GUIDE TO THE

SMITHSONIAN ARCHIVES

Smithsonian Institution Press 1996

Washington, D.C.

Archives and Special Collections of the Smithsonian Institution

Number 5

Library of Congress Cataloging-in-Publication Data

Smithsonian Archives.
    Guide to the Smithsonian archives.
        p.   cm. -- (Archives and special collections of the
    Smithsonian Institution ; no. 5)
        Includes indexes.
        1. Smithsonian Archives--Catalogs.   I. Title.   II. Series:
    Smithsonian Institution.   Archives and special collections of the
    Smithsonian Institution ; no. 5.
    Z7403.S64   1996
    [Q11]
    027.573--dc20   96-22215
                                                              CIP

CONTENTS

OVERVIEW

CONTENTS

DETAILED

ORAL HISTORY COLLECTION 612

PREFACE

On the occasion of the Smithsonian's 125th anniversary in 1971, the Smithsonian Institution Archives issued its first *Guide to the Smithsonian Archives*. That *Guide* marked the significant progress made by the Archives staff over a two year period. The Archives of the Institution had been kept since its founding, but only since 1969 was a staff of professional archivists in place to preserve and organize the holdings, and assist research by a wide range of administrators, building managers, curators and outside scholars. I am pleased to note that this fourth edition of the Guide commemorates another milestone in the Institution's history, our 150th anniversary.

In the twenty-five years since the first *Guide*, the Institution has grown and diversified. Programs new in 1971 have passed their quarter century mark and are now regularly transferring records to the Archives. From the Smithsonian Environmental Research Center, to the National Museum of African Art, to the Museum Support Center, new programs have generated new office files. This diversity—and the organizational processes which sustain it—is reflected in the holdings of the Archives. Research, exhibitions, collections management, publication, education, administration—every major area of Institutional life is represented among its multiple record types. Documents, photographs, films, oral histories, and architectural drawings arrive daily from a worldwide complex of museums and research institutes. In combination, the holdings form a rich resource for the study of numerous facets of American culture, science and technology, and provide the basis for understanding the nature and activity of the Smithsonian Institution from its inception to the present. As we send this *Guide* to the printer, we embark on another new phase of our work—archiving the electronic record.

The present volume is roughly ten times larger than the 72 pages comprising the first edition. However, the reliance on traditional methods of accessibility, such as printed guides, has been tempered in recent years with the new approaches that computers bring. I am pleased to note, therefore, that henceforward the Archives will turn to on-line descriptions of its collections as the primary method of researcher access. Rather than produce periodic revisions of a printed publication, the staff will routinely update a publicly accessible electronic file containing *Guide*-level entries. This edition, then, marks an end. I salute the exemplary work that the last four editions of the *Guide* represent, and note the beginning of a new tradition of excellence in the provision of electronic access to the Smithsonian Institution Archives.

J. Dennis O'Connor
Provost
May 1996

ACKNOWLEDGMENTS

Thousands of feet of records, hundreds of descriptive entries, dozens of people, and almost five years of time have gone into the making of this *Guide*. The staff of the Smithsonian Institution Archives have placed their talents, and some might add portions of their sanity, in service to this endeavor. The result is a remarkable source of information about a remarkable Institution. On the occasion of the Smithsonian's Sesquicentennial, the Office of Smithsonian Institution Archives is proud to issue this fourth edition of its guide to holdings.

Responsible for this achievement are, in alphabetical order, the following past and present staff members: Alan L. Bain, Batja Bell, William Cox, Kathryn L. Crossman, William A. Deiss, Terrica M. Gibson, Susan W. Glenn, Thomas W. Harley, Jr., Pamela M. Henson, Michael J. Horsley, Paulette Hughes, Josephine Jamison, Robert Shawn Johnstone, Bruce R. Kirby, Joan Mathys, William W. Moss, Tammy L. Peters, Kathleen M. Robinson, Anna M. Rogers, Gerald Rosenzweig, Leslie E. Sagle, Terri A. Schorzman, Mumia Shimaka-Mbasu, James A. Steed, Carolyn Taylor, Paul H. Theerman, Diane Vogt-O'Connor, James C. Wilson, Lynn M. Wojcik, and Ashley S. Wyant.

Special recognition should be given to several staff whose labors were particularly intense. First among these is Alan L. Bain, Project Director throughout the entire period and designer of the processes applied to all phases of *Guide* activity. Supporting him at various times were text editors William Deiss (1991-93) and James A. Steed (1994-96); and index editors Diane Vogt-O'Connor (1991-93) and James A. Steed (1993-96). William Cox, Susan W. Glenn, Kathleen M. Robinson, and Paul H. Theerman assumed responsibility for special proofing and production control work during the final production stages. Tammy L. Peters was responsible for typesetting and producing camera-ready copy. Her diligence and good humor were invaluable.

The Office of Information Technology, particularly Ralph Walker, Carla Roeper and Ken McCormick, and the Smithsonian Institution Press, particularly Alan Burchell, helped move the *Guide* through the entire production process.

Entries for records of the Department of Anthropology and the Bureau of Ethnology, which are kept by the National Anthropological Archives, are included through the cooperation of Mary Elizabeth Ruwell and John P. Homiak, Directors, and James R. Glenn and Janet Kennelly, archivists.

Finally, the Office of Smithsonian Institution Archives wishes to thank the Atherton Seidell Endowment Fund for its generous grant in support of publication costs, and Ross Simons, former Assistant Provost for Science, Robert Hoffmann, former Acting Provost, and J. Dennis O'Connor, Provost, for their interest in and support of this office.

Ethel (Edie) Hedlin
Director

INTRODUCTION

General

The Smithsonian Institution Archives, located in the Arts and Industries Building, Room 2135, 900 Jefferson Drive, S.W., Washington, D.C. 20560, is open to the scholarly and general public. The telephone number is (202) 357-1420; Internet address OSIAREF@OSIA.SI.EDU. Research hours are from 9:00 a.m. to 5:00 p.m., Monday through Friday. Researchers who want access before 10:00 a.m. should make special arrangements, since the Arts and Industries Building is closed to the public before that hour.

Although the Archives is open five days a week, many of its collections are stored at sites off the Mall. Thus, researchers should make arrangements with the reference staff in advance of their arrival if at all possible to ensure that records are available without delay.

The Archives is presently in the process of migrating its holdings to the Smithsonian Institution Research Information System, which will allow researcher access through the Internet. However, at this printing that work is not complete. Users who want Internet access should contact the Archives to learn about its availability.

Accessibility ♿

Physical access to the reading room of the Smithsonian Archives is available by elevator. For information about access to the *Guide* through the Internet, consult the preceding paragraph.

Upon demand, the Archives will provide an enlarged print, Braille, or audiotape copy of specific pages in the *Guide*. Presently the Archives has a staff member who can provide interpreting by sign language.

For access through TTY, telephone (202) 786-2745. For additional information on accessibility, telephone (202) 357-1420.

Scope of the Guide

The Smithsonian Archives program is chiefly concerned with official records of the Smithsonian and papers of Smithsonian staff. This guide to its holdings supersedes the 1983 *Guide to the Smithsonian Archives* and includes two-thirds of the Archives' holdings as of 1995. The *Guide* also includes archives of the Anthropology Department of the National Museum of Natural History and Bureau of American Ethnology, kept in the National Anthropological Archives; records of the Freer Gallery of Art and Arthur M. Sackler Gallery Archives; permanent object collection files of the National Museum of American Art and the National Portrait Gallery, kept in those museums; and some records processed by Smithsonian Archives staff but retained in other museums for curatorial use.

There are also manuscripts maintained in independent repositories. These include the National Anthropological Archives; Archives of American Art; Archives Center, National Museum of American History; Center for Folklife Programs and Cultural Studies Archives; Eliot Elisofon Photographic Archives, National Museum of African Art; Freer Gallery of Art and Arthur M. Sackler Gallery Library Archives; Hirshhorn Museum and Sculpture Garden Collection Archive; Human Studies Film Archives; National Museum of Natural History; National Air and Space Archives; and the National Museum of the American Indian Photograph Archives.

For further information about these repositories, please write to the Smithsonian Archives for a copy of its brochure *Smithsonian Institution Archival, Manuscript, and Special Collection Resources*, 1995.

Seventy-two cubic feet of Smithsonian records have been transferred to the National Archives. See the *Guide to the National Archives of the United States*, Washington, 1987.

Using this Guide

The rationale for organization of this guide is the distinction between Smithsonian records and other materials kept by the Smithsonian Archives. Part I, "Records of the Smithsonian Institution," includes official records arranged under administrative and several ad hoc headings, while Part II, "Special Collections," includes research materials under four headings: Papers of James Smithson and Secretaries; Other Papers and Records; Oral History Collection; and Smithsonian Videohistory Collection.

Appendix A is an index organized by form of record, including audio and videotapes, graphic illustrations, and photographs. Appendix B is an index to manuscript collections according to the discipline or area of interest reflected in the special collections. Appendix C, a bar graph showing the chronological coverage of each record unit, can also be used to find page references in the *Guide* for record unit numbers.

Finally, there is a volume index containing personal and organizational names, as well as some subject terms. Users should note that the index does not include all names which appear in the *Guide*. Cross references have been supplied in several instances, especially between different names for the same office. Where several variations of an agency name or expedition are given, a preferred name is provided to assist the researcher in finding all occurrences of the name. Although organizational titles provide access by subject, no subject indexing has been done. Index entries include the page number, followed by the record unit number in brackets.

Information supplied for each entry in this guide includes: the entry title for the record, giving the name of the originating office or person; the type of record (mostly in Part I); the chronological coverage, noting major gaps; and the volume of records in linear meters. However, in the case of small or non-document collections volume may be expressed as number of items, microforms, audiovisual records, or otherwise as appropriate. A history of the creating office or individual follows. The arrangement of the record unit is stated, and finding aids are noted if they exist.

The depth of an entry is determined by numerous factors: its size; its importance or research value; and the extent to which it has been processed. In many cases the processing of more recent records has been given preference over detailed descriptions of older records.

Reference Service

The Archives staff collects papers and records, prepares them for use, and services them for scholars. In order to balance staff effort in these areas of responsibility, limitations must be imposed on the time devoted to reference requests.

For researchers visiting the Archives, the staff will render all reasonable assistance. For telephone, fax, Internet, and letter inquiries, staff effort may be limited, depending on the nature of the request and the current reference load. In some cases, where the scope of the inquiry is large or where no finding aids exist, it may be necessary for the researcher to examine the material in person.

To protect its collections, the Smithsonian Archives requires researchers to conform to certain search room procedures. These generally require acceptable identification and registration of the user, acknowledgment of receipt of materials used, and adherence to rules for handling materials. Written copies of these rules are provided to researchers when they first register at the Archives.

Reproduction

1. The preferred method of reproduction is xerography, and the Archives may require that materials be reproduced in this fashion. Some items cannot be reproduced by xerography because of legibility problems, deteriorated conditions, or because information has been obscured during binding. Researchers will be charged the prevailing per-page rate.

2. Microfilming may be permitted in certain cases. When records are already available on microfilm, the Archives will lend a copy of the film to the university library or other responsible institution with which the researcher is affiliated at no cost. If the researcher wants a personal copy of the microfilm, the Archives will arrange for reproduction through an outside vendor. The Archives presently has no microfilming program, and researchers will have to rely on the services of outside vendors. In some cases, where the cost in staff time for supervision and in money are excessive, the Archives may decline to permit microfilming.

3. Payment for reproduction must be made before materials are shipped. Receipt of copies alone does not entitle a researcher to quote from them without the Archives' prior consent.

Permission to Quote from Smithsonian Archives

The Smithsonian Archives requires that researchers request permission from the Archives to quote from any documents in its holdings, specifying which documents are to be reproduced. All direct quotations must be credited to the Smithsonian Institution Archives.

Many documents in the physical possession of the Archives are not the literary property of the Institution. While the Archives staff will endeavor to inform researchers when permission to publish should be sought elsewhere, the responsibility for determining the status of property rights, and for securing permission to quote, remains with the researcher. Researchers should be cognizant of recent changes in the copyright law which affect literary property rights for unpublished papers.

Except in rare cases relating to projected documentary publications, permission to quote will be granted without question since the Archives is solely concerned to determine where its holdings are used.

Citation of Smithsonian Archives

Without specifying a specific form for citations, the Archives suggests that the following information be included:

1. Description of the document: for example, "Letter from Joseph Henry to Mary Henry, 11 August 1850."

2. Identification by Smithsonian Archives record unit number: for example, "Smithsonian Archives, record unit 7001."

3. Name and inclusive dates of the record unit: for example, "Joseph Henry Collection, 1808, 1825-1878, and related papers to *circa* 1903."

4. Additional physical location information: for example, "Box 1, folder 6, item 3"; or by box number only if nothing more is available.

Any box in the Smithsonian Archives can be located by a record unit number and a box number. In most cases, this physical location information is sufficient for subsequent location of items; but in case of reboxing or rearrangement of collections, box and folder information is not sufficient. A good description of the document or larger unit should be included in citations.

Restrictions

The scholarly purpose of the Smithsonian Archives program is to make information available to researchers; however, some restrictions on access to records are necessary to protect personal privacy, legitimate proprietary rights or to maintain reasonable administrative confidentiality.

Some 92 of the collections in this guide are restricted. Restriction does not indicate that the records are closed; rather, some staff review is necessary to ensure respect for personal privacy or administrative confidentiality. Since restrictions vary widely and change with time, they are not specified in the *Guide*. Researchers who want to work with restricted materials must make prior arrangement with Archives staff.

Record Groups in the Smithsonian Archives

This section will be of interest primarily to Archivists who desire more information about the Smithsonian Archives' principles of operation.

The Smithsonian Archives applies the term "record unit" to archives and special collections in this guide. Numbers may be used for an entire collection, series, several series, or sub-series, whichever best suits the purpose at hand.

Since archives are best interpreted in the context of the activity which generated them, it is necessary to preserve information about the administrative history and structure of originating offices and to place record units in that context in order to identify their provenance precisely. Traditional archival systems assign numbers in a classified order, but this method causes problems, especially for efficient shelving of records. Many systems in large archives therefore develop a second numbering system to locate archives that are not shelved in classified order. The Smithsonian Archives preserves provenance information by including administrative history in record unit entries and especially in the *Guide*'s table of contents, where entries are presented in classified order. Record unit numbers are assigned in numerical sequence, with certain exceptions noted below, and have no relationship to the provenance-related order of the *Guide*.

A few additional comments should be made about the Smithsonian Archives system. Official records are assigned numbers in sequence from 1 to 6999 in order of record unit creation, except that a block of numbers has been reserved for records of the Board of Regents. Manuscript collections and archives from non-Smithsonian offices are assigned numbers in a series ranging from 7000 to 9999, with numbers reserved for papers of Secretaries and for oral and videohistory transcripts and tapes. When first organized, the Archives shelved its records in record unit order in order to avoid having to create a second numbering system to control location. The acquisition of off-site storage has necessitated abandoning this approach. A location numbering system for record units and accessioned materials has been added to the Archives on-line accession database system and is used for retrieving records.

PART I
RECORDS OF THE
SMITHSONIAN INSTITUTION

BOARD OF REGENTS

RECORDS OF THE
BOARD OF REGENTS, 1846-

The Board of Regents is the governing body of the Smithsonian Institution, created by the Act of August 10, 1846, which established the Institution and gave form to the trust received from its English benefactor, James Smithson. The Board's composition has varied over time. At present it consists of two *ex officio* members, the Vice-President of the United States and the Chief Justice of the United States (by custom, its Chancellor), three members of the House of Representatives and three members of the Senate, appointed by resolution from those two bodies, and nine citizen-Regents, no two of whom may be residents of the same state, and two of whom must be residents of the District of Columbia. These members are appointed, upon recommendation of the Board, by joint resolution of the Congress.

The Secretary of the Smithsonian Institution is responsible for shaping the Institution's policies and directing its operations; but final authority resides with the Board of Regents, which is empowered to hold title to land, to accept gifts and trusts, to sue and be sued, and to exercise all the other powers usual to bodies of this kind.

(1)

Board of Regents, 1846-
Minutes of Meetings (2.7 linear meters).

The Smithsonian Institution was created by authority of an Act of Congress approved August 10, 1846. The Act entrusted direction of the Smithsonian to a body called the Establishment, composed of the President; the Vice-President; the Chief Justice of the United States; the Cabinet; the Mayor of Washington; and the Commissioner of the Patent Office. In fact, however, the Establishment last met in 1877; and control of the Smithsonian has always been exercised by its Board of Regents. The membership of the Regents consists of the Vice-President and the Chief Justice of the United States; three members each of the Senate and House of Representatives; two citizens of the District of Columbia; and nine citizens of the several states, no two from the same state. (Prior to 1970 the category of citizen-Regents not residents of Washington consisted of four members). By custom the Chief Justice is Chancellor. The office was at first held by the Vice-President. However, when Millard Fillmore succeeded to the presidency on the death of Zachary Taylor in 1851, Chief Justice Roger Brooke Taney was chosen in his stead; and the office has always been filled by the Chief Justice since that time.

These records are the official, edited minutes of the Board, compiled at the direction of the Secretary of the Smithsonian, who is also secretary to the Board. Manuscript minutes exist for the period from 1846 to 1856, and after 1891. Only printed versions exist for the years from 1857 to 1891.

ARRANGEMENT: (1) Bound minutes, 1846-1856, 1891-1968; (2) printed and loose minutes, 1876-1890, 1968-   ; and indexes, 1907-1946. FINDING AIDS: (1) Indexes, *circa* 1907-1946; (2) index for the *Annual Report;* (3) description in control file. SPECIAL CONDITIONS: (1) Restricted; (2) printed versions of minutes for the years 1857-1890 are available in the *Annual Reports of the Smithsonian Institution* for those years; (3) use of this record unit requires prior arrangement with the Archives staff.

(3)

Board of Regents, 1960-1984
Records (2.9 linear meters).

The Board of Regents is the governing body of the Smithsonian Institution, responsible for setting the Institution's policy and exercising oversight of its operations. For a more complete account of its history, see record unit 1.

These records deal largely with preparations for official meetings of the Board and with efforts to keep Regents informed of subjects of interest to them and upcoming issues for discussion at formal meetings.

ARRANGEMENT: (1) Records, 1960-1975, accession number T90113; (2) records, 1966-1979, accession number 83-052. FINDING AIDS: Folder list in control file. SPECIAL CONDITIONS: (1) Restricted; (2) use of this record unit requires prior arrangement with the Archives staff.

(2)

Board of Regents Executive Committee, 1846-1948
Records (0.9 linear meter).

The printed Smithsonian *Annual Reports* contain edited reports of the Executive Committee, which also were printed as separates such as those found in this record unit. Manuscript reports exist for 1867-1890, and while these are mostly the texts from which printed reports were made, they occasionally contain additional information. For the Permanent Committee, which was created under Charles Walcott's administration, more substantial typescript minutes exist.

These records document the meetings of the Committee. From them are taken the printed versions appearing in the *Annual Reports of the Smithsonian Institution.*

ARRANGEMENT: (1) Manuscript minutes of meetings of the Executive Committee, 1846-1849; (2) manuscript reports of the Executive Committee, 1867-1890; (3) typescript minutes of the Permanent Committee and the Executive Committee, 1915-1948; (4) printed reports (separated from the *Annual Report)* of the Executive Committee. FINDING AIDS: Indexes in the *Annual Report.* SPECIAL CONDITIONS: (1) Restricted; (2) use of this record unit requires prior arrangement with the Archives staff.

OFFICE OF THE SECRETARY

RECORDS OF THE
SECRETARY'S OFFICE, 1846-1985

The Secretary of the Smithsonian, appointed by the Board of Regents, is the Institution's chief executive officer. The Secretaries in this period were Joseph Henry, 1846-1878; Spencer F. Baird, 1878-1887; Samuel P. Langley, 1887-1906; Charles D. Walcott, 1907-1927; Charles G. Abbot, 1928-1944; Alexander Wetmore, 1944-1952; Leonard Carmichael, 1953-1964; and S. Dillon Ripley, 1964-1983. The Secretaries exert a strong influence on the Institution—in Henry's and Baird's case a formative one—and their records are thus potentially valuable for any study related to activities of the Smithsonian Institution. Unfortunately, secretarial records have never been described for subject access. Indexes to correspondents' names do exist and are listed below. Related material can be found in the records of the Assistant Secretaries as well as in the Secretaries' personal papers.

One large gap exists in these records. Although the Smithsonian Institution was founded in 1846, virtually all records of the Secretary's office postdate 1865, when a fire destroyed part of the original building. By chance, certain early secretarial records have survived, some in the secretarial records for 1863-1879 and more in the papers of William Jones Rhees, Chief Clerk of the Smithsonian.

A few comments on the archival characteristics of these records will be useful to researchers, especially those using microfilm. From 1863 to 1907, records were maintained in two files, one consisting of incoming correspondence and another of outgoing correspondence. The incoming consists of originals, while the outgoing consists of letterpress, a copy of the original transferred to tissue paper in bound volumes. Incoming letters usually were filed alphabetically by sender's name, while outgoing were in chronological order. Thus the search procedure involves examining records in two locations for the same correspondent or topic.

Register numbers appear on documents and indexes for the period 1863-1907. With one exception, noted below, the register system cannot now be used to retrieve documents, since numbers were assigned for current working use only. These numbers were assigned to incoming letters in order of receipt. The number and an abstract of the letter were entered in a register; hence, the term "register number."

Soon after Secretary Langley's death in 1906, the Secretary's office adopted the modern practice of keeping a single correspondence file combining incoming correspondence and carbon copies of outgoing correspondence. Records were no longer divided by secretarial administration. Instead, file units were arranged alphabetically, usually by proper name and sometimes, more recently, by activity or subject. These physical arrangement principles have persisted to the present.

Extensive card indexes provide access to these records by proper name, and the Archives staff can estimate the extent of available documentation when inquiries are made by proper name. Subject inquiries in most cases require examination of the records by the researcher. The *Preliminary Guide to the Smithsonian Archives,* 1971, listed several of these indexes as separate record units. In this *Guide,* record units 39, 40, 41, 47, and 48 from the 1971 *Guide* have been eliminated; indexes are mentioned in entries for related records. The indexes are as follows:

Incoming Correspondence	1863-1878
Outgoing Correspondence	1865-1889
Incoming Correspondence	1879-1882
Incoming Correspondence	1882-1887
Incoming and Outgoing Correspondence	1890-1906
Incoming and Outgoing Correspondence	1907-1924
Incoming and Outgoing Correspondence	1925-1949
Incoming and Outgoing Correspondence	1949-1964

In the first three of these indexes, the reference consists only of volume and page number, leading directly to the document. The fourth index gives a register number, which is then used to locate the documents. The remaining indexes have distinctive cards for incoming and outgoing correspondence, which are filed together. Outgoing cards refer to volume and page numbers and are used like the earlier indexes. Incoming cards indicate register numbers in some indexes; but the records must be located in an alphabetical file, without regard to register number. Most of these indexes, along with registers explained above, were maintained by the Secretary's office to facilitate the use of its active records. Errors in indexing and loss or misplacement of documents render these indexes less than reliable, a problem which researchers should keep in mind.

(43)

Office of the Secretary, 1835, 1838, 1846-1865
Records (0.2 linear meter).

Nearly all the Smithsonian's records were destroyed in a fire which damaged the original building in 1865. A few of the records saved are preserved here.

These records document several aspects of the Smithsonian's history, most notably the 1854-1855 debate over allocation of the Institution's income.

ARRANGEMENT: Chronologic. FINDING AIDS: Description in control file. SPECIAL CONDITIONS: Use of this record unit requires prior arrangement with the Archives staff.

(26)

Office of the Secretary (Joseph Henry, Spencer F. Baird), 1863-1879
Incoming Correspondence (12.7 linear meters).

This series consists mostly of correspondence addressed to Joseph Henry, much of which received his personal attention; also included are some copies of Henry letters, occasional returned original Henry letters, and a considerable number of letters to Baird.

ARRANGEMENT: Numerous alphabetical series numbered from volume 1 through volume 183; (1) volumes 1-75, 1863-1869, unbound and rearranged in two alphabetic series; (2) volumes 76-183, 1866-1879, alphabetic in several series. FINDING AIDS: (1) Card indexes, providing mostly proper name access; references are to volume and page numbers, although records for volumes 1-75 are located alphabetically; (2) most volumes indexed individually; (3) alphabetic arrangement of records serves as an additional finding aid. SPECIAL CONDITIONS: (1) Many items are missing, especially from the first 75 volumes; (2) record unit available on microfilm; (3) use of this record unit requires prior arrangement with the Archives staff.

(32)

Office of the Secretary, 1865-1879
Incoming Correspondence (0.3 linear meter).

These secretarial records apparently were separated from the main series before the latter were bound; they may be integrated into the main series later.

ARRANGEMENT: Alphabetic and chronologic. FINDING AIDS: None. SPECIAL CONDITIONS: Use of this record unit requires prior arrangement with the Archives staff.

(27)

Office of the Secretary (Joseph Henry), 1873-1878
Incoming Correspondence, Requests for Publications and Assistance (2.7 linear meters).

Mostly ephemeral; contains records of the Chief Clerk.

ARRANGEMENT: Alphabetic. FINDING AIDS: Each volume indexed individually. SPECIAL CONDITIONS: (1) Record unit available on microfilm; (2) use of this record unit requires prior arrangement with the Archives staff.

(28)

Office of the Secretary (Spencer F. Baird), 1879-1882
Incoming Correspondence (5.7 linear meters).

ARRANGEMENT: Chronologic by register number, 1-21,500; register number assigned by date received. FINDING AIDS: (1) Card index, providing proper name access; cards later were mounted and xeroxed; (2) card index, providing subject access. SPECIAL CONDITIONS: (1) Record unit available on microfilm; (2) use of this record unit requires prior arrangement with the Archives staff.

(29)

Office of the Secretary (Spencer F. Baird), 1882-1887
Incoming Correspondence (0.8 linear meter).

ARRANGEMENT: Alphabetic. FINDING AIDS: (1) A card index providing mostly proper name access; this is the primary finding aid available; (2) bound index; (3) register. SPECIAL CONDITIONS: Use of this record unit requires prior arrangement with the Archives staff.

Office of the Secretary (Spencer F. Baird, Samuel P. Langley), 1882-1890
Incoming Correspondence (2.5 linear meters).

ARRANGEMENT: Alphabetic, including a major subheading for government. FINDING AIDS: (1) Each volume indexed individually; (2) bound indexes to registers, April 30, 1883 to December 31, 1886; see record unit 36. Access is mostly by proper name in each case. SPECIAL CONDITIONS: Use of this record unit requires prior arrangement with the Archives staff.

Office of the Secretary (Samuel P. Langley), 1891-1906, with related records to 1908
Incoming Correspondence (13.4 linear meters).

These records document the administration of the Smithsonian during most of the tenure of Samuel P. Langley, its third Secretary.

Bureaus which were created or substantially changed during these years include the Bureau of American Ethnology (BAE), the Smithsonian Astrophysical Observatory (SAO), the National Zoological Park (NZP), and the Freer Gallery of Art. (Researchers interested in the BAE, the SAO, the NZP, or the Freer Gallery should also consult record unit 45, which contains much material on these topics.) Langley was responsible for the creation of the SAO and NZP; and both are covered in great detail here. Langley's own papers were destroyed by fire soon after his death; but a significant amount of his research in astrophysics and aerodynamics ("aerodromics," as he called it) is preserved in the records of the Secretary's office. These records also document the Institution's only two significant financial embarrassments: the embezzlement of Smithsonian trust funds by William W. Karr, and a smaller peculation in BAE funds.

ARRANGEMENT: (1) General correspondence, arranged alphabetically; (2) Smithsonian bureaus; (3) Hodgkins Fund documents and correspondence; (4) government departments. FINDING AIDS: (1) Description in control file; (2) card index providing mostly proper name access, usually with letter abstracted on the card; (3) special bound index to Hodgkins Fund correspondence. SPECIAL CONDITIONS: Use of this record unit requires prior arrangement with the Archives staff.

Office of the Secretary (Joseph Henry, Spencer F. Baird, Samuel P. Langley), 1865-1891
Outgoing Correspondence (8.2 linear meters).

ARRANGEMENT: Chronologic. FINDING AIDS: (1) Card index providing mostly proper name access; unreliable after 1889; (2) an index in each volume also provides mostly proper name access. SPECIAL CONDITIONS: (1) Deteriorating letterpress affects legibility; (2) record unit available on microfilm; (3) use of this record unit requires prior arrangement with the Archives staff.

Office of the Secretary (Samuel P. Langley), 1887-1907
Outgoing Correspondence (5.7 linear meters).

Shortly after Samuel P. Langley became Secretary, a new system of organizing outgoing correspondence was devised. Some of the records have not survived to the present; hence, there are gaps in series numbers.

ARRANGEMENT: (1) General, 59 volumes, 1892-1907; (2) Museum, 18 volumes, 1892-1907; (4) Ethnology, 7 volumes, 1892-1907; (5) National Zoological Park, 9 volumes, 1890-1907; (6) Astrophysical Observatory, 14 volumes, 1892-1907; (8) Publication Requests, 3 volumes, 1900-1907; (11) Assistant in Charge of the Office, 8 volumes, 1891-1907; (12) New Museum, 1 volume, 1903-1907; (13) Advisory Committee on Printing and Publication, 1 volume, 1906-1907; (20) Aerodromics, 10 volumes, 1891-1907; (25) Hodgkins Fund, 6 volumes, 1892-1907; also, unnumbered: (a) copies of museum business letters, 2 volumes, 1888-1889; (b) Internal and Confidential Correspondence, 9 volumes, 1887-1906. Each of the above sections is arranged chronologically. FINDING AIDS: (1) Card index, combining index for incoming and outgoing; provides access mostly by proper name, usually with the letter abstracted on the card; (2) indexes in bound volumes; (3) volume list in control file. SPECIAL CONDITIONS: (1) Deteriorating letterpress affects legibility; (2) record unit partially microfilmed; (3) use of this record unit requires prior arrangement with the Archives staff.

Office of the Secretary (Charles D. Walcott), 1903-1924
Records (14.6 linear meters).

These records document the administration of the Smithsonian Institution during the tenure of Charles D. Walcott, its fourth Secretary, who served from 1907 to 1927.

Of special interest is the Institution's entry into the field of the fine arts. While the National Gallery of Art (now the National Museum of American Art) and the Freer Gallery of Art had their beginnings a few years before 1907, it is in these records that their development can be traced most completely. The Smithsonian continued to pursue a wide variety of other interests as well.

Thus, the records deal with the following topics, among others: aviation; the American School of Archeology in China; the Carnegie Institution of Washington, D.C.; the Cinchona Botanical Station, Jamaica; many international Congresses; numerous national and international expositions, especially the Panama-California Exposition, San Diego, 1912-1916, and the Panama-Pacific Exposition at San Francisco, 1914-1915; the George Washington Memorial Association; the Harriman-Alaska Series; the Kahn Foundation for Foreign Travel of American Teachers; the Koren Expedition to Siberia; the Langley-Wright aerodrome controversy; the Montezuma solar observatory at Calama, Chile; solar observations at Mount Harqua Hala, Arizona, and Mount Wilson, California; the Naples Zoological Station; the National Academy of Sciences; the National Research Council; publication of Mary Vaux Walcott's *North American Wildflowers;* the Biological Survey of the Panama Canal Zone; the Alfred Duane Pell Collection; the Research Corporation; the Smithsonian-Roosevelt African Expedition; seismological studies; the Charles D. and Mary Vaux Walcott Research Fund; the Smithsonian Scientific Series; grants from the Hodgkins Fund; the Langley Aerodynamical Laboratory; the National Advisory Committee for Aeronautics; the Smithsonian Astrophysical Observatory; and the Bureau of Biological Survey. The records include correspondence, minutes, announcements, publications, fiscal records, photographs, manuscripts, and news clippings.

ARRANGEMENT: (1) Correspondence, 1903-1924; (2) Smithsonian administrative offices, 1907-1924; (3) records relating to cabinet departments and government offices, 1907-1924. FINDING AIDS: (1) Description in control file; (2) bound indexes, also on microfilm, prepared when records were created or received, providing mostly proper name access and usually abstracting the letter. SPECIAL CONDITIONS: Use of this record unit requires prior arrangement with the Archives staff.

(46)

Office of the Secretary (Charles D. Walcott, Charles G. Abbot, Alexander Wetmore), 1925-1949

Records (29.1 linear meters).

These records chiefly document the policy and administration of the Smithsonian under Charles G. Abbot, 1928-1944, though they overlap parts of the administrations of Secretaries Walcott and Wetmore.

Smithsonian bureaus which were founded, enlarged, or significantly changed during these years, and which are represented here, include the Smithsonian Astrophysical Observatory; the National Gallery of Art, now the National Museum of American Art; the National Gallery of Art, founded by Andrew Mellon; the National Zoological Park; the National Air Museum, now the National Air and Space Museum; and the Canal Zone Biological Area, now the Smithsonian Tropical Research Institute. Abbot's tenure was complicated by the Depression and World War II, which restricted many of the developments which seemed so promising under his predecessor. The principal event of his administration was Andrew Mellon's gift of a national art museum. Abbot created a Division of Radiation and Organisms within the Astrophysical Observatory, always his personal interest. With the use of Works Progress Administration funds he was also able to produce major improvements for the National Zoological Park. The Smithsonian continued its ties with the National Academy of Sciences, the Carnegie Institution, the National Advisory Committee for Aeronautics, the National Research Council, the National Geographic Society and similar organizations. During the war, the Smithsonian was instrumental in operating the Ethnogeographic Board and co-operated with the Office of Scientific Research and Development. Its co-operation with such bodies, and new ones like the Atomic Energy Commission, continued in the postwar years. Miscellaneous topics in the records include: the Johnson-Smithsonian Deep-Sea Expedition to the Puerto Rico Trench, 1933; the Eighth American Scientific Conference, Washington, 1940; the Smithsonian Scientific Series; *North American Wildflowers;* the Langley-Wright controversy; the River Basin Surveys; the abortive design competition for a museum of modern art, won by Eliel Saarinen; "The World Is Yours" radio broadcasts; Robert H. Goddard's rocket research; awarding of the Langley Medal; private funding of the Smithsonian, especially the Tamblyn and Brown conferences and the 1927 conference on the future of the Smithsonian; and Charles G. Abbot's research in solar radiation and climatic studies.

ARRANGEMENT: Alphabetic including two subunits for government, one for Smithsonian administration and budgets and one for international congresses. FINDING AIDS: (1) Card index, prepared when records were created or received, providing mostly proper name access and usually abstracting the letter; (2) folder list in control file. SPECIAL CONDITIONS: (1) Arrangement will be changed; (2) use of this record unit requires prior arrangement with the Archives staff.

(50)

Office of the Secretary (Alexander Wetmore, Leonard Carmichael), 1949-1964
Records (42.9 linear meters).

These records document part of the secretarial administration of Alexander Wetmore and the whole of Leonard Carmichael's tenure. During this period the Smithsonian's capacity to carry out research in its traditional scientific disciplines was substantially strengthened. At the same time the Institution was able to invest much more effort in promoting cultural and artistic activities.

Bureaus and offices which were created or underwent substantial change during this period and which are represented here include the United States National Museum; the Museum of Natural History; the Museum of History and Technology; the Smithsonian Astrophysical Observatory; the National Cultural Center, now the John F. Kennedy Center; the Bureau of American Ethnology; the National Portrait Gallery; the National Collection of Fine Arts; the National Zoological Park; the Smithsonian Oceanographic Sorting Center; and the Smithsonian Institution Traveling Exhibition Service. Subject headings appearing in these records include: the Arctic Research Laboratory; the Armed Forces Museum and the National Armed Forces Museum Advisory Board; the earth satellite program; the Canal Zone Biological Area, now the Smithsonian Tropical Research Institute; the Smithsonian's centennial; modernization of Smithsonian exhibits; the Link Foundation; the National Advisory Committee for Aeronautics; the National Air Museum, now the National Air and Space Museum; the National Gallery of Art; the Research Corporation; the Century 21 Exposition, Seattle, 1962; the Smithsonian Science Information Exchange; and the Smithsonian Scientific Series.

ARRANGEMENT: (1) Alphabetic subject series; (2) alphabetic series arranged by government division; (3) alphabetic series of miscellaneous organizations; (4) three alphabetic miscellaneous series. FINDING AIDS: (1) Folder list in control file; (2) bound indexes, also on microfilm. SPECIAL CONDITIONS: Use of this record unit requires prior arrangement with the Archives staff.

(99)

Office of the Secretary (S. Dillon Ripley), 1964-1971
Records (116.4 linear meters).

For an administrative history of the Office of the Secretary, see the introductory material at the beginning of this section of the *Guide*. In 1964 S. Dillon Ripley, formerly a Professor of Biology at Yale University and Director of its Peabody Museum of Natural History, succeeded Leonard Carmichael as eighth Secretary of the Smithsonian Institution.

These records reflect the growing scope and complexity of the Smithsonian during Ripley's tenure. They document the Smithsonian's changing administrative structure; growing relationships with universities, foundations, and other external groups; efforts to attract more government support for the Smithsonian; pursuit of new initiatives and programs; and the regular administrative activities of the Institution. The records for this period document the opening of the National Museum of History and Technology (now the National Museum of American History); creation of the Office of Academic Studies and the Office of Smithsonian Symposia and Seminars; founding of the Smithsonian Resident Associate Program; establishment of the Chesapeake Bay Center for Environmental Studies; opening of east and west wings of the National Museum of Natural History; opening of the Anacostia Neighborhood Museum; beginning of the Festival of American Folklife; opening of the National Portrait Gallery; establishment of the Woodrow Wilson International Center for Scholars; formation of the Smithsonian National Associates Program; and the opening of the Renwick Gallery.

ARRANGEMENT: Chronologic. FINDING AIDS: (1) Description in control file; (2) card indexes for each series shelved following records. SPECIAL CONDITIONS: Use of this record unit requires prior arrangement with the Archives staff.

(613)

Office of the Secretary (S. Dillon Ripley), 1972-1984
Records (201.4 linear meters).

For an administrative history of the Office of the Secretary during the tenure of S. Dillon Ripley, see record unit 99.

These records concern the operation of the Office of the Secretary from 1972 to the end of S. Dillon Ripley's tenure as Secretary of the Smithsonian Institution.

The records document the Smithsonian's on-going operations—internal, with other government offices and departments, and with foundations, universities, and other outside organizations. Among the events that are documented are the formation of the Harvard-Smithsonian Center for Astrophysics; renovations at the National Zoological Park; the opening of the Hirshhorn Museum and Sculpture Garden; creation of the Scientific Event Alert Network; opening of the Cooper-Hewitt Museum of Decorative Arts and Design in New York City; opening of the National Air and Space Museum; opening of a restored Arts and Industries Building; addition of the National Museum of African Art to the Smithsonian; first use of the Multiple-Mirror Telescope, Mount Hopkins, Arizona; donation of the Arthur M. Sackler Collection of Oriental Art to the Smithsonian; opening of the Museum Support Center; and the beginning of construction of the Center for African, Near Eastern, and Asian Cultures.

ARRANGEMENT: (1) Records, 1972, accession number T90103; (2) records, 1973, accession number T90104; (3) records, 1974, accession number T90105; (4) records, 1975, accession number T90106; (5) records, 1976, accession number T90107; (6) records, 1977, accession number 81-078; (7) records, 1978, accession number 82-124; (8) records, 1979, accession number 83-090; (9) records, 1980, accession number 84-129; (10) records, 1981, accession number 85-132; (11) records, 1982, accession number 86-041; (12) records, 1983, accession number 86-060; (13) records, 1984, accession number 87-066. FINDING AIDS: (1) Folder list in control file; (2) indexes prepared for each series, shelved with records. SPECIAL CONDITIONS: (1) Restricted; (2) use of this record unit requires prior arrangement with the Archives staff.

Assistant to the Secretary, 1957-1966
Records (5.7 linear meters).

The position of Assistant to the Secretary was created in 1959. James Bradley held the post for one year and was succeeded by Theodore W. Taylor, who served from 1960 to 1966. The Assistant was responsible for various projects as directed by the Secretary.

Projects represented in these records include the National Collection of Fine Arts, the National Portrait Gallery, and the acquisition of the Patent Office Building; Smithsonian Associates; National Armed Forces Museum Advisory Board; National Council on the Arts; extensive liaison with the Astrophysical Observatory and its stations around the world; and the Science Information Exchange.

The records consist of memoranda, correspondence, reports, contracts and agreements, drawings and blueprints, budgets, and other fiscal records.

ARRANGEMENT: Alphabetic subject file. FINDING AIDS: Folder list in control file. SPECIAL CONDITIONS: Use of this record unit requires prior arrangement with the Archives staff.

Special Assistant to the Secretary (Richard H. Howland), 1958-1985
Records (8.6 linear meters).

Special Assistants to the Secretary have discharged many duties over the years. Richard H. Howland first came to the Smithsonian Institution in 1960 as Head Curator and Chairman of the Department of Civil History, Museum of History and Technology. In 1964 Howland became a Special Assistant to newly arrived Secretary S. Dillon Ripley, who asked him to oversee restoration of the Smithsonian Building to its original nineteenth-century ambience.

These records deal in some degree with Howland's work as Head Curator but mostly describe his assignment as a Special Assistant. Records include wide correspondence with furniture dealers, professional organizations, learned societies, historical preservation groups, and prospective donors. There is also some material documenting Howland's work on the Smithsonian Associates' program of travel tours, as well as files of information on the Archaeological Institute of America and the American School of Classical Studies in Athens.

ARRANGEMENT: Records, 1958-1985, accession number 86-080. FINDING AIDS: Folder list in control file. SPECIAL CONDITIONS: Use of this record unit requires prior arrangement with the Archives staff.

Special Assistant to the Secretary for Fine Arts (Thomas M. Beggs), 1965
Records (0.1 linear meter).

The position of Special Assistant to the Secretary for Fine Arts was created in 1965. Thomas M. Beggs, who had served as Director of the National Collection of Fine Arts, 1948-1964, held the position until his retirement in 1965. He was charged with surveying American and foreign art museums concerning the development of contemporary art in this country.

These records primarily consist of form letters answering Beggs' survey. Other records pertaining to this collection such as charters and annual reports have been dispersed in the National Museum of American Art and Portrait Gallery Library.

ARRANGEMENT: Unarranged. FINDING AIDS: None. SPECIAL CONDITIONS: Use of this record unit requires prior arrangement with the Archives staff.

(341)

Special Assistant to the Secretary for Bicentennial Planning, 1969-1977
Records (1.2 linear meters).

The Special Assistant to the Secretary for Bicentennial Planning was responsible for developing various aspects of the Smithsonian's planning for the celebration of the Bicentennial of the American Revolution in 1976. For a full account of planning for the Bicentennial events, researchers should also consult the records of the Bicentennial Coordinator responsible for internal Smithsonian planning, record unit 337.

John J. Slocum was attached to the Office of the Secretary, but also reported on occasion to the Director of the National Museum of History and Technology since he was involved in procuring artifacts for use by the Museum in its exhibits. He was particularly involved in negotiations for a Pony Express first-day cover and for a Corliss steam engine, both of which the Museum wanted as features of its Bicentennial exhibitions. Slocum was also responsible for planning and leading a Smithsonian National Associates trip to Turkey during 1971, drawing on his earlier experience of the eastern Mediterranean in the American diplomatic service.

These records consist of correspondence between Slocum and various persons and organizations he dealt with in carrying out his duties. They also document some of his personal interests, notably numismatics and the work of the English Speaking Union.

ARRANGEMENT: Unarranged. FINDING AIDS: None. SPECIAL CONDITIONS: Use of this record unit requires prior arrangement with the Archives staff.

(620)

Special Assistant to the Secretary (Dorothy Rosenberg), 1971-1979
Records (0.4 linear meter).

Dorothy Rosenberg joined the Smithsonian Institution in 1959 as an Administrative Officer. In 1971 she began work for Under Secretary Robert A. Brooks and then for Secretary S. Dillon Ripley from 1973 to her retirement in 1979. Her duties involved management of the Secretary's Office, and she was liaison to the Board of Regents as well.

These records document especially sensitive matters and were kept apart from regular office records on that account.

ARRANGEMENT: Records, 1971-1979, accession number 82-096. FINDING AIDS: Folder list in control file. SPECIAL CONDITIONS: Use of this record unit requires prior arrangement with the Archives staff.

Special Consultant to the Secretary (James C. Bradley), 1966-1973
Records (2.8 linear meters).

James C. Bradley served as Under Secretary of the Smithsonian Institution, 1971-1972. After his retirement in 1972, Bradley agreed to serve as a Special Consultant to Secretary S. Dillon Ripley in order to assist in the completion of several projects with which he had been involved before his retirement.

These records chiefly document the completion of the Hirshhorn Museum and Sculpture Garden's building on the Mall. There are also some materials from Bradley's earlier career.

ARRANGEMENT: Unarranged. FINDING AIDS: Folder list in control file. SPECIAL CONDITIONS: Use of this record unit requires prior arrangement with the Archives staff.

Consultant to the Secretary (Frank A. Taylor), 1969-1980
Records (0.4 linear meter).

Following his retirement as Director General of Museums and Director of the United States National Museum in 1971, Frank A. Taylor continued to serve the Smithsonian as a Consultant to the Secretary, 1971-1977, and as a Research Associate for both the Office of Museum Programs, 1971- , and the Smithsonian Institution Archives, 1978- .

These records document Frank A. Taylor's work as both Consultant to Secretary S. Dillon Ripley, and as Research Associate for the Office of Museum Programs. Included are correspondence, memoranda, reports, handwritten notes, budgets, and newspaper clippings regarding four major projects: the Mid-American Center, Arkansas; the Smithsonian Museum Support Facility; the Director search, National Museum of History and Technology; and proposals for the last museum site on the Mall.

ARRANGEMENT: (1) Mid-American Center, 1969-1980; (2) Museum Support Facility, 1972-1978; (3) Director Search, National Museum of History and Technology; (4) last museum site on the Mall, 1977. FINDING AIDS: Folder list in control file. SPECIAL CONDITIONS: Use of this record unit requires prior arrangement with the Archives staff.

Secretary's Executive Committee, 1966-1981
Records (0.8 linear meter).

Shortly after S. Dillon Ripley became the Smithsonian's eighth Secretary in 1964, he created a group of advisors named the Secretariat. It was composed of the Secretary, Assistant Secretary, Director General of Museums, Assistant Secretary for Science, Assistant Secretary for History and Art, Assistant Secretary for Public Service, Treasurer, Director of the Office of Academic Programs, General Counsel, Director of the Office of Personnel and Management Resources, the Assistant to the Secretary, the Public Affairs Officer, the Director of the Office of International Activities, and the Secretary's Executive Assistant. From this committee the Secretary obtained such information and advice as he wished in making operating decisions for the Smithsonian. In 1971, as a result of a study of management practices at the Institution, the Secretary streamlined this group, renaming it the Executive Committee. Its members were the Assistant Secretaries for Science, History and Art, and Public Service; the Treasurer, the Executive Officer for Supporting Services, and, *ex officio,* the General Counsel. The new committee continued to advise the Secretary and was also given more responsibility for making decisions than its predecessor.

These records consist chiefly of minutes of the Executive Committee's discussions of policy issues presented to the Institution.

ARRANGEMENT: Unarranged. FINDING AIDS: Folder list in control file. SPECIAL CONDITIONS: (1) Restricted; (2) use of this record unit requires prior arrangement with the Archives staff.

REGISTERS, ABSTRACTS, MISCELLANEOUS INDEXES, 1850-1912

(42)

Office of the Secretary, 1850-1852
Correspondence Registers (0.1 linear meter).

These registers are for letters burned in the 1865 Smithsonian Building fire.

ARRANGEMENT: Chronologic. FINDING AIDS: None. SPECIAL CONDITIONS: Use of this record unit requires prior arrangement with the Archives staff.

(35)

Office of the Secretary, 1865-1873, 1882
Letters Written Registers (0.8 linear meter).

These registers record outgoing correspondence. Letters entered in the register were also abstracted briefly, and occasionally the abstract is the only version of the letter available.

ARRANGEMENT: Chronologic: (1) January 1865-June 1867; (2) August 1867-September 1868; (3) May 1871-December 1871; (4) January 1872-April 1873, 1882. FINDING AIDS: None. SPECIAL CONDITIONS: Use of this record unit requires prior arrangement with the Archives staff.

(36)

Office of the Secretary, 1865-1873, 1883-1912
Letters Received Registers (2.7 linear meters).

These registers record incoming correspondence. Letters entered in the registers were also abstracted briefly, and occasionally the abstract is the only version of the letter available.

ARRANGEMENT: Chronologic. There are four series of register numbers represented in existing register books: one which was in operation in 1865; a second which began and ended in 1873; a third which began in 1879, but which is first represented in these register books in 1883 and ends in 1894; and a fourth which began in 1895. FINDING AIDS: Bound indexes referring to register numbers as follows: 1870, 1873, 1874-1876, 1883-1886, *circa* 1887-1894. SPECIAL CONDITIONS: Use of this record unit requires prior arrangement with the Archives staff.

(37)

Office of the Secretary, 1864-1869
Abstracts of Incoming and Outgoing Correspondence (0.5 linear meter).

The date of compilation of these abstracts is unknown, although presumably it was done in part before the 1865 fire.

ARRANGEMENT: Chronologic with indications of source of abstract in official records: (1) October 30, 1864-July 19, 1869; (2) February 20, 1865-October 30, 1869. FINDING AIDS: None. SPECIAL CONDITIONS: Use of this record unit requires prior arrangement with the Archives staff.

(38)

Office of the Secretary (Joseph Henry, Spencer F. Baird), 1870-1876, 1883-circa 1894
Miscellaneous Indexes and Abstracts (0.9 linear meter).

ARRANGEMENT: Alphabetic and chronologic: (1) index of letters received, 1870; (2) index to letters attended to, 1873; (3) synopsis of letters received, 1874-1875; (4) synopsis of letters received, 1875-1876; (5) subjects of letters written, undated; (6) index of letters received, January 1-April 30, 1883; (7) index of correspondence, April 30, 1883-December 31, 1886, *circa* 1887-1894. FINDING AIDS: None. SPECIAL CONDITIONS: Use of this record unit requires prior arrangement with the Archives staff.

SPECIAL SERIES, 1892-1966

Several segments of secretarial records have come to the Smithsonian Archives as discrete units. The entries follow in chronologic order.

(46TA)

Office of the Secretary, 1892-1893, 1900-1947
Records Relating to Budget (2.3 linear meters).

This record unit was assigned a new record unit number since the publication of the 1983 *Guide.* For information concerning budget records, see record unit 49.

Office of the Secretary, 1892-1893, 1900-1947
Records Relating to Budget (2.3 linear meters).

ARRANGEMENT: Chronologic. FINDING AIDS: Card index to records of the Secretary's office for pertinent years. SPECIAL CONDITIONS: Use of this record unit requires prior arrangement with the Archives staff.

Office of the Secretary, 1912-1959
Records Relating to Research Corporation (1.2 linear meters).

This record unit was assigned a new record unit number since the publication of the 1983 *Guide.* For information concerning the Research Corporation, see record unit 51.

Office of the Secretary, 1912-1959
Records Relating to Research Corporation (1.2 linear meters).

The Research Corporation, a foundation granting funds for research in science and technology, has been associated with the Smithsonian since its foundation in 1912 with a gift from Frederic G. Cottrell. Cottrell was a chemist with the United States Bureau of Mines and an inventor of devices related to electrical precipitation of pollutants.

ARRANGEMENT: Temporary arrangement as follows: reports, minutes, agreements, project reports, fiscal papers, correspondence. FINDING AIDS: Card index to records of the Secretary's office for pertinent years. SPECIAL CONDITIONS: Use of this record unit requires prior arrangement with the Archives staff.

Office of the Secretary, 1912-1965
Records Relating to the Canal Zone Biological Area (4 linear meters).

From 1918 to 1923 various groups interested in tropical American research discussed the desirability of creating a research institute in Central or South America. In 1923, the Institute for Research in Tropical America (IRTA) was formed by a number of private foundations and universities, under the aegis of the National Research Council. The Smithsonian Institution was one of these early sponsors, and its ties with the Institute grew stronger still when the federal government took over the IRTA in 1940, calling it the Canal Zone Biological Area (CZBA) and placing the Smithsonian's Secretary on its governing board. The CZBA was located on Barro Colorado Island in the Panama Canal Zone. In 1946 control of CZBA was vested in the Smithsonian, which renamed it the Smithsonian Tropical Research Institute in 1966.

Records document the creation and development of the Canal Zone Biological Area, chiefly from 1923 to 1965, and cover all phases of its operations as a private and federal facility during that period. The researcher will find three general types of records in this unit: (1) the official records of IRTA and CZBA before 1946, some of which were created by the Smithsonian in its role as sponsor of the organization and some of which were interfiled at a later date; (2) office files of Thomas Barbour and IRTA, which often duplicate or complement other records; and (3) official records generated entirely by the Smithsonian in its operation of CZBA since 1946.

ARRANGEMENT: (1) Office files, 1912-1965; (2) general correspondence, 1918-1965; (3) general correspondence, by subject, 1912-1965; (4) records of the Institute for Research in Tropical America, 1919-1940. FINDING AIDS: Description in control file. SPECIAL CONDITIONS: Use of this record unit requires prior arrangement with the Archives staff.

(142)

Office of the Secretary, 1964-1966

Records of the Smithson Bicentennial (4.8 linear meters).

In 1965 the Smithsonian observed the 200th anniversary of the birth of its founding benefactor. These records document planning for that event.

ARRANGEMENT: Alphabetic by subject. FINDING AIDS: Folder list in control file. SPECIAL CONDITIONS: Use of this record unit requires prior arrangement with the Archives staff.

UNDER SECRETARIES AND ASSISTANT SECRETARIES

(175)

Assistant Secretary, 1932-1964
Records (0.3 linear meter).

John Enos Graf was Associate Director of the United States National Museum, 1931-1945, and, subsequently, an Assistant Secretary of the Smithsonian until 1957. John L. Keddy was appointed an assistant to the Secretary in 1946 and became an Assistant Secretary in 1947. Keddy's main duties were of an administrative nature.

These records of Graf and Keddy deal chiefly with Secretary Carmichael's efforts to reorganize and redirect the Smithsonian's research effort in 1953 and 1954. Smaller amounts of material deal with Graf's work in the National Museum and the work of the Commission on the Organization of the Executive Branch of Government in 1946.

ARRANGEMENT: Unarranged. FINDING AIDS: None. SPECIAL CONDITIONS: Use of this record unit requires prior arrangement with the Archives staff.

(137)

Under Secretary, 1958-1973
Records (14.4 linear meters).

The Office of Under Secretary was first established in 1971. It is the successor office to that of the Assistant Secretary (Administration), the position held by John L. Keddy from 1947 to 1960.

James C. Bradley came to the Smithsonian in 1959 as Assistant to the Secretary, a newly created position. In 1960, Bradley became one of the two Assistant Secretaries, and his primary responsibility was general administration. The title was changed in 1971 to Under Secretary. Bradley held the post until his retirement in 1972.

Robert Angus Brooks was Deputy Under Secretary, 1971-1972. On Bradley's retirement, the title of Assistant Secretary was revived and Brooks was appointed to that position. In May of 1973 the title again became Under Secretary and Brooks retained that post.

The Under Secretary is administratively responsible to the Secretary and is the second ranking official in the Institution. He assists the Secretary in formulation of programs, analysis and solution of problems involved in the determination of policies, execution of policy decisions, and maintenance of an effective management and administrative system to support the Institution's programs. The Under Secretary serves as the Secretary's liaison with Congress and various federal and non-federal agencies.

These records are mainly subject files kept by Bradley and Brooks in their capacities as Assistant Secretary and Under Secretary and concern the Woodrow Wilson International Center for Scholars, renovation of the Smithsonian Institution Building, the National Armed Forces Museum Advisory Board, legislation affecting the Smithsonian,

National Zoological Park, National Museum Act, personnel, Smithsonian Art Commission, National Portrait Gallery, Museum of History and Technology, budgets, congressional relations, Freer Gallery of Art, John F. Kennedy Center for the Performing Arts, plans for the Mall, National Air and Space Museum, National Collection of Fine Arts, Museum of Natural History, National Gallery of Art, Hirshhorn Museum and Sculpture Garden, Hillwood, regional museums, retirement funds, Smithsonian Astrophysical Observatory, relations with the White House, Folklife Festivals, and the Smithsonian Science Information Exchange. Also included is a speech file of James C. Bradley.

ARRANGEMENT: (1) Five alphabetic subject files, overlapping in dates and subjects, 1958-1973; (2) James Bradley speech file, 1958-1968. FINDING AIDS: Folder list in control file. SPECIAL CONDITIONS: Use of this record unit requires prior arrangement with the Archives staff.

(392)

Under Secretary, 1971-1984
Records (23 linear meters).

For information on the origins of the Office of the Under Secretary, see record unit 137. The second Under Secretary was Robert Angus Brooks, who served from 1973 until his death in 1976. Michael Collins served as the third Under Secretary from 1978 to 1980 and was succeeded by Phillip S. Hughes, 1980-   .

These records document the Under Secretary's involvement in all aspects of the Institution's operations from the perspective of a senior policy-maker, as well as contacts with governmental, corporate, and private bodies with which the Smithsonian conducted its affairs. A few records deal with Brooks's work as Deputy Under Secretary and Assistant Secretary and with Collins's directorship of the National Air and Space Museum.

ARRANGEMENT: (1) Office of the Under Secretary, records, 1972-1975, accession number xx-001; (2) Office of the Under Secretary, 1972-1974, accession number T91020; (3) Office of the Under Secretary, records, 1978-1979, with related records, 1971-1978, accession number 81-083; (4) Office of the Under Secretary, records, 1980-1981, accession number 84-103; (5) Office of the Under Secretary, 1980-1983, accession number 85-182; (6) Office of the Under Secretary, 1980-1984, accession number 86-059; (7) Office of the Under Secretary, 1983-1984, accession number 88-025. FINDING AIDS: Folder list in control file. SPECIAL CONDITIONS: (1) Restricted; (2) use of this record unit requires prior arrangement with the Archives staff.

(394)

Assistant Secretary for Administration, 1972-1982
Records (11.6 linear meters).

On August 15, 1976, Secretary Ripley appointed John F. Jameson Assistant Secretary for Administration. The title itself has been used in different ways at different times in the Institution's history. For a fuller understanding of its use, researchers should consult record units 137 and 175. In this instance the incumbent was the successor to the Under Secretary as the Secretary's principal lieutenant.

These records document the creation of the Office of the Assistant Secretary for Administration. Some records from the Office's administrative predecessor, the Office of the Under Secretary, are included as well. Researchers should note that the Assistant Secretary's functions passed to the Office of the Under Secretary, recreated in 1982.

The records concern the work of the Assistant Secretary as chief operating officer of the Institution, with special responsibility for budgetary and planning issues. The records also document early developmental stages of offices and programs which later became permanent administrative entities, such as the Museum Support Center, the Cooper-Hewitt Museum, and the National Air and Space Museum, or which were later terminated, like the National Armed Forces Museum Advisory Board. Some records from Robert Angus Brooks's tenure as Under Secretary are also included.

ARRANGEMENT: (1) Assistant Secretary for Administration, records, 1974-1976, accession number xx-002; (2) Assistant Secretary for Administration, records, 1972-1976, accession number xx-003; (3) Assistant Secretary for Administration, records, 1975-1978, accession number 81-028; (4) Assistant Secretary for Administration, records, 1976-1978, accession number 81-038; (5) Assistant Secretary for Administration, records, 1977-1980, accession number 82-063; (6) Assistant Secretary for Administration, records, 1977-1981, accession number 83-022; (7) Assistant Secretary for Administration, records, 1972-1982, accession number 84-093; (8) Assistant Secretary for Administration, records, 1979, 1981-1982, accession number 85-122. FINDING AIDS: Partial folder list in control file. SPECIAL CONDITIONS: Use of this record unit requires prior arrangement with the Archives staff.

(104)

Assistant Secretary for History and Art, 1965-1972
Records (11.3 linear meters).

The position of the Assistant Secretary for History and Art was planned by Secretary S. Dillon Ripley in 1964, but it was not filled until late 1967 when Charles Blitzer was named Acting Assistant Secretary for History and Art. Blitzer, who had been Director of the Office of Education and Training from 1965, became Assistant Secretary and served 1968-   .

The Assistant Secretary for History and Art served as the administrative link between the Secretary and the following Smithsonian bureaus: the Museum of History and Technology, the National Collection of Fine Arts, the National Portrait Gallery, the Freer Gallery of Art, the National Air and Space Museum, the Hirshhorn Museum and Sculpture Garden, the National Armed Forces Museum Advisory Board, the Smithsonian Archives, the Joseph Henry Papers, the Cooper-Hewitt Museum, the Office of Academic Studies, the Office of American Studies, the Woodrow Wilson International Center for Scholars, and the Archives of American Art.

These records contain correspondence, memoranda, and related material concerning the administration of bureaus listed above, as well as material concerning relationships with other Smithsonian offices. Also included are some files from Blitzer's previous position as Director of the Office of Education and Training.

ARRANGEMENT: (1) Bureau files, 1968-1971; (2) general subject files, 1968-1971; (3) alphabetic correspondence file, 1965-1969; (4) bureau files, 1968-1972; (5) general subject files, 1968-1972; (6) outgoing correspondence, 1968-1970. FINDING AIDS: Folder list in control file. SPECIAL CONDITIONS: Use of this record unit requires prior arrangement with the Archives staff.

Assistant Secretary for History and Art, 1965-1985
Records (24.7 linear meters).

For an administrative history of the Office of the Assistant Secretary for History and Art, see record units 104 and 281. Charles Blitzer served until 1983. John E. Reinhardt was Acting Assistant Secretary, 1983-1984, followed by Dean W. Anderson, 1984-1985. In 1985 the office was abolished as part of an administrative reorganization.

The Assistant Secretary for History and Art was responsible for overseeing the Smithsonian's programs concerned with those disciplines. These included the Anacostia Museum; the Archives of American Art; the Center for Asian Art (comprised of the Freer Gallery of Art and the Arthur M. Sackler Gallery); the Cooper-Hewitt Museum; the Hirshhorn Museum and Sculpture Garden (HMSG); the Joseph Henry Papers; the National Museum of African Art; the National Museum of American History; the National Museum of American Art (NMAA), including the Renwick Gallery and Barney Studio House; the National Portrait Gallery (NPG); and the Office of American Studies.

These records document an important change in the scope of the Smithsonian's concerns. Four of the bureaus and offices represented in these records existed in some form prior to 1964—the National Museum of American History, the Freer Gallery of Art, the National Museum of American Art, and the National Portrait Gallery. All the others were new enterprises for the Smithsonian and marked a great increase in the Institution's studies and collections in history and, especially, in art.

In addition, the records concern the administration of the bureaus and offices reporting to the Assistant Secretary for History and Art, including relations with the Board of Regents and the Office of the Secretary, prospective donors, budgeting and planning for federal and private financial support, relations with other museums and scholarly institutions, recruitment and other personnel matters, and the details of routine administration.

ARRANGEMENT: (1) Records, 1974-1981, accession number 82-093; (2) Special Assistant's files related to the Franklin D. Roosevelt Centennial (Susan Hamilton), 1980-1982, accession number 83-003; (3) records, 1978-1981, accession number 83-116; (4) budget reports and memoranda, 1980-1982, accession number 83-122; (5) project files, 1978-1980, accession number 84-019; (6) personnel files, 1975-1983, accession number 84-057; (7) records, 1971-1972, accession number 84-184; (8) reports, memoranda, and budget documents, 1982-1983, accession number 84-218; (9) appointment books and publicity on Charles Blitzer's appointment to the National Humanities Center, 1980-1982, and related materials, 1965, accession number 85-088; (10) budget files, 1983-1985, accession number 86-049; (11) administrative files, 1968-1985, accession number 86-156. FINDING AIDS: Folder list in control file. SPECIAL CONDITIONS: (1) Restricted; (2) use of this record unit requires prior arrangement with the Archives staff.

Assistant Secretary for History and Art, 1966-1980, with related records from 1961
Records (19.6 linear meters).

For an administrative history of the Office of the Assistant Secretary for History and Art, see record unit 104.

This record unit documents the tenure of Charles Blitzer as Assistant Secretary for History and Art from 1973 to 1979. There are also records pertaining to the Office of Education and Training, 1965-1968, which Blitzer had directed.

The celebration of the Bicentennial of the American Revolution was a major Smithsonian project from 1972 to 1977. These records document those efforts from first proposals to their completion or abandonment and include memoranda, budget proposals, and audio-visual recordings including a 16mm film of the Wells Fargo Essay Contest, "Towards our Third Century."

Changes in History and Art's organization during these years included the return of the Hillwood Estate to the Marjorie Merriweather Post Foundation in 1975, the transfer of the Smithsonian Institution Archives to the Assistant Secretary for Museum Programs, and the assignment of the office of the American Revolution Bicentennial Coordinator to History and Art. The Renwick Gallery was acquired as a showcase for design, crafts, and decorative arts and became part of the National Museum of American Art. The Smithsonian also acquired the Carnegie Mansion and renovated it to house the Cooper-Hewitt Museum of Decorative Arts and Design, which opened in 1976. The Hirshhorn Museum and Sculpture Garden was completed during this period and opened in 1974. The Museum of History and Technology became the National Museum of History and Technology (NMHT) in 1969.

The records consist of correspondence, memoranda, budgets, and associated materials documenting the changing activities of History and Art bureaus during a period of intense activity and growth.

ARRANGEMENT: (1) Bureau and office files, 1961-1980; (2) general correspondence files, 1964-1979; (3) budget files, 1972-1980; (4) Smithsonian offices and bureau files (other than History and Art), 1965-1979; (5) Director of Education and Training files, 1965-1968. FINDING AIDS: Folder list in control file. SPECIAL CONDITIONS: Use of this record unit requires prior arrangement with the Archives staff.

(337)

Assistant Secretary for History and Art, American Revolution Bicentennial Coordinator, 1968-1977
Records (17.8 linear meters and oversize).

The Bicentennial Coordinator's Office was created on July 1, 1971, to coordinate the work of a special Institution-wide committee intended to plan the Smithsonian's activities in observance of the Bicentennial of the American Revolution. The office was abolished in 1977 at the conclusion of the Bicentennial observance.

These records document the work of Susan A. Hamilton as Bicentennial Coordinator, acting under the direction of the Assistant Secretary for History and Art. They also cover preliminary planning for Bicentennial programs carried out between 1968 and the creation of the Office in 1971. For a fuller record of such activities, researchers should also consult the records of John J. Slocum, Special Assistant to the Secretary (record unit 341).

Records consist of correspondence, memoranda, publications, photographs, videotapes, a banner, and posters documenting the work of the Coordinator and the committee, as well as proposals and planning documents for both approved and rejected projects prepared to mark the Bicentennial. Plans for *Art in America: A Bibliography* and for an exhibition, *The Federal City: Plans and Realities,* are especially well represented.

ARRANGEMENT: (1) Bicentennial Coordinator's records, 1968-1977, accession number xx-016; (2) graphic arts materials (oversize), 1976, accession number xx-017; (3) Coordinator's records, 1971-1977, accession number 83-004; (4) Coordinator's records, 1971-1976, accession number 84-141. FINDING AIDS: Folder list in control file. SPECIAL CONDITIONS: Use of this record unit requires prior arrangement with the Archives staff.

(190)

Director General of Museums and Director, United States National Museum, circa 1921-1973

Records (11.6 linear meters).

The title of Director General of Museums was established in 1968 concurrent with the establishment of the Office of Special Museum Programs. In FY 1969 both titles, Director General of Museums and Director, United States National Museum (USNM), were assumed by Frank A. Taylor.

By 1957 the development of the programs of the Museum of History and Technology and the Museum of Natural History necessitated separate directorships for these two components of the National Museum. Frank A. Taylor became the first Director of the Museum of History and Technology, serving from 1958 to 1964. A. Remington Kellogg became Acting Director of the Museum of Natural History. Both individual directors continued under the general direction of the Director, USNM, Kellogg. Taylor was named Director, USNM, in the fall of 1962 upon the retirement of Kellogg. In June 1967 the Director, USNM, was relieved of line responsibility for the Museum of History and Technology and the Museum of Natural History. Under the direction of the Secretary, the Director, USNM, continued to carry out the directives of the National Museum Act of 1966 and continued to administer the Office of Exhibits, Conservation Analytical Laboratory, Office of the Registrar, and the Smithsonian Traveling Exhibition Service. The Office of Special Museum Programs was created in FY 1968 and Frank A. Taylor was named Director General of Museums. From FY 1969 until his retirement in January 1971, Taylor served as Director General of Museums and Director, USNM. In August 1972 Paul N. Perrot became Assistant Secretary for Museum Programs (Director, USNM). The Assistant Secretary for Museum Programs assumed essentially the same duties and responsibilities performed by the Director General of Museums.

Records are essentially those of Frank A. Taylor in his capacity as Director, USNM, 1962-1971, and Director General of Museums, 1968-1971. However, some records as Chairman of the Exhibits Modernization Committee, 1943-1959, and as Director of the Museum of History and Technology, 1958-1964, as well as related records are included.

ARRANGEMENT: (1) General file, 1960-1972, arranged alphabetically; (2) buildings, 1933-1971, arranged alphabetically; (3) United States National Museum, Office of the Director, 1964-1969, arranged chronologically; (4) National Museum of Natural History, 1965-1971, arranged chronologically; (5) National Museum of History and Technology, 1964-1971, arranged chronologically; (6) Conservation Analytical Laboratory, 1956-1972, arranged chronologically; (7) Office of Exhibits Programs, 1956-1972, arranged chronologically and special exhibits arranged alphabetically; (8) Smithsonian Institution Traveling Exhibition Service, 1955-1971, arranged chronologically; (9) legislative file, 1953-1972, arranged alphabetically; (10) National Museum Act, 1965-1972, arranged alphabetically; (11) museum education, 1964-1971, arranged chronologically; (12) museums file, 1949-1972, arranged alphabetically by state and foreign country; (13) museum assistance, 1961-1973, arranged alphabetically by state and foreign country; (14) special projects, 1966-1970, arranged alphabetically; (15) outside organizations, 1956-1972, arranged alphabetically; (16) National Science Foundation Belmont Conference, 1969-1970, arranged chronologically;

(17) American Association of Museums, 1955-1972, arranged chronologically; (18) International Council of Museums, 1957-1972, arranged chronologically; (19) Frank A. Taylor, personal, 1921-1971, arranged alphabetically; (20) miscellaneous and unfiled material, *circa* 1961-1972, unarranged. FINDING AIDS: Description in control file. SPECIAL CONDITIONS: Use of this record unit requires prior arrangement with the Archives staff.

(608)

Assistant Secretary for Museums, 1968-1989
Records (8.2 linear meters).

In 1985 the Office of the Assistant Secretary for Museums was created. The incumbent was responsible for the central planning, coordination, and oversight of the Institution's museums. He was also to advise the Secretary on all museum-related policies and programs and to serve as principal liaison between the Smithsonian and American and foreign museological organizations. Finally, he was to represent the Smithsonian in its dealing with federal agencies and foreign governments on museological matters. The first Assistant Secretary was Thomas L. Freudenheim, who served 1985-   .

These records document the development of the Office's mandate. There is extensive correspondence with Smithsonian bureaus and administrators, American and foreign government bodies at all levels, various learned societies, foundations, and other private organizations. The records also include correspondence of the Office of the Assistant Secretary for Museum Programs, chiefly on the part of Paul N. Perrot and William N. Richards, Jr., its Assistant Secretary and Acting Assistant Secretary, respectively.

ARRANGEMENT: (1) Records, 1979-1986, accession number 89-133; (2) records, 1968-1989, accession number 92-014. FINDING AIDS: Folder list in control file. SPECIAL CONDITIONS: Use of this record unit requires prior arrangement with the Archives staff.

(191)

Assistant Secretary for Museum Programs, 1972-1974
Drug Exhibit and Advisory Council on Historic Preservation Records (1.3 linear meters).

The Smithsonian Institution sponsored a major special exhibit entitled *Drugs* in May 1972. It sought to trace the historical roots and evolution of the use of hallucinogens and to educate the public in understanding drugs in our culture. The Office of the Assistant Secretary for Museum Programs sponsored an adjunct activities area for the presentation of panel discussions, lectures, theatrical shows, films, and other events.

The Assistant Secretary for Museum Programs is the representative of the Secretary of the Smithsonian on the Advisory Council for Historic Preservation. The Council is the federal agency charged with advising the President and Congress on matters of historic preservation with regard to the National Register of Historic Places, legislation, and the activities of the International Centre for the Study of the Preservation and Restoration of Cultural Property.

These records are the files of the Assistant Secretary for Museum Programs concerning these two activities. The records include correspondence, memoranda, newsletters, brochures, minutes of meetings, and other material.

ARRANGEMENT: (1) *Drugs* exhibit, 1972; (2) Advisory Council for Historic Preservation, 1972-1974. FINDING AIDS: Folder list in control file. SPECIAL CONDITIONS: Use of this record unit requires prior arrangement with the Archives staff.

(342)

Assistant Secretary for Museum Programs, 1972-1986, with related records from 1965 to 1976
Records (67.7 linear meters and oversize).

In 1972 Paul N. Perrot became Assistant Secretary for Museum Programs, assuming the duties formerly discharged by the Director General of Museums. For an administrative history of the earlier office, see record unit 190. In 1983 Perrot was succeeded by William N. Richards, Jr., Acting Assistant Secretary for Museum Programs. In 1986 the office was merged into a new office, the Assistant Secretary for Museums, held by Thomas L. Freudenheim.

This record unit documents the work of the Assistant Secretary for Museum Programs. The office directed the operations of the Conservation Analytical Laboratory, Office of Exhibits Central, Office of the Registrar, the Smithsonian Institution Archives, Smithsonian Institution Traveling Exhibition Service, and the Institution's functions under the National Museum Act of 1966 until its repeal in 1983. In addition, the office served as liaison with various regional, national, and international museum organizations.

Records document planning and equipping the Museum Support Center, the major facility constructed in suburban Maryland to care for the national collections, and occupied in 1983; administration of the Arts and Industries Building; exhibitions at the Evans Gallery of the National Museum of Natural History; Institute of Museum Services; and work with the American Association of Museums, International Council of Museums (ICOM), the International Centre for Conservation in Rome, the International Center Committee of the Advisory Committee for Historic Preservation, and the United Nations Economic and Social Council. The records of William N. Richards, Jr., as Special Assistant to the Assistant Secretary for Museum Programs, 1972-1983, and as Acting Assistant Secretary for Museum Programs, 1983-1985, are also included, as are some records dealing with Paul Perrot's work in the museum field prior to his tenure at the Smithsonian.

ARRANGEMENT: (1) Assistant Secretary for Museum Programs, records, 1972-1978, accession number xx-018; (2) Assistant Secretary for Museum Programs, International Council on Museums, 1965-1974, accession number xx-019; (3) Assistant Secretary for Museum Programs, 1966-1976, accession number xx-020; (4) Assistant Secretary for Museum Programs, personnel records, undated, accession number xx-021; (5) Assistant Secretary for Museum Programs, records, 1972-1976, accession number xx-022; (6) Assistant Secretary for Museum Programs, records, 1972-1979, accession number 81-021; (7) Assistant Secretary for Museum Programs, records, 1968-1979, accession number 82-058; (8) Assistant Secretary for Museum Programs, financial records, 1968-1977, accession number 82-092; (9) Assistant Secretary for Museum Programs, records, 1971-1981, accession number 83-014; (10) Assistant Secretary for Museum Programs, Institute of Museum Services records, 1978-1982, accession number 83-077; (11) Assistant Secretary for Museum Programs, architectural renderings and plans, *circa* 1975-1980, accession number 83-112; (12) Assistant Secretary for Museum Programs, records, 1972-1983, accession number 84-203; (13) Assistant Secretary for Museum Programs, records, 1980-1984, accession number 85-171; (14) Assistant Secretary for Museum Programs, records, 1972-1982, accession number 86-004; (15) Assistant Secretary for Museum

Programs, Dentzel Carousel records, *circa* 1981, accession number 86-063; (16) Assistant Secretary for Museum Programs, records, 1974-1984, accession number 86-066; (17) Assistant Secretary for Museum Programs, records, *circa* 1977-1986, accession number 87-021; (18) Assistant Secretary for Museum Programs, Museum Support Center and Arts and Industries Building records, accession number 88-037; (19) Executive Assistant to the Assistant Secretary for Museum Programs, records, 1973-1979, accession number 81-085; (20) Assistant to the Assistant Secretary for Museum Programs, records, 1977-1982, accession number 84-100; (21) Office of the Executive Assistant to the Assistant Secretary for Museum Programs, architectural drawings, 1974-1983, accession number 86-088. FINDING AIDS: Folder list in control file. SPECIAL CONDITIONS: Use of this record unit requires prior arrangement with the Archives staff.

(575)

Assistant Secretary for Museum Programs, 1975, 1978, 1980-1986
Records (6.2 linear meters).

For an administrative history of the Office of the Assistant Secretary for Museum Programs, see record unit 342.

This record unit documents the work of the Assistant Secretary for Museum Programs, Paul N. Perrot, over a substantial period of his tenure and the tenure of his successor, William N. Richards, Jr. Records concern issues of general Smithsonian administration and policy, as well as topics dealing with specific museums and Smithsonian programs.

Among the subjects documented are planning for the Quadrangle Museum Project, the work of the Smithsonian Institution Traveling Exhibition Service, and the National Museum Act of 1966.

ARRANGEMENT: Assistant Secretary for Museum Programs, records, 1975, 1978, 1980-1986, accession number 87-019. FINDING AIDS: Folder list in control file. SPECIAL CONDITIONS: Use of this record unit requires prior arrangement with the Archives staff.

(145)

Assistant Secretary for Public Service, 1961-1974
Records (5.7 linear meters).

The Office of the Assistant Secretary for Public Service was established in 1968. William W. Warner was appointed Acting Assistant Secretary for Public Service at that time; within a year he was appointed to the position on a permanent basis.

Prior to his appointment as Acting Assistant Secretary, Warner was the Consultant to the Secretary for International Activities, 1964; Special Assistant to the Secretary for International Activities, 1965; and the Director of the Office of International Activities, 1966.

In June 1972, Warner went on administrative sabbatical, and Julian T. Euell, Special Assistant in the Office since 1969, became Acting Assistant Secretary. Euell became Assistant Secretary for Public Service in November 1973.

The Assistant Secretary for Public Service is in charge of the following Smithsonian bureaus: the Smithsonian Associates; the Office of Public Affairs; the Division of Performing Arts; the Smithsonian Institution Press; the Anacostia Neighborhood Museum; the Office of Elementary and Secondary Education; the Office of Smithsonian Symposia and Seminars; Reading Is Fundamental, Inc.; and the *Smithsonian* magazine.

Other bureaus which reported to the Assistant Secretary for Public Service for part of this period included the Office of International Activities; the Smithsonian Museum Shops; and the Belmont Conference Center.

The records are arranged in four alphabetic series, in the order in which they were received from the originating office. The series overlap in chronology and subject matter and are probably just segments of one general alphabetic subject file that was weeded and separated as parts of the file became noncurrent.

Much of the pre-1968 material included in the records is material which Warner brought with him from his previous assignment as Assistant to the Secretary for International Activities. Others are files (mainly those relating to the Anacostia Neighborhood Museum) of Charles Blitzer (as Assistant Secretary for History and Art and as Director of Education and Training) which were transferred to Warner's office as responsibility for the Anacostia program was shifted.

ARRANGEMENT: Four alphabetic subject files, overlapping in subject matter and dates. FINDING AIDS: Folder lists in control file. SPECIAL CONDITIONS: Use of this record unit requires prior arrangement with the Archives staff.

(367)

Assistant Secretary for Public Service, circa 1968-1988
Records (20.1 linear meters).

For an administrative history of the Office of the Assistant Secretary for Public Service, see record unit 145. Julian T. Euell was named Acting, and then Assistant Secretary for Public Service in 1973. He held the position until 1983, when Peter Seitel succeeded him and served for a year. Ralph Rinzler held the office, 1984-   .

These records document the activities of the Assistant Secretary for Public Service in the 1970s and 1980s, with a small amount of material dating back to 1968. The records concern the offices reporting to the Assistant Secretary for Public Service, including the Anacostia Neighborhood Museum, the Smithsonian Institution Press, the Office of Public Affairs, *Smithsonian* magazine, the Office of Elementary and Secondary Education, the Office of Symposia and Seminars, the Resident Associates, the Division of Performing Arts, the Office of Interdisciplinary Studies, the Office of Telecommunications, the Smithsonian Institution Libraries, and the Visitors' Information and Associates' Reception Center. The relations of the Assistant Secretary for Public Service with other Smithsonian offices are also well documented. Also included is material on the *Aditi* exhibition and the *Festival of India.* Of special interest are the records of the Edinburgh International Festival, 1984, in which the Smithsonian participated with two conferences and a number of musical events. The Institution also mounted the largest exhibition which had ever traveled, called *Treasures from the Smithsonian Institution at the Royal Scottish Museum.*

ARRANGEMENT: (1) Records of the Assistant Secretary for Public Service, 1973-1974, accession number xx-030; (2) records of the Assistant Secretary for Public Service, 1968-1971, accession number 81-082; (3) records of the Assistant Secretary for Public Service, 1972-1980, accession number 83-068; (4) records of the Assistant Secretary for Public Service, accession number 84-116; (5) records of the Assistant Secretary for Public Service, 1975-1985, accession number 88-118; (6) records of the Assistant Secretary for Public Service, 1982-1985, accession number 89-039; (7) records of the Assistant Secretary for Public Service, 1983-1988, accession number 91-074; (8) records of the Assistant Secretary for Public Service, 1984, accession number 87-022; (9) records of the Assistant Secretary for Public Service, 1987, accession number 88-005. FINDING AIDS: Folder list in control file. SPECIAL CONDITIONS: (1) Restricted; (2) use of this record unit requires prior arrangement with the Archives staff.

(526)

Assistant Secretary for Research, circa 1984-1990, with related records from 1973
Records (7 linear meters).

For an administrative history of the Assistant Secretary for Science, the former title of the Assistant Secretary for Research, see record units 108, 254, and 329.

Robert S. Hoffmann succeeded David Challinor as Assistant Secretary for Research and served 1988-   .

These records consist primarily of administrative files of the Assistant Secretary for Research, 1987-1990, documenting his responsibility for the National Air and Space Museum, the National Museum of Natural History, the National Zoological Park, the Smithsonian Environmental Research Center, the Smithsonian Astrophysical Observatory, the Smithsonian Institution Archives, the Office of Fellowships and Grants, the Office of International Activities, the Smithsonian Tropical Research Institute, the Smithsonian Institution Libraries, and related environmental groups and projects. Only the *Panama Canal Alternatives Study,* 1973-1983, predates 1984. Of special interest are records documenting the closing of the Radiation Biology Laboratory in Rockville, Maryland.

For additional information, researchers should see record unit 393.

ARRANGEMENT: (1) Records of the Assistant Secretary for Research, *circa* 1981-1988, accession number 91-111; (2) records of the Assistant Secretary for Research, 1986-1990, accession number 91-175; (3) records of the Assistant Secretary for Research, *circa* 1973-1990, accession number 92-026. FINDING AIDS: Folder list in control file. SPECIAL CONDITIONS: (1) Restricted; (2) use of this record unit requires prior arrangement with the Archives staff.

(393)

Assistant Secretary for Research, 1985-1987, with related records from 1974 to 1987
Records (8.2 linear meters).

In October 1985, as part of a wider reorganization, a new office, Assistant Secretary for Research, was created. This office, together with the Assistant Secretary for Museums, superseded three predecessor offices, the Assistant Secretary for Science, the Assistant Secretary for History and Art, and the Assistant Secretary for Museum Programs. David Challinor, previously the Assistant Secretary for Science, and a specialist in forest ecology, became the first Assistant Secretary for Research and served through 1987.

These records document the operation of the Office of the Assistant Secretary for Research, which is responsible for overseeing the Institution's research activities in its various museums, the National Zoological Park, the Smithsonian Astrophysical Observatory, the Smithsonian Tropical Research Institute, and the Smithsonian Environmental Research Center. Records include budget and fiscal reports, research reports and research proposals from bureaus under the Office's jurisdiction.

The records also document the work of John H. Falk, a Special Assistant to the Assistant Secretary for Research, who also was on the staffs of the Chesapeake Bay Center for Environmental Studies and the Smithsonian Office of Educational Research.

This record unit also documents the activities of the Neotropical Lowlands Research Program, known before 1981 as the Amazon Ecosystem Research Program, and its principal investigators, Clifford Evans, Jr., and W. Ronald Heyer.

ARRANGEMENT: (1) Assistant Secretary for Research, records, 1985-1987, accession number 88-065; (2) Assistant Secretary for Research, Special Assistant (John H. Falk), records, *circa* 1975-1987, accession number 88-010; (3) Assistant Secretary for Research, Neotropical Lowlands Research Program, (Clifford Evans, Jr., and W. Ronald Heyer), records, 1974-1985, accession number 87-006. FINDING AIDS: Folder list in control file. SPECIAL CONDITIONS: (1) Restricted; (2) use of this record unit requires prior arrangement with the Archives staff.

(527)

Deputy Assistant Secretary for Research, circa 1979-1990
Records (4.9 linear meters).

Until late 1985, the Assistant Secretary for Research was called the Assistant Secretary for Science. Ross B. Simons served as Program Manager in that Office, 1976-1987. He was then named Deputy Assistant Secretary for Research and served 1987-   .

These records consist of the files of Ross B. Simons and document his responsibilities in the science bureaus of the Smithsonian Institution, particularly its environmental programs.

The records include correspondence and memoranda, reports, fellowship information, minutes of meetings, and budget files. Researchers should also consult the records of the Assistant Secretary for Science and the Assistant Secretary for Research.

ARRANGEMENT: Alphabetic. FINDING AIDS: Folder list in control file. SPECIAL CONDITIONS: (1) Restricted; (2) use of this record unit requires prior arrangement with the Archives staff.

(108)

Assistant Secretary for Science, 1963-1973
Records (9.5 linear meters).

The first person named Assistant Secretary for Science was Thomas Dale Stewart in 1964, although many of the functions of the office had previously been handled by one of the Assistant Secretaries. Sidney R. Galler was named to the position in 1965; and in 1971 David Challinor became Assistant Secretary for Science.

The Assistant Secretary for Science served as the administrative link between the Secretary and the following Smithsonian bureaus: Center for the Study of Man, the Chesapeake Bay Center for Environmental Studies, National Air and Space Museum, National Museum of Natural History, National Zoological Park, Office of Environmental Sciences, Radiation Biology Laboratory, Smithsonian Astrophysical Observatory, Smithsonian Science Information Exchange, and the Smithsonian Tropical Research Institute.

The records are arranged in four alphabetic subject files, overlapping in dates and subject matter. The files were probably segments of one general file which was weeded and separated as records became noncurrent.

ARRANGEMENT: (1) Four alphabetic subject files; (2) tapes of lectures, 1968-1969. FINDING AIDS: Folder list in control file. SPECIAL CONDITIONS: Use of this record unit requires prior arrangement with the Archives staff.

(254)

Assistant Secretary for Science, 1963-1978
Records (19.9 linear meters).

These records document the administration of Assistant Secretary for Science, David Challinor, 1971-   .

Bureaus whose actions are documented in these records include the Center for the Study of Man, Chesapeake Bay Center for Environmental Studies, Fort Pierce Bureau, National Air and Space Museum, National Museum of Natural History, National Zoological Park, Office of International Programs, Radiation Biology Laboratory, Smithsonian Astrophysical Observatory (SAO), Smithsonian Science Information Exchange (SSIE), and the Smithsonian Tropical Research Institute (STRI). These records also document offices which underwent administrative changes during the period, 1971-1976 including the Center for Natural Areas, Center for Short-Lived Phenomena, Office of Environmental Programs, Office of Environmental Sciences, Office of International and Environmental Programs, and the Office of Oceanography and Limnology. In addition, there is material concerning the office's involvement with federal and international agencies and private organizations regarding the preservation of endangered species and flora, conservation of the environment, ecological research, and the Research Awards Program which the office administered.

The pre-1971 records include materials transferred by Challinor and one of his assistants, Michael R. Huxley, from their previous assignment at the Office of International Activities (OIA), where Challinor served as Director, 1968-1971, and Huxley as Assistant Director, 1970-1971. The remainder of the pre-1971 material was inherited by Challinor from his predecessor, Sidney R. Galler.

These records consist of a correspondence register; files on bureaus administered by the office including reorganization proposals for SSIE, 1972-1973, photographs of the STRI facility at Barro Colorado Island, the Johnson-Sea-Link accident, 1973, SAO's Multiple-Mirror Telescope project, 1975-1976, and the Foreign Currency Program country files, 1972-1978, including the Nepal Tiger Ecology Project, 1972-1977; general office files including photographs of recipients of the Edward W. Browning Achievement Award, participants in the 1972 Galapagos Science Conference, Challinor's appointment books, and materials concerning organizations concerned with endangered species, flora, and ecology; OIA materials including information on the Sea Level Canal Study, 1970, the Mekong Basin Project, 1972, congressional bills pertaining to endangered species and flora, proposals for rules and regulations by international conservation organizations, scientific research agreements between the U.S. and foreign countries, and the Foreign Currency Program country files, 1965-1974; Research Awards Program award and program files and proposals, 1966-1977; newspaper clippings and journal articles; and printed materials.

ARRANGEMENT: (1) Correspondence register, 1971-1973; (2) files of bureaus under the Office of the Assistant Secretary for Science, 1963-1978; (3) general office files, arranged alphabetically by subject, 1966-1977; (4) Office of International Activities, 1967-1974; (5) Research Awards Programs, 1966-1977. FINDING AIDS: Description in control file. SPECIAL CONDITIONS: Use of this record unit requires prior arrangement with the Archives staff.

(329)

Assistant Secretary for Science, circa 1963-1986
Records (29.6 linear meters).

For an administrative history of the office of the Assistant Secretary for Science, see record units 108 and 254.

David Challinor served as Assistant Secretary for Science from 1971 to 1985, when his title was changed to Assistant Secretary for Research. Ross B. Simons served as Program Manager, 1976-   . Offices reporting to this Assistant Secretary included the Center for the Study of Man, the National Anthropological Film Center, the Chesapeake Bay Center for Environmental Studies (CBCES), the Office of Fellowships and Grants, the Office of Biological Conservation (OBC), the Research Institute for Immigration and Ethnic Studies, the National Museum of Natural History, the National Air and Space Museum, the Smithsonian Astrophysical Observatory, the Smithsonian Science Information Exchange (SSIE), the Radiation Biology Laboratory (RBL), the Fort Pierce Bureau, and the Smithsonian Tropical Research Institute (STRI). This period saw the termination of OBC, SSIE, and the Research Institute for Immigration and Ethnic Studies; the creation of the Office of Fellowships and Grants; the combination of CBCES and RBL into the Smithsonian Environmental Research Center; and the renaming of the Fort Pierce Bureau as the Marine Station at Link Port.

These records document the administration, under David Challinor, of the science bureaus of the Smithsonian, *circa* 1975-1985, and the International Environmental Sciences Program (IESP) during a period of intense environmental activity by the Institution. The IESP funded work in India, Egypt, Aldabra, and Brazil, among others. A subprogram of the IESP was the Environmental Sciences Program (ESP), which primarily funded research on the tropical ecosystem at STRI and the temperate ecosystem at CBCES. Smithsonian scientists were important participants in environmental organizations such as the Endangered Species Scientific Authority, the International Convention Advisory Commission, the Convention on International Trade in Endangered Species of Wild Flora and Fauna, and the International Union for the Conservation of Nature.

These records consist of correspondence and memoranda concerning operation of the science bureaus: their budgets, personnel, facilities, collections, and the filling of high level positions. Also included are files documenting the IESP and ESP and Smithsonian participation in other environmental organizations, and grant applications for scientific projects.

ARRANGEMENT: (1) Offices reporting to the Assistant Secretary for Science, *circa* 1963-1986; (2) administrative subject files, 1975-1985. FINDING AIDS: Description in control file. SPECIAL CONDITIONS: (1) Restricted; (2) use of this record unit requires prior arrangement with the Archives staff.

Assistant Secretary for Science, 1965-1971
Research Award Proposals, Awards, and Contracts (3 linear meters).

For an administrative history of this office, see record unit 108.

These files include the record copy of proposals for research awards for the fiscal years 1967 and 1968. Included are both new proposals and those proposals from previous fiscal years for which continued support was sought. The FY 1967 proposals and progress reports were generally made to Harry Hyman, Smithsonian Research Awards Administrator, 1966-1970, through Sidney R. Galler, Assistant Secretary for Science, 1966-1971. FY 1968 proposals were frequently accompanied by a covering memo from the Director of the participating museum. The memo was sent to Galler through Elbridge O. Hurlbut, Contracting Officer, and contained the Director's comments on the proposal. The proposals themselves were addressed to the Smithsonian Research Awards Program and also contained biographical information about the principal investigator, usually including a resume and list of publications. The files also contain records of research awards and contracts.

ARRANGEMENT: (1) FY 1967 new and continued proposals, arranged numerically; (2) FY 1968 proposals, arranged numerically; (3) FY 1968 proposals, arranged by bureau code number, and numerically within each bureau; (4) research awards, 1966-1971; (5) research awards, 1965; (6) contracts, 1966-1969. FINDING AIDS: Description in control file. SPECIAL CONDITIONS: Use of this record unit requires prior arrangement with the Archives staff.

UNITED STATES
NATIONAL MUSEUM

DIRECTOR, ASSOCIATE DIRECTOR, AND ASSISTANT SECRETARY AS DIRECTOR OF THE UNITED STATES NATIONAL MUSEUM, 1850-1975

Spencer F. Baird was appointed Assistant Secretary of the Smithsonian Institution in 1850, with primary responsibility for the direction of the United States National Museum (USNM). The title "Assistant Secretary" was not reserved exclusively for the administrator of the Museum; and throughout the history of the Institution there have been officials known as Assistant Secretaries who had other duties. In fact, there have often been two or more Assistant Secretaries present within the administrative hierarchy at the same time. The records listed below, however, are those of the official in charge of the United States National Museum, whatever his title. During the 1940s the title, Assistant Secretary, was permanently attached to other duties, and the responsibility for the Museum fell to an official known as Director, United States National Museum. A. Remington Kellogg was the first person to hold that position. Previously, the Secretary had been *ex officio* the Director of the United States National Museum. Incumbents included: (1) Spencer F. Baird, 1850-1881; (2) George Brown Goode, 1881-1896, including the years 1881-1887 when he served as Assistant Director of the Museum without the title of Assistant Secretary; (3) Charles D. Walcott, Acting Assistant Secretary, 1897-1898; (4) Richard Rathbun, 1897-1918; (5) William deC. Ravenel, 1918-1925, with the title Administrative Assistant to the Secretary, in charge of the United States National Museum; (6) Alexander Wetmore, 1925-1948; (7) A. Remington Kellogg, 1948-1962; and (8) Frank A. Taylor, 1962-1967.

In 1957 the United States National Museum created two administrative subdivisions: the Museum of Natural History and the Museum of History and Technology. In 1967 the United States National Museum as an administrative entity ceased to exist, and the Museum of Natural History and the Museum of History and Technology became separate administrative units. In 1969 the names of the museums were changed to the National Museum of Natural History (NMNH) and the National Museum of History and Technology, renamed the National Museum of American History (NMAH) in 1980.

In this *Guide,* records of the United States National Museum are considered separately from those of the National Museum of Natural History and the National Museum of American History. Only central administrative records of the United States National Museum will be found in the USNM section. Records of offices that now exist as part of NMNH or NMAH, or as obvious predecessors of currently existing administrative units, are listed under those museums. In order to maintain provenance, records listed under the sections of NMNH and NMAH whose date spans clearly falls within the time USNM was in operation will have USNM in their titles, and will also appear with USNM in parenthesis after the title in the index, even though the entries will be found in the sections for NMNH and NMAH.

All of the record units in this section constitute the files of the central administration of the United States National Museum. All of them are the files of the Assistant Secretary in charge of the United States National Museum or his direct subordinates. After 1882 most of the records were maintained by the Division of Correspondence and Documents (prior to 1886 the Department of Direction). The Division was in charge of the distribution and filing of correspondence of the Museum, including the acknowledgment of gifts, loans, and exchanges; the preparation of reports upon material sent for examination; replies to requests for technical information of all kinds; distribution of Museum publications; and the preparation, editing, and proofreading of the *Annual Report of the United States National Museum.* The first six record units listed are exceptions. Some of them were created prior to the establishment of the Division of Correspondence and Documents, and others were considered to be of such importance or confidentiality that they received the personal attention of the Assistant Secretary and were not maintained in the central files. The other categories of USNM records have been established for the convenience of the reader and do not necessarily reflect their provenance.

The organization of records in this section is complex. Prior to 1907, the main USNM series were divided between incoming and outgoing files; after that year a unitary system was used. In 1902, a numeric filing system was implemented, at first for incoming only (1902-1907) and, with establishment of the unitary system, for both incoming and outgoing correspondence. Throughout the period, additional, special files were maintained. Many of the records are related to accession records, either by subject matter or by relationship to accession records numbering systems. As noted in the explanation of registration records, the large Permanent Administrative File series changes in the 1940s and 1950s, and becomes mostly a registration-related record (kept by the Registrar after 1956). It is retained here for convenience since the numeric system is continuous.

(52)

Assistant Secretary (Spencer F. Baird), 1850-1877
Incoming Correspondence (8.1 linear meters).

For an administrative history of the Assistant Secretary, see the introduction to the United States National Museum.

ARRANGEMENT: (1) Chronologic, 1850-1852; (2) several alphabetic series, 1853-1868, 1871-1877; (3) United States explorations and government reports, 1852-1860; (4) foreign exchanges, 1859-1862; (5) accounts of sales, 1852-1861. FINDING AIDS: (1) All volumes are indexed individually by proper name; (2) records dating from 1850 to 1868 are represented in the card index; those from 1875 through 1877 have been erroneously indexed as part of the Secretary's records, volumes 184-209. The indexes in each volume are the most reliable. SPECIAL CONDITIONS: (1) Records dating from 1875 to 1877 have been assigned volume and page numbers which should be ignored for present research purposes; letters from 1869 to 1871 are missing altogether; (2) use of this record unit requires prior arrangement with the Archives staff.

Assistant Secretary (Spencer F. Baird), 1850-1877
Outgoing Correspondence (3.1 linear meters).

For an administrative history of the Assistant Secretary, see the introduction to the United States National Museum.

ARRANGEMENT: Chronologic, volumes 1-81. FINDING AIDS: (1) Card index, prepared by Archives staff from index to each volume; (2) index to each volume, created as records were created. SPECIAL CONDITIONS: (1) Deteriorating letterpress affects legibility; (2) record unit partially microfilmed; (3) use of this record unit requires prior arrangement with the Archives staff.

Secretary and Assistant Secretary, circa 1854-1890
Correspondence Registers (0.4 linear meter).

For an administrative history of the Secretary, see the introduction to the Office of the Secretary. For an administrative history of the Assistant Secretary, see the introduction to the United States National Museum.

ARRANGEMENT: (1) Secretary, outgoing registers, *circa* 1860-1890; (2) Assistant Secretary, incoming and outgoing registers, 1854-1872. FINDING AIDS: None. SPECIAL CONDITIONS: Use of this record unit requires prior arrangement with the Archives staff.

Assistant Secretary, 1858-1869 and undated
Correspondence with the Hudson's Bay Company (0.1 linear meter).

In the late 1850s, the Smithsonian Institution began receiving large collections of ethnographic and natural history material from arctic America, gathered by officers of the Hudson's Bay Company (HBC). The Smithsonian's relationship with HBC was primarily a result of Robert Kennicott's explorations on behalf of the Institution during the 1850s.

These records consist of correspondence written to Smithsonian Assistant Secretary Spencer F. Baird by officers of the HBC documenting their collecting activities on behalf of the Institution. Principal correspondents include George Barnston, Laurence Clarke, Jr., Charles P. Gaudet, Donald Gunn, William L. Hardisty, Strachan Jones, James Lockhart, Roderick Ross MacFarlane, W. Mactavish, and Bernard Rogan Ross. Also included is correspondence from Elliott Coues to Baird concerning an expedition to Labrador, 1860; and miscellaneous notes and lists concerning natural history specimens.

This correspondence was apparently pulled from Baird's official files. Researchers interested in the HBC should also consult record units 26, 33, 52, 53, 305, 7002, 7215, and 7221.

ARRANGEMENT: (1) Correspondence, 1858-1869 and undated, arranged alphabetically; (2) notes and lists on natural history specimens. FINDING AIDS: None. SPECIAL CONDITIONS: (1) Record unit available on microfilm; (2) use of this record unit requires prior arrangement with the Archives staff.

Assistant Secretary in charge of the United States National Museum, 1860-1908
Incoming Correspondence (19.6 linear meters).

This record unit comprises the primary incoming correspondence of the officer in immediate charge of the United States National Museum.

These records chiefly document museum accessions and Smithsonian expeditions and field collecting trips. Other topics include operations of certain museum divisions, and miscellaneous subjects. Accession records include: Alfred E. Hippisley Collection of Chinese Porcelain, 1909-1912; Horace Capron Collection of Japanese Art; John Croumbie Brown publications and manuscripts; Frances Lea Chamberlain collection of gems and minerals; Cardwell collection of Egyptian antiquities; Riggs collection of armor; Israel H. Harris fossil collection; Owen collection of fossils; J. Gwyn Jeffreys collection of shells; Thomas V. Keam collection of pottery; Chinese musical instruments; Frederick S. Perkins collection of copper implements; Troost collection of Crinoids; Robert Wilson Shufeldt collection of birds; Bradley collection of fossils; Ball Herbarium; Talcott Williams collection of Moroccan flora.

Records related to Smithsonian expeditions and field work include: William Louis Abbott collecting work, 1889-1901, in Central Africa, Somaliland, Kashmir, Turkestan, Siam, Burma; Beecher S. Bowdish collecting work in Puerto Rico and Cuba, 1901-1902; S. H. Boyd collecting work in Siam; William Harvey Brown collecting work in Africa; C. G. Calkins collecting work in Japan; John H. Camp collecting work in Africa; Charles Chaille-Long collecting work in Egypt; Heli Chatelain collecting work in Africa; Emile Deschamps collecting work in the Orient; Bruno Geisler collecting work in New Guinea; United States Navy expedition to Guam, 1899; Greely Relief Expedition, 1884; Pierre Louis Jouy collecting work in Arizona and New Mexico; Mark Brickell Kerr collecting work in Central and South America; C. A. King collecting work in Central America; John Francis Lebaron collecting work in Nicaragua; Roderick Ross MacFarlane collecting work in Canada; D. J. MacGowan collecting work in China and Manchuria; Mexican-United States Boundary Commission; A. J. Miller collecting work in Central America; R. B. Montcreiffe collecting work in Nicaragua; Edward William Nelson collecting work in Arizona; Herbert Gouvernour Ogden collecting work in Alaska; Charles Russell Orcutt collecting work in Mexico; Edward Palmer collecting work in Florida; Robert Edwin Peary Expedition to Northern Greenland; Cyrus Guernsey Pringle collecting work in Mexico; *Illustrated American* Expedition to Southern Utah and Northern New Mexico; Charles Wallace Richmond collecting work in Central America; William Woodville Rockhill Expedition to China and Tibet; William Edwin Safford collecting work in South America; Percy W. Shufeldt collecting work in Mexico; Robert Wilson Shufeldt collecting work in Louisiana; D. W. Snyder collecting work in Africa; Winfrid Alden Stearns Expedition to Labrador; Robert Stein Expedition to Ellesmere Land; Cyrus Thomas anthropological excavations in Pennsylvania and Ohio; Timothy E. Wilcox collecting work in Arizona; Henry D. Woolfe collecting work in Alaska and South America.

Records related to the origin or operation of subdivisions of the United States National Museum include: correspondence of Joseph William Collins, Section of Naval Architecture, United States National Museum; correspondence of Adolph Cluss regarding construction of United States National Museum building, 1881; correspondence of Wilbur Olin Atwater as Honorary Curator, Section of Foods, United States National Museum.

Miscellaneous topics include: Mexican-United States International Boundary Commission, 1891-1894; Smithsonian participation in the Medicinal Flora of America Commission.

ARRANGEMENT: Alphabetic by correspondent. FINDING AIDS: Description in control file. SPECIAL CONDITIONS: (1) Restricted; (2) inquiries related to specimens should be directed to the appropriate museum registrar; (3) use of this record unit requires prior arrangement with the Archives staff.

(201)

Assistant Secretary in charge of the United States National Museum, 1875-1902
Letters Received from Departments and Bureaus of the Government and Letters Received from Officials of the Museum (4.6 linear meters).

This record unit consists of two correspondence series maintained by the Division of Correspondence and Documents. The first series consists mostly of correspondence received by the central administration of the United States National Museum from Museum officials, curators, assistant curators, and aids. Most of the correspondence is routine and deals with administrative policy, requests for publications, staff problems, and exhibits. Materials of special interest include accounts of expeditions, reports on Smithsonian involvement at expositions, and data on significant accessions. Most of the correspondence is directed to George Brown Goode, with lesser amounts to Frederick William True, Samuel P. Langley, Spencer F. Baird, Charles D. Walcott, and Richard Rathbun.

The second series consists of correspondence received from United States government agencies. Much of the correspondence is routine, but some relates to collecting of specimens by government agencies and agents. Often, an individual employed by a government agency also served as an Honorary Curator in the United States National Museum, and his correspondence might be found in both series one and two.

ARRANGEMENT: (1) Letters received from officials of the Museum, 1880-1902; (2) letters received from departments and bureaus of the government, 1875-1902. FINDING AIDS: Description in control file. SPECIAL CONDITIONS: Use of this record unit requires prior arrangement with the Archives staff.

(54)

Assistant Secretary in charge of the United States National Museum (George Brown Goode), 1877-1896
Records (0.7 linear meter).

George Brown Goode's (1851-1896) association with the Smithsonian Institution began in 1872 when Spencer F. Baird invited him to work as a volunteer collector for the United States Commission of Fish and Fisheries (USCFF). Goode accepted and became Baird's chief pupil and assistant. In 1873, he was appointed Assistant Curator in the United States National Museum (USNM), a position he retained until 1877 when his title was changed to Curator. In 1881, when the new museum building was completed, Goode was appointed Assistant Director. In that year he prepared Circular No. 1 of the National

Museum, which proposed a comprehensive scheme of administration for the Museum. On January 12, 1887, Goode was appointed Assistant Secretary in charge of the National Museum and until his death in 1896 he remained the head administrative officer of the Museum. After coming to the USNM, Goode continued to serve the United States Commission of Fish and Fisheries in various capacities. He acted as statistical expert for the Halifax Fishery Arbitration Commission, 1877-1878; chief of the Fisheries Division of the Tenth Census, 1879-1880; and United States Commissioner at the Berlin International Fisheries Exposition, 1880, and the London International Fisheries Exposition, 1883. On the death of Spencer F. Baird in 1887, Goode assumed the position of Fish Commissioner, and held it until January 1888.

This record unit consists of incoming and outgoing correspondence received by Goode and concerns both the USNM and USCFF.

ARRANGEMENT: (1) Incoming correspondence from the Secretary, 1883-1897; (2) outgoing correspondence and memoranda, mostly with the Secretary, 1887-1896; (3) incoming correspondence, mostly concerning the United States Commission of Fish and Fisheries, 1877-1895. FINDING AIDS: (1) Indexes bound with the outgoing correspondence; (2) description in control file. SPECIAL CONDITIONS: Use of this record unit requires prior arrangement with the Archives staff.

(192)

United States National Museum, 1877-1975
Permanent Administrative Files (87.4 linear meters).

In 1902 the Museum's Division of Correspondence and Documents instituted a numeric filing system for the general correspondence of the United States National Museum. That correspondence, as found in this record unit, comprises most of the central administrative files of the Museum. Prior to 1902, museum correspondence had been filed alphabetically by correspondent (see record unit 189). Beginning in 1862 the accession records of the National Museum had been filed using a numeric system similar to that later adopted for correspondence. Finally in 1924 the two numbering systems were integrated.

Records prior to 1907 consist mostly of incoming correspondence (outgoing correspondence can be found in record unit 112). After 1907 the records contain both incoming and outgoing correspondence. Much of the material consists of routine public inquiries. In addition, these records document museum accessions and Smithsonian expeditions and field trips. Other topics include Smithsonian participation in expositions, operation of certain museum divisions, and miscellaneous subjects. Accession records include: data on the Herbert R. Bishop jade collection; William Joseph Hammer collection of incandescent lamps, 1905; Robert Ward collection of ferns, 1905-1906; transfer of the United States Patent Office collections to the United States National Museum, 1906-1909; Hubert G. Squires collection of Chinese porcelain; Hippisley collection of Chinese porcelain, 1909-1912; collections from the Arizona fossil forest; E. A. Wakefield collection of Basuto pottery; James D. S. Chalmers collection of minerals; McIntire collection of historical objects; Charles Fuller Baker collection of Philippine insects; Georg Herman Baur natural history collection from the Galapagos Islands; United States National Museum collection of postage stamps; Isaac Lea collection of gems and mollusks; George D. Seymour collection of clocks; Joseph Priestley collection of scientific apparatus; Robert C. Hall ethnological collection; Dwight J. Partello bequest; John B. Bernadou bequest; Bernard Rogan Ross ethnological collections; Mrs. James W. Pinchot collection of textiles; Richard Mansfield collection of theatrical costumes; B. F. Chandler herbarium; Morris Loeb collection of chemical compounds; Donn collection of Lincoln relics; Frank S. Collins herbarium and library; Oldroyd collection of Lincoln relics; Thomas Jefferson writing desk; Richard E. Byrd airplane *Josephine Ford;* Walter W. Holmes fossil bird bone collection; Brush-Swan electrical apparatus collection; collection of first ladies' gowns in the United States National Museum; Virgil Michael Brand coin collection; Charles Russell Orcutt natural history collections; Isobel H. Lenman collection of Old World archeology; American period costume collection in the United States National Museum; Charles A. Lindbergh collection of personal memorabilia; Nordenskold Mesa Verde collection; Joseph Nelson Rose collection of cacti; Osborne collection of Guatemalan textiles; United States National Museum collection of building stones; the Holt collection of birds from South America, 1936-1940; the Annie M. Hegeman lace and textile collection; the United States National Museum's collection of Jean Leon Gerome Ferris paintings; James Townsend Russell anthropological collection; the Harvey Harlow Nininger meteorite collection; the Hope Diamond.

Records related to Smithsonian expeditions and field work include: Mexican-United States Boundary Commission; expeditions and collecting in the Philippine Islands, 1903-1905; University of Pennsylvania Expedition to Babylonia, 1887-1888; Metropolitan Museum of Art Expedition to Egypt, 1909; Arthur deC. Sowerby collecting trips to China, 1909-1936; Owen Bryant-William Palmer Expedition to Java, 1905-1910; Smithsonian-Roosevelt African Expedition, 1909; Rainey African Expedition, 1911; Smithsonian-Harvard Expedition to Altai Mountains, Siberia, 1912; National Geographic Society-Yale University Expedition to Peru, 1915; Smithsonian-Universal Film Manufacturing Company African Expedition, 1920; David Crockett Graham collecting work in China, 1925-1940; Hugh McCormick Smith collecting work in Siam; Marsh-Darien Expedition, 1924; Smithsonian Biological Survey of the Panama Canal Zone, 1911-1912; Ellsworth Paine Killip collecting work in Europe, 1935, and Venezuela, 1943-1944; Henry Bascom Collins, Jr., field work in Mississippi and Louisiana, 1938; Herbert Girton Deignan's collecting work in Siam, 1936-1937; the Johnson-Smithsonian Deep Sea Expedition to the West Indies, 1933; Stanley John's collecting work in the British West Indies, 1935-1938; Charles W. Gilmore and Frank H. H. Roberts collecting work in Arizona, 1937; the National Geographic Society-Smithsonian Institution Archeological Expedition to Vera Cruz, Mexico, 1938-1939; Matthew William Stirling's field work in Mexico, 1940-1946; the National Geographic Society-University of Virginia Expedition to the South Pacific Islands, 1939; Walter W. Taylor, Jr.'s archeological field work in Mexico, 1940-1945; Floyd A. McClure's bamboo investigations in Mexico and Central and South America, 1943-1944; Henri Pittier's botanical field work in Venezuela, 1944-1946; Philip Hershkovitz field work in Colombia, 1946-1950; the Finn Ronn Antarctic Research Expedition, 1946-1948; Brina Kessel field work in Alaska, 1950; Clifford Evans, Jr., field work in Ecuador, 1954-1958; Marshall T. Newman field work in Peru, 1955-1957; James Paul Chapin collecting work in Africa, 1957; Ralph S. Solecki field work in Iraq, 1954-1959.

Records which document Smithsonian involvement in expositions include: South Carolina Interstate and West Indian Exposition, Charleston, 1902; Louisiana Purchase Exposition, St. Louis, 1904; Jamestown (Virginia) Tercentenary Exposition, 1907; International Photographic Exposition, Dresden, 1909; World's Columbian Exposition, Chicago, 1893; Panama-California Exposition, San Diego, 1915; Panama-Pacific International Exposition, San Francisco, 1915; International Silk Exposition, New York, 1921; Pageant of Progress Exposition, Chicago, 1922; Sesquicentennial Exposition, Philadelphia, 1926; Progress Exposition, New Haven, 1926; International Exposition, Seville, Spain, 1927; Century of Progress Exposition, Chicago, 1933; Great Lakes Exposition, Cleveland, 1936; New York World's Fair, 1939; Golden Gate International Exposition, San Francisco, 1939; Texas Centennial Exposition, Dallas, 1936; Greater Texas and Pan American Exposition, 1937; Port-au-Prince Bicentennial Exposition, Haiti, 1949.

Records related to the origin or operation of subdivisions of the United States National Museum include: development of the Division of Textiles; history of the United States National Herbarium, 1886-1908; development of the Division of Medicine; development of the Division of Mineral Technology, 1914; Smithsonian Traveling Exhibit Service; Division of Graphic Arts; Division of Numismatics.

Miscellaneous topics covered by these records include: establishment of Bermuda Biological Station, 1900-1904; United States military operations against insurgents in the Philippine Islands, 1904; the Lincoln Memorial Commission, 1913; proposed construction of a George Washington Memorial; National Museum involvement in search for the Port Orford meteorite; exhibition of the *Spirit of St. Louis;* National Museum exhibition of objects from World War I; use of the National Museum building by the Bureau of War Risk Insurance in World War I; proposed creation of a National Museum of Engineering and Industry under Smithsonian control; Samuel P. Langley's aerodrome experiments; Smithsonian activities during World War II, particularly the evacuation of USNM collections from Washington; A. Remington Kellogg's work on the Governmental Advisory Committee on Oceanography and the International Whaling Commission; United States National Museum correspondence with Phineas T. Barnum, 1882-1891; Washington A. Roebling's mineral collections.

Most of the correspondence is directed to the officer in immediate charge of the United States National Museum (Richard Rathbun, 1897-1918; William deC. Ravenel, 1918-1925; Alexander Wetmore, 1925-1948; A. Remington Kellogg, 1948-1962) with lesser amounts to John Enos Graf, who was appointed Associate Director, USNM, in 1931. Also, a smaller amount of correspondence is addressed to the Secretary of the Smithsonian (Spencer F. Baird, 1878-1887; Samuel P. Langley, 1887-1906; Charles D. Walcott, 1907-1927; Charles G. Abbot, 1928-1944; Alexander Wetmore, 1944-1952; Leonard Carmichael, 1953-1964) and to various museum curators. This correspondence was usually referred to the chief administrator of the United States National Museum for response.

ARRANGEMENT: Numeric. FINDING AIDS: (1) Description in control file; (2) partial card index. SPECIAL CONDITIONS: (1) Restricted; (2) inquiries related to specimens should be directed to the appropriate museum registrar; (3) use of this record unit requires prior arrangement with the Archives staff.

Assistant Secretary in charge of the United States National Museum, 1879-1907
Outgoing Correspondence (10 linear meters).

These records comprise the primary outgoing correspondence of the officer in immediate charge of the United States National Museum from the appointment of George Brown Goode as Assistant Director in 1881. Records from the years 1879-1881 mostly pertain to the United States Fish Commission, and Commission business is included through 1887. In 1888, Goode was made Assistant Secretary in charge of the United States National Museum. After Goode's death in 1896, the business of this office was administered for a time by the Executive Curator, Frederick William True. Richard Rathbun became Assistant Secretary in 1898, but most correspondence in this series in the period 1896-1902 is signed by the Executive Curator; after that, most is signed by the Assistant Secretary.

Several peculiarities of this record unit should be noted. Predominance of Fish Commission correspondence in the pre-1881 years has been described. Although letterpress volumes are numbered sequentially, dates do not always follow in strict chronologic order; sometimes special books were designated for an official to use when out of the city or when discharging special duties. Many letters were signed by subordinates, the Secretary, and by the Assistant Secretary as Acting Secretary. Apparently, the sequential numbering was imposed at a later date. These records were in the custody of the Registrar for many years. See record unit 189 for incoming correspondence. See also record unit 192.

ARRANGEMENT: Chronologic, letterpress volumes numbered sequentially with the prefix "L". FINDING AIDS: (1) Each volume indexed separately; (2) card index in record unit 116; (3) volume list in control file. SPECIAL CONDITIONS: (1) Record unit available on microfilm; (2) use of this record unit requires prior arrangement with the Archives staff.

Assistant Secretary in charge of the United States National Museum, 1883-1907
Internal Memoranda (2 linear meters).

These records consist of memoranda from the central administration of the United States National Museum, usually the Office of the Assistant Secretary, to staff of the Museum and other divisions of the Smithsonian. Most memoranda originate from subordinates.

ARRANGEMENT: Chronologic, 44 letterpress volumes numbered sequentially with prefix "M". FINDING AIDS: (1) Each volume indexed separately; (2) card index in record unit 116; (3) list of volumes in control file. SPECIAL CONDITIONS: (1) Record unit available on microfilm; (2) use of this record unit requires prior arrangement with the Archives staff.

Assistant Secretary in charge of the United States National Museum, 1885-1907
Reports on Inspected Specimens (26 microfilm reels).

These records consist of correspondence from the National Museum to persons who sent in specimens for examination. Most correspondence is signed by subordinate officials.

ARRANGEMENT: Numeric, 26 letterpress volumes numbered sequentially with prefix "R". FINDING AIDS: (1) Each volume is indexed individually; (2) card index in record unit 116; (3) list of volumes in control file. SPECIAL CONDITIONS: (1) Record unit available on microfilm only; (2) use of this record unit requires prior arrangement with the Archives staff.

(115)

Assistant Secretary in charge of the United States National Museum, 1887-1907
Transmission of Specimens (28 microfilm reels).

These records consist of receipts from the National Museum for specimens loaned or given to individuals and institutions. Before 1891, substantial correspondence is included; after that date, there are mostly copies of receipts. See also Specimen Distribution Records and Specimen Distribution Record Books, record units 186 and 120 respectively.

ARRANGEMENT: Chronologic, letterpress volumes 1-28 with the prefix "T". FINDING AIDS: (1) Each volume is indexed separately; (2) card index in record unit 116; (3) list of volumes in control file. SPECIAL CONDITIONS: (1) Record unit available on microfilm only; (2) use of this record unit requires prior arrangement with the Archives staff.

(116)

Assistant Secretary in charge of the United States National Museum, 1881-1904
Card Index to Correspondence (30 microfilm reels).

Index cards were prepared for the following series in the Assistant Secretary's office: Outgoing Letterpress Correspondence ("L"), record unit 112; Memoranda ("M"), record unit 113; Reports on Specimens ("R"), record unit 114; and Transmission of Specimens ("T"), record unit 115. The cards also index Accession Acknowledgements ("A") maintained by the Registrar, record unit 109.

ARRANGEMENT: Alphabetic. FINDING AIDS: None. SPECIAL CONDITIONS: (1) Apparently all series are not indexed for all years; indexes in individual series should be consulted; (2) record unit available on microfilm only; (3) use of this record unit requires prior arrangement with the Archives staff.

(408)

United States National Museum, 1881-1919 and undated
Preparators' Annual Reports (0.8 linear meter).

For a description of similar records and an explanation of the United States National Museum (USNM) reporting system, see record unit 158.

This record unit consists of weekly, monthly, and annual reports of USNM staff involved with the preparation of collections for study and exhibition. The reports were submitted to the Director of the USNM, and maintained by the Division of Correspondence and Documents. Included are reports of the Taxidermist, Osteological Preparator, Preparator of the Department of Arts and Industries, Modeler, and Printer. Also included are reports of the Division (before 1897, Department) of Comparative Anatomy.

ARRANGEMENT: Unarranged. FINDING AIDS: Folder list in control file. SPECIAL CONDITIONS: Use of this record unit requires prior arrangement with the Archives staff.

United States National Museum, 1881-1964
Curators' Annual Reports (12.7 linear meters).

The administration of the United States National Museum required curators to submit regular reports on the activities of the departments, divisions, and sections. Prior to about 1900 these reports were often made monthly and semi-annually as well as annually. The reports were traditionally submitted to the Director of the National Museum to be used in preparing the published *Annual Report of the United States National Museum.* The individual reports, however, were not reproduced in their entirety in the published *Annual Report* and generally contain more information than is to be found in the published version.

Reports were stored by the Division of Correspondence and Documents, and later by the Office of the Registrar.

Includes reports submitted to the Director of the United States National Museum by curators and administrators.

ARRANGEMENT: (1) Annual, semi-annual, and monthly reports, 1881-1897; (2) annual reports, FY 1898-FY 1930; (3) annual reports, FY 1931-FY 1934, FY 1936-FY 1956, FY 1958-FY 1960, FY 1964. FINDING AIDS: Description in control file. SPECIAL CONDITIONS: Use of this record unit requires prior arrangement with the Archives staff.

Assistant Secretary in charge of the United States National Museum, 1884-1939
Administrative Records (0.5 linear meter).

These records consist of copies of telegrams, official reports, memoranda, and correspondence between administrators of the Museum, other divisions of the Smithsonian, and government officials and other persons outside the Smithsonian.

ARRANGEMENT: (1) Telegrams, 1884-1907; (2) official reports, 1898; (3) memoranda between Executive Curator and the Assistant Secretary, 1896-1899; (4) memoranda, Executive Curator to the Secretary, 1896-1900; (5) memoranda, Acting Assistant Secretary to the Secretary, 1897-1898; (6) Assistant Secretary correspondence regarding the American Patent Centennial, 1891-1892; (7) copies of letters of introduction, 1884-1939. FINDING AIDS: Telegrams are indexed in each volume. SPECIAL CONDITIONS: (1) Record unit available on microfilm; (2) use of this record unit requires prior arrangement with the Archives staff.

Division of Correspondence and Documents, United States National Museum, 1890-1907
Records of Publication Distribution (0.5 linear meter).

ARRANGEMENT: (1) Publications distributed, 1895-1898; (2) publications, 1890-1907, 11 volumes (2 volumes missing from series). FINDING AIDS: Volumes indexed individually. SPECIAL CONDITIONS: Use of this record unit requires prior arrangement with the Archives staff.

Assistant Secretary, Acting (Charles D. Walcott), 1897-1898

Outgoing Correspondence (0.1 linear meter).

In January 1897, Charles D. Walcott, Director of the United States Geological Survey and Honorary Curator of Paleontology in the United States National Museum, assumed the duties of Acting Assistant Secretary. He resigned from the position June 30, 1898.

ARRANGEMENT: Chronologic. FINDING AIDS: None. SPECIAL CONDITIONS: Use of this record unit requires prior arrangement with the Archives staff.

Assistant Secretary in charge of the United States National Museum (Richard Rathbun), 1897-1918

Records (2.9 linear meters).

Richard Rathbun's career as an administrative officer of the United States National Museum (USNM) began in 1896, when he was appointed Assistant Secretary in charge of Office and Exchanges. After the resignation of Charles D. Walcott, Acting Assistant Secretary in charge of the USNM in 1898, Rathbun's duties were revised to include certain aspects of Museum administration. During this time the Executive Curator, Frederick William True, was the officer in immediate charge of the Museum. In January 1901, Rathbun was made Assistant Secretary in charge of the USNM, and so remained until his death in 1918. On the death of Secretary Samuel P. Langley in February 1906, Rathbun assumed the duties of Acting Secretary until the election of Charles D. Walcott in 1907. Major accomplishments of Rathbun's Assistant Secretarial years included the completion of the Children's Room of the Smithsonian Institution, 1901; the development of the National Gallery of Art, 1904-1910 (after 1937 known as the National Collection of Fine Arts); and the construction of the new National Museum Building completed in 1911.

ARRANGEMENT: (1) General correspondence, 1897-1918; (2) outgoing correspondence, 1898-1907; (3) reports on European museums, 1904 and 1907; (4) requests for and acknowledgments of receipt of United States National Museum Bulletin 70, *The National Gallery of Art,* by Richard Rathbun, January-April 1910; (5) historical research file, 1897-1918. FINDING AIDS: (1) Outgoing letterpress books, except volume 1, are individually indexed; (2) description in control file. SPECIAL CONDITIONS: Use of this record unit requires prior arrangement with the Archives staff.

Division of Correspondence and Documents, United States National Museum, 1907-1913

Logs of Letters to be Initialed (0.1 linear meter).

These logs apparently contain a record of outgoing correspondence signed by the Administrative Assistant, and forwarded to the Head Curators for information and initialing.

ARRANGEMENT: By department and alphabetic thereunder. FINDING AIDS: None. SPECIAL CONDITIONS: Use of this record unit requires prior arrangement with the Archives staff.

Director, United States National Museum (A. Remington Kellogg), 1925-1963 and undated
Records (2.1 linear meters).

A. Remington Kellogg (1892-1969) was Director of the United States National Museum (USNM), 1948-1962. He also served as Assistant Secretary of the Smithsonian Institution, 1958-1962. Prior to his appointment as Director, Kellogg had served as Assistant Curator and Curator in the Division of Mammals, USNM, beginning in 1928.

This record unit consists primarily of files created by Kellogg during his tenure as Director of the United States National Museum, 1948-1962. It includes smaller amounts of records kept by Kellogg as Assistant Secretary of the Smithsonian Institution, 1958-1962, and as Assistant Curator and Curator in the Division of Mammals, USNM, 1928-1948. The record unit also contains files created by other Smithsonian and USNM officials, including Alexander Wetmore, Kellogg's predecessor as chief administrative officer of the Museum, 1925-1948; Frank A. Taylor, Assistant Director of the USNM; and Albert C. Smith, Director of the Museum of Natural History. The records deal with Smithsonian and USNM administration and include budget files, 1949-1959, documenting fiscal development of the Smithsonian and its various bureaus, especially the USNM; reports on staff research submitted to the Smithsonian's Research Subcommittee, 1948-1962; a file concerning Smithsonian research funds and bequests made to the Institution, 1926-1957; and administrative files, 1925-1963, which document planning and development of the Museum of History and Technology and occupancy planning for the east and west wings of the Natural History Building.

For other records relating to Kellogg's service as Director of the United States National Museum, see record units 88 and 155.

ARRANGEMENT: (1) Budget files, 1949-1959; (2) Smithsonian Research Subcommittee, research reports, 1948-1962; (3) funds and bequests file, 1926-1957 and undated; (4) administrative files, 1925-1963 and undated. FINDING AIDS: Description in control file. SPECIAL CONDITIONS: Use of this record unit requires prior arrangement with the Archives staff.

Assistant Secretary in charge of the United States National Museum, 1936-1948
Letters of Detail (0.1 linear meter).

Letters of detail were sent to United States National Museum staff members from the Assistant Secretary and contained travel instructions and other information concerning field trips, attendance at conferences, and other official time spent away from the Museum.

ARRANGEMENT: Alphabetic. FINDING AIDS: None. SPECIAL CONDITIONS: Use of this record unit requires prior arrangement with the Archives staff.

Director, United States National Museum (A. Remington Kellogg), 1937-1968 and undated
Records (1.4 linear meters).

A. Remington Kellogg (1892-1969) was Director of the United States National Museum (USNM), 1948-1962; and from 1958 to 1962 he also served as Assistant Secretary of the Smithsonian Institution. Kellogg had served as Assistant Curator and Curator in the Division of Mammals, USNM from 1928 to 1948. Upon his retirement in 1962, Kellogg was appointed Research Associate in Vertebrate Paleontology, where he continued his studies in evolutionary marine mammalogy until his death.

This record unit consists primarily of records created by Kellogg during his tenure as Director of the United States National Museum, 1948-1962. Also included are files kept by Kellogg in his capacity as Assistant Secretary of the Smithsonian Institution, 1958-1962, and Research Associate in Vertebrate Paleontology, 1962-1968. Records prior to 1948 were created by Kellogg as Assistant Curator and Curator in the Division of Mammals, USNM. These records concern both Kellogg's own research and personal affairs, as well as USNM and Smithsonian business. They include correspondence, 1937-1968, between Kellogg and USNM and Smithsonian staff, professional colleagues, and personal acquaintances, as well as a subject file, 1940-1968.

For other records and papers of A. Remington Kellogg see record units 89, 155, 208, 7165, and 7170.

ARRANGEMENT: (1) General correspondence, 1937-1968 and undated; (2) subject file, 1940-1968 and undated. FINDING AIDS: Description in control file. SPECIAL CONDITIONS: Use of this record unit requires prior arrangement with the Archives staff.

Associate Director, United States National Museum, 1940-1943
Records (0.3 linear meter).

John Enos Graf was Associate Director of the United States National Museum (USNM) from 1931 to 1945. During the World War II era, Graf served as a member of the Committee on Conservation of Cultural Resources. Established in March 1941, the Committee was given responsibility for preparing plans for the protection of materials of cultural, scientific, or historical importance in the possession of agencies of the federal government. In 1941, Graf conducted a survey of significant Smithsonian collections to be evacuated in case of war.

These records include correspondence, memoranda, reports, meeting minutes, and related materials documenting Graf's work as a member of the Committee on Conservation of Cultural Resources and the 1941 survey of Smithsonian collections. A small amount of material was created by Carl W. Mitman, Chairman of the Smithsonian War Committee.

ARRANGEMENT: Unarranged. FINDING AIDS: None. SPECIAL CONDITIONS: Use of this record unit requires prior arrangement with the Archives staff.

United States National Museum, 1959-1960
Travel Reports (0.1 linear meter).

This record unit consists of reports on official travel submitted to the Director of the United States National Museum by the professional and technical staffs of the Museum of Natural History and the Museum of History and Technology. Included are reports documenting research trips, attendance at professional meetings, trips to examine and acquire collections, and field work.

ARRANGEMENT: Unarranged. FINDING AIDS: None. SPECIAL CONDITIONS: Use of this record unit requires prior arrangement with the Archives staff.

ADMINISTRATIVE ASSISTANT, UNITED STATES NATIONAL MUSEUM, 1882-1914

Administrative Assistant, United States National Museum, 1885-1914
Records (3.3 linear meters).

The Administrative Assistant was in charge of the general supervision of the expenditure of United States National Museum (USNM) appropriations; preparing proposals for supplies; issuing orders for the purchasing of supplies; settlement of accounts; awarding contracts; supervision of non-scientific or specimen-related correspondence; general supervision of employees, assignments to duty, granting leaves of absence; and conducting boards of inquiry and investigations of complaints. The Administrative Assistant also acted as special agent and at times was appointed representative of the Museum and the Smithsonian at international expositions. Prior to 1902 the incumbent was known as Chief Clerk.

William V. Cox was designated as the Museum's first Chief Clerk in 1885. When he left the Museum in 1902 the title of the position was changed to Administrative Assistant, and William deC. Ravenel was appointed to the post.

The records consist of outgoing letterpress book correspondence concerning general fiscal matters, estimates of appropriations, appropriation and expenditure statements, certified vouchers for the disbursement clerk, fiscal records pertaining to USNM exhibits at international expositions, and personnel matters. Originally these records had been kept in three separate series: (1) general museum business, (2) personnel, and (3) copied letters addressed to the Secretary transmitting vouchers for payment.

ARRANGEMENT: Chronologic, volumes 1-99. FINDING AIDS: (1) Volumes are individually indexed; (2) volume list in control file. SPECIAL CONDITIONS: Use of this record unit requires prior arrangement with the Archives staff.

Administrative Assistant, United States National Museum, 1882-1914
Incoming Correspondence and Internal Memoranda (5.7 linear meters).

For an administrative history of the Administrative Assistant, United States National Museum, see record unit 167.

ARRANGEMENT: Numeric filing scheme. FINDING AIDS: (1) Alphabetic card index; (2) box list in control file. SPECIAL CONDITIONS: (1) Records may be incomplete; (2) use of this record unit requires prior arrangement with the Archives staff.

RECORDS OF BUILDING CONSTRUCTION, 1879-1882, 1890, 1901-1919, 1928-1929

National Museum Building Commission, 1879-1882
Records (1.7 linear meters).

In 1876 the Board of Regents requested an appropriation from Congress to build a new museum, a necessity because of the incoming collections from the International Exhibition in Philadelphia. Congress complied and made an appropriation in 1879. The Regents appointed a building commission consisting of resident members of the Regents' Executive Committee and Secretary Spencer F. Baird. Cluss and Shulze of Philadelphia were made superintending architects. Construction began in April 1879 and was completed in 1881.

These records fully document the construction of the 1881 National Museum Building; included are fiscal records, specifications, bids and contracts, correspondence with the architects, and records of the Building Commission itself, including minutes of meetings. See also record unit 92.

ARRANGEMENT: (1) Vouchers submitted for payment, including payrolls, 1879-1882; (2) specifications, bids, and contracts, 1879-1881; (3) outgoing correspondence, 1879-1882; (4) incoming correspondence, 1879-1882; (5) minutes of meetings of the Commission, 1879-1880, with some letters bound in; (6) ledgers, 1879-1882; (7) plans, specifications, and contracts; (8) drawings, plans, and sketches, oversize. FINDING AIDS: (1) Indexes to outgoing correspondence bound in with volumes; (2) indexes to bids and contracts bound in with volumes. SPECIAL CONDITIONS: (1) Deteriorating letterpress may prevent any reproduction; (2) use of this record unit requires prior arrangement with the Archives staff.

Assistant Secretary, 1890, 1901-1916, 1923
Records Relating to Museum Construction (1.6 linear meters).

In 1903 Congress authorized the Board of Regents to begin a new museum building, construction to be under the direction of Bernard R. Green, Superintendent of Buildings and Grounds of the Library of Congress. Construction began in June 1904 and ended in 1911. Richard Rathbun, Assistant Secretary, spent much of his time from 1901 to 1911 planning and supervising construction of the new building, including extensive consultation with foreign and domestic museum experts.

These records, together with record units 80, 81, and 187, contain full documentation of construction of the 1911 National Museum Building from internal planning and contracts to construction details and costs. Rathbun prepared a history of the museum construction, which was published as "A Descriptive Account of the Building Recently Erected for the Departments of Natural History of the United States National Museum," *United States National Museum Bulletin 80,* Washington, 1913.

ARRANGEMENT: (1) General correspondence, 1901-1916, 1923; (2) subject files, 1890, 1901-1912; (3) photographs; (4) notes, extracts, and compilations from the correspondence and reports, 1901-1910; (5) Frank F. Graham and Thompson-Starrett lawsuits, 1907-1915; (6) space allocation files, 1908-1911. FINDING AIDS: Description in control file. SPECIAL CONDITIONS: Use of this record unit requires prior arrangement with the Archives staff.

Administrative Assistant, United States National Museum, 1902-1909, 1917-1919, 1928-1929
Records Relating to Museum Construction and Use of Facilities (0.3 linear meter).

For an administrative history of the Administrative Assistant, United States National Museum, see record unit 167. For an explanation of these construction records, see record unit 79.

ARRANGEMENT: (1) Correspondence, mostly copies, regarding construction of the Museum; (2) correspondence, 1917-1919, regarding use of the building by the Bureau of War Risk Insurance; (3) correspondence, 1928-1929, regarding repair of the dome of the building, provenance uncertain. FINDING AIDS: None. SPECIAL CONDITIONS: Use of this record unit requires prior arrangement with the Archives staff.

Superintendent of Construction for the United States National Museum Building, 1903-1911
Records (6.7 linear meters).

For an explanation of these records, see record unit 79.

ARRANGEMENT: (1) Ledger, 1903-1911; (2) record of contracts; (3) specifications; (4) outgoing correspondence, 1903-1911; (5) orders issued for materials; (6) incoming correspondence; (7) proposals; (8) daily reports; (9) applications; (10) contracts; (11) steel work; (12) drawings, blueprints, and floorplans, including oversize. FINDING AIDS: (1) Index to ledger; (2) index to outgoing correspondence, bound with volume. SPECIAL CONDITIONS: Use of this record unit requires prior arrangement with the Archives staff.

National Museum Construction, 1905-1909
Records (0.1 linear meter).

These records were sampled from a larger body of records related to construction of the National Museum Building (now the Natural History Building) between 1903 and 1911.

ARRANGEMENT: (1) Journal of stone received for use in building the third story, 1905-1906; (2) a record of government property on hand for building the National Museum, 1905-1909; (3) a daily report of services rendered and materials received, September 1907; (4) a record of the allocation of labor and materials, August 1907; (5) a time book of laborers' work, October-November 1908; (6) a monthly time book for the Graham contract (no. 25), December 1908-January 1909. FINDING AIDS: None. SPECIAL CONDITIONS: Use of this record unit requires prior arrangement with the Archives staff.

REGISTRAR AND RELATED RECORDS, 1834-1976

The chief accession records of the United States National Museum are the most important records in this section. Because they are related to other records in this section, and to some records included under "Director and Assistant Secretary as Director of the USNM, 1850-1975," a brief explanation is required.

Documentation of the USNM collection of specimens can be found in many records, and no attempt will be made here to describe all possible locations. Records directly related to the main accession file or its numeric system will be explained. Records of the Director of the USNM are closely related in subject matter to accession records. After 1924, numbers for several numeric record systems were assigned from the same number series, the most important of which were the accession records proper. See Office of the Registrar, 1834-1958 (accretions to 1976), record unit 305; and the Permanent Administrative Files of the USNM, record unit 192. Thus, users should approach accession records and USNM correspondence files together, especially if documentation of accessions is sought. This relationship also explains some peculiarities of the filing systems. Other specimen-related records listed under Assistant Secretary in charge of the USNM are Reports on Inspected Specimens, 1885-1907; and Transmission of Specimens, 1887-1907.

Yet another complicating factor is involved. During the 1940s or 1950s, the Permanent Administrative File ceased to be used as a file for the Director of the USNM, but the file itself persisted in the same numeric sequence as a record pertaining mostly to acquisition and accessioning of specimens, and after 1956 as a record of the Registrar. This file is, nevertheless, retained as the Permanent Administrative File of the Director of the USNM, because of its continuous numeric sequence; it is entered in this *Guide* under the section for administrative files of the USNM.

Office of the Registrar, 1834-1958 (accretions to 1976)
Accession Records (239.8 linear meters).

This record unit was assigned a new record unit number since the publication of the 1983 *Guide.* For information concerning the accession records maintained by the Office of the Registrar, see record unit 305.

Office of the Registrar, 1834-1958 (accretions to 1976)
Accession Records (239.8 linear meters).

Stephen C. Brown was appointed Registrar of the United States National Museum (USNM) in 1880 and served until his death in 1919. The Registrar functioned as the transportation, storage, and record clerk for the Museum and was responsible for shipping, accessions, storage, and the distribution of specimens. With the death of Brown in 1919, the position was abolished. Functions relating to accessions, examination and reports of specimens, and the distribution of specimens were reassigned to the Chief, Division of Correspondence and Documents. The duties of Shipping Clerk, which had been performed by Brown, were combined with those of the Property Clerk.

From 1919 until 1956, the Registrar's functions remained with the Division of Correspondence and Documents. Herbert S. Bryant and Helena Weiss served as Chiefs of the Division, 1918-1948 and 1948-1956, respectively. In 1956, the Division was renamed the Office of the Registrar, with Helena Weiss serving as Registrar until her retirement in 1971. Responsibilities of the Registrar included shipping, mail, transportation, distribution of publications, customs work, travel, correspondence, and accessions.

The Office of the Registrar underwent administrative and functional changes between 1971 and 1976. William P. Haynes served as Acting Registrar, 1972-1973; Richard H. Lytle served as Acting Registrar, 1972-1973, and Registrar pro tem, 1973-1975. In 1973 a Registrarial Council was created to study museum registration problems and to recommend changes to improve registration and control of specimens within the Institution.

Beginning in 1975, each Smithsonian museum had established its own Registrar to ensure proper documentation of all acquisitions, and to work with curators and conservators to ensure the security and availability of specimens. In addition to accessioning and shipment of specimens, other functions once part of the office of the Smithsonian Registrar, such as mail, customs work, and travel, were delegated to other offices within the Institution. The Council, which consisted of Museum Registrars headed by the Registrar of the Smithsonian Institution, continued as a forum for registrarial discussion.

The accession records of the United States National Museum (USNM) were maintained by the Office of the Registrar. The accession records constitute the official documentation of the national collections and include correspondence with donors, specimen lists, and subsequent correspondence documenting the history of the collections. Curators catalog specimens and maintain their own records of studies made of the collections. Ordinarily, these materials do not appear in the accession records.

Accession records dating from 1834 to 1857 were arranged alphabetically by donor within each year. From 1857 to 1862 the accession records were assigned sequential numbers within each year. Since 1862, the accession records have been numbered sequentially without regard to year. The year as printed or stamped at the top of each accession card within each accession file indicates the year the accession was received. Beginning in 1899, the accession year was based on the July-June fiscal year. The *Annual Report of the Smithsonian Institution* usually listed the names of the donors, accession numbers, and descriptions of specimens accessioned.

The provenance of accession records prior to 1880 varies widely. The earliest accessions, which predate the existence of the Smithsonian Institution, were for specimens collected by private individuals and members of the United States Exploring Expedition which were forwarded to the National Institute. Those specimens, along with the records documenting them, were transferred to the Smithsonian upon the demise of the National Institute, probably in 1862. It is uncertain who was responsible for maintaining accession records between 1846 and 1880. Attempts were made to assemble some form of registration system for maintaining control over the movements of specimens within and without the Smithsonian, possibly by the Chief Clerk or the Assistant Secretary of the Institution. Documents covering the years prior to 1880 were culled from the official correspondence of the Secretary and Assistant Secretary and made part of the accession record file.

Post-1880 accession files usually consist of an accession card and accession memorandum followed by incoming and outgoing correspondence, intra-office correspondence, and specimen lists, usually arranged chronologically. Undated documents were interfiled according to the context or placed after the accession memorandum. The accession records are arranged chronologically according to accession dates, with some exceptions. Dates within an accession file may vary widely, from documents preceding the actual accession to documents many years later. The numeric system is for permanent accessions. However, there are gaps in the numerical sequence, especially after 1924 when the numeric system used for permanent accession records became part of the overall numbering system used by the Division of Correspondence and Documents for the permanent administrative files of the USNM. These files (see record unit 192) consist of non-accession museum administrative records. Beginning in FY 1948, the permanent administrative files ceased to be used as a file for the Director of the USNM; but the accession file itself continued in the same numerical sequence as a record pertaining to acquisition and accessioning of specimens.

Fiscal year 1958 is used as the cut-off year for the USNM accession records in this record unit, since this was the last year in which the USNM existed as a single administrative unit prior to the creation of two divisions within the USNM, the Museum of Natural History and the Museum of History and Technology. Post-1958 accession records maintained the same numeric system and were kept by the Office of the Registrar until the period from 1973 to 1976, when each museum set up its own museum registrar; and the post-1958 accession records were divided up between the respective museums.

ARRANGEMENT: (1) Accession records, arranged alphabetically by donor within each year, 1834-1858; (2) accession records, arranged numerically within each year, 1858-1862; (3) accession records, arranged numerically only, 1862-1958; (4) non-permanent accession records; (5) pending accession files. FINDING AIDS: (1) *Annual Report of the Smithsonian Institution,* 1850-1873; (2) *Annual Report of the United States National*

Museum, 1874-1958; (3) Accession Record Books, 1859-1921, see record unit 110; (4) card index to correspondence on microfilm. SPECIAL CONDITIONS: (1) Record unit microfilmed; (2) restricted; (3) inquiries related to specimens should be directed to the appropriate curator; (4) use of this record unit requires prior arrangement with the Archives staff.

(127)

Registrar, 1880-1884
Outgoing Correspondence (0.1 linear meter).

For an administrative history of the Office of the Registrar, see record unit 305.

    These records include the correspondence of Stephen C. Brown with Spencer F. Baird at Woods Hole, Massachusetts, regarding operation of the Smithsonian.

ARRANGEMENT: Chronologic. FINDING AIDS: Volumes are indexed separately. SPECIAL CONDITIONS: Use of this record unit requires prior arrangement with the Archives staff.

(75)

Registrar, 1890-1919
Records (0.1 linear meter).

For an administrative history of the Office of the Registrar, see record unit 305.

    These records concern the operation of the Registrar's office and do not include accession records for Museum objects.

ARRANGEMENT: Unarranged. FINDING AIDS: None. SPECIAL CONDITIONS: Use of this record unit requires prior arrangement with the Archives staff.

(128)

Registrar, 1890-1919
Outgoing Correspondence and Annual Reports (0.4 linear meter).

For an administrative history of the Office of the Registrar, see record unit 305.

    These records include correspondence from the Registrar to Museum staff and others, mostly regarding transportation of specimens, and the annual report of the Registrar to the Assistant Secretary, including a statement of specimen distributions.

ARRANGEMENT: Chronologic. FINDING AIDS: Volumes are indexed separately. SPECIAL CONDITIONS: Use of this record unit requires prior arrangement with the Archives staff.

(199)

Registrar, 1948-1971
Records (0.4 linear meter).

For an administrative history of the Office of the Registrar, see record unit 305.

    These records include the files of the Registrar relating to budgets, personnel, organization, procedures, and policy. They do not contain accession records.

ARRANGEMENT: Alphabetic, by subject. FINDING AIDS: Description in control file. SPECIAL CONDITIONS: Use of this record unit requires prior arrangement with the Archives staff.

Registrar, 1958-1963
Telegrams (0.4 linear meter).

For an administrative history of the Office of the Registrar, see record unit 305. Apparently, the Office of the Registrar was in charge of maintaining copies of outgoing telegrams sent by the Smithsonian Institution.

This record unit consists primarily of copies of telegrams sent by officials of the Smithsonian Institution and the bureaus under its administration, 1958-1963. Occasional incoming telegrams are also found. The telegrams mostly concern procurement, personnel, and other administrative matters, but occasionally document the distribution of specimens, negotiations for collections, and field work.

ARRANGEMENT: Alphabetic and chronologic. FINDING AIDS: None. SPECIAL CONDITIONS: Use of this record unit requires prior arrangement with the Archives staff.

Registrar, 1853-1920
Specimen Distribution Record Books (2.6 linear meters).

For an administrative history of the Office of the Registrar, see record unit 305.

This is the record book of specimens distributed by the Smithsonian to individuals and institutions throughout the world. One volume includes distributions from Spencer F. Baird's personal collections. See also Transmission of Specimens and Specimen Distribution Records, record units 115 and 186.

ARRANGEMENT: (1) Main series, 1860-1920 (specimens dating from 1840 and earlier), 9 volumes and index; (2) specimens distributed, 1853-1862; (3) specimens distributed, 1861-1874; (4) reptiles, undated; (5) foreign exchanges, *circa* 1880-1890; (6) copies of invoices of specimens sent out for examination, 1900-1911; (7) specimen distribution index; (8) birds, S-Z, 1883-1892. FINDING AIDS: (1) Main series has a separately bound index; (2) index for the years 1874-1888; (3) card index. SPECIAL CONDITIONS: Use of this record unit requires prior arrangement with the Archives staff.

Registrar, 1853-1920
Specimen Distribution Records (4.3 linear meters).

For an administrative history of the Office of the Registrar, see record unit 305.

These records consist of correspondence and specimen listings and provide supplemental information to the entries maintained in the Specimen Distribution Record Books, record unit 120. Records which did not provide additional information were culled and discarded. Material concerns the distribution of specimens to schools, museums, public institutions, and individual scientists throughout the United States and overseas.

ARRANGEMENT: (1) Numbers D 0.0-D 0.1233, *circa* 1853-*circa* 1872; (2) D 0-D 32679, May 1872-March 1920. FINDING AIDS: Access to this record unit is provided through the Specimen Distribution Record Books, record unit 120. SPECIAL CONDITIONS: Use of this record unit requires prior arrangement with the Archives staff.

Registrar, 1859-1921
Accession Record Books (1.4 linear meters).

For an administrative history of the Office of the Registrar, see record unit 305.

The accession record books list incoming specimens of the United States National Museum in order of receipt. If the specimens are retained, the Registrar's control number assigned on receipt becomes the accession number. For the years 1859-1861, numbers begin anew each year; beginning in 1862, numbers are sequential without regard to year.

ARRANGEMENT: (1) Numeric beginning each year, 1859-1861; (2) numeric beginning in 1862 with number 1. FINDING AIDS: (1) Access by donor name provided by a card file in the Registrar's office; (2) three bound indexes for partial nineteenth century coverage. SPECIAL CONDITIONS: (1) Record unit available on microfilm; (2) use of this record unit requires prior arrangement with the Archives staff.

Registrar, 1875, 1880, 1904, 1919
Records Relating to Accessions (16 microfilm reels).

For an administrative history of the Office of the Registrar, see record unit 305.

ARRANGEMENT: (1) Index to donors, *circa* 1875; (2) index to donor names, accessions through *circa* 1886; (3) index to accession records checked out from the Registrar's office, undated; (4) accessions, 1919, no accession numbers; (5) accessions, 1904, numbers 10001-10100, do not correspond to permanent or temporary accession numbers in the main series. FINDING AIDS: None. SPECIAL CONDITIONS: (1) Record unit available on microfilm only; (2) use of this record unit requires prior arrangement with the Archives staff.

Registrar, 1884-1907
Accession Acknowledgements (52 microfilm reels).

For an administrative history of the Office of the Registrar, see record unit 305.

These records supplement the main accession files of the Registrar's office and thus comprise another source for documenting the national collections. They consist mostly of acknowledgements to donors for specimens sent to the National Museum. Beginning in June 1885, accession numbers are usually given on each acknowledgement, including accession numbers 15550 through 47007; accession numbers do not follow in sequence through the volumes.

ARRANGEMENT: Chronologic, volumes 1-52, with the prefix "A". FINDING AIDS: (1) Volumes are indexed separately; (2) card index, record unit 116. SPECIAL CONDITIONS: (1) Record unit available on microfilm only; (2) use of this record unit requires prior arrangement with the Archives staff.

Registrar, 1886-1907
Temporary Accession Record Books (0.1 linear meter and 5 microfilm reels).

For an administrative history of the Office of the Registrar, see record unit 305.

These record books list temporary accessions of the United States National Museum in order of accession action.

ARRANGEMENT: Numeric by accession number. FINDING AIDS: (1) Access by donor name provided by a card file in the Registrar's office; (2) bound index. SPECIAL CONDITIONS: (1) Record unit partially microfilmed; (2) use of this record unit requires prior arrangement with the Archives staff.

(121)

Registrar, 1891-1919
Examinations and Reports (0.7 linear meter).

For an administrative history of the Office of the Registrar, see record unit 305.

The Registrar recorded information about specimens received in the Museum and assigned each unit a control number, which is the accession number for those items which were retained. This record lists the specimens by control number and the name of the curator who was assigned to examine and report on them.

ARRANGEMENT: By control number, including a series for temporary accessions, numbers 24134-63871. FINDING AIDS: None. SPECIAL CONDITIONS: Use of this record unit requires prior arrangement with the Archives staff.

(126)

Registrar, 1894-1908
Record of Storage (0.1 linear meter).

For an administrative history of the Office of the Registrar, see record unit 305.

This is a record of specimens and objects stored and controlled by the Registrar's office. Information on contents is usually very limited.

ARRANGEMENT: Chronologic. FINDING AIDS: None. SPECIAL CONDITIONS: Use of this record unit requires prior arrangement with the Archives staff.

(122)

United States National Museum, 1850-1851, 1855-1969
Transportation Records (8.3 linear meters).

For an administrative history of the Office of the Registrar, see record unit 305.

These records are of incoming and outgoing shipments of the United States National Museum and other Smithsonian bureaus. Information recorded usually includes date, control number, address of sender and recipient, contents, and charges. Apparently a shipping office was set up in the new Natural History Building in 1912, and the main record was transferred there. Entries in the main record after 1912 reflect transportation activities related only to the National Museum. A separate record was set up in 1912 for other Smithsonian bureaus.

ARRANGEMENT: (1) Receipt of collections record, 1850-1851; (2) incoming transportation record for Smithsonian bureaus, 1855-1912, for United States National Museum, 1855-1969, with occasional outgoing record, 1855-1872; (3) incoming Smithsonian transportation record, 1912-1924; (4) outgoing transportation record for Smithsonian bureaus, 1885-1912, and for United States National Museum, 1885-1966. FINDING AIDS: Numeric list of transportation numbers for some volumes in control file. SPECIAL CONDITIONS: Use of this record unit requires prior arrangement with the Archives staff.

Transportation Clerk, 1850-1874, 1879-1884
Receipts for Packages (0.8 linear meter).

For an administrative history of the Office of the Registrar, see record unit 305.

These records include receipts from express companies for shipments from the Smithsonian. Entries usually give little or no information on contents of shipments, although more information is included for 1879-1884. One volume is for shipments by sea.

ARRANGEMENT: Chronologic, numbers assigned beginning each calendar year (sea shipment records excepted). FINDING AIDS: None. SPECIAL CONDITIONS: Use of this record unit requires prior arrangement with the Archives staff.

United States National Museum, 1864-1940
Register of Package Announcements and Express Bills Certified (0.4 linear meter).

For an administrative history of the Office of the Registrar, see record unit 305.

These records include a list of packages announced as being sent to the Smithsonian, listed and numbered in order of their announcement, and containing the following information when complete: transportation number, sender, origin, address sent to, how sent, date received, and expenses. The purpose was to control shipments of which the Smithsonian had been forewarned by letter or other means.

ARRANGEMENT: (1) Chronologic by date of announcement; (2) express bills certified. FINDING AIDS: None. SPECIAL CONDITIONS: Use of this record unit requires prior arrangement with the Archives staff.

Registrar, 1880, 1884, 1888, 1892-1893, 1897-1898, 1901
Exposition Shipping Records (0.3 linear meter).

For an administrative history of the Office of the Registrar, see record unit 305.

These records contain information concerning the shipment of exhibits and supplies to and from expositions in which the Smithsonian participated.

ARRANGEMENT: (1) Berlin International Fisheries Exposition, 1880; (2) Louisville International Exposition, 1884; (3) Cincinnati Industrial Exposition, 1884; (4) Ohio Valley and Central States Exposition, 1888; (5) Columbian Historical Exposition, Madrid, Spain, 1892; (6) World's Columbian Exposition, Chicago, 1893; (7) foreign shipments, 1893; (8) Tennessee Centennial Exposition, Nashville, 1897; (9) Omaha Trans-Mississippi and International Exposition, 1898; (10) Pan-American Exposition, Buffalo, New York, 1901. FINDING AIDS: None. SPECIAL CONDITIONS: Use of this record unit requires prior arrangement with the Archives staff.

United States National Museum, 1885-1929
Transportation Receipts (1.3 linear meters).

For an administrative history of the Office of the Registrar, see record unit 305.

These are records of shipments received by the Registrar's office and usually contain only scant information about specimens or objects.

ARRANGEMENT: Chronologic, control numbers 42598-169361. FINDING AIDS: None. SPECIAL CONDITIONS: Use of this record unit requires prior arrangement with the Archives staff.

Property Clerk, 1882-1890, 1900-1910, 1925-1930
Records (2.1 linear meters).

The Property Clerk of the United States National Museum was responsible for the inspection and distribution of all Museum supplies and furniture, for keeping commonly used supplies in stock, and for ordering special articles as needed. The title, Property Clerk, was not used until 1891, but persons had been appointed before that time to fill the same function. Persons responsible for property included Carl W. Schuermann, 1882-1886; J. Elfreth Watkins, Engineer of Property, 1888-1891; James S. Goldsmith, 1891-1898; William A. Knowles, 1898-1903; and Henry N. Spottswood, 1903-1904. Knowles was again appointed Property Clerk in 1904.

These records contain correspondence of the Property Clerk concerning requisitions, orders, solicitations of business, and administrative memoranda concerning operation of the Department of Property and Supplies. They also include early phone bills of the Smithsonian and annual reports of the Property Clerk which contain inventories of supplies on hand.

ARRANGEMENT: (1) Incoming correspondence, 1900-1910; (2) telephone bills, 1882-1886; (3) annual reports, 1925-1930; (4) orders for purchases, numbered 8741-28039 in order of issuance; (5) invoices, 1884-1890; (6) ledger, 1885-1887; (7) property receipts, 1886-1887; (8) small bills, 1884-1887. FINDING AIDS: None. SPECIAL CONDITIONS: (1) Provenance of records is uncertain; probably will be rearranged; (2) use of this record unit requires prior arrangement with the Archives staff.

NATIONAL MUSEUM
OF NATURAL HISTORY

The history of the National Museum of Natural History's collections begins with specimens collected by the United States Exploring Expedition, 1838-1842 and transferred to the Smithsonian Institution in 1858. The Smithsonian also received specimens by gift or purchase in the late 1840s. In 1850 newly appointed Assistant Secretary Spencer F. Baird donated his personal natural history collection to the Institution. During the 1850s and 1860s several expeditions which explored the American West also sent specimens to the Institution; and the dissolution of the National Institute brought additional collections in 1862. The collections were initially housed in the Smithsonian Institution Building. They were moved to the newly constructed National Museum Building (now the Arts and Industries Building) in 1881.

From the early 1880s until 1897, various departments and divisions within the United States National Museum (USNM) were responsible for zoological, botanical, geological, and anthropological collections. As a result of a major reorganization of the USNM in 1897, three Departments were created—Biology, Geology, and Anthropology—to administer the Museum's collections and research in those areas. Various curatorial divisions were established under each department. The collections were moved to a new building (now the National Museum of Natural History) devoted to natural history and anthropology in 1911. In 1947, the Department of Biology was abolished and replaced with two new Departments—Zoology and Botany.

In 1957, the USNM created two administrative subdivisions: the Museum of Natural History (MNH) and the Museum of History and Technology. The USNM was eliminated as an administrative entity in 1967, and MNH became a separate administrative unit. During 1963-1964, a major reorganization of the curatorial departments in MNH took place. The Departments of Entomology, Invertebrate Zoology, and Vertebrate Zoology were created to replace the old Department of Zoology; and the Departments of Mineral Sciences and Paleobiology were established in place of the old Department of Geology. Separate departments of Anthropology and Botany were maintained. In 1969, the Museum was renamed the National Museum of Natural History (NMNH). Directors of NMNH (before 1969, MNH) have included A. Remington Kellogg, Acting Director, 1957-1958; Albert C. Smith, 1958-1962; Thomas Dale Stewart, 1962-1966; Richard Sumner Cowan, 1966-1973; Porter M. Kier, 1973-1979; James F. Mello, Acting Director, 1979; Richard S. Fiske, 1980-1985; James C. Tyler, Acting Director, 1985, 1988; Robert S. Hoffmann, 1985-1988; and Frank H. Talbot, 1988-   .

DIRECTOR, ASSOCIATE DIRECTOR, ASSISTANT DIRECTOR, AND CENTRAL ADMINISTRATIVE OFFICES, 1948-1991

(155)

Director, National Museum of Natural History, 1948-1970
Records (18.9 linear meters).

For an administrative history of the Office of the Director, National Museum of Natural History (NMNH), see the introduction to NMNH.

These records are the administrative files of the Office of the Director, NMNH. Most of the records date from the 1950s. Those records created prior to 1959 are the records of the Director of the United States National Museum, although they are records relating primarily to that segment of the USNM which became the Museum of Natural History in 1957. Directors whose activities are documented include A. Remington Kellogg, Frank A. Taylor, Albert C. Smith, Thomas Dale Stewart, and Richard Sumner Cowan. Related records are to be found in record units 88 and 89.

ARRANGEMENT: (1) Subject files, 1948-1968, arranged alphabetically by major subject categories and numerically by sub-topic thereunder; (2) subject files, 1950-1970, arranged chronologically by calendar year and numerically by subject thereunder; (3) add acquisition, additional segments of series 2, 1968-1969; (4) file plans for series 1 and series 2. FINDING AIDS: Description in control file. SPECIAL CONDITIONS: Use of this record unit requires prior arrangement with the Archives staff.

(309)

Director, National Museum of Natural History, 1962-1978
Records (7.3 linear meters).

For an administrative history of the Office of the Director, National Museum of Natural History (NMNH), see the introduction to NMNH.

These records are chiefly the official administrative files of the Office of the Director of NMNH, 1976-1978. The files document Porter M. Kier's tenure as Director of NMNH. A few records predate this period and consist of files documenting funding for research conducted by NMNH scientists.

ARRANGEMENT: (1) Alphabetic subject file, 1976; (2) alphabetic subject file, 1977; (3) alphabetic subject file, 1978; (4) proposals and grants file, 1962-1978; (5) budget files, FY 1976. FINDING AIDS: Description in control file. SPECIAL CONDITIONS: Use of this record unit requires prior arrangement with the Archives staff.

(197)

Director, National Museum of Natural History, 1964-1973
Records (7.3 linear meters).

For an administrative history of the Office of the Director, National Museum of Natural History (NMNH), see the introduction to NMNH.

These records are chiefly files of the Director's Office, NMNH, 1964-1969, 1971-1972, and document the activities of directors Thomas Dale Stewart and Richard Sumner Cowan. During the earlier period a complicated subject-numeric filing system was in use. In 1971 a simpler subject-numeric plan was used and replaced before the end of that year by a straight alphabetic subject file, which is the current office filing system.

ARRANGEMENT: (1) Records of the Director's Office, NMNH, 1964-1969; (2) Flora of North America Project records, 1967-1973; (3) Summer Institute in Systematics records, 1970-1971; (4) records of the Director's Office, NMNH, 1971; (5) records of the Director's Office, NMNH, 1972; (6) miscellany, 1964-1972. FINDING AIDS: Description in control file. SPECIAL CONDITIONS: Use of this record unit requires prior arrangement with the Archives staff.

(364)

Director, National Museum of Natural History, 1969-1982
Records (1 linear meter).

For an administrative history of the Office of the Director, National Museum of Natural History (NMNH), see the introduction to NMNH.

These records chiefly document the role of NMNH in the organization and programs of the Association of Systematics Collections (ASC) during the tenures of Directors Richard Sumner Cowan, 1969-1973; Porter M. Kier, 1973-1979; and Richard S. Fiske, 1980-1982. The ASC was established on July 7, 1972 "... to foster the care, management, preservation, and improvement of systematics collections and to facilitate their utilization in science and society."

The records include correspondence, memoranda, reports, meeting materials, constitution and by-laws, and publications. They concern the initial discussions for a national program for systematics; the organization and incorporation of ASC; meetings and symposia of ASC; and Kier's service as ASC Vice-President. Also included are a few files documenting NMNH relations with the American Institute of Biological Sciences and the American Association for the Advancement of Science.

ARRANGEMENT: Unarranged. FINDING AIDS: None. SPECIAL CONDITIONS: (1) Restricted; (2) use of this record unit requires prior arrangement with the Archives staff.

(374)

Director, National Museum of Natural History, 1971-1990
Records (32 linear meters).

For an administrative history of the Office of the Director, National Museum of Natural History (NMNH), see the introduction to NMNH.

Porter M. Kier served as Director of NMNH from 1973 to 1979. Richard S. Fiske was appointed to the position in January 1980 and served until July 1985. Robert S. Hoffmann was named Director in October 1985 and remained in the position until January 1988. Frank H. Talbot was appointed Director in June 1988.

These records primarily document the administration of the NMNH during the tenures of Kier, Fiske, and Hoffmann. A small amount of files were created by Talbot and Acting Directors James F. Mello, 1979, and James C. Tyler, 1985 and 1988. Also included are a few records created during the tenure of Richard Sumner Cowan as Director in 1971-1972. The records document the research, exhibition, and educational missions of the

NMNH. They also document relations between the NMNH and Smithsonian bureaus and offices, educational organizations, and the museum community. Of special interest are files documenting the planning, construction, and the opening of the Museum Support Center, a facility constructed in suburban Maryland to care for the national collections and occupied in 1983; the opening and exhibition program of the Thomas M. Evans Special Exhibition Gallery; and the development of NMNH programs including the Molecular Systematics Laboratory and the Biological Diversity Program. Also included are fiscal and budgetary records, and files documenting special events at the NMNH.

ARRANGEMENT: (1) Director's files, 1973-1984, accession number 86-005; (2) Director's files, 1972-1982, accession number 86-038; (3) Director's files, 1972-1986, accession number 87-121; (4) Director's files, 1971-1988, accession number 88-161; (5) Director's files, 1985-1989, accession number 89-132; (6) Director's files, 1982-1990, accession number 90-054; (7) Director's files, 1983-1988, accession number 91-120; (8) Museum Support Center, 1983-1984, accession number 88-027; (9) fiscal records, 1979-1984, accession number 87-150; (10) special event files, 1983-1989, accession number 90-109. FINDING AIDS: Folder list in control file. SPECIAL CONDITIONS: (1) Restricted; (2) use of this record unit requires prior arrangement with the Archives staff.

(257)

Director, National Museum of Natural History, 1973-1975
Records (6.5 linear meters).

For an administrative history of the Office of the Director, National Museum of Natural History (NMNH), see the introduction to NMNH.

These records are the official administrative files of the Office of the Director of the National Museum of Natural History, 1973-1975. Porter M. Kier was appointed to that position on January 14, 1973.

ARRANGEMENT: (1) Alphabetic subject file, 1973; (2) alphabetic subject file, 1974; (3) alphabetic subject file, 1975; (4) reading file, 1975. FINDING AIDS: Description in control file. SPECIAL CONDITIONS: Use of this record unit requires prior arrangement with the Archives staff.

(362)

Director, National Museum of Natural History, 1974-1987
Special Programs Records (2.1 linear meters).

For an administrative history of the Office of the Director, National Museum of Natural History (NMNH), see the introduction to NMNH.

Marsha S. Cox, later known as Marsha E. Sitnik, was appointed Program Manager in the Office of the Director, NMNH, in 1983. Prior to her appointment she had served as Program Administrator in the Office of the Assistant Secretary for Science.

These records document special programs and projects undertaken in the NMNH. Included are files on the Caribbean Coral Reef Ecosystems Program, Scholarly Studies Program, Short-Term Visitors Program, a 1987 NMNH expedition to Henderson Island in the South Pacific, the 1987 NMNH Task Force on Research, the NMNH *Calendar,* and the NMNH Diving Board. Also included are files concerning the Charles Darwin Foundation for the Galapagos Islands, a program administered by the Assistant

Secretary for Science. The records consist of correspondence, memoranda, proposals, reports, budgets, and fiscal materials.

ARRANGEMENT: (1) Caribbean Coral Reef Ecosystems Program, 1985-1987; (2) Scholarly Studies Program, 1980-1987; (3) Short-Term Visitors Program, 1986-1987; (4) Henderson Island Expedition, 1982-1987; (5) NMNH Task Force on Research, 1987; (6) NMNH *Calendar,* 1984-1987; (7) NMNH Diving Board, 1983-1985; (8) Charles Darwin Foundation for the Galapagos Islands, 1974-1986. FINDING AIDS: Box list in control file. SPECIAL CONDITIONS: (1) Restricted; (2) use of this record unit requires prior arrangement with the Archives staff.

(533)

Director, National Museum of Natural History, 1982-1987
Records (0.4 linear meter).

For an administrative history of the Office of the Director, National Museum of Natural History (NMNH), see the introduction to NMNH.

These records include correspondence, memoranda, proposals, reports, and notes documenting efforts to obtain outside funding for research projects of the NMNH scientific staff.

ARRANGEMENT: Alphabetic. FINDING AIDS: Folder list in control file. SPECIAL CONDITIONS: (1) Restricted; (2) use of this record unit requires prior arrangement with the Archives staff.

(425)

Special Assistant to the Director, National Museum of Natural History, 1985-1987
Records (0.4 linear meter).

For an administrative history of the Office of the Director, National Museum of Natural History (NMNH), see the introduction to NMNH.

Ruth O. Selig was appointed Special Assistant to the Director, NMNH in 1985. She served in that capacity under NMNH Director Robert S. Hoffmann until 1987.

These records document Selig's work as Special Assistant to the Director and concern the McKinsey & Co. study of NMNH, 1986-1987; the establishment of the NMNH Development Office; and preparation of the NMNH Guidebook, 1985-1986.

ARRANGEMENT: Unarranged. FINDING AIDS: None. SPECIAL CONDITIONS: (1) Restricted; (2) use of this record unit requires prior arrangement with the Archives staff.

(384)

Associate Director for Special Projects, National Museum of Natural History, 1977-1991
Records (1.6 linear meters).

For an administrative history of the Office of the Director, National Museum of Natural History (NMNH), see the introduction to NMNH.

Catherine J. Kerby joined the staff of NMNH in 1976 when she was appointed Staff Assistant to the Director. Her title was changed to Special Assistant to the Director in 1984, Assistant Director for Special Projects in 1987, and Associate Director for Special Projects in 1991.

These records consist of correspondence, memoranda, reports, and related materials documenting a myriad of duties performed by Kerby during her career at NMNH. They include voluminous materials concerning the development of the National Museum of the American Indian (NMAI), especially activities of the NMAI Collection Management Task Force, and the movement of NMNH collections to the Museum Support Center. Also included are files created by Charles W. Hart, Jr., during his tenure as Staff Assistant to the Director, 1977-1979.

ARRANGEMENT: Unarranged. FINDING AIDS: Folder list in control file. SPECIAL CONDITIONS: (1) Restricted; (2) use of this record unit requires prior arrangement with the Archives staff.

(366)

Exhibits Committee, National Museum of Natural History, 1969-1989
Records (3.7 linear meters).

The National Museum of Natural History (NMNH) Exhibits Committee was formed in 1970 to advise the Director of NMNH on matters concerning temporary and permanent exhibitions at the Museum. The Committee, which included one representative from each of the scientific departments in the Museum, was responsible for advising in the selection of temporary exhibitions and the selection, support, and approval of the development and production of new exhibition halls. The Committee also assisted in the development of a long-range plan for museum exhibitions and was responsible for prioritizing the upkeep and improvement of existing exhibitions.

The Exhibits Committee was headed by a Chairman who served for roughly two years. The Chairmen represented by these records were: Ronald S. Goor (1970-1972), Leo J. Hickey (1973-1975), Douglas H. Ubelaker (1975-1977), Richard S. Fiske (1977-1979), Robert W. Read (1980-1981), Bruce D. Smith (1981-1983), and Richard S. Boardman (1983-1985).

These records consist of memoranda, correspondence, reports, meeting minutes, and plans and photographs of exhibitions and exhibition halls. Also included are some scripts of label text from various NMNH exhibitions. The bulk of the records are from the years 1970-1985, with a few items from 1987 and 1989.

ARRANGEMENT: Unarranged. FINDING AIDS: None. SPECIAL CONDITIONS: (1) Restricted; (2) use of this record unit requires prior arrangement with the Archives staff.

(363)

Office of Exhibits, National Museum of Natural History, circa 1955-1990 and undated
Records (16.7 linear meters).

The Office of Exhibits in the National Museum of Natural History (NMNH) was created in 1973 when a reorganization established independent exhibit offices in several Smithsonian museums. Prior to its establishment, natural history exhibitions were the responsibility of the Office of Exhibits, 1955-1969, and the Office of Exhibits Programs, 1969-1973. For administrative histories of these two offices see record unit 90.

Harry T. Hart was appointed Chief of the Office of Exhibits, NMNH, on March 18, 1973. Eugene F. Behlen replaced Hart on May 22, 1977, and he served as Chief until

1983. Carl A. Alexander was Acting Chief during 1983-1984. In 1984, administration of the Office of Exhibits became a duty of the newly established Assistant Director for Exhibits. Laurence P. O'Reilly was appointed to the position.

This record unit contains a variety of records documenting the planning, design, and production of permanent and temporary exhibitions at the NMNH. It also contains smaller amounts of records concerning exhibitions held at the National Museum of History and Technology, National Air and Space Museum, National Collection of Fine Arts, Anacostia Neighborhood Museum, and Arts and Industries Building. A few records documenting office administration are also found.

The records were created by the Office of Exhibits, 1955-1969; the Office of Exhibits Programs, 1969-1973; and the Office of Exhibits, NMNH, 1973-1990. Staff of the Office of Exhibits, NMNH, and its predecessor offices, represented in the records include John E. Anglim, 1956-1972; A. Gilbert Wright, 1963-1970; Dorothy Guthrie, 1965-1970; James A. Mahoney, 1969-1973; William F. Haase, 1969-1983; Harry T. Hart, 1970-1977; Eugene F. Behlen, 1977-1983; and Carl A. Alexander, 1969-1987. Also included are a few records of Laurence P. O'Reilly, 1984-1990.

The records offer primary documentation of natural history exhibition production at the Smithsonian, and they help to illustrate a period of intense exhibit modernization at the Institution. They include correspondence, memoranda, photographs, blueprints, layouts, scripts, work contracts, schedules, notes, and publications. Of special interest are records documenting the renovation of permanent exhibition halls during the 1960s; efforts to make NMNH exhibits more accessible to the handicapped; the development of the Insect Zoo; planning and preparation of the NMNH American Bicentennial Exhibition in the 1970s; activities of the NMNH Exhibits Committee; and professional activities of the staff.

ARRANGEMENT: (1) Exhibit files, *circa* 1956-1987 and undated, accession number 90-156; (2) exhibit files, *circa* 1958-1978 and undated, accession number 85-138; (3) exhibit files, *circa* 1959-1986 and undated, accession number 89-054; (4) exhibit files, *circa* 1960-1978 and undated, accession number 85-201; (5) exhibit files and administrative records, *circa* 1965-1978 and undated, accession number 88-042; (6) exhibit files, *circa* 1965-1982 and undated, accession number 87-064; (7) exhibit files, 1978-1980, accession number 89-152; (8) exhibit files, *circa* 1967-1988, accession number 91-044; (9) exhibit files, *circa* 1960-1990, accession number 91-160; (10) exhibit files, *circa* 1963-1989, accession number 92-097; (11) exhibit files, *circa* 1955-1973 and undated, accession number 84-097. FINDING AIDS: Folder list in control file. SPECIAL CONDITIONS: Use of this record unit requires prior arrangement with the Archives staff.

(564)

Office of Exhibits, National Museum of Natural History, 1974-1986, with related records from 1956
Records (1.6 linear meters).

For an administrative history of the Office of Exhibits, National Museum of Natural History (NMNH), see record unit 363.

These records consist primarily of scripts for NMNH permanent and temporary exhibitions. Also included are various reports on NMNH exhibitions, visitor surveys, and correspondence and memoranda concerning the preparation of background dioramas for the habitat groups hall in 1956.

ARRANGEMENT: Unarranged. FINDING AIDS: Folder list in control file. SPECIAL CONDITIONS: (1) Restricted; (2) use of this record unit requires prior arrangement with the Archives staff.

(416)

Public Information Officer, National Museum of Natural History, circa 1969-1991 and undated, with related material from 1959

Records (3 linear meters).

Thomas R. Harney joined the staff of the Smithsonian Institution in 1969 as Science Information Officer in the News Bureau of the Office of Public Affairs. In this capacity, he kept in touch with the National Museum of Natural History (NMNH) to inform the public of research developments and exhibitions through news releases and articles. In 1976, he was appointed Writer-Editor at NMNH, and in 1990 he became NMNH's Public Information Officer.

These records were created and collected by Thomas R. Harney and primarily document research, exhibitions, and public programs at NMNH. They include news releases, photographs, newspaper clippings, brochures, and related materials concerning permanent and special exhibitions at NMNH; a biographical information file containing photographs, notes, and published materials on NMNH staff; a subject file primarily concerning NMNH activities, but also containing materials regarding exhibitions at the National Air and Space Museum; 35mm color slides of NMNH exhibitions, staff, and events; and audiocassette tapes of press conferences and presentations at or about NMNH.

ARRANGEMENT: (1) Exhibition files, 1959, 1962-1964, 1966-1991 and undated; (2) biographical information file, *circa* 1960-1990 and undated; (3) subject file, 1962-1990 and undated; (4) slides, 1978-1990 and undated; (5) audiotapes, 1989 and undated. FINDING AIDS: Description in control file. SPECIAL CONDITIONS: Use of this record unit requires prior arrangement with the Archives staff.

(566)

Office of the Registrar, National Museum of Natural History, 1976-1989, with related records from circa 1960

Records (1.6 linear meters).

The Office of the Registrar, National Museum of Natural History (NMNH), was established in 1976 as a part of the decentralization of the Smithsonian's central Registrar's Office. At that time, NMNH and the National Museum of History and Technology were given control over their own registration activities. Margaret A. Santiago was appointed NMNH Registrar. The Office of the Registrar monitors the movement of collections at NMNH and is responsible for accessions, loans, and the shipment of specimens.

These records primarily document the operations of the Office of the Registrar and, to a lesser extent, the professional activities of Margaret A. Santiago. They include correspondence, memoranda, reports, and budget materials concerning the establishment of the office, registration procedures, collection management policies, workshops and training, office administration, and activities of the Smithsonian's Registrarial Council. Also included are records concerning Margaret A. Santiago's activities as a member of the American Association of Museums and the African American Museums Association, and photographs of the opening ceremonies of the new Office of the Registrar facilities in 1980.

ARRANGEMENT: Unarranged. FINDING AIDS: Folder list in control file. SPECIAL CONDITIONS: Use of this record unit requires prior arrangement with the Archives staff.

(429)
Senate of Scientists, National Museum of Natural History, 1963-1987
Records (3.7 linear meters).

In 1963, the Senate of Scientists was established to represent professional concerns of the scientific research staff of the National Museum of Natural History (NMNH). Modeled on faculty senates in universities, the Senate was structured to function as a trouble-shooter and source of collective opinion outside normal administrative channels. The Senate is managed by a council consisting of a chairman, chairman-elect, secretary, and one councilor elected by each curatorial department. Full membership in the Senate is restricted to scientists employed by NMNH, but associate membership is extended to research associates of the Museum and to scientists located in NMNH but employed by other government agencies.

Significant issues addressed by the Senate have included library service, parking policies, off-mall storage and curatorial facilities, technical assistance, automated data-processing facilities, funding for systematics research, and publications policies. In addition, the Senate has served as a stimulus to collegiality within NMNH, through its publications, seminars, teas, and dinner forums.

Chairmen of the Senate of Scientists have include Gordon D. Gibson, 1963-1964; Richard S. Boardman, 1964-1965, 1978-1979; W. Donald Duckworth, 1965-1966; Roy S. Clarke, Jr., 1966-1967; Francis M. Hueber, 1967-1968; Clifford Evans, Jr., 1968-1970; Martin A. Buzas, 1970-1971; Clyde F. E. Roper, 1971-1972; Thomas R. Waller, 1972-1973; W. Duane Hope, 1973-1974; Erle G. Kauffman, 1974-1975; Donald J. Ortner, 1975-1976; Richard H. Eyde, 1976-1977; Meredith Leam Jones, 1977-1978; Jack W. Pierce, 1979-1980; Herman J. Viola, 1980-1981; W. Ronald Heyer, 1981-1982; David L. Pawson, 1982-1983; William G. Melson, 1983-1984; Richard W. Thorington, Jr., 1984-1985; George R. Zug, 1985-1986; and Raymond B. Manning, 1986-1987.

These records document the establishment and activities of the Senate of Scientists. They were primarily created by the chairman of the Senate and include constitutions and amendments; committee files; minutes of council and annual meetings; records concerning dinner forums, seminars, and other Senate events; membership records; treasurer's files and financial records; files concerning Senate publications; project files; and photographs of Senate members. For additional information on the Senate of Scientists, see record unit 9508.

ARRANGEMENT: (1) Chairman's files and related materials, 1963-1983, accession number 89-091; (2) chairman's files, 1963-1965, accession number T90115; (3) treasurer's files, 1963-1982, accession number 90-161; (4) chairman's files, 1984-1986, accession number 87-136; (5) chairman's files, 1986-1987, accession number 88-019. FINDING AIDS: Folder list in control file. SPECIAL CONDITIONS: (1) Restricted; (2) use of this record unit requires prior arrangement with the Archives staff.

BIOLOGY AND ZOOLOGY, 1897-1958

(242)

Department of Biology, United States National Museum, 1897-1943
Records (2.3 linear meters).

For an administrative history of the Department of Biology, see record unit 143.

This record unit documents the administration of the Department of Biology under Head Curators True, 1897-1911, and Stejneger, 1911-1943. Records include correspondence of the Department, 1897-1943; quarterly reports, 1910-1940; annual reports, 1901, 1911-1941; and plans of operation, 1911-1940. In addition, a small amount of correspondence in this record unit is directed to James E. Benedict (1854-1940), who was appointed Chief of Exhibits in the Department of Biology in 1909. His title was changed to Assistant Curator in 1918, and he continued in that position until his retirement in 1930.

For other material relating to the Department of Biology, see the Leonhard Stejneger Papers, record unit 7074, and the Frederick William True Papers, record unit 7181.

ARRANGEMENT: (1) Incoming correspondence, 1897-1914; (2) general correspondence, incoming and outgoing, 1913-1943; (3) outgoing correspondence, 1897-1912; (4) quarterly reports, 1910-1940; (5) annual reports, 1901, 1911-1940; (6) plan of operations, 1911-1940. FINDING AIDS: Description in control file. SPECIAL CONDITIONS: Use of this record unit requires prior arrangement with the Archives staff.

(143)

Department of Zoology, United States National Museum, 1901-1954
Records (0.4 linear meter).

The Department of Biology was formed during the reorganization of the United States National Museum in 1897. At that time, the various departments in the biological sciences became divisions and the department was set up as the organizational unit controlling those divisions. The first Head Curator was Frederick William True who served from 1897 to 1911. In 1911, Leonhard Stejneger became Head Curator and held that position until his death in 1943. Waldo LaSalle Schmitt was the last Head Curator of the Department and served until its separation in 1947 into the Departments of Zoology and Botany. Schmitt continued as Head Curator of Zoology and Ellsworth Paine Killip was appointed Head Curator of Botany.

The correspondence in this record unit contains only a portion of the correspondence of the two Departments. Other material relating to the Department of Biology can be found in the Frederick William True Papers, record unit 7181, and the Leonhard Stejneger Papers, record unit 7074.

ARRANGEMENT: Alphabetic by correspondent. FINDING AIDS: Description in control file. SPECIAL CONDITIONS: Use of this record unit requires prior arrangement with the Archives staff.

(431)

Department of Biology, United States National Museum, circa 1901-1944, with related materials from 1894

Records (0.4 linear meter).

For an administrative history of the Department of Biology, see record units 143 and 242.

This record unit consists mostly of record books maintained by the Department of Biology. They include a register of employees of the Department, *circa* 1910-1940; a visitor's book, 1943-1944; a record of manuscripts submitted to the Head Curator of Biology for publication by the United States National Museum (USNM), 1931-1943; a record of requisitions, 1901-1916; and a record of specimens distributed, 1931-1943. Also included are lists, notes, and copies of correspondence concerning USNM marine invertebrate collections in the custody of Addison Emery Verrill of Yale University, *circa* 1894-1907.

ARRANGEMENT: Unarranged. FINDING AIDS: None. SPECIAL CONDITIONS: Use of this record unit requires prior arrangement with the Archives staff.

(243)

Department of Zoology, National Museum of Natural History, 1943-1958

Records (2.3 linear meters).

The Department of Zoology was created July 31, 1947, as part of a general reorganization of the United States National Museum. At that time, the Department of Biology was divided into the Departments of Zoology and Botany. Waldo LaSalle Schmitt, who had served as Head Curator of the Department of Biology since 1943, became the first Head Curator of Zoology. He held that position until his retirement in 1957.

This record unit consists of records of the Department of Zoology under Head Curator Waldo LaSalle Schmitt and includes outgoing correspondence, 1946-1957; correspondence with the public, 1947-1957; and administrative records, 1943-1958. Also included are records of the Department of Biology, 1943-1947.

For other records relating to the Departments of Biology and Zoology see record units 143, 242, 431, 7074, and 7181.

ARRANGEMENT: (1) Outgoing correspondence, 1946-1957; (2) correspondence with the public, 1947-1957; (3) administrative records, 1943-1958. FINDING AIDS: Description in control file. SPECIAL CONDITIONS: Use of this record unit requires prior arrangement with the Archives staff.

VERTEBRATE ZOOLOGY, 1825-1988

(136)
Department of Vertebrate Zoology, National Museum of Natural History, 1954-1970
Records (1.7 linear meters).

The Department of Vertebrate Zoology was created in 1964 by the separation of the Department of Zoology into vertebrate and invertebrate branches. Philip S. Humphrey became the first Chairman of the Department and served until 1968. George E. Watson took the post in 1968.

The majority of the records date from the creation of the Department in 1964, but they include material from the divisions of the Department of Zoology which later became the Department of Vertebrate Zoology. The records include internal correspondence concerning travel, departmental committees, hiring of curators, fiscal matters, and special projects of departmental interest.

ARRANGEMENT: Chronologic. FINDING AIDS: Folder list in control file. SPECIAL CONDITIONS: Use of this record unit requires prior arrangement with the Archives staff.

(382)
Department of Vertebrate Zoology, National Museum of Natural History, 1965-1987
Records (3.2 linear meters).

For an administrative history of the Department of Vertebrate Zoology, see record unit 136. Philip S. Humphrey, the first Chairman of the Department, served from 1964 to 1968. He was succeeded by George E. Watson, 1968 to 1972; Robert H. Gibbs, Jr., 1972 to 1978; George R. Zug, 1978 to 1983; and W. Ronald Heyer, 1984 to 1987. In September 1987, Richard W. Thorington, Jr., took the post.

This record unit consists of records of the Department of Vertebrate Zoology, primarily under the chairmanships of George E. Watson and Robert H. Gibbs, Jr., with additional material from the tenures of Philip S. Humphrey, George R. Zug, W. Ronald Heyer, and Richard W. Thorington, Jr. The records include memoranda, correspondence, and subject files relating to committees and professional societies; budget; annual reports; computerization; security; building renovations; space planning; collections management; division activities and staffing; international relations; relations with Congress; and information on professional societies and programs of interest to the Department. Subject files of special interest focus on the growing emphasis on computers in the Department; national and international information exchanges; space problems and the establishment of the Museum Support Center at Suitland, Maryland; construction of the Osteo-Preparation Laboratory in the east courtyard of the Natural History Building; appointment of Porter M. Kier as Director of NMNH; and involvement in international research programs in the Caribbean and Brazil.

ARRANGEMENT: (1) Chairmen's files, 1965-1974, accession number 85-136; (2) Chairmen's files, 1965-1983, accession number 89-142; (3) Chairmen's files, 1968-1987, accession number 93-021. FINDING AIDS: Folder list in control file. SPECIAL CONDITIONS: (1) Restricted; (2) use of this record unit requires prior arrangement with the Archives staff.

Belem Ecological Project, National Museum of Natural History, 1967-1971
Records (0.1 linear meter).

The Belem Ecological Project was a multidisciplinary study of environmental conditions of the Amazon delta in the vicinity of Belem, Brazil. The purpose of the project was to improve knowledge of tropical delta forest environments and determine the influence of human activities on those environments. The project was funded through a grant from the Army Research Office and ran from 1967 to 1971. Philip S. Humphrey, Chairman, Department of Vertebrate Zoology, National Museum of Natural History, was Principal Investigator.

These records primarily document the administration of the Belem Ecological Project. They consist of correspondence and memoranda between Philip S. Humphrey, Smithsonian administrators, and project staff including Thomas E. Lovejoy III; financial reports and fiscal records; and files on project personnel.

ARRANGEMENT: Unarranged. FINDING AIDS: None. SPECIAL CONDITIONS: Use of this record unit requires prior arrangement with the Archives staff.

Division of Birds, National Museum of Natural History, circa 1854-1959
Records (5.2 linear meters).

The collection of birds under the care of the Smithsonian was begun in 1850 when Spencer F. Baird, the newly appointed Assistant Secretary, came to the Institution and brought his collection of over 3600 birds. The Department of Ornithology, the predecessor of the present Division of Birds, was not established until 1880, however, when a general reorganization of the United States National Museum took place. From 1874 to 1881 Robert Ridgway was a member of the Smithsonian staff as an Assistant in ornithology. With the reorganization of the Museum, he became Curator of Birds in 1881 and retained that title until his death in 1929. Other curators of the Division have included Charles Wallace Richmond, Assistant and Associate Curator, 1895-1932; Joseph Harvey Riley, Assistant and Associate Curator, 1928-1941; S. Dillon Ripley, Assistant Curator, 1942-1943; and Walter A. Weber, Assistant Curator, 1943-1944. Herbert Friedmann was appointed Curator in 1929 and Herbert Girton Deignan, Assistant Curator, 1940-1942, was appointed Associate Curator in 1942.

ARRANGEMENT: (1) Outgoing correspondence, 1885-1930; (2) general correspondence, incoming and outgoing, 1874-1955; (3) general correspondence, incoming and outgoing, 1956-1959; (4) distribution and destruction records, *circa* 1854-1900, 1911-1934; (5) material related to the history of the Division of Birds. FINDING AIDS: Description in control file. SPECIAL CONDITIONS: Use of this record unit requires prior arrangement with the Archives staff.

Division of Birds, National Museum of Natural History, 1958-1986
Records (2.9 linear meters).

For an administrative history of the Division of Birds, see record units 105 and 270. George E. Watson and Richard L. Zusi continued as Curators in the Division with

Watson retiring in 1984. Paul Slud continued as Associate Curator through 1983. Storrs L. Olson held the position of Associate Curator from 1975 to 1981 when he became Curator of the Division.

This record unit consists primarily of correspondence and memoranda. Correspondence documents the Division's interaction with the public and ornithologists from universities, professional societies, and museums worldwide. Correspondence also concerns research, publications, professional societies, and the exchange of specimens. Memoranda document administrative matters such as collecting permits, asbestos removal, personnel, collections management and expansion, space planning, parking, Division meetings, and construction of the Osteo-Preparation Laboratory. Also included are forms and lists documenting the loan of specimens and equipment from the Division to individuals within the Smithsonian and to other museums and universities. Additional subject files include documentation of research funding, computerization, divisional policy, exhibit work, and drafts of annual reports.

ARRANGEMENT: (1) Loan and exchange of specimens, 1958-1977, accession number 81-016; (2) correspondence, memoranda, and subject files, 1962-1982, accession number 85-135; (3) correspondence and memoranda, 1978-1986, accession number 88-150. FINDING AIDS: Folder list in control file. SPECIAL CONDITIONS: (1) Restricted; (2) use of this record unit requires prior arrangement with the Archives staff.

(270)

Division of Birds, National Museum of Natural History, 1960-1973
Correspondence (1 linear meter).

For an administrative history of the Division of Birds, see record unit 105. Herbert Friedmann retired as Curator in 1960, as did Herbert Girton Deignan in 1961. Other curators represented in this material include Philip S. Humphrey, Curator, 1962-1964; George E. Watson, Assistant Curator, 1963, Associate Curator, 1964, and Curator, 1965-   ; Richard L. Zusi, Associate Curator, 1964-1967, and Curator, 1968-   ; and Paul Slud, Associate Curator, 1965-   .

This record unit consists of the official correspondence of the Division with the public and with ornithologists from museums and universities throughout the world. Topics include exchange of specimens, research projects, and scientific publications.

ARRANGEMENT: Alphabetic. FINDING AIDS: Description in control file. SPECIAL CONDITIONS: Use of this record unit requires prior arrangement with the Archives staff.

(151)

Division of Birds, National Museum of Natural History, 1930-1961
Annual Reports (0.3 linear meter).

For an administrative history of the Division of Birds, see record unit 105.

ARRANGEMENT: Chronologic. FINDING AIDS: None. SPECIAL CONDITIONS: Use of this record unit requires prior arrangement with the Archives staff.

Division of Birds, National Museum of Natural History
Card Index to Illustrations (2.2 linear meters).

Index to published illustrations of birds.

ARRANGEMENT: By taxonomic family. FINDING AIDS: None. SPECIAL CONDITIONS: Use of this record unit requires prior arrangement with the Archives staff.

Division of Birds, National Museum of Natural History, circa 1897-
Catalog of Generic and Specific Names (8.4 linear meters).

For an administrative history of the Division of Birds, see record unit 105.

Charles Wallace Richmond began this monumental project in the 1890s, and continued working on it until his death. He planned a card catalog of all described species and genera of birds, with names as originally spelled, complete references and dates of publication, type locality, name of collector, present location of type, and any other pertinent data. The catalog is still added to as new species are identified.

ARRANGEMENT: Alphabetic by genus and species. FINDING AIDS: None. SPECIAL CONDITIONS: Use of this record unit requires prior arrangement with the Archives staff.

Division of Birds, United States National Museum, circa 1878-1933
Data on Birds' Nests and Eggs (3.2 linear meters).

For an administrative history of the Division of Birds, see record unit 105.

This collection of data was originally started by Charles Emil Bendire (1836-1897), an Army surgeon, who served as Honorary Curator of the Department of Birds' Eggs (prior to 1885 known as the Section of Oology, and from 1885 to 1888 as the Section of Birds' Eggs) from 1884 until his death.

This collection consists mainly of information on birds' nests and eggs accumulated by Bendire. Over a period of many years he sent out questionnaires to prominent ornithologists and oologists requesting information on nests and eggs and breeding habits. The replies which Bendire received, often in the form of long, detailed letters, make up a large portion of this collection. Also included are notes taken by Bendire. The collection has been added to since Bendire's death by members of the staff of the Division of Birds. No effort has been made to identify correspondents. There is, however, some correspondence of Robert Ridgway and William LaGrange Ralph.

ARRANGEMENT: By family, genus, and species. FINDING AIDS: None. SPECIAL CONDITIONS: Use of this record unit requires prior arrangement with the Archives staff.

Division of Birds, National Museum of Natural History
Donor-Collector Cards (1.2 linear meters).

Five drawers of 3 x 5 cards listing donor or collector, catalog number of specimen, and locality.

ARRANGEMENT: Alphabetical by donor or collector. FINDING AIDS: None. SPECIAL CONDITIONS: Use of this record unit requires prior arrangement with the Archives staff.

Division of Birds, National Museum of Natural History, circa early 1800s-
Ornithological Reprints (360 volumes and 18.4 linear meters).

This unique collection forms a major resource for the study of ornithology and the history of ornithological research. The bound volumes are in specific order, but are indexed in a card catalog. The loose reprints are arranged alphabetically by the name of the author.

ARRANGEMENT: See description above. FINDING AIDS: Card index to bound volumes. SPECIAL CONDITIONS: Use of this record unit requires prior arrangement with the Archives staff.

Division of Birds, National Museum of Natural History, circa 1854-
Specimen Catalogs (117 volumes).

As specimens are identified, they are assigned a catalog number, which is entered in the catalog and permanently affixed to the specimen. Specimens are not entered when they are accessioned, but when they are identified. Often, much time elapses between accession and identification, and in some instances, specimens accessioned later than others are cataloged first. Information found in a catalog entry usually includes: name of specimen, donor, collector, locality in which specimen was found, catalog number, date on which specimen was collected, date entered in catalog, and remarks.

There are, in addition, two original catalogs (or fragments of catalogs) of the collection of Spencer F. Baird. These catalogs cover the period from about 1839 to 1850. The specimens listed in these catalogs were donated by Baird to the United States National Museum, and are represented in the main series of the catalogs.

ARRANGEMENT: By catalog number. FINDING AIDS: None. SPECIAL CONDITIONS: Use of this record unit requires prior arrangement with the Archives staff.

Division of Birds, National Museum of Natural History
Taxonomic Data File (13.6 linear meters).

For an administrative history of the Division of Birds, see record unit 105.

This file, probably started by Robert Ridgway, consists mostly of measurements of birds, locality data, and general notes. This file still receives periodic additions from staff members of the Division. This collection has little, if any, correspondence.

ARRANGEMENT: By genus or species. FINDING AIDS: None. SPECIAL CONDITIONS: Use of this record unit requires prior arrangement with the Archives staff.

(7215)

Collected Notes, Lists, and Catalogs on Birds, National Museum of Natural History, 1839, 1849-1851, 1855-1987
(11.3 linear meters).

This collection contains manuscript notes, lists, and catalogs concerning bird specimens. The catalogs are the primary documentation for many of the specimens of the Division of Birds. Although they vary in content, as a general rule they contain specimen-related data including catalogs of specimens collected, dates, localities, tag numbers, measurements, and remarks on the specimens. Less frequently, they contain journal entries of the collector describing field activities, affairs of the day, anthropological observations, personal financial accounts, and other personal matters. Also included is an edited manuscript on Arctic birds, apparently compiled from the notes of Bernard Rogan Ross, Roderick Ross MacFarlane, Robert Kennicott, and others.

ARRANGEMENT: (1) Field catalogs and notebooks, 1850, 1855-1987; (2) collected notes and lists, 1839, 1849, 1851, 1856, 1860-1862, 1873; (3) manuscript on Arctic birds, undated. FINDING AIDS: Partial description in control file. SPECIAL CONDITIONS: (1) Check finding aid for location; (2) use of this record unit requires prior arrangement with the Archives staff.

(245)

Pacific Ocean Biological Survey Program, National Museum of Natural History, circa 1961-1973, with data from 1923
Records (32.1 linear meters, 95 volumes, and oversize).

The Pacific Ocean Biological Survey Program (POBSP) was initiated in 1962 when the Smithsonian Institution entered into a grant agreement with the Department of Defense. During the period from January 1963 through June 1969, Smithsonian Institution employees undertook biological surveys in an area of the Pacific Ocean spanning the equator and extending from latitude 30 degrees north to 10 degrees south and from longitude 150 degrees to 180 degrees west, an area dotted with clusters of islands and atolls. The major goals of the program were to learn what plants and animals occurred on the islands, the seasonal variations in their numbers and reproductive activities, and the distribution and population of the pelagic birds of that area. Emphasis was placed on the banding of birds in an effort to determine migration, distribution, and abundance of pelagic sea birds. During the six and a half years of field work, 1,800,000 birds were banded; approximately 150,000 observations of pelagic birds at sea were made; and biological surveys of varying intensity were made on several islands.

The Principal Investigator of the POBSP was Philip S. Humphrey (1926-), who in 1962 came to the Smithsonian Institution as Curator of Birds. In 1964 Humphrey became Chairman of the newly created Department of Vertebrate Zoology, while retaining his position as Curator of Birds. In 1967 he left the Smithsonian to become Director of the Museum of Natural History and Chairman of the Department of Zoology at the University of Kansas. However, he remained as Principal Investigator of the Survey.

These records document the administration, field work, and research activities of the POBSP, especially its bird banding, island survey, and pelagic survey programs. Included are reports, correspondence, field records, office records, contracts, data, notes, manuscripts, maps, and photographs. The records also contain material from earlier field activities in the Pacific which was collected by the POBSP.

ARRANGEMENT: (1) Intra-office records, 1961-1970; (2) contracts, 1962-1969; (3) travel, 1962-1970; (4) correspondence, 1963-1972; (5) annual and Army reports, 1963-1969; (6) Hawaii office files, 1963-1969; (7) miscellaneous reports, 1963-1969; (8) *Pacific Bird Observer* files, 1964-1970; (9) field correspondence, 1963-1970; (10) monthly field summaries, 1965-1969; (11) field guide; (12) field notes, 1963-1968; (13) general banding files; (14) banding memoranda books, 1960-1961, 1963-1969; (15) band listings; (16) banding record books, 1963-1969; (17) banding and recovery schedules, 1963-1969; (18) foreign band recoveries; (19) Smithsonian band recoveries; (20) Smithsonian bands recovered by others; (21) reports on banding returns-by location; (22) reports on banding returns-by number; (23) banding reports; (24) at-sea data, 1963-1969; (25) at-sea data (non-POBSP), 1949-1970; (26) at-sea observation checklists, 1963-1967; (27) at-sea distribution and abundance charts; (28) at-sea record books, 1963-1964 and undated; (29) Southern Island Cruise reports, 1963-1968; (30) Southern Island Cruise field notes, 1963-1966; (31) Southern Grid Survey reports, 1965-1968; (32) Northern Grid Survey reports, 1963-1968; (33) Eastern Area Cruise reports, 1966-1968; (34) Eastern Grid Survey reports, 1967-1968; (35) Eastern Pacific Offshore Islands reports, 1967-1968; (36) *Townsend Cromwell* cruise reports, 1964-1965; (37) Leeward Islands Survey reports, 1963-1967; (38) island reports, *circa* 1954-1970, 1973; (39) island files, *circa* 1963-1970; (40) Kure Atoll files, *circa* 1963-1970, with data from 1951; (41) Sand Island-Johnston Atoll files, 1963-1973, with data from 1961; (42) specimen catalogs, 1963-1969; (43) general bird files, *circa* 1963-1971; (44) stomach data, 1963-1967; (45) insect, mammal, reptile, and amphibian data, 1963-1969; (46) botany data; (47) bathythermographic data, 1963-1968; (48) literature survey, 1964-1967; (49) manuscripts for publication or oral presentation, 1964-1970; (50) non-POBSP notes and manuscripts, 1923, 1951, 1956, 1961, 1963-1968, 1973 and undated; (51) maps and charts; (52) aerial photographs, 1926, 1932-1933, 1938-1943, 1945, 1955, 1957, 1965; (53) photographs, by location; (54) photographs, by Southern Island Cruise; (55) photographs, by animal; (56) photographs, unidentified; (57) negatives and slides; (58) card files; (59) oversize; (60) data books, 1963-1969. FINDING AIDS: Description in control file. SPECIAL CONDITIONS: (1) Record unit partially microfilmed; (2) check finding aid for location; (3) use of this record unit requires prior arrangement with the Archives staff.

(435)
Palearctic Migratory Bird Survey, National Museum of Natural History, 1966-1971
Records (10.7 linear meters).

The Palearctic Migratory Bird Survey (PMS), a survey of migratory birds, their ectoparasites and the viruses they carry, was conducted in the eastern Mediterranean from 1966 to 1971. The primary PMS operation site was in northern Egypt. Surveys were also conducted in Cyprus and Israel. The PMS involved scientists of the Smithsonian Institution, the United States Naval Medical Research Unit, and Yale University, and was funded by the Army Research Office, the Smithsonian Foreign Currency Program, and the Smithsonian Research Foundation. George E. Watson, Chairman, Department of Vertebrate Zoology, and Curator, Division of Birds, National Museum of Natural History, was Principal Investigator.

These records consist primarily of raw and synthesized bird-banding data compiled by the Palearctic Migratory Bird Survey. The usual data given includes species, sex, weight, and fat content. Also included is correspondence of Watson, mostly concerning banding work; reports; and administrative records.

ARRANGEMENT: Unarranged. FINDING AIDS: Box list in control file. SPECIAL CONDITIONS: Use of this record unit requires prior arrangement with the Archives staff.

(203)

Division of Comparative Anatomy, United States National Museum, circa 1885-1902, 1909
Records (0.1 linear meter).

From 1885 until about 1904, a Department of Comparative Anatomy existed within the United States National Museum. This Department (after 1897 a division in the Department of Biology) was responsible for the preparation and care of the osteological specimens of the Museum. From the early days of the museum collections, separate bone catalogs were kept, distinct from the other specimen catalogs. In addition, a series of vertebrate skulls and skeletons was exhibited in the main hall of the Smithsonian Building, and much material was in storage.

When the collections were moved from the Smithsonian Building to the Museum in 1883, a proposal was made that a Department of Comparative Anatomy be set up. Although Frederick William True and Frederic Augustus Lucas were listed as Curator and Assistant in such a Department as early as 1883, formal organization of the Department first came in 1885.

Lucas joined the Smithsonian Institution in 1882 as an osteological preparator and became Assistant Curator in 1887. True was the first full Curator and served from 1885 to 1890, when Frank Baker became Honorary Curator. In 1893, Lucas became Curator and remained in that capacity until he left the Smithsonian in 1904. Following Lucas's departure, the Division remained without a curator until it was gradually incorporated into the other zoological divisions.

ARRANGEMENT: (1) Memoranda for divisional reports, 1887-1902; (2) lists of specimens and records of divisional operations, *circa* 1885-1894, 1909; (3) material concerning Ohio Valley and Central States Exhibition, 1888; (4) daily calendar of Frederic Augustus Lucas, 1886-1895, 1898-1899. FINDING AIDS: Description in control file. SPECIAL CONDITIONS: Use of this record unit requires prior arrangement with the Archives staff.

(213)

Division of Fishes, United States National Museum, 1865-1941
Records (1.8 linear meters).

The origins of the Division of Fishes of the United States National Museum and its ichthyological work can be traced to the arrival of Spencer F. Baird as Assistant Secretary of the Smithsonian in 1850, along with his natural history collections. Baird brought Charles Frederic Girard to the Institution the same year and Girard remained until 1860, publishing a number of papers based on the Institution's collections of fishes. Theodore Nicholas Gill joined the Smithsonian in 1859 to help prepare the reports for the Northwestern Boundary Survey and spent much of his time working on the museum collections, although he was never an official division staff member. Fish deposited by the United States Fish Commission and its successor agencies have also contributed importantly to the collection.

The Division of Fishes and the United States Fish Commission were closely associated from the latter's founding in 1871. In addition to Baird's duties as Assistant Secretary, he was Commissioner of Fish and Fisheries from the Commission's founding until his death in 1887. He also assigned Smithsonian staff members to Fish Commission duties; and the distinction between the activities of the Fish Commission and the Division of Fishes is very nebulous in these papers, particularly for the early period.

Tarleton Hoffman Bean joined the staff as Assistant Ichthyologist in 1877 and became Curator following the formal organization of the United States National Museum in 1880. Fish Commission duties became too time-consuming, however; and he served only as an Honorary Curator from 1888 to 1905. His brother, Barton A. Bean, was appointed Assistant in 1882, Aid in 1886, and Curator in 1890. He retained this title until his retirement in 1932. Barton Warren Evermann held the title of Curator from 1906 to 1913, but apparently spent the greater part of his time on Bureau of Fisheries matters. Other curators represented in these records include George Sprague Myers, Assistant Curator, 1933-1936, and Leonard Peter Schultz, Assistant Curator, 1936-1938, who became Curator in 1938.

The records include the official correspondence of the Division, chiefly concerning identification, loan, and acquisition of specimens; requests for information from scientists and the public; research being conducted by the staff; and the administrative affairs of the Division. There is extensive correspondence with David Starr Jordan and Henry Weed Fowler.

ARRANGEMENT: (1) Outgoing correspondence, 1882-1914; (2) correspondence, 1865, 1867, 1869-1941; (3) divisional accession record, 1884-1936; (4) divisional distribution record, 1882-1934; (5) invoices, packing memoranda, and related materials concerning specimens sent out, 1895, 1911-1913, 1915, 1918-1923. FINDING AIDS: Description in control file. SPECIAL CONDITIONS: Use of this record unit requires prior arrangement with the Archives staff.

(415)

Division of Fishes, National Museum of Natural History, circa 1885-1978
Records (3 linear meters).

For an administrative history of the Division of Fishes, see record units 213 and 234.

These records consist primarily of incoming and outgoing correspondence compiled by the Division of Fishes, *circa* 1965-1978. Most of the correspondence is from ichthyologists, collectors, donors, and students and concerns the identification, exchange and distribution of specimens; collecting work; and requests for publications. Also found in the records are written copies of annual report submissions, *circa* 1891-1972, and budget estimates, *circa* 1885-1974.

Curators and other staff members of the Division of Fishes represented by correspondence in these records include Ernest A. Lachner, Curator in Charge, 1965-1966, Supervisor and Curator, 1967, and Curator, 1968-1978; Victor G. Springer, Associate Curator, 1965-1966, and Curator, 1967-1978; William Ralph Taylor, Associate Curator, 1965-1978; Stanley H. Weitzman, Associate Curator, 1965-1967, Supervisor and Curator, 1968-1969, and Curator, 1970-1978; and Robert H. Gibbs, Jr., Associate Curator, 1965-1968, Curator, 1969, Supervisor and Curator, 1970, and Curator, 1971-1978.

ARRANGEMENT: (1) Correspondence, *circa* 1965-1978; (2) annual reports, *circa* 1891-1972; (3) budget estimates, *circa* 1885-1974. FINDING AIDS: Box list in control file. SPECIAL CONDITIONS: Use of this record unit requires prior arrangement with the Archives staff.

(234)

Division of Fishes, National Museum of Natural History, 1922, 1927-1964
General Correspondence (3.3 linear meters).

For an administrative history of the Division of Fishes, see record unit 213.

These records consist of incoming and outgoing correspondence compiled by the Division of Fishes, 1922, 1927-1964. Most of the correspondence is from domestic and foreign ichthyologists, aquarists, collectors, colleges and universities, museum officials, and the general public and concerns the identification, exchange, and distribution of specimens; collecting work; publications; requests for information; professional societies; and museum administration. The majority of the correspondence is directed to the curatorial staff of the Division of Fishes, with lesser amounts to scientific and museum aids. Subjects of special interest which are documented in the correspondence include: Robert Rush Miller's work on the Fish and Wildlife Survey of Guatemala, 1946-1947; Miller's work on the Smithsonian Institution-Commonwealth of Australia-National Geographic Society Expedition to Arnhem Land, 1948; and Leonard Peter Schultz's activity as a member of the Bikini Scientific Survey, 1946, and Resurvey, 1947. A small amount of correspondence directed to George Sprague Myers and Leonard Peter Schultz predates their careers at the United States National Museum.

Curators and other staff members of the Division of Fishes represented by correspondence in these records include Earl D. Reid, Aid, 1925-1938, and Senior Scientific Aid, 1939-1945; George Sprague Myers, Assistant Curator in Charge, 1933-1936; Leonard Peter Schultz, Assistant Curator in Charge, 1936-1938, Curator, 1938-   ; Robert Rush Miller, Associate Curator, 1944-1948; Marie Poland Fish, Scientific Aid, 1944-1946; Donald S. Erdman, Scientific Aid, 1947-1949; Loren P. Woods, Associate Curator, 1947-1948; William T. Lepley, Scientific Aid, 1947-1953; Robert H. Kanazawa, Museum Aid and Museum Specialist, 1951-   ; William Ralph Taylor, Associate Curator, 1956-   ; Victor G. Springer, Associate Curator, 1963-   ; Robert H. Gibbs, Jr., Associate Curator, 1963-   ; and Stanley H. Weitzman, Associate Curator, 1963-   .

ARRANGEMENT: Alphabetic. FINDING AIDS: Description in control file. SPECIAL CONDITIONS: Use of this record unit requires prior arrangement with the Archives staff.

(7220)

Collected Notes, Lists, Catalogs, Illustrations, and Records on Fishes, National Museum of Natural History, circa 1835-1974 and undated
(4.9 linear meters and oversize).

This collection contains manuscript notes, lists, catalogs, illustrations, and ship records concerning fish specimens. The catalogs are the primary documentation for many of the specimens of the Division of Fishes. Although they vary in content, as a general rule they contain specimen-related data including catalogs of specimens collected, dates, localities, tag numbers, measurements, and remarks on the specimens. Less frequently, they contain journal entries of the collector describing field activities, affairs of the day, and personal matters.

ARRANGEMENT: (1) Collected notes, lists, and illustrations, *circa* 1835-1850, 1852, 1882-1883, 1911 and undated; (2) field notes, catalogs, and records, 1853-1856, *circa* 1877-1974. FINDING AIDS: Description in control file. SPECIAL CONDITIONS: (1) Check finding aid for location; (2) use of this record unit requires prior arrangement with the Archives staff.

(208)

Division of Mammals, National Museum of Natural History, circa 1867-1971
Records (8.8 linear meters).

The Department of Mammals of the United States National Museum was created in 1880. Prior to that time, the Smithsonian held an extensive collection of mammals which had been obtained from the private collection of Spencer F. Baird, from the United States Exploring Expedition and other government explorations, and from the collections of the National Institute, which was dissolved in 1861. Upon the formation of the Department, Elliott Coues was appointed Honorary Curator of Mammals. He continued as Honorary Curator until Frederick William True became Curator in 1883. In 1897, a major reorganization of the Museum made the Department a division within the new Department of Biology; and True became Head Curator of Biology. True also remained Curator of Mammals until 1909. In 1898, Gerrit Smith Miller, Jr., was appointed Assistant Curator of Mammals and from 1908 until his retirement in 1940 served as Curator. Other staff members of the Division of Mammals have included Marcus Ward Lyon, Jr., Aid, 1898-1906, and Assistant Curator, 1906-1909; Ned Hollister, Assistant Curator, 1910-1916; A. Remington Kellogg, Assistant Curator, 1928-1941, and Curator, 1941-1948; David H. Johnson, Associate Curator, 1941-1957, and Curator, 1957-1967; Raymond Maurice Gilmore, Associate Curator, 1944-1947; Henry W. Setzer, Associate Curator, 1949-1969, and Curator, 1969-   ; Charles O. Handley, Jr., Assistant Curator, 1950-1954, Associate Curator, 1954-1965, and Curator, 1965- ; and Richard W. Thorington, Jr., Associate Curator, 1969-   .

The records contain the correspondence of the Division staff and are chiefly concerned with identification, loan, and acquisition of specimens; requests for information from scientists and the public; expeditions, field trips, and collectors; research being carried out by the staff; and administration of the Division. Also included in the records are annual reports and invoices of the Division, *circa* 1867-1951; manuscripts of Miller and Lyon, consisting mostly of descriptions and revisions of classifications which were apparently published; and collected biographical information on and photographs of prominent naturalists and scientists, including a significant amount of material on John Muir.

ARRANGEMENT: (1) Annual reports of the Division of Mammals, 1905-1945; (2) outgoing correspondence, 1882-1907; (3) incoming correspondence, *circa* 1886-1907; (4) correspondence, 1907-1971; (5) invoices, *circa* 1867-1951; (6) manuscripts of Gerrit Smith Miller, Jr., and Marcus Ward Lyon, Jr., 1905-1907, 1909; (7) biographical material concerning prominent naturalists and scientists. FINDING AIDS: Description in control file. SPECIAL CONDITIONS: Use of this record unit requires prior arrangement with the Archives staff.

Division of Mammals, National Museum of Natural History, circa 1953-1988
Records (3.3 linear meters).

For an administrative history of the Division of Mammals, see record unit 208. Henry W. Setzer retired as Curator in 1979. Other curators represented in these records include Charles O. Handley, Jr., Assistant Curator, 1950-1954, Associate Curator, 1954-1965, and Curator, 1965-   ; Richard W. Thorington, Jr., Associate Curator, 1969-1976, and Curator, 1976-   ; James G. Mead, Assistant Curator, 1972-1976, Associate Curator, 1976-1982, and Curator, 1982-   ; and Michael D. Carleton, Assistant Curator, 1979-1983, Associate Curator, 1983-1987, and Curator, 1987-   .

These records consist of incoming and outgoing correspondence of the staff of the Division of Mammals and primarily concern the identification, loan, and acquisition of specimens; requests for information from colleagues and the public; the publication of scientific papers; and research projects of the staff.

ARRANGEMENT: Chronologic and alphabetic. FINDING AIDS: Box list in control file. SPECIAL CONDITIONS: (1) Restricted; (2) use of this record unit requires prior arrangement with the Archives staff.

Division of Mammals, National Museum of Natural History, 1860-1973 and undated
Biographical File (2.2 linear meters).

For an administrative history of the Division of Mammals, see record unit 208.

This biographical file was maintained by the Division of Mammals. It contains a variety of materials documenting the lives and careers of scientists from a wide range of fields including mammalogy, ornithology, ichthyology, herpetology, botany, entomology, paleontology, and geology. Also included are files on conservationists, taxidermists, historical figures, explorers, frontiersmen, and hunters. The files include biographical sketches, memoirs, obituaries, articles, bibliographies, news clippings, press releases, correspondence, and photographs.

Of special interest is extensive material documenting the career of taxidermist William L. Brown. Included are reminiscences of his fifty-one year career at the National Museum of Natural History and its predecessor, the United States National Museum; photographs taken on the Beach Anglo-Egyptian Sudan Expedition, 1928, and the Beach-Webb Alaskan Expedition, 1937; and correspondence concerning the Fenykovi elephant.

ARRANGEMENT: Alphabetic. FINDING AIDS: Description in control file. SPECIAL CONDITIONS: Use of this record unit requires prior arrangement with the Archives staff.

Collected Notes, Lists, Drawings, and Catalogs on Mammals, National Museum of Natural History, circa 1825-1972
(3.4 linear meters).

This collection contains field catalogs and notebooks, manuscript notes, lists, and drawings primarily concerning mammal specimens. Also included are lists, autographs, and related materials regarding mammalogists and naturalists who collected mammal specimens for the United States National Museum. The field catalogs and notebooks are the primary documentation for many of the specimens in the Division of Mammals. Although they vary in content, as a general rule they contain specimen-related data including lists of specimens collected, dates, localities, tag numbers, measurements, and remarks on the specimens. Less frequently, they contain journal entries of the collector describing field activities, affairs of the day, anthropological observations, personal financial accounts, and other personal matters.

Some of the manuscript notes contain information on other fauna and flora observed and collected. Charles S. Anderson manuscript notes also contain data on birds of Minnesota, and W. J. Spina manuscript notes deal with the birds, amphibians, reptiles, and plants of Pennsylvania.

ARRANGEMENT: (1) Field catalogs and notebooks, 1853, *circa* 1863-1972; (2) collected notes, lists, drawings, and catalogs, *circa* 1825-1941. FINDING AIDS: Description in control file. SPECIAL CONDITIONS: (1) Check finding aid for location; (2) use of this record unit requires prior arrangement with the Archives staff.

(407)

Mammal Identification Service, National Museum of Natural History, 1966-1976
Records (0.4 linear meter).

The Mammal Identification Service (MIS) was established in 1966. It was located in the Division of Mammals, National Museum of Natural History, and supported jointly by the Smithsonian and the National Institutes of Health (NIH). Charles O. Handley, Jr., Curator in the Division of Mammals, was Principal Investigator of the project. Gary L. Ranck was appointed Curator of MIS in 1966. Ranck resigned the following year and was replaced by Ronald H. Pine, who served until 1973. The MIS was terminated in 1974 when NIH support ceased.

The primary purpose of MIS was to provide rapid identifications of mammals of medical and epidemiological importance. In addition to providing identifications, MIS published manuals on the classification and identification of mammals, and trained paramedical workers in techniques for the collection and field preservation of specimens.

These records document the eight-year history of MIS and consist of correspondence of Handley, Ranck, and Pine concerning the creation of the project, the identification of mammal specimens, professional activities, and administrative matters; proposals submitted to NIH to provide funding for MIS; annual reports and a final report of the project; and administrative records.

ARRANGEMENT: Unarranged. FINDING AIDS: None. SPECIAL CONDITIONS: Use of this record unit requires prior arrangement with the Archives staff.

(161)

Division of Reptiles and Amphibians, National Museum of Natural History, 1873-1968
Records (4.4 linear meters).

The collection of reptiles and amphibians under the care of the Smithsonian Institution had its origins in the collection of Spencer F. Baird, which he presented to the Institution when he came to Washington to accept the position of Assistant Secretary in 1850. For the next three decades there was no curator officially in charge of the collection, and most of the early publications resulting from the collection were produced by Baird and Charles Frederic Girard, who from 1850 to 1860 was Baird's chief assistant.

In 1879 Henry Crecy Yarrow, an army surgeon who had served as naturalist on the United States Surveys West of the 100th Meridian led by Lieutenant George Wheeler, was appointed Honorary Curator of the Department of Herpetology, a position which he filled on a part-time basis until his resignation in 1889. During the early 1880s the Department was known variously as the Department of Herpetology, the Department of Reptiles, and the Department of Reptiles and Batrachians. By about 1885 the latter title had become standard. In 1947 the name was changed to the Division of Reptiles and Amphibians.

Curators since 1889 have included Leonhard Stejneger, Curator, 1889-1943, and Doris Mable Cochran, Assistant, Associate, and Curator, 1927-1968. James A. Peters, Associate Curator, 1964-1966, became Curator in 1966.

The records contain general correspondence of the Division's curators; Leonhard Stejneger material pertaining to the international congresses he attended as a representative of the United States National Museum; and administrative memoranda regarding the National Museum operations for the Division of Reptiles and Amphibians and the Departments of Biology, Vertebrate Zoology, and Zoology, pertaining to requisitions, budgetary matters, publication policy, expeditions of curators, museum exhibitions, and personnel matters. For additional records of the Division of Reptiles and Amphibians, see the Leonhard Stejneger Papers, record unit 7074, and the James A. Peters Papers, record unit 7175.

ARRANGEMENT: (1) General correspondence, incoming and outgoing, 1873-1968; (2) outgoing correspondence, 1882-1883, 1889-1922; (3) correspondence related to scientific congresses, 1895-1911; (4) administrative memoranda, 1946-1966. FINDING AIDS: Description in control file. SPECIAL CONDITIONS: Use of this record unit requires prior arrangement with the Archives staff.

(327)

Division of Reptiles and Amphibians, National Museum of Natural History, 1934-1985
Records (3.9 linear meters).

For an administrative history of the Division of Reptiles and Amphibians, see record unit 161.

James A. Peters served as Curator from 1966 until his death in 1972. George R. Zug served as Associate Curator from 1969 to 1974. In 1976 he was appointed Curator. W. Ronald Heyer was appointed Associate Curator in 1972. Since 1977 he has served as Curator.

These records consist primarily of incoming and outgoing correspondence of the professional staff of the Division of Reptiles and Amphibians. Included is correspondence concerning taxonomic questions, the identification and acquisition of specimens, field work and expeditions, and divisional administration. Most of the correspondence dates from 1969, and is executed by George R. Zug and W. Ronald Heyer. A small amount of correspondence predates 1969. The majority of this material was created by James A. Peters.

ARRANGEMENT: Alphabetic. FINDING AIDS: Description in control file. SPECIAL CONDITIONS: (1) Restricted; (2) use of this record unit requires prior arrangement with the Archives staff.

(1060501)

Collected Notes, Lists, and Catalogs on Reptiles and Amphibians, National Museum of Natural History, 1859-1866, 1877, 1882-1981
(2 linear meters).

This collection contains manuscript notes, lists, and catalogs concerning herpetological specimens. The catalogs are the primary documentation for many of the specimens of the Division of Reptiles and Amphibians. Although they vary in content, as a general rule they contain specimen-related data including catalogs of specimens collected, dates, localities, tag numbers, measurements, and remarks on the specimens. Less frequently, they contain journal entries of the collector describing field activities, affairs of the day, anthropological observations, personal financial accounts, and other personal matters.

ARRANGEMENT: Alphabetic. FINDING AIDS: Description in control file. SPECIAL CONDITIONS: Use of this record unit requires prior arrangement with the Archives staff.

(7445)

Collected Notes, Photographs, and Graphic Illustrations on Turtles, Division of Reptiles and Amphibians, United States National Museum, 1853-1953
(0.4 linear meter).

These records appear to have come originally from the Division of Reptiles and Amphibians. For an administrative history of this Division, see record unit 161.

This material, which probably began to be assembled in the 1930s, comprises an information file on turtles, containing a high proportion of visual material: chiefly photographs (often only negatives) and graphic illustrations, many in watercolor. Several of these are by illustrator Antonio Zeno Shindler, and one is by Spencer F. Baird. Working notes and correspondence pertaining to turtles make up the balance of the collection. Leonhard Stejneger appears initially to have collected the material, and Doris Mable Cochran continued the task.

ARRANGEMENT: Unarranged. FINDING AIDS: None. SPECIAL CONDITIONS: Use of this record unit requires prior arrangement with the Archives staff.

(508)

Division of Reptiles and Batrachians, United States National Museum, 1889-1926
Records (0.1 linear meter).

For an administrative history of the Division of Reptiles and Batrachians, see record unit 161.

These records consist of three bound letterpress books and a bound volume containing routine notations concerning procuring supplies and accepting and sending out specimens. The letterpress books also have interleaved single letters and memoranda. Most correspondence is over the signatures of curators Leonhard Stejneger and Doris Mable Cochran, or Richard G. Paine, an Aid in the Division.

ARRANGEMENT: (1) Requisitions of supplies, 1906-1910; (2) specimen invoices, 1895-1910; (3) Division copies of accession memoranda, 1921-1926; (4) catalog of reptile and amphibian specimens received, 1889-1890. FINDING AIDS: Letterpress books found in series 1-3 are indexed. SPECIAL CONDITIONS: Use of this record unit requires prior arrangement with the Archives staff.

(210)

Taxidermist, United States National Museum, 1883-1889
Records (0.3 linear meter).

The history of taxidermy in the Smithsonian Institution closely parallels the development of the public exhibition role of the United States National Museum. Prior to 1858, specimens in the possession of the Museum were made up chiefly for purposes of scientific study, and the art of the taxidermist was not in great demand. The transfer of the national collections from the Patent Office to the Smithsonian in 1858 provided the initial impetus for the development of the United States National Museum's exhibition series and of the skills needed to properly prepare and maintain it.

Between 1858 and 1872, the Museum used both outside contractors and some staff members to do necessary mounting work. Increased appropriations from Congress in 1872 allowed the hiring of a permanent taxidermist, Joseph Palmer. In 1874, his son William also joined the taxidermic staff. Both Palmers continued their association with the Smithsonian until their deaths, Joseph's in 1913 and William's in 1921. In his later years, Joseph Palmer worked chiefly with the Department of Anthropology, modeling figures for exhibit.

William Temple Hornaday became Taxidermist in 1882 and remained with the Museum until 1889. In the course of his taxidermic work at the Museum, Hornaday began to collect live animals to serve as models for his mountings. The public interest that these animals generated led to the creation of the Department of Living Animals in 1888 with Hornaday as its first Curator. This eventually became the nucleus of the National Zoological Park, which was started in 1890. Hornaday was named the first Superintendent, but policy differences arose which eventually led to his resignation in 1890. In 1896, he became Director of the New York Zoological Park and held that position for thirty years. On Hornaday's resignation, William Palmer was appointed chief Taxidermist.

This record unit includes an alphabetical file of correspondence of William Temple Hornaday as Taxidermist and Curator of Living Animals. The correspondence deals mainly with the collecting and shipping of specimens and live animals, Hornaday's trip to Montana in 1886, taxidermy, and the operations of Hornaday's departments. Correspondents include museum officials, collectors, shippers, and taxidermists.

ARRANGEMENT: Alphabetic. FINDING AIDS: Description in control file. SPECIAL CONDITIONS: Use of this record unit requires prior arrangement with the Archives staff.

Taxidermist, United States National Museum, circa 1903-1904, 1907-1908, 1936 and undated

Records (0.1 linear meter).

For a history of taxidermy at the United States National Museum (USNM), see record unit 210.

This record unit consists of log books containing a daily record of work performed and specimens received for preparation, 1903-1904, 1907-1908; and instructions for preparing specimens written by USNM taxidermist William L. Brown, *circa* 1936.

ARRANGEMENT: Unarranged. FINDING AIDS: None. SPECIAL CONDITIONS: Use of this record unit requires prior arrangement with the Archives staff.

INVERTEBRATE ZOOLOGY, 1835-1989

Department of Invertebrate Zoology, National Museum of Natural History, 1947-1975

Records (2.3 linear meters).

For an administrative history of the Department of Invertebrate Zoology, see record unit 249.

This record unit consists of an administrative subject file primarily documenting the operation of the Department of Invertebrate Zoology under Chairmen Donald F. Squires, 1964-1965; Raymond B. Manning, 1967-1971; and David L. Pawson, 1971-1976. Records predating the establishment of the Department in 1964 were created by its predecessor, the Department of Zoology.

ARRANGEMENT: Alphabetic. FINDING AIDS: Box list in control file. SPECIAL CONDITIONS: Use of this record unit requires prior arrangement with the Archives staff.

Department of Invertebrate Zoology, National Museum of Natural History, 1952-1973

Records (2.9 linear meters).

The Department of Invertebrate Zoology was created in 1963 when the Department of Zoology was divided into three new departments: Vertebrate Zoology, Invertebrate Zoology, and Entomology. The Divisions of Marine Invertebrates and Mollusks were under administrative control of the newly created Department. On July 1, 1965, the Division of Marine Invertebrates was abolished and three new divisions were formed—

Crustacea, Echinoderms, and Worms—and were joined with the existing Division of Mollusks to form the Department of Invertebrate Zoology. Chairmen of the Department have included Donald F. Squires, 1964-1965; Joseph Rosewater, Acting Chairman, 1966; Raymond B. Manning, 1967-1971; David L. Pawson, 1971- .

This record unit contains records of the Department of Invertebrate Zoology, 1964-1973, as well as records created by its predecessor, the Department of Zoology, 1952-1964. Most of the latter records document the Department of Zoology under Head Curators Herbert Friedmann, 1957-1961; Fenner A. Chace, Jr., Acting Head Curator, 1961-1962; and Horton H. Hobbs, Jr., 1962-1964. A small amount of records were created during the Head Curatorship of Waldo LaSalle Schmitt, 1947-1957. For administrative histories of the Department of Zoology see record units 143 and 243. Included in the record unit is general correspondence of the Department of Zoology, 1952-1964, and the Department of Invertebrate Zoology, 1964-1973; files of the Chairman of the Department of Invertebrate Zoology, 1964-1973; annual reports, 1956-1972; and administrative records, 1954-1972.

ARRANGEMENT: (1) Department of Zoology, general correspondence, 1952-1964; (2) Department of Invertebrate Zoology, general correspondence, 1964-1973; (3) Department of Invertebrate Zoology, Chairman's files, 1964-1973; (4) annual reports, 1956-1972; (5) administrative records, 1954-1972. FINDING AIDS: Description in control file. SPECIAL CONDITIONS: Use of this record unit requires prior arrangement with the Archives staff.

(423)

Department of Invertebrate Zoology, National Museum of Natural History, circa 1965-1989, with related records from 1945
Records (5 linear meters).

For an administrative history of the Department of Invertebrate Zoology, see record units 249 and 292.

This record unit consists primarily of correspondence and administrative records created by the Chairman of the Department of Invertebrate Zoology, *circa* 1965-1989. The records document the research, exhibition, and outreach functions of the Department. Also included are various record books created by the Division of Marine Invertebrates and the Department of Invertebrate Zoology, *circa* 1945-1974. The record books include a record of manuscripts reviewed by the staff, 1948-1974, and the administration of the Rathbun Memorial Fund, 1955 and 1965. In addition, there is a guest book, 1945-1965, and a day book, 1948-1949. For an administrative history of the Division of Marine Invertebrates, see record unit 233.

Most of the records were created by Department Chairmen David L. Pawson, Curator of Echinoderms, 1971-1976; W. Duane Hope, Curator of Worms, 1976-1981; Clyde F. E. Roper, Curator of Mollusks, 1981-1987; Roger F. Cressey, Jr., Curator of Crustacea, 1987-1988; and Charles W. Hart, Jr., Curator of Crustacea, 1989. The period 1965-1971 is not well represented by administrative records.

ARRANGEMENT: (1) Record books, *circa* 1945-1974, accession number 90-078; (2) general correspondence and administrative files, *circa* 1965-1981, accession number 84-032; (3) general correspondence and administrative files, *circa* 1967-1984, accession number 86-101; (4) research and administrative files, *circa* 1979-1989, accession number 92-020. FINDING AIDS: Box list in control file. SPECIAL CONDITIONS: (1) Restricted; (2) use of this record unit requires prior arrangement with the Archives staff.

Collected Manuscripts, Correspondence, Drawings, Photographs, and Notes on Invertebrate Zoology, United States National Museum, 1871-1951 and undated
(2.3 linear meters).

This collection consists of field notes; drawings and sketches; photographs; manuscripts; research notes; and specimen lists relating to invertebrate zoology, especially crustacea. Also included is a small amount of correspondence of Wesley Roswell Coe, 1950-1951, and Harriett Richardson, 1906-1914. Of special interest are photographs of the United States Fish Commission's laboratories at Woods Hole, Massachusetts, in the 1880s. The material is arranged alphabetically by individual or subject.

ARRANGEMENT: Alphabetic. FINDING AIDS: Description in control file. SPECIAL CONDITIONS: Use of this record unit requires prior arrangement with the Archives staff.

Division of Crustacea, National Museum of Natural History, circa 1908-1979
Records (10.8 linear meters).

The Division of Crustacea was established on July 1, 1965, as a result of an administrative reorganization in the Department of Invertebrate Zoology, National Museum of Natural History. Prior to that time, the national collection of crustacea was under the care of the Division of Marine Invertebrates. For administrative histories of the Division of Marine Invertebrates and the Department of Invertebrate Zoology, see record units 249 and 233.

These records consist primarily of incoming and outgoing correspondence of the curatorial staff of the Division of Crustacea, 1965-1979, and its predecessor, the Division of Marine Invertebrates, 1908-1965. Most of the correspondence dates from 1937, with a small amount created before that date. A few photographs and manuscripts are included in the records and are noted in the folder list. The correspondence deals with the same general topics as those described in record unit 233. Subjects of special interest which are documented in the correspondence include several Arctic expeditions conducted by Robert A. Bartlett, 1925-1935; the proposed Pacific Islands Scientific Expedition under the auspices of the National Geographic Society and the University of Virginia, 1939-1940; Smithsonian participation on the Pacific Science Board of the National Research Council, 1953; the United States Fish and Wildlife Service Alaska King Crab Investigation, 1940; and special research conducted by the Division as part of the Smithsonian war effort, *circa* 1941-1945.

Curators represented by correspondence in these records include Waldo LaSalle Schmitt, Curator, 1920-1947; Clarence R. Shoemaker, Assistant and Associate Curator, 1921-1944; Mildred S. Wilson, Assistant Curator, 1944-1946; Fenner A. Chace, Jr., Curator, 1946-1963; Paul Louis Illg, Associate Curator, 1947-1952; Frederick Merkle Bayer, Assistant and Associate Curator, 1947-1961; Thomas E. Bowman, Associate Curator and Curator, 1954- ; Charles E. Cutress, Jr., Associate Curator and Curator, 1961-1965; Marian H. Pettibone, Associate Curator, 1963-1965; Raymond B. Manning, Associate Curator and Curator, 1963- ; David L. Pawson, Associate Curator, 1964-1965; Meredith Leam Jones, Associate Curator, 1964-1965; W. Duane

Hope, Associate Curator, 1964-1965; J. Laurens Barnard, Associate Curator and Curator, 1964-   ; Roger F. Cressey, Jr., Associate Curator and Curator, 1965-   ; and Louis S. Kornicker, Associate Curator and Curator, 1965-   .

ARRANGEMENT: (1) General correspondence, 1908-1962; (2) general correspondence, 1962-1979. FINDING AIDS: Description in control file. SPECIAL CONDITIONS: Use of this record unit requires prior arrangement with the Archives staff.

(414)

Division of Crustacea, National Museum of Natural History, 1977-1981
Records (2.9 linear meters).

For an administrative history of the Division of Crustacea, see record unit 307. Brian F. Kensley was appointed Associate Curator in 1978. Charles W. Hart, Jr., joined the staff as Curator in 1979.

These records consist of incoming and outgoing correspondence of the curatorial staff of the Division of Crustacea. The correspondence concerns the identification, acquisition, and exchange of specimens; preparation and review of scientific papers and monographs; professional activities of the staff, especially involvement in The Crustacean Society; review of grant proposals; and divisional administration. Curators represented in the correspondence include Thomas E. Bowman, Raymond B. Manning, J. Laurens Barnard, Roger F. Cressey, Jr., Louis S. Kornicker, Brian F. Kensley, and Charles W. Hart, Jr. Also included is correspondence of Museum Specialist C. Allan Child.

ARRANGEMENT: Alphabetic. FINDING AIDS: Box list in control file. SPECIAL CONDITIONS: Use of this record unit requires prior arrangement with the Archives staff.

(325)

Division of Echinoderms, National Museum of Natural History, 1907-1982
Records (4.2 linear meters).

From 1880 until 1920, the study and curation of the United States National Museum collection of Echinoderms was under the administrative direction of the Division of Marine Invertebrates. In 1920 the collection of Echinoderms was removed from Marine Invertebrates to form a new Division of Echinoderms. Austin H. Clark, who had served since 1908 as Collaborator and Assistant Curator in the Division of Marine Invertebrates, was appointed Curator and remained in the position until his retirement in 1950. At that time, the Division of Echinoderms ceased to exist as an administrative entity, and the collections reverted to the care of the Division of Marine Invertebrates. On July 1, 1965, the Division of Echinoderms was reformed as a division of the newly created Department of Invertebrate Zoology. Professional staff of the present Division of Echinoderms includes David L. Pawson, Associate Curator and Curator, 1965-   ; Klaus Ruetzler, Associate Curator and Curator, 1965-   ; and Frederick Merkle Bayer, Visiting Curator and Curator, 1972-   .

These records consist primarily of incoming and outgoing correspondence of the curatorial staff of the Division of Echinoderms. Most of the correspondence dates from the creation of the new Division of Echinoderms in 1965 and concerns the identification, exchange, and distribution of specimens; collecting work and expeditions; publication of manuscripts; professional activities; and administrative matters. Also included are divisional annual reports, 1966-1982.

ARRANGEMENT: (1) General correspondence, 1907-1980; (2) annual reports, 1966-1982. FINDING AIDS: Description in control file. SPECIAL CONDITIONS: Use of this record unit requires prior arrangement with the Archives staff.

Division of Echinoderms, United States National Museum, 1920-1953
Annual Reports and Records (0.3 linear meter).

Austin H. Clark (1880-1954) came to the Smithsonian in 1908 as a Collaborator in the Division of Marine Invertebrates, and in 1910 he became Assistant Curator of the Division. In 1920 the collection of Echinoderms was removed from Marine Invertebrates to form a new Division of Echinoderms, with Clark as Curator, a position which he held until his retirement in 1950. From 1950 to 1954 he was an Associate in Zoology. The Division of Echinoderms, which ceased to exist as an administrative entity after Clark's retirement, was reestablished in 1965. For additional records of the Division see the Austin H. Clark Papers, record unit 7183.

ARRANGEMENT: (1) Annual and quarterly reports, 1920-1953; (2) Division correspondence and records, *circa* 1939-1943. FINDING AIDS: Description in control file. SPECIAL CONDITIONS: Use of this record unit requires prior arrangement with the Archives staff.

(233)
Division of Marine Invertebrates, National Museum of Natural History, 1853-1962
Records (7.9 linear meters).

The origins of the collection of marine invertebrates under the care of the Smithsonian Institution can be traced to the collections made by William Stimpson while serving as zoologist on the North Pacific Exploring Expedition, 1853-1856, and the specimens collected by the United States Exploring Expedition which were transferred to the Smithsonian in 1858. Stimpson seems to have been, nominally at least, in charge of the Smithsonian marine invertebrate collections until 1865. By that date the Smithsonian collection of crustacea numbered more than 10,000 jars—the largest in the world at that time. In 1867 Stimpson was authorized to take most of the collection of American invertebrates to the Chicago Academy of Sciences for study, where they were destroyed when the Academy was burned in the Chicago fire of 1871. Beginning in the 1870s, large collections of marine invertebrates came to the Smithsonian as a result of the various expeditions conducted by the United States Fish Commission. Many of these specimens were retained at Yale University by Addison Emery Verrill for study and identification and did not reach the United States National Museum until 1907.

The Department of Marine Invertebrates was created as an administrative unit of the United States National Museum in 1880. In 1897 the Department became the Division of Marine Invertebrates. In 1914 the Division of Marine Invertebrates was merged with the Division of Mollusks into a single division under the title of Marine Invertebrates. In 1920 the collection of Echinoderms was removed from Marine Invertebrates to form a new Division of Echinoderms. In 1921 Mollusks was again separated from Marine Invertebrates.

Richard Rathbun (1852-1918) served as Curator of Marine Invertebrates from 1880 to 1914. In 1897 Rathbun was appointed Assistant Secretary of the Smithsonian, and responsibility for the administration of the Division fell largely to the two assistant curators, James E. Benedict (1854-1930) and Mary Jane Rathbun (1860-1943). Benedict served as Assistant Curator from 1890 to 1909. Mary Jane Rathbun served as Copyist, 1886-1893; Aid, 1893-1894; Assistant Curator, 1894-1914; and Associate in Zoology, 1914-1943. Clarence R. Shoemaker (1874-1958) served as Aid, Assistant Curator, Associate Curator, and Associate in Zoology from 1911 to 1958. Waldo LaSalle Schmitt (1887-1977) came to the Division in 1915 and served as Curator from 1921 to 1947. Fenner A. Chace, Jr. (1908-   ) served as Curator from 1946 to 1963.

These records consist mostly of correspondence of the members of the staff of the Division of Marine Invertebrates with naturalists, collectors, colleagues, scientists, and museum officials, concerning identification, exchange, and distribution of specimens; collecting work; museum publications; and museum administration. Some correspondence of Richard Rathbun, 1884-1887, pertains to United States Fish Commission business. Also included are monthly and annual reports of the Division, 1881-1936; invoices of specimens received, 1854-1914, which date back to the collections made by Stimpson; invoices of specimens sent out, 1878-1921; catalog of duplicate specimens, 1872-1881; and miscellaneous material.

ARRANGEMENT: (1) Outgoing correspondence, 1884-1920; (2) incoming correspondence, 1861, 1877, 1881-1902; (3) incoming correspondence, 1903-1920; (4) incoming and outgoing correspondence, 1921-1937, 1939, 1961-1962; (5) Clarence R. Shoemaker correspondence, 1919-1958; (6) monthly and annual reports, 1881-1936; (7) invoices of specimens received, 1854-1914; (8) invoices of specimens sent out, 1878-1921; (9) catalog of duplicate specimens, 1872-1881; (10) historical material and typescript, 1906 and 1932. FINDING AIDS: Description in control file. SPECIAL CONDITIONS: Use of this record unit requires prior arrangement with the Archives staff.

(235)
Division of Marine Invertebrates, National Museum of Natural History, 1921-1965
Records (1.6 linear meters).

For an administrative history of the Division of Marine Invertebrates, see record unit 233.

This record unit includes annual reports of the Division of Marine Invertebrates, 1930-1965; examination and reports, 1921-1965; personnel records, 1947-1964; and an administrative file, 1946-1965.

ARRANGEMENT: (1) Annual reports, 1930-1965; (2) examination and reports, 1921-1965; (3) personnel records, 1947-1964; (4) administrative files, 1946-1965. FINDING AIDS: Description in control file. SPECIAL CONDITIONS: Use of this record unit requires prior arrangement with the Archives staff.

Division of Mollusks, National Museum of Natural History, 1851-1982 and undated
Records (19.6 linear meters).

The origin of the mollusk collections under the care of the Smithsonian Institution predates the formal establishment of the Department of Mollusks. Collections of shells began arriving at the Institution from many of the exploring expeditions conducted during the 1830s, 1840s, and 1850s. The Department of Mollusks was created as an administrative unit of the United States National Museum (USNM) in 1880. As a result of an administrative reorganization of the USNM in 1897, the name was changed to the Division of Mollusks. In 1914, the Division was merged with the Division of Marine Invertebrates under the latter title. In 1921, the Division of Mollusks regained independent status. At that time the coral and helminthological collections were turned over to the Division's care.

William H. Dall, Alaskan explorer and paleontologist with the United States Geological Survey, served as Honorary Curator of the Division of Mollusks from 1880 until his death in 1927. Paul Bartsch joined the Division as an Aid in 1896. He was promoted to Assistant Curator in 1906 and Curator in 1916, a post he retained until his retirement in 1946. At that time, Bartsch was appointed Associate in Zoology. Harald A. Rehder came to the Division in 1932 as Senior Scientific Aid. He served as Assistant Curator, 1934-1942; Associate Curator, 1942-1946; Curator, 1946-1965; and Senior Zoologist, 1965-1980. He was appointed Zoologist Emeritus upon his retirement in 1980.

Other staff members of the Division of Mollusks have included Robert Edwards Carter Stearns, Assistant Curator, 1884-1893, and Associate in Zoology, 1894-1909; Charles Torrey Simpson, Aid, 1889-1902; William B. Marshall, Aid, 1895-1896, 1903-1914, and Assistant Curator, 1914-1934; Horace G. Richards, Assistant Curator, 1932; Joseph P. E. Morrison, Senior Scientific Aid, 1934-1942, Assistant Curator, 1942-1946, and Associate Curator, 1946-1974; R. Tucker Abbott, Assistant Curator, 1946-1949, and Associate Curator, 1949-1954; Joseph Rosewater, Associate Curator, 1961-1969, and Curator, 1969-   ; Clyde F. E. Roper, Associate Curator, 1966-1972, and Curator, 1972-   ; Richard S. Houbrick, Associate Curator, 1977-1978, and Curator, 1979-   ; and Arthur H. Clarke, Associate Curator, 1977-1980.

These records document the operation and activities of the Division of Mollusks from its establishment in 1880 until 1982. A large part of the records consists of incoming and outgoing correspondence relating to all aspects of the Division's work. The correspondence documents the history of malacology during the nineteenth and twentieth centuries, the history and activities of the American Malacological Union, the development of the Smithsonian collection of mollusks, divisional administration, the research of divisional staff members, and relations between the Division and United States government agencies. The collection also contains various specimen-related records including catalogs of individual collections, specimen identification report books, invoices, requisitions, and log books. Also included are divisional annual reports and various administrative records.

For additional material pertaining to the Division, see the William H. Dall Papers, record unit 7073.

ARRANGEMENT: (1) General correspondence, 1858-1982 and undated; (2) correspondence with the Smithsonian, United States National Museum, and government agencies, 1887-1929; (3) outgoing correspondence, 1885-1937; (4) catalogs, report books, invoices, log books, lists, and related materials, 1851-1937 and undated; (5) annual reports, 1884-1969; (6) administrative records, 1950-1976. FINDING AIDS: (1) Description in control file; (2) each volume of outgoing correspondence and some of the catalogs are indexed separately. SPECIAL CONDITIONS: Use of this record unit requires prior arrangement with the Archives staff.

(202)

Section of Corals, Division of Mollusks, National Museum of Natural History, 1931-1962
Annual Reports (0.1 linear meter).

The United States National Museum's collection of corals was originally entrusted to the care of the Department of Marine Invertebrates. Of particular importance in that collection were the corals collected by the United States Exploring Expedition, 1838-1842. In 1914, Marine Invertebrates was merged with the Division of Mollusks to form a single Division of Marine Invertebrates. In 1921, the Division of Mollusks was reestablished and the coral and helminthological collections were turned over to it. The Curator of the Division of Mollusks, Paul Bartsch, began to refer to a Section of Corals in his annual reports although there was never a curator for the Section. This practice continued, with the reports in this record unit forming a separate section of the Division of Mollusks annual report, until the coral collection was transferred to the Division of Marine Invertebrates about 1962.

For an administrative history of the Division of Mollusks, see record unit 73.

ARRANGEMENT: Chronologic. FINDING AIDS: None. SPECIAL CONDITIONS: Use of this record unit requires prior arrangement with the Archives staff.

(7418)

Division of Mollusks, National Museum of Natural History, 1888-1988 and undated
Photograph Collection (0.1 linear meter).

For an administrative history of the Division of Mollusks, see record unit 73.

This collection was maintained by the Division of Mollusks. It contains photographs of Division curators, including William H. Dall, Paul Bartsch, Robert Edwards Carter Stearns, Charles Torrey Simpson, Harald A. Rehder, R. Tucker Abbott, Joseph Rosewater, and Richard S. Houbrick; malacologists, invertebrate zoologists, and other scientists including Henry Hemphill, John Brooks Henderson, Jr., Charles W. Johnson, Carlos de la Torre y de la Huerta, and James Zetek; annual meetings of the American Malacological Union, 1974-1986; the *Pele* Expedition, 1967; and National Museum of Natural History exhibitions.

ARRANGEMENT: Alphabetic. FINDING AIDS: None. SPECIAL CONDITIONS: Use of this record unit requires prior arrangement with the Archives staff.

Collected Notes, Lists, and Drawings on Mollusks, United States National Museum, circa 1835-1850, 1861-1863 and undated
(0.1 linear meter and oversize).

This collection includes manuscript notes and lists on the mollusks of New York and on *Naiades* in the Smithsonian. The only identified author is C. J. Robinson. The collection also contains original drawings of shells for the plates of *Histoire Naturelle des Iles Canaries* by Philip Baxter Webb and Sabin Berthelot, *circa* 1835-1850.

ARRANGEMENT: Unarranged. FINDING AIDS: None. SPECIAL CONDITIONS: Use of this record unit requires prior arrangement with the Archives staff.

(7461)

Collected Notes, Lists, Catalogs, Drawings, and Manuscripts on Mollusks, United States National Museum, circa 1869-1917 and undated
(0.1 linear meter).

This collection consists of notes, lists, catalogs, drawings, and manuscripts on mollusks. Much of the material relates to specimens in the Division of Mollusks, National Museum of Natural History.

The collection includes a manuscript on the mollusks of the Republic of Panama by James Zetek, 1917; a list of Florida shells collected for the Smithsonian by Henry Hemphill, *circa* 1884; notes on squid collected around Bermuda by Joseph William Collins, *circa* 1880; a report on a voyage from Washington, D. C., to South Carolina by Robert Platt, United States Navy, undated; and a catalog of shells collected in Florida by Robert Edwards Carter Stearns, 1869.

ARRANGEMENT: Unarranged. FINDING AIDS: None. SPECIAL CONDITIONS: Use of this record unit requires prior arrangement with the Archives staff.

(1030301)

Collected Field Notebooks, Journals, Catalogs, Notes, and Lists on Mollusks, National Museum of Natural History, 1893-1981 and undated
(1.7 linear meters).

This collection consists primarily of field notebooks, journals, logs, and catalogs concerning mollusk specimens. Many of the volumes contain primary documentation for specimens in the Division of Mollusks. Although they vary in content, as a general rule the field notebooks contain specimen-related information including names of specimens, date collected, locality or station data, catalog or field numbers, and remarks about the specimens. Several of the volumes contain journal entries of the collector describing field activities, affairs of the day, personal financial accounts, and other personal matters. A few of the volumes include photographs. The collection also contains miscellaneous notes, lists, bibliographic references, and related materials on mollusks.

ARRANGEMENT: Alphabetic. FINDING AIDS: Description in control file. SPECIAL CONDITIONS: Use of this record unit requires prior arrangement with the Archives staff.

Division of Worms, National Museum of Natural History, 1965-1975, with related materials from circa 1920
Records (1 linear meter).

The Division of Worms was established on July 1, 1965, as a result of an administrative reorganization in the Department of Invertebrate Zoology. Prior to 1965, the national collection of worms was under the care of the Division of Marine Invertebrates. For administrative histories of the Department of Invertebrate Zoology and the Division of Marine Invertebrates, see record units 249 and 233.

Professional staff of the Division of Worms included Meredith Leam Jones, Associate Curator and Curator, 1965-   ; Marian H. Pettibone, Associate Curator and Curator, 1965-   ; W. Duane Hope, Associate Curator and Curator, 1965-   ; and Mary E. Rice, Associate Curator and Curator, 1965-   .

These records primarily document activities of the Division of Worms from its establishment in 1965 until 1975. They include correspondence concerning the identification, exchange, and distribution of specimens, professional activities of staff members, and administrative matters; files concerning W. Duane Hope's work as an officer of the Association of Meiobenthologists; and an information file on worms, compiled by the Division of Marine Invertebrates, which contains newspaper clippings, articles, and correspondence of Waldo LaSalle Schmitt.

ARRANGEMENT: (1) Correspondence, 1965-1975; (2) information file on worms, *circa* 1920-1965; (3) files concerning the Association of Meiobenthologists, 1968-1971. FINDING AIDS: None. SPECIAL CONDITIONS: Use of this record unit requires prior arrangement with the Archives staff.

ENTOMOLOGY, 1850-1990

Division of Insects, United States National Museum, 1878-1906
Incoming Correspondence (0.7 linear meter).

The Smithsonian Institution, prior to 1882, confined its activities in entomology to the distribution of specimens to workers in the field and the publication of their research. Many of the specimens eventually were deposited with the United States Department of Agriculture which the Smithsonian had designated as repository for the collections in 1874. The need for better curation of the collection led to the appointment of the Department of Agriculture Entomologist, Charles Valentine Riley, as Honorary Curator of Insects and to the transfer of the collection to the United States National Museum in 1882. Riley's successor at the Agriculture Department, Leland Ossian Howard, became Honorary Curator on Riley's death in 1895 and held the post until his own death in 1950.

Other entomologists from Agriculture also served frequently as custodians of various parts of the collection.

In addition to the Department of Agriculture staff, the Museum also appointed a number of curators in the Division of Insects. For the time period covered by these records, those curators included John Bernhard Smith, Assistant Curator, 1886-1889, and William Harris Ashmead, Assistant Curator, 1897-1908.

These records are the official incoming correspondence for the Division of Insects regarding determination, acquisition and loan of specimens, and other scientific matters.

ARRANGEMENT: Alphabetic by personal name, occasionally by subject rather than by correspondent. FINDING AIDS: Description in control file. SPECIAL CONDITIONS: Use of this record unit requires prior arrangement with the Archives staff.

(139)

Division of Insects, United States National Museum, 1882-1918
Outgoing Correspondence and Records (0.7 linear meter).

For an administrative history of the Division of Insects, see record unit 138. In addition to the curators noted in record unit 138, this record unit documents the activities of James Chamberlain Crawford, Assistant and Associate Curator, 1908-1919.

These records include receipts for specimens; annual and monthly reports of the Division; and correspondence regarding acquisition, distribution, and loan of specimens.

ARRANGEMENT: (1) Outgoing correspondence, 1882-1907; (2) invoices and requisitions, 1901-1918. FINDING AIDS: Description in control file. SPECIAL CONDITIONS: Use of this record unit requires prior arrangement with the Archives staff.

(140)

Department of Entomology, National Museum of Natural History, 1909-1963
Records (6.5 linear meters).

The Department of Entomology was organized in the United States National Museum in July 1963. Prior to that time, it was the Division of Insects of the Department of Zoology. For the administrative history of the Division of Insects, see record units 138 and 139. Curators represented in these records include James Chamberlain Crawford, Assistant and Associate Curator 1908-1919; John Merton Aldrich, Associate Curator, 1919-1934; Edward Albert Chapin, Curator, 1934-1954; and John Frederick Gates Clarke, Curator, 1954-1963. In 1963 Clarke became the first Chairman of the newly created Department of Entomology.

These records comprise the official correspondence of the Division of Insects and its successor, the Department of Entomology, and include records of staff of the Department of Agriculture because of close cooperation in taxonomic entomology.

ARRANGEMENT: Alphabetic by personal name. FINDING AIDS: Description in control file. SPECIAL CONDITIONS: Use of this record unit requires prior arrangement with the Archives staff.

Department of Entomology, National Museum of Natural History, 1922-1971
Records (0.8 linear meter).

For an administrative history of the Department of Entomology, see record units 138, 139, 140, and 148.

These records contain annual reports of the Department and its predecessors, 1922-1970, including curators' and divisional reports, statistics on specimens and accessions, and publications lists; plans of operations, 1927-1951, 1953-1966; and requisitions for purchase of specimens, 1964-1971. Also included are reports to the Department on activities of staff of the Division of Insect Identification, United States Department of Agriculture, who were located in the National Museum of Natural History (NMNH). These reports are filed with the NMNH Department or Division reports for the corresponding year.

ARRANGEMENT: (1) Annual reports, 1922-1970; (2) plans of operation, 1927-1951, 1953-1966, and requisitions, 1964-1971. FINDING AIDS: Description in control file. SPECIAL CONDITIONS: Use of this record unit requires prior arrangement with the Archives staff.

Department of Entomology, National Museum of Natural History, circa 1948-1974
Records (3 linear meters).

For an administrative history of the Department of Entomology, see record units 138, 139, 140, and 148. Paul D. Hurd, Jr., became Chairman of the Department in 1970.

This record unit contains correspondence, memoranda, notes, reports, manuscripts, and other materials documenting the activities of the Department of Entomology and its staff, especially during the tenures of John Frederick Gates Clarke, Karl V. Krombein, and Paul D. Hurd, Jr., as chairmen. Some material concerning the professional activities of these three is also included.

ARRANGEMENT: (1) Administrative subject file, *circa* 1948-1973; (2) manuscripts, 1952-1971; (3) grants, *circa* 1954-1974; (4) correspondence, 1952-1955, 1959-1974. FINDING AIDS: Description in control file. SPECIAL CONDITIONS: Use of this record unit requires prior arrangement with the Archives staff.

Department of Entomology, National Museum of Natural History, circa 1963-1988, with related records from 1934
Records (7.8 linear meters).

For an administrative history of the Division of Insects and the Department of Entomology, see record units 138, 139, 140, and 148.

These records consist of administrative subject files and professional correspondence documenting the administration and activities of the Department of Entomology. Most of the records were created during the tenures of Chairmen Paul D. Hurd, Jr., 1971-1976; Donald R. Davis, 1976-1981; and Wayne N. Mathis, 1981-1987. A smaller portion of the records was created by earlier chairmen John Frederick Gates Clarke, 1963-1965, and Karl V. Krombein, 1965-1971, as well as by recent Chairman Ronald J. McGinley, 1987-   .

These records provide information about specimen collections; specimen acquisition, loan, and distribution; budgets; personnel; publications; professional meetings and societies; and research projects. Also included are a few early documents dating from before the 1963 establishment of the Department of Entomology. These early records come from either the Department's predecessor, the Division of Insects, or from United States Department of Agriculture entomologists working in the United States National Museum.

ARRANGEMENT: (1) Chairman's files, *circa* 1953-1978, accession number 82-056; (2) Chairman's files, *circa* 1950-1982, accession number 84-124; (3) Chairman's files, 1964-1979, accession number T89065; (4) Chairman's files, 1934-1936, 1955-1988, accession number 92-036; (5) Chairman's files, *circa* 1952-1956, 1964-1987, accession number 92-110. FINDING AIDS: Folder list in control file. SPECIAL CONDITIONS: (1) Restricted; (2) use of this record unit requires prior arrangement with the Archives staff.

(148)

Department of Entomology, National Museum of Natural History, 1963-1967
Records (0.5 linear meter).

The Department of Entomology was organized in the United States National Museum, now the National Museum of Natural History, in July 1963. See record units 138, 139, and 140 for an administrative history of the Department. In 1963 John Frederick Gates Clarke became Chairman and he was succeeded by Karl V. Krombein in 1965.

The great majority of the records concern donation or other receipt of specimens in the National Museum; distribution or loan of specimens from the Museum; requests for determination of specimens by other entomologists and the general public (a considerable proportion of the determinations were made for state departments of entomology); and general research questions from the public. The Department corresponded with institutions all over the world, including most major United States and Canadian natural history institutions; state entomology departments; and institutions in Latin America, Great Britain, Europe, Australia, and India.

Less prevalent is correspondence between entomologists concerning their research; correspondence concerning manuscripts for publication in the National Museum series or submitted by Department staff to other journals; applications for research grants, mostly by Departmental staff to outside agencies; occasional copies of itineraries for research trips; and a few manuscripts of articles. The most useful correspondence is between the chairmen, Clarke and Krombein, and other entomologists regarding their research and collecting expeditions.

ARRANGEMENT: Alphabetic. FINDING AIDS: Description in control file. SPECIAL CONDITIONS: Use of this record unit requires prior arrangement with the Archives staff.

(1020001)

Department of Entomology, United States National Museum, circa 1870-1930
Autographs of Entomologists (7 volumes).

See record units 138, 139, 140, and 148 for an administrative history of the Department.

These letters were drawn from a number of sources and assembled for handwriting identification. The correspondence may be important historically.

ARRANGEMENT: Alphabetic. FINDING AIDS: None. SPECIAL CONDITIONS: Use of this record unit requires prior arrangement with the Archives staff.

(7401)

Department of Entomology, National Museum of Natural History, circa 1850-1982
Biographies of Entomologists (0.8 linear meter).

See record units 138, 139, 140, and 148 for an administrative history of the Department of Entomology.

These records consist mainly of biographical sketches, memorials, newspaper obituaries, and articles on domestic and foreign entomologists. Many of the biographies contain photographs. Also included are a few articles on the history of entomology.

For additional biographical information on entomologists, see record unit 7323.

ARRANGEMENT: Mostly alphabetic. FINDING AIDS: None. SPECIAL CONDITIONS: Use of this record unit requires prior arrangement with the Archives staff.

(1020002)

Department of Entomology, circa 1850-
Biographies of Entomologists (0.6 linear meter).

This collection was combined with record unit 1020003 to form record unit 7323, Systematic Entomology Laboratory, United States Department of Agriculture, 1797-1988 and undated, Photographs and Biographical Information.

(7423)

Department of Entomology, National Museum of Natural History, circa 1934-1964 and undated
Newspaper Clippings (0.1 linear meter).

This record unit contains clippings of newspaper articles about entomology and entomologists. The clippings come from newspapers all over the United States, and the majority date from the mid-1950s to the early 1960s.

ARRANGEMENT: Chronologic. FINDING AIDS: None. SPECIAL CONDITIONS: Use of this record unit requires prior arrangement with the Archives staff.

(1020003)

Department of Entomology, National Museum of Natural History, circa 1880-
Photographs of Entomologists.

This collection was combined with record unit 1020002 to form record unit 7323, Systematic Entomology Laboratory, United States Department of Agriculture, 1797-1988 and undated, Photographs and Biographical Information.

Department of Entomology, National Museum of Natural History, undated
Photographs of Lepidopterists (0.1 linear meter).

This collection of photographs of noted lepidopterists active primarily from the 1840s through the 1950s was assembled over a period of years by staff of the Department of Entomology. Many of the lepidopterists pictured worked for either the United States National Museum or the United States Department of Agriculture. Included are photographs of August Busck, Carl Heinrich, William Schaus, and John Bernhard Smith. The majority of the images are not original prints; they were cut out of professional journals and books. Also included is one copper daguerreotype plate.

ARRANGEMENT: Alphabetic. FINDING AIDS: Folder list in control file. SPECIAL CONDITIONS: Use of this record unit requires prior arrangement with the Archives staff.

Collected Notebooks of Entomologists, United States National Museum, circa 1881-1931
(0.1 linear meter).

Most notebooks of entomologists are retained as part of that person's papers; but for convenience, others are retained in this collection. The notebooks for the most part contain information relating to specimens in the National Museum of Natural History.

ARRANGEMENT: Unarranged. FINDING AIDS: Description in control file. SPECIAL CONDITIONS: (1) Additional notebooks may be placed in this collection; (2) use of this record unit requires prior arrangement with the Archives staff.

Collected Records and Papers on Entomology, United States National Museum, circa 1866-1950
(0.8 linear meter).

This collection consists of miscellaneous records and papers created by entomologists Herbert Spencer Barber, Henry Guernsey Hubbard, Charles Valentine Riley, and Eugene Amandus Schwarz. For biographical information on Barber, Hubbard, Riley, and Schwarz, see record units 7103, 7107, 7076, and 7104. These papers represent work done for the United States Department of Agriculture at the United States National Museum. Included in this record unit are correspondence and memoranda; notes; photographs of maps and insect illustrations; record books of information on specimen purchases, loans, and exchanges; and typed and hand-written drafts of entomological manuscripts. The majority of the manuscript drafts were written by Barber and concern the insect family Lampyridae. Also included are two of Hubbard's field notebooks and photographs taken during his trip to the western United States and British Columbia.

ARRANGEMENT: Unarranged. FINDING AIDS: None. SPECIAL CONDITIONS: Use of this record unit requires prior arrangement with the Archives staff.

Collected Scientific Illustrations and Photographs of Insects, National Museum of Natural History, circa 1920-1980

(1.2 linear meters).

This collection consists of illustrations and black and white photographs of insects that were used for figures and plates in scientific research papers written by various Department of Entomology and United States Department of Agriculture entomologists. Illustrators include B. B. Baber, Lawrence M. Druckenbrod, Julia Ellen Edmonson, Molly Ann Dwyer Griffin, Elaine R. S. Hodges, Frank M. Hull, Andre del Campo Pizzini, Robert J. Sim, Arthur Smith, Jung Lea Smith, Robert Evans Snodgrass, and George L. Venable.

ARRANGEMENT: Unarranged. FINDING AIDS: Folder list in control file. SPECIAL CONDITIONS: Use of this record unit requires prior arrangement with the Archives staff.

Division of Coleoptera, National Museum of Natural History, 1963-1979

Records (0.8 linear meter).

The Division of Coleoptera in the National Museum of Natural History was created at the time of the establishment of the Department of Entomology in July 1963. The Department was organized by discipline into five divisions: Neuropteroids, Lepidoptera, Coleoptera, Myriapoda and Arachnida, and Hemiptera. For an administrative history of the Department of Entomology, see record units 138, 139, 140, and 148. Curators represented in these records include Oscar L. Cartwright, Terry L. Erwin, and Paul J. Spangler. Cartwright was appointed Associate Curator of Insects in 1948, became Curator of Coleoptera when the Division was created in 1963, and was named Emeritus Entomologist when he retired in 1970. Erwin was hired in 1970 as Assistant Curator, became Associate Curator in 1973, and Curator in 1976. Spangler was appointed Associate Curator of Insects in 1962 and was assigned to the Division of Coleoptera in 1963.

These records consist of incoming and outgoing correspondence of the Division of Coleoptera concerning the acquisition, identification, loan, and distribution of specimens from 1963 to 1971. Also included are records documenting visitors to the Division from 1965 to 1979.

ARRANGEMENT: (1) Alphabetic correspondence file, 1963-1971; (2) visitor record book, 1968-1969, 1976; (3) requests for visitor passes, 1965-1979. FINDING AIDS: Description in control file. SPECIAL CONDITIONS: Use of this record unit requires prior arrangement with the Archives staff.

Division of Hemiptera, National Museum of Natural History, 1963-1984, with related records from 1949

Records (1.4 linear meters).

The Division of Hemiptera was created when the Department of Entomology was established in July 1963. The Department was organized by discipline into five divisions:

Neuropteroids, Lepidoptera, Coleoptera, Myriapoda and Arachnida, and Hemiptera. For an administrative history of the Department of Entomology, see record units 138, 139, 140, and 148.

For administrative purposes, the Division of Hemiptera also processed transactions relating to Hymenoptera, until a separate division could be created. Since Hymenoptera did not separate from Hemiptera until 1984, the title Division of Hemiptera and Hymenoptera was frequently used during the 1960s and 1970s. Curators represented in these records include Richard Charles Froeschner, Karl V. Krombein, Paul D. Hurd, Jr., and Gerald I. Stage.

Froeschner was appointed Associate Curator in 1963. Krombein was Chairman of the Department from 1966 to 1970, and a Senior Entomologist from 1971 to 1980, at which time his title was changed to Senior Scientist. Hurd succeeded Krombein as Chairman in 1970, and in 1977 he became a Curator in the Division of Hemiptera and Hymenoptera. Hurd's title was changed to Senior Scientist in 1980, and he remained with the Division until his death in 1982. Stage was an Assistant Curator from 1966 to 1970.

These records consist of incoming and outgoing correspondence of the Division of Hemiptera concerning the identification, acquisition, distribution, and loan of specimens from 1963 to 1984. Related correspondence created between 1949 and 1963 by Louise M. Russell, Entomologist at the Insect Identification and Parasite Introduction Branch, United States Department of Agriculture, is also included. Russell gave her correspondence concerning insects of the order Homoptera to Richard Froeschner when he became an Associate Curator in the Division. These records also include annual reports for the Division of Hemiptera written by Froeschner, and administrative memoranda of the Division. A small amount of correspondence created by Froeschner before he came to the Division is also included.

ARRANGEMENT: (1) Correspondence, 1949-1984; (2) annual reports, 1964-1974; (3) administrative memoranda, 1968-1975; (4) Froeschner pre-Division correspondence, 1954, 1960, 1962. FINDING AIDS: Description in control file. SPECIAL CONDITIONS: (1) Restricted; (2) use of this record unit requires prior arrangement with the Archives staff.

(427)

Division of Lepidoptera, National Museum of Natural History, 1963-1990, with related records from 1942
Records (4.5 linear meters).

The Division of Lepidoptera was created in July 1963, when the Department of Entomology was established. At that time, the Division was also responsible for the national collection of Diptera specimens. In 1968, the Division was renamed Lepidoptera and Diptera, to reflect the actual assignment of insect orders. This title remained until 1974, when all Diptera activities were moved under the Division of Neuropteroids; see record unit 422. For an administrative history of the Department of Entomology, see record units 138, 139, 140, and 148.

Curators represented by these records include William D. Field, Associate Curator, 1947-1975, and Curator, 1976-1980; John Frederick Gates Clarke, Curator, 1954-1963, Chairman, 1963-1965, Senior Entomologist, 1965-1975, and Research Associate, 1976-1990; Donald R. Davis, Associate Curator, 1961-1964, and Curator, 1964-   ; and W. Donald Duckworth, Associate Curator, 1962-1974, and Curator, 1974-1984.

These records consist of professional correspondence and administrative files documenting the activities and research of the Division of Lepidoptera. The correspondence for the most part concerns the loan, acquisition, identification, and distribution of insect specimens. A small amount of the correspondence dates to before the 1963 establishment of the Department of Entomology; the earliest letter is dated 1942. This early correspondence comes from either the Department's predecessor, the Division of Insects, or from lepidopterists working for the United States Department of Agriculture within the United States National Museum.

The administrative records include files describing various private collections of Lepidoptera specimens, reading lists and information sheets for amateur entomologists, memoranda and correspondence, and statistical information about the Division's specimen collection.

ARRANGEMENT: (1) General correspondence, 1963-1990, with related records from 1942; (2) administrative files, *circa* 1966-1987. FINDING AIDS: Box list in control file. SPECIAL CONDITIONS: (1) Restricted; (2) use of this record unit requires prior arrangement with the Archives staff.

(422)

Division of Neuropteroids and Diptera, National Museum of Natural History, 1963-1989, with related records from 1938
Records (2.1 linear meters).

The Division of Neuropteroids was created in July 1963, when the Department of Entomology was established at the United States National Museum. The title of the Division was changed in 1974 to Neuropteroids and Diptera, when research and transactions involving the Diptera collection were placed under the same administration as the work of the neuropterists. For an administrative history of the Department of Entomology, see record units 138, 139, 140, and 148.

Curators represented by these records include Grace E. Glance, Associate Curator, 1948-1957; Oliver S. Flint, Jr., Associate Curator, 1961-1965, and Curator, 1965- ; and Richard W. Baumann, Associate Curator, 1972-1975.

These records consist of professional correspondence and administrative files documenting the research and activities of the neuropteroid portion of the Division of Neuropteroids and Diptera. No records concerning Diptera are included in this record unit. Most of the correspondence was created by Oliver S. Flint, Jr., and concerns the acquisition, loan, identification, and distribution of neuropteran specimens. A small amount of correspondence from Flint's predecessor, Grace E. Glance, is included, as are some letters written by Richard W. Baumann. The earliest correspondence dates back to 1938 and was created by Glance in her position as an entomologist researching neuropteroids in the United States Department of Agriculture's Bureau of Entomology and Plant Quarantine from 1925 to 1948. The administrative records in this collection were also created by Flint and include memoranda and correspondence, budget and grant information, and annual reports and manuscripts.

ARRANGEMENT: (1) Alphabetic correspondence, 1963-1980, with related materials from 1938; (2) administrative files, 1963-1989. FINDING AIDS: Folder list in control file. SPECIAL CONDITIONS: (1) Restricted; (2) use of this record unit requires prior arrangement with the Archives staff.

BOTANY, 1825-1990

(220)

Division of Plants, United States National Museum, 1870-1893
Records (2.9 linear meters).

The foundations of the present Department of Botany of the National Museum of Natural History are the extensive collections of plants gathered by the government exploring expeditions of the 1800s and those assembled by the United States Department of Agriculture in connection with its investigations. The Smithsonian had original control of the specimens collected by the expeditions, and these were forwarded to John Torrey at Columbia College in New York, who had offered to house and prepare the collections without remuneration. When Torrey returned the specimens in 1868, lack of facilities and manpower led Joseph Henry to arrange for the Department of Agriculture to act as repository for the collections. There it was merged with the existing collections of the Department. Charles Christopher Parry was named Botanist of the Department of Agriculture in 1868 to care for the collection and served until 1871. George Vasey was appointed Botanist and Curator of the National Herbarium in 1872.

Lester Frank Ward, who had been appointed Honorary Curator of Fossil Plants in the United States National Museum in 1881, put together another collection of plants for comparison with his fossil specimens. This collection grew to the point where Ward was also named Honorary Curator of the Department of Recent Plants in 1885. In 1889, Vasey was given charge of the collection and appointed Honorary Curator of the Department of Botany. He retained this title until his death in 1893.

In 1894, arrangements were made by Frederick Vernon Coville, Vasey's successor, to have the collections housed at Agriculture moved to the Museum. There they were merged with Ward's collection although transfer of appropriations and personnel did not occur until 1896. Since that time, administration of the United States National Herbarium has come from the United States National Museum's Division of Plants and its successors.

Most of these records are the official files of George Vasey as Botanist of the United States Department of Agriculture and Curator of the United States National Herbarium from 1872 to 1893. They include incoming and occasional outgoing correspondence, mostly to Vasey, but sometimes to Jeremiah M. Rusk, Secretary of Agriculture; Edwin Willits, Assistant Secretary of Agriculture; Frederick Watts, George B. Loring, and John Eaton, Commissioners of the Department of Agriculture; and C. A. Cammon, Assistant Commissioner of the Department. All correspondence was referred to Vasey for response; and he either answered it himself or referred it to one of the Assistant Botanists, Joseph Nelson Rose, Frederick Vernon Coville, or Lyster Hoxie Dewey. Correspondents include leading United States and foreign botanists; colleagues; directors and curators of United States and foreign herbaria; custodians of botanical nurseries; naturalists; plant collectors; dealers in patent medicines; feed companies; seed growers; ranchers; farmers; geological surveys of the United States and Canada; Department of Agriculture staff members and administrative officers; Smithsonian Institution administrators; newspaper publishers and editors; scientific societies; the United States Experimental Grass and Forage Station at Garden City, Kansas; and in particular, botanists from the agricultural and mining colleges and their agricultural experiment stations.

This record unit contains requests for botanical specimens and seeds; determination, identification, and description of plants, grasses, and seeds, requests for plants to protect embankments; purchase of specimens; transfer of specimens to the National Herbarium; exchange of plant collections; lists of specimens in herbaria; information on plant collection methods; collecting in the field; botanical experiments; publishing taxonomies and other articles on botanical collections; requests for Department of Agriculture publications on American grasses; requests for Smithsonian publications; requests by Vasey for botanical publications; Smithsonian requests for material regarding the National Herbarium for its *Annual Report;* requests for jobs with the Department of Agriculture; staff salary increases and transfers of staff members; activities of colleagues and their collections; personal matters; and drafts of manuscripts.

Also included are outgoing letterpress correspondence from Vasey, administrative officers of the Department of Agriculture, and Assistant Botanists regarding the above subjects.

ARRANGEMENT: (1) Incoming and occasional outgoing correspondence, A-Z, 1870-1893; (2) outgoing correspondence of the Division of Botany, Department of Agriculture, 1886-1893; (3) outgoing correspondence of the Assistant Botanists, Division of Botany, Department of Agriculture, 1891-1893. FINDING AIDS: Description in control file. SPECIAL CONDITIONS: Use of this record unit requires prior arrangement with the Archives staff.

(221)

Division of Plants, United States National Museum, 1886-1928 and undated
Records (6.4 linear meters).

These records are the official files of Joseph Nelson Rose as Assistant Botanist at the United States Department of Agriculture, 1888-1896, and Assistant and Associate Curator of the Division of Plants, United States National Museum, 1896-1911 and 1917-1928. They also document Rose's professional career. For an administrative history of the United States National Herbarium and the Division of Plants, see record unit 220.

These records include incoming and outgoing correspondence with leading United States and foreign botanists, colleagues, herbarium and nursery curators, florists, agrostologists, field agents, amateur plant collectors, Department of Agriculture officials, Smithsonian Institution administrators, agricultural experiment stations, editors, and friends. The records concern examination, identification, and reports on botanical specimens; identification of specimens for publications; transfer of specimens to the United States National Herbarium; exchange of specimens; requests to Rose for information on the flora of Texas and Mexico; requests for bulbs, seeds, and plants; the purchase of cacti collections; research and collecting expeditions; nomenclature; illustrations for journals; collaboration on collecting specimens and publishing; requests for jobs; requests for recommendations of colleagues to systematize cultivated plants; proposals for a building to house the National Herbarium in order to expand the collection; meetings of scientific societies; and requests for *Who's Who* autobiographical information.

The records also include manuscripts and correspondence regarding Rose's joint Cactaceae project with Nathaniel Lord Britton; manuscripts and correspondence concerning Rose's joint project with John Donnell Smith regarding Hauyeae; notes, bibliographic references, and abstracts of correspondence relating to Rose's research on cacti; reviews; and occasional newspaper clippings concerning botanists.

ARRANGEMENT: (1) Incoming and occasional outgoing correspondence, 1886-1928; (2) outgoing correspondence, 1894-1919; (3) manuscript and correspondence related to the Joseph Nelson Rose and John Donnell Smith project on Hauyeae, 1911-1912; (4) Joseph Nelson Rose and Nathaniel Lord Britton project on Cactaceae, 1919-1923, and Rose's work on cacti, 1903-1922; (5) outgoing correspondence, 1894-1909, 1911-1912; (6) incoming and occasional outgoing correspondence, oversize, 1886-1928; (7) notes, bibliographic references, and abstracts of correspondence concerning Rose's research on cacti. FINDING AIDS: Description in control file. SPECIAL CONDITIONS: Use of this record unit requires prior arrangement with the Archives staff.

(272)

Department of Botany, National Museum of Natural History, 1885-1970
Records (4.8 linear meters).

For an administrative history of the Department of Botany, see record units 220 and 226. Jason Richard Swallen succeeded Ellsworth Paine Killip as Head Curator of the Department and served from 1950 to 1964. In 1964 the administrative title was changed to Chairman; chairmen represented in these records include William L. Stern, 1965-1967, and Mason E. Hale, Jr., 1968-1970.

These records consist of a variety of record and ledger books documenting loans, accessions, requisitions, and the mounting of specimens; annual and quarterly reports; files relating to World War II problems of loans and storage; exchange files, including correspondence with other institutions; a botanical reference file composed of replies to public inquiries; and an administrative subject file maintained by William L. Stern.

ARRANGEMENT: (1) Accession books, 1885-1943; (2) record of plants identified, 1889-1895 and undated; (3) requisition books, 1895-1952; (4) mounting books, 1895-1935; (5) loan books, 1894-1947; (6) memoranda of packing, 1901-1926; (7) record of specimens on hand, 1894-1899; (8) record of examination and report, 1900-1929; (9) financial notes, 1915-1916; (10) index to shipping invoices, 1948-1957; (11) visitor's book, 1930-1965; (12) annual and quarterly reports, 1912-1966; (13) files relating to World War II, 1941-1950; (14) exchange records, 1920-1969; (15) botanical reference file, 1926-1970; (16) administrative subject file, 1951-1968. FINDING AIDS: Description in control file. SPECIAL CONDITIONS: Use of this record unit requires prior arrangement with the Archives staff.

(236)

Division of Plants, United States National Museum, 1889-1896, 1902
Records (0.1 linear meter).

For an administrative history of the Division of Plants, see record unit 220.

These records consist of incoming correspondence to Ellen W. Cathcart, scientific assistant in the Division of Botany, United States Department of Agriculture, and concern the identification, determination, and exchange of cryptogams. Some of the correspondence was addressed to Frederick Vernon Coville, Curator of the United States National Herbarium, but was referred to Cathcart for reply.

(222)

Division of Plants, United States National Museum, 1894-1903
Records (0.7 linear meter).

These records are the official files of Charles Louis Pollard (1872-1945) as Assistant Curator of the Division of Botany, United States Department of Agriculture (USDA), 1894-1895, and the Division of Plants, United States National Museum (USNM), 1895-1903. Pollard also edited *Plant World* from 1899 to 1907.

These records document the activities of both divisions, as well as Pollard's scientific and administrative activities from 1894 to 1903. The records of both divisions have been maintained together and contain incoming and outgoing correspondence with botanists, entomologists, horticulturists, USDA and USNM administrative staff; foresters and colleagues; seed laboratories; and natural history and scientific societies. The correspondence chiefly concerns the examination, identification, collection, and exchange of botanical specimens, especially violets, mosses, grasses, ferns, fern-like plants, food plants, herbs, shrubs, and trees.

The correspondence also includes accession lists, annual reports, requests and approvals for field work, nomenclatorial work, and routine correspondence in reference to the publication of *Plant World* and other publications concerning botanical specimens. Also included are some of Pollard's manuscripts: "New American Species of *Chamaecrista*"; "A New Violet from New Jersey"; "The Genus *Oxytria* of Rafinesque"; and "The Two Violets."

ARRANGEMENT: (1) Incoming and occasional outgoing correspondence, 1894-1903; (2) outgoing correspondence, 1894-1903. FINDING AIDS: Description in control file. SPECIAL CONDITIONS: Use of this record unit requires prior arrangement with the Archives staff.

(223)

Division of Plants, United States National Museum, 1899-1947
Records (4.2 linear meters).

These records are the official files of William Ralph Maxon as Aid, Assistant and Associate Curator, and Curator of the United States National Herbarium, Division of Plants, United States National Museum, 1899-1946. For an administrative history of the Division of Plants, see record unit 220.

These records include incoming and outgoing correspondence with United States and foreign botanists; colleagues; directors of museums and herbaria; Smithsonian administrators; botanical collectors; and friends concerning identification, examination, and reports on botanical specimens; botanical gifts; loans or exchanges with other herbaria and collectors; information concerning ferns; carbon copies of Frederick Vernon Coville correspondence in regard to recommendations made by Maxon and Joseph Nelson Rose to have leading botanists receive honorary research positions with the National Herbarium; activities of staff members; salaries and annual leave; explorations and collecting expeditions; Maxon's expedition to Cuba, 1907, as well as to the West Indies, Mexico, Central America, South America, and Asia; professional potential of colleagues; information concerning the affairs of other botanical institutions; manuscripts; requests for publications and reprints; scientific society meetings; and editing and review of scientific articles. There is also correspondence concerning the American Fern Society and its publication, the *American Fern Journal,* 1924-1931.

ARRANGEMENT: (1) Incoming and occasional outgoing correspondence, 1899-1947; (2) outgoing correspondence, 1899-1931; (3) outgoing correspondence concerning the American Fern Society and the *American Fern Journal,* 1924-1931. FINDING AIDS: Description in control file. SPECIAL CONDITIONS: Use of this record unit requires prior arrangement with the Archives staff.

(224)

Division of Plants, United States National Museum, 1902-1922
Records (0.8 linear meter).

For an administrative history of the Division of Plants, see record unit 220.

These records contain official outgoing letterpress correspondence of Paul Carpenter Standley while Assistant Curator of the Division of Plants, United States National Museum, 1909-1922, regarding identification, examination, and reports on specimens sent to the Division; exchange and purchase of national collections; explorations and collecting expeditions; and botanical studies by Standley and other botanists. The records also include letterpress copies of manuscripts.

ARRANGEMENT: (1) Outgoing correspondence, 1902-1922; (2) manuscripts, undated. FINDING AIDS: Description in control file. SPECIAL CONDITIONS: Use of this record unit requires prior arrangement with the Archives staff.

(225)

Division of Plants, United States National Museum, 1904-1911
Records (0.1 linear meter).

For an administrative history of the Division of Plants, see record unit 220.

Joseph Hannum Painter was an Aid in the Division of Plants, United States National Museum, 1904-1908. These records contain Painter's incoming and outgoing correspondence with botanists and Smithsonian staff concerning the shipment of specimen collections; identification of specimens; mounting of collections; and Painter's work on the yellow pond lily, *Nymphaea.* Also included are copies of outgoing payments made by Joseph Nelson Rose for specimen collections, equipment, staff salaries, and labor, *circa* 1908-1911.

ARRANGEMENT: (1) Incoming and occasional outgoing correspondence, 1904-1908; (2) outgoing correspondence, 1905-1911. FINDING AIDS: Description in control file. SPECIAL CONDITIONS: Use of this record unit requires prior arrangement with the Archives staff.

(226)

Department of Botany, United States National Museum, 1918-1949
Records (2.2 linear meters).

In 1947, the Division of Plants of the Department of Biology became the Department of Botany. The new Department consisted of the Divisions of Cryptogams, Grasses, and

Phanerogams. These records are the official files of Ellsworth Paine Killip as Aid, Assistant Curator, Associate Curator, and Curator of the Division of Plants, and as Head Curator of the Department of Botany. For an administrative history of the Division of Plants, see record unit 220. These records also include professional correspondence between Killip and his colleagues documenting their personal and professional activities. Occasional letters and copies of letters to and from William Ralph Maxon, which were apparently forwarded to Killip, are also found in these records.

This record unit includes incoming and outgoing correspondence with United States and foreign botanists; directors and botanists of United States and foreign herbaria; museum curators; colleagues; friends; editors; and scientific societies concerning examination and identification of botanical specimens; exchange of specimen collections; explorations and collecting expeditions, especially Killip's expeditions to South America; information on mounting specimens; requests for photographs pertaining to Killip's publications; requests for publications and reprints; reviews of monographs; checking manuscripts for taxonomy and nomenclature; scientific society meetings; nominations for officers and members of scientific societies; evaluations of colleagues for positions; recommendations for job openings; personal matters; also outgoing correspondence containing references to Killip's collecting expeditions to Colombia; his work on South American plants; determinations of plants received; maps; passports; manuscripts; and a few copies of outgoing letters of Paul Carpenter Standley, Assistant Curator, 1921.

ARRANGEMENT: (1) Incoming and occasional outgoing correspondence, 1918-1949; (2) outgoing correspondence, 1920-1927; (3) miscellaneous letterpress book, 1921-1924. FINDING AIDS: Description in control file. SPECIAL CONDITIONS: Use of this record unit requires prior arrangement with the Archives staff.

(227)

Department of Botany, National Museum of Natural History, 1936-1965
Records (1.8 linear meters).

These records are the official files of Jason Richard Swallen while he was employed by the Bureau of Plant Industry, United States Department of Agriculture, 1936-1946, and the Department of Botany, United States National Museum, 1946-1964. Swallen succeeded Ellsworth Paine Killip as Head Curator of Botany in 1950. He was also Curator of Grasses from 1946 to 1964. For an administrative history of the Department of Botany, see record units 220 and 226.

This record unit includes some correspondence belonging to Mary Agnes Chase, which was forwarded to Swallen; Ernest R. Sohn, Associate Curator of Botany, 1956; and Thomas R. Soderstrom, Curator of Grasses, 1964-1965. Correspondents include United States and foreign botanists; agricultural experiment stations; field botanists; state geological surveys; foresters; curators of herbaria; wildlife technicians; collectors of botanical specimens; grass companies; government officials; colleagues; and scientific societies concerning examination, identification, and determination of botanical specimens, especially grasses and corn; exchanges of specimen collections; loans of specimens; requests for and shipment of botanical collections; nomenclature; agrostology investigations; studies of grasses, especially Swallen's work for Julian Alfred Steyermark's *Flora of Guatemala;* requests for photographs pertaining to publications; photographs of flora sent to Swallen by collectors in the field; editing articles and requests to review papers; manuscripts; reports; requests for recommendations for job openings; recommendations and evaluations of colleagues for job positions; elections of officers of scientific societies; and requests for Swallen to seek election to office in scientific societies.

ARRANGEMENT: (1) General correspondence, 1936-1965; (2) outgoing correspondence, 1939-1944. FINDING AIDS: Description in control file. SPECIAL CONDITIONS: (1) Record unit available on microfilm; (2) use of this record unit requires prior arrangement with the Archives staff.

(428)
Department of Botany, National Museum of Natural History, circa 1947-1990, with related records from 1926
Records (6.6 linear meters).

For an administrative history of the Department of Botany, see record units 220, 226, and 272. Edward S. Ayensu became Chairman of the Department of Botany in 1970. He served until 1976, when he was succeeded by Dieter C. Wasshausen, who directed the Department until 1982. Mark M. Littler was appointed Chairman in 1982. He was succeeded by Laurence E. Skog in 1987.

This record unit primarily documents the operation of the Department of Botany under Head Curators Ellsworth Paine Killip, 1947-1950, and Jason Richard Swallen, 1950-1964; and Chairmen William L. Stern, 1965-1967, Mason E. Hale, Jr., 1967-1970, Ayensu, Wasshausen, Littler, and Skog. Records created prior to the formation of the Department of Botany in 1947 are those of its predecessor, the Division of Plants. They include incoming and outgoing correspondence with United States and foreign botanists, curators of museums and herbaria, Smithsonian staff, and botanical collectors concerning the identification, acquisition, loan, and exchange of specimens; research and publications; professional affairs; and administrative matters.

Records include administrative and program files concerning collection management, exhibitions, space and facilities, budget and fiscal matters, grant proposals, and departmental reviews; correspondence documenting Hale's field work in Antarctica, 1981; records concerning the death of E. Yale Dawson in 1966; records and audiotapes from memorial services for Hale, Thomas R. Soderstrom, and Richard H. Eyde; annual reports, *circa* 1960-1989; plans of operations, *circa* 1950-1960; and records of the Department's Herbarium Services Unit, 1970-1980, which mostly concern collection management and the identification of specimens.

ARRANGEMENT: (1) General correspondence and administrative records, *circa* 1948-1977, with records from 1926, accession number 83-032; (2) administrative records, *circa* 1942-1963, accession number 90-057; (3) administrative records, *circa* 1965-1985, with records from 1947, accession number 90-123; (4) administrative records, *circa* 1964-1990, with records from 1948, accession number 92-091; (5) administrative records, *circa* 1960-1970, accession number 81-073; (6) Herbarium Services Unit, 1970-1980, accession numbers T89025 and 81-067. FINDING AIDS: Preliminary description in control file. SPECIAL CONDITIONS: (1) Restricted; (2) use of this record unit requires prior arrangement with the Archives staff.

Division of Cryptogams, United States National Museum, 1946-1951
Records (0.5 linear meter).

These records are the official files of George Albert Llano as Associate Curator of the Division of Cryptogams, Department of Botany, United States National Museum, 1948-1951. Records also document Llano's scientific and personal activities. For an administrative history of the Department of Botany, see record units 220 and 226.

Records include incoming and outgoing correspondence with botanists; curators of herbaria; superintendents of national parks; departmental staff members; friends; and publishers concerning examination, identification, and reports of lichens and mosses sent to the Division; exchange of lichen collections; taxonomy; requests to attend scientific meetings; requests to loan botanical specimens from other herbaria; Llano's field work collecting lichens in arctic Alaska, 1949; publication of manuscripts; reviewing articles; personal matters pertaining to the scientific activities of friends; references to colleagues; publication problems; and problems concerning the retention of specimens by other botanists which prevented Llano from reviewing them as part of his research.

ARRANGEMENT: (1) Incoming and outgoing correspondence, 1946-1951; (2) incoming and outgoing correspondence, oversize, 1946-1951. FINDING AIDS: Description in control file. SPECIAL CONDITIONS: Use of this record unit requires prior arrangement with the Archives staff.

Division of Grasses, United States National Museum, 1884, 1888, 1899-1963
Records (6.8 linear meters).

Albert Spear Hitchcock joined the United States Department of Agriculture in 1901 as Assistant Agrostologist under Frank Lamson-Scribner. In 1905 he was put in charge of the grass herbarium and became Systematic Agrostologist. After 1928, he held the title of Principal Biologist in charge of Systematic Agrostology of the Department of Agriculture and kept that title until his death in 1935. His relationship with the Smithsonian began in 1912 when he became Custodian of Grasses, Division of Plants, United States National Museum (USNM). At that time, the grass herbarium was apparently transferred to the National Museum. Hitchcock remained Custodian without remuneration until his death.

Mary Agnes Chase joined the Department of Agriculture in 1903 as a botanical illustrator and eventually became Scientific Assistant in Systematic Agrostology, 1907; Assistant Botanist, 1923; and Associate Botanist, 1925. Upon Hitchcock's death in 1935, Chase succeeded to his positions as Principal Botanist in charge of Systematic Agrostology and Custodian of the Section of Grasses, Division of Plants, USNM. She retired from the Department of Agriculture in 1939, but retained her post at the Museum. When the Department of Botany was formed in 1947, the Section became the Division of Grasses and Chase was made a Research Associate in the Department, apparently retaining her honorary custodianship of the grass herbarium. She died in 1963.

These records are the official files of Hitchcock and Chase when they worked for the Agrostology Section of the Bureau of Plant Industry, United States Department of Agriculture, and the Division of Grasses of the Department of Botany, United States

National Museum. For an administrative history of the Department of Botany, see record units 220 and 226. These records also document the scientific careers of Hitchcock and Chase and include personal papers predating their tenures with those agencies. Records of the Department of Agriculture were probably transferred to the National Museum when Hitchcock became Custodian of Grasses in 1912.

This record unit includes incoming and outgoing correspondence with United States and foreign botanists; directors and curators of herbaria; agronomists; collectors of botanical specimens; seed laboratories; floral companies; Department of Agriculture and Smithsonian Institution staff members; agricultural schools and agricultural experiment stations; colleagues; friends; publishers; and scientific societies concerning identification, examination, and reports on plants and grasses; exchange and transfer of specimens; gifts and loans of specimen collections; information regarding plants and grasses for sheep and other livestock; explorations and botanical collecting expeditions; taxonomy; nomenclature; sick and annual leave; requests for positions with the Department of Agriculture; recommendations for colleagues for positions; recommendations for fellowships; recommendations for publication of manuscripts; requests for publications; election to scientific societies; administrative status of the Section of Grasses of the United States National Herbarium, 1938; Mary Agnes Chase Fund, 1953-1961; feminist movement; pacifism and politics in Europe before and during the Second World War; and political and economic conditions during the Chinese Civil War, especially in Foochow, 1949.

The records also include photograph albums documenting field trips by Hitchcock to South America, Africa, Canada, and in the United States, and by Chase to Brazil in 1924-1925; a bound volume of letters received by Chase on her eightieth birthday in 1949; biographies; manuscripts; newspaper clippings; photographs; and a scrapbook.

ARRANGEMENT: (1) Incoming and occasional outgoing correspondence, A-Z and oversize, 1884, 1888, 1899-1963; (2) outgoing correspondence of the Agrostology Section of the Bureau of Plant Industry, United States Department of Agriculture, 1905-1923; (3) reports, 1923-1924; (4) scrapbook of Albert Spear Hitchcock, 1893-1921; (5) photograph albums, 1919-1929; (6) letters received by Mary Agnes Chase on her eightieth birthday, 1949. FINDING AIDS: Description in control file. SPECIAL CONDITIONS: Use of this record unit requires prior arrangement with the archives staff.

(230)
Division of Phanerogams, National Museum of Natural History, 1920-1961
Records (0.4 linear meter).

This record unit includes incoming and outgoing correspondence of Emery Clarence Leonard, Aid, Assistant and Associate Curator of the Division of Plants, 1918-1947, and Associate Curator of Phanerogams, Department of Botany, 1947-1962. For an administrative history of the Department of Botany, see record units 220 and 226.

Records include correspondence with botanists; colleagues; friends; herbarium curators; directors of arboreta; private collectors of plants; and publishers concerning specimen identification; recommendation of books to be used in the identification of plants; requests for reprints; purchase and acquisition of collections; reference to colleagues and herbaria; history of private collections; personal accounts of daily activities of friends and colleagues; and personal memoranda regarding Leonard's salary, promotion, and recommendation that he be made a Research Associate.

ARRANGEMENT: Alphabetic by correspondent. FINDING AIDS: Description in control file. SPECIAL CONDITIONS: Use of this record unit requires prior arrangement with the Archives staff.

(237)

Department of Botany, National Museum of Natural History, 1889-1968
Autographs of Botanists (0.1 linear meter).

See record units 220 and 226 for an administrative history of the Department of Botany.
Most of the correspondence making up this collection was written to John Donnell Smith, Research Associate in the Division of Plants from 1905 to 1928.

ARRANGEMENT: Alphabetic. FINDING AIDS: Description in control file. SPECIAL CONDITIONS: Use of this record unit requires prior arrangement with the Archives staff.

(7219)

Collected Notes and Lists on Botany, United States National Museum, circa 1871 and undated
(0.1 linear meter).

This collection includes manuscript lists and notes on the flora of Indian Territory, San Diego, and unidentified locales. The authors of these manuscripts are unidentified.

ARRANGEMENT: Unarranged. FINDING AIDS: None. SPECIAL CONDITIONS: Use of this record unit requires prior arrangement with the Archives staff.

(1010014)

Collected Notes, Lists, and Catalogs on Plants, National Museum of Natural History, 1825-1966 and undated, with related material to 1977
(12.8 linear meters).

This record unit consists primarily of field notes and specimen lists of National Museum of Natural History curators and people who collected specimens for the Museum. In most cases the field notes document collections housed in the Department of Botany. Included in this record unit for convenience are materials which are not strictly field notes, such as unpublished manuscripts of books and correspondence.

ARRANGEMENT: Alphabetic. FINDING AIDS: Description in control file. SPECIAL CONDITIONS: Use of this record unit requires prior arrangement with the Archives staff.

Division of Mineralogy and Petrology, National Museum of Natural History, 1932-1963
Records (1.3 linear meters).

The Division of Mineralogy and Petrology of the Department of Geology was established in 1911. Prior to that date it was known as the Division of Mineralogy. In 1942, the Division of Mineralogy and Petrology was combined with the Division of Physical and Chemical Geology (systematic and applied) under the former name. The Department of Geology was abolished in 1963 as part of a reorganization in the National Museum of Natural History. At that time, the Division of Mineralogy and Petrology became the newly created Department of Mineral Sciences.

Edward P. Henderson joined the staff of the United States National Museum (USNM) in 1929 as Assistant Curator in the Division of Physical and Chemical Geology (systematic and applied). In 1942, he became Associate Curator in the Division of Mineralogy and Petrology. He remained in that position until 1963, when he was named Associate Curator in charge of the newly created Division of Meteorites of the Department of Mineral Sciences. He was made Curator in 1965 and on his retirement in 1966 was appointed Research Associate. For records of Henderson's years as Curator and Research Associate in the Division of Meteorites, see record unit 269.

This record unit consists primarily of Edward P. Henderson's official correspondence files as Associate Curator of the Division of Mineralogy and Petrology. A smaller amount of files were created by Roy S. Clarke, Jr., who was appointed Chemist in the Division of Mineralogy and Petrology in 1957. Correspondence before 1942 was carried out by Henderson in his capacity as Assistant Curator of the Division of Physical and Chemical Geology (systematic and applied). The correspondence is both incoming and outgoing and deals exclusively with the national collection of meteorites under the care of the Division of Mineralogy and Petrology. Of special interest is correspondence concerning efforts to acquire the Harvey Harlow Nininger Meteorite Collection, 1957-1963. Correspondents include geologists and mineralogists, meteorite collectors and dealers, Smithsonian and USNM staff and administrators, government agencies, research foundations, and the general public.

For other records of the Division of Mineralogy and Petrology, see record unit 266. For records of the Division of Meteorites, see record unit 269.

ARRANGEMENT: Alphabetic. FINDING AIDS: Description in control file. SPECIAL CONDITIONS: Use of this record unit requires prior arrangement with the Archives staff.

Division of Mineralogy, National Museum of Natural History, 1958, 1964-1970
Records (2.1 linear meters).

The Division of Mineralogy was established in 1963 as part of a reorganization in the geological sciences at the Museum of Natural History (MNH). At that time the Department of Geology was abolished and replaced by two new Departments, Mineral Sciences and Paleobiology. The Divisions of Mineralogy and Meteorites were created under the Department of Mineral Sciences. Staff of the Division of Mineralogy included Paul E. Desautels, Associate Curator, 1963- ; and John S. White, Jr., Museum Specialist, 1963- .

This record unit consists primarily of incoming and outgoing correspondence documenting the operation of the Division of Mineralogy, 1964-1970. Most of the correspondence was conducted by Desautels and White, with lesser amounts by George S. Switzer in his capacity as Chairman of the Department of Mineral Sciences. It concerns the acquisition of collections, identification of specimens, and professional activities of the staff. Also included are records concerning the opening of the Gem and Mineral Hall in the MNH in 1958.

ARRANGEMENT: (1) Incoming and outgoing correspondence, 1964-1970; (2) Gem and Mineral Hall opening, 1958. FINDING AIDS: Box list in control file. SPECIAL CONDITIONS: Use of this record unit requires prior arrangement with the Archives staff.

Division of Mineralogy, National Museum of Natural History, 1960-1989
Records (5.3 linear meters).

For an administrative history of the Division of Mineralogy, see record unit 336.

This record unit consists of incoming and outgoing correspondence and memoranda documenting the operation of the Division of Mineralogy primarily from 1971 to 1989. The correspondence concerns the acquisition of collections, identification of specimens, research and professional activities of the staff, requests for information, and divisional administration.

Most of the correspondence was carried out by Paul E. Desautels, Associate Curator, 1963-1973, and Curator, 1973-1983; John S. White, Jr., Museum Specialist, 1963-1974, Associate Curator, 1974-1984, and Curator, 1984- ; and Pete J. Dunn, Museum Specialist, 1973- . Smaller amounts of correspondence were created by Joel E. Arem, Crystallographer, 1971-1974; Daniel E. Appleman, Crystallographer, 1974- ; and Jeffrey E. Post, Associate Curator, 1984- .

ARRANGEMENT: Alphabetic and chronologic. FINDING AIDS: Box list in control file. SPECIAL CONDITIONS: (1) Restricted; (2) use of this record unit requires prior arrangement with the Archives staff.

Department of Mineral Sciences, National Museum of Natural History, 1936, 1938, 1948-1977 and undated

Records (3.3 linear meters).

The Department of Mineral Sciences was created in 1963 as part of a reorganization in the National Museum of Natural History. At that time the Department of Geology was divided into two new departments, with the Division of Mineralogy and Petrology becoming the Department of Mineral Sciences and the Divisions of Invertebrate Paleontology and Paleobotany and Vertebrate Paleontology joined to form the Department of Paleobiology. George S. Switzer became the first Chairman of the Department of Mineral Sciences in 1963 and served until 1968. Other incumbents included Brian H. Mason, 1968-1973, and William G. Melson, 1973-1978. Staff of the Division of Mineralogy and Petrology included William F. Foshag, Assistant Curator, 1919-1929, Curator, 1929-1948, and Acting Curator, 1948-1956; Edward P. Henderson, Associate Curator, 1942-1963 (also Assistant Curator in the Division of Physical and Chemical Geology from 1929 to 1942); George S. Switzer, Associate Curator, 1948-1956, Acting Curator, 1957, and Curator, 1958-1963; Paul E. Desautels, Associate Curator, 1957-1963; and Roy S. Clarke, Jr., Chemist, 1957-1963. In 1963 Henderson and Clarke were assigned to the Division of Meteorites, and Desautels to the Division of Mineralogy. Therefore, after 1963, they are not represented in this correspondence.

This record unit consists of correspondence documenting the operation of the Department of Mineral Sciences, 1963-1977, and its predecessor, the Division of Mineralogy and Petrology of the Department of Geology, 1948-1963. With the exception of a few letters, correspondence of the Division of Mineralogy and Petrology prior to 1948 is not included in the record unit. The correspondence is both incoming and outgoing and concerns the identification and acquisition of specimens; participation in professional societies and mineral exhibitions; the publication of scientific manuscripts and departmental and divisional administration. Correspondents include geologists and mineralogists, gemologists, jewelers, mineral collectors and dealers, colleges and universities, mining companies, publishers, government agencies, and the general public. Correspondence prior to 1963 is mostly directed to Curator George S. Switzer and Associate Curator Paul E. Desautels. Correspondence after 1963 is primarily carried out by Departmental Chairmen Switzer, Brian H. Mason, and William G. Melson. The correspondence is arranged alphabetically by correspondent.

ARRANGEMENT: Alphabetic. FINDING AIDS: Description in control file. SPECIAL CONDITIONS: Use of this record unit requires prior arrangement with the Archives staff.

Department of Mineral Sciences, National Museum of Natural History, 1953-1988

Records (0.4 linear meter).

For an administrative history of the Department of Mineral Sciences prior to 1978, see record unit 266.

Daniel E. Appleman was appointed Chairman of the Department of Mineral Sciences in 1978 and served through 1982. Robert F. Fudali served as Chairman from 1983 until 1988.

This record unit consists of incoming and outgoing correspondence and memoranda written by Robert F. Fudali during his tenure as Chairman, 1983-1988, concerning departmental administration and his professional activities, and annual reports of the Department of Mineral Sciences, 1963-1986, and its predecessor, the Division of Mineralogy and Petrology of the Department of Geology, 1953-1963.

ARRANGEMENT: Unarranged. FINDING AIDS: Folder list in control file. SPECIAL CONDITIONS: (1) Restricted; (2) use of this record unit requires prior arrangement with the Archives staff.

(269)

Division of Meteorites, National Museum of Natural History, 1963-1970 and undated *Records (1.2 linear meters).*

The Division of Meteorites was established in 1963 as part of a reorganization in the National Museum of Natural History (NMNH). At that time the Department of Geology was divided into two new departments, Paleobiology and Mineral Sciences. Prior to 1963, the NMNH collection of meteorites was under the care of the Division of Mineralogy and Petrology of the Department of Geology (see record unit 268). Staff of the Division of Meteorites included Edward P. Henderson, Associate Curator in charge, 1963-1964, Curator, 1965-1966, and Research Associate, 1966-   ; Roy S. Clarke, Jr., Chemist, 1963-1966, Associate Curator, 1966-   ; Kurt Fredriksson, Curator in charge, 1964-1966, Curator, 1967-   , including the years 1967-1968 when he also served as Supervisor; Brian H. Mason, Curator, 1965-   , including 1968 when he also served as Supervisor; Robert F. Fudali, Geochemist, 1967-   ; Eugene Jarosewich, Chemist, 1967-   ; and Joseph A. Nelen, Chemist, 1967-   .

This record unit consists of correspondence documenting the operation of the Division of Meteorites, 1963-1970. The correspondence is both incoming and outgoing and concerns the identification and acquisition of specimens; the publication of scientific manuscripts; exhibits; participation in professional societies; and divisional administration. Of special interest is correspondence concerning the acquisition of the Arthur R. Allen Meteorite Collection, 1963-1964, and Edward P. Henderson's collecting work in Australia, 1963-1965. Correspondents include geologists and mineralogists, meteorite collectors and dealers, Smithsonian and NMNH staff and administrators, government agencies, and the general public. The correspondence is primarily directed to Curators Henderson (after 1966, Research Associate), Clarke (prior to 1966, Chemist), Fredriksson, and Mason.

ARRANGEMENT: Alphabetic. FINDING AIDS: Description in control file. SPECIAL CONDITIONS: Use of this record unit requires prior arrangement with the Archives staff.

Division of Meteorites, National Museum of Natural History, circa 1970-1988
Records (1.4 linear meters).

For an administrative history of the Division of Meteorites and information on its staff prior to 1970, see record unit 269.

This record unit consists of incoming and outgoing correspondence and memoranda documenting the operations of the Division of Meteorites, 1970-1988. The records concern the identification and acquisition of specimens, divisional administration, and professional activities of its staff members. Staff members represented by correspondence include Brian H. Mason, Curator, 1970-1984; Roy S. Clarke, Jr., Associate Curator, 1970-1973, and Curator, 1973-   ; Kurt Fredriksson, Curator, 1970-1973, and Geochemist, 1973-   ; Robert F. Fudali, Geochemist, 1970-   ; Eugene Jarosewich, Chemist, 1970-1973; Joseph A. Nelen, Chemist, 1971-1973; and Glenn J. MacPherson, Associate Curator, 1984-   .

ARRANGEMENT: (1) Division of Meteorites, records, 1970-1974, accession number 89-095; (2) Division of Meteorites, records, *circa* 1970-1988, accession number 89-097. FINDING AIDS: Folder list in control file. SPECIAL CONDITIONS: (1) Restricted; (2) use of this record unit requires prior arrangement with the Archives staff.

Division of Petrology and Volcanology, National Museum of Natural History, 1975-1987
Records (0.4 linear meter).

The Division of Petrology was established in the Department of Mineral Sciences in 1964. In 1973, the name was changed to the Division of Petrology and Volcanology. Curators in the Division have included William G. Melson, Associate Curator in Charge, 1964-1973, and Curator, 1973-   ; Thomas E. Simkin, Geologist, 1972-1973, Associate Curator, 1973-1974, and Curator, 1974-   ; Richard S. Fiske, Curator, 1975-   ; and Sorena Sorensen, Associate Curator, 1984-   .

This record unit consists of correspondence and memoranda documenting the operations of the Division of Petrology and Volcanology from 1975 to 1984. Most of the correspondence is written by the professional staff of the Division, but also included are letters of Museum Specialist Harold H. Banks, Jr. The records document the acquisition and identification of specimens, divisional administration, and professional activities of the staff.

ARRANGEMENT: Chronologic. FINDING AIDS: Folder list in control file. SPECIAL CONDITIONS: (1) Restricted; (2) use of this record unit requires prior arrangement with the Archives staff.

Department of Geology, National Museum of Natural History
Biographical File (2.5 linear meters).

For an administrative history of the Department of Geology, see record unit 156.

This biographical file was maintained by the United States National Museum's Department of Geology and several of its curators. Included in the file are biographies, obituaries, memoirs, and memorial service programs and addresses of prominent scientists, particularly American geologists and paleontologists, as well as some notable Smithsonian Institution personnel. Also included are newspaper feature stories about geologists and their important geological discoveries or contributions to their field of study. Many of the publications include published prints or an occasional photograph of the subject. Also attached by the Department to some of the publications is correspondence, 1836-1958, usually written by the subject.

ARRANGEMENT: Alphabetic. FINDING AIDS: Description in control file. SPECIAL CONDITIONS: Use of this record unit requires prior arrangement with the Archives staff.

(7421)

Department of Mineral Sciences, National Museum of Natural History, circa 1919-1976 and undated
Photograph Collection (0.5 linear meter).

For an administrative history of the Department of Mineral Sciences, see record unit 266.

This photograph collection was maintained by the Department of Mineral Sciences and its predecessor, the Department of Geology. It includes photographs of curators and other departmental staff members, donors to the national collection of minerals and gems, geologists, paleontologists, mineralogists, and gemologists. Paul E. Desautels, William F. Foshag, Edward P. Henderson, George Frederick Kunz, George P. Merrill, Washington A. Roebling, Waldemar Theodore Schaller, and Henry Stephens Washington are but a few of the scientists represented by photographs in the collection.

ARRANGEMENT: Alphabetic. FINDING AIDS: List of photographs in control file. SPECIAL CONDITIONS: Use of this record unit requires prior arrangement with the Archives staff.

(7291)

Collected Catalogs, Correspondence, and Specimen Lists on Mineral Sciences, United States National Museum, 1894-1910 and undated
(0.3 linear meter).

This collection consists of accession catalogs maintained by the Department of Geology, 1900-1910, and by the Division of Mineralogy of the Department of Geology (prior to 1897, the Department of Minerals), 1894-1910; catalogs, specimen lists, and an alphabetic index of the Frederick A. Canfield Mineral Collection which was bequeathed to the United States National Museum in 1926; and outgoing correspondence concerning the Petrographic Reference Collection of the Department of Geology, 1896-1906.

ARRANGEMENT: Unarranged. FINDING AIDS: Description in control file. SPECIAL CONDITIONS: Use of this record unit requires prior arrangement with the Archives staff.

PALEOBIOLOGY, 1850-1984

(248)
Division of Vertebrate Paleontology, United States National Museum, 1882-1922 and undated
Records (0.1 linear meter).

For an administrative history of the Division of Vertebrate Paleontology, see record unit 156.

These records consist of incoming correspondence primarily to Frederic Augustus Lucas, a Curator in the Division, from Charles E. Beecher, William Cooper, Nelson Horatio Darton, James W. Gidley, George Brown Goode, James Hall, John Bell Hatcher, Othniel Charles Marsh, William McAdams, Henry Fairfield Osborn, and Charles D. Walcott. Also included is correspondence from Fred Brown to Marsh concerning specimens collected in Wyoming by Brown for Marsh at Yale University. Presumably, this correspondence accompanied the specimens when they were later given to the United States National Museum. Included with a letterpress book of outgoing correspondence, 1900-1909, are copies of the Division's annual reports for fiscal years 1901 to 1909.

ARRANGEMENT: (1) Incoming correspondence, 1888-1904, 1909-1912, 1922 and undated; (2) correspondence from Fred Brown to Othniel Charles Marsh, 1882-1887; (3) outgoing correspondence, 1900-1909, and annual reports, 1901-1909. FINDING AIDS: Description in control file. SPECIAL CONDITIONS: Use of this record unit requires prior arrangement with the Archives staff.

(156)
Division of Vertebrate Paleontology, National Museum of Natural History, circa 1889-1957
Records (2.7 linear meters).

Work in vertebrate paleontology at the Smithsonian Institution predates the formal establishment of a Department of Vertebrate Paleontology in 1887. Joseph Leidy and Edward Drinker Cope, among others, studied the fossil collections which had been gathered by the various government exploring expeditions and sent to the Smithsonian. With the reorganization of the United States National Museum, 1880, the Department of Comparative Anatomy was given charge of the collections until the creation of the Department of Vertebrate Paleontology in 1887, with Othniel Charles Marsh as Honorary Curator. Since its creation, the Department has undergone a number of organizational and title changes.

In 1894, the Department became a Section of the Department of Paleontology. The reorganization of 1897 created a Division of Stratigraphic Paleontology in the Department of Geology, and Vertebrate Paleontology was made a Section of that Division. It became a separate Division in 1908 but in 1911 was again made a Section, this time in the Division of Paleontology. In 1924 this Division was renamed the Division of Stratigraphic Paleontology, and Vertebrate Paleontology again became a Division.

Since Marsh's death in 1889, curators of the Division have included Frederic Augustus Lucas, intermittently from 1889 to 1904; Charles W. Gilmore, Assistant and

Associate Curator, 1911-1923, and Curator, 1923-1945; and James W. Gidley, Assistant Curator, 1911-1931. Charles Lewis Gazin, Assistant and Associate Curator, 1932-1946, was appointed Curator following Gilmore's death. David H. Dunkle and Peter P. Vaughn were named Associate Curators in 1946 and 1957, respectively.

These records document the history of the Division of Vertebrate Paleontology, 1889-1957, and to a greater extent, the professional and administrative activities of Charles W. Gilmore when he was a staff member of the Division, 1905-1945.

ARRANGEMENT: (1) Daybooks and journals, kept by Charles W. Gilmore, 1905-1931; (2) journal, *circa* 1910-1923; (3) general correspondence, 1898-1901, 1905-1945; (4) vertebrate fossil identifications, 1889-1904; (5) examination and reports and outgoing correspondence, 1911-1923, 1930-1940, 1946-1957; (6) article drafts, notes, speeches, and radio talks. FINDING AIDS: Description in control file. SPECIAL CONDITIONS: Use of this record unit requires prior arrangement with the Archives staff.

(424)

Division of Vertebrate Paleontology, National Museum of Natural History, circa 1947-1974 and undated
Records (2.5 linear meters).

For an administrative history of the Division of Vertebrate Paleontology prior to 1957, see record unit 156. The Department of Geology was divided in 1963 into Departments of Mineral Sciences and Paleobiology, with Vertebrate Paleontology a Division of the latter.

Curators of the Division have included Charles Lewis Gazin, 1946-1968; Associate Curators David H. Dunkle and Peter P. Vaughn, 1946-1967, and 1957-1959, respectively; Nicholas Hotton III, Associate Curator, 1959-1968, and Curator, 1969-   ; Clayton E. Ray, Associate Curator, 1964-1968, Supervisor and Curator, 1968-1971, and Curator, 1971-   ; and Robert J. Emry, Associate Curator, 1971-1981, and Curator, 1982-   .

These records consist of incoming and outgoing correspondence documenting the operation of the Division of Vertebrate Paleontology, *circa* 1955-1974. Also included are plans of operation, *circa* 1947-1960; public inquiries for identification of specimens and information; and glass plate negatives which document the field work of Frederick William True and James W. Gidley, as well as paleontological exhibits.

Curators represented by correspondence include Charles Lewis Gazin, David H. Dunkle, Clayton E. Ray, Nicholas Hotton III, and Robert J. Emry.

ARRANGEMENT: (1) General correspondence, *circa* 1955-1974; (2) plans of operation, *circa* 1947-1960; (3) public inquiries for identification and information, *circa* 1957-1970; (4) glass plate negatives, undated. FINDING AIDS: Box list in control file. SPECIAL CONDITIONS: Use of this record unit requires prior arrangement with the Archives staff.

Collected Notebooks, Manuscripts, Drawings, Photographs, and Correspondence on Vertebrate and Invertebrate Paleontology, United States National Museum, circa 1850-1940 and undated

(1.7 linear meters).

For an administrative history of the Division of Vertebrate Paleontology, see record unit 156.

This collection consists of original drawings of fossil specimens and artists' interpretations of extinct animals; photographs of specimens, sites, exhibitions and museums; correspondence; notes written by James W. Gidley on primates; and drawings of birds and reptiles found during the Northern Pacific Railroad Route Expedition.

ARRANGEMENT: (1) Field notes, 1886-1908, 1939 and undated; (2) manuscripts, 1903-1911, 1923 and undated; (3) photographs, 1937 and undated; (4) related material, 1865, 1883-1887, 1890-1891, 1898-1899, 1911 and undated; (5) drawings, photographs, notes and related material, *circa* 1850-1940, accession number 90-145. FINDING AIDS: Description in control file. SPECIAL CONDITIONS: Use of this record unit requires prior arrangement with the Archives staff.

Collected Field Notebooks on Vertebrate Paleontology, National Museum of Natural History, 1874-1975

(2 linear meters).

This collection contains field notebooks of collectors who collected specimens for the Division of Vertebrate Paleontology. They are the primary documentation for many of the specimens in the Division of Vertebrate Paleontology. Although they vary in content, as a general rule they contain specimen-related data including catalogs of specimens collected, dates, localities, tag numbers, measurements, and remarks on the specimens. Less frequently, they contain journal entries of the collector describing field activities, affairs of the day, anthropological observations, personal financial accounts, and other personal matters. Included with some of the notebooks are expense accounts from field trips.

ARRANGEMENT: Alphabetic by collector. FINDING AIDS: Description in control file. SPECIAL CONDITIONS: Use of this record unit requires prior arrangement with the Archives staff.

Department of Paleobiology, National Museum of Natural History, 1930-1932, 1937-1984 and undated, with related materials from 1882

Records (4.6 linear meters and oversize).

The paleontological collections of the United States National Museum (USNM) were located in the Department of Geology from its creation in 1880 until its dissolution in 1963. The Department of Paleobiology was created in 1963 as part of a reorganization in the National Museum of Natural History. At that time the Department of Geology was divided into two departments, with the Divisions of Invertebrate Paleontology and Paleobotany and Vertebrate Paleontology joined to form the Department of

Paleobiology, while the Division of Mineralogy and Petrology became the Department of Mineral Sciences. G. Arthur Cooper became the first Chairman of the Department of Paleobiology in 1963 and served until 1967. Other Chairmen included Porter M. Kier, 1967-1972; Richard E. Grant, 1972-1977; Martin A. Buzas, 1977-1982; and Ian G. MacIntyre, 1982-   .

This record unit documents the activities of the Department of Paleobiology from its establishment in 1963 until 1984. Records prior to 1963 were mostly created by the Division of Invertebrate Paleontology and Paleobiology, Department of Geology, and extensively document the curatorial career of G. Arthur Cooper. Chairmen of the Department of Paleobiology represented in the records include Cooper, Porter M. Kier, Richard E. Grant, Martin A. Buzas, and Ian G. MacIntyre. Records document research and professional activities of curators and other staff scientists; budget planning and other administrative matters; departmental reviews; plans for the movement of collections to the east wing of the National Museum of Natural History during the 1960s and the Museum Support Center in the 1980s; cooperative relations with the Paleontology and Stratigraphy Branch, United States Geological Survey; establishment of the A. Remington Kellogg Memorial Fund; and exhibitions, including the Exhibits Modernization Program at the USNM.

Records include annual reports; budget estimates and plans of operation; research proposals and progress reports; administrative files of the Department of Paleobiology; subject files maintained by the Department of Paleobiology and the Division of Invertebrate Paleontology and Paleobotany, Department of Geology; correspondence and memoranda with Smithsonian bureaus, offices and staff; a correspondence file of Chairman Martin A. Buzas; correspondence files of the Division of Invertebrate Paleontology and Paleobotany, Department of Geology, mostly concerning the identification and acquisition of specimens; exhibition scripts; blueprints and drawings, mostly of specimen storage cases; and outgoing memoranda of Richard S. Boardman, a curator in the Department of Paleobiology, which concern his research and professional activities.

ARRANGEMENT: (1) Annual reports, 1948-1974, 1978-1982; (2) budget estimates and plans of operation, 1950-1977, 1979-1984; (3) research progress reports, 1948-1963; (4) research proposals, 1957-1980 and undated; (5) administrative files, 1963-1982; (6) Martin A. Buzas correspondence, 1977-1982 and undated; (7) Department of Paleobiology, subject files, 1963-1984, with materials from 1924; (8) correspondence with Smithsonian bureaus, offices and staff, 1949-1974, with materials from 1882; (9) Division of Invertebrate Paleontology and Paleobotany, subject files, 1932, 1941-1963; (10) Division of Invertebrate Paleontology and Paleobotany, general correspondence, 1930-1965, with materials from 1896; (11) exhibition scripts, 1938, 1952, 1956-1971; (12) blueprints and mechanical drawings, 1916, 1931-1971; (13) Richard S. Boardman, outgoing memoranda, 1958-1974. FINDING AIDS: Description in control file. SPECIAL CONDITIONS: (1) Correspondence A-J in series 10 is missing; (2) use of this record unit requires prior arrangement with the Archives staff.

(543)
Department of Paleobiology, National Museum of Natural History, circa 1940-1980
Records (0.4 linear meter).

For an administrative history of the Department of Paleobiology, see record unit 328.

This record unit contains personnel files of curators, museum specialists, and affiliated personnel of the Department of Paleobiology, *circa* 1940-1980. Records include correspondence, biographical sketches, curricula vitae, and photographs. Staff and affiliated individuals documented include Ray S. Bassler, G. Arthur Cooper, David H. Dunkle, Douglas Ralph Emlong, Lorenzo Ford, Charles Lewis Gazin, M. Grant Gross, Leo J. Hickey, Lawrence B. Isham, Mildred Joseph, Erle G. Kauffman, Jesse Merida, and Franklin L. Pearce.

ARRANGEMENT: Alphabetic. FINDING AIDS: Box list in control file. SPECIAL CONDITIONS: Use of this record unit requires prior arrangement with the Archives staff.

DEPARTMENT OF ANTHROPOLOGY AND BUREAU OF AMERICAN ETHNOLOGY, 1878-1990

The Department of Anthropology and the Bureau of American Ethnology (BAE) were merged into the newly created Smithsonian Office of Anthropology (SOA) in 1965. In 1968 the SOA was retitled the Department of Anthropology. For administrative histories of the BAE and the Department of Anthropology, see record units NAA 1 and NAA 5.

These records are located in the Smithsonian's National Anthropological Archives. Reference requests should be addressed to the National Anthropological Archives, National Museum of Natural History, Smithsonian Institution, Washington, D.C. 20560.

(NAA 1)

Bureau of American Ethnology, 1879-1908
Records (8.2 linear meters).

The Bureau of Ethnology was founded in 1879 after Congress appropriated funds for the continuation of research among North American Indians that had been begun by the Geographical and Geological Survey of the Rocky Mountain Region. The name was changed in 1897 to the Bureau of American Ethnology (BAE) to emphasize the geographic limit of its interests. Under John Wesley Powell, its Director from 1879 to 1902, the BAE became a major force in the growth of the nascent science of anthropology by undertaking several broad and basic anthropological research projects, sponsoring extensive and intensive field research by its staff and collaborators, initiating several series of anthropological publications, and joining both professional and amateur anthropologists throughout the country in unofficial efforts to promote the growth of the discipline. In addition, the BAE prepared exhibits for several large expositions of the later 19th and early 20th centuries and, on instruction from the Secretary of the Smithsonian Institution, made collections of anthropological specimens for deposit in the United States National Museum. In addition to its research and publications program, it developed a manuscript repository, an illustrative section that included photographic work, and a library.

In overseeing these many efforts, Powell was able to rely heavily on capable lieutenants, particularly William John McGee, who joined the staff with the title Ethnologist-in-Charge in 1893. Powell also enjoyed a marked degree of independence from the central Smithsonian administration; and, while he was Director of the United States Geological Survey from 1880 to 1894, the BAE had considerable support from the Survey. Following Powell's death, dissatisfaction with these arrangements on the part of the Institution, irregularities in the administration of the BAE, and considerable criticism within Congress combined to lead the Smithsonian to investigate the BAE's activities. This resulted in tighter control by the Secretary of the Institution. Although its purposes and functions remained basically similar to those developed under Powell, greater emphasis was placed upon research and publication under his successors: William Henry Holmes, Chief, 1902-1909; Frederick Webb Hodge, Ethnologist-in-Charge, 1910-1918; Jesse Walter Fewkes, Chief, 1918-1928; Matthew William Stirling, Chief, 1928-1954, Director, 1954-1957; Frank H. H. Roberts, Jr., Director, 1957-1964; and Henry B. Collins, Acting Director, 1964-1965.

The BAE had three significant but temporary sub-units under its administration. The Mounds Survey, which concentrated on the eastern part of the United States, was undertaken on instructions from Congress. From 1882 to 1895 it was led by Cyrus Thomas assisted by a number of specially appointed field workers. The Institute for Social Anthropology was in operation from 1943 to 1952 and the River Basin Surveys from 1946 to 1969. See record units NAA 4 and NAA 6 below for descriptions of these last two projects.

The extant records of the BAE include not only the material described in this and the following series, but are also found in a collection of numbered manuscripts located in the National Anthropological Archives. Earlier archivists separated many letters, reports, fiscal records, and other material from their series and cataloged them as individual items. For a description of the series of numbered manuscripts, see *Catalog to the Manuscripts at the National Anthropological Archives,* G. K. Hall, Boston, 1975.

This record unit consists mainly of bound letterpress copy books used for the outgoing correspondence of administrative personnel. The material varies considerably in content. Much of it concerns housekeeping functions, the distribution of publications, and inquiries received from the public. It also includes copies of outgoing letters that reflect the BAE's wide contact in the world of anthropology and science in general. Considerable amounts of it contain reports on general developments within the BAE and among its staff, but this is extremely uneven. Some private correspondence is included, particularly in the letterbooks of W. J. McGee. Since both Powell and McGee were at times in their careers connected with the United States Geological Survey and retained active interests in geology throughout their lives, material relating to the Survey and to geological studies and organizations is included.

ARRANGEMENT: (1) General outgoing correspondence, 1879-1907; (2) outgoing transmittal correspondence, 1893-1903; (3) outgoing correspondence relating to the BAE library, 1896-1897; (4) outgoing correspondence regarding editorial work, 1894-1903; (5) requisitions for printing and binding, 1896-1903; (6) outgoing correspondence of William Henry Holmes, 1890-1893, 1903-1905; (7) outgoing correspondence of W. J. McGee, 1893-1903; (8) outgoing correspondence of Frank Hamilton Cushing, 1896-1899; (9) outgoing correspondence of Chief Clerk Frank M. Barnett, April 13 and 21, 1903; (10) accounts, 1897-1907; (11) BAE annual reports, 1898-1903; (12) records regarding the International Archeological Commission, 1902-1903;

(13) outgoing correspondence regarding the joint meeting of the American and British Associations for the Advancement of Science, 1897. FINDING AIDS: (1) Most volumes indexed by correspondent; (2) separate index arranged by year and correspondent for 1878-1883. SPECIAL CONDITIONS: These records are located in the Smithsonian's National Anthropological Archives.

(NAA 2)

Bureau of American Ethnology, 1878-1965
Records (31.2 linear meters).

For an administrative history of the Bureau of American Ethnology (BAE) and general remarks concerning its records, see record unit NAA 1.

These records consist mainly of incoming correspondence, much of which is related to the outgoing correspondence described in record unit NAA 1. A small number of items represent correspondence of the Geographical and Geological Survey of the Rocky Mountain regions and relate to its ethnological work. Much of the material consists of inquiries from the general public, but also includes letters concerning accounts; reports from Bureau of American Ethnology staff members and collaborators, including substantive anthropological and biographical data; and material relating to the collection of specimens for the United States National Museum, the purchase and donation of manuscripts for the BAE archives, and the preparation and acquisition of the BAE photographic collection. Some of the letters relate to certain BAE projects, particularly the Mounds Survey, Garrick Mallery's study of Indian sign language, Henry Crecy Yarrow's study of mortuary customs, James Pilling's compilation of bibliographies relating to Indian languages, and John Wesley Powell's collection of data on Indian languages.

ARRANGEMENT: (1) Incoming correspondence, 1878; (2) incoming correspondence, 1879-1888; (3) incoming correspondence, 1888-1906; (4) incoming correspondence, 1907; (5) incoming correspondence from Matilda Coxe Stevenson, 1890-1918; (6) incoming correspondence from Charles D. Walcott, 1907; (7) incoming correspondence from the Smithsonian Institution, 1889-1908; (8) incoming correspondence from the United States National Museum, 1889-1909; (9) incoming correspondence from government agencies, 1888-1908; (10) incoming and outgoing correspondence, 1909-1950; (11) incoming and outgoing correspondence, 1950-1965. FINDING AIDS: (1) Index by year and name of correspondent, 1878-1888; (2) registers of letters received, 1947-1963. SPECIAL CONDITIONS: These records are located in the Smithsonian's National Anthropological Archives.

(NAA 3)

Bureau of American Ethnology, 1893-1966
Administrative Records (5.2 linear meters).

For an administrative history of the Bureau of American Ethnology (BAE) and general remarks concerning its records, see record unit NAA 1.

These records consist largely of material relating to fiscal, property, and personnel matters. Considerable reference correspondence with the general public and records regarding the acquisition, loan, and transfer of collections are also included. The records relating to the investigation of the BAE in 1903 provide data on the general operations of the BAE from around 1893 to 1903 and on the activities and attitudes of individual staff members.

ARRANGEMENT: (1) Requisitions, 1893-1898; (2) records relating to the investigation of the administration of the BAE, 1903; (3) correspondence regarding cooperative ethnological investigations, 1928-1935; (4) correspondence of Matthew W. Stirling, 1928-1957; (5) administrative file, 1950-1960; (6) fiscal records, 1945-1966. FINDING AIDS: Draft register. SPECIAL CONDITIONS: These records are located in the Smithsonian's National Anthropological Archives.

(NAA 4)
Bureau of American Ethnology, Institute for Social Anthropology, 1942-1952
Records (30 linear meters).

For an administrative history of the Bureau of American Ethnology (BAE), see record unit NAA 1.

The Institute for Social Anthropology (ISA) was established in 1943 as an autonomous unit of the Bureau of American Ethnology. It grew out of efforts by the Inter-American Society of Anthropology and Geography and operated throughout most of its existence with support provided by committees of the Department of State. The ISA's purpose was to promote cooperation with other American states in anthropological training and research. Its headquarters were in Washington, D.C., under the direction of Julian H. Stewart from 1943 to 1946 and George M. Foster from 1946 to 1952. Staff members were stationed in Brazil, Colombia, Mexico, Peru, and Guatemala, where they taught university classes, directed the field work of students, and assisted with the preparation of publications. In 1952, the ISA came under the sponsorship of the Institute of Inter-American Affairs, and its functions were absorbed by that organization at the close of the year.

The records chiefly contain administrative files concerning arrangements for financing the Institute and other fiscal matters, recruitment and use of personnel, and cooperation with State Department and other government and private organizations. Some of the correspondence includes reports by individual staff members on their activities.

ARRANGEMENT: (1) Annual reports, 1942-1952; (2) organizational and personnel files, 1942-1952; (3) records relating to cooperation with the Department of State, 1946-1951; (4) correspondence, 1942-1952; (5) records relating to cooperative arrangements with Latin American countries, 1942-1952; (6) records relating to other organizations, 1942-1952; (7) accounts and fiscal records, 1946-1952; (8) budget records, 1944-1951. FINDING AIDS: Draft register. SPECIAL CONDITIONS: These records are located in the Smithsonian's National Anthropological Archives.

(NAA 5)
Department of Anthropology, National Museum of Natural History, 1897-1990, with related materials dating from circa 1828
Records and Manuscripts (95.9 linear meters).

The Department of Anthropology was organized in 1897 as part of a general reorganization of the United States National Museum (USNM). Its creation followed a long history of involvement in anthropology that began in the earliest years of the Smithsonian Institution, with support for and publication of the researches of Ephraim George Squier and Edwin Hamilton Davis, Henry Rowe Schoolcraft, and John Wesley Powell. The early United States National Museum had well defined departments and collections in ethnology, prehistoric ceramics, and archaeology, under such specialists as William Henry Holmes, Otis Tufton Mason, Charles Rau, and Thomas Wilson. The Department's immediate predecessor was a Division of Anthropology that included these and several other departments. The Division was, however, merely a grouping of departments and lacked essential organizational elements such as specific functions or administrative personnel.

The Department in 1897 was based on a broad concept of anthropology and included divisions of ethnology, historical archeology, prehistoric archeology, technology, graphic arts, medicine, religions, and history and biography. Over the next twenty years, several divisions were made either independent units or parts of the USNM's Department of Arts and Industries. By 1920, the major divisions within the Department were ethnology, archeology, and physical anthropology. The Department also remained responsible for small sections of ceramics, musical instruments, and art textiles until they were transferred to the new Museum of History and Technology in the early 1960s.

From 1879 to 1965, anthropology at the Smithsonian was divided between the Department (including its predecessors) and the Bureau of American Ethnology (BAE). The primary concern of the Department was the collection of anthropological specimens; the BAE was mainly concerned with research. The division of labor was not, however, complete. Artifacts and other materials collected by BAE staff were added to the collections of the Department, while Department staff were involved in research in the collections, field research (often through temporary assignments to the BAE), and research on non-material culture. The Department and the BAE had distinctly different areas of geographic concern, however. The BAE was interested primarily in Indians of the Western Hemisphere, while the Department curated collections from the entire world. The growth of the Department's non-American collections after World War II led to new staff curatorial specialties for Oceania, Africa, and Asia.

In 1965, many of the functions of the Bureau of American Ethnology were transferred to the Department during a reorganization of the National Museum of Natural History. This new Smithsonian Office of Anthropology was renamed the Department of Anthropology in 1968. The curatorial staff placed primary emphasis on research, while much of the management of the collections was turned over to support staff. The scientific staff was originally organized into divisions of cultural anthropology and physical anthropology, but in the later 1960s this structure gave way to one with greater independence for individual curators, each of whom reported directly to the Department Chair. Several Departmental support units were created in the 1960s and 1970s, including an automatic data processing inventory unit, a processing laboratory, an illustrations section, a conservation laboratory, and an archives, designated the National Anthropological Archives (NAA) in 1968. In 1977, a collections manager was appointed to organize the automatic data processing and inventory units and to take charge of the processing laboratory. Until 1968, when it was placed under the immediate charge of the Director, National Museum of Natural History, the River Basins Survey (formerly administered by the BAE and for which see record unit NAA 6) was also part of the Department's responsibility. In 1986 an American Indian Program was started for coordination of programs for American Indians and to provide assistance in maintaining relations with American Indian tribes.

In 1989, the Department was organized into six divisions: ethnology, physical anthropology, archeology, the National Anthropological Archives, the Human Studies Film Archives, and the Office of *The Handbook of North American Indians.* An executive committee made up of the heads of these divisions was formed to advise the chairman. At the same time, the position of Deputy Chairman was created.

Head Curators and Chairs include William Henry Holmes, 1897-1902, 1910-1920; Otis Tufton Mason, Acting Head Curator, 1902-1903, Head Curator 1904-1908; Walter Hough, Acting Head Curator, 1908-1909, 1920-1923, Head Curator, 1923-1935; Frank M. Setzler, 1935-1960; Thomas Dale Stewart, 1960-1962; Waldo R. Wedel, 1963-1965; Richard B. Woodbury, 1965-1967; Saul H. Riesenberg, 1967-1970; Clifford Evans, Jr.,1970-1975; William W. Fitzhugh, 1975-1980; Douglas H. Ubelaker, 1980-1984; Adrienne L. Kaeppler, 1985-1988; and Donald J. Ortner, 1988-   .

The records of the Department of Anthropology are relatively discontinuous. Mainly they concern museum functions relating to anthropology as it is conceived today—ethnology, archeology, and physical anthropology. As units concerned with other studies were transferred from the Department, related records were generally transferred with them. In addition to these transfers, evidence exists of considerable culling of early files. Furthermore, much of the Department's earliest material was filed among the records of the United States National Museum, now in the Smithsonian Archives. Moreover, some essentially administrative materials have been incorporated in papers of curatorial staff deposited in NAA, as well as NAA's series of numbered manuscripts.

These records contain some significant special collections. Antiquities permits for undertaking archeological work on federal lands were routinely reviewed by the Smithsonian Institution between 1906 and 1981. The Smithsonian's Office of the Secretary transferred this file to the Department in the 1960s; the file was placed with NAA in 1973. Since 1981, submission of applications and reports has been very irregular.

Departmental records contain two archeology reference files, one of materials dating between 1828 and 1961; the other between 1861 and 1916. Both are arranged geographically, and much of the material consists of reports of archeological finds by both professional and amateur archaeologists. The Archeology Map Collection consists mostly of printed maps for reference purposes, supplemented by manuscript maps of archeological sites.

Other special collections include a Manuscript and Pamphlet File, chiefly relating to ethnology, but including materials on archeology, physical anthropology, and cultural history, and also containing some administrative records. Records of the Urgent Anthropology Program and the Office of *The Handbook of North American Indians* document these two Smithsonian ventures, the one to support research on cultures undergoing rapid change, the other to publish a comprehensive reference work on Native Americans.

For further information, see James R. Glenn, *Guide to the National Anthropological Archives, Smithsonian Institution* (Washington, D.C.: National Anthropological Archives, 1992).

ARRANGEMENT: A. Records of the Head Curators and Department Chairs, including (1) reports, 1921-1967; (2) minutes of staff meetings, 1963-1972; (3) memoranda exchanged with Smithsonian units, 1965-1972; (4) memoranda from Smithsonian administrators, 1964-1971; (5) subject files, 1828-1975 (mostly dating from

1889 to 1975); (6) River Basin Surveys file, 1965-1969; (7) research statements, proposals, and awards, 1961-1977; (8) publications files, 1960-1974; (9) condemnations, 1910-1965; (10) special exhibits, 1951-1952; (11) data concerning employees, 1912-1965; (12) records concerning Smithsonian fellows, 1972-1974; (13) miscellaneous administrative files, 1891-1980; (14) invoices concerning specimens, 1904-1920; (15) leaflets for public distribution, 1955-1966; (16) Federal Antiquities Act permits and reports, 1904-1982; (17) exhibit labels and miscellaneous documents, 1870s-1950s; (18) photographs of specimens and other subjects, 1880s-1950s; (19) miscellany, 1960s; (20) records of the Urgent Anthropology Program, *circa* 1966-   ; (21) unprocessed material; B. records of the Division of Archeology, including (22) reports, 1899-1959; (23) general files, 1899-1959; (24) correspondence, 1931-1956; (25) subject file, 1935-1974; (26) archeological reference file, 1828-1962; (27) archeological reference file, 1861-1916; (28) miscellany, 1963-1974; (29) maps; C. records of the Division of Ethnology, including (30) reports, 1920-1964; (31) manuscript and pamphlet file, mostly 1870s-1930s; (32) research plans and reports, 1946-1965; (33) data on employees, 1924-1957; (34) special exhibits, 1932-1946; (35) management plans, 1951-1955; (36) registers of visitors, 1942-1965; D. records of the Division of Cultural Anthropology, (37) accession lists, 1920-1968; E. records of the Section of Animal Products, including (38) general file, 1884-1887; F. records of the *Handbook of North American Indians,* including (39) manuscripts for volume 8 (California); and (40) records of the illustrations section for volumes 8 (California), 9 and 10 (Southwest), and 15 (Northeast) only; and G. records of the Anthropological Laboratory/Conservation and Restoration Laboratory, including (41) records, 1939-1973. FINDING AIDS: Description in control file. SPECIAL CONDITIONS: These records are located in the Smithsonian's National Anthropological Archives.

(NAA 6)

River Basin Surveys, circa 1945-1969
Records, Archeological Documents, Photographs, Cartographic Materials (120 linear meters).

The creation of the River Basin Surveys (RBS) grew out of preliminary work by the Committee for the Recovery of Archeological Remains, an ad hoc group of anthropologists. The Committee's concern was the preservation of archeological evidence threatened by public works programs, especially the construction of dams and reservoirs, that were carried out after World War II. The result of the Committee's work was a cooperative arrangement among the Smithsonian, the National Park Service, the Corps of Engineers, many universities, and other public and private organizations to exchange information and finance and carry out salvage archeological work throughout the United States. The RBS was organized in 1947 to carry out the Smithsonian's part of the program. It was particularly active in field work in the Missouri Basin, the West Coast, Texas, and the southeastern states. Through most of its existence, the RBS was an autonomous unit of the Bureau of American Ethnology. Headquarters were in Washington, D.C., and there was a major field office in Lincoln, Nebraska. There were also field offices for relatively short periods of time in Austin, Texas, and Eugene, Oregon. When the Bureau was disbanded in 1965, the RBS became a unit of the Smithsonian Office of Anthropology (Department of Anthropology since 1968). In 1966, the headquarters were moved to Lincoln; in 1968, the RBS was placed administratively under the Director of the National Museum of Natural History. In 1969, the RBS was transferred to the National Park Service, but provision was made for the deposit of its records and manuscripts in the Smithsonian.

The files of the central office and field offices include correspondence, memoranda of telephone conversations, reports, information files, housekeeping files, subject files, a few field notebooks, and photographic material. The site files consist mainly of photographs and completed forms for data collected in the field and the laboratory. The files of Harold Huscher and Carl Miller, separated because of continued work in analyzing the data they contain, include correspondence, notes, archeological forms, and photographs. Huscher's material largely concerns work along the Chattahoochee River. Miller's files concern work in Virginia and North Carolina. Much of the material regarding sites is controlled by the system for designating sites developed by the Smithsonian. This consists of a three-part code that includes a number to indicate the state, an alphabetical abbreviation to indicate county, and a number for each site within a county.

ARRANGEMENT: (1) Records of the Washington, D.C., office, 1945-1966; (2) records of the Lincoln, Nebraska, office, 1945-1969; (3) records of the Eugene, Oregon, office, 1947-1951; (4) records of the Austin, Texas, office, 1947-1952; (5) Harold Huscher's files, *circa* 1958-1966; (6) Carl Miller's files, *circa* 1949-1965; (7) research and publications files, *circa* 1948-1952; (8) site files, 1945-1969; (9) photographic documents, *circa* 1945-1969; (10) cartographic documents, undated. FINDING AIDS: (1) Draft registers for Washington and Lincoln office files; (2) list of site files by Smithsonian designation. SPECIAL CONDITIONS: These records are located in the Smithsonian's National Anthropological Archives.

NATIONAL MUSEUM OF AMERICAN HISTORY

The history of the National Museum of American History's (NMAH) collections dates from the very beginning of the Institution, when Secretary Joseph Henry began to amass a collection of scientific apparatus for historical and demonstration purposes. In 1849 the Institution made a major purchase of fine arts prints, which became the core of the graphic arts collections. In 1858, the United States Patent Office transferred to the Smithsonian the national collections, including specimens from the Wilkes Exploring Expedition, 1838-1842. In 1862, upon the demise of the National Institute, a local scientific and learned society, many of its collections came to the Smithsonian. And, most notably, after the Centennial Exposition of 1876, the Smithsonian received many objects from exhibitors at Philadelphia. Thus by the 1880s, rich collections from many different sources, some specific to natural history and geology, but many others relating to the human world, had come to the Smithsonian.

Various departments and divisions within the United States National Museum (USNM) were responsible for these objects. In 1881 George Brown Goode, Assistant Secretary in charge of the USNM, established the Department of Arts and Industries under the Division of Anthropology. (The relative hierarchical position of *department* and *division* will reverse after 1897.) The Department was "to include all the collections illustrating the utilization of the earth and its products by man, and the history and method of arts and industries within historic times." The Department collected objects related to various forms of transportation, the textile industry, materia medica, products of manufacturing and commercial firms, historical relics of prominent Americans, scientific instruments and apparatus, graphic arts, military artifacts, and coins and medals.

After Goode's death in 1896, the USNM underwent a major reorganization, and in 1897 the Department of Arts and Industries was abolished and the collections dispersed among various divisions of the new Department of Anthropology. Many of the historical collections were curated by a newly-established division within the Department, History and Biography (the name truncated to the Division of History in 1904) under the direction of A. Howard Clark. The Division was responsible for collections in philately, numismatics, political and military memorabilia, costumes, and furnishings. Other divisions of Anthropology dealt with technology, medicine, textiles, graphic arts, and photography, while the Department's Division of Ethnology curated objects of everyday life, ceramics, glass, and musical instruments.

Beginning in 1919, curation of the historical collections regained some administrative coherence. William deC. Ravenel, Administrative Assistant in charge of the USNM, re-established the Department of Arts and Industries, independent of and equal to the Department of Anthropology within the Museum. The new Department assumed responsibility for objects related to mechanical technology, mineral technology, textiles, medical sciences, and from 1920 graphic arts and photography as well—although ceramics, glass, and musical instruments collections continued to be curated within

Anthropology's Division of Ethnology, and political, military, costume and furnishings collections continued under its Division of History. That Division and the new Department together provided the skeleton of a history and technology museum. From 1921 on, the Division of History was independent of the Department of Anthropology. From 1921 to 1924 and again from 1932 to 1948, the Division functioned as an independent curatorial office within USNM; between 1924 and 1932 it was joined with the Department of Arts and Industries. In 1948, the Division of History was given departmental status. With the increase in staff and curatorial divisions under the Departments of History and Engineering and Industries (as Arts and Industries was renamed in 1938), the Department of Anthropology turned over to those departments many historical collections.

Head Curators of the Department of Engineering and Industries and its predecessor were William deC. Ravenel, 1919-1932; Carl W. Mitman, 1932-1948; and Frank A. Taylor, 1948-1957. Head Curators and Curators of the Department of History and its predecessors were A. Howard Clark, 1897-1918; Theodore T. Belote, 1919-1948; Charles Carey (acting), 1948-1951; and Mendel L. Peterson, 1951-1957.

The creation of the Museum of History and Technology (MHT) within USNM on July 1, 1957, gathered the historical collections under one museum. Frank A. Taylor was appointed Director of MHT on April 16, 1958, and was primarily responsible for the planning and supervision of the construction of the museum building, which opened in 1964. With the creation of MHT, the old Departments of History and Engineering and Industries of the USNM were reconfigured as Departments of Civil History, Armed Forces History, Science and Technology, and Arts and Manufactures. John C. Ewers, Assistant Director of MHT, succeeded Taylor as Director, 1964-1965, followed in 1966 by Robert P. Multhauf, Chairman of the Department of Science and Technology and Curator of Physical Sciences. USNM ceased to exist as an administrative entity in 1967, and at that time MHT became a separate museum within the Institution.

In January 1969, Daniel J. Boorstin, a University of Chicago history professor, was appointed Director. That year MHT was renamed the National Museum of History and Technology (NMHT), and all curatorial divisions were realigned under the Departments of Cultural History, National and Military History, Science and Technology, Industries, and Applied Arts. Boorstin resigned as Director in 1973.

Brooke Hindle, a historian of early American science and technology, was appointed Director of NMHT in February 1974. Before completing his term in June 1978, Hindle reorganized the curatorial departments at NMHT. Cultural History continued as a department, while new Departments of National History, History of Science, and History of Technology were created. Otto Mayr, Chairman of the former Department of Science and Technology and Curator of Mechanical and Civil Engineering, succeeded Hindle as Acting Director of the Museum.

Roger G. Kennedy, a historian of American architecture, was appointed Director of NMHT in October 1979. One year later, on October 13, 1980, President Carter signed a bill authorizing the Museum's name change to the National Museum of American History. A major reorganization of NMAH occurred shortly thereafter, in which the Departments of Social and National History and the History of Science and Technology were established. Also during this reorganization the National Numismatic Collection and the National Philatelic Collection—each reporting to the Director—were created from the former Divisions of Numismatics and Postal History. In 1981, the Department of Social and National History was renamed Social and Cultural History.

In 1990, the National Philatelic Collection became the National Postal Museum; it moved into the newly renovated Washington City Post Office in 1993. Kennedy resigned as Director on December 1, 1992. Spencer Crew, a historian and Chairman of the Department of Social and Cultural History, and Deputy Director, 1991-1992, became Acting Director, and he was named Director of the Museum on January 24, 1994. Later that year, Crew combined the two departments in to a single Department of History.

For further information about the administrative structure of NMAH and its predecessors, see the introductions to the Departments of the History of Science and Technology and of Social and Cultural History.

DIRECTOR, DEPUTY DIRECTOR, AND ASSISTANT DIRECTOR, 1920-1988

(276)

Director, National Museum of History and Technology, 1944-1975
Records (13.3 linear meters).

These records partially cover the administrations of Alexander Wetmore and A. Remington Kellogg as Directors of the United States National Museum, but more fully the tenures of Frank A. Taylor, John C. Ewers and Robert P. Multhauf as Director of the Museum of History and Technology, and Daniel J. Boorstin and Brooke Hindle as Director of the National Museum of History and Technology (NMHT). Most of the records cover the years from 1960 to 1975 and relate to activities of the Office of the Director and the daily internal administration of the NMHT, but also included are a few records concerning general Smithsonian issues.

Records include correspondence and memoranda with educational institutions, government agencies, professional associations, scholars, domestic and foreign museums, and NMHT curators concerning cooperative programs with other organizations; special events in the NMHT, including fundraising activities and lecture series; NMHT policies, organization and planning of the Museum, publication of curators' research, acquisition of objects for the national collections, exhibits, and security; blueprints, floor plans, and photographs of the Museum's facilities; exhibit records, including photographs, blueprints, floor plans, and a small number of scripts; and files, including memoranda and reports, concerning the Museum's relationship with other Smithsonian bureaus, offices, and the central administration.

ARRANGEMENT: (1) General correspondence, 1954-1975; (2) security files, 1963-1975; (3) committees, 1953-1975; (4) exhibits, 1950-1975; (5) Secretary's office, Smithsonian bureaus and offices and related organizations, 1944-1975; (6) publications, 1957-1973; (7) non-Smithsonian museums, 1950-1975; (8) departmental files, 1954-1975; (9) departmental correspondence, 1955-1963. FINDING AIDS: Folder list in control file. SPECIAL CONDITIONS: Use of this record unit requires prior arrangement with the Archives staff.

Director, National Museum of American History, circa 1945-1987 and related records, 1920-1930
Records (68 linear meters).

The National Museum of American History (NMAH) was created on October 3, 1980. For an administrative history of its predecessors, see the introduction to NMAH.

These records document the tenures of Frank A. Taylor, John C. Ewers, and Robert P. Multhauf as Directors of the Museum of History and Technology; of Daniel J. Boorstin, Brooke Hindle, and Roger G. Kennedy as Directors of the National Museum of History and Technology; and of Roger G. Kennedy as Director of NMAH. Most of the records document the period from 1960 to 1986, although pre-1958 records document the work of Alexander Wetmore and A. Remington Kellogg as Directors of a predecessor organization, the United States National Museum.

Records document activities of the Office of the Director and the daily internal administration of NMAH but also include a few records concerning general Smithsonian issues.

Records include correspondence and memoranda with educational institutions, government agencies, professional associations, scholars, domestic and foreign museums, and NMAH curators concerning cooperative programs with other organizations; special events in the NMAH, including fundraising activities, lecture series, and musical events; NMAH policies; organization and planning of the Museum; publication of curators' research; acquisition of objects for the national collections; exhibits; security; blueprints, floor plans, and photographs of the Museum's facilities; exhibition records, including photographs, blueprints, floor plans, and a small number of scripts; and files, including memoranda and reports, concerning the Museum's relationship with other Smithsonian bureaus, offices, and the central administration.

ARRANGEMENT: (1) Director's files, 1963-1977, accession number 81-097; (2) Director's files, 1957-1978, accession number 82-065; (3) Director's files, 1945-1981, accession number 83-071; (4) Director's files, 1959-1976, 1979-1982, accession number 84-120; (5) Director's files, *circa* 1977-1981, accession number 85-118; (6) Director's files, 1981-1982, accession number 86-109; (7) Director's files, *circa* 1950-1977, and related records, 1920-1930, accession number T90040. FINDING AIDS: Folder list in control file. SPECIAL CONDITIONS: (1) Restricted; (2) use of this record unit requires prior arrangement with the Archives staff.

Director, National Museum of History and Technology, 1948-1965
Exhibition Records (4.5 linear meters).

For an administrative history of the Director, see the introduction to the National Museum of American History.

This record unit contains some information on post-World War II exhibition planning at the Smithsonian. However, in the main, it documents the involvement of the Office of the Director in exhibition planning at the Museum from its creation in 1957 through 1965.

Records contain information on the planning of exhibitions for a new Museum of History and Technology and their subsequent installation and modification. They track efforts to select contractors, choose exhibition items, and plan and construct exhibition halls. Records of the Director's dealings with Smithsonian administrators and colleagues are also included.

ARRANGEMENT: Records, accession number 89-090. FINDING AIDS: Folder list in control file. SPECIAL CONDITIONS: Use of this record unit requires prior arrangement with the Archives staff.

(279)

Director, National Museum of History and Technology, 1953-1978
Special Projects Records (0.8 linear meter).

For an administrative history of the Director, National Museum of History and Technology (NMHT), see the introduction to the National Museum of American History.

These records of special projects in NMHT as well as throughout the Smithsonian focus on several major activities including the Computer History Project in cooperation with the American Federation of Information Processing Societies (AFIPS); the bicentennial celebration of James Smithson's birth; acquisition of a flag from each of the fifty states; and a proposed historical studies center. Records for the Computer History Project include press releases, audit reports, minutes of its Advisory Committee and memoranda and correspondence relating to a computer history exhibit, an oral history project on computer history, and the role of the principal investigators in the AFIPS project. For the Smithson Bicentennial, records include newspaper and magazine articles, photographs, and correspondence with speakers, foreign and domestic invitees, charitable foundations, and the International Council of Museums. The states' flags project produced correspondence with governors and other state executive officials concerning the states' flags, while the proposal for a historical studies center yielded proposed budgets, correspondence, and copies of federal legislation.

This record unit also contains correspondence and memoranda concerning the *Atoms for Peace* exhibit by the Atomic Energy Commission; correspondence, memoranda, magazine articles, and photographs relating to a McGraw-Hill publication editorial advocating a proposed national museum of engineering and industry; a speech by Leonard Carmichael, news releases, correspondence, and memoranda concerning a National Conference of Business Paper Editors; and correspondence and teachers' guidebooks to various Smithsonian exhibit halls for the Washington Area School Study Council.

ARRANGEMENT: (1) Computer History Project (AFIPS), 1967-1978; (2) Smithson Bicentennial, 1964-1965; (3) states' flags project, 1969-1972; (4) historic studies center, 1964-1966; (5) miscellaneous special projects, 1953-1963. FINDING AIDS: Folder list in control file. SPECIAL CONDITIONS: Use of this record unit requires prior arrangement with the Archives staff.

(278)

Director, National Museum of History and Technology, 1956-1978
Annual Reports and Smithsonian Years (0.8 linear meter).

These annual reports were prepared by curators and administrators from the National Museum of History and Technology (NMHT) as well as from two previous museum administrative entities, the United States National Museum and the Museum of History and Technology, that had responsibility for objects subsequently housed in NMHT. The reports were then submitted in a condensed form for publication in the *Annual Report of the Smithsonian Institution* and, since fiscal year 1965, in the *Smithsonian Year.*

Included in these annual summaries are a general discussion prepared by the Office of the Director, NMHT, and curatorial divisions and departments of the year's major events including exhibits, special museum activities, photographs of events and museum objects, bibliographies of curators, and accession data.

ARRANGEMENT: Chronologic. FINDING AIDS: Folder list in control file. SPECIAL CONDITIONS: Use of this record unit requires prior arrangement with the Archives staff.

(621)

Office of the Director, National Museum of History and Technology, 1957-1973
Exhibition Records (1.2 linear meters).

For an administrative history of the Director, see the introduction to the National Museum of American History.

This record unit documents the involvement of the Office of the Director in exhibition planning at the Museum of History and Technology from its creation in 1957 through its development into the National Museum of History and Technology. These records concern the tenures of Frank A. Taylor, John C. Ewers, Robert P. Multhauf, and Daniel J. Boorstin.

These records contain information about planning exhibitions for a new Museum of History and Technology and their subsequent installation and modification. They track efforts to choose exhibition items, plan and construct exhibition halls, and prepare the building systems for operation. Records of the Director's activities with Smithsonian administrators and colleagues are also included.

ARRANGEMENT: Records, accession number 89-088. FINDING AIDS: Folder list in control file. SPECIAL CONDITIONS: Use of this record unit requires prior arrangement with the Archives staff.

(583)

Director, National Museum of American History, circa 1982-1988
Records (16.4 linear meters).

The National Museum of American History (NMAH) was created on October 3, 1980, from the former National Museum of History and Technology (NMHT). For an administrative history of the Director, National Museum of American History, see the introduction to NMAH.

These records document the tenure of Roger G. Kennedy, Director, NMHT, 1979-1980, and Director, NMAH, 1980-   , as well as some of the work of Douglas E. Evelyn, Deputy Director. The records concern activities of the Office of the Director and the administration of NMAH. Of special note are records regarding the conclusion in 1982 of the collections inventory mandated by Congress in 1979 and the 1983 beginning of work on the first major renovation of exhibition spaces since 1964.

Records include correspondence and memoranda with educational institutions, government agencies, professional associations, scholars, domestic and foreign museums, and NMAH curators concerning programs with other organizations; special events held at NMAH, including lecture series and fundraising; policies and planning for NMAH operations; the acquisition of objects for the national collections; and exhibition records, including floor plans, sketches, blueprints, and scripts.

ARRANGEMENT: (1) Director's records, 1982-1984, accession number 87-070; (2) Director's records, *circa* 1983-1987, accession number 88-120; (3) Director's records, 1982-1987, accession number 89-086; (4) Director's records, 1986, accession number 91-075; (5) Director's records, 1987, accession number 91-076; (6) Director's records, *circa* 1986-1988, accession number 92-107. FINDING AIDS: Folder list in control file. SPECIAL CONDITIONS: (1) Restricted; (2) use of this record unit requires prior arrangement with the Archives staff.

(285)
Director and Deputy Director, National Museum of History and Technology, 1920s-1970s
Photograph File (4.6 linear meters).

The Offices of the Director and Deputy Director, National Museum of History and Technology (NMHT) maintained these photographs as a reference file. The majority of the photographs document the history of NMHT and its predecessors; included are views of exhibits, buildings, events, and some specimens.

ARRANGEMENT: Unarranged within the following series: (1) buildings; (2) events; (3) special exhibits; (4) permanent exhibits; (5) specimens; (6) miscellany; (7) slides. FINDING AIDS: Description in control file. SPECIAL CONDITIONS: Use of this record unit requires prior arrangement with the Archives staff.

(277)
Deputy Director, National Museum of History and Technology, 1958-1978
Records (2.9 linear meters).

For an administrative history of the National Museum of History and Technology (NMHT), see the introduction to the National Museum of American History.

These records, generated by John C. Ewers, Assistant Director, 1959-1964, and Silvio A. Bedini, Assistant Director, 1965-1972, and Deputy Director, 1972-1978, document the role of these positions within NMHT administrative hierarchy. A small portion of the records also covers Ewers's position as NMHT Director from 1965 to 1966. Included in these records are files pertaining to the Conservation Analytical Laboratory, the early planning stages of NMHT's involvement in the Bicentennial of the American Revolution (BAR) celebration, and a proposed joint program on the BAR between the National Science Foundation and NMHT. Also included are records concerned with the Museum's more routine activities such as NMHT and traveling exhibits, departmental meetings, building management, and budgetary matters. Records include correspondence with other Smithsonian museums, memoranda between museum administrators and curators, reports, requests for use of NMHT facilities, floor plans, minutes of committee meetings, conference proceedings, and legislative history of the Joseph H. Hirshhorn Museum and Sculpture Garden.

ARRANGEMENT: According to special topics or activities. FINDING AIDS: Folder list in control file. SPECIAL CONDITIONS: Use of this record unit requires prior arrangement with the Archives staff.

Assistant Director for Administration, National Museum of American History, circa 1955-1988

Records (14.8 linear meters).

The Assistant Director for Administration is responsible for overseeing budget and financial planning, personnel, contracting, procurement, special exhibition projects, and building management of the National Museum of American History.

The activities of this office date back to 1958, when William E. Boyle was appointed Administrative Assistant in what was then called the Museum of History and Technology (MHT). Boyle became Administrative Officer for the Museum in 1963, retaining that post until 1965. In 1963, Virginia Beets joined Boyle as an Administrative Officer, and succeeded him as head of the office in 1966.

Robert G. Tillotson joined the staff in 1967 as Administrative Officer, with the same responsibilities as Beets. In December 1969, Tillotson became Assistant Director for Administration. Despite the difference in title, Beets continued in a similar capacity to that of Tillotson until she resigned her position in 1973 to become Museum Registrar. Tillotson chose Jean J. Middleton as his Administrative Officer in 1976. In 1979, Tillotson left the office to accept the position of Executive Director of the National Philatelic Collection, and Middleton resigned her post to join Tillotson as assistant.

Throughout 1980, the duties of the Assistant Director for Administration were temporarily handled by Luis del Rio, Executive Officer. During that year, NMHT had its name changed to the National Museum of American History (NMAH). In 1981, Ronald E. Becker was appointed Assistant Director for Administration. Becker selected Richard J. Nicastro to become his Assistant Administrator from 1983 to 1984 and Administrative Officer in 1985. Elizabeth E. Greene replaced Nicastro as Administrative Officer in 1986, when Nicastro became Deputy Assistant Director for Exhibits, NMAH.

Records include correspondence and memoranda with NMAH curators, government agencies, collections committees for NMAH, professional associations, and academicians; information pertaining to the Doubleday Lecture Series; staff appointments; accounting ledgers; congressional budget submission reports and hearing files; NMAH five-year funding prospectus; federal and trust fund appropriation requests, allocations, and distribution summary logs; inventory lists; building management records; lectures and financial contracts; operation reviews for NMAH; travel allotments and balance sheets; and purchase agreements.

ARRANGEMENT: (1) Assistant Director for Administration files, 1955-1982, accession number 84-070; (2) Assistant Director's files, 1977-1983, accession number 84-225; (3) Assistant Director's files, 1977-1983, accession number 85-158; (4) Assistant Director's files, 1981-1983, accession number 86-110. FINDING AIDS: Folder list in control file. SPECIAL CONDITIONS: (1) Restricted; (2) use of this record unit requires prior arrangement with the Archives staff.

HISTORY OF SCIENCE AND TECHNOLOGY, 1882-1988

The Department of the History of Science and Technology had responsibility for curatorial divisions in three distinct areas: scientific and industrial collections, medical collections, and military collections. All three areas were present in the Department of Arts and Industries of the United States National Museum (USNM), which had responsibility for them from 1881 to 1897, but their subsequent history was less clear. There has generally been a unity in the treatment of the scientific and technological collections, centered upon the Department of Arts and Industries and its successors. However, the medical collections were administrative vagabonds until gaining final independent curatorial status within the science and technology collections in 1938. The military history collections were associated with those of political history and national memorabilia and only joined with science and technology from 1980. In addition, at times ceramics and glass, textiles, graphic arts, and photographic collections were curated as part of the science and technology collections, sometimes as part of collections in social and cultural history, and thus their administrative placement has varied over the years.

The core of the Department has been the divisions concerned with scientific and technical apparatus and artifacts. The curation of these collections was administratively cohesive from 1881 to the present, except for the years 1897 to 1919, when these activities were dispersed into the Department of Anthropology. Otherwise, the administrative structure has been the Department of Arts and Industries (USNM), 1881-1897; its re-establishment, 1919-1938; and its successors, from 1938.

When the Department of Arts and Industries was established in 1881 with George Brown Goode as its Curator, it included sections to deal with artifacts in such areas as fisheries and naval architecture, transportation and engineering, and physical apparatus. In 1897, these sections were combined in the new Department of Anthropology as the Division of Technology (called the Division of Mechanical Technology after 1912). The Museum also set up an independent Department of Mineral Technology in 1904 (Division after 1913) responsible for mining apparatus.

When William deC. Ravenel re-established the Department of Arts and Industries in 1919, it oversaw the Divisions of Mechanical Technology and Mineral Technology, and (discussed below) Medicine, Textiles (a division established independent of departmental affiliation in 1912), and, in 1920, Graphic Arts. Following Ravenel's retirement in 1932, John Enos Graf and then Carl W. Mitman succeeded him as Head Curator of Arts and Industries.

In 1931 the Department established the Division of Engineering, incorporating the old Divisions of Mineral and Mechanical Technology as sections, and adding a new Section of Aeronautics. Mitman, Curator of Mechanical Technology since 1920, was the Division's Curator until 1932, when he was succeeded by Frank A. Taylor, who had become Assistant Curator of Mineral and Mechanical Technology in 1928. The Division held collections relating to engineering, transportation, physical sciences, tools, horology, and aeronautics. Subsequent heads of the Division included: Frank A. Taylor, Curator until 1948, then Head Curator of the Department; Robert P. Multhauf, Curator of the Division, 1955-1956; and Robert S. Woodbury, Curator of the Division, from 1956. For further information on the Division of Engineering and its predecessors, see record unit 297.

The Section of Aeronautics was under Paul Garber, Assistant Curator until 1942, when it became a Division, under Garber as Associate Curator, 1942-1946, Curator from 1946, and Fred C. Reed, Associate Curator, 1942-1947. The Division of Aeronautics was separated from the Department in 1947 to form the nucleus of the National Air Museum.

Medical and textile divisions came into the new Department of Arts and Industries with its 1919 re-establishment. The two divisions were closely linked. From 1916, both came under the direction of Frederick L. Lewton, and they were administratively joined from 1931 to 1938. In that year, they definitively separated, with the creation of the Division of Medicine and Public Health and with Textiles becoming part of a new Division, Crafts and Industries. For further information on the medical and textiles divisions see record units 244 and 472.

The Division of Crafts and Industries held collections in the areas of textiles, wood technology, chemical and agricultural industries, and manufactures. Frederick L. Lewton, Curator of Textiles from 1912, served as Curator of the Division, 1938-1946. He was succeeded by William N. Watkins, 1947-1957. Other staff of the Division of Crafts and Industries and its predecessors included: O. E. Roberts, Jr., Curator of the Loeb Collection of Chemical Types, 1924-1930; Wallace E. Duncan, Assistant Curator of Chemical Industries, 1939-1942; Joseph W. Schutz, Assistant Curator of Chemical Industries, 1942-1943; Elizabeth W. Rosson, Assistant Curator of Textiles, 1944-1946; Mary Windhorst, Assistant Curator of Textiles, 1946-1948; Fred C. Reed, Associate Curator of Manufactures and Agricultural Industries, 1947-1951; Grace L. Rogers, Assistant Curator of Textiles, from 1948; Edward C. Kendall, Associate Curator of Manufactures and Agricultural Industries, 1951-1956; and Philip W. Bishop, Curator of Industrial Cooperation, from 1957.

The final component of the Department of Arts and Industries/Engineering and Industries was Graphic Arts, organized as a section by Curator Sylvester Rosa Koehler within the old Department of Arts and Industries in 1886, and as a Division within Anthropology from 1897, and within Arts and Industries from 1920. From 1897, the Division of Graphic Arts also included the Section of Photography, which began as an independent section in 1883. For further information, see record units 206 and 529.

With the creation of the Museum of History and Technology in 1957, the science and technology collections formed two of the museum's four departments: Science and Technology, and Arts and Manufactures. The new organization resulted in a great expansion of curatorial divisions deriving from sections of the old Divisions of Engineering and of Craft and Industries. Multhauf was made Head Curator of the Department of Science and Technology, which included Divisions of Physical Sciences, Mechanical and Civil Engineering, Transportation, Agriculture and Wood Products, Electricity, and Medical Sciences. Philip W. Bishop was Head Curator of the Department of Arts and Manufactures, with Divisions of Textiles, Graphic Arts, Industrial Cooperation, and Ceramics and Glass (from the USNM's Division of Ethnology, Department of Anthropology).

Changes in organization through 1969 included: in 1959, the Division of Agriculture and Wood Products became part of the Department of Arts and Manufactures and in 1960 was renamed the Division of Agriculture and Forest Products; in 1961 the Division of Industrial Cooperation was renamed the Division of Manufactures and Heavy Industries; in 1964, the title of Head Curator was changed to that of Chairman; in 1965 was created a Section of Mathematics and Antique Instruments (later the Section of Mathematics); and in 1966, when Multhauf became the Director of MHT, Faye Cannon (prior to 1976, Walter F. Cannon), Curator of Physical Sciences, took over as Chairman of the Department of Science and Technology.

In 1969 MHT was reorganized as the National Museum of History and Technology (NMHT). The four departments were re-established as five, by the formation of a hybrid Department of Applied Arts and reorganization of the existing four departments.

The Department of Science and Technology retained Divisions of Physical Sciences, Mechanical and Civil Engineering, Medical Sciences, and Electricity, which was renamed the Division of Electricity and Nuclear Energy to reflect the changing nature of the collections. Removed from the Department, however, was the Division of Transportation; it was reassigned to the Department of Industries, successor to the Department of Arts and Manufactures. There it joined Agriculture and Mining (formerly Agriculture and Forest Products), Ceramics and Glass, and Manufactures and Heavy Industries.

The Divisions of Textiles and of Graphic Arts and Photography (as Graphic Arts became known) were moved from Arts and Manufactures into the new Department, Applied Arts, where they joined the Divisions of Numismatics and Postal History. Henceforth Graphic Arts proper would no longer be associated with the science and technology collections, although Textiles and Photographic History (as a separate Division) would later briefly rejoin them.

Departmental chairs included, for Science and Technology, Bernard S. Finn, 1969-1973, Robert M. Vogel, 1973-1975, and Otto Mayr, 1976-1977; for Industries, John H. White, Jr., 1969-1975, and John T. Schlebecker, Jr., 1975-1977; and for Applied Arts, Carl H. Scheele, 1969-1975, and Vladimir Clain-Stefanelli, 1975-1977.

During the period from 1969 to 1978, the Division of Graphic Arts and Photography split; and the Divisions of Agriculture and Mining and of Manufacturing merged to form a Division of Extractive Industries, Department of Industries, in 1976.

The reorganization of NMHT in 1978 saw reversion to four departments, two roughly in scientific and technological areas, two in areas of social, cultural, and national history. The Department of Applied Arts was abolished. Departments pertaining to science and technology were formed as the Department of History of Science, with Finn as Chairman, and the Department of History of Technology, with Schlebecker as Chairman. The former department included continuing Divisions of Physical Sciences, Medical Sciences, the Division of Electricity and Modern Physics (renamed from Division of Electricity and Nuclear Energy), and new Divisions of Mechanisms, formed from Mechanical and Civil Engineering, and Mathematics, upgraded from a Section. The Department of the History of Technology included—from the old Department of Industries—the Divisions of Mechanical and Civil Engineering, Extractive Industries, and Transportation, and the Divisions of Textiles and of Photographic History from the old Department of Applied Arts. The Division of Ceramics and Glass was transferred to the Department of Cultural History.

In 1980, in the organization of National Museum of American History, the Department of History of Technology merged with the Department of History of Science to form the Department of the History of Science and Technology. From the Divisions of the two combining Departments, Textiles moved out to the Department of Social and National History. The Divisions of Military History and of Naval History moved in. For their prior history see the Introduction to the Department of Social and Cultural History.

Chairs of the new Department included Finn, 1980-1982, and Arthur P. Molella, Curator of Electricity and Modern Physics, 1983- . Significant administrative developments, 1980-1988, included: in 1984, the Military and Naval History Divisions merged to form the Division of Armed Forces History; in 1985, the Division of Extractive Industries was renamed the Division of Agriculture and Natural Resources; in 1986, the Division of Mechanical and Civil Engineering merged back with the Division of Mechanisms to create the Division of Engineering and Industry, and the Division of Photographic History was moved into the Department of Social and Cultural History; and in 1987, the Division of Computers, Information, and Society was established, while the Division of Physical Sciences combined with the Division of Mathematics to become the Division of Physical Sciences and Mathematics.

(219)

Department of Arts and Industries, United States National Museum, circa 1887
Exhibit Labels (0.1 linear meter).

For an administrative history of the Department of Arts and Industries, see the introduction to the Department of the History of Science and Technology.

A collection of tools and materials used in Japanese lacquer work was presented to the United States National Museum by the Department of Education of the Japanese Government through Shiro Akabane, Secretary of the Japanese Legation in Washington, D.C. The donation was apparently made between 1885 and 1887.

This record unit consists of descriptive labels prepared for the collection by Edwin H. Hawley, preparator in the Department of Arts and Industries.

ARRANGEMENT: Unarranged. FINDING AIDS: None. SPECIAL CONDITIONS: Use of this record unit requires prior arrangement with the Archives staff.

(84)

Department of Engineering and Industries, United States National Museum, 1891-1957
Records (2 linear meters).

For an administrative history of the Department of Engineering and Industries and its predecessors, see the introduction to the Department of the History of Science and Technology.

These records originated mostly in the office of the Head Curator of the Department of Engineering and Industries, United States National Museum, under Carl W. Mitman and Frank A. Taylor, but include records of several other curators, primarily Smith Hempstone Oliver and Paul E. Garber.

The records include general correspondence, memoranda, and administrative files concerning departmental accessions, administrative policy and budgetary matters, exhibits, and requests for photographs for publication; minutes of a steering committee to establish a Smithsonian endowment fund; outgoing correspondence and summaries of the work of the Sections of Fisheries and Naval Architecture under Joseph William Collins, 1891-1894; an incomplete set of scripts and programs, scrapbooks, correspondence, and news clippings concerning radio programs on technology and science aired on "The World Is Yours"; and subject files consisting of correspondence and memoranda covering areas and individuals in the engineering and technological sciences.

ARRANGEMENT: (1) General correspondence, 1893-1895, 1905-1956; (2) outgoing correspondence, Sections of Fisheries and Naval Architecture, 1891-1894; (3) administrative files, 1919-1957; (4) subject files, 1919-1957; (5) "The World Is Yours" files, 1936-1940. FINDING AIDS: Description in control file. SPECIAL CONDITIONS: Use of this record unit requires prior arrangement with the Archives staff.

(375)

Department of the History of Science and Technology, National Museum of American History, circa 1925-1937, 1954-1985
Records (2.9 linear meters).

For an administrative history of the Department of the History of Science and Technology and its predecessors, see the introduction to the Department.

This record unit documents administrative operations and exhibition programs of the Department of the History of Science and Technology and its predecessors, chiefly from 1958 to 1985. Some records pertain to technological exhibitions and other activities of curatorial divisions located in the Arts and Industries Building in the 1920s and 1930s.

Records consist of correspondence and memoranda between Museum staff and chairmen of the Department, including Frank A. Taylor, Head Curator of the Department of Engineering and Industries through 1956; Robert P. Multhauf, Acting Head Curator, 1957, Head Curator of the Department of Science and Technology, 1958-1963, and Chairman, 1964-1966; Faye Cannon (prior to 1976, Walter F. Cannon), 1966-1968; Bernard S. Finn, 1969-1972, Robert M. Vogel, 1973-1975; Otto Mayr, 1976-1977; Finn, Chairman of the Department of the History of Science, 1978-1980, and of the Department of the History of Science and Technology, 1980-1982; and Arthur P. Molella, 1983-   .

Also included in the records is documentation about the Hall of Physics and the Hall of Chemistry; script for the Brooklyn Bridge Centennial Exhibition; exhibition floor plans and drawings; agreements for incoming loans of artifacts from private collectors and other museums; photographs of the architect's drawing for the Museum building; photographs of Museum exhibitions and special events; photographs of exhibitions located in the Arts and Industries Building; curatorial travel reports; budgetary records; patent specifications; conservation requirements for artifacts; information on the Museum's collection inventory project; and minutes of meetings.

ARRANGEMENT: (1) Department of the History of Science and Technology, Chairmen's files, *circa* 1925-1983, accession number 85-207; (2) Department Chairmen's files, 1974-1985, accession number 87-174; (3) Department records, 1954-1980, accession number 88-181. FINDING AIDS: Folder list in control file. SPECIAL CONDITIONS: Use of this record unit requires prior arrangement with the Archives staff.

(240)

Section of Agriculture, Division of Agriculture and Mining, National Museum of History and Technology, circa 1923-1973
Records (1.8 linear meters).

The Section of Agriculture, Division of Agriculture and Mining, dates back to 1921, when "specimens and models of agricultural implements and objects relating to the history of agriculture in this country" began to be collected. From 1921 to 1932, these collections were kept as part of the textile collections. In 1932, a Section of Agricultural History was set up in the Division of Textiles, Department of Arts and Industries, and a separate catalog started. The Section became the Section of Agricultural Industries, Division of Crafts and Industries, Department of Engineering and Industries, in 1938 and retained that title until 1957. Frederick L. Lewton, Curator of Textiles, was in charge of the agricultural collections from 1921 to 1946. In 1947 Fred C. Reed became Associate Curator for the Section of Agricultural Industries and Manufactures. Reed was replaced as Associate Curator by William N. Watkins in 1951 and Edward C. Kendall in 1952.

When the Museum of History and Technology was created in 1957, the Division of Agriculture and Wood Products was established in the Department of Science and Technology. This became the Division of Agriculture and Forest Products, Department of Arts and Manufactures in 1960, and the Division of Agriculture and Mining, Department of Industries, in 1969. Kendall continued as Associate Curator until 1965, and John T. Schlebecker, Jr., became Curator in that year.

Records document the curatorial and administrative activities of the Section of Agriculture, Division of Agriculture and Mining, and its predecessors and include correspondence, memoranda, exhibits scripts, and reports. Annual reports covering the Sections of Chemical Industries, Chemical Technology, Foods, Manufactures, and Organic Chemistry are also contained in the records, most likely because these sections also reported administratively to the Division of Textiles, until 1938, and to the Division of Crafts and Industries, 1938-1957, and curators often had responsibility for more than one section. Annual reports for the Division of Agriculture and Mining, 1969-1973, also contain material concerning the Section of Mining.

Of special interest is extensive documentation, in the form of scripts, blueprints, correspondence, and notes of work on the Hall of Forest Products, 1960-1967, which was never installed; and correspondence on and papers presented at the Symposium on Eighteenth-Century Agriculture, 1966-1969. Some material on the professional activities of Division staff, particularly Edward C. Kendall and John T. Schlebecker, Jr., is also included.

ARRANGEMENT: (1) Subject file, 1944-1973; (2) memoranda, *circa* 1946-1973; (3) public inquiries, 1941, 1946-1973; (4) reading files, 1960-1973; (5) annual reports, *circa* 1923-1973; (6) exhibits, *circa* 1948-1973; (7) Symposium on Eighteenth-Century Agriculture, 1966-1969. FINDING AIDS: None. SPECIAL CONDITIONS: Use of this record unit requires prior arrangement with the Archives staff.

Division of Armed Forces History, National Museum of American History, circa 1960-1988

Records (5.8 linear meters).

The record unit chiefly concerns the Division of Naval History, one component in the Division of Armed Forces History. For an administrative history of the Division's Military History component, see record unit 396.

Beginning in the 1880s, naval collections were curated by the Section of Historical Relics, United States National Museum, and its various successors through to the Division of History. In 1935, the Division established the Military and Naval Collection, and, in 1947, it formed a Section of Naval History. The Section was given divisional status in 1948 and was placed under the direction of Mendel L. Peterson. Additional details on the pre-1980 history of the Division are located in the introduction to the Department of Social and Cultural History. After 1980, the Divisions of Naval and Military History were placed in the new Department of the History of Science and Technology, and, in 1984, they were merged to form the Division of Armed Forces History.

The main function of the Division of Naval History was to trace the historical development of the United States Navy, beginning with maritime operations during the colonial and Revolutionary War period through subsequent years of change leading to the advent of the modern navy. Research focused mainly on United States naval personnel, vessels, weapons, uniforms, insignia, navigational instruments, and flags. Division staff were also involved in marine archeology, research, attending conferences, and collecting maritime artifacts.

Staff of the Division included Mendel L. Peterson, Acting Curator of Naval History, 1958-1960; Philip K. Lundeberg, Associate Curator, 1959-1961, Curator of Naval History, 1962-1984, Curator of Armed Forces History, 1984-   ; Melvin H. Jackson, Associate Curator of Naval History, 1962-1965; Harold D. Langley, Curator of Naval History, 1969-1984, Curator of Armed Forces History, 1984-   ; and Lee Houchins, Research Associate of Naval History, 1978-1984.

Most of the documentation in this record unit concerns the curatorial and staff activities of the Division of Naval History, but also includes some records pertaining to the Division of Armed Forces History. These records consist of correspondence and memoranda documenting research activities, planning exhibitions for the Hall of Naval History, construction of ship models such as the USS *Constitution,* arrangements for acquiring the gunboat *Philadelphia,* studies of the submarine *Nautilus* and the Sperry gyrocompass, presentation in 1965 of Sir Francis Drake's Cadiz Letter to the Museum, and involvement with the restoration of the USS *Constellation.* Also included are administrative files of the Division; public inquiries; blueprints for the Hall of Naval History; exhibition scripts; and photographs of ship models, naval vessels, exhibitions, and staff.

ARRANGEMENT: (1) Division of Naval History, 1960-1975, accession number 81-023; (2) Division of Naval History, 1960-1980, accession number 85-202; (3) Division of Naval History, 1977-1988, accession number 90-097. FINDING AIDS: Folder list in control file. SPECIAL CONDITIONS: Use of this record unit requires prior arrangement with the Archives staff.

Division of Electricity and Modern Physics, National Museum of History and Technology, 1886-1978
Records (1.4 linear meters).

The earliest artifacts relating to electricity date to 1885, with collections forming part of the Section of Steam Transportation, Department of Arts and Industries. In 1889 the Section made a significant acquisition when it acquired the original Alfred Vail telegraphic receiver. George C. Maynard curated the collections during most of this early period, serving in various capacities from 1885 until 1918. For a history of this unit and its successors through the early years of the Division of Engineering, see record unit 297.

In the reorganization of 1938, the Section of Electrical Engineering and Communications was created in the Division of Engineering, Department of Engineering and Industries. Frank A. Taylor, the dominant figure in the Division throughout the 1930s and 1940s, was placed in charge. The Section was renamed the Section of Electricity in 1947 and the Division of Electricity in 1957. In 1969 it became the Division of Electricity and Nuclear Energy and in 1978, the Division of Electricity and Modern Physics. Staff members of the curating divisions since 1938 have included Frank A. Taylor, Curator of the Division and in charge of the Section, 1932-1948; Carl W. Mitman, in charge of the Section while Taylor was on war duty, 1943-1946; Kenneth M. Perry, Associate Curator, 1948-1956; W. James King, Jr., Associate Curator, 1956-1958, Acting Curator, 1958-1961; Robert P. Multhauf, Acting Curator (while Head Curator of the Department), 1961-1963; Bernard S. Finn, Associate Curator, 1963-1965, Curator, 1965-   ; and Paul Forman, Associate Curator, 1972-1975, Curator, 1976-   .

The records of the Division of Electricity and Modern Physics and its predecessors relate to the Division's responsibility for electrical artifacts. Included is early correspondence, primarily of George C. Maynard, but also including J. Elfreth Watkins and Carl W. Mitman, concerning the inventions of Alexander Graham Bell, Samuel F. B. Morse, Alfred Vail, and inventors of dynamos and incandescent electric lighting; correspondence of more recent curators with manufacturers of electrical equipment, donors of artifacts, and historians and researchers concerning dates and patents of electrical equipment, objects in the Division's collection, and exhibits, particularly on early electrical appliances; reading files; annual reports and plans of operation; exhibit files, consisting of scripts, photographs, correspondence and memoranda, and floor plans, primarily for the Hall of Electricity; and requisitions.

ARRANGEMENT: (1) General correspondence, 1886-1927; (2) general correspondence, 1939, 1952, 1955-1974; (3) general correspondence, 1962-1978; (4) appliance exhibit correspondence, 1970-1977; (5) reading files, 1970-1975; (6) annual reports and plans of operation, 1954-1970; (7) exhibit files, 1896-1973; (8) requisitions, 1963-1978. FINDING AIDS: Description in control file. SPECIAL CONDITIONS: Use of this record unit requires prior arrangement with the Archives staff.

Franklin Delano Roosevelt Exhibition, Division of Electricity and Modern Physics, National Museum of American History, circa 1981-1982
Records (0.8 linear meter).

On January 30, 1982, the National Museum of American History (NMAH) mounted *FDR: The Intimate Presidency,* a major exhibition recounting Roosevelt's relationship with the American people through mass media, particularly radio broadcasting. The exhibition was created to commemorate the one-hundredth anniversary of Roosevelt's birth. Arthur P. Molella, Curator of the Division of Electricity and Modern Physics, oversaw organization of the exhibition and was involved with research, catalog publication, and symposia. When the exhibition closed on August 1, 1982, it toured under the auspices of the Smithsonian Institution Traveling Exhibition Service.

Records include correspondence and memoranda between Molella and historical societies, museums, and NMAH departments and divisions pertaining to the development of the exhibition. Also included are exhibition scripts documenting the early political years of Roosevelt and his presidency, especially emphasizing his skillful use of radio and the fireside chats during the 1930s and 1940s; exhibition blueprints and floor plans; research notes, particularly about the history of radio technology; exhibit proposals; minutes of meetings; photocopies of articles on Roosevelt radio programs and New Deal-era murals; symposium literature; photographs; and newspaper clippings concerning exhibition reviews.

ARRANGEMENT: Unarranged. FINDING AIDS: Folder list in control file. SPECIAL CONDITIONS: Use of this record unit requires prior arrangement with the Archives staff.

Division of Engineering, United States National Museum, 1886-1956
Records (1.4 linear meters).

Although the Division of Engineering was not established until 1931, its origins date back to 1885, when the Section of Steam Transportation was created in the Department of Arts and Industries, United States National Museum (USNM). The divisions and sections dealing with physical apparatus, physical science, technology, electricity, engineering, transportation and their modern counterparts all share a common derivation from this Section, wherein curators often served in several positions at the same time.

In 1885 J. Elfreth Watkins was appointed Curator of the Section of Steam Transportation, which was successively known as Transportation and Engineering, and Technological Collections. During his absence from 1892 to 1895, William Crawford Winlock served in that capacity.

When the USNM was reorganized in 1897, the Section became the Division of Technology of the Department of Anthropology, renamed the Division of Mechanical Technology in 1912. Watkins served as Curator until 1903, with George C. Maynard as Assistant Curator, 1901-1912, and Curator, 1912-1918.

The Museum also established an independent Department of Mineral Technology in 1904, responsible for mining apparatus, with Charles D. Walcott as Honorary Curator, 1904-1912. The Department became a Division in 1913, under Chester G. Gilbert,

Curator until 1919. The Division also included Carl W. Mitman, Aide, 1914-1915, Assistant Curator, 1915-1919; and Joseph E. Pogue, Assistant Curator, 1917-1918, Curator, 1918-1919.

In 1919 both Divisions were placed in the new Department of Arts and Industries, with Mitman as Curator of Mechanical Technology and Gilbert continuing as Honorary Curator of Mineral Technology, a position he held until 1935. However, in 1921 Mitman took the title of Curator of the Divisions of Mineral and Mechanical Technology, serving in this capacity until 1931. Other staff included Paul M. Frank, Assistant Curator of Mineral Technology, 1921-1923; Paul E. Garber, Assistant Curator of Mineral and Mechanical Technology, 1924-1931; and Frank A. Taylor, Assistant Curator, 1928-1931.

In 1931 the Division of Engineering was established, with the Divisions of Mineral and Mechanical Technology becoming two of its three sections; the third was the Section of Aeronautics. The Division continued through 1957, although the Section of Aeronautics left in 1942, gaining divisional status. After 1938 the Division of Engineering reported to the Department of Engineering and Industries, successor to Arts and Industries.

The Division held collections relating to engineering, transportation, physical sciences, tools, horology, and until 1942, aeronautics. Staff of the Division included: Mitman, Curator of the Division and in charge of Mineral Technology, 1931-1938, Head Curator of the Department of Arts and Industries, 1932-1938, Head Curator of the Department of Engineering and Industries, 1938-1948; Taylor, Assistant Curator of Mechanical Technology, 1932, Curator of the Division and in charge of Mechanical Technology, 1932-1948, Head Curator of the Department of Engineering and Industries, 1948-1957; Garber, Assistant Curator of Aeronautics, 1931-1942; Smith Hempstone Oliver, Associate Curator of Land Transportation, 1946-1956, and of Horology, 1955-1956; Kenneth M. Perry, Associate Curator of Electricity, 1948-1956, and of Marine Transportation, from 1955; Robert P. Multhauf, Associate Curator of Engineering, 1954-1955, and Curator of the Division, 1955-1956; W. James King, Jr., Associate Curator of Electricity, from 1956; Robert S. Woodbury, Curator of the Division, from 1956; and Edward A. Battison, Associate Curator of Light Machinery, from 1956.

This record unit documents the activities of the Division of Engineering (USNM) and its predecessors. Included is early correspondence between curators J. Elfreth Watkins and William Crawford Winlock and administrators of the USNM and the Smithsonian; an incomplete general correspondence file, R-Z, of Carl W. Mitman and Chester G. Gilbert, *circa* 1904-1919; annual and quarterly reports of the divisions; histories of the Division of Technology, 1906; administrative files including budgets, plans of operations, object inventories, and lists of objects packed for evacuation during World War II; postcards and photographs of museums and exhibits from Mitman's study of European engineering, industrial, and science museums in 1932; files, including minutes of an organizing committee and correspondence between Mitman and Holbrook Fitz John Porter, concerning an effort to establish a National Museum of Engineering and Industry under the auspices of the Smithsonian; and files, including correspondence and biographical information, documenting the Divisions of Mineral and Mechanical Technology's efforts to establish a biographical file on American inventors, engineers, and industrialists.

ARRANGEMENT: (1) General correspondence, 1886-1896; (2) outgoing correspondence, 1886, 1891-1903; (3) general correspondence, 1904-1905, 1913-1919; (4) annual and quarterly reports and division histories, 1895-1956; (5) special reports, exhibit records, and related materials, 1896-1946; (6) files related to proposed National Museum of Engineering and Industry, 1920-1932; (7) biographical file. FINDING AIDS: Folder list in control file. SPECIAL CONDITIONS: Use of this record unit requires prior arrangement with the Archives staff.

(397)

Division of Engineering and Industry, National Museum of American History, circa 1948-1988

Records (9.2 linear meters and oversize).

For a history of the antecedent divisions and units to the Division of Engineering and Industry before 1957, see record unit 297.

With the establishment of the Museum of History and Technology (MHT) in 1957, the Division of Engineering—minus its collections in physical science, electricity, and transportation—became the Division of Mechanical and Civil Engineering, in the Department of Science and Technology. Administrative changes in 1978 established two new Departments, History of Science and History of Technology. The Division of Mechanisms was split from the Division of Mechanical and Civil Engineering, and the divisions split between the departments. The creation of the Department of the History of Science and Technology in 1980 returned the divisions to the same department, and in 1986 they merged to form the Division of Engineering and Industry.

Curators and staff of the Division included Frank A. Taylor, Curator of the Division of Engineering, 1933-1955; Robert P. Multhauf, Associate Curator of the Division of Engineering, 1954, and Curator, 1955-1957; Robert M. Vogel, Assistant Curator of Mechanical and Civil Engineering, 1958-1961, Associate Curator, 1962-1966, Curator, 1967-1985, and Curator of Engineering and Industry, 1986-1988; Edwin A. Battison, Associate Curator of Mechanical and Civil Engineering, 1958-1969, Curator, 1970-1977, and Research Associate of Mechanisms, 1978-1980; Carlene E. Stephens, Museum Technician of Mechanical and Civil Engineering, 1974-1977, Museum Specialist, 1977-1983, Curator of Mechanisms, 1984-1985, and Curator of Engineering and Industry, 1986-   ; Otto Mayr, Curator of Mechanical and Civil Engineering, 1970-1977, and Curator of Mechanisms, 1978-1984; Robert C. Post, Museum Specialist, Mechanical and Civil Engineering, 1973-1974; David F. Noble, Curator of Mechanisms, 1983-1985; Tom D. Crouch, Curator of Engineering and Industry, 1986; and Steven Lubar, Curator of Engineering and Industry, 1987-   .

Records consist of curatorial and staff correspondence and memoranda pertaining to horology, exhibit proposals, manufacturers of engineering equipment, models, collections management, minutes of meetings, acquisitions, and installation of exhibits. Also included are blueprints for the Hall of Heavy Machinery; exhibit scripts from *Power and the Early Steam Engine,* and for *Building the Brooklyn Bridge: The Design and Construction;* inquiries from private collectors, companies, universities, and individuals; Edwin A. Battison research notes; files of Robert M. Vogel and Carlene E. Stephens; personal papers and publications; records from the exhibition *The Clockwork Universe: German Clocks and Automata, 1550-1650;* administrative files; photographs, contact sheets, and slides of the Division's exhibits and specimens; and the motion picture film *Die Welt Als Uhr* (The World as a Clock).

ARRANGEMENT: (1) Division of Mechanical and Civil Engineering, 1960-1977, accession number 81-071; (2) Division of Mechanical and Civil Engineering, 1948-1981, accession number 86-113; (3) Division of Mechanisms, 1975-1980, accession number 88-127; (4) Division of Mechanical and Civil Engineering, 1957-1988, accession number 89-108; (5) Division of Mechanical and Civil Engineering, 1967-1986, accession number 91-022; (6) Division of Mechanical and Civil Engineering, 1956-1976, accession number 92-028. FINDING AIDS: Partial folder list in control file. SPECIAL CONDITIONS: Use of this record unit requires prior arrangement with the Archives staff.

(206)

Division of Graphic Arts and Photography, National Museum of History and Technology, 1882-1969
Records (2 linear meters).

For an administrative history of the photographic component of the Division of Graphic Arts and Photography prior to 1969, see record unit 529. In 1882, George Brown Goode, Assistant Director in charge of the United States National Museum (USNM), contacted the Boston art scholar Sylvester Rosa Koehler for assistance in creating a graphic arts collection. Over the next four years, Koehler and Goode proceeded to make plans for such a collection at the Smithsonian. When the Section of Graphic Arts was established in 1886 in the Department of Arts and Industries, Koehler became its part-time Curator.

The Section of Graphic Arts was made a Division of the Department of Anthropology when USNM was reorganized in 1897. After Koehler's death in 1900, the graphic arts collections were administered for a time by the Smithsonian Library. In 1904, Paul Brockett was made Custodian of the Division, and, in 1912, Ruel Pardee Tolman became his aide.

When another reorganization of USNM occurred in 1919, the Division of Graphic Arts, in 1920, began reporting to the re-established Department of Arts and Industries. It remained within this Department and its successors until 1957. Tolman was placed in charge of the Division as Assistant Curator, 1920-1931, and Curator, 1932-1946. Jacob Kainen, an aide in the Division since 1942, became Curator in 1946 when Tolman was named Director of the National Collection of Fine Arts. Eugene N. Ostroff, Associate Curator, 1960-1965, became Curator in 1966 upon Kainen's retirement.

In 1957, the Division was located in the Department of Arts and Manufactures, Museum of History and Technology. From 1897, the Division had contained a Section of Photography, and in the 1969 reorganization of the Museum, the Section was abolished and the Division was renamed Graphic Arts and Photography.

Research of the Division's graphic arts component centered on the history of printing technology. The Division documented the techniques, materials, and equipment used in writing, drawing, line engraving, etching, photogravure, lithography, halftone printing, silk-screen stencil, papermaking, calligraphy, and bookbinding. The Division also prepared exhibitions of tools, heavy machinery, and supplies used in the printmaking process, most of which were featured in the Hall of Graphic Arts.

Curators and staff of the Division included Sylvester Rosa Koehler, Curator, 1886-1900; Paul Brockett, Custodian, 1904-1920; Ruel P. Tolman, museum aide, 1912-1919, Assistant Curator, 1920-1931, Curator, 1932-1946; Ralph Clifton Smith, museum aide, 1921-1926; C. Allen Sherwin, museum aide, 1935-1937; Jacob Kainen, museum aide, 1942-1945, Curator, 1946-1966; Eugene J. Fite, museum aide, 1947-1950, Assistant

Curator, 1951; Fuller O. Griffith III, museum aide, 1955-1957, Assistant Curator, 1958-1960, Associate Curator, 1961-1964; Peter Morse, Associate Curator, 1965-1967; Eugene N. Ostroff, Associate Curator, 1960-1966, Curator, 1966-   ; and Elizabeth M. Harris, Assistant Curator, 1966-   .

These records consist of curatorial correspondence, accession lists, blueprints for the Hall of Graphic Arts, historical information about the Division, annual reports, staff lecture notes and papers, materials pertaining to *The Printing Ink Exhibition,* biographies of important contributors in the field of printing technology, exhibition labels and photographs, correspondence logs, and newspaper clippings pertaining to activities of the Division.

ARRANGEMENT: (1) Correspondence, 1903-1969; (2) accession reports, invoices, and correspondence logs, 1887-1962; (3) annual reports, 1882-1958; (4) exhibition records, 1914-1960; (5) lectures and publicity, 1920-1937. FINDING AIDS: Folder list in control file. SPECIAL CONDITIONS: Use of this record unit requires prior arrangement with the Archives staff.

(413)
Division of Graphic Arts, National Museum of History and Technology, 1887-1978
Records (2.4 linear meters).

For an administrative history of the Division of Graphic Arts prior to 1969, see record unit 206.

From 1969 to 1971, activities pertaining to graphic arts were found in the Division of Graphic Arts and Photography, Department of Applied Arts. In 1972, it was re-established as the Division of Graphic Arts when photographic activities were removed to a newly-established Division of Photographic History. After 1977, it reported to the Department of Cultural History.

The curators during these years included Eugene N. Ostroff, Curator, 1966-1971; Peter C. Marzio, Associate Curator, 1971-1975, and Curator, 1976-1978; and Elizabeth M. Harris, Assistant Curator, 1966-1970, and Associate Curator, 1971-   .

These records include Division of Graphic Arts records dating from its establishment, including the work of curators Sylvester Rosa Koehler, Jacob Kainen, and Peter C. Marzio. Also included are lecture notes and papers of curators Ruel P. Tolman, Kainen, and Marzio; inventory lists of Graphic Arts objects; working outline for *The Steam Engine in the Graphic Arts* exhibition; loans and grants files; correspondence, newspaper clippings, and biographical information pertaining to acclaimed painter and etcher Charles W. Dahlgreen; *Do It the Hard Way: Rube Goldberg and Modern Times* exhibition records; photographs of exhibitions in the Hall of Graphic Arts; and planning files for the Hall of News Reporting.

ARRANGEMENT: (1) Division of Graphic Arts, 1970-1973, accession number T89109; (2) Division of Graphic Arts, 1917-1919, 1934-1967, accession number T89110; (3) Division of Graphic Arts, 1887-1978, accession number T89111; (4) Division of Graphic Arts and Photography, 1969-1971, accession number 85-134; (5) Division of Graphic Arts, 1971-1978, accession number 82-113. FINDING AIDS: Folder list in control file. SPECIAL CONDITIONS: Use of this record unit requires prior arrangement with the Archives staff.

Division of Medical Sciences, National Museum of History and Technology, circa 1890-1977
Records (5.5 linear meters).

Smithsonian interest in the medical sciences dates back to the Toner Lecture Series, which was established by Joseph M. Toner in 1872. The Secretary of the Institution served on the Board of Trustees for the fund that supported the series, and the Smithsonian published the lectures, which took place between 1873 and 1890, in its Miscellaneous Collections.

In 1881, the Section of Materia Medica was established in the Department of Arts and Industries, United States National Museum (USNM), to curate medical specimens. Until 1900, the United States Navy detailed a Navy surgeon to act as honorary curator for the Section of Materia Medica. The surgeons included James Milton Flint, 1881-1884, 1887-1891, and 1895-1900; Henry G. Beyer, 1884-1887; John C. Boyd, 1891-1892; William S. Dixon, 1892-1893; C. H. White, 1893; C. U. Gravatt, 1893-1894; R. A. Marmion, 1894; and Daniel McMurtrie, 1894-1895.

In 1897, the Section of Materia Medica became the Division of Medicine in the Department of Anthropology. Upon his retirement from the Navy, Flint volunteered to remain and served as Honorary Curator, 1900-1912. Until 1917, responsibility for the collections moved first to Walter Hough, Division of Ethnology, and then to Frederick L. Lewton, Division of Textiles. Lewton appointed Joseph Donner as Assistant Curator of the materia medica collection in 1917 and Charles Whitebread in 1918. Whitebread served as Assistant Curator, 1918-1938, and Associate Curator, 1939-1948.

Between 1931 and 1938, the Division merged with the Division of Textiles, under Lewton's direction. In 1938 the Division was separated from the Division of Textiles and established as the Division of Medicine and Public Health in the newly established Department of Engineering and Industries, and in 1957 it was renamed the Division of Medical Sciences, reporting to the new Department of Science and Technology. Staff of the Division included George S. Thomas, Associate Curator, 1948-1952; George B. Griffenhagen, Associate Curator, 1952-1956, Curator, 1956-1959; John B. Blake, Associate Curator, 1957-1959, Curator, 1959-1961; Sami K. Hamarneh, Associate Curator, 1960-1962, Curator, 1963-1972, Historian, 1972-1977; and Audrey B. Davis, Assistant Curator, 1968-1969, Associate Curator, 1970-1977.

These records document the activities of the Division of Medical Sciences and its predecessors, chiefly 1917-1975. Included is correspondence concerning the Division's collections, exhibits, and research into the history of medicine, dentistry, and pharmacy; memoranda; annual reports; and administrative files. Of special interest is an extensive file of James A. Tobey of the National Health Council, relating to efforts to organize an exhibit on advances in public health that was mounted at the Smithsonian, 1922-1924. There is extensive documentation on the Hall of Rehabilitative Medicine, including correspondence, exhibition scripts, promotional literature from rehabilitative institutions and manufacturers of rehabilitative supplies, as well as a manuscript by Victor Cohn, a *Washington Post* science and medical reporter, on the life of Sister Elizabeth Kenny.

ARRANGEMENT: (1) Outgoing correspondence, 1967-1975; (2) correspondence, 1903, 1905, 1917-1952; (3) correspondence, 1952-1955; (4) correspondence, 1957-1961; (5) correspondence, 1962-1967; (6) correspondence, 1968-1970, 1975; (7) public inquiries, by subject, 1956-1968; (8) public inquiries, by correspondent, 1957-1968; (9) public inquiries, 1968-1970; (10) public inquiries, 1970-1975; (11) public inquiries, 1975-1976; (12) annual reports and plans of operation, 1959-1975; (13) administrative subject file, *circa* 1890-1976; (14) memoranda, 1913, 1917-1948; (15) memoranda, 1958, 1962-1967, 1969-1970, 1972-1975; (16) exhibit records, 1922-1924; (17) Sami K. Hamarneh files, *circa* 1959-1977; (18) Audrey B. Davis files, 1968-1976; (19) Everett A. Jackson correspondence, 1970-1976; (20) correspondence, 1953-1960; (21) correspondence, 1956-1962; (22) Hall of Rehabilitative Medicine files, 1969-1977; (23) Audrey B. Davis files, 1971-1976. FINDING AIDS: Folder list in control file. SPECIAL CONDITIONS: Use of this record unit requires prior arrangement with the Archives staff.

(471)

Division of Medical Sciences, National Museum of American History, circa 1955-1986

Records (1.4 linear meters).

For an administrative history of the Division of Medical Sciences to 1977, see record unit 244; for subsequent departmental affiliations, see the Introduction to the Department of the History of Science and Technology, which the Division joined in 1980.

Since 1977, staff members of the Division have included Audrey B. Davis, Curator, 1978- ; Barbara Melosh, Curator, 1983- ; Ramunas A. Kondratas, Assistant Curator, 1977-1983, Associate Curator, 1984- ; and Sami K. Hamarneh, Associate Curator, 1960-1962, Curator, 1963-1972, Historian, 1972-1977, and Curator Emeritus, 1982-1985.

Records consist of curatorial correspondence and memoranda pertaining to exhibition planning, acquisitions, curatorial research, and collections management. In addition there are minutes of meetings with organizations including the American Association of Health and Medical Museums, as well as the American Academy of the History of Dentistry; proposals, scripts, photographs, and other related information pertaining to the exhibitions *Pain and Its Relief* and *Women in Science;* Audrey B. Davis research files; letters of inquiry from medical academies, government agencies, private collectors, and universities; illustrations of medical specimens; symposium and sponsored lecture files; travel reports; and information on early medical practice.

ARRANGEMENT: (1) Division of Medical Sciences, 1955-1978, accession number 82-021; (2) Division of Medical Sciences, 1965-1986, accession number 94-026. FINDING AIDS: Partial folder list in control file. SPECIAL CONDITIONS: Use of this record unit requires prior arrangement with the Archives staff.

(396)

Division of Military History, National Museum of American History, circa 1968-1981

Records (2.5 linear meters).

Beginning in the 1880s, military collections were curated by the Section of Historical Relics, United States National Museum, and its various successors through to the Division of History. In 1935, the Division established the Military and Naval Collection, and, in 1947, it formed a Section of Military History. The Section was given Division status in 1948 and was placed under the direction of Mendel L. Peterson. Additional details on the history of the Division are located in record unit 383, and in the introduction to the Department of Social and Cultural History.

The Division of Military History was responsible for tracing the historical development of the United States Army from its inception as a colonial militia to its current role in the missile age. Research focused on United States Army firearms, artillery, ammunition, edged weapons, uniforms, medals, and flags. In addition to collecting military and foreign artifacts the Division published military histories and conducted studies of arms collections in other museums.

Staff members of the Division included Craddock R. Goins, Jr., Curator, 1959- , and Donald E. Kloster, Associate Curator, 1973- .

These records consist of public inquiries from museums, universities, historical societies, and private collectors regarding gun models, saber types, military heraldry, uniform insignia, history of the United States Army, the preservation of artifacts, and paintings illustrating scenes from American military history. Also included are copies of responses to public inquiries by the two curators; photographs, scripts, and correspondence concerning the exhibitions *Victory at Yorktown, Von Steuben,* and *Belgian Gunmaking and American History;* and memoranda from administrative offices, some of which pertain to planning for the Bicentennial of the American Revolution.

ARRANGEMENT: (1) Division of Military History, 1977-1980, accession number 84-061; (2) Division of Military History, 1968-1981, accession number 85-130. FINDING AIDS: Folder list in control file. SPECIAL CONDITIONS: Use of this record unit requires prior arrangement with the Archives staff.

(216)

Divisions of Mineral and Mechanical Technology, United States National Museum, circa 1900-1921
Storage and Condemnation Records (0.3 linear meter).

For an administrative history of the Divisions of Mineral and Mechanical Technology, United States National Museum, see record unit 297.

These records include correspondence, memoranda, and lists concerning the storage and condemnation of specimens and materials belonging to the Divisions of Mineral and Mechanical Technology.

ARRANGEMENT: Unarranged. FINDING AIDS: None. SPECIAL CONDITIONS: Use of this record unit requires prior arrangement with the Archives staff.

(529)

Division of Photographic History, National Museum of American History, circa 1883-1984
Records (4.5 linear meters).

For an administrative history of the Division of Graphic Arts, which contained the Section of Photography from 1897 to 1969, see record unit 206.

The history of photography at the Smithsonian Institution dates from the 1850s. In 1859, Secretary Joseph Henry proposed that a photographic record be assembled of Native American delegations visiting Washington, D.C. In 1867, with the support of

Ferdinand V. Hayden, a geologist, and William H. Blackmore, a wealthy English collector and speculator, Washington photographers Alexander Gardner and Antonio Zeno Shindler began photographing the Native American delegates. These images and others formed the earliest Smithsonian photograph collection.

In 1883, the Section of Photography was established in the Department of Preparation, with Thomas William Smillie as photographer. Smillie, a former photographer at the United States Fish Commission, had been employed by the Institution as its official photographer since 1870. Smillie was named Custodian of the Section in 1896, but also continued to function as the Institution's photographer until his death in 1917. His successors also retained these dual responsibilities until 1943, when the duties were separated and Gurney I. Hightower became the Institution's official photographer.

In 1897, the Section became a part of the Division of Graphic Arts, where it remained until 1969. At that time, the Division was redesignated Graphic Arts and Photography. In 1972, the two functions divided, and the Division of Photographic History was established in the Department of Applied Arts. At that time, Eugene N. Ostroff, Associate Curator and Curator of Photography under the previous divisions, was made Curator of Photographic History. Successively, the Division was affiliated with the Department of History of Technology, 1978-1980, and then the Department of the History of Science and Technology.

The Division of Photographic History and its predecessors primarily documented the history of photographic science and technology in America since the nineteenth century. The Division collected cameras, patent models, motion picture apparatus, and photographs such as daguerreotypes, tintypes, and calotypes.

Curators and staff of the Division included Thomas W. Smillie, photographer, 1871-1895, Custodian and photographer, 1896-1917; Loring W. Beeson, Custodian and photographer, 1917-1920; Arthur J. Olmsted, Custodian and photographer, 1920-1930, Assistant Curator and photographer, 1931-1941, Associate Curator and photographer, 1942, Associate Curator, 1943-1946; Alexander J. Wedderburn, Associate Curator, 1947-1960; Eugene N. Ostroff, Associate Curator of Photography, 1960-1966, Curator, 1966-1972, Curator of Photographic History, 1972-   ; and David E. Haberstich, Assistant Curator, 1970-1976.

These records consist mostly of curatorial and staff correspondence and memoranda documenting activities of the Division and its predecessors, especially during the tenures of Thomas W. Smillie, Alexander J. Wedderburn, and Eugene N. Ostroff. The records also include information on the Hall of Photography, organized by Ostroff; newspaper clippings pertaining to the field of photography; historic photographs; annual reports; and administrative files.

ARRANGEMENT: (1) Division of Photographic History, 1886-1969, accession number T90064; (2) Division of Photographic History, 1883-1922, accession number 82-026; (3) Division of Photographic History, 1961-1979, accession number 87-032; (4) Division of Photographic History, 1955-1974, accession number 88-122; (5) Division of Photographic History, 1980-1984, accession number 90-028. FINDING AIDS: Folder list in control file. SPECIAL CONDITIONS: Use of this record unit requires prior arrangement with the Archives staff.

Division of Physical Sciences, National Museum of History and Technology, 1955-1966 and undated
Records (1.2 linear meters).

For an administrative history of the Division of Physical Sciences see record unit 293.

This record unit includes the research files of Robert P. Multhauf, Curator in the Division of Physical Sciences. The records contain scripts for Hall of Chemistry exhibitions; historical information and illustrations pertaining to chemistry, chemical apparatus, and industrial laboratories; biographies of distinguished chemists; and selected early twentieth-century scientific catalogs and articles on chemistry. Also included are the research files of Eduard Farber, a visiting scholar.

ARRANGEMENT: (1) Division of Physical Sciences, 1955-1966, accession number 87-112. FINDING AIDS: Folder list in control file. SPECIAL CONDITIONS: Use of this record unit requires prior arrangement with the Archives staff.

Division of Physical Sciences, National Museum of History and Technology, 1956-1976
Records (0.9 linear meter).

In 1890 a Section of Physical Apparatus was established in the Department of Arts and Industries with William Crawford Winlock as Honorary Curator. In 1897 the Section became the Mechanical Phases collection in the Division of Technology, curated by J. Elfreth Watkins. For its history through the Division of Engineering, Department of Engineering and Industries, see record unit 297.

In 1938 the Section of Physical Sciences and Measurement was created from the Section of Mechanical Technology of the Division of Engineering. Frank A. Taylor, Curator of Engineering, assumed curatorial responsibility for Physical Sciences and Measurement, serving in this capacity until 1955. His successor, Robert P. Multhauf, was Curator of the Section from 1955 to 1957.

In 1957 the Section of Physical Sciences and Measurement became the Division of Physical Sciences, Department of Science and Technology, in the Museum of History and Technology (MHT). Multhauf served as Curator of the Division until the position was assigned to Faye Cannon (prior to 1976, Walter F. Cannon) in 1965.

Research and collections of the Division of Physical Sciences principally focused on the history of astronomy, meteorology, chemistry, classical physics, geology, astrophysics, and mathematics. Curators and staff of the Division included Robert P. Multhauf, Curator of the Section of Physical Sciences and Measurement, 1955-1957, Curator of the Division of Physical Sciences, 1957-1965; Faye Cannon, Associate Curator, 1962-1964, Curator, 1965- ; Lester Clark Lewis, Curator, 1962; Uta C. Merzbach, Associate Curator, 1964-1967; Deborah J. (Mills) Warner, Assistant Curator, 1964-1966, 1968-1969, Associate Curator, 1970- ; and Jon B. Eklund, Assistant Curator, 1968-1969, Associate Curator, 1970- .

These records consist of public inquiries about scientific instruments; layout plans, scripts, and photographs for exhibitions; proposals for the Hall of Physics, Mathematics, and Astronomy in MHT; general curatorial correspondence with domestic and foreign science museums, universities, manufacturers and collectors of scientific instruments, and professional societies; administrative files consisting of annual reports, staff memoranda, and planning statements; records documenting Cannon's role in the bicentennial celebration of James Smithson's birth; and information pertaining to internship research.

ARRANGEMENT: (1) Administrative files, 1961-1976; (2) exhibitions, 1956-1976; (3) general correspondence, 1956-1976; (4) public inquiries, 1962-1976; (5) bicentennial celebration of Smithson's birth, 1964-1967; (6) internship research, 1962-1965. FINDING AIDS: None. SPECIAL CONDITIONS: Use of this record unit requires prior arrangement with the Archives staff.

(332)

Division of Physical Sciences and Mathematics, National Museum of American History, 1956-1988 and undated
Records (3.3 linear meters and oversize).

For a history of the Division of Physical Sciences prior to 1965, see record unit 293.

In 1965 a Section of Mathematics and Antique Instruments was created in the Division of Physical Sciences under Uta C. Merzbach, Associate Curator. The Section was renamed the Section of Mathematics in 1968, and Merzbach reported to Silvio A. Bedini, Assistant Director for the Museum. In 1970 the Section of Mathematics became part of the Division of Electricity and Nuclear Energy. Merzbach became involved in the Computer History Project (CHP), which included Henry S. Tropp as Principal Investigator. CHP was a joint research effort between the Smithsonian Institution and the American Federation of Information Processing Societies (AFIPS) to gather information on the development of computer technology. The project closed in 1974.

From 1974 to 1977, the Section of Mathematics reported to the Chairman of the Department of Science and Technology. In 1978 it became the Division of Mathematics in the Department of History of Science; and in 1987, it merged with the Division of Physical Sciences to form the Division of Physical Sciences and Mathematics.

The Division of Mathematics and its predecessors were concerned with the history of mathematical calculating instruments, both domestic and foreign, dating back to the eighteenth century. The Division prepared exhibitions for the Hall of Mathematics and collected artifacts such as planimeters, slide rules, mechanical calculators, digital electronic computers, and astrolabes. Curators and staff of the Division and its predecessors included Robert P. Multhauf, Curator of Physical Sciences and Measurement, 1955-1957, Curator of Physical Sciences, 1957-1964; Uta C. Merzbach, Associate Curator of Physical Sciences, 1964, Associate Curator of Mathematics and Antique Instruments, 1965-1968, Associate Curator of Mathematics, 1968-1970, Curator of Mathematics, 1970-1988; and Henry S. Tropp, Principal Investigator of the Computer History Project, 1971-1974.

These records include administrative files of the Division of Mathematics and its predecessors; Merzbach correspondence with computer industries, university professors, and pioneers or experts in the field of computing science; exhibition scripts, research material, and blueprints for the Hall of Mathematics; Computer History Project research files, correspondence, floor plans, and budgetary information; and photographs of exhibitions, artifacts, and Division staff.

ARRANGEMENT: (1) Administrative records, 1962-1988; (2) Uta C. Merzbach correspondence, 1958-1985; (3) Computer History Project and Division research files, 1956-1985; (4) Computer History Project correspondence, *circa* 1966-1974; (5) exhibition blueprints, 1963-1980. FINDING AIDS: Description in control file. SPECIAL CONDITIONS: Use of this record unit requires prior arrangement with the Archives staff.

(239)

Division of Transportation, National Museum of History and Technology, circa 1927-1973 and undated

Records (8.5 linear meters and oversize).

The collections of the Division of Transportation date back to 1885, in the Section of Steam Transportation in the Department of Arts and Industries. For an administrative history of this unit and its successors through the Division of Engineering, Department of Engineering and Industries, see record unit 297.

In 1938 the Section of Transportation and Civil Engineering was established in the Division of Engineering. Frank A. Taylor served as Curator of the Division of Engineering, 1932-1948, and had direct responsibility for the Museum's transportation collections. (Taylor was away on war duty from 1943 until 1946, but retained his title.) In 1947 the Section was divided into two units: the Section of Marine Transportation and the Section of Land Transportation. Taylor served as Department Head and had specific curatorial responsibility for the Section of Marine Transportation until 1954, when Kenneth M. Perry was named an Associate Curator of the Department and was assigned the Marine Section until 1965. Smith Hempstone Oliver directed the Section of Land Transportation as Associate Curator, 1946-1956.

In 1957 a new Division of Transportation was created as one of several divisions in the Department of Science and Technology. In 1969 Transportation was assigned to the Department of Industries in the National Museum of History and Technology.

The Division of Transportation documents the evolution of rail, marine, and road transportation in the United States from the eighteenth century to the present. Its collections include locomotives, streetcars, motor vehicles, bicycles, carriages, motorcycles, and various vessels and vehicles which capture three centuries of transportation history. Curators of the Division have included Howard I. Chapelle, Curator, 1957-1967; John H. White, Jr., Assistant Curator, 1958-1961, Associate Curator, 1961-1966, Curator, 1966-   ; Melvin H. Jackson, Associate Curator, 1966-1968, Curator, 1969-   ; George W. Hilton, Associate Curator, 1966-1968, Curator, 1968-   ; and Donald H. Berkebile, Assistant Curator, 1973-   .

These records chiefly document the operations of the Division of Transportation from its creation in 1957, and the operations of the Section of Land Transportation, 1946-1957. Lesser amounts of records relate to the administration of the land transportation collections prior to 1946 and to the marine transportation collections before 1957.

ARRANGEMENT: (1) Correspondence, *circa* 1927-1973; (2) memoranda, 1951-1952, 1955-1973; (3) administrative records, 1955-1972 and undated; (4) exhibit records, 1958-1969 and undated. FINDING AIDS: Description in control file. SPECIAL CONDITIONS: Use of this record unit requires prior arrangement with the Archives staff.

Division of Transportation, National Museum of American History, 1946-1985
Records (8.2 linear meters).

For an administrative history of the Division of Transportation through 1973, see record unit 239. In 1978 the Division of Transportation was part of the Department of History of Technology, which merged with the Department of History of Science to form the Department of the History of Science and Technology in 1980.

These records consist of curator's day journals, 1946-1956; a manuscript copy, *Wheels and Wheeling: The Smithsonian Cycle Collection,* 1974; and administrative files of the Division of Transportation concerning such matters as gifts and grants, annual budgets, minutes of meetings, publications, and historical inquiries regarding objects. Also included are records concerning exhibition planning, including fundraising, travel, and production files for the Hall of American Maritime Enterprise at NMAH.

Curatorial staff represented in the records include Smith Hempstone Oliver, Associate Curator, 1946-1956; Howard I. Chapelle, Curator, 1957-1966, Senior Historian, 1967-1971; John H. White, Jr., Assistant Curator, 1958-1961, Associate Curator, 1961-1966, Curator, 1966-1985, Senior Historian, 1986-   ; Donald H. Berkebile, Assistant Curator, 1973-1975, Associate Curator, 1975-1980; Melvin H. Jackson, Associate Curator, 1966-1968, Curator, 1969-1977, Honorary Curator, 1978-1979; Robert C. Post, Curator, 1980-1981; and William L. Withuhn, Curator, 1983-   .

ARRANGEMENT: (1) Curator's day journals, 3 volumes, 1946-1956, accession number 85-211; (2) Division of Transportation, 1961-1970, accession number 84-128; (3) Division of Transportation, 1970-1975, accession number T91013; (4) *Wheels and Wheeling: The Smithsonian Cycle Collection* manuscript text, 1974, accession number 83-061; (5) Division of Transportation, 1971-1978, accession number T91011; (6) Division of Transportation, 1970-1977, accession number 89-109; (7) Division of Transportation, 1973-1977, accession number 81-024; (8) Division of Transportation, 1964-1985, accession number 90-103. FINDING AIDS: Folder list in control file. SPECIAL CONDITIONS: Use of this record unit requires prior arrangement with the Archives staff.

SOCIAL AND CULTURAL HISTORY, 1938-1994

The Department of Social and Cultural History was responsible for collections of political, social, and cultural history. It included a number of different curatorial areas—including political memorabilia, costumes, furnishings, textiles, graphic arts, photography, ceramics and glass, and musical instruments—that either were continuously associated with American history, or that came to the Museum through the ethnological collections of the Department of Anthropology. In addition, the Department's predecessors were also responsible for military, philatelic, and numismatic collections, but these were placed elsewhere in 1980, when the Department was formed.

At first, all historical collections were curated within the Department of Arts and Industries, established in 1881 by George Brown Goode, Assistant Secretary in charge of the United States National Museum (USNM). He arranged historical artifacts into sections of historical relics, ceramics and glass, furnishings, coins and medals, costumes, and musical apparatus. A philatelic collection was established in 1888. Staff included A. Howard Clark, Curator of Historical Relics, 1883-1889, and of Historical Collections (as the section was renamed), 1889-1897; J. King Goodrich, Acting Curator in charge of Costumes, 1883; A. P. Niblack, Assistant Curator of Costumes, 1883; Paul Edmond Beckwith, Aid in the Section of Historical Collections, 1884-1897; and Edwin H. Hawley, Custodian of Musical Apparatus, 1885-1897.

When USNM was reorganized in 1897, the Section of Historical Collections became the Division of History and Biography, Department of Anthropology. It was renamed the Division of History in 1904. It was responsible for collections of political memorabilia, military relics, philately, numismatics, costumes, and furnishings. Prior to 1919, staff included A. Howard Clark, Custodian of History and Biography, 1897-1903, and Curator of the Division of History, 1904-1918; Paul Edmond Beckwith, Assistant Curator of History and Biography, 1897-1903, and Assistant Curator of the Division of History, 1904-1907; Theodore T. Belote, Assistant Curator of the Division of History, 1908-1918; and, beginning in 1913, Joseph B. Leavy, Philatelist of the National Postage Stamp Collection.

The USNM reorganization in 1897 assigned other collections elsewhere in the Anthropology Department. Its Division of Ethnology contained a Section of Ceramics (although the ceramics and glass collections were the *de facto* responsibility of the Division of History until 1908), as well as objects of everyday life. Beginning in 1903, Ethnology also contained a Section of Musical Instruments. The Division of Graphic Arts included a Section of Photography in addition to graphic arts collections. A Section on Textiles, which had a brief existence in the 1880s, was re-established in 1912 as a departmentally-independent Division of Textiles, reporting directly to the Assistant Secretary in charge of USNM. For administrative histories of the Divisions of Textiles and Graphic Arts, see record units 472, 206, and 529.

In the 1919 reorganization of USNM that re-established the Department of Arts and Industries, the Division of History initially remained under the Department of Anthropology. But between 1921 and 1924, the Division became an independent curatorial office reporting to William deC. Ravenel, Administrative Assistant in charge of USNM and Director of the Department of Arts and Industries. The Division merged with the Department of Arts and Industries in 1924 to form the Department of Arts and Industries and Division of History. On Ravenel's retirement in 1932, the Division became an independent unit again, reporting to John E. Graf, Associate Director of USNM. When Graf became Assistant Secretary of the Smithsonian Institution in 1945, the Division reported to Alexander Wetmore, Director of USNM and Secretary of the Institution. In addition to military collections, the Division remained accountable for costumes, antiquarian artifacts (known as the Domestic Section in 1937), political memorabilia, numismatics, and philately. Theodore T. Belote served as Curator, 1919-1948; Joseph B. Leavy, Philatelist, 1913-1921; and Catherine L. Manning, Philatelist, 1921-1943, and Assistant Curator, 1944-1951.

In 1947, collections of the Division of History were arranged as the Sections of Civil History (political memorabilia, costumes, and domestic objects), Military History, Naval History, Numismatics, and Philately. The following year the Division was reorganized as the Department of History, and each section became a corresponding division. Charles Carey (Aid, 1921-1924, and Assistant Curator, 1925- 1948) became Acting Head Curator of the Department, 1948-1951; and Mendel L. Peterson, Curator of the Divisions of Military and Naval History, served as Head Curator, 1951-1957.

In 1957, with the creation of the Museum of History and Technology (MHT), the divisions of the Department of History were reorganized into two of the new museum's four departments: Civil History and Armed Forces History. The Department of Civil History held Divisions of Political History, Philately and Postal History, Numismatics, and Cultural History (from the Division of Ethnology, Department of Anthropology), and a unit called Growth of the United States (Division in 1967). The Division of Cultural History contained the Section of Musical Instruments from Ethnology, and, in 1966, this section was made a separate division. A. N. B. Garvan was Head Curator, 1957-1960; Richard H. Howland, Head Curator, 1961-1964, and Chairman, 1964-1967; and C. Malcolm Watkins, Curator of Cultural History, Acting Chairman, 1968-   .

The Department of Armed Forces History included the Divisions of Military History and Naval History, under the leadership of Mendel L. Peterson, Head Curator, 1957 1964, and Chairman, 1964-1969.

In 1969, MHT was reorganized as the National Museum of History and Technology (NMHT). The four departments were re-established as five, by the formation of a hybrid Department of Applied Arts and by the reorganization of the existing four departments. The Department of Civil History became the Department of Cultural History, gathering or establishing Divisions of Costume and Furnishings, Musical Instruments, Ethnic and Western Cultural History, and Preindustrial Cultural History. Department chairmen were Watkins, 1969-1973; Rodris C. Roth, Curator of Costume and Furnishings, and Acting Chairman, 1973-1974; and Richard E. Ahlborn, Curator of Ethnic and Western Cultural History, Chairman, 1975-1977. 05 The old Department of Armed Forces History became the core of the new Department of National and Military History, as the Division of Political History joined the Divisions of Military History, Naval History, and the newly established Division of Historic Archeology. Edgar M. Howell, Curator of Military History, served as Chairman of this Department from 1969 to 1973; and Margaret Brown Klapthor, Curator of Political History, was Chairman from 1974 to 1977.

Removed from the former Department of Civil History to the newly established Department of Applied Arts were the Divisions of Numismatics and of Postal History (renamed from Philately and Postal History), where they joined the Divisions of Textiles and the newly named Graphic Arts and Photography.

Major administrative changes during the period from 1969 to 1977 included the splitting of the Division of Graphic Arts and Photography into two separate divisions in 1972, and the abolition of the Division of Historic Archeology in 1973.

The reorganization of NMHT in fiscal year 1978 saw reversion to four departments, two roughly in scientific and technological areas, two in areas of social, cultural, and national history. The Department of Applied Arts was abolished. The Divisions of Numismatics and of Postal History from that Department were added to the Department of National and Military History to form the Department of National History. Vladimir Clain-Stefanelli, immediate past Chairman of Applied Arts and Curator of Numismatics, continued as chair in the new Department from 1978 to 1979.

The three other divisions of the old Department of Applied Arts also found new homes. The Divisions of Textiles and Photographic History were assigned to the Department of History of Technology. The Division of Graphic Arts was placed in the Department of Cultural History, which now also included the Division of Ceramics and Glass (previously in the Department of Industries, NMHT, and Department of Arts and Manufactures, MHT). A new Division of Domestic Life was formed, consolidating artifacts and furnishings from the former Divisions of Costume and Furnishings and Preindustrial Cultural History. The remaining collections formed the Division of Costume. Ethnic and Western Cultural History was renamed the Division of Community Life, while the Division of Musical Instruments continued from before. Chairmen of the Department of Cultural History during this period were Anne C. Golovin, Curator of Domestic Life, (Acting) 1978, Peter C. Marzio, Curator of Graphic Arts, 1978, and Claudia B. Kidwell, Curator of Costume, 1979-1980.

In 1980, NMHT was renamed the National Museum of American History (NMAH), with attendant reorganization. The Department of Cultural History merged with the Department of National History to form the Department of Social and National History. However, the military history divisions were transferred to the Department of the History of Science and Technology. Thus Social and National History—known as Social and Cultural History from 1981—included Divisions of Ceramics and Glass, Community Life, Costume, Domestic Life, Graphic Arts, Musical Instruments (Musical History from 1987), Political History, and Textiles. Kidwell served as Chairman during these years. The Division of Photographic History shifted between the two departments until it was permanently established as a part of Social and Cultural History in 1986. The Divisions of Postal History and of Numismatics were not assigned to either department, but instead became the National Philatelic Collection (in 1990, the National Postal Museum) and the National Numismatic Collection, each reporting to the Director of NMAH.

Chairs of the Department of Social and Cultural History after Kidwell included: Anne C. Golovin, Curator of Domestic Life, (Co-chair) 1982; Elizabeth M. Harris, Curator of Graphic Arts, (Co-chair) 1982; Gary B. Kulik, Assistant Curator of Textiles, 1983-1986; Tom D. Crouch, Curator of Engineering and Industry, 1986-1990; Spencer Crew, Curator of Community Life, 1990-1992; and Anne C. Golovin, Acting Chairman, 1992, and Chairman, 1993-1994.

In the administrative reorganization of 1994, both departments were abolished and all divisions were consolidated into a single Department of History.

(251)

Department of Cultural History, National Museum of History and Technology, 1957, 1964-1975
Records (0.9 linear meter).

For an administrative history of the Department of Cultural History and its predecessor, the Department of Civil History, see the introduction to the Department of Social and Cultural History.

During the period 1966-1967, the Divisions of Musical Instruments and Growth of the United States were established in the Department. Growth of the United States was a unit in the Department, *circa* 1957 to 1967, and was administered by the Assistant Director of the Museum of History and Technology from 1965 to 1967.

These records include the files of the Chair of the Department of Civil History, Richard H. Howland, 1964-1968; C. Malcom Watkins, Acting Chair, 1968, Chair of Cultural History, 1969-1973; Rodris C. Roth, Acting Chair, 1973-1974; and Richard E. Ahlborn, Chair, 1975- .

The records consist of administrative files, including memoranda and correspondence concerning exhibits, general museum and departmental policies, the acquisition of objects, and the search for a curator; general correspondence with donors, reseachers, and non-Smithsonian museum administrators concerning the acquisition of objects, exhibits, museum programs, and C. Malcolm Watkins's reseach on southwestern United States and New England cultural life; reading files; and plans of operations, annual reports, and budget proposals.

ARRANGEMENT: (1) Administrative files, 1957, 1964-1975; (2) general correspondence, 1964, 1968-1974; (3) reading files, 1971-1974; (4) annual reports, budgets, and plans of operations, 1968-1974. FINDING AIDS: Description in control file. SPECIAL CONDITIONS: Use of this record unit requires prior arrangement with the Archives staff.

(331)
Department of Cultural History, National Museum of History and Technology, 1968-1979 and undated, with related records from 1954, 1961-1964
Records (1.6 linear meters).

For an administrative history of the Department of Cultural History and its predecessor, the Department of Civil History, see the introduction to the Department of Social and Cultural History and record unit 251.

The records of the Department of Cultural History consist of correspondence and subject files created during the tenures of C. Malcolm Watkins and Richard E. Ahlborn as chairmen. The records include correspondence, memoranda, annual reports, budget files, travel reports, and photographs. They document departmental administration, National Museum of History and Technology committee activities, exhibitions, and museum and department collection policies and activities. Included is information on the exhibition, *A Nation of Nations,* the Hall of Everyday Life in the American Past, the Historical Archaeology Project, and the symposium, *Kin and Communities: The Peopling of America.* Staff members whose activities are documented include Anne C. Golovin, Cynthia A. Hoover, Claudia B. Kidwell, Peter C. Marzio and Rodris C. Roth.

In addition to departmental activities, the records document the professional and curatorial activities of Ahlborn and Watkins. Included are research awards proposals, travel reports, correspondence with curators, archaeologists, and the general public, and lectures.

ARRANGEMENT: (1) Correspondence, 1972-1979; (2) subject files, 1954, 1961-1964, 1968-1979. FINDING AIDS: Description in control file. SPECIAL CONDITIONS: Use of this record unit requires prior arrangement with the Archives staff.

Division of Ceramics and Glass, National Museum of American History, circa 1938-1987, with related records from 1914

Records (6.6 linear meters).

Among the Smithsonian's earliest ceramic and glass artifacts were those acquired at the 1876 Philadelphia Centennial Exposition and from archeological sites throughout North America. Edward Foreman, Curator for the ethnological collections at the United States National Museum (USNM), cataloged ceramic artifacts from 1881 to 1883, as did his successor, Otis T. Mason, from 1884 to 1902. The curator for the Section of Historical Collections, A. Howard Clark, cataloged glass artifacts during the same years.

In 1897, the Section of Ceramics was established in the Division of Ethnology, Department of Anthropology. The glass collections were added to the Section but remained the curatorial responsibility of Clark, Curator of the newly organized Division of History. Paul Edmond Beckwith, Assistant Curator for the Division of History, was responsible for the Section from 1903 to 1907. From 1907 to 1920, a National Gallery of Art (NGA) was established and administered by USNM, and selections of contemporary porcelain and glass were placed with NGA during this period.

From 1908 to 1935, the Section of Ceramics became the curatorial responsibility of Walter Hough, Curator of Ethnology. Mrs. Julian James, a patron of the Division of History at USNM, assisted Hough with maintaining the collections, as did private collectors and donors such as Eliza Ruhamah Scidmore and Olive Risley Seward. Samuel W. Woodhouse served as Collaborator of the Section from 1933 to 1943. In 1935, Herbert W. Krieger replaced Hough as Curator of Ethnology and was responsible for the Section.

In 1957, the Section was removed from the Division of Ethnology to become the Division of Ceramics and Glass, Department of Arts and Manufactures (and successor departments). In 1978, the Division transferred to the Department of Cultural History and continued under its successor departments. Additional details on the history of the Division are located in the introductions to the Departments of Social and Cultural History and the History of Science and Technology.

Curators and staff of the Division included Paul V. Gardner, Acting Curator, 1958-1960, Associate Curator, 1961, Curator, 1962-1977, and Curator Emeritus, 1978- ; J. Jefferson Miller II, Assistant Curator, 1962, Associate Curator, 1963-1969, Curator, 1970-1977, Consultant, 1978, and Curator Emeritus, 1979- ; Susan H. Myers, Assistant Curator, 1980-1983, and Curator, 1984- ; and Ivor Noel Hume, Research Associate, 1980-1984.

These records include the correspondence and memoranda of Paul V. Gardner, J. Jefferson Miller II, and Susan H. Meyers pertaining to private donations, loans, exhibition planning, identification of ceramic and glass pieces, conferences and seminars, staff research, and administrative matters. Also included are inquiries from collectors, museums, historical associations, university professors, ceramics and glass manufacturers, and publishers; minutes of meetings; research notes of J. Jefferson Miller II, for the publication *English Yellow-Glazed Earthenware;* newspaper clippings; Kiln Club information and photographs; exhibition photographs, blueprints, and scripts; and research material on the Hans Syz Collection in the Division.

ARRANGEMENT: (1) Division of Ceramics and Glass, 1950-1979, accession number T89041; (2) Division of Ceramics and Glass, 1954-1978, accession number T89042; (3) Alfred Duane Pell Collection, 1914-1940, accession number T90058; (4) Division of Ceramics and Glass, 1938-1970, accession number 82-114; (5) Division of Ceramics and Glass, 1955-1980, accession number 84-086; (6) Division of Ceramics and Glass, 1964-1987, accession number 90-149. FINDING AIDS: Folder list in control file. SPECIAL CONDITIONS: Use of this record unit requires prior arrangement with the Archives staff.

(519)

Division of Costume and Furnishings, National Museum of History and Technology, 1972-1974
Records (0.4 linear meter).

For an administrative history of the furnishings component of the Division of Costume and Furnishings prior to 1969, see record unit 261.

In 1883 a Section of Costumes was established under the Department of Arts and Industries, Division of Anthropology, United States National Museum (USNM), but was abolished in 1884. Costume collections subsequently were curated by the Section of Historical Relics and its various successors through to the Division of History, under the direction of A. Howard Clark until 1918 and Theodore T. Belote, 1919-1948. Otis T. Mason of the Department (later, Division) of Ethnology aided Clark with costumes of ethnological importance.

The Period Costume Collection was established in 1911 and featured a series of dresses worn by former First Ladies. Collector and donor Mrs. Julian James and Walter Hough, Head Curator of the Department of Anthropology, acted as co-supervisors. When Mrs. James died in 1922, Belote curated the collections. Upon its formation in 1943, the Civil Section of the Division of History assumed responsibility for the costume collections. Until 1969, they remained under that Section and its various successors through to the Division of Political History, Section of American Costume. Curators Margaret Klapthor and Anne W. Murray were chiefly concerned with costumes, establishing the First Ladies Hall and the Hall of American Costume during these years. For additional details on the history of the Section under the Division of Political History, see record unit 252.

When the Museum was reorganized in 1969, the new Division of Costume and Furnishings and the existing Division of Political History each curated portions of the costume collections. Staff for the new Division was assembled from the Divisions of Cultural History (now defunct) and Political History. Rodris C. Roth served as Associate Curator (chiefly furnishings), 1969-1971, and Curator, 1972- , and Claudia B. Kidwell as Assistant Curator (chiefly costume), 1969- . Murray continued as Curator Emerita, 1969- .

Research of the Division of Costume and Furnishings primarily focused on the history of clothing and household objects in America with emphasis on the industrial period. It studied how changing economic, social, and technological factors affected the clothing and appearance of Americans. In addition, the Division was concerned with documenting and interpreting everyday wares used in the home, and the activities surrounding them. The Division staff and their predecessors collected a wide range of artifacts for study including clothing of men, women and children; jewelry; military and diplomatic uniforms; heating and lighting devices; clothing and gowns of Presidents and First

Ladies; metal, synthetic and wooden wares; theatrical garments; furniture and accessories; household appliances; working class apparel; and architectural elements.

These records chiefly consist of curatorial responses to public inquiries. Included is correspondence from private collectors, museum curators, clothing manufacturers, college professors, historical associations, and individuals.

ARRANGEMENT: (1) Division of Costume and Furnishings, 1972-1973, accession number T89058; (2) Division of Costume and Furnishings, 1973-1974, accession number 82-101. FINDING AIDS: Folder list in control file. SPECIAL CONDITIONS: Use of this record unit requires prior arrangement with the Archives staff.

(258)
Division of Cultural History, National Museum of History and Technology, 1952-1967 and undated
Records (0.1 linear meter).

Prior to the creation of the Division of Cultural History in 1957, the cultural history collections were the curatorial responsibility of the Division of Ethnology, Department of Anthropology. With the establishment of the Museum of History and Technology in 1957, the Division of Cultural History became a part of the Museum's new Department of Civil History. Musical Instruments, which formed part of the collections of the Division of Cultural History, became a separate Division in 1966.

C. Malcolm Watkins, who joined the Smithsonian as an Associate Curator of Ethnology in 1948, was appointed Curator of Cultural History in 1957. Other curators of the cultural history collections included G. Carroll Lindsay, Assistant Curator of Ethnology, 1956-1957, Associate Curator, 1958; Rodris C. Roth, Assistant Curator, 1957-1959, Associate Curator, 1960-   ; John D. Shortridge, Associate Curator, 1958-1960; John N. Pearce, Assistant Curator, 1960-1963, Associate Curator, 1964; Cynthia A. Hoover, Assistant Curator, 1961-1963, Associate Curator, 1964-   ; Anthony N. Hathaway, Junior Curator, 1961, Assistant Curator, 1962-1963; Howard Mayer Brown, Associate Curator, 1965; Richard E. Ahlborn, Associate Curator, 1966-   ; and John T. Fesperman, Jr., Concert Director, 1966.

These records consist of the administrative files of the Division of Cultural History and its staff, as well as records from the Division of Ethnology relating to cultural history activities. Included are annual reports of these divisions; budget estimates and plans of operations of the Division of Cultural History, including estimates and plans for the Division before it underwent an administrative reorganization in 1969; newspaper clippings concerning an exhibit on life in early America; research progress reports of curators and research associates; correspondence relating to lists of objects borrowed by the United States Department of Agriculture for an exhibit in Hamburg, Germany; and related materials.

ARRANGEMENT: (1) Annual reports, 1957-1967; (2) budget estimates and plans of operations, 1956-1957 and undated; (3) newspaper clippings, research reports, and related materials, 1952-1966 and undated. FINDING AIDS: Description in control file. SPECIAL CONDITIONS: Use of this record unit requires prior arrangement with the Archives staff.

Division of Domestic Life, National Museum of History and Technology, circa 1955-1977 and undated

Records (1 linear meter).

The earliest domestic life artifacts received by the Institution consisted of relics of George Washington and items of ethnologic importance. Some objects were assigned to the Department of Ethnology, United States National Museum (USNM). Others were curated by the Section of Historical Relics and its various successors through to the Division of History, under the direction of A. Howard Clark until 1918 and Theodore T. Belote, 1919-1948.

From 1943 to 1957, the Civil Section of the Division of History and its successors cared for the furnishings collections, as part of the political history and costumes collections. Charles Dorman assisted Margaret Brown Klapthor and Anne Wood Murray with this responsibility. In 1957 the domestic life collections were assigned to the new Division of Cultural History, along with staff and collections from the former Division of Ethnology. C. Malcolm Watkins became Curator of Cultural History and Rodris C. Roth became Assistant and, subsequently, Associate Curator. In 1969, Cultural History was given departmental status. The Department featured a new Division of Costume and Furnishings, which now curated the furnishings collections from the former Division of Cultural History. It also included a new Division of Preindustrial Cultural History, with collections from the defunct Growth of the United States (GOUS) unit. Watkins served as Curator for the latter Division and Anne C. Golovin, from GOUS, was Associate Curator.

In 1977, the Division of Domestic Life was established, where domestic life artifacts from the Divisions of Costume and Furnishings and Preindustrial Cultural History were combined. Roth was made Curator of the new Division, and Golovin became Associate Curator.

Research of the Division of Domestic Life mainly focuses on American household artifacts such as furniture, lighting devices, and modern appliances; or metalware and small wooden objects commonly used in the home, which date from the early seventeenth century. The Division staff and their predecessors have acquired a variety of items formerly owned by leading American statesmen, as well as handmade objects from average households illustrating the development of the American home.

Curators and staff of domestic life collections have included C. Malcolm Watkins, Curator of Cultural History, 1957-1968, Chairman of the Department of Cultural History and Curator of Preindustrial Cultural History, 1969-1972, Senior Curator, 1973- ; Rodris C. Roth, Assistant Curator of Ethnology, 1957, Assistant Curator, 1958-1959, Associate Curator, 1960-1968, of Cultural History, Associate Curator, 1969-1972, Curator, 1972-1977, of Costume and Furnishings, Curator of Domestic Life, 1977- ; John N. Pearce, Assistant Curator of Cultural History, 1960-1963, Associate Curator, 1964; G. Carroll Lindsay, Assistant Curator of Ethnology, 1956-1957, Associate Curator of Cultural History, 1958; Anne C. Golovin, Assistant Curator of Growth of the United States, 1963-1968, Associate Curator of Preindustrial Cultural History, 1969-1977, Associate Curator of Domestic Life, 1977- ; Richard E. Ahlborn, Associate Curator of Cultural History, 1966-1968; Susan H. Myers, museum technician, 1971-1974, museum specialist, 1975-1977, of Preindustrial Cultural History; Richard H. Howland, Head Curator, 1961-1964, Chairman, 1964-1967, of the Department of Civil History; Peter C. Welsh, Associate Curator, 1961-1962, Curator, 1963-1968, of Growth of the United States; and Wilcomb E. Washburn, Acting Curator of Political History, 1958, Curator, 1959-1965.

These records document activities of the Division of Cultural History, the Division of Preindustrial Cultural History and, to some extent, the Growth of the United States, the Division of Domestic Life, and the Department of Cultural History. Records include the correspondence and memoranda of C. Malcolm Watkins, Rodris C. Roth, Anne C. Golovin, Richard E. Ahlborn, Susan H. Myers, and Richard H. Howland; administrative files; minutes of meetings; information pertaining to educational programs and special events; inventories and other documentation concerning furnishings of historical houses in Washington, D.C.; annual reports for the Growth of the United States, Division of Cultural History, and the Division of Preindustrial Cultural History; committee files; identification reports of artifacts submitted for historical verification; and reports for public relations projects of the Division of Preindustrial Cultural History and the Museum. Also included are reading files and responses to public inquiries, most of which pertain to objects in the national collections or to the examination of items for historical authentication.

Additional details on the history of domestic life collections are located in record units 251 and 331, and in the introduction to the Department of Social and Cultural History.

ARRANGEMENT: (1) Administrative files, 1955-1977 and undated; (2) public inquiries, 1970-1977; (3) reading files, 1968-1977. FINDING AIDS: Folder list in control file. SPECIAL CONDITIONS: Use of this record unit requires prior arrangement with the Archives staff.

(381)
Division of Historic Archeology, National Museum of History and Technology, circa 1952-1976
Records (4.1 linear meters).

Specialization within the field of underwater historic archeology was established by Mendel L. Peterson, who served as Associate Curator and Curator of the Divisions of Military and Naval History, 1948-1957, Head Curator of the Department of History, 1951-1957; Head Curator and Chairman of the Department of Armed Forces History, 1957-1969; and Curator of the Division of Historic Archeology, 1969-1973.

Peterson began taking an interest in underwater historic archeology in 1952 and conducted extensive research and led expeditions to underwater shipwreck sites in the Florida Straits, the Bahamas, and the West Indies. Grants from the Explorers Research Corporation and the National Geographic Society in the 1960s supported his explorations of the coral reefs off Bermuda. In 1965, Peterson published *History under the Sea: A Handbook for Underwater Exploration,* which remains a standard reference source on surveying underwater archeological sites and for laboratory techniques for preserving artifacts from underwater excavations.

When the Division of Historic Archeology was formally established in 1969, emphasis on underwater historic archeology became more focused. Peterson supervised the Division's Underwater Exploration Project which involved further exploration of the

Caribbean and thorough investigations of previously discovered underwater sites. The Division was abolished in 1973 when Peterson retired.

This record unit includes correspondence and memoranda between Peterson and curators of the Department of Armed Forces History, the *Bertrand* Committee, the Caribbean Research Institute, the Explorers Research Corporation, and various professional organizations and individuals participating in the Underwater Exploration Project.

Records also include *Bertrand* Committee reports and blueprints for the raising of the steamboat *Bertrand* in 1969; photographs and illustrations of underwater shipwreck sites, artifacts, and preservation methods; photographs of engineer and inventor Waldemar A. Ayres, experimenting with oxygenating plastic membrane panels in the waters off Long Island Sound; original manuscripts and bibliographical information for the publication *History under the Sea;* subject files concerning preservation of artifacts and use of electrolytic reduction on metallic objects; information on cannon markings and their identification; budgetary records; and proposals for the Hall of Underwater Exploration, National Museum of History and Technology.

ARRANGEMENT: (1) Division of Historic Archeology, 1952-1973, accession number 87-096; (2) Division of Historic Archeology, 1956-1976, accession number 82-067; (3) Division of Historic Archeology, 1969-1970, 1975-1976, accession number 82-069. FINDING AIDS: Folder list in control file. SPECIAL CONDITIONS: Use of this record unit requires prior arrangement with the Archives staff.

(485)
Division of Musical History, National Museum of American History, circa 1954-1994
Records (25 linear meters).

A collection of musical instruments was established in 1881, consisting of American Indian instruments acquired during the Wilkes Expedition, gifts from diplomats, and instruments of foreign manufacture acquired at the 1876 Philadelphia Centennial Exposition. In 1882, the collection was enlarged with the addition of nineteenth-century wind instruments, music boxes, and banjos donated by New York music dealer J. Howard Foote.

Edwin H. Hawley became Custodian of the Collection in 1885, remaining until his death in 1918. Renamed the Section of Musical Instruments in 1886, it reported to the Department of Arts and Industries through 1896, the Department of Anthropology, 1897-1902, and subsequently formed a part of the Division of Ethnology of that Department until 1957. George Brown Goode supplemented the collection by a tour to Europe in 1892, and the collection grew further through the donation of keyboard instruments by Hugo Worch, a Washington, D.C., piano dealer, between 1914 and 1921. Worch was Honorary Custodian of Musical Instruments, 1920-1938, and George D. McCoy was Curator of the Section, 1927-*circa* 1929; otherwise it came under the responsibility of ethnology curators Walter Hough, 1918-1935, and Herbert W. Krieger, 1935-1957. After Worch, there was no musically trained full-time staff member to care for these collections.

With the creation of the Museum of History and Technology in 1957, the Section of Musical Instruments became part of the Division of Cultural History, Department of Civil History. In 1966, the Section was given divisional status in the Department. For its subsequent departmental affiliation, see the introduction to the Department of Social and Cultural History. In 1987, the Division was renamed the Division of Musical History.

The Division of Musical History primarily interprets the development and importance of music in American culture since the eighteenth century through the study of American and foreign musical instruments, musical scores, illustrations of musical objects, and historical literature. The Division has restored musical instruments to playable condition, sponsored concerts, prepared exhibits for the Hall of Musical Instruments at the National Museum of American History, recorded musical performances and sounds using Smithsonian instruments, arranged seminars in eighteenth-century performance conventions, and published histories of classical as well as contemporary music.

Curators and staff of the Division included John D. Shortridge, Associate Curator of Musical Instruments, 1958-1960; John T. Fesperman, Jr., Concert Director, 1966, Associate Curator, 1967-1971, Curator, 1972-1987, Curator of Musical History, 1987-   ; Cynthia A. Hoover, Assistant Curator of Musical Instruments, 1961-1963, Associate Curator, 1964-1974, Curator, 1975-   ; James M. Weaver, Concert Director, 1967-1972, Assistant Curator of Musical Instruments, 1973-1975, Associate Curator, 1976-1986, Curator, 1987-   ; Sheridan Germann, Research Associate, 1980; and museum specialists Helen R. Hollis, Robert E. Sheldon, J. Scott Odell, Elizabeth McCullough, and Gary Sturm.

This record unit consists of curatorial and staff correspondence and memoranda pertaining to the Tower Concert series, exhibitions at the Hall of Musical Instruments, staff research and publications, organ building, acquisition of musical instruments, and funding for seminars and musical performance recordings. Also included are inquiries from private collectors, musicians, universities, and instrument manufacturers; minutes of meetings; floor plans for the Hall of Musical Instruments; recital announcements; audiotapes of Fesperman's organ performances; contracts with publishing companies; Fesperman's research material for the publications *Flentrop in America* and *Organs in Mexico;* exhibition proposals, scripts, loan agreements, and brochures from *Contemporary Musical Instrument Makers;* funding information, progress reports, photographs, and program booklets from Music at the Smithsonian, as well as the Tower Concert series; audiotapes and cassette recordings of concert performances, interviews with musicians, and music used for exhibitions; administrative records; photographs and slides of American and European chamber organs; correspondence between Fesperman and organ builder F. A. Flentrop; and staff research notes.

ARRANGEMENT: (1) Division of Musical Instruments, 1963-1979, accession number T90041; (2) Division of Musical Instruments, 1962-1975, accession number 82-115; (3) Division of Musical Instruments, 1964-1981, accession number 84-173; (4) Division of Musical Instruments, 1958-1980, accession number 85-155; (5) Division of Musical Instruments, 1975-1983, accession number 87-104; (6) Division of Musical Instruments, 1962-1982, accession number 88-050; (7) Division of Musical History, 1959-1988, accession number 92-066; (8) Division of Musical History, 1954-1994, accession number 94-109; (9) Division of Musical Instruments, 1960-1974, accession number 95-068. FINDING AIDS: Folder list in control file. SPECIAL CONDITIONS: Use of this record unit requires prior arrangement with the Archives staff.

Division of Political History, National Museum of History and Technology, circa 1950-1969
Records (0.8 linear meter).

The collections of the Division of Political History date back to 1883, when they were part of the Section of Historical Relics, United States National Museum. The political artifacts consisted largely of George Washington memorabilia. By 1886, the collections had expanded to include relics of former presidents Thomas Jefferson, Abraham Lincoln, and Ulysses S. Grant. Care of the collections was assigned to the Section and its various successors through to the Division of History, under the direction of A. Howard Clark until 1918 and Theodore T. Belote, 1919-1948.

In 1943, the Division of History formed a Civil Section that included political memorabilia, costumes, and furnishings. The Section became the Division of Civil History in 1948, and was given departmental status upon the creation of the Museum of History and Technology (MHT) in 1957. At that time the Division of Political History was formed. The Division retained responsibility for political collections as well as costumes, which were curated by its Section of American Costume. Responsibility for furnishings was transferred to the new Division of Cultural History. Margaret Brown Klapthor, who began her museum career as an aide in the Civil History Section in 1944, was concerned with political memorabilia, costumes, especially the First Ladies' gowns, and furnishings. She was assisted by Anne Wood Murray; both women planned the First Ladies Hall and the Hall of American Costume, which opened in 1964. Charles Dorman assisted Klapthor in maintaining the furnishings collections. Curator Wilcomb E. Washburn primarily served as Director of Growth of the United States, an exhibition unit within the Department, which was disbanded in 1968.

The Division of Political History is primarily responsible for research documenting American political history and items of political significance since the late eighteenth century. Research interests of the Division and its predecessors include political campaigns and memorabilia, inaugural gowns and other garments worn by the First Ladies, artifacts from the White House, furnishings and personal accessories of former Presidents, histories of distinguished American politicians and their families, gifts from foreign dignitaries, history of the women's suffrage movement, development of modern political mass communications media, and themes in American government.

Curators and staff of the Division included Wilcomb E. Washburn, Acting Curator, 1958, Curator, 1959-1965; Margaret B. Klapthor, Assistant Curator, 1949-1951, Associate Curator of Civil History, 1952-1957, Associate Curator of Political History, 1957- ; Herbert R. Collins, Assistant Curator, 1961- ; Charles G. Dorman, Assistant Curator, 1957-1960; Anne W. Murray, Assistant Curator, 1957-1963, Associate Curator, 1964-1967, and Curator Emerita, 1968- ; Keith E. Melder, Assistant Curator, 1962-1963, Associate Curator, 1964- ; and Claudia B. Kidwell, Assistant Curator, 1965- .

These records consist of general curatorial correspondence, mostly public inquiries, concerning the First Ladies Hall and objects associated with presidents and other prominent figures; administrative files pertaining to exhibits and the operation of the Department of Civil History and MHT; annual reports of the Divisions of Civil History and Political History; curators' research reports; and examinations and reports on objects submitted to the Division for historical authentication.

Additional details on the history of the Division are located in the introduction to the Department of Social and Cultural History. For additional information on the costume and furnishings collections, see record units 519, 261, and 258.

ARRANGEMENT: (1) Administrative files, 1964-1969; (2) general correspondence, 1964-1968; (3) annual reports, 1950-1968; (4) research reports, 1957-1968; (5) examinations and reports, 1956-1968. FINDING AIDS: Description in control file. SPECIAL CONDITIONS: Use of this record unit requires prior arrangement with the Archives staff.

(473)
Division of Political History, National Museum of American History, circa 1960-1982
Records (7.3 linear meters).

For an administrative history of the Division of Political History prior to 1969, see record unit 252. In 1969 the Division was placed in the Department of National and Military History and its successors. Additional information is to be found in the introduction to the Department of Social and Cultural History.

Curators and staff of the Division included Wilcomb E. Washburn, Curator, 1959-1965; Margaret B. Klapthor, Associate Curator, 1957-1970, Curator, 1971- ; Herbert R. Collins, Assistant Curator, 1961-1970, Associate Curator, 1971-1977, Curator, 1978-1981; Edith P. Mayo, Assistant Curator, 1976-1979, Associate Curator, 1980- ; and Keith E. Melder, Assistant Curator, 1962-1963, and Associate Curator, 1964- . In addition this record unit includes the records of Anne W. Murray and Claudia B. Kidwell.

Records consist of curatorial correspondence and memoranda pertaining to acquisitions, collections management, restoration of specimens, and exhibition proposals and installation. Also included are public inquiries concerning exhibits, political campaign items, presidential information, American politicians, and inaugural gowns of the First Ladies; records documenting the Division of Political History's preparation of the States section for *1876: A Centennial Exhibition* at the Arts and Industries Building; exhibition photographs, scripts, and concepts for the Hall of American Costume, the First Ladies Hall, and the Hall of Historic Americans; documentation referring to plans for the Bicentennial of the American Revolution exhibit, *We the People;* subject files about the United States Presidents; and research notes of Herbert R. Collins for his publications *Presidents on Wheels, Threads of History,* and *Wills of the United States Presidents.*

ARRANGEMENT: (1) Division of Political History, 1973-1979, accession number 81-055; (2) Division of Political History, 1960-1982, accession number 92-005. FINDING AIDS: Folder list in control file. SPECIAL CONDITIONS: Use of this record unit requires prior arrangement with the Archives staff.

(472)
Division of Textiles, National Museum of American History, circa 1947-1982
Records (0.8 linear meter).

The Smithsonian established a Section of Foods and Textiles as a part of the United States National Museum (USNM) in 1883. Romyn Hitchcock, an experienced microscopist and chemist, was selected as Curator of Textiles and also acted as Assistant

Curator along with Honorary Curator W. O. Atwater in the analysis of food products. Many of the textile specimens assigned to Hitchcock were acquired at the close of the 1876 Philadelphia Centennial Exposition. The Section was renamed the Section of Textiles shortly before its demise in 1890.

In 1912, the Division of Textiles was re-established, reporting to the Assistant Secretary in charge of USNM. Frederick L. Lewton became Curator of the Division. From 1916, Lewton was also responsible for medical collections, and between 1931 and 1938 the collections were administered jointly by a single Division of Textiles and Medicine. In the latter year textiles became a Section within the newly established Division of Crafts and Industries, of which Lewton served as Curator through 1946.

Textiles was reestablished as a division in 1957 and was moved among many different departments until its affiliation with the Department of Social and Cultural History in 1981. For an account of these administrative changes, see the introduction to the Department of the History of Science and Technology, whose antecedent departments oversaw the Division prior to 1980.

The principal function of the Division of Textiles is to document the historical, cultural, and economic development of American textile fabrics, implements, and machinery since the seventeenth century. In addition to American technical progress in the production of textiles, work of the Division focused on the earliest methods of textile making throughout the world. Research interests of the Division and its predecessors included tapestry, weaving, household and costume textiles, woolen goods, silks, sewing threads, hand spinning-wheels, sewing machines, patent models, textile techniques from fiber to fabric, fiber identification, dyes, quilts, and other needlework. The Division staff also has developed exhibitions, presented lectures on the history of textile manufacturing, published catalogs, and collected and conserved objects.

Staff of the Division included Rita J. Adrosko, Associate Curator, 1963-1970, and Curator, 1971- ; Grace Rogers Cooper, Assistant Curator, 1949-1956, Associate Curator, 1957, and Curator, 1958-1976; Gary B. Kulik, Assistant Curator, 1979-1981, and Associate Curator, 1982; William N. Watkins, Curator, 1947-1957; Milton Eisler, Conservator, 1960-1963; Maureen Collins McHugh, Conservator, 1963-1970; Kathrine Dirks, museum technician, 1971-1980, and Conservator, 1981- ; Doris M. Bowman, needlework and lace specialist, 1960- ; Lois Vann, museum specialist, 1961- ; and Barbara Suit Janssen, museum specialist, 1975- .

For the most part, this record unit documents curatorial and staff activities of the Division of Textiles after the creation of the Museum of History and Technology in 1957; however, some records also date from the time the Division was a Section of the Division of Crafts and Industries in the United States National Museum.

Records consist of inquiries from private collectors, textile corporations, universities, and historical societies pertaining to collections of the Division; copies of curatorial responses to public inquiries; budgetary information; accession lists; correspondence referring to identification of textile specimens, their preservation needs, and tours of the Textile Hall; and curatorial reports.

ARRANGEMENT: (1) Division of Textiles, 1947-1971, accession number T91009; (2) Division of Textiles, 1977-1979, accession number 81-007; (3) Division of Textiles, 1967-1979, accession number 81-022; (4) Division of Textiles, 1980-1982, accession number 83-134. FINDING AIDS: Folder list in control file. SPECIAL CONDITIONS: Use of this record unit requires prior arrangement with the Archives staff.

NATIONAL NUMISMATIC COLLECTION AND
NATIONAL POSTAL MUSEUM, 1915-1991

(359)

National Numismatic Collection, National Museum of American History, circa 1921-1985
Records (13.1 linear meters).

The origins of the National Numismatic Collection date back to the early years of the Smithsonian Institution. When James Smithson died, among his personal effects were several coins and medals, including one with his likeness. At least two of the gold sovereigns bequeathed to the United States by Smithson are preserved in the National Numismatic Collection.

In 1862, the National Institute began sending its numismatic collection to the Institution. The Smithsonian also acquired numismatic objects from the 1876 Philadelphia Centennial Exposition. George Brown Goode, Assistant Secretary in charge of United States National Museum (USNM) and an avid collector of coins and medals, promoted the early growth of numismatic holdings at the Smithsonian. In 1881, he organized the numismatic objects as a Section in the Department of Arts and Industries, Division of Anthropology. By 1886 the Section had been eliminated and its objects assigned to the custody of A. Howard Clark, Curator of the Section of Historical Relics. They then fell under its successors: the Section of Historical Collections, Department of Arts and Industries, 1889-1897, the Division of History and Biography, Department of Anthropology, 1897-1904, and the Division of History, 1904-1948. Between 1897 and 1947, numerous collections were received, such as the George Bunker Glover bequest of Far Eastern coins and the United States Mint Collection.

In 1947, the Section of Numismatics was created in the Division of History, and the next year, the Section was given divisional status in the new Department of History. That same year Stuart M. Mosher succeeded the retiring Curator in charge, Theodore T. Belote, as Associate Curator of the Division of Numismatics, a position he held until his death in 1956. Vladimir Clain-Stefanelli became Curator at that time, and, shortly after his appointment, Elvira Eliza Clain-Stefanelli, joined the Division as Assistant Curator.

As a result of museum reorganizations, the Division of Numismatics was affiliated with the Departments of Civil History, 1957-1968, Applied Arts, 1969-1977, and National History, 1978-1979. In 1980, the Division was organized as the National Numismatic Collection in the National Museum of American History (NMAH), reporting to the Director. In 1981, the Clain-Stefanellis were made Historians of the National Numismatic Collection, followed by the 1984 appointment of Coralee C. Gillilland as Curator. Important acquisitions included the Willis H. DuPont Collection of Russian coins and the Josiah K. Lilly, Jr., Collection of gold coins ranging from ancient to modern times.

The National Numismatic Collection researches the history of numismatics worldwide, beginning with the earliest types of money, with the primary goal of presenting "social, economic and political history through money: the organization of monetary systems, the effect of money on events in history, and the value of the figurative language of coins and paper currency as witness to the art and culture of a society." The National Numismatic Collection primarily collects ancient and contemporary coinage, paper currency, medals and decorations, financial documents, minting equipment, and tokens.

Curators and staff included Theodore T. Belote, Curator in charge of numismatic collections, 1919-1948; Stuart M. Mosher, Associate Curator of Numismatics, 1948-1956; Vladimir Clain-Stefanelli, Curator of the Division of Numismatics, 1956-1979, Curator, 1980, and Historian, 1981-1982, of the National Numismatic Collection; Elvira Eliza Clain-Stefanelli, Assistant Curator, 1957-1961, Associate Curator, 1961-1968, Curator, 1969-1979, of Numismatics, and Curator, 1980, and Historian, 1981-1985, of the National Numismatic Collection; and Coralee C. Gillilland, Curator of the National Numismatic Collection, 1984-   .

This record unit consists of curatorial correspondence and memoranda pertaining to publications, exhibitions, acquisitions, numismatic conferences in foreign countries, and materials on loan; annual reports of the Division of Numismatics; budgetary files; American Numismatic Association convention information; exhibition scripts for the Hall of Monetary History and Medallic Art; policies regarding United States Treasury Department coinage laws, purchases, and transfers; blueprints and floor plans for the Hall of Numismatics; staff publications; correspondence with coin dealers, the American Bankers Association, and the Federation Internationale de la Medaille; and reports on counterfeit money.

The records also include photographs of numismatic exhibits at USNM, the exhibition *History of Machines and Banking,* coinage and early minting machines, and various United States mints; the Clain-Stefanellis' research notes, manuscripts, and published articles; historical information on United States mints; copies of congressional numismatic joint resolutions, acts, and bills; domestic coin exchange charts; information on the Willis H. DuPont Collection and the Josiah K. Lilly, Jr., Collection; exhibition brochures; historical information on the National Institute; and staff publications.

ARRANGEMENT: Alphabetic by name and subject. FINDING AIDS: Folder list in control file. SPECIAL CONDITIONS: (1) Restricted; (2) use of this record unit requires prior arrangement with the Archives staff.

(580)

National Postal Museum, National Museum of American History, 1915-1991
Records (4.5 linear meters).

The philatelic collections date back to 1887, when Spencer F. Baird bequeathed his personal stamp collection to the Institution. The stamps were placed in the custody of A. Howard Clark, Curator of the Section of Historical Relics, United States National Museum (USNM). The collections then fell under various successor units: the Section of Historical Collections (1889-1897), the Division of History and Biography, Department of Anthropology (1897-1904), and the Division of History (1904-1948). In 1908, David W. Cromwell, a well-known New York philatelist, began making a series of donations to the Smithsonian Institution, which by 1915 housed some twenty thousand United States and foreign postage stamps. These stamps, as well as Baird's collection and others acquired by the Division over the years, were placed on display at the Arts and Industries Building.

In 1911, the Post Office Department began transferring to the USNM holdings of stamps and related objects from its Postal Museum. This collection eventually amounted to some two hundred thousand items, mostly consisting of domestic and foreign stamps, envelopes, and postal cards as well as albums of models, photographs of Post Office facilities, and die proofs. The Post Office Department agreed to make periodic transfers of United States issues and foreign stamps to the Smithsonian, to insure the continual growth of what became known as the National Postage Stamp Collection. From 1913 to 1921, Joseph B. Leavy served as the first Philatelist of the Collection.

The Collection was organized as the Section of Philately in the Division of History through 1947, and became the Division of Philately in the new Department of History in 1948. In 1957, the Division was renamed Philately and Postal History (changing again to Postal History in 1969). It was affiliated with the Departments of Civil History, 1957-1968, Applied Arts, 1969-1977, and National History, 1978-1979, as a result of museum reorganizations. In 1980, the Division was organized as the National Philatelic Collection in the National Museum of American History, reporting to the Director. A decade later, in 1990, the National Philatelic Collection became the National Postal Museum.

Curators at the National Postal Museum research the history of the American postal system and collect American postage, special stamp editions of famous individuals or subjects, postal stationery, Post Office equipment and uniforms, and foreign stamps primarily for what they show about American history. Curators and staff included Joseph B. Leavy, Philatelist, 1913-1921; Catherine L. Manning, Philatelist, 1921-1943, Assistant Curator of Philately, 1944-1951; Franklin R. Bruns, Jr., Assistant Curator of Philately, 1951, Associate Curator in charge, 1952-1957, Associate Curator, 1971-1977, and Supervisor, 1978-1979; Francis J. McCall, Assistant Curator of Philately, 1957, Acting Curator, 1958, Associate Curator, 1959-1963; George T. Turner, Acting Curator of Philately, 1959-1961, and Associate Curator, 1962; Richard H. Howland, Acting Curator of Philately, 1962-1963; Carl H. Scheele, Assistant Curator of Philately, 1960-1963, Acting Curator, 1964-1968, Associate Curator, 1969, Curator in charge, 1970-1977; Reidar Norby, Assistant Curator of Philately, 1969, Associate Curator, 1970-1983, Curator, 1984-1988; Robert G. Tillotson, Executive Director of the National Philatelic Collection, 1980-1982; Herbert R. Collins, Executive Director of the National Philatelic Collection, 1982-1990, Director of the National Postal Museum, 1990; and James R. Bruns, Curator, 1984-1989, and Deputy Executive Director, 1990, of the National Philatelic Collection, and Acting Director of the National Postal Museum, 1991- .

These records consist of staff correspondence and memoranda of the National Postal Museum and its predecessors; early photographs of exhibitions; planning information for the Hall of Philately; newspaper clippings, articles, and research files documenting the origin and extensive history of the National Postal Museum; proposals, preliminary contracts, minutes of meetings, and blueprints for a National Postal Museum; and administrative files.

ARRANGEMENT: (1) Division of Postal History, 1915-1979, accession number 86-120; (2) National Postal Museum, 1922-1991, accession number 92-009. FINDING AIDS: Folder list in control file. SPECIAL CONDITIONS: Use of this record unit requires prior arrangement with the Archives staff.

EXHIBITIONS AND PUBLIC PROGRAMS, 1957-1992

(599)

Division of Education and Visitor Information, National Museum of American History, circa 1974-1981
Records (0.4 linear meter).

In 1974, a Division of Public Information and Education was created from the Office of Elementary and Secondary Education, National Museum of History and Technology (NMHT). The following year Alice Reno Malone was appointed Coordinator of Education for the Division and reported to the Deputy Director of NMHT. She was later joined by education specialists Robert S. Harding and Elizabeth M. Sharpe. In 1976 the Division of Public Information and Education was renamed the Division of Education and Visitor Information, with Malone submitting Division reports to the Director of NMHT. The Division was placed under the Office of Public and Academic Programs in 1980. It was abolished when NMHT was renamed the National Museum of American History (NMAH).

The Division of Education and Visitor Information was responsible for providing Museum visitors with a variety of programs that interpreted the exhibitions and collections of NMAH. The Division was involved in interpretative lesson tours, outreach activities, films and orientation sessions, demonstrations, lectures, teachers workshops, publications, and discovery corner presentations.

These records include staff memoranda; correspondence with educators and outside consultants on public programs; annual and monthly reports of the Division; NMAH exhibition proposals; budgetary files; information on docent training programs, NMAH tours, and internships; and educational newsletters.

ARRANGEMENT: Unarranged. FINDING AIDS: Folder list in control file. SPECIAL CONDITIONS: Use of this record unit requires prior arrangement with the Archives staff.

(551)

Department of Exhibits, National Museum of American History, 1957-1992
Records (18 linear meters).

The Department of Exhibits was created in 1973 to design and produce exhibitions within the National Museum of American History (NMAH), then known as the National Museum of History and Technology. Prior to 1973 the Office of Exhibits Programs was responsible for the design and production of NMAH exhibitions.

The Department of Exhibits is responsible for the design, production, installation, and disassembly of the permanent and temporary exhibitions at the National Museum of American History. The records include the project files and the administrative files of the Department dating from its establishment in 1973. Also included are project files and administrative files of the Office of Exhibits Programs, 1969-1973, and the Office of Exhibits, 1959-1968. Staff represented in the records include John E. Anglim, Chief, Office of Exhibits, 1957-1968, Chief, Office of Exhibits Programs, 1969-1970, and

Director, Office of Exhibits Programs, 1971-1972; Benjamin W. Lawless, Assistant Director of the Museum for Design and Production, 1974-1976, and Assistant Director for Exhibits, 1977-1981; J. Michael Carrigan, Assistant Director for Exhibitions and Public Spaces, 1982- ; and Richard J. Nicastro, Deputy Assistant Director for Exhibitions and Public Spaces, 1985- .

Records consist of exhibition design, production, and installation information including proposals and narratives, scripts, schedules, graphic designs, construction contracts and specifications, floor plans, blueprints, schematic drawings, and photographs. The records also include Department of Exhibits administrative files such as correspondence, memoranda, monthly progress reports, budget information, space planning, and meeting minutes of the Museum Advisory Committee, 1983.

ARRANGEMENT: (1) Schematic drawings and photographs for the exhibition, *The Telephone,* 1957, accession number 83-138; (2) Division of Exhibits Production, 1959-1981, accession number 82-013; (3) Department of Exhibits, 1961-1990, accession number 91-016; (4) Department of Exhibits, 1968-1987, accession number 89-105; (5) Department of Exhibits, 1971, 1976-1982, accession number 84-014; (6) Department of Exhibits, 1971-1984, accession number 87-176; (7) Department of Exhibits, 1979-1986, accession number 88-096; (8) Department of Exhibits, 1979-1992, accession number 92-087; (9) Department of Exhibits, 1985-1990, accession number 91-137; (10) Department of Exhibits, 1987-1988, accession number 89-042; (11) Department of Exhibits, 1987-1989, accession number 91-004; (12) Department of Exhibits, 1985-1992, accession number 93-059. FINDING AIDS: Folder list in control file. SPECIAL CONDITIONS: Use of this record unit requires prior arrangement with the Archives staff.

(360)
Office of Public Affairs, National Museum of American History, circa 1970-1985
Records (15.2 linear meters).

In the early 1970s, the Office of Public Affairs reported to the Director of the National Museum of History and Technology (NMHT). Also included as part of the Office was the special events staff. In 1972, Rebecca B. Clapp was appointed Special Events Assistant for the Office of Public Affairs and Special Events, and became Special Events Officer in 1975. Geraldine B. Sanderson succeeded Clapp the following year and was made Public Information Officer in 1978. In 1980, Sanderson began reporting to the Director of the Office of Public and Academic Programs.

When NMHT was renamed the National Museum of American History (NMAH) in 1980, the Office of Public Affairs again reported to the Director of the Museum. In 1982, Mary W. Dyer succeeded Sanderson as the Public Information Officer. From 1984 to 1985, the Office of Public Affairs was under the Department of Public Programs.

The Office of Public Affairs is responsible for preparing, coordinating, and distributing information to the public and the media concerning activities at NMAH. Staff has included Rebecca B. Clapp, Special Events Assistant, 1972-1974, and Special Events Officer, 1975; Geraldine B. Sanderson, Special Events Officer, 1976-1977, and Public Information Officer, 1978-1981; and Mary W. Dyer, Public Information Officer, 1982-1985.

These records consist of staff memoranda and correspondence, brochures, events calendars, and public notices for NMAH programs and exhibitions; articles; newspaper clippings, and news-related information documenting Museum events; exhibition brochures, catalogs, and scripts; film reels of public service announcements; audiotape recordings of musical performances and lectures; photographs, contact sheets, and slides of exhibition objects, media events, and the public visiting NMAH; guest lists, proposals, and schedules about the Doubleday Lecture Series; videotape of Museum exhibitions; and Folklife Festival information.

ARRANGEMENT: (1) Office of Public Affairs, 1970-1979, accession number 82-066; (2) Office of Public Affairs, 1976-1985, accession number 87-013; (3) Office of Public Affairs, 1981-1985, accession number 88-040; (4) Office of Public Affairs, 1982-1985, accession number 88-047. FINDING AIDS: Folder list in control file. SPECIAL CONDITIONS: Use of this record unit requires prior arrangement with the Archives staff.

(584)

Department of Public Programs, National Museum of American History, circa 1980-1992, with related records from 1968

Records (22.1 linear meters).

In 1980 an Office of Public and Academic Programs was established at the National Museum of History and Technology, subsequently the National Museum of American History (NMAH). Josiah O. Hatch, a Special Assistant to the Director of the Museum, was assigned as Director of the Office. Hatch submitted reports for Public and Academic Programs to Douglas E. Evelyn, Deputy Director of NMAH.

When the Smithsonian Institution's Division of Performing Arts became defunct in 1983, part of its staff was reassigned to the Office of Public and Academic Programs. In 1984, the Office was reorganized as the Department of Public Programs. It included sections of production, education, the Program in Black American History, performances, publications, and the Office of Public Affairs. Hatch became its head as the Assistant Director for Public Programs. The next year, Lonn W. Taylor succeeded Hatch.

The Department of Public Programs is responsible for a variety of tasks associated with providing the public with opportunities for learning. It works with the Museum's other departments to produce educational materials such as scholarly publications, kits and guides, and information on various topics of interest that interpret NMAH exhibitions. The Department also sponsors or coordinates programs and performances using Museum collections; presents special programs on important aspects of American life and culture that cannot be exhibited through artifacts alone; and organizes colloquia, symposia, and lectures. Staff has included Josiah O. Hatch, Director of the Department of Public Programs, 1980-1983, and Assistant Director for Public Programs, 1984; Lonn W. Taylor, Deputy Assistant Director for Public Programs, 1984, and Assistant Director, 1985- ; Harold A. Closter, Production Director, 1983-1986, Program Manager, 1987-1990, and Deputy Assistant Director, 1991- ; Bernice Johnson Reagon, Director of the Program in Black American History, 1983-1987; James M. Weaver, Director of Performance Programs, 1983-1986; Shirley E. Cherkasky, Coordinator of Museum Programs, 1983- ; Elizabeth M. Sharpe, Education Specialist, 1985-1986, and Deputy Assistant Director for Public Programs, 1987- ; and Manuel J. Melendez, Performing Arts Production Specialist, 1984-1991.

These records mostly consist of staff correspondence and memoranda documenting administrative and program-oriented activities of the Department of Public Programs. The records pertain to fundraising, social history lectures and seminars, the Senior Series

Program, budget, educational outreach proposals, grant information, planning for the Program of Hispanic American History, and the Country Music Program. In addition, there are budget reports; videotapes, audiotapes, abstracts, and planning documents from the Conference on Music in America at the Smithsonian Institution; minutes of meetings; information on educational projects for NMAH exhibitions; research material consisting of exhibition scripts, blueprints, and photographs; outline of Highlight Tours at NMAH; and brochures, articles, and newspaper clippings on NMAH special events.

The record unit also includes records which date back to the Division of Performing Arts. Performing Arts records primarily consist of working files; videotapes and audiotapes of performances from the Country Music Program, Jazz at the Smithsonian, and the Festival of American Folklife; and budgetary information.

ARRANGEMENT: (1) Office of Public and Academic Programs, 1971-1980, accession number 83-008; (2) Department of Public Programs, 1978-1983, accession number 84-087; (3) Department of Public Programs, 1980-1987, accession number 89-112; (4) Department of Public Programs, 1972-1985, accession number 89-129; (5) Department of Public Programs, 1968-1986, accession number 90-148; (6) Department of Public Programs, 1985-1988, accession number 91-138; (7) Department of Public Programs, 1975-1990, accession number 92-090; (8) Department of Public Programs, 1973-1991, accession number 93-010; (9) Department of Public Programs, 1986-1990, accession number 94-032; (10) Department of Public Programs, 1983-1991, accession number 95-008; (11) Department of Public Programs, 1983-1992, accession number 95-075. FINDING aids: Folder list in control file. SPECIAL CONDITIONS: Use of this record unit requires prior arrangement with the Archives staff.

(595)

Office of Special Events, National Museum of American History, circa 1980-1987
Records (6.5 linear meters).

In 1980, the special events staff was part of the Office of Public Affairs, which reported to the Director of the Office of Public and Academic Programs in the National Museum of History and Technology (NMHT). Geraldine B. Sanderson, Public Information Officer for the Office of Public Affairs, was also responsible for special events. When NMHT was renamed the National Museum of American History (NMAH) in 1980, the special events staff was separated from Public Affairs to become the Office of Special Events. Susan B. Beaudette was appointed Museum Program Coordinator for the Office, reporting to the Director of NMAH. In 1983, Anne Walton became Special Events Assistant to Beaudette. The Office of Special Events was placed under the Office of External Affairs in 1986.

The Office of Special Events is primarily responsible for planning exhibition openings, symposia, award presentations, musical and dance performances, official ceremonies, and staff holiday celebrations at NMAH. The Office is also involved in the Folklife Festival and the Doubleday Lecture Series. Staff has included Geraldine B. Sanderson, Public Information Officer, 1978-1980; Susan B. Beaudette, Museum Program Coordinator, 1981-1985; and Anne Walton, Special Events Assistant, 1983-   .

These records consist of staff correspondence and memoranda, Doubleday Lecture Series planning files, contracts, and invitation lists; floor plan drawings for events; information on opening exhibition tours and receptions; newspaper clippings, press releases, and articles pertaining to events; symposium information; photographs and contact sheets of lecturers, exhibition openings, and special guests; and financial reports.

ARRANGEMENT: (1) Office of Special Events, 1980-1983, accession number 87-018; (2) Office of Special Events, 1981-1987, accession number 93-131. FINDING AIDS: Folder list in control file. SPECIAL CONDITIONS: Use of this record unit requires prior arrangement with the Archives staff.

SPECIAL PROJECTS, 1963-1984

(377)

Dwight D. Eisenhower Institute for Historical Research, National Museum of American History, circa 1964-1984
Records (3.3 linear meters).

The Dwight D. Eisenhower Institute for Historical Research was originally conceived as a center for the study of war-related issues and the contributions of the military establishment. It was to be an integral part of a proposed National Armed Forces Museum which would be a Smithsonian bureau. Although the proposed Museum and the Institute eventually became two distinct entities, their histories are linked by this common origin and by the later transfer of staff and records.

An act of Congress in 1961 established the National Armed Forces Museum Advisory Board (NAFMAB) to begin planning for the museum, the study center, and the acquisition of a suitable site. An administrative history of the National Armed Forces Museum Advisory Board can be found in record unit 581.

By 1973 prospects for building a National Armed Forces Museum had dimmed considerably, and the Smithsonian moved to establish the Eisenhower Institute in the National Museum of History and Technology (NMHT). Forrest C. Pogue was named Director of the Institute, under the broad supervision of the NMHT Director in cooperation with NAFMAB.

The activities of the Institute included research, publications, lectures, and conferences concerning the contributions of the armed forces to American society and culture. Pogue was allowed to continue his research on General George C. Marshall.

In its first full year of operation, 1975, the Eisenhower Institute reported to the Department of National and Military History, but in 1976 the Institute assumed separate status under the Director. In 1979 James S. Hutchins, past Director of NAFMAB, joined Pogue as Historian. In 1980 the name of the Museum changed to the National Museum of American History (NMAH).

By 1984, Hutchins had moved to the Division of Armed Forces History, where he remained as Historian, 1984-   . Pogue retired at the end of 1984. The remainder of the staff members were reassigned; the Eisenhower Institute, never a priority of Smithsonian management, became inactive.

These records consist of a few files relating to NAFMAB, including some documents concerning its history, its project to raise the Union monitor *Tecumseh,* and the later meetings of the Board. Most of the record unit consists of files of Pogue's activities, speeches, professional memberships, and relationships of the Institute with Smithsonian and outside historians.

ARRANGEMENT: (1) Eisenhower Institute for Historical Research, 1964-1980, accession number 88-014; (2) Eisenhower Institute for Historical Research, 1967-1984, accession number 85-218. FINDING AIDS: Partial folder list and file plan in control file. SPECIAL CONDITIONS: (1) Restricted; (2) use of this record unit requires prior arrangement with the Archives staff.

(581)

National Armed Forces Museum Advisory Board, circa 1960-1975
Records (6.2 linear meters).

The National Armed Forces Museum Advisory Board (NAFMAB) was created by Act of Congress in 1961 to plan for the establishment of a national museum to honor America's armed forces. The museum, which was to be a Smithsonian bureau, would include a study center named in honor of President Dwight D. Eisenhower. John Nicholas Brown served as Chairman of the Board, 1963-1975.

Colonel John H. Magruder III served as the Director of NAFMAB from 1963 until his death in 1972. He struggled unsuccessfully to bring the museum into existence, gathering military weapons and artifacts and lobbying tirelessly to acquire various sites for the project. When the museum plan seemed doomed, he recast it as a Bicentennial Outdoor Museum Park. He also acquired the rights to the Civil War monitor *Tecumseh,* which had sunk in Mobile Bay during a battle in 1864. Divers were sent to the Bay and a number of artifacts retrieved from the vessel, but the plan to recover the entire wreck failed.

None of Magruder's efforts succeeded, in part because of the American involvement in the Vietnam War and some unfortunate publicity which likened the museum to a Disneyland of war. With Magruder's death, the project was weakened further. In 1973 the Smithsonian decided to salvage at least a part of the 1961 law by bringing the study center into existence. The Eisenhower Institute for Historical Research was established in the National Museum of History and Technology (NMHT). For an administrative history of the Eisenhower Institute, see record unit 377.

James S. Hutchins was named Acting Director and then Director of NAFMAB, 1973-1975; but in effect he presided over its demise. Although the legislation was never formally repealed, Smithsonian management in the 1970s did not favor the museum. The Advisory Board was ordered to divest itself of the material that had been gathered; and in 1975 the Board recommended that all further efforts to build the museum cease. Hutchins was eventually transferred to the staff of the Eisenhower Institute.

These records document the managerial activities of NAFMAB, including collecting and accessioning, planning for a site, exhibits design, and carrying out various projects. Also included is a multi-volume chronology of events, 1946-1973, in addition to copies of files of NMHT curator Mendel L. Peterson, who represented the Smithsonian on a preliminary committee established by President Eisenhower. Files on the *Tecumseh* include photographs of the diving operations and items retrieved from the ship.

ARRANGEMENT: (1) National Armed Forces Museum Advisory Board, *circa* 1960-1975, accession number T89062; (2) National Armed Forces Museum Advisory Board, 1965-1973, accession number T90038. FINDING AIDS: Partial folder list in control file. SPECIAL CONDITIONS: (1) Use of this record unit requires prior arrangement with the Archives staff; (2) a few NAFMAB records exist in record unit 377.

The Smithsonian Journal of History, 1963-1972
Records (1.7 linear meters).

The *Smithsonian Journal of History* was a scholarly quarterly specializing in illustrated articles. The *Journal* had its inception in the 1964 meetings of the Association of Curators and won financial support from the Secretary of the Smithsonian in December 1964. The first issue published was Spring 1966. Articles were contributed by professional historians and were not limited to any particular subject, area of interest, nation, or time period. The "Notes and Queries" section of each issue carried notes of important research programs, museum acquisitions, and exhibits both at the Smithsonian and at other historical museums. This section also printed requests for information about important or unusual objects. Due to financial and schedule problems, the *Journal* was forced to terminate publication after the Winter 1968-1969 issue.

Although officially the responsibility of the Director of the National Museum of History and Technology, administrative decisions were handled by an Editorial Board. Faye Cannon (Walter F.) served as Editor for the first five issues. Upon Cannon's resignation in July 1967, Peter C. Welsh became Editor for the last seven issues. The *Journal's* Board of Advisors was a group of noted historians who served as advisors on selection of manuscripts and related activities.

Records document publication of the *Journal* from solicitation of manuscripts to final layout, including correspondence and memoranda between editors and authors, illustrations for published articles, and to a small extent, original copy submitted for publication. Also included are records for staff information, e.g., information regarding various presses.

ARRANGEMENT: (1) Office and museum business, 1963-1972; (2) requisitions, 1965-1970; (3) journal business, 1964-1971; (4) journal content, 1965-1969; (5) production of journal, 1965-1968; (6) correspondence, 1965-1969; (7) press information, 1964-1965; (8) societies and clubs, 1964-1966; (9) published articles file, 1966-1969. FINDING AIDS: Description in control file. SPECIAL CONDITIONS: Use of this record unit requires prior arrangement with the Archives staff.

Steering Committee for the History of Science and Technology, National Museum of History and Technology, circa 1968-1972
Records (0.1 linear meter).

In 1968 a Steering Committee for the History of Science and Technology was organized in the Museum of History and Technology (MHT). MHT was renamed the National Museum of History and Technology (NMHT) in 1969. Nathan Reingold and Bernard S. Finn served as Chairmen. The Committee reviewed and appointed graduate students, postdoctoral associates, and Ph.D. candidates to research programs in science and technology at the Museum. It also sponsored history of science and technology lectures, symposia, and colloquia at the Museum.

These records include correspondence and memoranda of the Chairmen, research appointment contracts, minutes of meetings, budgetary information, and research program announcements.

ARRANGEMENT: Unarranged. FINDING AIDS: Folder list in control file. SPECIAL CONDITIONS: Use of this record unit requires prior arrangement with the Archives staff.

NATIONAL ZOOLOGICAL PARK

Originally conceived by Samuel P. Langley, Secretary of the Smithsonian, as a place in which to house endangered species and to conduct research, the National Zoological Park (NZP) was established by an Act of Congress in 1889. A National Zoological Park Commission, comprised of the Secretary of the Interior, the President of the Board of Commissioners of the District of Columbia, and the Secretary of the Smithsonian Institution, was formed under the Act to select and purchase land for the National Zoo. One hundred and sixty-six acres in the valley of Rock Creek, located in northwest Washington, D.C., were eventually purchased for the Park. Frederick Law Olmsted, landscape architect, was consulted with regard to the design of the landscape and the location of the buildings. Copies of his drawings and sketches by his firm are presently located at the National Zoological Park.

The financial burden of the NZP was to be shared by Congress and the District of Columbia, a fact which altered Langley's vision, enlarging his purpose to one of securing a wide variety of species for the enjoyment of the District's residents. In 1890, Congress passed another Act which placed the National Zoological Park under the Board of Regents of the Smithsonian, to administer the Park and to receive and care for the animals "for the advancement of science and the instruction and recreation of the people."

The first inhabitants of the Zoo were the 185 animals under the care of William Temple Hornaday, Curator of Living Animals, United States National Museum, that had been sheltered by fences behind the Smithsonian Institution Building. These animals had been shipped to Washington to be used as Hornaday's taxidermy models. Previously, those which had not been killed and preserved for the mammal collection had been shipped to the Philadelphia Zoo.

Hornaday became the first Superintendent of the Zoo, but resigned soon afterwards over differences of opinion with Langley. Frank Baker, Assistant Superintendent of the United States Life Saving Service and Professor of Anatomy at Georgetown University, was appointed Acting Manager of the NZP in 1890, and from 1893 to 1916 he held the position of Superintendent. The early history of the NZP was marked by the demands for building construction, park layout and roads, and acquisition of animals—all on an extremely tight budget. Despite these difficulties, the Park and its animal collections began to take shape. In 1891, Dunk and Gold Dust, the Zoo's first elephants, and French, the first lion, arrived.

Upon Baker's retirement in 1916, Ned Hollister, Assistant Curator of Mammals at the United States National Museum, was appointed to succeed him. During Hollister's tenure as Superintendent, the NZP continued to operate on modest appropriations. As a result, few new animals were purchased, and housing for existing animals remained inadequate. However, the popularity of the Park continued to grow, and in 1924, 2.4 million people visited the Zoo. Superintendent Hollister died in 1924 and was succeeded by Alexander Wetmore, a biologist at the Biological Survey, United States Department of Agriculture, who served only five months before leaving to become Assistant Secretary of the Smithsonian Institution.

In 1925, William M. Mann, entomologist at the Department of Agriculture, became the fifth NZP Superintendent. The title of the NZP head administrator was changed in 1926 to that of Director, and Mann held that position until his retirement in 1956. Several major collecting expeditions helped add to the NZP animal stock during the era of the Great Depression and World War II. Included were the Smithsonian-Chrysler Fund Expedition to Tanganyika, 1926; the National Geographic Society-Smithsonian Institution Expedition to the East Indies, 1937; and the Smithsonian-Firestone Expedition to Liberia, 1940. Mann's tenure also witnessed the construction of new animal houses and support buildings, including several which were built by the Public Works Administration, a New Deal relief program.

When Mann retired in 1956, the Zoo veterinarian, Theodore H. Reed, was appointed Acting Director. He was made Director in 1958 and remained in the position until 1983. Under Reed's direction the NZP and its programs evolved rapidly. A 1962 master plan led to a series of phased renovation and construction projects. The Education-Administration Building, 1977; the William M. Mann Memorial Lion-Tiger Exhibit, 1976; and Beaver Valley, 1979, were just a few of the projects completed during Reed's tenure. The NZP benefited considerably by the creation of the Friends of the National Zoo (FONZ) in 1958. Originally concerned with capital improvements and modernization, the focus of FONZ activities changed to education by the mid-1960s. Eventually, FONZ took charge of parking, food, and souvenir concessions at the Zoo with proceeds used to augment educational work and scientific research. Several important animal acquisitions were made during the period, notably the white tigress, Mohini, in 1960, the gift of a pair of Komodo dragons from the government of Indonesia in 1964, and the arrival of a pair of giant pandas from the People's Republic of China in 1972. Programs in scientific research and conservation were developed under Reed. A Scientific Research Department was created in the mid-1960s to conduct studies on animal behavior, reproduction, and breeding. In 1975, the General Services Administration transferred over 3,000 acres of land in Front Royal, Virginia, to the Smithsonian Institution to establish the NZP's Conservation and Research Center (CRC). The goal of CRC is to conduct research on and to develop breeding programs for endangered and exotic species. Michael H. Robinson succeeded Reed as NZP Director in 1984.

Researchers interested in the history of the NZP should also see record unit 7293, William M. Mann and Lucile Quarry Mann Papers, *circa* 1885-1981; record unit 7411, John F. Eisenberg Papers, *circa* 1962-1982 and undated; record unit 9513, Lucile Quarry Mann Interviews, 1977; record unit 9568, Theodore H. Reed Interviews, 1989-1993; and record unit 9553, Conservation of Endangered Species Interviews, 1990.

DIRECTOR AND ASSISTANT DIRECTOR, 1887-1986

(74)

National Zoological Park, 1887-1966

Records (38.7 linear meters).

For an administrative history of the National Zoological Park (NZP), see the introduction to NZP.

These records document the development of the NZP from the site survey work begun by William Temple Hornaday in 1888 through the beginnings of its modernization plans in 1965. The tenures of directors Hornaday, Baker, Hollister, Wetmore, Mann, and Reed are represented in this record unit. Included are records of the National Zoological Park Commission; maps, blueprints, photographs, and correspondence regarding acquisition of land for the NZP and construction of NZP buildings; administrative records such as payrolls, personnel, budget, and departmental and park police reports; diaries of the Directors and other staff; and scrapbooks following the development and growth of the NZP. The records also contain correspondence concerning specimen exhibitions and facilities provided by the NZP to several expositions, including the Pan-American Exposition, 1901, the Louisiana Purchase Exposition, 1904, and the Panama-Pacific International Exposition, 1915.

The acquisition, care, and feeding of NZP animals is also extensively documented in correspondence contained in these records. Of particular interest are the records of expeditions abroad for the purpose of collecting animals for the NZP, including the Smithsonian-Theodore Roosevelt Expedition, 1909, the Smithsonian-Chrysler Fund Expedition to East Africa, 1926, and the Smithsonian-Firestone Expedition, 1940. In addition, records documenting Samuel P. Langley's research on the flight of birds, Frank Baker's survey of private and public zoological parks and his buffalo census are included.

ARRANGEMENT: (1) Diaries of the Director, 1895-1930; (2) diaries, ledgers, memoranda, and memo books, 1890-1931 and undated; (3) bound accessions and removal books, 1918-1924; (4) National Zoological Park Commission papers, 1889-1891; (5) congressional documents containing Secretary Samuel P. Langley's reports on National Zoological Park expenditures, 1888-1905; (6) Director's official outgoing correspondence, 1889-1927; (7) letters to the Smithsonian Institution, Director's official outgoing correspondence to the Smithsonian Institution administrators, 1900-1931; (8) letters from the Smithsonian Institution, copies of official outgoing correspondence from Smithsonian Institution administrators regarding the National Zoological Park, 1900-1907; (9) animal voucher book, 1905-1918; (10) voucher abstracts, 1905-1927; (11) requisitions for printing and binding, requisitions to the Government Printing Office, 1915-1931; (12) incoming correspondence and letter registers to the correspondence, arranged by subject and alphabetically by correspondent thereunder, 1887-1900; (13) general correspondence, incoming and outgoing, arranged by major topic and alphabetically by subject thereunder, 1899-1930; (14) general correspondence, incoming and outgoing, arranged by major topic and alphabetically by subject thereunder, 1930-1965; (15) daily report of Animal Department, 1904-1915, 1942-1966; (16) time roll, Department of Living Animals, United States National Museum, and National Zoological Park, 1890-1892; (17) National Zoological Park payroll and time roll, 1891-1921, 1927-1932; (18) requisitions and orders for planting, repairs, alterations, and shop requests, 1904-1942, 1960-1966; (19) scrapbooks, 1887-1931; (20) miscellaneous, *circa* 1890-1918 and undated. FINDING AIDS: (1) Outgoing correspondence letterpress books are indexed; (2) letter registers for incoming correspondence, 1887-1900; (3) description in control file. SPECIAL CONDITIONS: Use of this record unit requires prior arrangement with the Archives staff.

(326)

Director, National Zoological Park, circa 1920-1984
Records (13 linear meters).

Theodore H. Reed joined the staff of the National Zoological Park (NZP) in 1955 when he accepted appointment as Veterinarian. When NZP Director William M. Mann retired in 1956, Reed became Acting Director. He was appointed Director in 1958. Reed continued to lead the NZP until 1983. At that time he was made Senior Advisor, a position he held until his retirement in 1984. For an administrative history of the NZP prior to 1955, see the introduction to NZP.

These records provide comprehensive documentation of the development of the NZP during Reed's twenty-seven-year tenure as Director, and include a few records created during his service as Senior Advisor, 1983-1984, and a small amount of material created during the administration of Reed's predecessor, William M. Mann. Included are records documenting the modernization, renovation, and construction of NZP buildings, exhibitions, and facilities; administrative reorganizations and the creation of a managerial hierarchy at the zoo; the development of NZP programs in animal management, zoological research, animal health and pathology, education and information, construction management, graphics and exhibits, and police and safety; the evolution of the idea for an NZP breeding farm and its realization in the creation of the Conservation and Research Center in Front Royal, Virginia, in 1975; and the establishment and the programs of the Friends of the National Zoo.

Also included is a subject file documenting NZP history and administration; records concerning the administration of the NZP by the Smithsonian Institution; correspondence of Reed; files on the NZP animal collection which contain acquisition, exchange, exhibition, and life history information; records documenting relations between the NZP and domestic and foreign zoological parks and aquariums; and files relating to the NZP's membership in the American Association of Zoological Parks and Aquariums.

ARRANGEMENT: (1) National Zoological Park offices, officials, and programs, 1955-1984 and undated; (2) Smithsonian Institution bureaus and offices, 1960-1982; (3) subject file, *circa* 1920-1982; (4) general correspondence, 1971-1976; (5) National Zoological Park animal collection files, 1932-1941, 1946-1977 and undated; (6) American Association of Zoological Parks and Aquariums files, 1961-1984; (7) United States zoological parks and aquariums, 1957-1979; (8) foreign zoological parks and aquariums, 1958-1980. FINDING AIDS: Description in control file. SPECIAL CONDITIONS: (1) Restricted; (2) use of this record unit requires prior arrangement with the Archives staff.

(380)

Director, National Zoological Park, 1928-1986 and undated
Records (5.7 linear meters).

For an administrative history of the National Zoological Park (NZP) prior to 1984, see record unit 326 and the introduction to NZP. Michael H. Robinson succeeded Theodore H. Reed as Director of NZP in 1984.

These records primarily document the administration of NZP during the latter part of Theodore H. Reed's tenure as Director. A small amount of material documents the activities of Reed's successor, Michael H. Robinson. Included are budget records; minutes from meetings; and files concerning NZP collections, exhibitions, research, staff, and educational programs. Of particular interest are records documenting the renovation of the Small Mammal House and the design of the Great Ape House. The collection also includes an animal information file containing memoranda and correspondence between NZP and animal dealers, other zoos, and the general public. These files were created by William M. Mann, Ernest Pillsbury Walker, and J. Lear Grimmer, as well as Reed.

ARRANGEMENT: Unarranged with the following series apparent: (1) alphabetic subject file, 1957-1985; (2) NZP offices and activities, 1961-1986; (3) animal information file, 1928-1970. FINDING AIDS: Folder list in control file. SPECIAL CONDITIONS: (1) Restricted; (2) use of this record unit requires prior arrangement with the Archives staff.

(404)

Assistant Director for Research, National Zoological Park, 1979-1985, with related material from 1969
Records (14.8 linear meters).

The Office of Animal Programs (OAP) was established in 1979, replacing the Office of Animal Management at the National Zoological Park (NZP). For an administrative history of the Office of Animal Management, see record unit 385. John F. Eisenberg was named Assistant Director for Animal Programs, responsible for all animal and education programs at NZP. Eisenberg resigned in 1982, and Dale L. Marcellini became Acting Assistant Director for Animal Programs. Devra G. Kleiman assumed Marcellini's position in 1983. In 1984 Kleiman's title was changed to Assistant Director for Zoological Research and Educational Activities. Her title was changed again in 1985 to Assistant Director for Research.

The majority of these records document the research and administrative activities of John F. Eisenberg as Assistant Director for Animal Programs, and Dale L. Marcellini and Devra G. Kleiman as Acting Assistant Directors for the Office. Included are general correspondence and subject files, budgets, personnel actions, research proposals and reports, and grant requests; information on American and foreign zoos, conferences and research trips, and NZP and Friends of the National Zoo (FONZ); and administrative correspondence and memoranda from various NZP and Smithsonian offices. These records also include files concerning the acquisition, exchange, breeding, and exhibition of animal collections at NZP and other zoos. Staff participation in American Association of Zoological Parks and Aquariums meetings and committees is also documented in these records. This record unit also contains files created by Jaren G. Horsley as Executive Assistant to the Office of Animal Programs.

A small amount of material in the record unit dates from before the 1979 establishment of OAP. These records are from either OAP's predecessor, the Office of Animal Management, or are from Eisenberg's earlier position as Resident Scientist in the Department of Scientific Research at NZP. Some of Eisenberg's work on the Smithsonian-Venezuela Research Project is documented in these records. For additional material pertaining to Eisenberg's earlier work at NZP, see the John F. Eisenberg Papers, record unit 7411.

ARRANGEMENT: (1) Karisoke Research Centre (Rwanda) correspondence, 1980-1982; (2) Eisenberg conferences and research trips, 1977-1982; (3) Eisenberg general correspondence, 1977-1982; (4) Eisenberg read file, 1977-1981; (5) Smithsonian-Venezuela Research Project, 1973-1983; (6) FONZ subject and budget files, 1978-1985; (7) NZP budget, 1979-1985; (8) NZP personnel actions, 1969-1985; (9) Committee for Evaluation of Professional Activities, 1982-1983; (10) Smithsonian offices, 1977-1985; (11) alphabetic subject file, 1974-1985; (12) animal files, 1977-1984; (13) United States and foreign zoos, 1978-1983; (14) American Association of Zoological Parks and Aquariums, 1977-1985; (15) Horsley file, 1980-1984; (16) Kleiman file, 1982-1983; (17) Office of Animal Programs meetings, 1978-1984; (18) NZP offices, 1977-1985. FINDING AIDS: Box list in control file. SPECIAL CONDITIONS: (1) Restricted; (2) use of this record unit requires prior arrangement with the Archives staff.

ANIMAL RECORDS AND PROGRAMS, 1887-1988

(386)

Animal Registration Records, National Zoological Park, 1887-1976
Records (15.1 linear meters).

Throughout its history, the National Zoological Park (NZP) has maintained records documenting animal accessions, health, breeding, behavior, and removals from the collection. Records prior to the 1889 establishment of NZP document the animals that were housed on the Mall, cared for by the United States National Museum's Department of Living Animals.

From 1889 to 1971, NZP had a centralized system of recording animal information. Records were stored in the administrative offices and were maintained by either the head keeper or the secretary to the animal department. In November 1971, NZP animals were divided into research and exhibit collections. To facilitate recordkeeping, the new exhibit divisions of mammals, birds, and reptiles/amphibians started maintaining the records on the animals within their collections. In 1975, NZP adopted the computerized International Species Inventory System (ISIS) to maintain animal-related records. For additional information, see Julie Hamman's *Guide to Animal-Related Records at the National Zoological Park, 1887-1985,* Occasional Papers Number 1, Smithsonian Archives, Washington, D.C., 1988.

These records document the manual recordkeeping system which tracked the animal collections at NZP before the introduction of ISIS in 1975. Included are accession cards and ledgers containing the accession number, common and scientific name, date of accession (whether through birth, purchase, loan, or exchange), breeding, health, and occasionally the final disposition of each animal. Removal ledgers and cards detail the cause of death, final disposition, or sale or exchange of animals, and may also include a history of the animal's illness and a tag number assigned to the carcass if it was sent to the United States National Museum. Miscellaneous specimen cards represent attempts at new forms of recordkeeping, such as index cards recording the history of NZP holdings of a particular species. Also included are animal purchase and exchange ledgers and a procurement ledger documenting the purchase of general supplies for NZP, especially food and bedding for the animals.

ARRANGEMENT: (1) Animal accession cards, 1890-1975; (2) animal removal cards, 1911-1942; (3) miscellaneous specimen cards, 1888-1957; (4) animal accession ledgers, 1887-1976; (5) animal removal ledgers, 1906-1952; (6) animal purchase and exchange ledgers, 1897-1932; (7) general procurement ledger, 1927-1932. FINDING AIDS: Description in control file. SPECIAL CONDITIONS: Use of this record unit requires prior arrangement with the Archives staff.

(389)

Animal Records, National Zoological Park, 1943-1988 and undated
Records (2.1 linear meters).

In addition to the centralized animal registration records maintained at the National Zoological Park (NZP) (see record unit 386), keepers also kept records for their own reference within their departments.

This material consists of record books with information about the health, behavior, breeding, births, deaths, and diet of animals at the National Zoological Park, as well as keepers' diaries and daily reports, and annual lists of NZP's holdings. Also included are daily checksheets for the giant pandas that record their diet, activities, and behavior.

ARRANGEMENT: Unarranged with the following series apparent: (1) Head keepers' daily reports, 1972-1974; (2) status of the collections, 1983-1988; (3) giant panda daily checksheets, 1975-1984; (4) miscellaneous record books and keepers' diaries, 1943-1979. FINDING AIDS: Description in control file. SPECIAL CONDITIONS: Use of this record unit requires prior arrangement with the Archives staff.

(385)

Office of Animal Programs, National Zoological Park, 1949, 1951, 1956-1982 and undated
Records (2.6 linear meters).

Prior to the early 1960s, management of the animal collections at the National Zoological Park (NZP) was primarily the responsibility of the animal keepers. In 1961, the Animal Department was created, with Waldfried T. Roth in charge as General Curator. Roth resigned in 1964, and Donald R. Dietlein was appointed Manager of the Department. The Animal Department was renamed the Department of Living Vertebrates in 1968, with Donald D. Bridgwater as Head. The Department of Living Vertebrates was abolished in 1971, and administration of the animal collection passed to Floris M. Garner, Assistant Director for Zoological Programs. Garner resigned the following year, and the Office of Animal Management (OAM) was created. Jaren G. Horsley was General Curator of OAM until 1979, when animal management was reorganized and became the Office of Animal Programs. At that time, John F. Eisenberg was appointed Assistant Director for Animal Programs. Eisenberg resigned his position in 1982.

These records primarily document the management of animal collections at NZP from the late 1960s through the early 1980s, with a small amount of material covering the years before that date span. Included are administrative memoranda and correspondence concerning the acquisition, shipment, breeding, health, and feeding of the animals, as well as information on personnel, safety, budget, and research. Also included are annual reports, animal inventories, and keepers' reports.

ARRANGEMENT: Unarranged. FINDING AIDS: Folder list in control file. SPECIAL CONDITIONS: (1) Restricted; (2) use of this record unit requires prior arrangement with the Archives staff.

PUBLIC AFFAIRS AND EDUCATION, 1899-1988

(365)

Office of Public Affairs, National Zoological Park, 1899-1988 and undated, with related material from 1805
Records (19.5 linear meters).

The Office of Public Affairs (OPA) did not exist as an administrative entity at the National Zoological Park (NZP) until 1978. Prior to the early 1960s, dissemination of public information was carried out by the staff of the Office of the Director. In 1962, the Information and Education Division was created, headed by Marion P. McCrane, 1962-1968, and Sybil E. Hamlet, 1968-1972, to handle public affairs and exhibit labels.

In 1972, the Information and Education Division became the Division of Interpretation, with Saul W. Schiffman as Chief. The new division's duties were expanded to include exhibit production. In 1974, information and education work was again separated from exhibits production by the creation of the Office of Education and Information and the Office of Graphics and Exhibits. Judith White was named Chief of the Office of Education and Information in 1975. This office was renamed the Office of Education in 1978, when information duties were transferred to the newly established Office of Public Affairs.

The OPA was headed by Patricia Hurley in 1978 and Robert J. Hoage, 1979-   . With the assistance of Sybil Hamlet and Michael Morgan, the OPA provided public information about NZP programs and activities and coordinated special events.

The records of the Office of Public Affairs were, for the most part, created and maintained by Hamlet, Public Information Officer at NZP for over twenty years. Also included are some general correspondence and memoranda created by Hamlet's predecessor, McCrane. The records consist of daily and weekly animal reports written by the keepers; drafts of exhibit label text; memoranda and correspondence concerning NZP special events; notes, correspondence, clippings, photographs, and manuscripts about animals at NZP and other zoos; incoming and outgoing correspondence concerning animals, NZP events and programs, and zoos in general; and administrative memoranda and correspondence.

Files on the history of NZP contain articles, notes, and drafts of a manuscript written by Hamlet. Also included are photographs and lantern slides of animals; original artwork, primarily of "Smokey Bear" and the giant pandas, "Ling-Ling" and "Hsing-Hsing"; architectural drawings and maps of NZP buildings and grounds; and scrapbooks of clippings about NZP people, events, and animals. Materials dating from the 1800s to the 1930s in the historical research files consist of either photocopies of or notes taken from original documents.

ARRANGEMENT: (1) Animal reports, 1964-1986; (2) exhibit label cards, undated; (3) general subject files, *circa* 1868-1988 and undated; (4) animal information files, 1855-1986 and undated; (5) animal correspondence, 1964-1980 and undated; (6) general correspondence, 1962-1985 and undated; (7) memoranda, 1962, 1964-1979, 1981-1982, 1987 and undated; (8) history of the NZP, 1805-1987 and undated; (9) lantern slides and photographs, 1956-1957, 1972, 1974 and undated; (10) artwork, 1950, 1961, 1972-1973 and undated; (11) architectural drawings and maps, 1889, 1892, 1894, 1896-1920, 1938, 1959-1962, 1974 and undated; (12) scrapbooks, 1899-1901, 1903, 1905, 1924-1978 and undated. FINDING AIDS: Description in control file. SPECIAL CONDITIONS: Use of this record unit requires prior arrangement with the Archives staff.

(395)

Office of Education, National Zoological Park, circa 1938-1980 and undated
Motion Pictures and Videotapes (2.6 linear meters).

This collection consists of motion pictures taken by veterinarians, keepers, directors, and other staff at the National Zoological Park (NZP) for research and documentation purposes. These motion pictures, along with footage shot for television news and other programs, were kept by the Office of Education as part of their mission to disseminate information to the public.

The motion pictures depict the medical treatment, transport, feeding, and behavior of animals at NZP and other zoological parks; the activities of keepers and other zoo personnel; animal-collecting expeditions and visits to foreign zoos by Lucile Quarry Mann and William M. Mann; and animal-related events at NZP. Also included is a reel-to-reel videotape on giant panda social and reproductive development, and a microfilmed report concerning the expansion of NZP.

ARRANGEMENT: Unarranged. FINDING AIDS: List in control file. SPECIAL CONDITIONS: (1) Only selected motion pictures were copied to videotape for preservation purposes and are available for viewing by researchers; (2) use of this record unit requires prior arrangement with the Archives staff.

NATIONAL MUSEUM OF AMERICAN ART

The history of the National Museum of American Art (NMAA) collection dates to the beginning of the Smithsonian Institution when, in 1846, the act establishing the Smithsonian authorized the Board of Regents to collect objects of art. Called the Gallery of Art, the collection included prints and drawings collected by George P. Marsh and North American Indian portraits and paintings by John Mix Stanley and Charles B. King. Portions of the collection were transferred from the Old Patent Office Building and the National Institute in 1858 and 1862, respectively. In 1865, fire destroyed a sizable portion of the collection, then housed in the Smithsonian Building. The surviving prints and drawings were loaned temporarily to the Library of Congress, while the paintings and sculptures were sent to the Corcoran Gallery of Art. These deposits were recalled in 1895 and were added to the George C. Catlin collection, which had been acquired in 1879.

In 1904 President Theodore Roosevelt recommended to Congress that the art collection contemplated in the act creating the Smithsonian be established as a national gallery of art and that the Institution be authorized to accept additions to the collection. Congress failed to take action on the recommendation. In 1906, the Gallery of Art achieved official status when the Supreme Court of the District of Columbia, interpreting the Smithsonian's organic act, defined the Gallery of Art to be in fact the National Gallery of Art. The Harriet Lane Johnston collection, donated to the Smithsonian in 1906, and the William T. Evans collection, donated in 1907, formed the nucleus for the new Gallery.

The National Gallery of Art (NGA) was administered by the United States National Museum (USNM) from 1907 until 1920, when Congress granted the Gallery enough funds to become a separate Smithsonian bureau. William Henry Holmes, Chief of the Bureau of American Ethnology, 1902-1909, and Head Curator of the Department of Anthropology, 1910-1920, held the position of Curator of the National Gallery, 1907-1920. When NGA became a separate bureau in 1920, Holmes resigned his position with the USNM and became the first Director of the Gallery. Holmes retired in 1932 and Ruel P. Tolman, Curator of the Division of Graphic Arts, USNM, became Acting Director. In 1937, the National Gallery of Art had its name changed to the National Collection of Fine Arts (NCFA), when the old name was assigned to the collection donated by Andrew W. Mellon to the United States. Tolman became Director of NCFA in 1946, and held the position until his retirement in 1948. Since 1948, the directors of NCFA have included Thomas M. Beggs, 1948-1964, David W. Scott, 1965-1969, Robert Tyler Davis, interim Director, 1969, and Joshua C. Taylor, 1970-1979. In 1980, NCFA was renamed the National Museum of American Art. Taylor continued as Director of NMAA from 1980 until his death in 1981. Harry Lowe was appointed Acting Director and held the post until mid-1982 when Charles C. Eldredge became Director. Eldredge was succeeded in 1988 by Elizabeth Broun, who was appointed Acting Director in 1988 and Director in 1989. She served 1989-   .

The NMAA collection has had many homes. Before 1906, the Gallery exhibited its collection in the Art Room of the Smithsonian Library. Between 1907 and 1909 the collection was divided between the Arts and Industries Building and the Corcoran Gallery of Art. In 1910 the collection was consolidated and moved to a hall in the newly constructed Natural History Building where, in March of that year, the Gallery opened the first exhibition to be staged in the building. In 1924 and again in 1939 architectural plans for the Gallery were drawn up, but funds were never appropriated for a building. In 1968 the collection was moved to the old Patent Office Building which was renamed the Fine Arts and Portrait Galleries Building. In 1972, NCFA gained additional gallery space with the acquisition of the Renwick Gallery. In 1981, the FA & PG Building was renamed the American Art and Portrait Gallery Building.

DIRECTOR, ASSISTANT DIRECTOR, AND DEPUTY DIRECTOR, 1892-1992

(311)

Office of the Director, National Collection of Fine Arts, 1892-1960
Records (7.3 linear meters).

Records document the administration of William Henry Holmes, first Curator of the National Gallery of Art (NGA), 1907-1920, and Director of the Gallery, 1920-1932. To a lesser extent the records document the administration of Ruel P. Tolman, Acting Director of NGA, 1932-1937, and the National Collection of Fine Arts (NCFA), 1937-1946, and Director of NCFA, 1946-1948, and the early years of Thomas M. Beggs' directorship of NCFA, 1948-1960.

Records document the routine operations of the NGA when it was a department of the United States National Museum; when it became a separate bureau of the Smithsonian; and the early years of NCFA. The files include internal correspondence as well as numerous public inquiries about artists, works of art, exhibitions, and donations of art and bequests. The Charles Lang Freer collection gift and the effects of early copyright laws regarding photographing art are documented here. These records also include photographs of staff, collections, exhibitions, and the galleries. Exhibition materials such as catalogs, installation photographs, shipping forms and condition reports mostly document loan exhibitions and some new acquisitions. Frequent sponsors of loan exhibitions included the Pan American Union, American Federation of Arts, Pennsylvania Society of Miniature Painters, and local groups such as the Landscape Club, Metropolitan State Art Contest, and the Society of Washington Artists.

In addition, these records document campaigns to raise public and private support for the national art collection. There is correspondence with art galleries and reports of visits to galleries throughout the United States, including the Carolina Art Association, the Mint Museum of Art (Charlotte, North Carolina), and the Metropolitan Museum of Art.

Minutes and reports show the functions and activities of the National Gallery of Art Advisory Committee, National Gallery of Art Commission, and Smithsonian Gallery of Art Commission.

Important Smithsonian correspondents include Charles G. Abbot, Cyrus Adler, Richard Rathbun, William deC. Ravenel, Charles D. Walcott, and Alexander Wetmore. There is also considerable correspondence with Leila Mechlin of the American Federation of Arts and Florence N. Levy, who was affiliated with the *American Art Annual.*

ARRANGEMENT: (1) Incoming and outgoing correspondence, 1892-1960; (2) National Gallery of Art and National Collection of Fine Arts advisory boards, 1908-1960; (3) administrative records, 1901-1947; (4) undated exhibition photographs, arranged alphabetically; (5) exhibition material, 1906-1948, arranged chronologically. FINDING AIDS: Description in control file. SPECIAL CONDITIONS: Use of this record unit requires prior arrangement with the Archives staff.

(312)

Office of the Director, National Collection of Fine Arts, 1912-1965
Records (9.9 linear meters).

These records document, for the most part, the administration of Thomas M. Beggs, Director of the National Collection of Fine Arts (NCFA), 1948-1964. Some records were pulled from the files of previous directors.

Records consist of administrative memoranda, budget, travel, and personnel files; lectures by NCFA staff; correspondence with art collectors and institutions; photographs of temporary exhibitions and accessions; exhibition material including brochures, correspondence, and photographs (the exhibition, *The Art and Archeology of Vietnam* is particularly well documented); and information on the proposed Smithsonian Gallery of Art (never constructed), and the Eliel Saarinen design, 1939.

Important NCFA and Smithsonian staff whose material appears include William Henry Holmes, William deC. Ravenel, Ruel P. Tolman, and Charles D. Walcott.

ARRANGEMENT: (1) Incoming and outgoing correspondence, 1912-1965; (2) Smithsonian Art Commission material, 1938, 1949-1964; (3) installation photographs of exhibitions; (4) exhibition material, 1948-1964, arranged chronologically. FINDING AIDS: Folder list in control file. SPECIAL CONDITIONS: Use of this record unit requires prior arrangement with the Archives staff.

(438)

Office of the Director, National Museum of American Art, 1969-1991
Records (7.4 linear meters).

For an administrative history of the Office of the Director, National Museum of American Art, see the introduction to NMAA. Upon the death of Director Joshua C. Taylor in April 1981, Harry Lowe was named Acting Director and served until July 1982. Charles C. Eldredge was appointed Director in 1982 and held the position until 1988. Elizabeth Broun served as Acting Director, 1988-1989, and then Director, 1989- .

These records primarily document the tenure of Charles C. Eldredge as Director and the first few years of the tenure of Elizabeth Broun. A small amount of material relates to previous directors.

During his six years in office, Eldredge directed the first refurbishment of the public galleries of the Museum since its opening in 1968. During his tenure the Museum staff was reorganized and new programs were started. The position of Chief Curator was created, and Elizabeth Broun was hired to fill it. The curatorial staff surveyed the entire permanent collection and a number of peripheral works were deaccessioned. A scholarly journal, *Smithsonian Studies in American Art,* was initiated; and the American Art Forum, an organization for patrons, was established.

These records consist primarily of administrative subject files maintained by the Office of the Director, documenting the Director's relationship with bureau and Smithsonian staff, and with outside people and organizations. Also included are files on the National Museum of American Art Commission, its meetings, and its commissioners.

ARRANGEMENT: (1) Records of the Office of the Director, 1969-1986, accession number 88-068; (2) records of the Office of the Director, 1982, accession number 88-080; (3) records of the Office of the Director, 1968-1981, accession number 88-131; (4) records of the Office of the Director, 1981-1988, accession number 88-170; (5) records of the Office of the Director, 1986-1990, accession number 92-101; (6) records of the Office of the Director, 1986-1991, accession number 93-056. FINDING AIDS: Description in control file. SPECIAL CONDITIONS: (1) Restricted; (2) use of this record unit requires prior arrangement with the Archives staff.

(322)

Office of the Director, National Museum of American Art, 1970-1983, with records dating from 1934

Records (12.8 linear meters).

For an administrative history of the Office of the Director, National Museum of American Art (NMAA), see the introduction to NMAA.

Joshua C. Taylor served as Director until his death in April 1981. Harry Lowe was Acting Director, 1981, and Charles C. Eldredge was appointed Director, 1982-   .

After moving into its new home in the Patent Office Building in 1968, the National Collection of Fine Arts (NCFA), as it was known until 1980, enjoyed a decade of growth under Taylor. A major event of the period was the opening of the Renwick Gallery in 1972. The Bicentennial of the American Revolution was celebrated in 1976 with a major exhibition entitled *America as Art,* curated by Richard N. Murray.

These records document the tenure of Joshua C. Taylor as Director, 1970-1981. Some records date back to 1934. In addition there is a folder of correspondence with David E. Finley dated 1938-1977. Included are files on NMAA offices, Smithsonian offices, various art commissions, other museums, events, and exhibitions.

ARRANGEMENT: (1) Alphabetic subject files, 1938-1979; (2) general correspondence, 1971-1976; (3) associations, committees, and councils, 1972-1982; (4) exhibition files, 1970-1981; (5) NCFA Commission minutes and NCFA reports, 1971-1979; (6) alphabetic subject files, 1969-1981; (7) art museums, associations, councils, etc., 1943-1981; (8) NCFA Commission and NCFA reports, 1976-1979; (9) personal correspondence, awards, and papers, 1935-1981; (10) teaching and student files, 1960-1981; (11) "at-a-glance" calendars, 1976-1981; (12) publications, 1934-1983. FINDING AIDS: Folder list in control file. SPECIAL CONDITIONS: (1) Restricted; (2) use of this record unit requires prior arrangement with the Archives staff.

Office of the Director, National Collection of Fine Arts, 1895-1975
Records Relating to the John Gellatly Collection (0.1 linear meter).

For an administrative history of the Office of the Director, National Collection of Fine Arts (NCFA), see the introduction to the NMAA.

The John Gellatly Collection was amassed by wealthy collector John Gellatly and his first wife, Edith Rogers Gellatly, in New York City during the late nineteenth and early twentieth centuries. Mrs. Gellatly died in 1913, and in 1929 Gellatly gave the Collection to the National Gallery of Art of the Smithsonian Institution. The Collection was moved to Washington and opened to the public in 1933 at the renamed National Collection of Fine Arts, then housed in the Natural History Building.

Gellatly married Charlayne Whiteley Plummer in 1930. After his death in 1931, she initiated legal proceedings to regain the Collection. Litigation continued until 1947, when the courts decided in favor of the Smithsonian Institution.

The Collection itself consists of some 1640 items, ranging from paintings to jewelry to sculpture, from around the world and from the United States.

These records consist of archival items purchased from Miss Mary P. Plummer in 1969, as well as correspondence and other material from NCFA files. The records were maintained by the Director until 1972, when they were deposited in the NCFA Library.

This record unit consists of photographs of Mr. and Mrs. Gellatly, reprints of several journal articles concerning the Collection, several pieces of correspondence, notes describing various Collection objects, a manuscript called *A Summary of the Gellatly Collection,* and a letter of artist Childe Hassam to John Gellatly.

ARRANGEMENT: Unarranged. FINDING AIDS: Box list in control file. SPECIAL CONDITIONS: Use of this record unit requires prior arrangement with the Archives staff.

Office of the Director, National Collection of Fine Arts, 1964-1969
Special Services Records (2.7 linear meters).

During David W. Scott's tenure as Director of the National Collection of Fine Arts (NCFA), 1965-1969, the public affairs program for the Museum emanated from the Director's Office under the supervision of Special Services. This Division began its operations in FY 1966 when John Latham was appointed Assistant for Special Services. When Latham resigned in May 1967, Jane Marsh became Acting Assistant and held that position until FY 1968, when Mary Nell Sherman was appointed Assistant for Special Services. Benjamin Ruhe, a staff member from the Smithsonian's Office of Public Affairs, assumed the responsibilities of the public relations section of Special Services in 1967.

The programs supervised by Special Services included programming various exhibition openings, conducting private tours for distinguished visitors, programming special lecture series and symposia, arranging congressional and ambassadorial teas, preparing press kits, maintaining magazine and newspaper contacts, and preparing the NCFA monthly calendar. Special Services was also responsible for the rotating art exhibitions held in the White House and the Executive Office Building, and the White

House Fellows' Seminars on American Art. During 1967 the Division established a docent program, and began a community relations program with local businesses and schools in the Washington, D.C., area for the NCFA opening in the Fine Arts and Portrait Galleries Building.

These records consist of memoranda and correspondence pertaining to the various programs carried out by Special Services, NCFA art collection material, exhibition material, lecture material, budget, reports, staff biographies, newspaper clippings, magazine articles, radio and television material, tour information, and information on the White House Fellows' Seminar.

ARRANGEMENT: (1) General office files, 1965-1969; (2) exhibition material, 1965-1969; (3) scrapbooks, 1964-1967. FINDING AIDS: Folder list in control file. SPECIAL CONDITIONS: Use of this record unit requires prior arrangement with the Archives staff.

(318)

Consultant Designer, National Collection of Fine Arts, 1966-1969
Records (0.5 linear meter).

William C. Hofer was hired on special status as a resident Consultant Designer to the National Collection of Fine Arts in FY 1967.

Records contain plans and specifications for the renovation of the old Patent Office Building as well as information on interior furnishings and equipment for the Museum. Also included are designs for the renovation of part of the Renwick Gallery.

ARRANGEMENT: By subject. FINDING AIDS: Folder list in control file. SPECIAL CONDITIONS: Use of this record unit requires prior arrangement with the Archives staff.

(439)

Deputy Director, National Museum of American Art, 1983-1992
Records (15.2 linear meters).

The position of Deputy Director was created in 1983 and held that year by Harry Lowe, only to be abolished in the general reorganization of 1984. In 1986 Charles J. Robertson was named Deputy Director and has served 1986-   .

These records consist of the files of Charles J. Robertson as Deputy Director. They include administrative subject files, arranged by year; exhibition files; and files concerning National Museum of American Art Commission meetings and retired commissioners. Some of the events documented in these records include the ninetieth birthday and subsequent death of Adelyn D. Breeskin, the lawsuit concerning ownership of the Romaine Brooks paintings, and the exhibition of the Hemphill Collection. Also included are budget files and files on acquisitions.

ARRANGEMENT: (1) Records of the Deputy Director, accession number 88-136; (2) records of the Deputy Director, accession number 91-009; (3) records of the Deputy Director, accession number 91-110; (4) records of the Deputy Director, accession number 93-057. FINDING AIDS: Folder list in control file. SPECIAL CONDITIONS: (1) Restricted; (2) use of this record unit requires prior arrangement with the Archives staff.

Curator, Assistant, Acting, and Deputy Director, National Museum of American Art (Harry Lowe), circa 1967-1983
Records (6.2 linear meters).

These records consist of the files of Harry Lowe, who served the National Museum of American Art in various capacities from 1965 to 1983. Lowe was Curator of Exhibits and Curator, Exhibition and Design, 1965-1972. From 1973 to 1974 he served as Assistant Director for Operations and, from 1975 to 1980, as Assistant Director. In 1981 he held the post of Acting Director; then in 1982, Assistant Director; and in 1983, Deputy Director.

These records consist of files maintained by Harry Lowe in his positions as Curator of Exhibits and Assistant, Acting, and Deputy Director.

ARRANGEMENT: Unarranged. FINDING AIDS: Partial folder list in control file. SPECIAL CONDITIONS: Use of this record unit requires prior arrangement with the Archives staff.

Assistant to the Director, National Collection of Fine Arts, 1972-1978
Records (1.2 linear meters).

The position of Assistant to the Director was created in 1978 to formalize the relationship of Richard N. Murray to Director Joshua C. Taylor. Murray came to the Smithsonian in 1972 as a Visiting Research Associate and soon began working closely with Taylor. In 1976 and 1977 Murray had the title of Coordinator of the Bicentennial Exhibition at the National Collection of Fine Arts. He served officially as Assistant to the Director, 1978-1979, when he left the Institution.

These records primarily document *America as Art,* the major exhibition and catalog which Murray produced for the Bicentennial in 1976. Also included are a small number of administrative subject files pertaining to other matters.

ARRANGEMENT: Unarranged. FINDING AIDS: None. SPECIAL CONDITIONS: Use of this record unit requires prior arrangement with the Archives staff.

CENTRAL ADMINISTRATION, 1908-1985

Assistant Director, Museum Resources, National Museum of American Art, circa 1978-1987
Records (2.5 linear meters).

The position of Assistant Director, Resources, was created in 1983 during a reorganization of the National Museum of American Art (NMAA). Charles J.

Robertson, who joined the staff in 1978 as Associate Administrator, served as Assistant Director, Resources, 1983-1984; Assistant Director, Museum Resources, 1985-1986; and Deputy Director, 1986- .

These records consist of subject files created by Robertson as Assistant Director, Resources, and Assistant Director, Museum Resources, mostly 1983-1984. Also included are exhibition records of Robertson as Associate Administrator and as Assistant Director.

For additional administrative records concerning NMAA, see record units 447 and 475. Records of the Deputy Director can be found in record unit 439.

ARRANGEMENT: (1) Museum Resources Division, accession number 88-003; (2) Assistant Director for Museum Resources, accession number 88-079. FINDING AIDS: Folder list in control file. SPECIAL CONDITIONS: (1) Restricted; (2) use of this record unit requires prior arrangement with the Archives staff.

(313)

Central Administrative File, National Collection of Fine Arts, 1908-1974
Records (16.4 linear meters).

Records document the administrations of David W. Scott, National Collection of Fine Arts (NCFA) Director, 1965-1969, Robert Tyler Davis, interim Director, 1969, and Joshua C. Taylor, Director, 1970- . Some records, most noticeably correspondence with Smithsonian Art Commission members, have been pulled from the files of previous administrations.

The Central Administrative File was established in order to receive records of the Director, Assistant Director, and copies and original incoming and outgoing correspondence carried on by museum curators, administrators, technicians, and research assistants. This system was discontinued in 1975.

Records include Smithsonian Art Commission and NCFA Commission reports and correspondence with Commission members, 1908-1972; NCFA fiscal material; memoranda among NCFA staff; NCFA policies and procedures; correspondence with Smithsonian administrators; exhibition material; gifts and purchases; material concerning the renovation of the old Patent Office Building; correspondence with professional organizations; correspondence with state, local, and private art galleries; correspondence with universities concerning art programs and exhibits; and correspondence with federal agencies and foreign art museums. Projects and museums supported by NCFA or responsible to NCFA and documented in these records include the Barney Studio House, Bicentennial Inventory of American Paintings, Cooper Union Museum, Renwick Gallery, and the White House art program seminars.

Important correspondents, organizations, and art museums whose material appears in the records include the American Federation of Arts, Archives of American Art, Adelyn D. Breeskin, Alexander Calder, Edith Halpert (Downtown Gallery), William Henry Holmes, Harry Lowe, Stanton MacDonald-Wright, Paul Manship, National Council on the Arts, National Gallery of Art, George Rickey, and S. Dillon Ripley.

ARRANGEMENT: (1) Smithsonian Art Commission and NCFA Commission, 1908-1972; (2) NCFA reports, 1965-1974; (3) NCFA staff, 1959-1974; (4) NCFA subject files, 1960-1974; (5) exhibition files, 1964-1972; (6) NCFA history and related material, 1940-1969; (7) NCFA, Fine Arts and Portrait Galleries file, 1956-1973; (8) general files, A-Z, 1963-1972; (9) Smithsonian Institution files, 1964-1972; (10) federal government files, 1958-1973; (11) state and foreign country files, 1948-1973; (12) International Art Program, 1965-1971; (13) Renwick Gallery, 1965-1974; (14) Cooper Union Museum, 1965-1972; (15) crafts, 1966-1972; (16) White House, 1963-1970; (17) artist and sculpture file, 1963-1972. FINDING AIDS: (1) Card index by correspondent indexes a portion of the records; (2) folder list in control file. SPECIAL CONDITIONS: Use of this record unit requires prior arrangement with the Archives staff.

(447)

Office of Administration, National Collection of Fine Arts, 1964-1980
Records (3.9 linear meters).

For a description and history of the Central Administrative File, see record unit 313. Harry W. Zichterman and Louise W. Robinson served as administrative officers, 1965-1968. Zichterman was Administrative Officer, Planning and Budget, 1969-1970. He was succeeded by George Riggs, Administrative Officer, 1971-1972; Harry Jordan, Administrative Officer, 1973, and Assistant Director for Administration and Management, 1974-1976; and H. Eugene Kelson, Administrator, 1977-1980.

These records document the day-to-day administration of the National Collection of Fine Arts during the tenures of Zichterman, Robinson, Riggs, Jordan, and Kelson under the directorship of David W. Scott, 1965-1969; Interim Director Robert Tyler Davis, 1969; and Director Joshua C. Taylor, 1970- . They include staff lists and organization charts, as well as correspondence and memoranda concerning exhibits and budget.

ARRANGEMENT: (1) Administrative files, 1964-1980; (2) financial and budget records, 1964-1978; (3) exhibition files, 1964-1980. FINDING AIDS: Folder list in control file. SPECIAL CONDITIONS: Use of this record unit requires prior arrangement with the Archives staff.

(475)

Office of Administrative Services, National Museum of American Art, 1968-1985
Records (4.1 linear meters).

For an administrative history of the Office of Administrative Services, see record unit 447.

H. Eugene Kelson served as Administrator until 1982. In 1983 Sherwood A. Dowling assumed the title. In 1985 Dowling's title was changed to Administrative Officer and he served in that capacity, 1985- .

Charles J. Robertson served as Associate Administrator, 1978-1982. In 1983 he became Assistant Director, Resources, and in 1985, Assistant Director, Museum Resources.

These records consist primarily of the files of Robertson and Kelson as Associate Administrator and Administrator, respectively, including Robertson's files as Treasurer of the American Association of Museums, 1982-1984. A few files date back to the late 1960s and the 1970s. Also included is an occasional memorandum of Robertson's in his new position as Assistant Director, Resources. For Robertson's files after 1982, see record unit 446.

ARRANGEMENT: Unarranged. FINDING AIDS: Folder list in control file. SPECIAL CONDITIONS: (1) Restricted; (2) use of this record unit requires prior arrangement with the Archives staff.

Staff Meeting Coordinator, National Museum of American Art, 1972-1983
Records (0.4 linear meter).

The position of Staff Meeting Coordinator was created by Director Joshua C. Taylor in 1973 to coordinate attendance and the agendas of staff meetings, a duty which had previously been carried out by the Agenda Committee. Andrea Brown served as Staff Meeting Coordinator until 1977. She was succeeded by Raylene Decator and Kristin Olive, who held the position until 1983. Margy Sharpe served as Staff Meeting Coordinator in 1983, when the position was apparently abolished.

These records primarily consist of minutes of the meetings, notes, memoranda, correspondence and other data for the monthly staff meetings.

ARRANGEMENT: Unarranged. FINDING AIDS: None. SPECIAL CONDITIONS: (1) Restricted; (2) use of this record unit requires prior arrangement with the Archives staff.

CURATORIAL DEPARTMENTS, 1961-1990

Department of Painting and Sculpture, National Collection of Fine Arts, 1963-1969
Records (0.8 linear meter).

The Department of Painting and Sculpture developed as an administrative unit when Richard P. Wunder was appointed Curator, Painting and Sculpture, in FY 1964. In 1967, Painting and Sculpture became a Department. Wunder resigned in FY 1968.

These records are the files of Wunder, Curator of the Department of Painting and Sculpture. Records include material on the National Collection of Fine Arts' lending program, 1964-1968, and conservation reports.

ARRANGEMENT: General correspondence, 1963-1969. FINDING AIDS: Folder list in control file. SPECIAL CONDITIONS: Use of this record unit requires prior arrangement with the Archives staff.

Department of Painting and Sculpture, National Museum of American Art, circa 1969-1986
Records (5.7 linear meters).

For an administrative history of the Department of Painting and Sculpture, National Museum of American Art (NMAA), see record units 315, 317, and 458.

In 1984 the Departments of Twentieth Century Painting and Sculpture and Eighteenth and Nineteenth Century Painting and Sculpture were again united as the Department of Painting and Sculpture. Harry Z. Rand served as Curator, Twentieth Century Painting and Sculpture, until 1983. In 1984 his title, and that of Virginia M. Mecklenburg and William H. Truettner, changed to Curator, Painting and Sculpture. All three served 1984- . Adelyn D. Breeskin remained as Senior Curatorial Advisor until her death in 1986.

This record unit consists of administrative files of the Department and documents the activities of its curators, Rand, Mecklenburg, Truettner, and Breeskin. The files contain information about Department relations with other NMAA offices concerning loans, shipments, requests for information, conservation, and exhibits. Exhibitions represented in some detail include *Jose De Creeft,* 1983.

ARRANGEMENT: Unarranged. FINDING AIDS: Folder list in control file. SPECIAL CONDITIONS: (1) Restricted; (2) use of this record unit requires prior arrangement with the Archives staff.

(458)

Department of Twentieth Century Painting and Sculpture, National Museum of American Art, circa 1961-1980
Records (17.8 linear meters).

For an administrative history of the Department of Twentieth Century Painting and Sculpture, see record units 315 and 317.

Walter Hopps remained as Curator from 1974 to 1977 and then served as Adjunct Curator until his departure later that year. Harry Z. Rand joined the staff in 1977 as Associate Curator, with the additional title of Chairman in 1978. Rand was named Curator in 1979. The staff included Virginia M. Mecklenburg, Associate Curator, and Lynda Roscoe Hartigan, Assistant Curator. Adelyn D. Breeskin remained as Consultant to the Department.

These records document the work of the Department and its curators in the late 1960s and in the 1970s, with some material dated as early as 1961. The files include correspondence concerning proposed and rejected works of art, some administrative actions, and the Department's relationship with other museums. The majority of the records concern major exhibitions mounted by the Department during the period, including *Made in Chicago, Robert Rauschenberg,* and *America as Art.* Also included are files of Breeskin and Hopps, their correspondence, speeches, and travel.

ARRANGEMENT: Unarranged. FINDING AIDS: Folder list in control file. SPECIAL CONDITIONS: (1) Restricted; (2) use of this record unit requires prior arrangement with the Archives staff.

(315)

Department of Twentieth Century Painting and Sculpture, National Collection of Fine Arts, 1965-1974
Records (11.6 linear meters).

The Department of Twentieth Century Painting and Sculpture maintains works of artists born after 1880 or who were working by 1900. However, there is still some overlap with the artwork maintained by the National Collection of Fine Arts (NCFA), Department of Eighteenth and Nineteenth Century Painting and Sculpture.

The administrative history of the Department dates back to 1964 when Adelyn D. Breeskin, a specialist in contemporary art, became Special Consultant to NCFA.

Breeskin became Acting Curator of the newly created Department of Contemporary Art in 1967 and Curator of the Department in 1968. The Department's name was changed to Contemporary Painting and Sculpture in 1970 and in 1974 it was changed to its present title. Walter Hopps was appointed Curator of the Department in 1974 and Breeskin became a consultant within the Department.

Records contain exhibition material, including staff research notes on artists and artwork; administrative records concerning the shipment of exhibited artwork, loan correspondence, security and display of the exhibited material, photographs of display items, and installation photographs; staff correspondence including correspondence and memoranda from Adelyn D. Breeskin and David W. Scott; and memoranda and correspondence concerning NCFA loans of art work to the White House, cabinet offices, and United States embassies.

ARRANGEMENT: (1) Exhibition records, 1969-1974; (2) department correspondence files, 1965-1972; (3) lending program, 1969-1970. FINDING AIDS: Folder list in control file. SPECIAL CONDITIONS: Use of this record unit requires prior arrangement with the Archives staff.

(459)

Department of Eighteenth and Nineteenth Century Painting and Sculpture, National Museum of American Art, 1965-1983
Records (4.9 linear meters).

For an administrative history of the Department of Painting and Sculpture, see record unit 317. In 1970 the Department of Painting and Sculpture was divided into two units: the Department of Contemporary Art, which was concerned with artists active in the twentieth century, and the Department of Eighteenth and Nineteenth Century Painting and Sculpture.

William H. Truettner joined the staff in 1969 as Associate Curator. In 1977 he was named Curator.

These records document exhibitions organized by the Department staff. Also included are administrative files and general correspondence.

ARRANGEMENT: Unarranged. FINDING AIDS: Folder list in control file. SPECIAL CONDITIONS: (1) Restricted; (2) use of this record unit requires prior arrangement with the Archives staff.

(461)

Curatorial Department, National Museum of American Art, 1982-1990
Records (3.7 linear meters).

For an administrative history of the Curatorial Department, see record unit 460, the records of its predecessor, the Department of Painting and Sculpture, which existed 1984-1989. In 1989 the Departments of Painting and Sculpture and of Graphic Arts were combined to form the Curatorial Department. Virginia M. Mecklenburg became Curator-in-Charge, Painting and Sculpture, in 1987 and Chief Curator in 1990.

These records consist of correspondence and memoranda documenting the activities of the Curatorial Department and its predecessors. Included are general correspondence; correspondence with artists, dealers, and institutions; and the files of Harry Z. Rand concerning his research and curation of *The Art of Paul Manship.*

ARRANGEMENT: (1) Curatorial Department, 1982-1988, accession number 91-062; (2) Curatorial Department, 1985-1990, accession number 93-117. FINDING AIDS: Folder list in control file. SPECIAL CONDITIONS: (1) Restricted; (2) use of this record unit requires prior arrangement with the Archives staff.

(457)

Department of Prints and Drawings, National Collection of Fine Arts, 1965-1978
Records (1.6 linear meters).

The Department of Prints and Drawings was created in 1967. Jacob Kainen served as Curator, 1967-1969. Janet L. Flint was named Acting Curator in 1970 and Curator in 1971. She held the position 1971-   .

These records consist of files documenting the *Twenty-third, Twenty-fourth,* and *Twenty-fifth National Exhibitions of Prints.* Also included is a small group of administrative records concerning accessions, publications, the Smithsonian Art Commission, and relations with other Museum offices.

ARRANGEMENT: (1) Department of Prints and Drawings, records, 1968-1978, accession number 85-051; (2) Department of Prints and Drawings, records, 1965-1971, accession number 88-071. FINDING AIDS: Folder list in control file. SPECIAL CONDITIONS: Use of this record unit requires prior arrangement with the Archives staff.

(476)

Department of Graphic Arts, National Museum of American Art, 1968-1987
Records (6.6 linear meters).

For an administrative history of the Department of Prints and Drawings, see record unit 457.

In 1983 the Department of Prints and Drawings was renamed the Department of Graphic Arts. Joann G. Moser, who joined the staff in 1985 as Curator, became Curator-in-Charge, 1987-   .

These records consist of files documenting exhibitions organized by the Department of Prints and Drawings and the Department of Graphic Arts, 1968-1987, under the leadership of Moser. Also included is a small amount of material left behind by curators Jacob Kainen and Janet L. Flint.

ARRANGEMENT: (1) Department of Graphic Arts, 1968-1987, accession number 93-030; (2) Department of Prints and Drawings, 1969-1977, accession number 91-092. FINDING AIDS: Folder list in control file. SPECIAL CONDITIONS: (1) Restricted; (2) use of this record unit requires prior arrangement with the Archives staff.

(465)

Office of the Director, Renwick Gallery, 1964-1983
Records (4.1 linear meters).

The Renwick Gallery opened in January 1973 as the curatorial branch of the National Collection of Fine Arts (now the National Museum of American Art), responsible for the presentation of American craft and design. The building, which had been the original Corcoran Gallery of Art, houses a permanent collection of furniture as well as temporary exhibitions.

The Office of the Director of the Renwick Gallery was established in 1974. Lloyd E. Herman held the position 1974-   . Records which predate the establishment of the

Office of the Director were created by David W. Scott, Director, National Collection of Fine Arts (NCFA), 1965-1969; Robert Tyler Davis, interim Director, NCFA, 1969; and Joshua C. Taylor, Director, NCFA, 1970-1973.

This record unit primarily documents the tenure of Lloyd Herman, Director of the Gallery, but also contains the records of Scott, Davis, and Taylor, directors of the National Collection of Fine Arts. The records pertain to temporary exhibitions as well as the permanent collections of the Renwick Gallery. Prior to 1973 the records illustrate the establishment of the collections as well as the restoration of the Renwick. Exhibitions represented are *Woodenworks,* 1972-1975, *Shaker,* 1972-1975, and *American Pieced Quilts,* 1973-1975. Also included are general office files, which include incoming and outgoing correspondence, exhibition schedules, newspaper clippings, photographs, and publications. Meetings and reports files and special events files are included.

ARRANGEMENT: (1) Renwick Gallery, records, 1967-1975, accession number 85-038; (2) Renwick Gallery, Office of the Director, accession number 85-141. FINDING AIDS: Folder list in control file. SPECIAL CONDITIONS: (1) Restricted; (2) use of this record unit requires prior arrangement with the Archives staff.

REGISTRAR, 1858-1995

(453)

Office of the Registrar, National Museum of American Art, 1963-1987
Records (30.3 linear meters).

The position of Registrar was first established in 1965. Prior to that time registrarial duties were performed by the United States National Museum registrar. Marjorie S. Zapruder served as Registrar from 1965 until 1967, when Elizabeth Strassmann was appointed. Strassmann held the position until 1973. She was succeeded by W. Robert Johnston, who served as Registrar, 1974-   .

This record unit documents the activities of the Office of the Registrar staff and consists of temporary loan files; temporary exhibition files, including shipping, insurance information and loan agreements; general correspondence files; administrative files; and the files of the Smithsonian Art Commission, 1963-1975.

ARRANGEMENT: (1) Office of the Registrar, 1963-1975, accession number 85-042; (2) Office of the Registrar, 1980, accession number 85-080; (3) Office of the Registrar, 1975-1985, accession number 85-147; (4) Office of the Registrar, 1983-1985, accession number 87-098; (5) Office of the Registrar, 1968-1982, accession number 87-135; (6) Office of the Registrar, 1982-1987, accession number 92-144; (7) Office of the Registrar, 1974-1986, accession number 93-092. FINDING AIDS: Folder list in control file. SPECIAL CONDITIONS: (1) Restricted; (2) use of this record unit requires prior arrangement with the Archives staff.

Fine Arts Lending Program, National Collection of Fine Arts, circa 1965-1978
Records (2 linear meters).

In the 1940s, the National Collection of Fine Arts (NCFA) began to loan various works of art to offices in the federal government, so that more of the collection could be seen than was possible in the space allotted to NCFA in the Natural History Building. In the mid-1960s, with the move to a new building imminent, an effort was made to locate or recall many long-term loans and tighten administration of the lending program. Rowland Lyon was named Curator of Information and Lending and served until his death in 1966. Donald R. McClelland became Associate Curator for the Lending Program, 1967-1968. Between 1969 and 1972, McClelland held the title of Coordinator of Special Projects. In 1973 he assumed the title of Coordinator for the Lending Program and served 1973-   .

These records consist of administrative files of the Fine Arts Lending Program during the tenures of Lyon and McClelland and include information about loans to the White House. Other records relating to the Lending Program can be found in record unit 453, the Office of the Registrar.

ARRANGEMENT: Unarranged. FINDING AIDS: Partial folder list in control file. SPECIAL CONDITIONS: Use of this record unit requires prior arrangement with the Archives staff.

Office of the Registrar, National Museum of American Art, circa 1858-
Accession Records (84.4 linear meters).

For an administrative history of the Office of the Registrar, National Museum of American Art (NMAA), see record unit 453. W. Robert Johnston served as Registrar, 1974-1989. In 1990 Melissa L. Kroning was appointed Acting Registrar, and in 1991, Registrar. She served 1991-   .

These records document the acquisition, maintenance, and scholarly study of the Museum's permanent collection and items that were later deaccessioned. Included are condition reports; donor receipts; correspondence offering, acknowledging, accepting, and confirming gifts; catalog entry sheets; purchase orders; invoices; copyright and licensing forms; reports recording exhibition and location histories; internal memoranda regarding the mechanics of maintaining objects; photographs; meeting minutes which note approvals of objects; credit lines for objects; acquisition questionnaires; curators' descriptions of objects; newspaper clippings; and exhibition catalogs.

These records are maintained permanently at the National Museum of American Art, along with photographs of objects. Information on the latter may be found in record unit 5000102. Inactive loan files are transferred to the Smithsonian Institution Archives. For information about inactive loans, see record unit 453.

ARRANGEMENT: Numeric by accession number. FINDING AIDS: *Brief Report of National Museum of American Art Accessions,* a computer printout of NMAA objects, arranged alphabetically by the name of the artist. SPECIAL CONDITIONS: Some files contain confidential information and may be closed.

Office of the Registrar, National Museum of American Art, circa 1970-
Photographs of Objects (113.8 linear meters).

For an administrative history of the Office of the Registrar, National Museum of American Art (NMAA), see record units 453 and 5000101.

These records consist of images of the NMAA's permanent collection documented in record unit 5000101. The files include prints, slides, negatives, and transparencies of the collection, including deaccessioned works of art.

ARRANGEMENT: Alphabetic by the name of the artist. FINDING AIDS: None. SPECIAL CONDITIONS: (1) These records are located at the National Museum of American Art; (2) researchers desiring copies of these photographs must contact the Office of the Registrar in writing.

Exhibitions Coordinator, National Museum of American Art, 1982-1991
Records (5.7 linear meters).

The position of Exhibitions Coordinator was created as part of the Office of the Registrar, National Museum of American Art (NMAA), in 1987. The Exhibitions Coordinator is responsible for the organization of checklists, vouchers, other paperwork associated with exhibitions, and interoffice communications concerning exhibitions. Margy P. Sharpe held the position from 1987 to 1990, and Katherine McCleery has been Exhibitions Coordinator, 1991-   .

These records consist of exhibition files maintained by the Exhibitions Coordinator. Included in the files are correspondence, staff memoranda, checklists, vouchers, and exhibition photographs. Exhibitions represented include *Zoo to Art,* 1985, and *Still Life by Henry Lee McFee,* 1986.

ARRANGEMENT: (1) Exhibitions Coordinator, exhibition files, accession number 88-078; (2) NMAA/NPG Exhibitions Coordinator, accession number 88-137; (3) NMAA Exhibitions Coordinator, accession number 89-061; (4) NMAA Exhibitions Coordinator, accession number 91-115; (5) NMAA Exhibitions Coordinator, accession number 92-112. FINDING AIDS: Partial folder list in control file. SPECIAL CONDITIONS: Use of this record unit requires prior arrangement with the Archives staff.

EXHIBITION AND DESIGN, 1963-1991

Office of Exhibition and Design, National Collection of Fine Arts, 1963-1973
Exhibition Records (6.8 linear meters).

Harry Lowe was appointed the first Curator of Exhibits for the National Collection of Fine Arts (NCFA) in FY 1964. In FY 1970, the title of the Office was changed to

Exhibition and Design. When Lowe became the NCFA Assistant Director for Operations in FY 1973, David B. Keeler was appointed Chief, Office of Exhibition and Design.

The Office of Exhibition and Design is responsible for the design, preparation, installation, and maintenance of both changing and permanent exhibition galleries, and for the aesthetic development of all other public and non-public areas of the NCFA section of the Fine Arts and Portrait Galleries Building.

Records include research, correspondence, and photographs concerning the design and installation of exhibitions; information on national art conferences; Harry Lowe's correspondence as Curator of Exhibits; correspondence with art galleries, museums, and private collectors, who loaned art work to NCFA; exhibition schedules and research on exhibits considered by an exhibits committee; correspondence and memoranda from NCFA staff, who represented the Smithsonian on Washington, D.C., art projects; and Smithsonian Institution Traveling Exhibition Service records.

ARRANGEMENT: (1) Exhibit committee reports, schedules, and rejected exhibit proposals, 1963-1970; (2) inactive committees, 1964-1968; (3) Smithsonian Institution Traveling Exhibition Service, 1963-1966; (4) Office of Exhibits, exhibition material, 1964-1969; (5) Curator of Exhibits, records, 1964-1973; (6) Office of Exhibits, installation photographs, 1965-1969; (7) lenders' correspondence, 1965-1970; (8) Office of Exhibition and Design, office files, 1964-1973. FINDING AIDS: Folder list in control file. SPECIAL CONDITIONS: (1) Provenance not known for all records; some records may be rearranged; (2) use of this record unit requires prior arrangement with the Archives staff.

(448)

Office of Exhibition and Design, National Collection of Fine Arts, 1964-1978
Records (4.1 linear meters).

For an administrative history of the Office of Exhibition and Design, see record unit 314. David B. Keeler served as Chief of the Office of Exhibition and Design, 1973-   .

These records consist of correspondence, photographs and slides which document the design and installation of exhibitions at the National Collection of Fine Arts and the Renwick Gallery when Keeler served as Chief. Of special interest are records concerning the Patent Office Building opening, 1968, and the exhibition, *America as Art,* 1976. The records also document the tenure of Harry Lowe as Curator of Exhibits, 1964-1972.

ARRANGEMENT: (1) Harry Lowe, Curator of Exhibits, 1964-1972; (2) exhibits, 1968-1978; (3) Renwick Gallery exhibitions, 1973-1974. FINDING AIDS: Folder list in control file. SPECIAL CONDITIONS: Use of this record unit requires prior arrangement with the Archives staff.

(452)

Office of Exhibition and Design, National Museum of American Art, 1975-1981
Exhibition Posters (300 items).

For an administrative history of the Office of Exhibition and Design, see record units 314 and 448.

This record unit consists of approximately 300 posters which document exhibitions at the National Collection of Fine Arts and later the National Museum of American Art.

ARRANGEMENT: Unarranged. FINDING AIDS: None. SPECIAL CONDITIONS: Use of this record unit requires prior arrangement with the Archives staff.

Department of Design and Production, National Museum of American Art, 1964-1991
Records (2 linear meters).

The Office of Exhibition and Design changed its name to the Department of Design and Production in 1982. David B. Keeler served as Chief from 1973 to 1985. In 1986 James W. Volkert was appointed Chief and served until 1989. He was succeeded by Val Lewton, who held the position, 1990-   .

These records consist of correspondence, memoranda, photographs, and blueprints which document the installation of exhibitions at the National Museum of American Art and the Renwick Gallery under Keeler, Volkert, and Lewton. Also included are exhibition scripts, catalogs, work orders, and administrative records of the Department of Design and Production.

ARRANGEMENT: Unarranged. FINDING AIDS: Description in control file. SPECIAL CONDITIONS: Use of this record unit requires prior arrangement with the Archives staff.

MUSEUM AND PUBLIC PROGRAMS, 1967-1987

(466)

Office of Museum Programs, National Collection of Fine Arts, 1968-1978
Postcards (0.4 linear meter).

For an administrative history of the Office of Museum Programs, see record unit 456. The National Collection of Fine Arts (NCFA) museum shop came under the direction of this Office.

This record unit consists of postcards reproduced from NCFA artwork, especially the S.C. Johnson & Son, Inc., Collection. The Office of Museum Programs was responsible for the creation of the postcards, which were sold in the NCFA museum shop.

ARRANGEMENT: Unarranged. FINDING AIDS: None. SPECIAL CONDITIONS: (1) Use of this record unit requires prior arrangement with the Archives staff; (2) permission to publish must be obtained from the Museum's Office of Visual Resources.

(504)

Office of Museum Programs, National Museum of American Art, circa 1981-1987
Records (4.5 linear meters).

For an administrative history of the Office of Museum Programs, see record unit 456.

These records consist of materials on the *National Survey of Accessibility in Museums in the United States,* 1986, carried out by the Office of Museum Programs.

Some exhibition records are also included, most notably *More Than Land or Sky: Art from Appalachia.*

Other records relating to the *National Survey of Accessibility in Museums in the United States* can also be found in record unit 456.

ARRANGEMENT: Unarranged. FINDING AIDS: Folder list in control file. SPECIAL CONDITIONS: (1) Restricted; (2) use of this record unit requires prior arrangement with the Archives staff.

(454)

Office of Public Affairs, National Museum of American Art, 1967-1975, 1982, 1986
Publicity Material, Tapes, Dissertations, Thesis (0.4 linear meter).

The first Public Affairs Officer, also called the Art Information Officer, of the National Museum of American Art was Benjamin Ruhe, who served from 1969 to 1975. Ruhe was officially attached to the central Smithsonian Office of Public Affairs until 1974, when an Office of Public Affairs was established as part of the Museum. In 1975 Margery A. Byers was named Chief of the Office of Public Affairs and served 1975-   .

Some of these records predate the official existence of the Office. Included are announcements, press releases, newspaper clippings, and catalogs on the Sao Paulo Biennale for 1967, 1969, and 1973; the sixth Biennale of Paris of 1969, and the Venice Biennale of 1968, 1970, and 1972. Also included is the audiotape and transcript of the ninetieth birthday party given for Adelyn D. Breeskin in 1986. In addition, the records contain two dissertations and a master's thesis, *Social Psychological Influences upon the Expression and Inhibition of Curiosity,* by Caryl Amsterdam Marsh, 1978; *America's Contemporary Craftsmen: A Way of Work, A Way of Life,* by Alice Jane Kling, 1982; and *A Comparison of Two Methods for Creating Empathy with Art in Grade-school Children,* by Judith Ellen Sobol, 1970.

ARRANGEMENT: Unarranged. FINDING AIDS: None. SPECIAL CONDITIONS: Use of this record unit requires prior arrangement with the Archives staff.

(455)

Office of Public Programs, National Museum of American Art, circa 1979-1985
Audiovisual Tapes (4.9 linear meters).

The Office of Public Programs was created in 1983 as part of the Division of Museum Programs (previously the Office of Education and later the Office of Educational Programs) established during the general reorganization of 1982 under Director Charles C. Eldredge. Alison R. Abelson served as Audiovisual Specialist in the Office of Education, 1980-1981. In 1982 she became Media Program Head; and in 1983 her title changed to Producer, Art Documentaries, where she served, 1983-   .

This record unit consists of audiotaped and videotaped interviews primarily conducted by Alison R. Abelson. In addition to extensive interviews with sculptor Reuben Nakian, the records also include interviews with former curator Jacob Kainen by Joshua C. Taylor, as well as various tapes on other art subjects, some produced by groups outside the Museum. Also included are a few edit notes and logs.

ARRANGEMENT: Unarranged. FINDING AIDS: Tape list in control file. SPECIAL CONDITIONS: Use of this record unit requires prior arrangement with the Archives staff.

EDITOR, 1926-1970

(462)

Office of the Editor, National Museum of American Art, 1926, 1949, 1951, 1954, 1958, 1965-1977, 1979-1986
Records (4.9 linear meters).

For an administrative history of the Office of the Editor, see record unit 319.

Georgia M. Rhoades served as Editor from 1968 until 1972. In 1973, Rhoades was replaced by Carroll S. Clark, who held that position until 1984. Gaye L. Brown served as Editor, 1985-   .

This record unit consists of museum exhibition catalogs, press releases, handouts, pamphlets, posters, and exhibition checklists. Some material predates the formal establishment of the Office.

Additional exhibition catalogs can be found in record unit 333.

ARRANGEMENT: (1) Exhibition announcements, 1926, 1949, 1951, 1954, 1958, 1965-1977, 1979-1986, accession number 86-092; (2) publications, 1960s-1980s, accession number 86-159. FINDING AIDS: None. SPECIAL CONDITIONS: Use of this record unit requires prior arrangement with the Archives staff.

(319)

Publication Editor, National Collection of Fine Arts, 1967-1970
Records (0.5 linear meter).

The functions of the Publication Editor date back to FY 1968 when Georgia M. Rhoades was appointed Editor, National Collection of Fine Arts (NCFA). In FY 1969 the Office was officially titled the Editorial Office and in FY 1970 the title was changed to Publication Editor, with Rhoades remaining Editor of the Office.

Responsibilities of the Publication Editor included the editing of NCFA catalogs; assisting NCFA staff in the writing of articles for publication in professional and semi-professional art journals; securing the printing of invitations for exhibition openings; securing the printing of posters; editing and writing articles for *Artyfacts,* a weekly information newsletter for NCFA staff; and investigating fund procedures for NCFA publications.

This record unit documents staff activity and consists of catalog specifications, correspondence with art magazines, proposals for publication funding, publication budgets, price lists, copyright material, and administrative memoranda.

ARRANGEMENT: By subject. FINDING AIDS: Folder list in control file. SPECIAL CONDITIONS: Use of this record unit requires prior arrangement with the Archives staff.

EDUCATION, 1961-1991

(443)

Department of Education, National Collection of Fine Arts, 1961-1978
Records (7 linear meters).

George Gallenkamp became the first Curator of Education for the National Collection of Fine Arts (NCFA) in 1965. He worked to establish educational programs within the Museum until his resignation in 1966. In 1967, Susan C. Sollins joined the staff as Visual Information Specialist and by 1968, as Assistant for Museum Programs, was responsible for parts of the education program. She became Chief of Museum Programs in 1970. Darrel L. Sewell replaced Sollins that same year as Associate Curator of Education when the Department of Education was formally established, combining the various programs concerning public education. Sewell served until 1973 when Peter Bermingham became Curator of the Department, a post he held until 1978.

These records include Gallenkamp's files as a staff member, 1965-1966, old exhibition files, miscellaneous subject files, information concerned with secondary education programs, interns, workshops and docents. Some of the docent records include information on the docent program in general, docent reports and docent research papers. Also included is information on various NCFA collections such as the Roy Neuberger Collection, the Johnson Wax Collection, and the Irene and Herbert F. Johnson Collection. Along with these files are quarterly, semiannual, annual and biennial reports for the NCFA.

ARRANGEMENT: Arranged by subject. FINDING AIDS: Folder list in control file. SPECIAL CONDITIONS: Use of this record unit requires prior arrangement with the Archives staff.

(456)

Office of Educational Programs, National Museum of American Art, circa 1968-1991, with materials dating from 1920
Records (6.2 linear meters).

The Office of Educational Programs had its origins in the Office of Museum Programs, established in 1968 to coordinate the activities of the Junior Museum, the docent program, the publication of postcards, and other events to educate the public. Susan C. Sollins, who held the title of Visual Information Specialist, was placed in charge of the Office as Chief in 1970. When she departed in 1970, her duties were transferred to the Department of Education, where Darrel L. Sewell was named Associate Curator of Education in 1970. He became Curator of Education, 1971-1972, and was succeeded by Peter Bermingham, 1973-1978.

Bermingham was succeeded by Barbara Shissler (from 1980, Barbara Shissler Nosanow). She served as Curator of Education, 1979-1982. From 1983 to 1984, Nosanow's title was Assistant Director, Programs. In 1985 her title changed again to Assistant Director, Museum Programs. She remained in the office until her departure in 1988, when Judith O'Sullivan was named Acting Assistant Director, Museum

Programs. In 1989 James W. Volkert became Acting Assistant Director, Museum Programs. In 1990 the name of the Office was changed to the Office of Educational Programs. Nora M. Panzer was appointed Acting Chief and held the position, 1990-   .

This record unit consists of files concerning the administration of Educational Programs under the various heads of that Office. Records include monthly calendars and scrapbooks of the docent program, information on exhibitions, records of the *National Survey of Accessibility in Museums in the United States,* and a photograph album of artist Alma Thomas. Other records pertaining to the *Survey* can be found in record unit 504.

ARRANGEMENT: (1) Office of Museum Programs, 1968-1984, accession number 91-061; (2) Office of Museum Programs, 1978-1991, accession number 91-154; (3) Office of Museum Programs, 1980-1986, (with materials dating from 1920), accession number 89-122; (4) Office of Museum Programs, 1984-1987, accession number 89-118; (5) Office of Museum Programs, 1985-1989, accession number 93-034; (6) Office of Museum Programs, 1986-1989, accession number 91-060; (7) Office of Museum Programs, 1986-1989, accession number 92-136. FINDING AIDS: None. SPECIAL CONDITIONS: (1) Restricted; (2) use of this record unit requires prior arrangement with the Archives staff.

SPECIAL PROGRAMS, 1965-1986

(321)

Office of Program Support, National Museum of American Art, 1965-1981, with related records from 1954
Records (35.6 linear meters).

The historic mission and activities of the Office of Program Support date back to the mid-1940s, when the Department of State administered United States exhibition activities overseas. In 1954 this activity was transferred to the United States Information Agency (USIA). The USIA organized and circulated art exhibitions abroad and, in the years immediately preceding 1965, supported American participation in international art shows.

In November 1965 the Smithsonian Institution and the USIA agreed that the Smithsonian would assume the responsibility for an international exchange program of art exhibitions; support American entries in international art exhibitions, in particular, the Venice and Sao Paulo Biennales; and service the United States Information Services' field requests, when possible. The USIA would continue to be responsible for national exhibitions presented in the Soviet Union and East European countries.

The International Art Program (IAP), the office responsible for the USIA activities in this area, was transferred to the control of the National Collection of Fine Arts (NCFA). Three program employees were detailed to NCFA; the USIA agreed to continue providing financial assistance for projects begun before the program transfer had been made.

In July 1966, IAP personnel, Lois A. Bingham, Chief, Margaret P. Cogswell, Deputy Chief, and William M. Dunn, Exhibits Officer, became permanent NCFA staff members.

Between 1965 and 1970, most of the exhibition budget for IAP was directed to the large international shows, most notably the Biennales. After the threatened boycott of American artists at the Venice Biennale in 1970, the Smithsonian began considering its role in the international art shows, not wanting to get involved in politics and the consequences of such activity in its relations with artists. At the same time, the USIA no longer felt that the international shows were the most useful means of reaching audiences abroad. As a result, both agreed that IAP would provide smaller exhibitions for USIA use—a minimum of six a year. NCFA, however, continued to assist American entries in the larger international shows by encouraging private institutions to provide support for them.

In 1973, IAP became the Office of Exhibitions Abroad (OEA), reflecting the changes in its mission. Lois Bingham continued as Chief of OEA.

By 1976-1977, OEA's funding and budgetary support for packaging shows for USIA was waning. In 1977, the Office title was changed to the Office of Program Support, with Bingham as Chief of the Office. The program of the new office became more restrictive, working with NCFA staff in assisting and developing NCFA projects. For other types of exhibitions, the Office was to seek outside financial support. In FY 1980, Bingham became Coordinator of Program Support; and by the end of 1981 the Office ceased all operations.

These records provide detailed documentation on the administrative as well as exhibition activities carried out by USIA, IAP, and OEA from 1954 through 1981. Exhibition records include correspondence with embassies, working committees, organizers, artists; fund-raising letters; loan agreements; condition reports; exhibition reports and catalogs; press releases and newspaper clippings; photographs of artwork, installations, and publicity material (ambassadors, artists, and local committees), as well as biographies of artists involved with the shows. In addition, there are color slides, tape recordings, and film covering some of the exhibitions. Well documented are the Sao Paulo Biennale and the Venice Biennale dating from 1955 and 1964, respectively.

Administrative records include correspondence and memoranda, histories of the programs, USIA and Smithsonian agreements, and information on the office reorganizations. There is also information on program planning, budgetary material, travel policy, and trips taken by the staff. In addition, there are records on exhibitions sponsored by the Museum of Modern Art and the USIA, resource files broken down by collections and collectors, and professional art organizations, staff meeting notes, and personal diaries.

ARRANGEMENT: (1) Exhibitions, 1954-1981, arranged by year and numerically thereunder; (2) audiovisual materials; (3) administrative records. FINDING AIDS: Folder list in control file. SPECIAL CONDITIONS: Use of this record unit requires prior arrangement with the Archives staff.

Office of Research and Professional Training, National Collection of Fine Arts, 1970-1978

Records (0.8 linear meter).

The National Collection of Fine Arts (NCFA), Office of Research and Professional Training, was created in 1970. It served as a reference resource for internal and external inquiries, and coordinated training and volunteer programs, internships and research fellowships at NCFA.

Lois M. Fink served as the Coordinator of Research, 1970-1973, and in the same capacity as Curator of Research, 1973-   .

These records document the activities of Lois M. Fink as head of the Office of Research and Professional Training from 1970 to 1978. Included are incoming and outgoing correspondence regarding internships and visiting scholar programs, and reference inquiries; memoranda sent within the Office and to Museum Director Joshua C. Taylor; a large amount of exhibition and publishing materials; correspondence concerning the NCFA exhibition entitled *Academy: The Academic Tradition in American Art: Commemorating the 150th Anniversary of the National Academy of Design,* 1975; expense account records; research program schedules and reports; and volunteer records.

ARRANGEMENT: Unarranged. FINDING AIDS: None. SPECIAL CONDITIONS: Use of this record unit requires prior arrangement with the Archives staff.

Office of Research Support, National Museum of American Art, circa 1973-1986

Records (4.1 linear meters).

The administrative history of the Office of Research Support dates from 1973 when it was first established as the Office of Slides and Photography. Eleanor E. Fink served as Slide and Photograph Librarian, 1973-1976, reporting to the Library. In 1977, her title was Chief of the Office. Later in 1977 the Office became independent and was renamed the Office of Visual Resources, with Fink as Chief until 1982. In 1983 the title changed to the Office of Research Support, with Fink as Chief, 1983-   .

Throughout this period the Office had charge of the Slide and Photograph Archives, the Peter Juley and Son Collection, and the Photography Laboratory; and Fink served as the chair of a committee on the computer indexing of visual materials. The Smithsonian Art Index, established in 1976 to document artworks in other Smithsonian collections, became the responsibility of the Office of Visual Resources in 1978.

These records consist of administrative subject files which document the tenure of Eleanor E. Fink in the Office of Research Support and its predecessors. Also included is the development of the Smithsonian Art Index.

ARRANGEMENT: Unarranged. FINDING AIDS: Folder list in control file. SPECIAL CONDITIONS: Use of this record unit requires prior arrangement with the Archives staff.

Smithsonian Traveling Exhibition Service, 1950-1962
Records (3 linear meters).

Funds from the Alice Pike Barney Memorial Fund, established in 1951, and a grant from the Department of State, enabled the National Collection of Fine Arts (NCFA) to create the Smithsonian Traveling Exhibition Service. Annemarie H. Pope was appointed Chief of the Service. By 1962, the Service was circulating 135 exhibits to 316 museums within the United States and two exhibits abroad. Occasionally, exhibits were prepared for the use of the United States Information Agency.

These records document exhibits circulated by the Smithsonian Traveling Exhibition Service from its inception. Though under the auspices of NCFA, the Service received private funds for its operations and was never housed with the Museum. The exhibits traveled throughout the United States, sometimes abroad, and were occasionally shown at NCFA. Official forms and letters were sent to the NCFA Director, Thomas M. Beggs, for signature because of NCFA titular responsibility. When the Service became independent of NCFA in 1965, it appears the exhibition records for exhibits no longer on tour were transferred to NCFA for its files.

Exhibition records contain shipping forms, correspondence, exhibition brochures, and photographs.

ARRANGEMENT: (1) Exhibition files, 1950-1962; (2) general files, 1951-1959. FINDING AIDS: Folder list in control file. SPECIAL CONDITIONS: Use of this record unit requires prior arrangement with the Archives staff.

LIBRARY, 1910-1986

National Museum of American Art and Portrait Gallery Library, circa 1910-1986
Exhibition Catalogs (8.6 linear meters).

For an administrative history of the National Museum of American Art and Portrait Gallery Library, see record unit 463, and for an administrative history of the National Museum of American Art (NMAA), see the introduction to NMAA.

This record unit consists of brochures, booklets, and books, collected by the National Museum of American Art and Portrait Gallery Library, cataloging exhibitions at the National Gallery of Art (now the National Museum of American Art), the National Collection of Fine Arts, the National Museum of American Art, and the Renwick Gallery. Also included are a few catalogs from exhibitions mounted by the Smithsonian Institution Traveling Exhibition Service (SITES) from exhibitions containing Smithsonian collections borrowed for use at other institutions, from exhibitions abroad, and from joint exhibitions. The set appears to be fairly complete for the NMAA and its predecessors. These catalogs range in format from the one-page flyers of the early twentieth century to the lavish publications of the 1980s.

Further exhibition material is available in other Smithsonian Archives records, especially record units 315, 348, 349, and 351. SITES exhibition records are included in record units 290, 316, and 487.

ARRANGEMENT: Alphabetic. FINDING AIDS: Description in control file. SPECIAL CONDITIONS: Use of this record unit requires prior arrangement with the Archives staff.

(463)

National Museum of American Art and Portrait Gallery Library, 1916, 1922, 1929-1930, 1946-1984
Records (3.3 linear meters).

The Fine Arts and Portrait Gallery Library was established in 1964 as a joint operation of the National Collection of Fine Arts (NCFA) and the National Portrait Gallery (NPG). Previously there had been collections of art books and materials in various Smithsonian buildings; but there was no official library. The official Library was first housed in the Arts and Industries Building but moved in 1968 into the newly renovated old Patent Office Building along with the two museums. The building was then renamed the Fine Arts and Portrait Gallery Building. In 1980, the building's name was again changed to the National Museum of American Art and Portrait Gallery Building. As a result of the name change, the Library became the National Museum of American Art and Portrait Gallery Library.

William B. Walker was appointed Librarian in 1965 and held that position until 1979. Katherine Ratzenberger was named Acting Librarian in 1980, followed by Acting Librarian Susan Gurney in 1981. Cecilia H. Chin served as Librarian, 1982-   .

These records document the opening of the National Collection of Fine Arts and the National Portrait Gallery in the Patent Office Building in 1968. Included are press kits; photographs; development files; pamphlets of the opening; catalogs from the Henry Ward Ranger Exhibition, 1929-1930; an annotated copy of *The National Gallery of Art, Catalog of Collections I,* 1922, by William Henry Holmes; and minutes of the Smithsonian Art Commission, 1963-1964. There are a few records predating 1964 in this record unit, including House and Senate bills and congressional records relating to Smithsonian interests and activities.

Also included are newsletters, association information, library count sheets, policies, minutes of meetings, surveys, a variety of reports, brochures, volunteer and internship information, and other general administrative records.

ARRANGEMENT: (1) Records documenting the opening of the National Collection of Fine Arts and Portrait Gallery Library in 1968, accession number 87-025; (2) House and Senate bills, subcommittee hearing transcripts, and transcripts of the Congressional Record concerning Smithsonian interests and activities, 1916, 1946-1970, accession number 88-084; (3) miscellaneous records from the Office of the Director, National Museum of American Art and Portrait Gallery Library, accession number 89-117. FINDING AIDS: None. SPECIAL CONDITIONS: Use of this record unit requires prior arrangement with the Archives staff.

NATIONAL PORTRAIT GALLERY

In 1919 interested citizens began active lobbying for a national portrait gallery. That year the Smithsonian Institution, through its National Gallery of Art (renamed the National Collection of Fine Arts in 1937), the American Federation of Arts, and the American Mission to Negotiate Peace endorsed the National Art Commission. Its purpose was to commission American artists to create a pictorial record of World War I through portraits of leaders of America and the Allied Nations. The result was twenty portraits which went on exhibit in the Natural History Building in May 1921 and again in 1923 after traveling in exhibitions throughout the United States. These portraits formed an early nucleus for what became the National Portrait Gallery's permanent collection.

From 1921 the National Gallery of Art Commission regularly discussed the not-yet-official National Portrait Gallery (NPG) and accepted donations of portraits for its future opening.

Congress officially established the National Portrait Gallery in 1962 as a bureau of the Smithsonian Institution, "a free and public museum for the exhibition and study of portraiture and statuary depicting men and women who have made significant contributions to the history, development, and culture of the people of the United States, and of the artists who created such portraiture and statuary."

The Smithsonian Board of Regents appointed the first NPG Commission in 1963, which elected John Nicholas Brown as its first head. The first NPG Commission defined two main objectives for the Gallery based on its congressional mandate: acquisition and exhibition of portraits and statuary of those who have made significant contributions to the history, development, and culture of the United States; and establishment of the Gallery as a research center for American biography, iconography, and history. To carry out the first objective, the Commission established guidelines for accepting portraits: the best likeness possible; original portraits from life, if possible; and exhibitions of permanent collection portraits of subjects who have been dead for at least ten years, as well as Presidents and First Ladies. The standards for accepting portraits thus vary considerably from those for other galleries. In every instance, the historical significance of the subject is judged before the artistic merit of the portrait or the prominence of the artist is considered.

In the 1960s and 1970s, NPG initiated several programs to carry out its second objective, providing a research center for American biography, iconography, and history, by establishing the Catalog of American Portraits and the Charles Willson Peale Papers.

Between 1964 and 1969, NPG began adding to the small collections of portraits acquired on its behalf by the National Collection of Fine Arts (NCFA). The National Gallery of Art (the name given the gift to the nation of the Andrew Mellon collection in 1937) transferred thirty-four portraits which Mellon had designated for a future national portrait gallery in his 1937 bequest. NCFA and the National Museum of History and Technology also transferred portraits from their collections, including works from the original Smithsonian collection.

From 1969 to 1981 there were several programmatic innovations, an active special exhibitions schedule, and continued growth of collections. The Living Self-Portrait series, started in 1978, brought in living portrait subjects to give autobiographical lectures, while the Portrait in Motion series, which began the following year, offered live interpretations of personalities whose portraits are in the collections, either through readings by or about the portrait subject.

In 1974, Paul Mellon donated a group of 761 engraved portraits by C. B. J. F. de Saint-Memin, and in 1979 Time, Incorporated, donated over 850 pieces pieces of cover art used on *Time* magazine covers.

Congress increased the Museum's ability to add to its collections when it passed an act in 1976 allowing it to collect portraits in all media, most notably photography. In 1981, 5,419 glass negatives from the Matthew Brady Studio were acquired as a group from the Frederick Hill Meserve Collection.

For many years the nucleus of the NPG collections was stored with and shown by the National Collection of Fine Arts wherever that bureau was housed. The first official NPG exhibition was shown in 1965 in the Arts and Industries Building. NPG moved from the Arts and Industries Building in 1967 to its present quarters in the old Patent Office Building. The building was renamed the Fine Arts and Portrait Galleries Building in 1968, and NPG officially opened to the public on October 7, 1968. The building was renamed the American Art and Portrait Galleries Building in 1981.

Directors of NPG since the Museum became a separate Smithsonian bureau have been Charles Nagel, 1964-1969; Marvin Sadik, 1969-1981; and Alan M. Fern, 1982-   .

DIRECTOR AND CENTRAL ADMINISTRATION, 1963-1990

(426)

Office of the Director, National Portrait Gallery, 1964-1990, with related material from 1937
Records (19.7 linear meters).

For an administrative history of the National Portrait Gallery (NPG), see the introduction to NPG.

These records document the administrations of Directors Charles Nagel, 1964-1969; Marvin Sadik, 1969-1981; and Alan M. Fern 1982-   .

Appointed in 1964, Charles Nagel initiated programs to provide a research center for American biography, iconography, and history. To achieve this objective, he established the Catalog of American Portraits and the Charles Willson Peale Papers. During his tenure, Nagel acquired small collections such as portraits set aside by Andrew Mellon, to be transferred to a national portrait gallery once one was established, transfers from the National Museum of History and Technology, and the National Collection of Fine Arts. In addition to documenting these actions, the records also contain information about NPG's move from the Arts and Industries Building in 1967 to its present quarters in the old Patent Office Building.

Records for the tenures of Marvin Sadik and Alan M. Fern mostly document major programmatic innovations, such as the Living Self-Portrait and Portrait in Motion series, as well as general expansion in the Gallery's educational, scholarly, and acquisition activities. The records also document exhibition schedules, the donation in 1974 of Paul Mellon's 761 engraved portraits by C. B. J. F. de Saint-Memin, the donation by Time, Incorporated, of 850 pieces of art used on *Time* magazine covers, and the 5,419 glass negatives from the Matthew Brady Studio, which were acquired in 1981 from the Frederick Hill Meserve Collection.

This record unit contains internal correspondence between the Directors and NPG staff; correspondence with other Smithsonian bureaus as well with local, national, and international art institutions and artists; numerous public inquiries about artists, works of art, exhibitions, donations of art and bequests; color and black and white photographs; exhibition records including exhibition designs, catalogs, installation photographs, checklists, names and addresses of financial and art donors, shipping and loan forms, insurance forms, reports concerning the security of the collections and the Gallery, and condition reports which mostly document loan exhibitions; information about new acquisitions; and NPG committee minutes.

ARRANGEMENT: (1) Office of the Director, 1964-1985, accession number 86-090; (2) Office of the Director, 1965-1986, accession number 87-061; (3) Office of the Director, 1971-1985, accession number 87-069; (4) Office of the Director, 1937-1976, accession number 87-168; (5) Office of the Director, 1975-1987, accession number 88-167; (6) Office of the Director, *circa* 1965-1985, accession number 90-043; (7) Office of the Director, 1959, 1969-1990, accession number 92-061; (8) Office of the Director, *circa* 1972-1990, accession number 93-025. FINDING AIDS: Folder list in control file. SPECIAL CONDITIONS: (1) Restricted; (2) use of this record unit requires prior arrangement with the Archives staff.

(379)

Administrative Office, National Portrait Gallery, 1963-1987
Records (9.2 linear meters).

The Administrative Office was established in 1966 by Charles Nagel, who served as the first Director of the National Portrait Gallery (NPG), 1964-1969. The primary responsibility of the Office was to organize temporary exhibitions of portraits and statuary of men and women who have made contributions to the history, development, and culture of the United States. The Office also administered the acquisition of portraits and photographs for the NPG and co-ordinated special exhibition schedules.

This record unit documents the activities and efforts of the Administrative Office to acquire objects and portraits and includes correspondence with art collectors and artists.

The records include correspondence and memoranda with various art collectors, artists, domestic and foreign museums, educational institutions, government agencies, professional associations, and scholars; NPG curators' correspondence with institutions regarding borrowing exhibition objects; exhibition records and scripts, including photographs, slides, posters, donor information, and memoranda; programs and plans for exhibitions and special events in the NPG, including fundraising activities; plans for the establishment of the Catalog of American Portraits and the Charles Willson Peale Papers project; NPG policies and organization; plans to establish a research center for

American biography, iconography, and history; acquisition of portraits and photographs; publication of curators' research; security of collections and the building; blueprints for exhibition galleries; photographs of the building; and reports concerning NPG's relationship with Smithsonian bureaus and offices, the United States Congress, and the public.

ARRANGEMENT: (1) Administrative Office records, 1963-1970, accession number 87-170; (2) Administrative Office records, 1964-1974, accession number 87-169; (3) Administrative Office records, 1965-1985, accession number 88-051; (4) Administrative Office records, 1967-1986, accession number 87-171; (5) Administrative Office records, 1967-1987, accession number 90-167. FINDING AIDS: Folder list in control file. SPECIAL CONDITIONS: (1) Restricted; (2) use of this record unit requires prior arrangement with the Archives staff.

DEPARTMENTS AND OFFICES, 1860-1988

(2020001)

Curatorial Departments, National Portrait Gallery, circa 1864-
Permanent Collection Records (108.7 linear meters).

The Curatorial Departments oversee the conservation of art work, the authenticating of sitters and artists, and research in American portraiture. Research by staff is incorporated into exhibitions and catalogs or transferred to the research file of the Catalog of American Portraits.

Permanent collection records document portraits in the permanent and study collections, artists and their collected works, and associative and decorative objects. These files are available to researchers on a restricted basis. They typically contain a photograph of the portrait or object; research on the sitter, object, or artist; conservation report; exhibition records; and official documentation, such as records on the transfer of ownership to the National Portrait Gallery (NPG); the accession report; loan agreements; and insurance records.

Ellen G. Miles was Associate Curator, 1978; Associate Curator of Painting and Sculpture, 1979-1994; and Curator of Painting and Sculpture, 1994-   . Wendy Wick Reaves became Curator of Prints and Drawings, 1979; Frederick Voss became Curator of the *Time* Collection, 1985; and Mary Panzer became Curator of Photographs, 1992. The records also contain the files of other NPG curators, including Robert G. Stewart, Associate Curator, 1964, Curator, 1965, and Curator of Painting and Sculpture, 1979-1994; Monroe Fabian, Assistant Curator, 1969-1971, Associate Curator, 1972-1978, and Associate Curator of Painting and Sculpture, 1979-1986; and William F. Stapp, Curator of Photographs, 1979-1991.

ARRANGEMENT: Portrait records are divided between curatorial departments according to media. FINDING AIDS: (1) *Permanent Collection Illustrated Checklist,* arranged alphabetically by sitter with index to artists' names; (2) computerized collections information system with multiple access points. SPECIAL CONDITIONS: (1)

Restricted; (2) records are located at the National Portrait Gallery; (3) researchers should contact appropriate curatorial departments to request access; (4) painting and sculpture collection records are housed with associative and decorative object records in the Office of the Registrar, through which access is granted.

(552)

Department of Design and Production, National Portrait Gallery, circa 1977-1988
Records (4.8 linear meters).

The Department of Design and Production was created in 1970 to support the exhibition program of the National Portrait Gallery by providing exhibition-related services throughout the Gallery. Initially called the Department of Exhibits and Design, its services range from exhibition design and script writing and editing to all facets of exhibition production, including woodworking, plastics, taxidermy, painting, framing and silkscreening. In addition to exhibition production and installation work, the Department is also responsible for supporting brochure design, creation of interpretive panels, illustration work, and graphics for various offices within the Gallery.

James J. Shelton was named Chief of the Department in 1970 and J. Michael Carrigan hired as Assistant Chief. In 1973 the Department was renamed the Department of Exhibits Design and Production. Carrigan became the Chief of the Department the following year, succeeded by Nello Marconi, who served as Chief, 1977-   . During Marconi's tenure the Department was renamed the Department of Design and Production.

The records consist of departmental correspondence; memoranda; manuscripts; exhibition layouts, gallery floor plans, and blueprints of interior spaces; drawing notes and sketches; lighting designs; production schedules; exhibition project submittals; photographs, slides, and negatives; exhibition catalogs; and newspaper clippings. The records date from the tenure of Nello Marconi as Chief of the Department.

ARRANGEMENT: (1) Department of Design and Production, *circa* 1977-1986, accession number 87-010; (2) Department of Design and Production, 1979-1982, accession number 84-080; (3) Department of Design and Production, 1979-1983, accession number 85-107; (4) Department of Design and Production, 1980-1988, accession number 90-112. FINDING AIDS: Folder list in control file. SPECIAL CONDITIONS: Use of this record unit requires prior arrangement with the Archives staff.

(555)

Department of Education, National Portrait Gallery, 1969-1980
Records (0.8 linear meter).

The Department of Education, National Portrait Gallery (NPG), was part of the Office of the Historian from 1969 to 1971. It became a separate entity in 1971 when James R. Vivian III was appointed Curator of Education. He was succeeded by Dennis A. O'Toole, who served from 1972 through 1978. In January 1979 Kenneth Yellis was appointed Curator of Education and served in that capacity through 1980.

The Department of Education is responsible for preparing educational materials and organizing exhibitions related to the history of the United States, its culture, biography, and the history of the art of portraiture, as reflected in the collections of the NPG.

This record unit documents the activities of the Department of Education and its staff. The bulk of the records contain information about specific programs of the Department, including the Education Aide Program, the Docent Program and the Volunteer Program. Other records document the NPG's current and future exhibitions, educational activities, plans designed primarily for visually handicapped visitors to the Haptic Gallery, and motion pictures.

These records consist of correspondence, memoranda, notes, curators' reports to the Director, Marvin Sadik, and minutes of staff meetings. The correspondence largely contains letters of appreciation from teachers, students, elementary and secondary school administrators, and the general public.

ARRANGEMENT: Department of Education, 1969-1980, accession number 85-092. FINDING AIDS: Folder list in control file. SPECIAL CONDITIONS: Use of this record unit requires prior arrangement with the Archives staff.

(361)

Office of Exhibitions, National Portrait Gallery, circa 1968-1976
Exhibition Records (5.2 linear meters).

Prior to 1974, individual curators within the National Portrait Gallery (NPG) were responsible for developing and coordinating exhibitions. In 1974, the Office of Exhibitions was established, and Beverly J. Cox was named Curator of Exhibitions and head of the Office. The Office of Exhibitions was charged with the responsibility for developing exhibitions, administering and negotiating exhibition loans, and coordinating plans for both changing and permanent exhibition galleries.

The exhibition records include correspondence and memoranda of NPG Director Marvin Sadik and his staff with artists and art organizations, businesses and individuals; correspondence and memoranda with local, state and private galleries, federal agencies and foreign art museums; research notes on artists and artwork; loan agreements; condition reports; exhibition reports, scripts, checklists, schedules and catalogs; architectural designs and plans; exhibition floor plans and charts; photographs of exhibition objects and artists; biographies of artists; press releases; newspaper clippings; magazine and journal articles; excerpts from books; and lecture materials. In addition, there are photographs and slides of objects which were not exhibited.

Administrative records include exhibition plans, budgetary materials, travel and shipping documentation, and insurance policies.

ARRANGEMENT: (1) *Abroad in America: Visitors to the New Nation, 1776-1914;* (2) *American Presidency in Cartoons, 1789-1977;* (3) *American Self-Portraits, 1670-1972;* (4) *Augustus Saint-Gaudens: The Portrait Relief;* (5) *Charles Frederich: The Washington Years, 1837-1848;* (6) *Christian Gallager: Portrait Painter to Federal America;* (7) *Elisha Kent Kane;* (8) *A Glimmer of Their Beauty: Black Sounds in the Twenties;* (9) *Homage to Thomas Eakins;* (10) *James Weldon Johnson;* (11) *John Muir;* (12) *Mary McLeod Bethune;* (13) *A Man for All Seasons: The Life and Portraits of John Quincy Adams;* (14) *A Nineteenth-Century Gallery of Distinguished Americans;* (15) *Presidents' Medals, 1789-1977;* (16) *Portraits from the American Stage, 1771-1971;* (17) *Portraits from "The Americans: The Democratic Experience";* (18) *The Spirit of Fact: The Daguerreotypes of Southworth and Hawes, 1843-1862;* (19) *Sculpture Court;* (20) *This New Man: A Discourse in Portraits;* (21) *Thomas Alva Edison;* (22) *Washington: From Banneker to Douglass, 1791-1870;* (23) *Washington in the New Era, 1870-1970;* (24) *Wedgewood Portraits and the American Revolution.* FINDING AIDS: Description in control file. SPECIAL CONDITIONS: Use of this record unit requires prior arrangement with the Archives staff.

Office of the Historian, National Portrait Gallery, 1972-1984
Records (1.2 linear meters).

The Office of the Historian, National Portrait Gallery (NPG), was established in 1966 when Daniel J. Reed was appointed the first Historian. Reed resigned in 1968 and Virginia Purdy became Acting Historian. Beverly J. Cox was appointed Historian in 1970. A year later, Lillian B. Miller was appointed Historian and Cox became Assistant Historian. Cox left the Office to become Coordinator of Exhibitions in 1973. Miller continued to serve as Historian until 1974 when she became Editor of the Charles Willson Peale Papers. Marc Pachter was appointed Historian in 1975 and served in that capacity through 1984.

The Historian was appointed to direct the research program of the NPG in American iconography, biography and history; to explore the art of portraiture in the United States and the Western world; and to conduct studies of men and women of any nation who made significant contributions to the history, development, and culture of the United States. From 1966 through 1967, the Historian also supervised the activities of the Catalog of American Portraits at NPG.

The Office also prepared biographical information on individuals whose portraits were offered to the NPG by gift or purchase. It undertook to prepare succinct and informative labels for portraits in the permanent collections or items on exchange; wrote catalogs; and conducted research on objects represented in portraits, statuary, prints, miniatures, and engravings.

This record unit documents the activities of the Office's first three Historians. Most of the records were created during Marc Pachter's tenure. They include much correspondence between Pachter and art historians, artists, national and international art institutions, and funding organizations. There is also correspondence with Amy E. Henderson, Assistant Historian, Kenneth Young and J. Michael Carrigan, exhibition designers, and Mona Dearborn, Keeper of the Catalog of American Portraits. In addition, the records document symposia and discussion panels organized by the Office and the production and display of exhibitions.

ARRANGEMENT: Office of the Historian, 1972-1984, accession number 92-149. FINDING AIDS: Box list in control file. SPECIAL CONDITIONS: Use of this record unit requires prior arrangement with the Archives staff.

Office of Public Affairs, National Portrait Gallery, circa 1962-1983
Records (9 linear meters).

The Office of Public Affairs was created to prepare, coordinate and disseminate information about the activities of the National Portrait Gallery (NPG) to the public and the news media. This work was carried out through the Director's Office from 1962 until 1972, when Nancy F. Bush was appointed NPG's first Public Affairs Officer. Bush held the position through 1973 and was followed by Carol Cutler, 1974-1978; Susanne Roschwalb, 1978-1979; and Sandra Westin, 1979-   .

This record unit consists of correspondence between Nancy F. Bush, Carol Cutler, Susanne Roschwalb, and Sandra Westin and NPG Directors Marvin Sadik and Alan M.

Fern and other NPG staff, as well as artists, other art museums, and cultural institutions in the United States and abroad, discussing acquisitions, exhibitions, lectures, seminars, and special events.

The records document planning and presentation of NPG exhibitions. Among these are *Abroad in America: Visitors to the New Nation, 1776-1914; The Black Presence in the Era of the American Revolution, 1770-1800; We Were But A Handful;* and *Why Not A Woman.* Exhibitions and associated special events are often documented by photographs, videotapes, and audiotapes.

ARRANGEMENT: (1) Office of Public Affairs, 1962-1981, accession number 84-069; (2) Office of Public Affairs, 1975-1983, accession number 87-173. FINDING AIDS: Folder list in control file. SPECIAL CONDITIONS: Use of this record unit requires prior arrangement with the Archives staff.

(553)

Editor of Publications, National Portrait Gallery, 1968-1982
Catalogs (1.2 linear meters).

The Editor of Publications is responsible for producing publications which document the National Portrait Gallery's (NPG) exhibitions. In 1968 National Portrait Gallery Director Marvin Sadik appointed Robert Gordon Stewart as the first Editor of Publications for the NPG. He was followed by Frances Stevenson Wein, 1975-   .

These illustrated catalogs document major and minor exhibitions, providing detailed discussions of exhibition themes. Additional catalogs, pamphlets, and booklets highlight specific features of the permanent collection such as the NPG's presidential portraits.

Catalogs also document special exhibitions which contain the Gallery's portraits, manuscripts, personal memoranda, and other objects, including items borrowed from private and public collections in the United States and abroad. Exhibitions reflecting such a broad use of materials include *The Black Presence in the Era of the American Revolution, 1770-1800; Return to Albion: Americans in England, 1760-1940; Abroad in America: Visitors to the New Nation, 1776-1914;* and *Portraits from "The Americans: The Democratic Experience."*

ARRANGEMENT: Exhibition catalogs and brochures, 1968-1982, accession number 85-083. FINDING AIDS: None. SPECIAL CONDITIONS: Use of this record unit requires prior arrangement with the Archives staff.

SPECIAL PROJECTS

(2030001)

Catalog of American Portraits, National Portrait Gallery
Research Files (494.1 linear meters).

Since 1966 the National Portrait Gallery has administered the Catalog of American Portraits (CAP), a reference collection and research facility containing photographs and documentation for more than 100,000 portraits of historically significant Americans, or by American artists. New material is added regularly from various sources, including an ongoing survey of portraits held in public and private collections across the country.

Initial administration of the CAP came from the Museum's Office of the Historian, with Daniel Reed, Historian, supervising the activities of CAP from 1966 to 1967. In 1967 Helen Maggs Fede was appointed the first Keeper of the Catalog, the administrative head of the Office. After her death a few months later, the Acting Historian, Virginia Purdy, administered CAP from 1967 to 1969. Wilford Cole was appointed Keeper of the Catalog in 1969 and held that position until 1974. Mona Dearborn served as Keeper from 1974 to 1984. Richard K. Doud was Keeper from 1984 to 1988, and Linda Thrift has been Keeper since 1989.

Under Cole, the first portrait survey, cataloging information in the southeastern United States, began. The database grew from random efforts to a more controlled information collection policy. Until 1976, however, field surveys concentrated on portraits of individuals pertinent to the American Revolution and the Bicentennial celebration. In 1978, CAP began an intense and systematic seven-year national survey funded in part by grants.

Today the staff of the CAP researches portraits, edits information from the field survey, incorporates portrait material into an online imaging database, and continues to provide reference service to researchers. Generally, only one-of-a-kind likenesses are recorded, such as paintings, drawings, and sculpture. Photographs, engravings, and lithographs are not included. The CAP files usually contain a photograph of the portrait, standard catalog data, a description, history of ownership, biographical sketches of subjects and artists, bibliographic references, and exhibition and conservation history. Often, archival correspondence and primary research material are included as well.

The CAP's online imaging database provides retrieval capabilities on almost every field of data, including the subject's principal historical distinction, portrait descriptions, time periods, regions, events, related people, and certain ethnic affiliations. Researchers may visit, write, telephone, fax, or e-mail their inquiries. Limited searching is also available on the National Portrait Gallery's World Wide Web (http://www.npg.si.edu) and America Online (NPGOnline) sites.

ARRANGEMENT: (1) Portrait files, alphabetic by sitter; (2) artist files, alphabetic by artist. FINDING AIDS: Computerized database provides multiple access points. SPECIAL CONDITIONS: (1) Some private collections information is restricted; (2) the records are located at the Catalog of American Portraits, National Portrait Gallery.

(2040001)

Peale Family Papers, National Portrait Gallery, 1735-1885
Research Files (44.1 linear meters).

The Peale Family Papers project was established in 1974 as the Papers of Charles Willson Peale and his Family. Initial funds came from the Smithsonian Institution and the National Endowment for the Humanities (NEH), with an endorsement from the National Historical Publications and Records Commission. Additional two year funding was provided in 1976 by the Smithsonian, NEH, and the Andrew Mellon Foundation. In 1978 Congress appropriated full funding for the project through the budget of the National

Portrait Gallery. The name of the project was changed to the Peale Family Papers in 1984.

The Peale Family Papers was organized to collect, study, and publish in microform and book editions the papers of Charles Willson Peale, artist, naturalist, inventor, and founder of the first important museum in North America, and his family. The papers and research document the history of art, science, and family life in America from 1735 to 1885, with an emphasis on the history and culture of the northeast region, particularly Philadelphia, Baltimore, Boston, and New York.

Lillian B. Miller has been Editor since the beginning of the project. Michael D. Schaffer was Assistant Editor, 1974-1977. Sidney Hart has served successively as Research Historian, 1976-1977, Assistant Editor, 1977-1986, Associate Editor, 1986-1991, and Senior Associate Editor, 1991-   . David C. Ward has served as Research Historian, 1982-1986, Assistant Editor, 1986-1991, and Associate Editor, 1991-   . Leslie Reinhardt became Editorial Assistant in 1991.

The Peale Family Papers contain photocopies of documents collected worldwide by the staff, including Charles Willson Peale Revolution-era diaries, travel diaries, museum records, lectures and autobiography; family writings; Titian Ramsay Peale journals documenting the Long expedition, 1819-1820, and the United States Exploring Expedition (Wilkes), 1837-1842; Benjamin Franklin Peale's writings about coins, medals, and the United States Mint; files on the portraiture and still life paintings of Sarah Miriam Peale, the portraits of Raphael Peale and James Peale, and on the miniatures of Anna Claypoole Peale; and Rembrandt Peale's writing on the mastodon, as well as materials on his portraits.

Peale Family Papers staff assemble and prepare the documents by indexing, annotating, and editing them. They create research files that include genealogies, newspaper articles, and biographical information on portrait sitters and correspondents of the Peales.

In 1980, a microfiche edition of *The Collected Papers of Charles Willson Peale and his Family* was published. In 1983 the project published the first volume of a planned seven-volume letterpress edition of *The Selected Papers of Charles Willson Peale and His Family*.

ARRANGEMENT: (1) Master document files arranged chronologically; (2) research files; (3) Rembrandt Peale *catalogue raisonne* files; (4) Sarah Miriam Peale *catalogue raisonne* files; (5) painting files for various Peale artists. FINDING AIDS: (1) Calendar of all letters from 1735 to 1827, arranged chronologically; (2) card indexes in chronological order, and by subject and family member, thereunder; SPECIAL CONDITIONS: (1) Restricted; (2) the records are located at the Peale Family Papers, National Portrait Gallery.

NATIONAL AIR AND SPACE MUSEUM

The National Air Museum (NAM) was created as a separate bureau of the Smithsonian Institution by an Act of Congress in 1946. Twenty years later, its name was changed to the National Air and Space Museum (NASM) as part of a congressional act authorizing a separate building to house its collections.

Before 1946 the aeronautical collections had been assigned to the custodial care of the United States National Museum's Department of Anthropology, Division of Mechanical Technology, 1887-1919; the Department of Arts and Industries, Division of Mechanical Technology, 1919-1931; and the Division of Engineering, 1931-1946. In 1946 Carl W. Mitman was appointed Assistant to the Secretary for NAM. Upon Mitman's retirement in 1952, Curator Paul E. Garber was named Head Curator.

The position of Director was not established until 1958, when Philip S. Hopkins was appointed, serving from 1958 to 1964. Hopkins was succeeded by S. Paul Johnston, who held the position from 1964 to 1969. Frank A. Taylor was appointed Acting Director and held that position until Michael Collins was appointed Director in 1971. Collins guided the Museum through construction and opening of the new facility. Collins resigned in 1978 and was succeeded by Melvin B. Zisfein, Acting Director, 1978-1979; Noel W. Hinners, Director, 1979-1982; Walter J. Boyne, Acting Director, 1982, Director, 1983-1986; Donald S. Lopez, Acting Director, 1986; James C. Tyler, Acting Director, 1986-1987; and Martin O. Harwit, Director, 1987-   .

The NASM collection dates back to the closing of the 1876 Centennial Exposition in Philadelphia when the Smithsonian received a group of kites from the Chinese Imperial Commission. In 1889, the Stringfellow engine became the first object accessioned into the collection. The twentieth century brought an explosion in flight technology and the emergence of air power as a deciding factor in World War II. The collections of the NAM were housed in the Arts and Industries Building, in a shed in the south yard known as the "Air and Space Building," and outdoors in "Rocket Row." The beginning of the conquest of space in the 1950s and 1960s helped to drive the renaming of the Air Museum and finally congressional passage in 1971 of appropriations for the construction of the new Museum.

After the groundbreaking ceremony held in November 1972, work on the new building proceeded on two fronts—the actual construction of the edifice and work by the staff on two dozen exhibition halls. The staff moved into the Museum in 1975 and completed preparations for the July 1, 1976, opening, part of the Smithsonian's contribution to the Bicentennial celebration. During the 1980s, the Museum began to focus more directly on its research component. Fellowships were established in the curatorial departments, outreach in the form of lectures and other public programs increased, and the NASM Archives was created.

DIRECTOR, DEPUTY DIRECTOR, ASSOCIATE DIRECTOR, AND ASSISTANT DIRECTOR, 1912-1989

(162)

National Air and Space Museum, 1912-1971
Records (11.8 linear meters).

For an administrative history of the National Air and Space Museum (NASM), see the introduction to NASM.

This record unit consists primarily of correspondence documenting the activities of the Museum director and its curators. Records include public inquiries and staff replies concerning aeronautical history and artifacts, requests and arrangements for lectures by the NASM staff, accession acknowledgements, exhibitions, fiscal matters, NASM reports, and personnel information, especially concerning Carl W. Mitman.

Important correspondents include Paul E. Garber, Esther C. Goddard, Philip S. Hopkins, S. Paul Johnston, and Carl W. Mitman. Institutions collaborating with NASM include the United States Army, Navy, and Air Force; the National Aeronautics and Space Administration; and the Civil Aeronautics Board.

ARRANGEMENT: (1) Incoming and outgoing correspondence, 1912-1958; (2) incoming and outgoing correspondence, 1956-1958; (3) incoming and outgoing correspondence, 1934-1960; (4) incoming and outgoing correspondence, 1961-1965, 1967; (5) Department of Education and Information, incoming and outgoing correspondence, 1968-1970; (6) Department of Astronautics, incoming and outgoing correspondence, 1966-1967; (7) outgoing chronological file, 1959-1970 (sampled); (8) personnel; (9) budget, contracts, transportation, travel, requisitions, rents, and utilities, 1948-1959; (10) reports, storage facilities, and miscellaneous. FINDING AIDS: Folder list in control file. SPECIAL CONDITIONS: Use of this record unit requires prior arrangement with the Archives staff.

(306)

Office of the Director, National Air and Space Museum, 1971-1978 and undated
Records (2.5 linear meters).

For an administrative history of the National Air and Space Museum (NASM), see the introduction to NASM.

These records are the official files of astronaut Michael Collins as Director, 1971-1978. To a large extent, the files concern the planning and funding of the new NASM building, its construction, the preparation of exhibits, and the opening of the Museum on July 1, 1976.

On day-to-day administrative matters, documentation is uneven or lacking in some areas. Correspondents do, however, include Smithsonian and NASM staff, congressmen and other government officials, members of the aerospace and other industries, museum directors, astronauts, and the public.

ARRANGEMENT: (1) Administrative subject files, 1971-1978; (2) reading files, 1971-1976; (3) photographs, 1971-1978 and undated; (4) artifacts. FINDING AIDS: Description in control file. SPECIAL CONDITIONS: Use of this record unit requires prior arrangement with the Archives staff.

Office of the Director, National Air and Space Museum, circa 1972-1989
Records (13.5 linear meters).

For an administrative history of the National Air and Space Museum (NASM), see the introduction to NASM.

These records provide documentation on the development of NASM after the huge success of its 1976 opening. The emphasis of the Museum's administration turned to revitalization of research efforts, professionalization of the staff, initiation of new projects and new exhibitions, an expanded program of publications, and plans to build both a new restaurant and an extension of the Museum at Dulles Airport.

The records primarily document the tenure of Walter J. Boyne as Acting Director and Director of NASM, 1982-1986, with small amounts of material pertaining to Michael Collins, Noel W. Hinners, James C. Tyler, Donald S. Lopez, and Martin O. Harwit. Also included are some records created by Boyne as Executive Officer, 1978-1979, Assistant Director for Resource Management and Operations, 1980, and Assistant Director, 1981.

ARRANGEMENT: (1) Director's files, *circa* 1972-1982, accession number 83-091; (2) director's files, 1981-1986, accession number 87-074; (3) director's files, 1983-1984, accession number 90-056; (4) director's files *circa* 1984-1986, accession number 89-073; (5) director's files, *circa* 1985-1986, accession number 89-120; (6) director's files, *circa* 1984-1989, accession number 91-097. FINDING AIDS: Description in control file. SPECIAL CONDITIONS: (1) Restricted; (2) use of this record unit requires prior arrangement with the Archives staff.

Deputy Director, National Air and Space Museum, 1961-1988
Records (10.3 linear meters).

The position of Deputy Director was created in 1971 when Director Michael Collins appointed Melvin B. Zisfein to the office. Zisfein, who was also Acting Director in 1978, served until 1981 when he left the Museum. Walter J. Boyne was named Deputy Director in 1981 and held the office, along with that of Acting Director, until 1983, when he became Director. In 1983 Boyne chose Donald S. Lopez to be Deputy Director for Curatorial Sciences. In 1984 the title was shortened to Deputy Director.

These records consist of files of both Zisfein and Lopez as Deputy Director. Included are administrative subject files, chronological correspondence files, and files on Guggenheim fellowships, 1979-1986. Some correspondence was created by Toni E. Thomas, Special Assistant to Donald S. Lopez.

ARRANGEMENT: (1) Records of the Deputy Director, 1961-1981, accession number 84-096; (2) records of the Deputy Director, 1979-1987, accession number 88-104; (3) records of the Deputy Director, fiscal year 1983, accession number 86-167; (4) records of the Deputy Director, 1986-1988, accession number 91-105. FINDING AIDS: Folder list in control file. SPECIAL CONDITIONS: (1) Restricted; (2) use of this record unit requires prior arrangement with the Archives staff.

Deputy Director, National Air and Space Museum, 1974-1976
Records (0.1 linear meter).

For an administrative history of the Deputy Director, see record unit 346.

These records consist of National Air and Space Museum (NASM) meeting reports and exhibit status reports in regard to preparations for the opening of the NASM building in July 1976.

ARRANGEMENT: Status reports and meeting reports. FINDING AIDS: None. SPECIAL CONDITIONS: Use of this record unit requires prior arrangement with the Archives staff.

Associate Director for Research, National Air and Space Museum, 1984-1987
Records (2.9 linear meters).

The position of Associate Director for Research was created by Director Walter J. Boyne in 1983 to develop a center for the study of the history of aerospace science at the National Air and Space Museum, highlighting its role in research and technology. Paul A. Hanle, formerly Associate Curator of the Department of Science and Technology, 1976-1977; Curator, 1978-1979; Acting Chairman of the Space Science and Exploration Department, 1980; and Chairman of the Department, 1981-1983, was appointed to the new office. By 1986 he was in charge of educational planning, education, publications and special projects, volunteer services, and university programs. When Hanle left the Museum in 1987, the position was abolished.

Some of the projects undertaken during Hanle's tenure included the Space Telescope History Project, the Air and Space Bibliography, and the Smithsonian History of Aviation Project.

These records consist primarily of administrative subject files concerning meetings, budgets, publications, lectures, professional appointments, seminars, grants, and projects.

ARRANGEMENT: Unarranged. FINDING AIDS: Folder list in control file. SPECIAL CONDITIONS: (1) Restricted; (2) use of this record unit requires prior arrangement with the Archives staff.

Assistant Director for Exhibits, National Air and Space Museum, circa 1963-1986
Records (4.9 linear meters and 3 oversize drawers).

The Exhibits Division was created in 1974 with Francis A. Baby as its Chief. Baby served until 1978 when Frank A. Nelms became Acting Chief. In 1979 Melvin B. Zisfein held the title of Acting Chief. In 1980 the Exhibits and Presentations Division was formed with Richard D. Crawford as Acting Chief. Edward Bedno was selected as Chief in 1981, with Crawford succeeding him in 1982. Crawford served in the position of Chief in 1983 and then as Assistant Director for Exhibits and Production Operations. Later that year Nadya A. Makovenyi became Chief of Exhibits, then Assistant Director for Exhibits and Public Spaces, 1984- .

These records provide documentation of the creation and preparation of exhibits for the most important period in the history of the National Air and Space Museum (NASM): the planning, fabrication, and installation of two dozen major galleries for the new museum building, which opened in 1976. Also included is material on exhibits in the Arts and Industries Building, where the museum collections were located before 1975, and on smaller, changing, exhibitions, as well as on the plans for the NASM restaurant. The records consist of correspondence, memoranda, reports, policy statements, procedure lists, reviews, contracts, some photographs, and a number of oversize plans and drawings.

ARRANGEMENT: (1) Exhibit records, *circa* 1963-1976, accession number 84-161; (2) exhibit records, 1982-1984, accession number 84-172; (3) exhibit records, 1971-1984, accession number 85-014; (4) exhibit records, *circa* 1972-1980, accession number 87-033; (5) exhibit records, *circa* 1970-1977, accession number 87-073; (6) exhibit records, *circa* 1980-1986, accession number 91-063. FINDING AIDS: Folder list in control file. SPECIAL CONDITIONS: Use of this record unit requires prior arrangement with the Archives staff.

(354)

Assistant Director for Development, National Air and Space Museum, circa 1986-1989
Records (0.8 linear meter).

Fundraising and other development activities of the National Air and Space Museum were originally the responsibility of the Office of Public Affairs, although both curators and upper management had long been involved by virtue of their contacts with the aerospace industry. A Membership and Development Officer, reporting to the Chief of Public Affairs, was first named in 1986 when Marilyn E. Lyons took the title. In 1987 Susan Beaudette, and in 1988, John M. Carlin, served in the position. Carlin's title was changed to Assistant Director for Development in 1989.

These records document the work of the Development Office in the *Beyond the Limits* exhibition of 1987, concerning computers and flight, and the Glennan-Webb-Seamans Project to establish a clearinghouse on sources for studying space history and to encourage scholarship in, and preservation of, these sources.

The records include correspondence and memoranda, lists of corporate and individual donors, plans for conferences and receptions, and reports on the projects. Also included is a folder on the Rowland Emmett exhibition and material on fundraising software.

ARRANGEMENT: Unarranged. FINDING AIDS: None. SPECIAL CONDITIONS: (1) Restricted; (2) use of this record unit requires prior arrangement with the Archives staff.

CENTRAL AND ADMINISTRATIVE FILES, 1933-1978

(537)

National Air and Space Museum, circa 1933-1970
Records (0.5 linear meter).

For an administrative history of the National Air and Space Museum (NASM), see the introduction to NASM.

This record unit consists of fragmentary records of NASM and the National Air Museum (NAM) whose exact provenance is not known. The records include some correspondence with members of the Museum's Advisory Board and a few sets of agendas, lists of attendees, and minutes of a few meetings; a report of an outside consultant concerning the operation of the reference collection which eventually became the NASM Archives; several programs for NAM ceremonies; and a small amount of Paul E. Garber material, including several annual reports, copies of some correspondence, and lists of aircraft. Also included is ephemeral correspondence between the public and the NASM Library. Only a sample of this was retained.

ARRANGEMENT: Unarranged. FINDING AIDS: None. SPECIAL CONDITIONS: Use of this record unit requires prior arrangement with the Archives staff.

(351)

National Air and Space Museum, circa 1963-1964
Photographs (0.8 linear meter).

For an administrative history of the National Air and Space Museum (NASM), see the introduction to NASM.

These records consist primarily of photographs taken at various NASM luncheons, ceremonies, and presentations, 1963-1964.

ARRANGEMENT: Unarranged. FINDING AIDS: None. SPECIAL CONDITIONS: Use of this record unit requires prior arrangement with the Archives staff.

(345)

Executive Officer, National Air and Space Museum, circa 1974-1978
Records (0.8 linear meter).

The position of Executive Officer was created in 1973 and assigned to John Whitelaw, who had previously served as Administrative Officer, 1971-1972. Whitelaw remained as Executive Officer until 1978, when Walter J. Boyne became Acting Executive Officer. Boyne became Executive Officer in 1978 and held the title until 1979 when the position was abolished.

These records are the administrative subject files of John Whitelaw as Executive Officer, *circa* 1974-1978. Much of the material consists of copies of memoranda, budgets, and reports, mainly routine.

ARRANGEMENT: Unarranged. FINDING AIDS: None. SPECIAL CONDITIONS: Use of this record unit requires prior arrangement with the Archives staff.

CURATORIAL DEPARTMENTS, 1960-1991

(330)
Department of Aeronautics, National Air and Space Museum, 1966-1986
Records (9.5 linear meters).

The Department of Aeronautics had its origin in the Section of Aeronautics under the United States National Museum. During fiscal year 1965, the National Air Museum was divided into five departments, one of which was the Department of Aeronautics. Paul E. Garber, who joined the staff in 1919 and had been Assistant Curator for Aeronautics since 1933, was named Assistant Director for Education and Information. The Department of Aeronautics was divided into three sections: Flight Craft, Flight Propulsion, and Flight Materiel, headed by Curators Louis S. Casey, Kenneth E. Newland, and Robert B. Meyer, respectively.

In 1971 Donald S. Lopez became Assistant Director for Aeronautics. In 1980 his title was changed to Chairman, Aeronautics Department. Lopez served as Chairman until 1983 when he became Deputy Director of the Museum, and Edmund T. Wooldridge, Jr., became Chairman, serving until 1986.

These records consist of the correspondence files of the Aeronautics Department, 1966-1986. The files document day-to-day concerns with exhibitions, loans, and research during a period which included planning for the new Museum, moving, installation of major exhibition halls, and the emergence of the National Air and Space Museum as the most popular museum in the world. Also included are internal memoranda, the *Milestones of Flight* First Day Cover series, and files of correspondence with artists and modelers.

ARRANGEMENT: (1) Correspondence with individuals, museums, organizations, and military organizations, 1966-1976; (2) correspondence with individuals, 1977-1986; (3) correspondence with museums, 1977-1986; (4) correspondence with organizations, 1977-1986; (5) correspondence with military organizations, 1977-1986; (6) internal memoranda, 1966-1986; (7) *Milestones of Flight* First Day Cover series; (8) correspondence with artists and modelers; (9) miscellaneous subject files. FINDING AIDS: Description in control file. SPECIAL CONDITIONS: Use of this record unit requires prior arrangement with the Archives staff.

(344)
Department of Aeronautics, National Air and Space Museum, circa 1981-1989
Records (1.6 linear meters).

For an administrative history of the Department of Aeronautics, see record unit 330.

Edmund T. Wooldridge, Jr., served as Chairman of the Department of Aeronautics, 1983-1986. Von D. Hardesty became Acting Chairman in 1986 and then Chairman,

1986-1988, when Donald S. Lopez became Acting Chairman. In 1989 Dominick A. Pisano was appointed Acting Chairman.

These records consist primarily of the correspondence files of the Department for fiscal years 1987-1989, divided into separate series for museums, people, organizations, and international correspondence. Also included is a chronological file of staff memoranda and some miscellaneous correspondence of Curator Robert C. Mikesh, *circa* 1981-1986.

ARRANGEMENT: (1) Correspondence with museums, A-Z, 1986-1988; (2) correspondence with people, A-Z, 1986-1988; (3) correspondence with organizations, A-Z, 1986-1988; (5) international correspondence, 1986-1988; (5) miscellaneous correspondence of Robert C. Mikesh; (6) correspondence files, 1988-1989. FINDING AIDS: None. SPECIAL CONDITIONS: Use of this record unit requires prior arrangement with the Archives staff.

(398)

Department of Astronautics, National Air and Space Museum, 1965-1980, with materials dating from circa 1953
Records (8.3 linear meters).

Frederick C. Durant III joined the National Air and Space Museum (NASM) as Assistant Director (Astronautics) in 1965. In 1975 his title was changed to Chairman, Department of Astronautics. He served until 1980, when he left the Museum.

These records document the activities of Frederick C. Durant III as Assistant Director (Astronautics) and Chairman of the Department of Astronautics, 1965-1980. A small number of Durant's personal files, which predate his arrival at NASM, are also included.

The most important events of this period were the planning and building of the new museum, the preparation and installation of exhibits, and the opening of the building. Of special interest is correspondence with American astronauts, writer Arthur C. Clarke, and Gene Roddenberry, creator of the *Star Trek* television series. Durant's personal interests in stamp collecting, in magic, and in the Cosmos Club are also represented. Also included are his lecture notes, research notes, and reprint files.

For other records of the Department of Astronautics, see record units 347 and 348.

ARRANGEMENT: (1) Correspondence with individuals, 1957-1980; (2) correspondence with organizations, 1957-1980; (3) subject files and personal correspondence, 1953-1980; (4) personal correspondence, 1962-1973. FINDING AIDS: Description in control file. SPECIAL CONDITIONS: Use of this record unit requires prior arrangement with the Archives staff.

(353)

Center for Earth and Planetary Studies, National Air and Space Museum, circa 1974-1975, with related materials from circa 1966
Maps and Photographs (8 oversize drawers).

The Center for Earth and Planetary Studies (CEPS) was established in 1974 as part of a formal program of research at the National Air and Space Museum (NASM). At the same time, the National Aeronautics and Space Administration (NASA) transferred its collection of lunar scientific maps and photographs to CEPS. Farouk El-Baz, a lunar geologist and a member of the International Astronomical Union Taskgroup for Lunar Nomenclature, was appointed first Research Director in 1974. CEPS, working with

NASA, undertook both lunar and earth mapping projects, such as the *Apollo-Soyuz* Test Project, which utilized astronauts in earth orbit to study and map earth features.

This record unit consists entirely of oversize materials, mostly lunar surface maps and a few maps of Egypt's surface taken from space, 1966-1973, transferred from NASA.

For other records concerning lunar nomenclature, the lunar surface, and space maps of Egypt, see the papers of Farouk El-Baz, record unit 7415.

ARRANGEMENT: Unarranged. FINDING AIDS: None. SPECIAL CONDITIONS: Use of this record unit requires prior arrangement with the Archives staff.

(480)
Center for Earth and Planetary Studies, National Air and Space Museum, 1981-1991
Records (3.3 linear meters).

For an administrative history of the Center for Earth and Planetary Studies (CEPS), see record unit 353. Farouk El-Baz served as Director of CEPS, 1974-1982. In 1982 Ted A. Maxwell was named Acting Research Director. He then held the title of Chairman, 1983-1988. Thomas R. Watters was appointed Acting Chairman, 1989-   .

These records consist of correspondence files of Farouk El-Baz, Ted A. Maxwell, and Thomas R. Watters as heads of CEPS. Oversize materials can be found in record unit 353.

ARRANGEMENT: Unarranged. FINDING AIDS: Box list in control file. SPECIAL CONDITIONS: (1) Restricted; (2) use of this record unit requires prior arrangement with the Archives staff.

(348)
Department of Space Science and Exploration, National Air and Space Museum, circa 1960-1986
Records (10 linear meters).

For an administrative history of the Department of Astronautics, the predecessor to the Department of Space Science and Exploration, see record unit 398.

In 1980 Frederick C. Durant III left the Smithsonian. The Department of Astronautics was renamed the Department of Space Science and Exploration, and Paul A. Hanle became Acting Chairman. Hanle served as Chairman, 1981-1985, when David H. DeVorkin became Chairman, serving through 1986.

These records consist of administrative files of Durant and Hanle from the Department of Astronautics and the Department of Space Science and Exploration. Included are correspondence, budget materials, exhibit scripts, annual reports, files of former Curator Richard C. Hallion, correspondence of Durant concerning the American Institute of Aeronautics and Astronautics, and administrative files of David H. DeVorkin as Chairman.

ARRANGEMENT: (1) Administrative files of the Department, accession number 84-197; (2) administrative files of David H. DeVorkin as Chairman, accession number 88-057. FINDING AIDS: Folder list in control file. SPECIAL CONDITIONS: (1) Restricted; (2) use of this record unit requires prior arrangement with the Archives staff.

Department of Space Science and Exploration, National Air and Space Museum, circa 1972-1985
Records (3.7 linear meters).

For an administrative history of the Department of Space Science and Exploration, see record units 398 and 348.

These records consist of administrative files of the Department of Astronautics and the Department of Space Science and Exploration. They contain exhibit records, including scripts, status reports, and planning documents, as well as records concerning interns, publications, lectures, collections management, position descriptions, and professional meetings.

ARRANGEMENT: Unarranged. FINDING AIDS: Folder list in control file. SPECIAL CONDITIONS: (1) Restricted; (2) use of this record unit requires prior arrangement with the Archives staff.

Department of Space History, National Air and Space Museum, circa 1976-1990
Beyond the Limits Exhibition Records (8.6 linear meters).

For an administrative history of the Department of Space History, see record units 347, 348 and 398. For additional departmental exhibition records, see record unit 352.

In 1987 Joseph N. Tatarewicz served as Acting Chairman of the Department, followed by James H. Sharp. In 1988, Gregg F. Herken became Chairman and served 1988-   .

This record unit documents the curation of the *Beyond the Limits* exhibition in 1987 by Paul E. Ceruzzi of the Department of Space History. It includes the concept and label script, correspondence with donors, material concerning funding, reports, plans, photographs, and material concerning the design and production of the exhibition.

ARRANGEMENT: Unarranged. FINDING AIDS: Folder list in control file. SPECIAL CONDITIONS: Use of this record unit requires prior arrangement with the Archives staff.

COOPERATIVE PROGRAMS, PUBLIC AFFAIRS, AND SPECIAL EVENTS, 1971-1990

Office of Cooperative Programs, National Air and Space Museum, 1987-1990
Records (1 linear meter).

The Office of Cooperative Programs was created in 1987 to develop lectures, films, and seminars for the public and lectures for the staff. Helen C. McMahon was selected as its first manager and served 1987-   .

These records document three projects carried out by the Office of Cooperative Programs: the University Workshop on the History of Aviation, 1988; the Legacy of Strategic Bombing lecture series, 1989-1990; and the symposium on Preserving the History of the Aerospace Industry, April 1990.

The records include correspondence, budgets, contracts, schedules, biographies, and brochures.

ARRANGEMENT: (1) Office of Cooperative Programs records, accession number 90-081; (2) Office of Cooperative Programs records, accession number 91-168; (3) Office of Cooperative Programs records, accession number 92-043. FINDING AIDS: None. SPECIAL CONDITIONS: Use of this record unit requires prior arrangement with the Archives staff.

(339)

Office of Public Affairs, National Air and Space Museum, circa 1971-1989
Records (11.5 linear meters).

The first Public Information Officer of the National Air and Space Museum (NASM) was Lynne C. Murphy, who reported to the Director and served from 1976 to 1978. She was succeeded by Rita C. Bobowski, later known as Rita C. Cipalla, who held the title until 1980 when it was changed to Chief, Public Affairs and Museum Services. In 1987 the title was shortened to Chief, Public Affairs, and Cipalla continued to serve 1989-   .

The primary function of the Office of Public Affairs was the handling of all NASM events: openings, lectures, presentations, luncheons, and ceremonies.

These records consist primarily of special events files. Also included is a small amount of administrative material and records of the annual Frisbee Festival, 1977-1983 (series 3). Other Frisbee Festival materials can be found throughout the record unit.

ARRANGEMENT: (1) Public Affairs records, *circa* 1971-1983, accession number 84-142; (2) Public Affairs records, 1981-1984, accession number 87-082; (3) Public Affairs records, 1977-1983, accession number 84-153; (4) Public Affairs records, 1984-1985, accession number 88-061; (5) Public Affairs records, 1986-1987, accession number 89-002; (6) Public Affairs records, 1987, accession number 90-095; (7) Public Affairs records, 1987-1989, accession number 91-090. FINDING AIDS: Folder list in control file. SPECIAL CONDITIONS: Use of this record unit requires prior arrangement with the Archives staff.

(340)

Office of Special Events, National Air and Space Museum, 1979-1990
Records (2.1 linear meters).

The Office of Special Events originated as part of the public affairs activities of the National Air and Space Museum, and special events assistants and coordinators reported to the Chief of the Office of Public Affairs until June 1990. At that time Special Events became part of the Development Office, reporting to the Assistant Director for Development, John M. Carlin. For an administrative history of the Office of Public Affairs, see record unit 339.

These records consist primarily of files of special events for calendar year 1990, but also include a small number of files from previous years. Each file documents a specific event, such as a reception, a lecture, a dinner, an exhibition opening, or a staff party. The files include invitations, announcements, lists of guests, timetables, menus, memoranda, and occasionally photographs of the event. Researchers should consult record unit 339 for special events files dated 1971-1989.

ARRANGEMENT: Chronologic. FINDING AIDS: None. SPECIAL CONDITIONS: Use of this record unit requires prior arrangement with the Archives staff.

(409)

Office of Special Events, National Air and Space Museum, circa 1987-1990
Records (1.2 linear meters).

For an administrative history of the Office of Special Events, see record unit 340.

These records consist of files documenting events held at the National Air and Space Museum. The events include receptions, parties, award ceremonies, coffees, meetings, luncheons, dinners, lectures, and exhibition openings.

ARRANGEMENT: Chronologic. FINDING AIDS: Folder list in control file. SPECIAL CONDITIONS: Use of this record unit requires prior arrangement with the Archives staff.

SPACEARIUM, 1957-1989

(356)

Albert Einstein Spacearium, National Air and Space Museum, circa 1957-1989
Records (5.7 linear meters).

In 1974 the Presentation and Education Division at the National Air and Space Museum was organized to develop and implement educational programs and operate the theater and planetarium planned for the new museum, then being built. A thirty-foot domed planetarium, called the Experimentarium, went into operation in the Arts and Industries Building to serve as a pilot for the seventy-foot structure being planned. In 1975 the Federal Republic of Germany gave the United States, as a Bicentennial gift, a Zeiss planetarium projector for the planetarium. The planetarium was dedicated as the Albert Einstein Spacearium and opened in July 1976.

Von Del Chamberlain served as Chief of the Presentation and Education Division, 1974-1978, and Charles G. Barbely was Planetarium Officer, 1976-1978. In 1978, Presentation and Education was divided, with the Planetarium remaining with Presentation under Von Del Chamberlain until 1980. In that year the Planetarium became independent and the position of chief was vacant. In 1981 the Planetarium was placed under the Exhibits and Presentation Division, with Richard D. Crawford as Chief and Thomas H. Callen II as Chief of the Planetarium Unit. James H. Sharp served as Chief of the Unit, 1983- . Since 1983, the Planetarium has been moved around the administrative hierarchy a number of times, from Space Science and Exploration, to Museum Operations, to Exhibits and Production Operations, and finally to Interpretive Programs, 1989- .

This record unit consists of administrative records, such as reports, correspondence, and attendance records, in addition to records concerning each show, including scripts, correspondence, and proposals. The actual audio and video tapes are in record unit 520. Material from the 1950s and 1960s concerns a proposed Washington Planetarium.

ARRANGEMENT: (1) Spacearium records, 1957-1979, accession number 84-001; (2) Spacearium records, 1985, accession number 90-080; (3) Spacearium records, 1986-1989, accession number 91-002; (4) Spacearium records, 1973-1981, accession number 84-146; (5) Spacearium records, 1979-1982, accession number 86-084. FINDING AIDS: Folder list in control file. SPECIAL CONDITIONS: Use of this record unit requires prior arrangement with the Archives staff.

(520)

Albert Einstein Spacearium, National Air and Space Museum, circa 1970-1989
Videotapes and Audiotapes (11.5 linear meters).

For an administrative history of the Albert Einstein Spacearium, see record unit 356.
    This collection consists of videotapes and audiotapes of Spacearium presentations.

ARRANGEMENT: Unarranged. FINDING AIDS: Box list in control file. SPECIAL CONDITIONS: Use of this record unit requires prior arrangement with the Archives staff.

BUILDING RECORDS, 1972-1976

(358)

Contractors' Files, National Air and Space Museum, 1972-1976
Records (27 linear meters).

For an administrative history of the National Air and Space Museum (NASM), see the introduction to NASM.
    This record unit documents the construction of the new Museum building, from ground-breaking in 1972 until its opening in July 1976. The majority of the records were in the custody of the Building Management Division of the Museum, while a smaller amount came from the Smithsonian's Office of Design and Construction.
    These records consist of bids, correspondence, employee lists, meeting reports, and architectural drawings and plans associated with the work of each contractor. Approximately half the records concern the work of the principal contractor, the Gilbane Building Company, while the remainder document the work of various other contractors dealing with foundations, structural steel, food service equipment, carpentry, and landscaping.

ARRANGEMENT: Contractors' files, accession number 85-188. FINDING AIDS: Folder list in control file. SPECIAL CONDITIONS: Use of this record unit requires prior arrangement with the Archives staff.

SMITHSONIAN ASTROPHYSICAL OBSERVATORY

Established in 1890 by Secretary Samuel P. Langley, the Smithsonian Astrophysical Observatory (SAO) was one of the earliest to practice the "new astronomy," or astrophysics. Originally housed in a shed behind the Smithsonian Building, the Observatory initially focused its research on the study of solar radiation and the solar constant—the amount of energy from the sun that strikes the outer edge of the earth's atmosphere. Langley was Director of the Observatory until his death in 1906. Charles G. Abbot, who came to SAO in 1895 as an assistant, was appointed Director in 1907. Under Abbot's direction several solar observing stations were established in the United States, South America, and Africa to carry out research on solar radiation. On Abbot's retirement in 1944, Loyal B. Aldrich was appointed Director of SAO.

In 1955, the Smithsonian and Harvard University joined in an agreement to conduct astrophysical research, and the scientific headquarters of SAO was moved to Cambridge, Massachusetts. Fred Lawrence Whipple, Chairman of the Astronomy Department at Harvard, was named Director, replacing Aldrich, who retired. The move to Cambridge and a close alliance with the Harvard College Observatory generated an expansion of the SAO research program. Contributions to the national space program were made by optical tracking of satellites at SAO stations around the world. Orbiting astronomical observatory experiments, meteoritical and cometary studies, and theoretical astrophysics investigations were also undertaken. A major SAO observatory located at Mount Hopkins, Arizona, was opened in 1968. The Multiple-Mirror Telescope, a joint project of SAO and the University of Arizona, was dedicated at Mount Hopkins in 1979. The Mount Hopkins Observatory was renamed the Fred Lawrence Whipple Observatory in 1981.

In 1973, the Smithsonian and Harvard University established at Cambridge the Center for Astrophysics (CFA) to coordinate the related research activities of SAO and the Harvard College Observatory under a single director. George B. Field became Director of CFA and of both observatories. The consolidated CFA research program was organized into seven divisions under Associate Directors: Atomic and Molecular Physics, High Energy Astrophysics, Optical and Infrared Astronomy, Planetary Sciences, Radio and Geoastronomy, Solar and Stellar Physics, and Theoretical Astrophysics. Major SAO studies in hydrogen masers, submillimeter wavelength interferometers, and infrared telescopes were undertaken in the 1970s and 1980s. Field returned to teaching and research in 1983, and was replaced as Director by Irwin I. Shapiro.

Two abbreviations have been used in reference to the Smithsonian Astrophysical Observatory, APO (Astrophysical Observatory) and SAO. The use of SAO apparently began sometime after the move to Cambridge.

Materials documenting the history of SAO are also found in the records of Secretaries Langley (record unit 31), Charles D. Walcott (record unit 45), Abbot (record unit 46), and Leonard Carmichael (record unit 50); Langley's personal papers (record unit 7003),

Abbot's personal papers (record unit 7005), and Whipple's personal papers (record unit 7431); an oral history interview with Whipple (record unit 9520); and a video history of the Multiple-Mirror Telescope (record unit 9542).

DIRECTOR, DEPUTY DIRECTOR, AND ASSISTANT DIRECTOR, 1893-1987

(474)

Smithsonian Astrophysical Observatory, 1893-1899
Records (0.1 linear meter).

Robert C. Child was appointed Assistant in the Astrophysical Observatory (APO) in 1893. In 1894 his title was changed to Aid, Acting in Charge, APO, a position he retained until 1896. Charles G. Abbot joined the APO as an Assistant in 1895. The following year he became Aid, Acting in Charge, APO.

This record unit consists of correspondence written to Child and Abbot by Samuel P. Langley, Secretary of the Smithsonian and APO Director. The correspondence concerns APO solar constant experiments, especially rules and precepts for photo-bolometric work; facilities, equipment, and apparatus; and APO publications.

ARRANGEMENT: Chronologic. FINDING AIDS: None. SPECIAL CONDITIONS: Use of this record unit requires prior arrangement with the Archives staff.

(85)

Smithsonian Astrophysical Observatory, 1923-1954
Records (2.9 linear meters).

These records consist mostly of correspondence between staff at the observing stations and Charles G. Abbot and others on the Observatory staff in Washington, regarding details of operating the stations and personnel problems. Also included are budgets, reports, and other administrative records. See also record unit 46. The stations for which records are included here are Montezuma, on the western slope of the Andes; Mount Saint Katherine, Egypt; Mount Brukkaros, Southwest Africa; Table Mountain, California; and Tyrone, New Mexico.

ARRANGEMENT: Most letters, filed by correspondent's name, under major headings of station names as follows: (1) California stations; (2) Saint Katherine Station; (3) Montezuma Station; (4) Tyrone Station; (5) budgets, reports, and articles about the observatory. FINDING AIDS: None. SPECIAL CONDITIONS: Use of this record unit requires prior arrangement with the Archives staff.

Smithsonian Astrophysical Observatory, circa 1954-1966
Records (26.5 linear meters).

These records consist of various administrative records accumulated since the move of the Smithsonian Astrophysical Observatory to Cambridge. The records consist of four groups of records which were retired to the Waltham Federal Records Center during the 1960s, and no order is apparent. Evidently some of the records are from a central file maintained by SAO, while others were accumulated from various offices. Retrieval is difficult.

ARRANGEMENT: By Federal Records Center Accession, essentially unarranged. FINDING AIDS: Folder list and transfer lists in control file. SPECIAL CONDITIONS: Use of this record unit requires prior arrangement with the Archives staff.

Director, Smithsonian Astrophysical Observatory, 1971-1987
Records (12.7 linear meters).

For an administrative history of the Smithsonian Astrophysical Observatory (SAO), see the introduction to SAO. Fred Lawrence Whipple retired as Director of SAO in 1973. He was succeeded by George B. Field, who served in the position until 1983. Irwin I. Shapiro was appointed Director in January 1983.

These records document the administration and scientific programs of SAO under the leadership of Field, 1973-1983, and Shapiro, 1983-1987. A small amount of material was created during Whipple's tenure as Director. The records consist of correspondence, memoranda, proposals, reports, budgets, publications, and related materials documenting the research activities of SAO divisions of Atomic and Molecular Physics, High Energy Astrophysics, Optical and Infrared Astronomy, Planetary Sciences, Radio and Geoastronomy, Solar and Stellar Physics, and Theoretical Astrophysics; the development and operation of the Multiple-Mirror Telescope; the research program of the Fred Lawrence Whipple Observatory (before 1981, the Mount Hopkins Observatory); the Satellite Tracking Program, including its evolution from Baker-Nunn cameras to laser-ranging systems, and its termination in 1983; SAO research programs in hydrogen masers, submillimeter wavelength interferometers, and infrared telescopes; the development of the Langley-Abbot Solar Research Program; relations with Harvard University, and SAO's role as a member of the Center for Astrophysics; the establishment of the SAO visiting scientist and post-doctoral fellowship programs; SAO involvement in site testing for an observatory on Mount Graham, Arizona; a proposed Institute for X-Ray Astronomy at SAO; and budgets, facilities, information management, personnel actions, publication programs, and other administrative matters.

Also included is incoming and outgoing correspondence of Field and Shapiro with professional colleagues, staff of SAO and the Harvard College Observatory, students, and the general public concerning scientific research, professional affairs, administrative issues, and requests for information.

ARRANGEMENT: (1) Director's records, 1971-1979, accession number 81-092; (2) Director's records, 1972-1981, accession number 83-026; (3) Director's records, 1972-1984, accession number 87-016; (4) Director's records, 1973-1980, accession number 85-109; (5) Director's records, 1973-1987, accession number 90-029. FINDING AIDS: Folder list in control file. SPECIAL CONDITIONS: (1) Restricted; (2) use of this record unit requires prior arrangement with the Archives staff.

(468)

Deputy Director, Smithsonian Astrophysical Observatory, circa 1963-1983
Records (15.2 linear meters).

As a result of a 1973 administrative reorganization of the Smithsonian Astrophysical Observatory (SAO), the position of Assistant Director (Administration) was abolished. At that time, a new position with the title of Assistant Director was created to handle procurement and fiscal control; facilities management; information systems; budget planning; personnel management; and other administrative matters. John G. Gregory was appointed Assistant Director in 1973. In 1982, the title was changed to Deputy Director and Gregory remained in the position. For an administrative history of the office of the Assistant Director (Administration) see record unit 256.

These records were created primarily by John G. Gregory as Assistant Director, 1973-1982, and Deputy Director, 1982-1983. A small amount of material was created by his predecessors, Carlton W. Tillinghast, 1961-1969, and Robert V. Bartnik, 1970-1973. The records include correspondence, memoranda, reports, budgets, and publications documenting SAO research projects, especially the Multiple-Mirror Telescope, the Fred Lawrence Whipple Observatory (before 1981, the Mount Hopkins Observatory), and the Infrared Telescope Program; activities of SAO scientific divisions; the Satellite Tracking Program and its phase-out in 1983; SAO involvement in the Boyden Observatory in South Africa, 1964-1977; the establishment of the Center for Astrophysics in 1973; SAO relations with Smithsonian bureaus and offices; SAO relations with the Harvard College Observatory; and general administrative matters such as personnel, budgeting, facilities, information management, planning, program reviews, and audits.

ARRANGEMENT: (1) Deputy Director's files, *circa* 1963-1983, accession number 85-073; (2) Deputy Director's files, *circa* 1966-1982, accession number 84-039; (3) Deputy Director's files, *circa* 1968-1982, accession number 84-013; (4) Deputy Director's files, *circa* 1973-1983, accession number 85-112. FINDING AIDS: Transfer lists in control file. SPECIAL CONDITIONS: (1) Restricted; (2) use of this record unit requires prior arrangement with the Archives staff.

(256)

Assistant Director (Administration), Smithsonian Astrophysical Observatory, 1964-1973
Records (1.2 linear meters).

Under the administrative control of the Office of the Director, the Assistant Director (Administration) was responsible for coordinating the Smithsonian Astrophysical Observatory's (SAO) service requirements and maintaining liaison with Smithsonian headquarters in Washington, D.C. Responsibilities of the Assistant Director (Administration) included contracting, procurement, and fiscal control; personnel management; budget planning and control; and management information programs. Prior to 1973, the title of the position was Assistant Director (Management). Kenneth H. Drummond became the first Assistant Director (Management) when the position was created in 1959 and served until 1961. Carlton W. Tillinghast held the office from 1961 until his death in 1969. Robert V. Bartnik was appointed to the position in 1970 and served until 1973.

This record unit consists primarily of administrative files maintained by Robert V. Bartnik in his capacity as Assistant Director (Administration), 1970-1973. A smaller amount of material was created by his predecessor, Tillinghast, 1964-1969. The files are arranged alphabetically by subject and include correspondence, memoranda, charts, reports, and scientific papers. The records are primarily administrative in nature and concern personnel, fiscal planning, conferences and meetings, computer operations, and building and office space matters. Of special interest are files documenting SAO relations with other astronomical organizations including the Cambridge Radio Observatory Committee and the Northeast Radio Observatory Corporation. Also contained in the record unit is material concerning SAO projects, including the Earth Physics Satellite, Project Celescope, the Satellite Tracking Program, and the Environmental Sciences Program. A small amount of correspondence of Leon Campbell, Jr., Special Assistant to the Director, 1969-1971, is included in the records.

ARRANGEMENT: Alphabetic. FINDING AIDS: Description in control file. SPECIAL CONDITIONS: Use of this record unit requires prior arrangement with the Archives staff.

(259)

Assistant Director (Management), Smithsonian Astrophysical Observatory, 1956-1967
Records (3.3 linear meters).

Prior to 1959 the duties of this office were performed by the Executive Officer, Vaughan Harmon. For an administrative history of the Office of the Assistant Director (Management), see record unit 256.

This record unit consists primarily of records maintained by Assistant Director Carlton W. Tillinghast, 1961-1969, with smaller amounts created by his predecessor, Kenneth H. Drummond, 1959-1961, and the Executive Officer, Vaughan Harmon. Also included are correspondence and memoranda addressed to SAO Director, Fred Lawrence Whipple. This material was usually referred to the Assistant Director for action. Records include general correspondence, 1957-1964, concerning SAO administration and scientific projects including Project Celescope; the Harvard Radio Meteor Project; SAO-International Year of the Quiet Sun Comet Project; the Meteorite Photography and Recovery Project (Prairie Network); and the Satellite Tracking Program. Of special interest is correspondence regarding the closing of SAO's Table Mountain, California, station in 1961. The record unit also includes administrative files, 1956-1966; Satellite Tracking Program records, 1957-1964, including administrative and tracking station files; and a buildings file, 1957-1966.

Around 1964, a numerical-subject records management system was instituted at SAO. Records were assigned a number code based on subject classification and filed numerically. Often records prior to 1964 were refiled using the numerical-subject system. Retrieval of records using the system is difficult.

ARRANGEMENT: (1) General correspondence and administrative files, 1957-1964; (2) administrative files, 1956-1966; (3) Satellite Tracking Program, administrative files, 1959-1967; (4) Satellite Tracking Program, station files, 1957-1964; (5) buildings file, 1957-1966. FINDING AIDS: Description in control file. SPECIAL CONDITIONS: Use of this record unit requires prior arrangement with the Archives staff.

(253)

Assistant Director (Science), Smithsonian Astrophysical Observatory, 1961-1973
Records (6.1 linear meters).

Under the administrative control of the Office of the Director, the Assistant Director (Science) was responsible for coordinating the Smithsonian Astrophysical Observatory's (SAO) scientific investigations. Charles A. Lundquist became Assistant Director (Science) when the post was created in 1962. When Lundquist resigned in 1973, the position was abolished as a part of the reorganization of SAO and the Harvard College Observatory into the Center for Astrophysics. At that time, seven Associate Directors were appointed to administer SAO scientific programs.

This record unit consists of administrative records maintained by Charles A. Lundquist as Assistant Director (Science) which primarily concern SAO scientific projects. Projects represented in the records include the Satellite Tracking Program, Celescope Project, Gravitational Redshift Space Probe Experiment, Hydrogen Maser Program, Very Long Baseline Interferometer, Earth Albedo Project, Meteor Research Program, Meteor Simulation Project (Wallops Island), Radio Meteor Project, Southwest Meteor Spectral Patrol, Meteorite Photography and Recovery Project (Prairie Network), Mount Hopkins Observatory, Multiple-Mirror Telescope Project, National Geodetic Satellite Program, SAO Earth Physics Satellite (Cannonball), Big Dish Radio Telescope, Central Bureau for Astronomical Telegrams, and the Star Catalogue. The record unit also includes files dealing with SAO and Smithsonian administration; records concerning National Aeronautics and Space Administration scientific projects and administration; general correspondence of Lundquist, 1962-1972; and an organizational file. A small amount of material predates Lundquist's appointment as Assistant Director (Science) in 1962.

ARRANGEMENT: (1) SAO project files, 1961-1973; (2) National Aeronautics and Space Administration files, 1962-1973; (3) SAO administrative files, 1962-1973; (4) Smithsonian Institution administrative files, 1963-1973; (5) general correspondence, 1962-1972; (6) organizational file, 1962-1973. FINDING AIDS: Description in control file. SPECIAL CONDITIONS: Use of this record unit requires prior arrangement with the Archives staff.

DEPARTMENTS AND PROJECTS, 1956-1985

(260)

Project Celescope, Smithsonian Astrophysical Observatory, 1958-1968
Records (2.6 linear meters).

Conceived in 1958, Project Celescope was an experiment undertaken by the Smithsonian Astrophysical Observatory (SAO) to study the atmospheres of the hotter stars by means of photometric measurements in those regions of the ultraviolet that are accessible only from above the earth's atmosphere. Measurements were obtained by mounting telescopes in an orbiting satellite that would focus starlight on ultraviolet-sensitive television cameras. Project Celescope was funded by the National Aeronautics and Space Administration (NASA) as part of their Orbiting Astronomical Observatory (OAO) program. The project reached a climax on December 7, 1968, when NASA launched the second OAO satellite containing the Celescope experiment. More than 8,500 photographs of over 2,800 areas of the sky were made during the experiment's lifetime.

From 1958 to 1965, Project Celescope existed as a separate division of SAO. In 1965 the project was placed under administrative control of the newly created Department of Flight Operations. The project's primary staff included Fred Lawrence Whipple, Project Director; Robert T. Davis, Project Scientist; and Francis R. Nitchie, Jr., Engineering Administrator, 1958-1962. In 1962, the title of the latter position was changed to Project Manager. Project Managers included G. K. Megerian, 1962; Charles A. Lundquist, Acting Project Manager, 1963; and John J. Burke, 1964-1968.

This record unit documents the operation of Project Celescope from its inception in 1958 until shortly before the launch of the experiment in December 1968. Records include correspondence, memoranda, TWX messages, contracts, invitations, bids and proposals; reports; and related materials concerning the technical development of Celescope; involvement of NASA in the project; SAO administration of the project; and the selection and work of contractors producing instruments for the project.

ARRANGEMENT: (1) Outgoing correspondence, 1958-1967; (2) National Aeronautics and Space Administration correspondence, 1958-1968; (3) interoffice memoranda, 1958-1967; (4) TWX messages, 1959-1967; (5) Electro-Mechanical Research, Inc., correspondence, 1961-1967; (6) technical directives file, 1963-1967; (7) contracts file, 1958-1965. FINDING AIDS: Description in control file. SPECIAL CONDITIONS: Use of this record unit requires prior arrangement with the Archives staff.

(302)

Meteorite Photography and Recovery Project (Prairie Network), Smithsonian Astrophysical Observatory, circa 1962-1975
Records (0.4 linear meter).

The Meteorite Photography and Recovery Project, also known as the Prairie Network, was created in 1962 and supported by a grant from the National Aeronautics and Space

Administration. The Prairie Network was a system of 16 automatic camera stations organized in the midwestern United States to acquire orbital and trajectory data on extremely bright meteors. The data was then used to recover any resultant meteorites. Richard E. McCrosky was the scientist in charge of the project from 1962 until its termination in 1975.

This record unit consists primarily of administrative records and includes fiscal records, grant and contract proposals, camera station reports, requisitions and purchase orders, travel records, personnel records, and annual reports.

ARRANGEMENT: Unarranged. FINDING AIDS: None. SPECIAL CONDITIONS: Use of this record unit requires prior arrangement with the Archives staff

(255)

Moonwatch Division, Smithsonian Astrophysical Observatory, 1956-1975
Records (8.5 linear meters).

The Moonwatch Division of the Smithsonian Astrophysical Observatory was created in 1956 as part of the Satellite Tracking Program established to track and photograph the artificial earth satellites to be launched during the International Geophysical Year, 1957-1958. The surprise launch of Sputnik in 1957 generated much enthusiasm for the satellite program. Amateur astronomers, often supported by local businesses and schools, formed groups of volunteers who manned rows of telescopes searching for satellites. The Moonwatch Division directed and instructed the observers, loaned them equipment, and tabulated the data collected. Scientists were named in other parts of the world to help establish Moonwatch teams in many foreign countries. Gradually many "teams" came to be composed of a single observer, highly skilled in satellite tracking and often affiliated with a local observatory or university. Until its termination in 1975, the Moonwatch Division coordinated this network of volunteers and amassed a total of nearly 400,000 observations of satellites. Directors of the Division included Armand N. Spitz, 1956-1957; Leon Campbell, Jr., 1957-1962; Richard C. Vanderburgh, 1962-1964; William P. Hirst, 1964-1968; and Albert Werner, 1968-1975.

The Volunteer Flight Officer Network (VFON) was established in 1963 by Denver Moonwatch team leader Herbert E. Roth to collect eyewitness reports of satellites and meteor sightings from airline pilots and other flight personnel. Roth was employed by United Airlines, which agreed to support the project by providing printing and mailing funds. In 1966 the VFON became affiliated with Moonwatch, which advised Roth and assumed a part of the mailing expenses. In 1969 Moonwatch assumed complete administrative control of VFON under a contract with the United States Air Force. Before its termination in 1975, the VFON had grown to include the employees of 118 airlines in fifty-seven countries and had collected approximately 4,200 observations. Roth served as its sole Director.

These records document the history of the Moonwatch Division and the Volunteer Flight Officer Network. They include the outgoing correspondence of Albert Werner, 1968-1975; general correspondence of the Moonwatch Division, 1957-1975; Moonwatch station files, 1956-1975, including correspondence and other data from American and foreign Moonwatch teams; Moonwatch administrative files, 1956-1975; Moonwatch project files, 1956-1975, including correspondence and reports on various comets, satellites, and other projects assigned to Moonwatch to track; incoming and outgoing correspondence of Herbert E. Roth, 1966-1975; general correspondence of the VFON, 1966-1975; VFON airline files containing correspondence and sighting reports from member airlines; VFON administrative files, 1966-1975; Moonwatch and VFON Newsletters and Bulletins, 1956-1975; and a small number of slides, tapes, and movies, 1966 and undated.

ARRANGEMENT: (1) Outgoing correspondence of Albert Werner, 1968-1975; (2) Moonwatch correspondence, 1957-1975; (3) Moonwatch station files, 1956-1975; (4) Moonwatch administrative files, 1956-1975; (5) Moonwatch project files, 1962-1973; (6) Herbert E. Roth correspondence, 1966-1975; (7) VFON miscellaneous correspondence, 1969-1975; (8) VFON airline files, 1963-1975; (9) VFON administrative files, 1963-1975; (10) newsletters and bulletins, 1956-1975; (11) slides, tapes, and movies, 1966 and undated. FINDING AIDS: Description in control file. SPECIAL CONDITIONS: Use of this record unit requires prior arrangement with the Archives staff.

(262)

Mount Hopkins Department, Smithsonian Astrophysical Observatory, 1966-1970
Records (0.7 linear meter).

In October 1965, Smithsonian Astrophysical Observatory (SAO) Director Fred Lawrence Whipple visited the southwestern United States for the purpose of choosing a site for a new branch observatory. The location selected was Mount Hopkins in the Santa Rita Mountains of Arizona. Development of the site began in 1966, and the observatory was officially opened on October 23, 1968. Research activities at Mount Hopkins included optical and laser satellite tracking for geodetic and geophysical studies, spectroscopic observation of both stellar and planetary bodies, and gamma-ray astronomy.

During 1965 and 1966, the Mount Hopkins Observatory project was administered by the Office of the Director. Jack A. Coffey served as the first Project Administrator from December 1965 to December 1966 (except during March and April 1966, when Raymond Watts served in the position). In 1967, the newly created Programs Management Office assumed responsibility for Mount Hopkins, with John J. Burke as Chief Administrative Officer. In 1969, the Mount Hopkins Department was established, with Ronald R. LaCount as Manager. Charles Tougas was appointed Field Manager of the Mount Hopkins site in 1966. He was assisted by Werner Kirchhoff, who served as Special Technical Advisor.

These records document the early history of the Mount Hopkins Observatory and concern site development, the construction of buildings, the development of astronomical instruments for use at Mount Hopkins, and projects conducted by SAO and the National Aeronautics and Space Administration at the Observatory. The records include a contracts file, 1966-1970; a projects file, 1967-1970; administrative records, 1966-1970; and photographs and color slides of the Observatory, 1969.

ARRANGEMENT: (1) Contracts file, 1966-1970; (2) projects file, 1967-1970; (3) administrative records, 1966-1970; (4) photographs and color slides, 1969. FINDING AIDS: Description in control file. SPECIAL CONDITIONS: Use of this record unit requires prior arrangement with the Archives staff.

Radio Meteor Project, Smithsonian Astrophysical Observatory, circa 1960-1971
Records (27.6 linear meters).

Created in 1958, the Radio Meteor Project analyzed the meteoric mass, velocity, orbital parameters, and physical phenomena associated with the atmospheric entry of micrometeoroids at heights of 86 to 110 km. Data was gathered by a multi-station radar system, based in Havana, Illinois. From 1958 to 1966, the project was under the administrative control of the Harvard College Observatory (HCO), with project staff including both HCO and Smithsonian Astrophysical Observatory (SAO) scientists. Principal funding for the project was from contracts with the National Science Foundation and the National Aeronautics and Space Administration. In 1966, administration of the project was transferred to SAO. The project was terminated in 1971, and the radar facility at Havana was transferred to the University of Illinois. SAO administrative officers of the Radio Meteor Project included Dorik Mechau, 1966; C. Hagge, 1966-1970; and Harris E. Rosenthal, 1970-1971. Chief scientific investigators of the project included Gerald S. Hawkins, Richard B. Southworth, and Richard E. McCrosky.

This record unit consists of films of meteors detected by the radar system at Havana, Illinois, *circa* 1960-1970; computer printouts containing data on meteors observed, *circa* 1966-1971; and computer tapes, *circa* 1965-1970.

ARRANGEMENT: Unarranged. FINDING AIDS: Box list in control file. SPECIAL CONDITIONS: Use of this record unit requires prior arrangement with the Archives staff.

Satellite Tracking Program, Smithsonian Astrophysical Observatory, 1956-1968
Satellite Tracking Station Records (10.9 linear meters).

Created in 1956 as part of the International Geophysical Year, the Satellite Tracking Program (STP) of the Smithsonian Astrophysical Observatory (SAO) was a world-wide network of stations responsible for the optical tracking of satellites. From 1956 until June 1959, the program was funded by a grant from the National Science Foundation. In July 1959, funding was assumed by the National Aeronautics and Space Administration (NASA). The goal of STP was to obtain photographs of satellites sufficient in number and accuracy to allow the determination of highly precise orbits. Data derived from the orbits provided information concerning variations in the density and temperature of the upper atmosphere and helped construct new representations of the earth's gravitational potential and geometrical figure. Twelve camera stations were established around the world between 36 degrees north and 36 degrees south of the equator. Stations were located at Jupiter, Florida (closed in 1967); Organ Pass, New Mexico (moved to Mount Hopkins, Arizona, in 1968); Maui, Hawaii; Curacao, Netherlands West Indies (moved to Natal, Brazil, in 1966); Arequipa, Peru; Villa Dolores, Argentina (moved to Comodoro Rivadavia, Argentina, in 1966); Shiraz, Iran (moved to Debre Zeit, Ethiopia, in 1966); Olifantsfontein, South Africa; Naini Tal, India; San Fernando, Spain; Tokyo, Japan (closed in 1968); and Woomera, Australia (moved to the Space Research Site at Island Lagoon, Australia, in 1964). Cooperative programs enabled STP to track satellites at United States Air Force stations at Oslo, Norway, and Johnston and Kwajalein Islands in the Pacific Ocean; the Royal Canadian Air Force Station at Cold Lake, Alberta; Harvard University's Agassiz Station; and the geodetic station at the National Technical University of Athens, Greece. A special satellite tracking camera, designed by James G. Baker and Joseph Nunn, was installed in each station.

When it was created in 1956, STP was a part of SAO's Upper Atmosphere Studies Division. The twelve satellite tracking camera stations were administered by the Photographic Observation Section, under the direction of Karl G. Henize. In 1961, STP became a separate Department of SAO. At that time the Station Operations Division (SOD) was created within STP for the administrative direction and logistical support of all satellite tracking camera stations, for maintenance of equipment and development of new equipment and techniques, and for technical support in observing procedures. SOD was organized into three sections—Administrative, Operations, and Engineering. Richard C. Brock became the first Chief of the Station Operations Division in June 1961. Other incumbents included Jan Rolff, 1962-1964, and Carl W. Hagge, Acting Chief, 1964-1965. In 1965, SOD was abolished and replaced by the Satellite Tracking and Data Acquisition Department (STADAD). STADAD assumed the duties of its predecessor and was also responsible for administering SAO's Meteor Simulation Project station at Wallops Island, Virginia. STADAD comprised five divisions—Optical Tracking Division, Moonwatch Division, Wallops Island Division, Engineering Division, and Administrative Support Division. John I. Hsia was appointed the first Manager of STADAD in 1965. Other incumbents included Jack A. Coffey, 1966-1968, and Harry Albers, 1968-   .

This record unit consists mostly of records documenting the administration and operation of the STP tracking stations and includes files on the stations kept by the Photographic Observation Section, 1956-1961; SOD, 1961-1965; and STADAD, 1965-1968. The station files consist of incoming and outgoing correspondence and memoranda, reports, and technical data concerning satellite tracking operations; station fiscal matters; the construction and maintenance of station buildings and facilities; conferences and meetings held at the stations; the procurement of equipment and supplies for the stations; station personnel; and special projects conducted at each station. Also included are administrative records of SOD and STADAD, station files and administrative records of the Engineering Section of SOD and STADAD, mostly concerning the operation of the Baker-Nunn tracking cameras at each station; station financial statements; and records documenting relations between SAO and foreign countries or states where tracking stations were located.

Many of the files in this record unit are arranged in a numerical-subject records management system instituted at SAO around 1964. In the system, records were assigned a number code based on subject classification and filed numerically. Often records prior to 1964 were refiled using the numerical-subject system. Retrieval of records using the system is difficult.

ARRANGEMENT: (1) Station files, 1956-1965; (2) station files, 1962-1965; (3) station files, 1962-1968; (4) administrative records, 1959-1967; (5) agreements file, 1956-1967; (6) administratively confidential station files, 1961-1966; (7) station financial statements, 1961-1967; (8) Engineering Section, station files, 1959-1963; (9) Engineering Section, station files, 1962-1968; (10) Engineering Section, administrative records, 1961-1967. FINDING AIDS: Description in control file. SPECIAL CONDITIONS: Use of this record unit requires prior arrangement with the Archives staff.

Satellite Tracking Program, Smithsonian Astrophysical Observatory, 1957-1968
Baker-Nunn Films (4 linear meters).

For an administrative history of the SAO Satellite Tracking Program (STP), see record unit 263.

This collection consists of ten Baker-Nunn films taken at each STP tracking station for each year from 1957 to 1968. A data sheet is included with each film.

ARRANGEMENT: By station. FINDING AIDS: None. SPECIAL CONDITIONS: Use of this record unit requires prior arrangement with the Archives staff.

Satellite Tracking Program, Smithsonian Astrophysical Observatory, 1957-1983
Records (26.7 linear meters and oversize).

For an administrative history of the Satellite Tracking Program (STP), see record unit 263.

As a result of an administrative reorganization of the Smithsonian Astrophysical Observatory (SAO) in 1973, the Satellite Tracking Program was placed under the management of the newly created Geoastronomy Division (after 1977, the Radio and Geoastronomy Division). At that time, Michael R. Pearlman was appointed Manager of STP.

During the 1970s, several of the STP's Baker-Nunn camera stations were replaced by laser-ranging tracking systems, as SAO's mission of operational tracking evolved into the support of scientific programs, particularly in earth dynamics. By the mid-1970s, STP laser ranging stations were operational in Arizona, Australia, Brazil, and Peru. STP also had cooperating agreements to track satellites with laser systems located in Spain and Greece. Baker-Nunn camera stations continued to make significant observations until 1978. Satellite data acquired by STP stations was used in investigations of polar motion, earth and ocean tides, crustal motion and deformation, and in the determination of the gravity field and its temporal variations. STP was terminated in 1983 when the National Aeronautics and Space Administration (NASA) contract to operate all NASA satellite tracking stations was awarded to the Bendix Corporation.

This record unit consists mostly of records documenting the administration, operation and scientific work of the STP Baker-Nunn camera and laser-ranging stations. The majority of the files were created after the SAO reorganization in 1973 and maintained by the Radio and Geoastronomy Division. The records include correspondence, memoranda, reports, drawings, blueprints, plans, schematics, charts, publications, manuals, maps, and data concerning station operations; station personnel; the design of stations and facilities; satellites tracked; equipment development, especially the laser-ranging system; agreements with host nations, states, and organizations; procurement requests and property inventories; weather at stations; and general administration. Also included is correspondence of STP Manager Michael R. Pearlman; photographs and slides of stations, personnel, equipment, and facilities; and information on foreign countries where stations were located.

ARRANGEMENT: Unarranged. FINDING AIDS: Box list in control file. SPECIAL CONDITIONS: (1) Restricted; (2) use of this record unit requires prior arrangement with the Archives staff.

(303)

Southwest Meteor Spectral Patrol, Smithsonian Astrophysical Observatory, 1968-1972

Records (0.2 linear meter).

The Southwest Meteor Spectral Patrol (SWMSP) was a meteor observing program carried out by the Smithsonian Astrophysical Observatory (SAO) to obtain spectral data during meteor showers. Funded under a National Aeronautics and Space Administration contract, SWMSP made observations at SAO's Organ Pass, New Mexico, and Wallops Island, Virginia, stations from 1968 through 1972. Claude Linton directed SWMSP from August to November 1968. Roy Proctor replaced Linton in November 1968 and remained in charge of the project until its termination in 1972.

This record unit contains material documenting the administrative and scientific work of SWMSP and includes budget and other fiscal records; project reports; correspondence and memoranda, mostly concerning the termination of SWMSP in 1972 and spectral data gathered during observations.

ARRANGEMENT: Unarranged. FINDING AIDS: None. SPECIAL CONDITIONS: Use of this record unit requires prior arrangement with the Archives staff.

(467)

Division of High Energy Astrophysics, Smithsonian Astrophysical Observatory, 1973-1985

Records (0.8 linear meter).

The High Energy Astrophysics Division of the Smithsonian Astrophysical Observatory is primarily involved in the study of X-ray emission from celestial sources, including such objects as pulsars, quasars, neutron stars, and black holes. X-ray astronomy must be carried out from space. The Division was established in 1973 to analyze data from satellite-borne X-ray detection instruments and to develop and plan instrumentation for future orbiting observatories. In the period covered by these records the efforts of the High Energy Astrophysics Division centered on data from the *Uhuru* and *Einstein* satellites and planning for the Advanced X-ray Astrophysics Facility. Riccardo Giacconi was named Associate Director of the Division in 1973. In 1981 Harvey D. Tananbaum became Associate Director of the Division.

This record unit consists of administrative memoranda distributed by Benson Rowe, the Program Manager for the Division. The memoranda concern budgets and expenditures, personnel actions, travel and work requests, and other administrative matters. They do not contain the product of the Division's scientific research, although budgeting and administrative support for that research are well documented.

ARRANGEMENT: Chronologic. FINDING AIDS: None. SPECIAL CONDITIONS: (1) Restricted; (2) use of this record unit requires prior arrangement with the Archives staff.

Radio and Geoastronomy Division, Smithsonian Astrophysical Observatory, 1978-1983
Records (1.2 linear meters).

The Radio and Geoastronomy Division was formed in fiscal year 1979 by the combination of two existing divisions, Radio Astronomy and Geoastronomy. The first of these two was formed in 1973 under the reorganization of the Smithsonian Astrophysical Observatory (SAO) conducted by new Director George B. Field. Arthur Edward Lilley, Professor of Radio-Astronomy at Harvard University, was appointed Associate Director of SAO in charge of this Division, a position he retained through the merger.

The Division of Geoastronomy was formed in 1970 under the direction of George Charles Weiffenbach, who joined SAO in 1969. Weiffenbach retained the directorship until 1976, when John C. Gregory took over as acting Associate Director until the merger of the two divisions.

These records were created primarily by Arthur Edward Lilley as head of the Division. Basic administrative records include files on the Northeast Radio Observatory Corporation and its Haystack Observatory in Westfield, Massachusetts; international astronomical organizations; and projects of two investigators of the Division, Mario Grossi and Giuseppe Colombo. Other records concern the Satellite Tracking Program, chiefly including material in support of SAO's contract with the National Aeronautics and Space Administration for FY 1980; a proposal to support the Goddard Space Flight Center in its Laser Tracking Network, including the proposal to take over the network completely; information about foreign tracking stations; and information about relocating a tracking station to India through agreement with the India Space Research Corporation.

ARRANGEMENT: (1) General files, 1978-1982; (2) satellite and laser geodesy files, 1979-1983. FINDING AIDS: Folder list in control file. SPECIAL CONDITIONS: (1) Restricted; (2) use of this record unit requires prior arrangement with the Archives staff.

CONTRACTS AND PROCUREMENT, 1956-1987

Contracts and Procurement Office, Smithsonian Astrophysical Observatory, 1956-1984
Contracts and Grants Records (16 linear meters).

The Contracts and Procurement Office is authorized to negotiate and administer federal and private contracts and grants for the Smithsonian Astrophysical Observatory (SAO). The Office is also responsible for providing supplies, services, materials, and equipment in response to requests from the SAO's scientific and administrative staff. Records maintained by the Office contain information on the formulation and administration of contracts and grants, which are especially useful for documenting SAO research projects.

These records primarily document the administration of contracts and grants supporting the Satellite Tracking Program, Project Celescope, the Meteor Research Program, and the Gravitational Redshift Space Probe Experiment. Also included are files documenting other contracts and grants, mostly with the National Aeronautics and Space Administration, the United States Army, and the United States Air Force. The records include correspondence with contracting and granting agencies, Smithsonian Institution officials, and project personnel; budgets, financial reports, and other fiscal information; progress and final reports; meeting minutes; property inventories; audits; contracts, amendments, and revisions; technical reports, drawings of instruments, and other information on project equipment; and correspondence with project subcontractors.

ARRANGEMENT: (1) Satellite Tracking Program, 1956-1984, accession number 88-067; (2) Project Celescope, 1958-1968, accession number 85-220; (3) Meteor Research Program and miscellaneous contracts and grants, 1965-1972, accession number 85-227; (4) Gravitational Redshift Space Probe Experiment, 1971-1976, accession number 85-219. FINDING AIDS: Box list in control file. SPECIAL CONDITIONS: (1) Restricted; (2) use of this record unit requires prior arrangement with the Archives staff.

(521)

Contracts and Procurement Office, Smithsonian Astrophysical Observatory, 1963-1984
Contracts and Grants Proposals (18.5 linear meters).

For a description of the Smithsonian Astrophysical Observatory's (SAO) Contracts and Procurement Office, see record unit 522.

These records consist of correspondence, memoranda, drafts, revisions, final copies, budgets, notes, and background data documenting proposals to outside organizations for contracts and grants to support the scientific research program of the SAO. Included are records concerning proposals submitted to government agencies (especially the National Aeronautics and Space Administration), universities, foreign governments, and private corporations.

ARRANGEMENT: (1) Contract and grant proposals, 1963-1980, accession number 85-213; (2) contract and grant proposals, 1980-1984, accession number 88-060. FINDING AIDS: Folder list in control file. SPECIAL CONDITIONS: (1) Restricted; (2) use of this record unit requires prior arrangement with the Archives staff.

(530)

Contracts and Procurement Office, Smithsonian Astrophysical Observatory, 1963-1968
Trust Fund Subcontracts (0.8 linear meter).

For a description of the Smithsonian Astrophysical Observatory's (SAO) Contracts and Procurement Office, see record unit 522.

These records document subcontracts issued by the SAO and funded with private funds of the Smithsonian Institution. Included are proposals, contracts, correspondence, memoranda, and reports concerning agreements with contractors to develop instruments and provide equipment for SAO projects and programs.

ARRANGEMENT: By contract number. FINDING AIDS: Folder list in control file. SPECIAL CONDITIONS: Use of this record unit requires prior arrangement with the Archives staff.

(525)

Contracts and Procurement Office, Smithsonian Astrophysical Observatory, 1965-1978
Quotations, Proposals, and Bids (8.2 linear meters).

For a description of the Smithsonian Astrophysical Observatory's Contracts and Procurement Office, see record unit 522.

These records document quotations, proposals, and bids from contractors, equipment makers, and other vendors to provide facilities and instruments for the Smithsonian Astrophysical Observatory and its programs. Of special interest are voluminous files concerning the development and planning for the Multiple-Mirror Telescope facility at Mount Hopkins, Arizona.

ARRANGEMENT: By quotation, proposal, or bid number. FINDING AIDS: Folder list in control file. SPECIAL CONDITIONS: Use of this record unit requires prior arrangement with the Archives staff.

(524)

Contracts and Procurement Office, Smithsonian Astrophysical Observatory, 1965-1986
Contracts and Grants Records (4.1 linear meters).

For a description of the Smithsonian Astrophysical Observatory's (SAO) Contracts and Procurement Office, see record unit 522.

These records consist mostly of proposals, reports, correspondence, and memoranda documenting SAO research projects funded by grants from Smithsonian Institution sources, including the Smithsonian Research Foundation, Scholarly Studies Program, Smithsonian Foreign Currency Program, Smithsonian Research Awards Program, Fluid Research Fund, and Smithsonian restricted private funds. Also included are files concerning SAO contracts and grants received from non-government agencies including universities, corporations, and private research organizations.

ARRANGEMENT: (1) Smithsonian Institution grants, 1967-1983, accession number 85-214; (2) Scholarly Studies Program grants, 1984-1986, accession number 88-063; (3) Smithsonian Research Foundation grants and non-government contracts and grants, 1965-1984, accession number 86-007. FINDING AIDS: Box list in control file. SPECIAL CONDITIONS: (1) Restricted; (2) use of this record unit requires prior arrangement with the Archives staff.

(523)

Contracts and Procurement Office, Smithsonian Astrophysical Observatory, 1969-1984
Contracts and Grants Records (6.8 linear meters).

For a description of the Smithsonian Astrophysical Observatory's (SAO) Contracts and Procurement Office, see record unit 522.

These records document the administration of contracts and grants received by the SAO from the National Aeronautics and Space Administration (NASA), the United States Air Force, and the United States Navy. They include correspondence and memoranda with contracting agencies, Smithsonian Institution officials, project personnel, and subcontractors; progress and final reports; technical reports and information on instrumentation; contracts, amendments, and revisions; budgets, financial reports, and other fiscal records; and property inventories and audits. The records provide information on SAO research projects in planetary sciences, theoretical astrophysics, high-energy astrophysics, radio astronomy, solar and stellar physics, atomic and molecular processes, geoastronomy, and optical and infrared astronomy.

ARRANGEMENT: (1) Contracts and grants with NASA, the United States Air Force, and the United States Navy, 1969-1984, accession number 86-009; (2) NASA grants, 1974-1984, accession number 86-022. FINDING AIDS: Box list in control file. SPECIAL CONDITIONS: (1) Restricted; (2) use of this record unit requires prior arrangement with the Archives staff.

(538)

Contracts and Procurement Office, Smithsonian Astrophysical Observatory, 1984-1987
Contracts and Grants Proposals (5.3 linear meters).

For a description of the Smithsonian Astrophysical Observatory's (SAO) Contracts and Procurement Office, see record unit 522.

These records consist of correspondence, memoranda, drafts, revisions, final copies, budgets, notes, and background data documenting proposals to outside organizations for contracts and grants to support the scientific research program of the SAO. Included are records concerning proposals submitted to government agencies, especially the National Aeronautics and Space Administration, universities, foreign governments and space programs, and private corporations. See also record unit 521 for additional contract and grant proposals.

ARRANGEMENT: By proposal number. FINDING AIDS: Folder list in control file. SPECIAL CONDITIONS: (1) Restricted; (2) use of this record unit requires prior arrangement with the Archives staff.

FREER GALLERY OF ART

The Freer Gallery of Art (FGA) was conceived by its founder, Charles Lang Freer (1854-1919), as a museum and a research institution. A Detroit industrialist, Freer collected more than 9,420 art objects and manuscripts before his death, including one of the largest collections of works by James McNeill Whistler; works by contemporary American artists including Childe Hassam, Winslow Homer, John Singer Sargent, Abbott Handerson Thayer, Thomas Wilmer Dewing, Dwight William Tryon, and Augustus Saint-Gaudens; and major collections of Chinese, Japanese, Egyptian, Near Eastern, and Indian objects. In 1904, Freer informally proposed to President Theodore Roosevelt that he give to the nation his art collection, funds to construct a building, and an endowment fund to provide for the study and acquisition of "very fine examples of Oriental, Egyptian, and Near Eastern fine arts." The deed of gift was executed in 1906 after the Smithsonian Institution's Board of Regents accepted Freer's offer on behalf of the government. Construction on the building to house the collection began in 1916 and was completed in 1921. On May 9, 1923, the FGA was opened to the public. The Gallery is an Italian Renaissance-style building of Massachusetts granite and Tennessee marble. The building was designed by American architect and landscape planner Charles A. Platt (1861-1933).

In 1920, John Ellerton Lodge (1878-1942), Curator of the Asiatic Department of the Museum of Fine Arts, Boston, was appointed the Freer's first Director. Lodge was the personal choice of Freer and continued to maintain his staff position at the Museum of Fine Arts until 1931. Lodge was Director of the Gallery until 1942; and in 1943, Archibald G. Wenley (1898-1962), who had been sent by Lodge to China, Japan, and France to study Asian languages, literature and history, became Director. Wenley held the position until 1962. Wenley was followed by John A. Pope (1906-1982), 1962-1971; Harold P. Stern (1923-1977), 1971-1977; Thomas Lawton (1931-   ), 1977-1987; and Milo C. Beach (1939-   ), 1988-   .

(4010001)

Central Files, Freer Gallery of Art, circa 1919-1982
Records (15.9 linear meters).

Apparently, outside of most registrarial and construction records, the Freer Gallery of Art (FGA) maintained one central file for correspondence and memoranda of its staff during its early years. Some documents concerning antiques and works of art sold to the Gallery along with photographs were interfiled with these records. Some time in the 1960s and 1970s the Gallery moved away from a centralized filing system.

The Central Files document the early development of the FGA and its administrative and research activities. They include information on the relationship of the Gallery to the Smithsonian and problems between Freer supporters and the Smithsonian concerning perceptions over proper use of the Freer endowment. Records include correspondence and memoranda among FGA staff, FGA staff and Smithsonian administrators and among Gallery staff, colleagues, other museums, government agencies and antique and art collection dealers.

Records include memoranda, correspondence, photographs, reports, invoices, and vouchers. Internal Gallery operations include information about exhibition openings, guard force requirements, correspondence with dealers, and purchasing of art objects and manuscripts. Records documenting these activities include plans of operations, budgetary and annual reports, position descriptions, and staff salaries. Research activities are documented through correspondence and reports on site excavations, information on exhibition catalogs and articles written by staff and examination of antiques and works of art forwarded to the Gallery for analysis and description. Also documented are staff activities for the government during World War II, especially translation of Japanese correspondence, documents, and shipping operations.

Staff members whose activities are documented in these records include Directors John Ellerton Lodge and Archibald G. Wenley, and to a lesser extent, John A. Pope, Harold P. Stern, and Thomas Lawton. Curators, specialists and administrative staff whose correspondence is included in this file are Grace D. Guest, Katherine N. Rhoades, William R. B. Acker, Carl W. Bishop, Richard Ettinghausen, Hin-cheung Lovell, and Esin Atil.

Major subject files include correspondence with the Detroit Trust Company, 1920-1922, and Frank J. Hecker, 1920-1923, concerning Freer's will, funds for the construction of the Gallery, Freer's collection, and the transfer of the collection from Detroit to Washington in 1920; an index of vouchers pertaining to Freer's purchases of objects, 1893-1919; correspondence with Charles A. Platt, 1920-1933; and correspondence between Lodge and Rhoades, 1920-1942, which documents viewpoints held by each individual on Freer's intentions and the relationship between the Gallery and the Smithsonian.

Gallery correspondence with other museums is well represented by its association with the Metropolitan Museum of Art, 1920-1981; the Art Institute of Chicago, 1937-1961; the Museum of Fine Arts, Boston, 1943-1979; and the British Museum regarding description and photographs of antiques, 1921-1961.

Records include important information on the publication series *Ars Orientalis* and *Ars Islamica;* the transfer of the Islamic Culture and Art Archives to the Freer, 1943; material about the Freer Medal and recipient Yashiro Yuko in 1965; visit by Emperor Hirohito of Japan, 1975; correspondence with Alva Studios, 1954-1982; correspondence with Avery Brundage, 1952-1973, and A. W. Bahr, 1923-1957, regarding their Chinese art and antique collections; correspondence with Smithsonian Secretary Charles D. Walcott, 1922-1926; and files on Fritz Low-Beer, art dealer, 1946-1961, reflecting the association of the Gallery with dealers world-wide concerning its interests in Far Eastern, Near Eastern, and Indian antiques and works of art. Correspondence with Kuang-zung Tung (Dong Guangzhong), 1923-1934, contains information on the Chinese Civil War and its influence over the Freer expeditions, problems with Chinese bandits, and Imperial action. Photographs in these files include Tung, Bishop, Wenley, various Chinese cities, the Yangtze River, and work at the excavation sites.

ARRANGEMENT: Alphabetic, though information on certain subjects may exist in different locations due to filing problems. FINDING AIDS: None. SPECIAL CONDITIONS: These records are located in the Freer Gallery of Art and Arthur M. Sackler Gallery Archives, Smithsonian Institution.

Personnel and Special Events, Freer Gallery of Art, 1920s-1980s
Photographs (1 linear meter).

These photographs were created by staff from the Freer Gallery of Art (FGA) to document special events of the Gallery and to serve as a portrait file of FGA personnel.

Photographs document FGA award presentations, exhibition openings, receptions, staff members, and visitors. Special events documented include visits by the King of Nepal, 1960, and the Crown Prince of Japan, 1965; the 50th anniversary of the FGA in 1973; opening of the *Art of the Arab World* exhibition, 1975; a memorial reception for Agnes E. Meyer; and the retirement party for Director John A. Pope.

FGA staff documented by the photographs include Curators James F. Cahill, Esin Atil, and Richard Ettinghausen; Directors Thomas Lawton, John Ellerton Lodge, Harold P. Stern, and Archibald G. Wenley; Assistant Director Sarah Newmeyer; and Smithsonian Secretary S. Dillon Ripley and his wife, Mary Livingston Ripley.

ARRANGEMENT: (1) Personnel photographs, arranged alphabetically; (2) special events photographs, arranged chronologically. FINDING AIDS: None. SPECIAL CONDITIONS: These records are located in the Freer Gallery of Art and Arthur M. Sackler Gallery Archives, Smithsonian Institution.

Building Construction Records, Freer Gallery of Art, 1916-
Records (5.3 linear meters and 15 oversize drawers).

These records were assembled by the Freer Gallery of Art (FGA) staff to document the history of the Freer Museum building designed by Charles A. Platt. Gallery construction began in 1916. Construction was carried out by the George A. Fuller Company. The building was completed in 1921.

Records include architectural drawings, specifications, blueprints and photographs documenting the groundbreaking of the Gallery, construction, and development of the exterior and interior of the building. Later records provide documentation on the building's facade, the interior courtyard and James McNeill Whistler's Peacock Room. In addition there are photographs of the Smithsonian Institution Building, Arts and Industries Building, the Post Office Building, the United States Capitol, the Washington Monument, and the Central Market.

ARRANGEMENT: (1) Construction photographs, arranged chronologically; (2) building photographs, arranged by view; (3) blueprints, arranged by architectural firm. FINDING AIDS: There is a finding aid for the blueprints. SPECIAL CONDITIONS: These records are located in the Freer Gallery of Art and Arthur M. Sackler Gallery Archives, Smithsonian Institution.

SMITHSONIAN ENVIRONMENTAL
RESEARCH CENTER

The Smithsonian Environmental Research Center (SERC) was established on July 1, 1983, when the Radiation Biology Laboratory was merged with the Chesapeake Bay Center for Environmental Studies.

The history of the Radiation Biology Laboratory (RBL) can be traced to May 1, 1929, when the Division of Radiation and Organisms was established by Secretary Charles G. Abbot. Initially funded mostly by the Research Corporation, the Division's purpose was to undertake investigations of the effect of radiation on living organisms. In 1941, the Division was administratively placed under the Smithsonian's Astrophysical Observatory. Staff in charge of the Division included Frederick S. Brackett, Research Associate in Charge, 1929-1930, and Chief, 1931-1932; Charles G. Abbot, Director, 1933-1941; Earl S. Johnston, Assistant Director in Charge, 1941-1948; Robert B. Withrow, Chief, 1948-1958; and William H. Klein, Acting Chief, 1958-1959, and Chief, 1959-1965.

On February 16, 1965, the Division of Radiation and Organisms was abolished. Its work was continued by the newly established Radiation Biology Laboratory (RBL), an independent Smithsonian bureau reporting to the Assistant Secretary for Science. The research program at RBL was three-pronged—regulatory biology, or how sunlight regulates growth and development of biological organisms; solar radiation measurements; and carbon dating of samples submitted by Smithsonian and outside scientists. In 1970, RBL relocated from the old Astrophysical Observatory buildings in the south yard of the Smithsonian Institution Building to facilities in Rockville, Maryland. William H. Klein served as Director of RBL during its eighteen-year history.

The Chesapeake Bay Center for Field Biology (CBCFB) was created on July 1, 1965, to conduct research and promote education in ecosystem biology. CBCFB was established at Java Farm, a 368-acre tract of land located seven miles south of Annapolis, Maryland, on the western shore of the Chesapeake Bay. Java Farm was bequeathed to the Smithsonian Institution by Robert Lee Forest in 1962. Adjoining property was purchased with funds contributed by private foundations, and the Center's site eventually grew to 2,400 acres including 14 miles of shoreline on the Rhode River.

From 1965 to 1969, CBCFB was an administrative unit of the Smithsonian Office of Ecology. In 1969, its name was changed to the Chesapeake Bay Center for Environmental Studies (CBCES), and it was placed under the administration of the newly created Office of Environmental Sciences. CBCES became an independent Smithsonian bureau in 1973, reporting to the Assistant Secretary for Science. Directors of the CBCES (before 1969, CBCFB) included Kyle R. Barbehenn, 1965-1968; Francis S. L. Williamson, 1968-1975; and J. Kevin Sullivan, Acting Director, 1975-1976, and Director, 1976-1983.

In February 1966, the Smithsonian joined in an agreement with the Johns Hopkins University and the University of Maryland to collaborate in biological research and education at CBCFB. In 1971, the three institutions joined with the Virginia Institute of

Marine Sciences to form the Chesapeake Research Consortium (CRC) to "foster and facilitate research germane to the region of the Chesapeake Bay." CBCES became a major component of the CRC research program.

William H. Klein was appointed Director of the newly created SERC in 1983. The mission of SERC is to continue basic research with the goals of measuring physical, chemical, and biological interactions in environmental settings. Operations of SERC were conducted at two sites—the old RBL laboratory at Rockville, Maryland, and the former CBCES facilities at Edgewater, Maryland. The Rockville laboratory closed on November 22, 1986, and all SERC activities were relocated to Edgewater. Klein retired in 1987, and was replaced by David L. Correll as Acting Director. Correll was appointed Director in 1989.

(286)
Office of the Director, Chesapeake Bay Center for Environmental Studies, 1964-1976 and undated
Records (4.7 linear meters).

For an administrative history of the Office of the Director, Chesapeake Bay Center for Environmental Studies (CBCES), see the introduction to the Center.

This record unit was created primarily by Francis S. L. Williamson as Director of CBCES, 1968-1975. There are also records created by his predecessor, Kyle E. Barbehenn, 1965-1968, and by J. Kevin Sullivan as Assistant Director, 1971-1975, Acting Director, 1975-1976, and Director, 1976, as well as correspondence of Smithsonian administrators Phillip C. Ritterbush, Helmut K. Beuchner, and Irvin Eugene Wallen.

These records include incoming and outgoing correspondence, memoranda, proposals, reports, photographs, and publications documenting the history of CBCES, and its predecessor, the Chesapeake Bay Center for Field Biology. Included are materials concerning the establishment of the Center; land acquisition, including files on foundations that contributed funds for the purchase of property; facilities development; the cooperative agreement between the Smithsonian, the Johns Hopkins University, and the University of Maryland for research at CBCES; the development and activities of the Chesapeake Research Consortium, Inc.; research conducted by CBCES staff and visiting scientists; proposals for research at CBCES; CBCES projects including the Rhode River Watershed Program, the Rhode River Environmental Education Project, and the Poplar Island Erosion Control Study; relations with Smithsonian administration and bureaus, government agencies, community groups, and research organizations; and environmental issues, especially those affecting the Chesapeake Bay.

ARRANGEMENT: (1) General correspondence, 1964-1975 and undated; (2) administrative records, 1964-1976 and undated. FINDING AIDS: Description in control file. SPECIAL CONDITIONS: Use of this record unit requires prior arrangement with the Archives staff.

Office of the Director, Chesapeake Bay Center for Environmental Studies, 1965-1983
Records (7.4 linear meters).

For an administrative history of the Office of the Director, Chesapeake Bay Center for Environmental Studies (CBCES), see the introduction to the Center.

These records primarily document the operation of CBCES under Director J. Kevin Sullivan, 1976-1983. Also included are records created by Sullivan as Assistant Director, 1972-1975, and Acting Director, 1975-1976. A small amount of material created by Directors Kyle R. Barbehenn, 1965-1968, and Francis S. L. Williamson, 1968-1975, is also present.

The records consist of correspondence, memoranda, proposals, reports, publications, and related materials documenting the CBCES research and education programs; CBCES relations with environmental organizations, citizen groups, and government agencies concerned with the welfare of the Chesapeake Bay; CBCES activities as a member of the Chesapeake Research Consortium; land use and facilities at CBCES; plans to merge CBCES with the Radiation Biology Laboratory; Sullivan's research on fisheries; and CBCES administration of and research on the Poplar Islands. Also included are copies of the CBCES newsletter, *Rhode River Review.*

ARRANGEMENT: Unarranged. FINDING AIDS: Folder list in control file. SPECIAL CONDITIONS: (1) Restricted; (2) use of this record unit requires prior arrangement with the Archives staff.

Office of the Director, Smithsonian Environmental Research Center, 1965-1986, with related records from circa 1918
Records (10.3 linear meters).

For an administrative history of the Office of the Director, Smithsonian Environmental Research Center (SERC), see the introduction to the Center.

These records primarily document the research programs and administration of the Radiation Biology Laboratory (RBL), 1965-1983, and SERC, 1983-1986, under Director William H. Klein. Also included are smaller amounts of material created by the Smithsonian Astrophysical Observatory (SAO) and the Division of Radiation and Organisms (R&O).

The records include incoming and outgoing correspondence of Klein and Assistant Director Walter Shropshire, Jr., 1965-1986; correspondence, proposals, and reports documenting research conducted under contracts with the Eppley Foundation, the National Aeronautics and Space Administration, the National Oceanic and Atmospheric Administration, the United States Department of Energy, the Atomic Energy Commission, the National Science Foundation, and the National Institutes of Health; files concerning the establishment of RBL in 1965, its facilities in the Smithsonian Institution Building and the move to Rockville, Maryland, in 1970; records relating to the merger of RBL and the Chesapeake Bay Center for Environmental Studies to form SERC in 1983; correspondence, memoranda, and reports concerning the Carbon-Dating Laboratory; correspondence with equipment suppliers; requests for information from the general public; staff reviews of scientific manuscripts; budget files of R&O, RBL, and

SERC; a manuscript by Earl S. Johnston on sunlight and plants; photographs of SAO, R&O, and RBL personnel including Charles G. Abbot, Loyal B. Aldrich, and Klein; photographs of equipment and facilities; glass plate negatives of SAO expeditions to Chile, 1918, and Africa and India, 1925; and glass plate negatives containing solar radiation data.

ARRANGEMENT: Unarranged. FINDING AIDS: Folder list in control file. SPECIAL CONDITIONS: (1) Restricted; (2) use of this record unit requires prior arrangement with the Archives staff.

(399)

Associate Director for Education Programs, Chesapeake Bay Center for Environmental Studies, 1974-1983
Records (2.9 linear meters).

John H. Falk joined the staff of the Chesapeake Bay Center for Environmental Studies (CBCES) in 1974 as Education Coordinator. In 1975 he was appointed Associate Director for Education Programs. Educational programs at CBCES included research on the design and implementation of outdoor-centered learning experiences, science education field trips for school groups, the development of public programs emphasizing environmental education, and the dissemination of research findings for use in planning and legislation affecting the Chesapeake Bay. Falk's position was abolished in 1983 after the Smithsonian Environmental Research Center was established.

These records document educational programs at the CBCES under Associate Director John H. Falk. They consist of correspondence, memoranda, reports, and printed materials concerning CBCES educational programs, especially the Summer Ecology Program and the Work-Learn Program in Environmental Studies; the dissemination of environmental information, particularly the publication of the *Rhode River Review;* office administration; relations with Smithsonian bureaus and offices; and Falk's educational research. Photographs of CBCES staff are found in the records.

ARRANGEMENT: Unarranged. FINDING AIDS: Folder list in control file. SPECIAL CONDITIONS: (1) Restricted; (2) use of this record unit requires prior arrangement with the Archives staff.

(387)

Carbon-Dating Laboratory, Smithsonian Environmental Research Center, 1962-1986
Records (5.3 linear meters).

A Carbon-Dating Laboratory was established in the Division of Radiation and Organisms, Smithsonian Astrophysical Observatory, in September 1962. The function of the Laboratory was to analyze samples of archeological and geological interest submitted by Smithsonian and outside researchers. The Laboratory also conducted basic research in the techniques of dating by the use of the carbon-14 method. Joel J. Sigalove, a geochemist, directed the Laboratory during its first year of operations. Austin Long was appointed Geochemist in 1963 and put in charge of the carbon-dating work. Long resigned in 1968 and was replaced by Robert Stuckenrath, who directed the Laboratory with the title of Anthropologist. Stuckenrath remained in the position until carbon-dating work ceased when the Rockville laboratory of the Smithsonian Environmental Research Center closed in November 1986.

These records document the operation of the Carbon-Dating Laboratory during its twenty-four year history. They include logbooks containing raw data on samples analyzed; incoming and outgoing correspondence of Sigalove, Long, and Stuckenrath with Smithsonian and outside scientists concerning the analysis of samples submitted for dating; information on dates provided by the Laboratory which were published in the journal *Radiocarbon;* and miscellaneous laboratory and record books.

ARRANGEMENT: Unarranged. FINDING AIDS: Folder list in control file. SPECIAL CONDITIONS: (1) Restricted; (2) use of this record unit requires prior arrangement with the Archives staff.

HIRSHHORN MUSEUM AND SCULPTURE GARDEN

The Hirshhorn Museum and Sculpture Garden was a gift to the nation from the financier and avid collector of modern art, Joseph H. Hirshhorn. Hirshhorn began his collecting with prints in 1917, and it became his lifelong passion. Hirshhorn's collection is best known for its nineteenth and twentieth century sculpture, including the works of Rodin, Picasso, Matisse, Giacometti, Calder, and Moore. He also collected widely and enthusiastically from the works of contemporary American painters, including, among many others, Thomas Eakins, Willem de Kooning, Raphael Soyer, and Larry Rivers.

Hirshhorn had long planned to keep his collection together in a museum so that its art could be accessible and give others the pleasure it had given him. Because of the strength of the collection, many museums throughout the United States and around the world courted Hirshhorn with offers of a museum and support for his holdings. Smithsonian Secretary S. Dillon Ripley very much wanted to see a museum of contemporary art in Washington, which had no significant contemporary museum at the time. Ripley worked to persuade Hirshhorn that he should choose Washington and the Smithsonian from among many competitors for his art. In this effort he had the powerful assistance of President Lyndon Johnson and his wife, Lady Bird, who enthusiastically wooed Hirshhorn over several years. Finally in 1966 Hirshhorn announced that he would give his entire collection to the Smithsonian, to be housed in a museum named for him and constructed on the Mall by the federal government. The initial gift numbered more than 6,000 pieces of art, and Hirshhorn bequeathed the Museum an additional 6,000 items and an endowment of five million dollars at his death.

The Hirshhorn Museum opened to the public in October 1974 under the direction of Abram Lerner, who had been appointed in 1967 after curating Hirshhorn's personal collection in New York and advising him on art purchases since 1955. Lerner retired in October 1984 and was succeeded by James T. Demetrion, formerly director of the Des Moines Art Center.

(510)
Office of the Director, Hirshhorn Museum and Sculpture Garden, 1974-1984, with related records from 1954
Records (10.8 linear meters).

The contemporary art collection of Joseph H. Hirshhorn was given to the Smithsonian Institution in 1966. In 1974 the collection, now named the Hirshhorn Museum and Sculpture Garden (HMSG), opened to the public, with Abram Lerner as its first Director. However, both the Museum and its Director had deeper roots. Hirshhorn, who began collecting art in 1917, began to work with Lerner in 1954. In 1955 Lerner became curator of Hirshhorn's collection, stored in leased space in New York City, and was continuously associated with Hirshhorn and the collection until retiring as Director in 1984.

These records document the growing Hirshhorn collection and its evolution into the present-day HMSG. There is some material from the period before Hirshhorn's 1966 gift of his collection to the nation, but most of the records date after the gift. Included are records documenting the scope of the original donation, choice of an architect for the new museum on the national Mall, construction of the building, planning for layouts and display of the collection, and evolution of the Museum's programs. There is some correspondence with President Lyndon B. Johnson as well as a 1955 plan in which Lerner outlined to Hirshhorn his proposal to curate the collection. The collection contains many photographs, mostly of works of art, as well as installation drawings dealing with construction and design of exhibitions.

ARRANGEMENT: (1) Records of the Director's Office, 1954-1974, accession number 82-105; (2) records of the Director's Office, 1963-1984, accession number 85-022. FINDING AIDS: Folder list in control file. SPECIAL CONDITIONS: (1) Restricted; (2) use of this record unit requires prior arrangement with the Archives staff.

(512)
Department of Administration and Museum Support Services, Hirshhorn Museum and Sculpture Garden, 1969-1981
Records (2.8 linear meters).

A Department of Administration was created in 1971 to oversee the daily operations of the Hirshhorn Museum and Sculpture Garden (HMSG). It was also responsible for coordinating the various stages of exhibition preparation to ensure completion of each exhibition. Joseph Sefekar was the first Administrator and served until 1978. The Office was renamed the Department of Administration and Museum Support Services in 1979, and Nancy L. Kirkpatrick became its Director, a position she retained through 1981.

This record unit documents the administrative procedures employed by HMSG. The records provide information about the process of recruiting staff for the new Museum. There are also budget and financial records, which track the costs of exhibits as they were produced.

ARRANGEMENT: (1) Administrative records, 1969-1981, accession number 85-091. FINDING AIDS: Partial folder list in control file. SPECIAL CONDITIONS: Use of this record unit requires prior arrangement with the Archives staff.

(469)
Department of Painting and Sculpture, Hirshhorn Museum and Sculpture Garden, circa 1974-1991, with related materials from 1967
Curatorial Records (18 linear meters).

The Department of Painting and Sculpture was created in 1967, shortly after the Hirshhorn Museum and Sculpture Garden (HMSG) was founded. The Department had offices in New York City until 1974, when construction was completed on the museum building in Washington, D.C. Curators represented in these records include Charles W. Millard III, Chief Curator, 1974-1986; Cynthia Jaffee McCabe, Associate Curator, 1967-1973, Curator, 1974-1978, Curator of Exhibitions, 1979-1986; Judith K. Zilczer, Research Assistant, 1974-1975, Historian, 1975-1989, Associate Curator of Painting, 1990, Curator of Painting, 1990-   ; Howard N. Fox, Museum Technician, 1975-1978, Assistant Curator for Exhibitions, 1979-1981, Associate Curator for Exhibitions, 1982-1985; and Ned Rifkin, Chief Curator for Exhibitions, 1986-1991.

These records consist of professional correspondence and administrative and research files of a number of curators from the Department of Painting and Sculpture. Included are correspondence and memoranda with HMSG staff, artists, galleries, and other museums; loan agreements, checklists, scripts, and installation plans for HMSG exhibitions; biographical information on, and interviews with, artists; photographs, slides, and transparencies of works of art; files concerning lectures and classes given by curators; intern and fellowship program information; curators' activity reports to HMSG administration; minutes from committee meetings; and audio recordings of lectures and interviews about HMSG exhibitions.

Records dating from before the 1974 opening of the Museum consist mainly of correspondence to either Joseph H. Hirshhorn or Abram Lerner, first Director of HMSG, mostly concerning art for sale or donation to the new Museum.

ARRANGEMENT: (1) Charles W. Millard III curatorial files, 1967-1987, accession number 91-056; (2) Charles W. Millard III curatorial files, 1974-1984, accession number 86-148; (3) Cynthia Jaffee McCabe curatorial files, 1974-1986, with related materials from 1971, accession number 87-045; (4) Judith K. Zilczer curatorial files, 1974-1985, accession number 86-019; (5) Judith K. Zilczer curatorial files, *circa* 1974-1986, accession number 87-048; (6) Judith K. Zilczer curatorial files, *circa* 1980-1988, accession number 89-074; (7) Judith K. Zilczer curatorial files, 1975-1991, accession number 92-024; (8) Judith K. Zilczer curatorial files, 1981, 1985-1991, accession number 92-039; (9) Howard N. Fox curatorial files, 1976-1985, accession number 86-147; (10) Howard N. Fox curatorial files, 1979-1983, accession number 87-047; (11) Ned Rifkin curatorial files, 1986-1991, accession number 92-018; (12) Ned Rifkin curatorial files, 1987-1991, accession number 92-040. FINDING AIDS: Box list in control file. SPECIAL CONDITIONS: (1) Restricted; (2) use of this record unit requires prior arrangement with the Archives staff.

(481)

Department of Painting and Sculpture, Hirshhorn Museum and Sculpture Garden, circa 1974-1992, with related materials from 1968

Exhibition Records (36.6 linear meters).

For an administrative history of the Department of Painting and Sculpture, see record unit 469.

These records document the planning, development, and installation of exhibitions by the Department of Painting and Sculpture, Hirshhorn Museum and Sculpture Garden (HMSG). Included are biographical and bibliographical research files on artists; correspondence with museums, galleries, and artists concerning loan of artwork; loan reports; shipment records; installation notes and photographs; budget and fundraising files; checklists, photographs, slides, and transparencies of artwork; and label copy and handouts for exhibitions. These records also contain catalog production files, including draft and final versions of catalog text, as well as galley proofs. Openings of exhibitions are documented with press releases and other publicity, photographs, invitations to openings, and reviews of exhibitions in newspapers and magazines. Files concerning lectures and seminars related to exhibitions are also included.

Major exhibitions represented by these records include: *Inaugural Exhibition; Soto: A Retrospective Exhibition; The Sculpture and Drawings of Elie Nadelman, 1882-1946; The Golden Door: Artist-Immigrants of America, 1876-1976; 14 Canadians: A Critic's Choice; The Noble Buyer: John Quinn, Patron of the Avant-Garde; Miro, Selected Paintings; Fernando Botero; Different Drummers; Alberto Giacometti, 1901-*

1966; Artistic Collaboration in the Twentieth Century; and *Francis Bacon: an Exhibition.*

A small amount of general administrative files of the Department of Painting and Sculpture is also included, as is some correspondence of Inez Garson, Assistant Curator, 1971-1974, Curator for Archives, 1978-1981; and Phyllis Rosenzweig, Curatorial Assistant, 1974-1976, Associate Curator, 1976-   . Records dating from before the 1974 opening of the Museum were created by members of the Department of Painting and Sculpture office in New York and mostly concern the selection of artwork for the *Inaugural Exhibition.*

ARRANGEMENT: (1) Exhibition records, 1969-1972, accession number 83-082; (2) exhibition records, 1974-1976, accession number 83-092; (3) exhibition records, 1975-1976, accession number 83-099; (4) exhibition records, *circa* 1973-1976, accession number 83-106; (5) exhibition records, 1968-1977, accession number 83-108; (6) exhibition records, 1974-1983, accession number 84-198; (7) exhibition records, 1976-1981, accession number 84-227; (8) exhibition records, 1978-1984, accession number 85-076; (9) exhibition records, *circa* 1975-1982, accession number 85-089; (10) exhibition records, 1981-1983, accession 85-128; (11) exhibition records, 1980-1983, accession number 85-143; (12) exhibition installation photographs, 1974-1982, accession number 86-123; (13) exhibition records, 1981-1984, accession number 86-149; (14) exhibition records, 1974-1977, accession number 87-167; (15) exhibition records, 1986-1989, accession number 89-053; (16) *Artistic Collaboration in the Twentieth Century* exhibition records, 1978-1984, accession number 89-068; (17) *Francis Bacon* exhibition records, 1981-1990, accession number 92-019; (18) exhibition records, 1970-1992, accession number 93-134. FINDING AIDS: Box list in control file. SPECIAL CONDITIONS: (1) Restricted; (2) use of this record unit requires prior arrangement with the Archives staff.

(516)

Department of Exhibits and Design, Hirshhorn Museum and Sculpture Garden, 1971-1989
Records (4.5 linear meters).

The Department of Exhibits and Design, Hirshhorn Museum and Sculpture Garden (HMSG), is responsible for arranging permanent and temporary HMSG exhibits and monitoring conditions in the Museum's exhibit galleries. From 1971 to 1976 the Department operated under the Director's Office. In 1976 Joseph Shannon was made Acting Chief of the Department. He served as Chief from 1977 to 1986. Edward P. Schiesser succeeded Shannon, 1986-   .

These records include the correspondence of Shannon and Schiesser; minutes of meetings; exhibition proposals; installation floor plans; scripts; conservation planning; budgets; photographs of HMSG, artworks, and artists; and plans to modify the Museum's Sculpture Garden.

ARRANGEMENT: Records, 1971-1989, accession number 94-144. FINDING AIDS: Folder list in control file. SPECIAL CONDITIONS: Use of this record unit requires prior arrangement with the Archives staff.

(514)

Department of Education, Hirshhorn Museum and Sculpture Garden, 1973-1986
Records (3.8 linear meters).

The Department of Education of the Hirshhorn Museum and Sculpture Garden (HMSG) was set up to interpret the Museum's collections to a broad and varied public. It produces information on the HMSG's collections designed to appeal to professional artists and art scholars, but also to the general public and to children. In support of its aims, the Department uses a wide variety of media, including a corps of trained volunteer docents, as well as printed materials of all sorts, films, lectures, and concerts. The Department of Education was created in 1973, and Edward Lawson was recruited from New York's Whitney Museum to be its Chief, a position he held, 1973-   .

These records include a series of audiotapes produced to train the first class of docents for HMSG's opening in 1974, as well as similar tapes prepared in later years. In addition, the records document special programs and projects designed for children. Correspondence dealing with relations with the broader Washington and national arts community is included, as are the correspondence, budget records, and other elements of museum administration. The records include numerous photographs.

ARRANGEMENT: (1) Docent training tapes, 1974-1982, accession number 83-065; (2) Department of Education, records, 1973-1981, accession number 84-068; (3) Department of Education, records, 1973-1984, accession number 87-051; (4) Department of Education, records, 1973-1983, accession number 87-180; (5) Department of Education, records, 1974-1986, accession number 89-015. FINDING AIDS: Description in control file. SPECIAL CONDITIONS: Use of this record unit requires prior arrangement with the Archives staff.

(513)
Office of Public Affairs, Hirshhorn Museum and Sculpture Garden, circa 1973-1984
Records (13.5 linear meters).

The Hirshhorn Museum and Sculpture Garden's (HMSG) first employee devoted explicitly to public affairs was Sidney Lawrence, first hired as a Museum Specialist (publicity) in 1976. In 1978 he became the Public Affairs Officer, Publications and Information Services Department. Lawrence became Public Information Officer, Office of Public Affairs, Department of Administrative and Museum Support Services, serving 1980-   .

The Office of Public Affairs is responsible for disseminating information on the Hirshhorn's various activities as broadly as possible among the audiences the Museum serves. To this end, it distributes many kinds of publicity—press kits, news releases, advertising spots, and the like. These materials are targeted at a wide variety of audiences, including professional artists and critics, knowledgeable patrons, school children, and casual visitors. The subject matter includes touring exhibits, exhibits from the HMSG's own collections, lectures, films, publications, and community-based activities which the Museum sponsors.

These records include exhibition catalogs, news releases, news clippings and articles from the serious and popular press, mailings, public correspondence seeking more information on artists and art-related topics, invitations to openings and other special events, and many photographs.

ARRANGEMENT: (1) Office of Public Affairs, records, 1974-1977, accession number 82-107; (2) Office of Public Affairs, exhibition records, 1977-1979, accession number 84-201; (3) Office of Public Affairs, exhibition records, 1979-1981, accession number 85-077; (4) Public Information Office, exhibition records, *circa* 1979-1981, accession number 85-090; (5) Public Information Office, exhibition records, *circa* 1980-1983, accession number 85-129; (6) Public Information Office, records, 1982-1983, accession number 85-144; (7) Public Information Office, records, 1976-1979, accession number 85-206; (8) Office of Public Affairs, exhibition records, 1978-1985, accession number 89-060. FINDING AIDS: Box and folder list in control file. SPECIAL CONDITIONS: (1) Restricted; (2) use of this record unit requires prior arrangement with the Archives staff.

Office of the Registrar, Hirshhorn Museum and Sculpture Garden, circa 1970-1985
Loan and Exhibition Records (9.8 linear meters).

The Office of the Registrar is responsible for preserving all documentation on the provenance of works of art in the Hirshhorn Museum and Sculpture Garden's (HMSG) collection. In addition, it is responsible for documenting, shipping, and inspecting all the art that the HMSG loans to other institutions or borrows from other collections for use in its own exhibitions.

Prior to acceptance of Joseph Hirshhorn's gift by the United States Congress, registrarial duties were managed by Abram Lerner. In 1968 the first Registrar, Myron O'Higgins, was employed and, in 1969, Thomas J. Girard. In 1970 James J. Elias and Frank B. Gettings served as Associate Registrars. In 1971 Sandra L. Pearson became Acting Registrar. She was made Registrar in 1972. Nancy Sage was Registrar in 1973, followed by Douglas Robinson, 1974-   .

These records consist of insurance records, art condition reports, facility condition reports, shipping documents and invoices, and photographs, as well as pamphlets and catalogs.

ARRANGEMENT: (1) Office of the Registrar, outgoing loans, *circa* 1970-1984, accession number 90-107; (2) Office of the Registrar, exhibition files, 1974-1985, accession number 90-120. FINDING AIDS: Folder list in control file. SPECIAL CONDITIONS: (1) Restricted; (2) use of this record unit requires prior arrangement with the Archives staff.

ANACOSTIA MUSEUM

The Anacostia Museum grew out of an idea that was first discussed at a conference on museums and education sponsored by the Smithsonian in August 1966. Soon thereafter, Smithsonian Secretary S. Dillon Ripley formed a committee to plan "an experimental store-front museum" in a Washington, D.C., neighborhood. In March 1967, the Smithsonian secured the Carver Theater in Anacostia as the site for the project.

Anacostia community leaders formed an advisory council to guide the venture and build local support. In June the Institution appointed John R. Kinard as Director of the Museum, a position he held until his death in 1989. Smithsonian staff cooperated with local citizens to convert the theater into an exhibition space, and to select objects for display. The theater was renamed the Anacostia Neighborhood Museum, and opened to the public on September 15, 1967.

The Museum relied largely on special grants for support until 1970, when it became a line item in the Institution's federal budget. Charles Blitzer, Director of the Office of Education and Training, was the Institution's chief liaison with the Museum until those duties were transferred to William W. Warner, Acting Assistant Secretary for Public Service, in November 1968. Assistant Secretary for History and Art John E. Reinhardt took over administration of the Museum in 1983.

In October 1974, the Exhibit Branch of the Museum moved into the new Exhibits Design and Production Laboratory in Fort Stanton Park. This facility served as the core for a larger museum building that was completed in 1987. The new structure was large enough to accommodate all the functions of the Museum in one location for the first time.

The Museum implemented an acquisition program in 1977, and first used original artifacts in the 1979 exhibition *Out of Africa: From West African Kingdoms to Colonization.* Other exhibitions have examined such subjects as urban problems, the history of Anacostia, African American art and heritage, and African culture. In April 1987 the Museum had its name changed to the Anacostia Museum. This reflected the Museum's increased mandate to examine, preserve, and interpret African American history and culture, not only locally and regionally, but nationally and internationally as well.

(265)

Director, Anacostia Neighborhood Museum, 1966-1975
Records (1.3 linear meters).

John R. Kinard became Director of the Anacostia Neighborhood Museum in June 1967, three months before it opened. The Museum was at first largely experimental, but as it developed, it became a center for the study of Anacostia, its citizens, and the experience of African Americans throughout the country. In addition to guiding the Museum through its formative years, Kinard played important roles both in the national museum profession and within the local community. For additional biographical information on Kinard, see record unit 9538.

These records consist of official files documenting the activities of the Museum and its staff, topical files on the local community, records of community group participation in the creation of the Museum, and exhibition material.

ARRANGEMENT: Alphabetic. FINDING AIDS: Folder list in control file. SPECIAL CONDITIONS: Use of this record unit requires prior arrangement with the Archives staff.

(349)

Director, Anacostia Museum, 1972-1987, with related records from 1970
Records (0.8 linear meter).

These records reflect the varied interests and activities of John R. Kinard as Director of the Anacostia Museum. The files consist primarily of official correspondence with museum professionals, community leaders and activists, officials of Washington, D.C., and Smithsonian management. Kinard's involvement with organizations such as the African American Museums Association, the Anacostia Historical Society, the Anacostia Coordinating Council, and the Afro-American Bicentennial Corporation is documented. Materials include photographs and clippings from newspapers and magazines, some of which describe Kinard's May 5, 1987, speech at the 51st annual conference of the Southern African Museums Association held in Pietermaritzburg, South Africa.

ARRANGEMENT: (1) General correspondence, 1972-1982; (2) status reports from outside organizations, 1972-1987; (3) newspaper and magazine clippings, 1977-1987. FINDING AIDS: Series list in control file. SPECIAL CONDITIONS: (1) Restricted; (2) use of this record unit requires prior arrangement with the Archives staff.

(350)

Administrative Officer, Anacostia Neighborhood Museum, 1971-1978
Records (0.4 linear meter).

Audrey Archer joined the Museum in 1968 as an Administrative Assistant and became the Administrative Officer in 1975. Although Archer's duties included responsibility for the entire Museum, these records concern only the Exhibit Design and Production Laboratory, which was designed and constructed during her tenure, and which was occupied by the Exhibit Branch of the Museum in 1974. For an administrative history of the Exhibit Branch and the Exhibits Training Program, see record unit 378.

These records document the administrative and financial activities of the Exhibits Design and Production Laboratory during its planning, construction, and first years of operation. Records contain feasibility studies of the project and correspondence and agreements about the acquisition of land for the facility. Also included are copies of construction contracts, as well as memoranda and correspondence with architects and contractors regarding the planning and progress of the building. The financial requirements of the project are documented by staff memoranda regarding possible sources of support, funding proposals, correspondence with donors, and requisition forms. A fire that damaged the Laboratory in July 1976 is documented by photographs, reports, and memoranda.

Administrative records of the Exhibits Training Program are also included. The records contain briefing sheets, periodic progress reports, and correspondence with

Smithsonian administrators and financial sponsors. Also included are grant proposals, curricula outlines, correspondence concerning job placements for graduating students, and statements of expenses.

ARRANGEMENT: Unarranged. FINDING AIDS: None. SPECIAL CONDITIONS: Use of this record unit requires prior arrangement with the Archives staff.

(390)

Education Department, Anacostia Museum, 1967-1989
Records (7 linear meters).

The Education and Development Department was established in 1967 as one of the two original branches of the Museum. Its early responsibilities focused on interpreting the Museum's exhibitions to the public. However, as the Museum established itself, the Department reached beyond this early mandate and became an active member of the Anacostia community. Its accomplishments included the development of educational outreach services which used ethnic-based materials; the creation in July 1969 of a Mobile Division to facilitate the Museum's involvement in the community; the formation of a Youth Advisory Council and other cultural arts groups; and the establishment of a Children's Room in February 1972. Renamed the Education Department by 1973, it also played a leading role in developing programs at the Museum which focused on urban problems and the concerns of incarcerated community members.

Zora B. Martin-Felton joined the Museum at its founding as Program Director, and by 1971 was named Supervisory Program Manager of the Education and Development Department. In 1979 she became an Education Specialist, and in 1989 was referred to as Chief of the Education Department. Fletcher A. Smith came to the Museum in July 1969 as the Coordinator of the new Mobile Division. He later took the title of Program Manager of the Division, which was renamed the Outreach Services Branch. The Branch was terminated after Smith's resignation in September 1978.

The records include incoming and outgoing correspondence and memoranda from Zora Martin-Felton and other staff of the Education Department, as well as program reports, budget justifications, and planning statements. These materials are scattered throughout the records and have many chronological gaps. The records also describe the development of educational materials for Museum exhibitions, and of workshops and programs for local teachers and students. In addition, the records detail the evolution of Department initiatives such as the Youth Advisory Council and the Outreach Services Branch, and contain planning materials for special events sponsored by the Department and the Museum. Some research materials for programs and exhibitions are also included.

ARRANGEMENT: (1) Records, 1967-1976, accession number T89008; (2) records, 1967-1986, accession number 88-070; (3) records, 1969-1989, accession number 91-021. FINDING AIDS: Folder list in control file. SPECIAL CONDITIONS: (1) Restricted; (2) use of this record unit requires prior arrangement with the Archives staff.

Exhibits Department, Anacostia Neighborhood Museum, 1967-1984, 1987
Records (5.7 linear meters).

The exhibits program of the Museum began in December 1967 when the Director appointed Larry Erskine Thomas as Research and Design Coordinator. After the program was divided into the Exhibit Branch and the Anacostia Studies Branch in January 1969, the two Branches together were designated the Research and Design Department, and Thomas became Supervisory Program Manager. In 1974 construction began on the Exhibits Design and Production Laboratory, also known as the Exhibits Center; and it was occupied by the Exhibit Branch in October of that year. At the same time, Charles W. Mickens took charge of the Exhibit Branch and the Laboratory as Exhibits Program Manager.

In 1975 the Research and Design Department was eliminated, and the two Branches each became directly responsible to the Director. Two new subdivisions were formed within the Exhibit Branch: Design and Installation, supervised by Larry Thomas, and Exhibit Production, managed by James E. Mayo. Mickens was made responsible to the Director for the entire Branch, and under his supervision the Laboratory became fully operational in October 1975. By 1982, the Branch was called the Exhibits Department. Mickens retired as Exhibits Program Manager in 1977, and the position was left vacant until the appointment of Victor Govier in 1979. After Govier's departure in May 1984, the position remained vacant through 1987.

An Exhibits Training Program was implemented with a group of eleven students in September 1976. The program was originally intended to play a central role in the function of the Laboratory, with the goal of increasing the representation of minorities in the museum professions. After the training of the first class of students was completed, however, the program was discontinued in May 1978.

Charles W. Mickens managed the Exhibits Training Program as part of his duties until Ronald Wildy was hired as Training Coordinator in November 1976. Wildy resigned in January 1977, and James Mayo supervised the program until John Bradshaw was hired as Training Officer in April of that year. Bradshaw remained in the position until the program was terminated.

This record unit documents the administration of the Exhibits Design and Production Laboratory for approximately its first ten years of operation, and describes the mission, philosophy, planning, and construction of the facility. The records contain planning materials for many of the Museum's early exhibitions, which reflect the involvement of community organizations as well as museum professionals. The materials also document the Exhibits Training Program in some detail.

ARRANGEMENT: (1) Administrative files, 1973-1984, 1987; (2) Exhibits Department subject files, 1967-1976; (3) Exhibits Training Program, 1975-1978. FINDING AIDS: Folder list in control file. SPECIAL CONDITIONS: Use of this record unit requires prior arrangement with the Archives staff.

COOPER-HEWITT MUSEUM

The Cooper-Hewitt Museum was established in 1896 as the Cooper Union Museum for the Arts of Decoration. Its parent organization, the Cooper Union for the Advancement of Science and Art, was founded in 1859 by Peter Cooper as a free school for the working classes of New York City. In his original plans for Cooper Union, Peter Cooper made provisions for a museum, but these plans were not immediately carried out.

In 1895, Peter Cooper's granddaughters, Eleanor Garnier Hewitt, Sarah Cooper Hewitt, and Amy Hewitt Green, asked the trustees of the Cooper Union for room in which to install a Museum for the Arts of Decoration, modeled after the *Musee des Artes Decoratifs* of Paris. The purpose of the museum was to provide the art students of Cooper Union, students of design, and working designers with study collections of the decorative arts. The trustees assigned the fourth floor of the Cooper Union's Foundation Building to the sisters, and the Museum was opened to the public in 1897.

Until the death of Sarah Cooper Hewitt, the management of the Museum was essentially in the hands of the Hewitt sisters as Directors. Following Sarah's death in 1930, the trustees of the Cooper Union appointed a board of four Directors, with Constance P. Hare as chairman, to administer the Museum. When Edwin S. Burdell became Director of the Cooper Union in 1938, the Museum was made part of his administrative responsibility, the Board of Directors was abolished, and an Advisory Council on the Museum, responsible for matters relating to the Museum's collections, was set up. Curators and custodians of the Museum included Mary A. Peoli, 1898-1904; Mary S. M. Gibson, 1904-1945; and Calvin S. Hathaway, 1933-1963 (Assistant Curator, 1933-1946, Curator, 1946-1951, and Director, 1951-1963).

In 1963, the Cooper Union began consideration of plans to discontinue the Museum because of the financial demands of the other divisions of the Union and the absence of a close relationship between the programs of the Museum and the Art School. The announcement of the plans led to a considerable public outcry, and a Committee to Save the Cooper Union Museum, headed by Henry F. duPont, was established. With the help of a study on the future of the Museum, prepared by a committee of the American Association of Museums, negotiations took place among the Committee, the Cooper Union, and the Smithsonian Institution leading to the Museum's transfer to the Smithsonian on July 1, 1968. The Museum was renamed the Cooper-Hewitt Museum of Design at the time of the transfer, and became the Cooper-Hewitt Museum of Decorative Arts and Design in 1969. In 1970, the Museum moved into its present home, the Carnegie Mansion, which was renovated and reopened to the public in 1976. That year the Museum was renamed the Cooper-Hewitt Museum, the Smithsonian Institution's National Museum of Design; it was designated the Cooper-Hewitt, National Design Museum in 1994. Heads of the Museum since 1963 have been Christian Rohlfing, Acting Administrator, 1963-1968; Richard P. Wunder, Director, 1968-1969; Lisa Taylor, Director, 1969-1987; and Dianne H. Pilgrim, Director, 1988-   .

DIRECTOR AND GENERAL ADMINISTRATION, 1881-1988

(267)

Cooper-Hewitt Museum, 1881, 1895-1976
Records (19.9 linear meters).

These records document the administration of the Museum from its establishment until its reopening in 1976 in the Carnegie Mansion. While there is some material concerning the activities of Eleanor Garnier Hewitt and Sarah Cooper Hewitt, the majority of the records deal with the management of the Museum following Sarah Cooper Hewitt's death in 1930. Records of Mary S. M. Gibson, Curator, 1904-1945; Calvin S. Hathaway, Curator, 1946-1951, and Director, 1951-1963; H. Christian Rohlfing, Acting Administrator, 1963-1968; Richard P. Wunder, Director, 1968-1969; and Lisa Suter Taylor, Director, 1969-   , are included.

The records include correspondence, memoranda, reports, publications, notes, photographs, and forms concerning the administrative operation of the Museum, including finance, personnel, buildings and equipment, and fundraising activities; the acquisition, care, and use of the Museum's collections; exhibits, programs, and activities sponsored by the Museum; research activities of the staff and outside researchers; and Museum publications. Correspondents include staff of the parent organizations, the Cooper Union and the Smithsonian Institution, museums, art historians, donors, contributors, and the general public. A few documents deal with the activities and history of the Cooper and Hewitt families, and of the Cooper Union.

ARRANGEMENT: (1) General correspondence, 1881, 1897, 1907-1973; (2) museum file, *circa* 1895-1971; (3) central museum files, 1968-1976, with materials from 1915; (4) Smithsonian file, 1968-1972, with records from 1951; (5) staff correspondence, 1971-1975; (6) annual reports, 1916-1968; (7) personnel records, *circa* 1933-1971; (8) fund-raising records. FINDING AIDS: Description in control file. SPECIAL CONDITIONS: Use of this record unit requires prior arrangement with the Archives staff.

(492)

Director, Cooper-Hewitt Museum, 1969-1992, with related records from 1948
Records (20.3 linear meters and 5 oversize drawers).

These records document the administration of the Cooper-Hewitt Museum under Directors Lisa Suter Taylor and Dianne H. Pilgrim. Taylor's appointment in October 1969 marked the first appointment of a woman as director of a Smithsonian museum. Previously, she had been a program director with the Smithsonian Associates. Taylor was made Director Emeritus after her retirement in June 1987. Pilgrim became Director in November 1988 after serving as Curator and Chair of the Department of Decorative Arts at the Brooklyn Museum.

Other staff also created some of the records. H. Christian Rohlfing joined the Cooper-Hewitt Museum in 1954 and, as Acting Administrator, oversaw its transition to a Smithsonian bureau. He then served as Assistant Director for Collections Management from 1979 until his retirement in 1982. Harold F. Pfister joined the Museum in 1982 as Assistant Director. He became Acting Director upon Taylor's retirement and resigned in 1988. Peter M. Scherer became Administrative Assistant to the Director in 1979 and rose to Special Assistant to the Director before leaving the Museum in 1983.

These records contain the Director's correspondence files from 1975 to 1991, as well as smaller files created by Rohlfing, Pfister, and Scherer. In addition, the records include administrative and subject files from 1970 to 1988. These files document museum functions such as acquisitions, collections management, and budgeting, as well as larger initiatives such as the Museum Mile street festival, which was conceived by the Cooper-Hewitt and inaugurated in June 1979. They also contain a complete collection of the Museum's newsletter from its first issue in the fall of 1977 through the spring 1990 issue; and photographs, plans, and drawings of proposed renovations to the Carnegie Mansion.

The records contain exhibition files dating from 1972 to 1992, with some gaps. The files include exhibition designs; publicity and press reviews; visitor comments; correspondence with other institutions and museums regarding the loan of objects; label copy; budgets and funding materials; lists of objects; and contracts. Also documented are Museum publications such as *Cities* (1982); *The Phenomenon of Change* (1984); and the *Smithsonian Illustrated Library of Antiques,* a twelve-part series begun in 1979 and published in association with the Book-of-the-Month Club. Publication files consist of correspondence with authors, contributors, subscribers, and publishers; progress reports; photographs of artwork; requests for reproduction permission; background research files; publicity and advertising files; production files; and contracts.

ARRANGEMENT: (1) Director's files, 1969-1977, with related records from 1948, accession number T89053; (2) Director's files, 1975-1980, accession number 85-193; (3) Director's files, 1977-1985, accession number 88-072; (4) Director's files, 1970-1992, accession number 94-053. FINDING AIDS: Description in control file. SPECIAL CONDITIONS: (1) Restricted; (2) use of this record unit requires prior arrangement with the Archives staff.

(545)

Administrator, Cooper-Hewitt Museum, 1962-1988
Records (6.6 linear meters).

In 1963 the Cooper Union trustees announced that the Cooper Union Museum would be closed, and Director Calvin S. Hathaway resigned. Curator of Exhibitions H. Christian Rohlfing was named Acting Administrator, and in this capacity he helped to guide the Museum's transfer to the Smithsonian Institution in 1968. In 1969 Rohlfing became Administrator of the renamed Cooper-Hewitt Museum, and in fiscal year 1972 he assumed the dual title of Administrator and Curator of Collections. John Dobkin became Program Management Officer in FY 1974 and was appointed Administrator in FY 1975. Dobkin and Rohlfing both held the title of Administrator until FY 1978, when Dobkin resigned and Rohlfing relinquished the post to assume purely curatorial responsibilities. The position of Administrator was vacant until FY 1979, when Daniel J. O'Leary became Assistant Director for Administration and Barbara V. Foss and Peter M. Scherer were appointed Administrative Assistants to the Director. O'Leary left the next year, and Foss was replaced by Chauncie McKeever in FY 1981. In FY 1983 McKeever left, Scherer was appointed Special Assistant to the Director, and Linda Dunne was named Administrator. Scherer left in FY 1984.

These records were created mostly by administrators Rohlfing, Dobkin, and Dunne. They document the activities of the Museum Advisory Board and the acquisitions committee and contain files on fundraising, membership, product development, sales, education, collections management, and exhibitions. The records also include audit reports and annual reports; grant proposals; architectural plans of the Miller House; and public relations files, including news clippings from the reopening of the Museum in 1976. In addition, the records contain periodic budget projections and reports for the programs, administrative departments, and payroll of the Museum dating from 1983 to 1988, along with the memoranda and spreadsheets which document their development.

ARRANGEMENT: (1) Records, 1962-1983, accession number 84-230; (2) budget records, 1983-1988, accession number 94-054. FINDING AIDS: Description in control file. SPECIAL CONDITIONS: (1) Restricted; (2) use of this record unit requires prior arrangement with the Archives staff.

(597)

Cooper-Hewitt Museum, 1968-1975
Reading Files (1.2 linear meters).

These records consist of copies of outgoing administrative and curatorial correspondence and internal memoranda dating from July 1968, when the Museum was transferred to the Smithsonian Institution.

ARRANGEMENT: Chronologic. FINDING AIDS: Description in control file. SPECIAL CONDITIONS: Use of this record unit requires prior arrangement with the Archives staff.

(633)

Committee to Save the Cooper Union Museum, 1963-1971, with related material from 1932
Records (0.1 linear meter).

On June 25, 1963, the president and Board of Trustees of the Cooper Union for the Advancement of Science and Art announced their plans to close the Cooper Union Museum for the Arts of Decoration. They temporarily closed the Museum in order to study the possibilities of dispersing the collections to other New York institutions. These actions aroused much comment in the press and among art patrons.

On July 9, 1963, the Committee to Save the Cooper Union Museum announced its formation to the Trustees of the Cooper Union. The Committee was chaired by Henry F. duPont and eventually numbered 260 members. The Committee raised funds to form a charitable trust, and on September 17 it offered to assume responsibility for the Museum from the Cooper Union. However, in November the Trustees accepted an offer by the American Association of Museums (AAM) to form a committee of advisors to aid in the study of the Museum's future. Shortly thereafter, the Museum was reopened to the public.

On behalf of the Committee to Save the Cooper Union Museum, duPont asked the Smithsonian Institution to become responsible for the Museum. The AAM committee substantially endorsed duPont's proposal. On October 9, 1967, the Committee, the Trustees of the Cooper Union, and the Smithsonian jointly announced an agreement that the Museum and its library would be transferred to the Institution. The Committee to

Save the Cooper Union Museum remained in existence to maintain the Cooper Union Museum Charitable Trust.

These files were assembled by the management and staff of the Cooper Union Museum, and later the Cooper-Hewitt Museum, to document their activities during discussions from 1963 to 1970 about the Museum's future and its transfer from the Cooper Union to the Smithsonian Institution. The records contain correspondence and memoranda of Museum Directors Lisa Suter Taylor, Richard P. Wunder, and Calvin S. Hathaway; Administrator Christian Rohlfing; and Associate Curator of Exhibitions Edward L. Kallop reflecting their interaction with the Cooper Union administration, the Committee to Save the Cooper Union Museum, the Smithsonian Institution, and other museum professionals during the period. Also included are press releases, minutes of meetings, lists of Committee members, and information about funds raised by the Committee. In addition, the records contain copies of legal and technical documents regarding the transfer.

The Museum's relationship with the Smithsonian from 1932 to 1968, and with the Smithsonian's National Collection of Fine Arts from 1965 to 1971, is documented through files containing correspondence, memoranda, newsletters, press clippings, and invitations exchanged by administrators and curators of each institution regarding museum business.

ARRANGEMENT: (1) Committee to Save the Cooper Union Museum, 1963-1970; (2) National Collection of Fine Arts correspondence file, 1965-1971; (3) Smithsonian Institution correspondence file, 1932-1968. FINDING AIDS: Folder list in control file. SPECIAL CONDITIONS: Use of this record unit requires prior arrangement with the Archives staff.

(288)

Friends of the Museum of the Cooper Union, 1934-1963
Records (0.3 linear meter).

From its inception, the Cooper Union Museum was dependent on the Hewitt sisters and their friends for donations. After Sarah Hewitt's death in 1930, it was feared that public interest, especially that of sponsors, in a museum of decorative arts would decrease. In 1934, the Museum's Board of Directors and interested persons founded the Friends of the Museum of the Cooper Union. In addition to collecting dues from members, the Friends of the Museum solicited annually for funds, and, from 1936, met annually for tea parties and lectures. The funds collected were used to purchase objects for the Museum, to pay costs for extra personnel and maintenance, and to encourage the study of decorative arts.

These records document the Friends of the Museum's annual appeals and annual meetings. Included are correspondence requesting donations; invitations to the meetings and exhibit openings; correspondence with guest speakers; receipt and expense reports; copies of speeches given at the annual meetings; and membership lists.

ARRANGEMENT: (1) Annual appeals, 1934-1963; (2) annual meetings, 1936-1961. FINDING AIDS: Description in control file. SPECIAL CONDITIONS: Use of this record unit requires prior arrangement with the Archives staff.

DECORATIVE ARTS, DRAWINGS AND PRINTS, EXHIBITIONS, AND TEXTILES, 1930-1992

(506)

Department of Decorative Arts, Cooper-Hewitt Museum, 1941-1992
Records (16 linear meters).

For an administrative history of the Department of Decorative Arts, see record unit 282.

These records consist of the administrative, correspondence, and exhibition files of the Department of Decorative Arts. Curator David R. McFadden and his predecessors created most of the records, but some were compiled by assistants in the Department, guest curators, and exhibition organizers. Some files, created before the Department was organized, document exhibition research and the storage of objects that later came under the curatorial care of Decorative Arts.

The administrative records contain object documentation files; staff meeting notes, memoranda, and reports; files on the work of interns and graduate students in the Department; materials documenting the Cooper-Hewitt Museum's participation in the Decorative Arts Association (DAA); and subject files. The correspondence files contain letters exchanged by Department staff and the general public, other museums, artifact donors, and professional associates regarding the collections and exhibitions of the Museum. The exhibition records consist largely of files on lenders to exhibitions curated or organized by the Department. In addition, the files include exhibition proposals and budgets; research files and bibliographies; installation plans and blueprints; object checklists and photographs; publicity files and press clippings; and catalog publication files.

ARRANGEMENT: (1) Records, 1941-1989, accession number 85-194; (2) records, 1977-1992, accession number 94-060. FINDING AIDS: Description in control file. SPECIAL CONDITIONS: (1) Restricted; (2) use of this record unit requires prior arrangement with the Archives staff.

(282)

Department of Decorative Arts, Cooper-Hewitt Museum, 1967-1978
Records (1 linear meter).

The Department of Decorative Arts was established in 1949 to collect, preserve, exhibit, and act as an information source for three-dimensional objects used in architectural, residential, and personal environments. In addition, the Department maintained the Museum's wallpaper pattern collections until the creation of a separate Department of Wallpapers in 1976.

These records chiefly document the administration of Janet Thorpe, Assistant Curator, 1967-1969, and Associate Curator, 1969-1973, and Catherine Lynn Frangiamore, Assistant Curator, 1969-1974. Also included are materials concerning Thomas E. Lennox, Assistant Curator, 1964-1967; J. Stewart Johnson, Curator, 1974-1976, and David R. McFadden, Curator, 1978-   . Records include correspondence with donors concerning gifts to the Museum, and with interested persons concerning the wallpaper pattern collections; materials concerning the Carnegie Mansion, staff meetings, student interns, researchers, and exhibitions; and chronological files, 1967-1974.

ARRANGEMENT: (1) Administrative files, arranged alphabetically by subject, 1967-1978; (2) general correspondence, 1967-1978; (3) chronological files, 1967-1974. FINDING AIDS: Description in control file. SPECIAL CONDITIONS: Use of this record unit requires prior arrangement with the Archives staff.

(289)

Cooper-Hewitt Museum, 1897-1973
Public Information Materials (2.7 linear meters).

These materials consist of newspaper and journal articles concerning the Museum's exhibitions, the closing of the Cooper Union Museum of Decorative Arts in 1963, the Museum's transfer to the Smithsonian Institution in 1968, and the Museum's relocation to the Carnegie Mansion in 1970. Included are exhibition albums consisting of photographs, catalogs, news releases, and announcement cards, 1952-1956; exhibit posters; a register of the Cooper Union staff members, 1955-1956; a booklet on restoration published by the Museum, 1961; a lithograph print of Peter Cooper; reprints about the Cooper Union Museum and the Cooper Union for the Advancement of Science and Art; and a museum visitor register, 1968-1969.

ARRANGEMENT: (1) Printed materials, 1921-1969; (2) exhibition albums, 1952-1956; (3) scrapbooks, 1962-1968; (4) scrapbooks, oversize, 1897-1973; (5) museum visitor register, 1968-1969; (6) oversize materials. FINDING AIDS: Description in control file. SPECIAL CONDITIONS: Use of this record unit requires prior arrangement with the Archives staff.

(283)

Department of Drawings and Prints, Cooper-Hewitt Museum, 1968-1978
Records (0.5 linear meter).

The Department of Drawings and Prints was established in 1946. It is responsible for the care, storage, cataloging, and study of its holdings. It also provides information on its drawing and print collections to users.

These records document the administration of Elaine Evans Dee, Curator, 1968- , and Xenia Cage, Museum Technician, 1968-1980. They include general correspondence, mostly inquiries regarding the collections, photograph orders, and job applications; and materials concerning exhibitions and the American Federation of Arts committee meetings, 1972-1978.

ARRANGEMENT: (1) General correspondence, arranged alphabetically, 1968-1978; (2) correspondence, photograph requests, arranged chronologically, 1970-1978; (3) exhibitions, arranged chronologically, 1970-1978; (4) the American Federation of Arts, 1972-1978. FINDING AIDS: Description in control file. SPECIAL CONDITIONS: Use of this record unit requires prior arrangement with the Archives staff.

Department of Exhibitions, Cooper Union Museum for the Arts of Decoration, 1930-1969
Records (6.5 linear meters).

The Department of Exhibitions was first organized as the Exhibits Section in 1946. Prior to 1946, persons in charge of exhibitions were assistants to the curator of the Cooper Union Museum for the Arts of Decoration. Alliene E. Dodge, D. Graeme Keith, James I. Rambo, Everett P. Lesley, Jr., and William R. Osmun were Assistants, Exhibits Section, during the period from 1946 to 1953. The assistants were under the supervision of the museum curator, and later, under the museum director.

In 1953 the Exhibits Section was redesignated the Department of Exhibitions, and the title of Assistant was changed to Keeper. Lesley, Osmun, and H. Christian Rohlfing held the title of Keeper during the period from 1953 to 1958. The title of Keeper, Department of Exhibitions, was changed to Curator, Department of Exhibitions, in 1958. Rohlfing held the title of Curator, and Edward L. Kallop became Associate Curator in 1957. When Rohlfing became Acting Administrator of the Museum in 1963, the position of Curator remained vacant. The department was discontinued as an administrative unit when the Cooper Union Museum transferred to the Smithsonian Institution in 1968.

The Department of Exhibitions was responsible for the design, preparation, installation, maintenance, and dismantling of "special" or theme exhibitions of museum and non-museum collections for the general public, including exhibitions for other branches of the Cooper Union for the Advancement of Science and Art.

Records document, for the most part, the Department under the administration of Calvin S. Hathaway, Curator, 1946-1951, and Director, 1951-1963. Included is correspondence of Hathaway with members of the exhibition staff, and with collectors and institutions concerning the exhibits in the Museum; exhibit files, arranged alphabetically by the title of the exhibits, and including photographs, pamphlets, floor plans, drawings, publicity materials, specimen lists and descriptions, and correspondence; and annual reports.

ARRANGEMENT: (1) Administrative files, 1934-1936, 1942, 1946-1947; (2) special exhibits, 1930-1969. FINDING AIDS: Description in control file. SPECIAL CONDITIONS: Use of this record unit requires prior arrangement with the Archives staff.

Exhibitions Department, Cooper-Hewitt Museum, 1973-1992
Exhibition Records (13.1 linear meters and oversize).

For an administrative history of the Exhibitions Department prior to 1968, see record unit 280. The Museum reinstated its exhibits office in fiscal year 1973 with the appointment of Dorothy Twining Globus as Exhibits Specialist. Lucy Fellowes was retained as Exhibitions Researcher in FY 1977. Globus became Exhibition Coordinator in FY 1978 and Curator of Exhibitions in FY 1987. Robin Parkinson was Exhibition Designer from FY 1978 through FY 1985, and Michael Legnasky was Designer in FY 1988, but the position has otherwise been vacant.

These records document the conceptualization, development, design, and execution of several exhibitions held by the Cooper-Hewitt Museum from 1973 through 1992, and of exhibitions rejected or cancelled by the Museum. Exhibition files include proposals; research files; correspondence with object lenders, scholars, and exhibition designers; photographs, slides, and checklists of objects; installation floor plans and blueprints, including layout drawings by Robin Parkinson; scripts and label copy; publicity materials; press reviews; funding and budget records; catalog publication notes; and bibliographies. In addition, the records contain slides that were shown in some exhibitions.

ARRANGEMENT: Chronologic. FINDING AIDS: Description in control file. SPECIAL CONDITIONS: (1) Restricted; (2) use of this record unit requires prior arrangement with the Archives staff.

(287)

Cooper-Hewitt Museum, 1974-1979
Exhibition Records (3.3 linear meters).

These records document Cooper-Hewitt Museum exhibitions from 1974 to 1979, especially the Museum's *Museum Without Walls* project; *Immovable Objects/Lower Manhattan, from Battery Park to the Brooklyn Bridge,* 1975; and the Museum's first exhibition at the Carnegie Mansion, *MAN transFORMS/Aspects of Design,* 1976.

These records were assembled by Dorothy Twining Globus, Exhibits Specialist, and Lucy Fellowes, Exhibits Researcher, and consist of correspondence with museum administrators, architects and designers, and interested persons concerning the exhibits, catalogs, and loans of objects. In addition, there are research notes, photographs, printed materials, budgets, newspaper and journal articles, notes taken at meetings, and blueprints and drawings. Oversize materials consist of blueprints and drawings of floor plans and layouts of the exhibits, and graphic print posters for a "metamorphic" theme (*MAN transFORMS*).

ARRANGEMENT: (1) Exhibitions, arranged chronologically, 1977-1979; (2) exhibition research materials, 1974-1977; (3) *MAN transFORMS,* oversize materials; (4) blueprints and drawings, oversize. FINDING AIDS: Description in control file. SPECIAL CONDITIONS: Use of this record unit requires prior arrangement with the Archives staff.

(539)

Department of Textiles, Cooper-Hewitt Museum, 1976-1991
Records (0.4 linear meter).

The textile collection of the Cooper Union Museum rose to preeminence with John Pierpont Morgan's 1902 donation of three significant collections of medieval European cloth designs. Mary S.M. Gibson took charge of the museum collections as Curator in 1904, and was responsible for the general oversight of the textile department until Jean Reed was hired as Assistant Keeper for Textiles in 1935 and Elizabeth Haynes became Keeper of Lace and Embroidery in 1937. In 1941 Reed was replaced by Alvena Vajda Secklar, who was succeeded by Dorothy G. Shepherd in 1942, and by Lili Blumendau in 1944.

Haynes died in June 1948 and three months later Alice Baldwin Beer was hired as Keeper of Needlework. Beer became Keeper of Textiles in 1950, and at the same time Jean E. Mailey replaced Blumendau as Assistant Keeper. Mailey resigned in 1957, and the designation "Keeper" was changed to "Curator" in October 1958. Sarah Frantz was Assistant Curator of Textiles from 1958 to 1961, and Christa C. Mayer held the post from 1961 to 1967. Milton F. Sonday of the Textile Museum in Washington, D.C. became Assistant Curator in December 1967.

In 1970 Beer retired and became Consultant for Textiles, and in fiscal year 1977 Sonday was appointed Curator of Textiles. In 1979 Beer was named Curator Emeritus, a position she held until her death in November 1981. Textile Conservator Lucy Commoner began work in FY 1977, and the appointment of Gillian Moss as Textiles Assistant in FY 1984 led to her assignment as Assistant Curator of Textiles in FY 1985.

These records consist of departmental correspondence and office memoranda from 1976 to 1991. Files for 1984 and 1988 are missing. The records were created mostly by Milton Sonday and Gillian Moss, and concern subjects such as exhibition loans, textile scholarship, catalogs and publications, public inquiries, the donation and acquisition of objects, research on collections, activities in other museums, and administrative needs. The records include some files on the exhibition *Lace,* which was shown at the Cooper-Hewitt Museum from August to November 1982.

ARRANGEMENT: Chronologic. FINDING AIDS: Description in control file. SPECIAL CONDITIONS: (1) Restricted; (2) use of this record unit requires prior arrangement with the Archives staff.

EDUCATION, MEMBERSHIP, AND PUBLIC INFORMATION, 1890-1990

(324)

Office of the Program Coordinator, Cooper-Hewitt Museum, 1976-1982
Records (2.2 linear meters).

The Office of the Program Coordinator, a unit of the Education Division, develops programs for the general public which deal with various aspects of the decorative arts. Included in each semester's offerings are lecture series, tours, workshops, weekend seminars, luncheon lectures, and an assortment of special programs for young people. Funding is provided in part by registration fees, and in part through the contributions of private foundations and corporations.

Jane Clark served as Program Coordinator from the beginning semester in 1976 to 1978, when she was succeeded by Jennifer Jarvis. Since 1979, the position has been shared by Jarvis and Susan Yelavich.

These records document the activities of the Program Coordinator and the development and administration of the Office from the fall semester of 1976 to the fall semester of 1982. Included is correspondence with organizers for travel programs, speakers, instructors, performers, guides, vendors and registrants; syllabi, course descriptions and teaching aids; student profile and program evaluation forms; contracts with course leaders; photographs and biographical information for selected instructors; newspaper and magazine articles concerning various programs; fiscal records for course supplies; transcripts of some lectures; program guides and agendas; and staff notes and memoranda.

ARRANGEMENT: (1) Programs, 1976-1982; (2) correspondence, 1979-1981. FINDING AIDS: Description in control file. SPECIAL CONDITIONS: Use of this record unit requires prior arrangement with the Archives staff.

(546)

Development Office, Cooper-Hewitt Museum, 1970-1990
Records (3.3 linear meters).

For an administrative history of the Development Office from 1976, see record unit 436. Prior to the establishment of the Office, fundraising was done by a variety of Cooper-Hewitt Museum staff, including curators, administrators, and the Director.

These records document the efforts of the Development Office to generate private financial support for Museum exhibitions from 1978 to 1990. Files were created for each exhibition and contain memoranda concerning possible sources of support and lists of potential donors; solicitation letters and correspondence with potential donors; information about corporate donors such as annual reports; promotional material and press releases for exhibitions; exhibition proposals and budget requirements; newspaper and magazine clippings about exhibitions; and funding summaries of donors solicited and their responses.

Records also consist of files for year-end appeals from 1983 to 1988, which include lists of donors, acknowledgment letters and other correspondence with donors; files for benefits held from 1982 to 1989 to raise money for the Museum, consisting mostly of copies of response forms; files documenting memorial funds established in honor of significant staff members or figures in design; and correspondence files with donors of $500 or less.

ARRANGEMENT: (1) Exhibition funding files, arranged alphabetically by exhibition title, 1978-1990; (2) year-end appeal files, arranged chronologically, 1983-1988; (3) benefits, arranged chronologically, 1982-1989; (4) memorial fund files, 1974-1982; (5) donors under $500, arranged alphabetically by donor name, 1970-1990. FINDING AIDS: Description in control file. SPECIAL CONDITIONS: (1) Restricted; (2) use of this record unit requires prior arrangement with the Archives staff.

(284)

Department of Membership and Programs, Cooper-Hewitt Museum, 1973-1978
Records (2.1 linear meters).

In 1974 the Museum held its first annual benefit auction of objects donated for sale. The funds earned from the first three auctions were used for the renovation of the Carnegie Mansion. Following completion of that project in 1976, the auctions were held to support the Museum's educational programs.

The first auction was coordinated by Dorothy Twining Globus, an Exhibits Specialist in the Museum. Mary Kerr, Assistant Registrar, coordinated the second auction in 1975.

In 1976, responsibility for the auctions was combined with a new membership program under Kerr as Membership Coordinator.

These records consist of correspondence with prospective donors; invitations to auction previews, supper parties, and the auctions; drafts for invitations, announcements, and the auction catalogs; photographs of items for auction; auction bids; expense statements; and sales receipts. Also included are newspaper and journal articles, materials pertaining to special events, and inactive volunteer files.

ARRANGEMENT: (1) Auctions, 1973-1978; (2) special events programs, 1976-1978. FINDING AIDS: Description in control file. SPECIAL CONDITIONS: Use of this record unit requires prior arrangement with the Archives staff.

(436)

Office of Membership and Development, Cooper-Hewitt Museum, 1976-1987
Records (0.4 linear meter).

For an administrative history of the Office of Membership and Development, see record unit 284. The office was managed by Mary Kerr from its inception in 1976 until 1983, when Eileen White became Development Manager. In 1986, George Nichols became Development Officer, and Susan Sweetser was Membership Officer. Nichols was appointed Membership and Development Officer in 1987.

These records contain reports and memoranda describing the Museum's membership operation, and document the selection and operation of automated mailing and tracking systems. Samples of solicitations and data from periodic membership drives are included, as are membership statistics and financial reports.

ARRANGEMENT: Unarranged. FINDING AIDS: Folder list in control file. SPECIAL CONDITIONS: (1) Restricted; (2) use of this record unit requires prior arrangement with the Archives staff.

(547)

Public Information Office, Cooper-Hewitt Museum, 1890, 1943-1984
Records (0.8 linear meter).

While under the auspices of the Cooper Union, the Museum had no staff or offices devoted exclusively to publicity, and it relied upon the Public Relations Office of the parent organization to issue press releases about its exhibitions and activities. In 1943 responsibility for publicity was included in the duties of D. Graeme Keith, Assistant to the Curator in charge of Services. He was replaced in 1944 by Allison Delarue. Mary A. Noon assumed responsibility for maintaining records on the Museum's history and publicity when she became Recorder in 1946. When the Museum was transferred to the Smithsonian Institution in 1968, Noon continued in this function as Museum Specialist.

An independent Public Relations Office was not established until 1977, one year after the Cooper-Hewitt Museum reopened to the public in the Carnegie Mansion. Isabelle Silverman was the Museum's first Public Relations Officer, and in 1979 she became Public Relations Manager. She was named Public Information Manager in 1983.

Many of these records predate Silverman's arrival at the Museum, and consist of subject files that were apparently assembled by Mary Noon and others to document the history and activities of the Museum under the Cooper Union. They contain curatorial correspondence; press releases; fact sheets; information leaflets; news clippings; and photographs of activities at the Museum. Also included are information files about important figures in the Museum's history.

These records also describe the work of the Public Information Office on the Museum's first exhibitions under Smithsonian auspices. The exhibitions *Immovable Objects/Lower Manhattan from Battery Park to the Brooklyn Bridge,* 1975, and *MAN transFORMS/Aspects of Design,* 1976, are documented through press releases, news clippings, and files on the opening receptions.

ARRANGEMENT: Unarranged. FINDING AIDS: Description in control file. SPECIAL CONDITIONS: Use of this record unit requires prior arrangement with the Archives staff.

REGISTRAR AND CONSERVATION, 1937-1992

(540)
Office of the Registrar, Cooper-Hewitt Museum, circa 1937-1992
Records (1.2 linear meters).

Soon after he was hired as Assistant Curator in 1933, Calvin Hathaway introduced a new system for accessioning and cataloging the collections of the Cooper Union Museum. By 1942 Hathaway had become Associate Curator, and his system was maintained by secretarial staff under the supervision of Mary A. Noon, Assistant to the Curator for Collections. Noon became Acting Head of the Museum in 1945, and in 1947 Dorothea C. Shipley was appointed Catalog Supervisor. Paul Dreschler replaced her in 1951, and Mary Fonner Blackwelder was named to the post in 1956.

Shortly after the Museum was transferred to the Smithsonian Institution Blackwelder assumed the position of Registrar, where she remained until February 1975. Elizabeth Burnham was Registrar from FY 1976 through FY 1978, and Albina De Meio served in that function from FY 1980 through FY 1981. Cordelia Rose was appointed Registrar in FY 1982.

These records document the administrative and program activities of the Office of the Registrar from 1973 to 1992, with some files dating from 1959. Records consist of staff meeting notes, administrative memoranda, quarterly reports, and annual reports to the Smithsonian's central Office of the Registrar in response to Office Memorandum 808, "Collections Management Policy." Also included are reports and budgets for the Museum's acquisitions fund; memoranda and correspondence concerning the Smithsonian Institution Registrar's Council and its predecessors, the Registrarial Council of the Smithsonian Institution and the Council of Registrars, from its inception in January 1973 through 1987; and insurance registers, projections, and claims. The records also contain labels describing various objects on exhibition, *circa* 1937 to 1968; accession card corrections and changes from 1959 and undated; contracts from the 1960s; lists of income and object purchases; and the correspondence of Mary Blackwelder from 1970 to 1971.

ARRANGEMENT: Arranged by subject, and chronologically thereunder. FINDING AIDS: Description in control file. SPECIAL CONDITIONS: (1) Restricted; (2) use of this record unit requires prior arrangement with the Archives staff.

(541)

Office of the Registrar, Cooper-Hewitt Museum, 1958, 1975-1987
Exhibition Files (16.4 linear meters).

For an administrative history of the Office of the Registrar, see record unit 540.

These records pertain to the exhibitions of the Cooper-Hewitt Museum, beginning with the first held under the auspices of the Smithsonian, *Immovable Objects/Lower Manhattan from Battery Park to the Brooklyn Bridge,* which opened in June 1975, and ending with *Louis Sullivan: The Function of Ornament,* which closed in September 1987. In addition, a file is included for the exhibition *Clay and Color: The Ceramics of Picasso,* which opened in the Cooper Union Museum in March 1958.

The records largely document the loan of objects by public and private institutions, organizations, and individuals for exhibition in the Museum. Exhibition documentation consists of correspondence with lenders regarding special conditions and restrictions on loans; loan agreements; packing, shipping, and insurance information; object specifications, provenance, and insurance values; object packing, condition and conservation photographs and reports; inventory lists; exhibition budgets; installation plans; label copy; and press reviews. The extent of documentation varies with each exhibition. Many of the exhibition files correspond to object photographs contained in record unit 542, and are linked to the photographs by loan numbers.

ARRANGEMENT: Arranged chronologically by exhibition, and alphabetically by lender thereunder. FINDING AIDS: Description in control file. SPECIAL CONDITIONS: (1) Restricted; (2) use of this record unit requires prior arrangement with the Archives staff.

(542)

Office of the Registrar, Cooper-Hewitt Museum, 1977-1987
Object Photographs and Condition Reports (9.8 linear meters).

For an administrative history of the Office of the Registrar, see record unit 540.

These records consist of notebooks created by the Registrar's Office to document the objects loaned to the Cooper-Hewitt Museum for exhibition. Documentation consists of color photographs or photocopies of photographs of objects showing methods of packing for shipment or damage to objects. Notebooks also contain condition reports, floor plans showing placement of objects in exhibitions, exhibition label facsimiles, lists of objects shown in exhibitions, and values of objects in different currencies. The first exhibition documented here is *The Royal Pavilion at Brighton,* which opened in March 1977, and the last is *Robert Adam and Kedleston Hall,* which opened in June 1987. Documentation of exhibits is by no means complete. Many of the notebooks correspond to exhibition files contained in record unit 541, and are linked to the files by loan number.

ARRANGEMENT: Chronologic. FINDING AIDS: Description in control file. SPECIAL CONDITIONS: (1) Restricted; (2) use of this record unit requires prior arrangement with the Archives staff.

Paper Conservation Laboratory, Cooper-Hewitt Museum, 1974-1987
Records (0.8 linear meter).

These records document the design, construction, furnishing, and equipping of the Cooper-Hewitt Museum's Paper Conservation Laboratory during 1979 and 1980 under the guidance of Konstanze Bachmann, Paper Conservator, and Elaine Evans Dee, Curator of Prints and Drawings. The files contain Dee's February 1975 proposal for the laboratory, and also include floor plans; lists of furnishings, equipment, and supplies; and price quotes. In addition, the records contain budget and cost estimates, correspondence with suppliers and contractors, and floor plan markups.

The records also document the first five years of the New York State Conservation Consultancy (NYSCC). The organization was an outgrowth of a program at the New York University Institute of Fine Arts, and was funded by grants from the New York State Council on the Arts (NYSCA). Bachmann was Coordinator of the NYSCC from its inception in 1982 through 1987. The goal of the program was to encourage an awareness of the need for collections conservation in New York museums and historical societies. The program offered lectures and seminars on various aspects of conservation; free conservation surveys; bibliographies and lists of conservators and conservation suppliers; and free bulletins on conservation topics.

Records of the program contain the original NYSCC grant proposal submitted by Bachmann to the NYSCA in February 1981 and grant applications, budgets, grant reviews, and annual reports for each subsequent year through 1987. The files also include mailing lists; seminar information; program correspondence from 1981 to 1987; lists of conservation surveys conducted under NYSCA and NYSCC auspices from 1974 to 1986; and selected survey reports. In addition, the records contain copies of the first twenty NYSCC bulletins, as well as brochures and publicity materials.

ARRANGEMENT: (1) Design and construction records of the Paper Conservation Laboratory, 1975, 1979-1980; (2) records of the New York State Conservation Consultancy, 1974-1987. FINDING AIDS: Description in control file. SPECIAL CONDITIONS: (1) Restricted; (2) use of this record unit requires prior arrangement with the Archives staff.

LIBRARY, 1864-1977

Library, Cooper-Hewitt Museum, 1864-1977
Publications and Reports (1.6 linear meters).

These publications and reports were accumulated over time in the Library of the Cooper-Hewitt Museum. Most were produced before the Cooper Union Museum was transferred to the Smithsonian Institution in 1968, and some predate the establishment of the Cooper

Union Museum itself in 1896. The publications include an incomplete series of annual reports for the Cooper Union for the Advancement of Science and Art, beginning with the fifth report published in 1864. The series ends with an excerpt from the Smithsonian *Annual Report* for FY 1969, when the Museum was first listed as a bureau of the Institution.

The materials also contain volumes one through three of the *Chronicle of the Museum for the Arts of Decoration of the Cooper Union;* biographical information about significant figures in the Museum's history; checklists, descriptions, and essays based on the Museum's collections; reports by the Director, Treasurer, and Secretary of the Council for the Cooper Union Museum from 1907 to 1927; texts of talks given at the Museum; and histories of the Museum written by staff members.

ARRANGEMENT: Unarranged. FINDING AIDS: Description in control file. SPECIAL CONDITIONS: Use of this record requires prior arrangement with the Archives staff.

WOODROW WILSON INTERNATIONAL CENTER FOR SCHOLARS

The Woodrow Wilson International Center for Scholars (WWICS) was established by Act of Congress on October 24, 1968, to be a "living memorial expressing the ideals and concerns of Woodrow Wilson...symbolizing and strengthening the fruitful relations between the world of learning and the world of public affairs." The Center was placed within the Smithsonian Institution under the independent administration of a fifteen-member Board of Trustees appointed by the President, eight chosen from private life and seven from public positions. Chairmen of the Board of Trustees have included Hubert H. Humphrey, 1969-1972; William J. Baroody, Sr., 1972-1979; Max Kampelman, 1979-1982; and William J. Baroody, Jr., 1982-   . Funding for the Center is derived from both private support and public appropriations.

The Wilson Center carries out its mission primarily through the selection of fellows and short-term guest scholars from the United States and around the world. Applicants submit a research proposal to be undertaken in one of the program areas, and fellows are chosen by impartial panels. The Center brings together the fellows and other prominent figures to discuss important national and international social and political subjects in forums and debates. WWICS also publishes *The Wilson Quarterly* and sponsors the "Dialogue" radio program. The Center opened its fellowship and guest scholar programs on October 19, 1970. Benjamin H. Read was appointed Acting Director of WWICS in March 1969 and became Director in September 1969, a position which he retained until February 1973. Albert Meisel (Deputy Director of WWICS since 1970) served as Acting Director from February until September 1973, when James H. Billington was appointed Director. Billington served until his departure in 1987, when Prosser Gifford was appointed Acting Director. Charles Blitzer became Director, 1988-   .

DIRECTOR, DEPUTY DIRECTOR, AND CENTRAL ADMINISTRATION, 1969-1989

(275)

Office of the Director, Woodrow Wilson International Center for Scholars, 1969-1979 and undated
Records (3.3 linear meters).

For an administrative history of the Woodrow Wilson International Center for Scholars (WWICS), see the introduction to the Center.

This record unit consists mostly of files maintained by Benjamin H. Read and James H. Billington during their service as Directors of WWICS. A few records were created by Albert Meisel as Acting Director of WWICS. The records document the early history of WWICS and concern fundraising; recruitment of fellows and scholars; the development of WWICS programs; conferences and symposia sponsored by WWICS; and national and international affairs. The record unit includes general correspondence, 1969-1975; outgoing correspondence, 1970-1979; program files, including records dealing with WWICS programs in International Affairs, Environmental Studies, Ocean Studies, and State and Local Government; and voluminous files regarding the WWICS Sustainable Growth Program.

ARRANGEMENT: (1) General correspondence, 1969-1975; (2) outgoing correspondence, 1970-1979; (3) program files, 1969-1977 and undated; (4) Sustainable Growth Program files, 1972-1976. FINDING AIDS: Description in control file. SPECIAL CONDITIONS: Use of this record unit requires prior arrangement with the Archives staff.

(560)

Deputy Director, Woodrow Wilson International Center for Scholars, 1971-1989
Records (2.9 linear meters).

Albert Meisel was appointed Deputy Director of the Woodrow Wilson International Center for Scholars (WWICS) in 1970 and held the position until 1973. In 1973 he served as Acting Director. In 1974 the title was changed to Assistant Director, and Michael J. Lacey held the position until 1975. In 1976 the position was again titled Deputy Director. George R. Packard served as Deputy Director from 1976 until 1979, when Prosser Gifford assumed the position. Gifford served from 1979 to 1987. In 1987 he was also Acting Director until leaving the Center in 1988, when Samuel F. Wells, Jr., was appointed Deputy Director.

These records consist of the files of George R. Packard and Prosser Gifford as Deputy Directors of WWICS. They consist of correspondence and reports concerning events, fundraising, and publications. Also included are records of financial contributions to the Center, 1971-1989.

ARRANGEMENT: (1) Records of the Deputy Director, 1976-1985, accession number 87-052; (2) records of financial contributions, 1971-1989, accession number 92-073. FINDING AIDS: None. SPECIAL CONDITIONS: (1) Restricted; (2) use of this record unit requires prior arrangement with the Archives staff.

(585)

Woodrow Wilson International Center for Scholars, 1970-1975
Tape Recordings of Events (0.4 linear meter).

For an administrative history of the Woodrow Wilson International Center for Scholars (WWICS), see the introduction to the Center.

This record unit consists of tape recordings of various events held in the early years of the Wilson Center. Included are dinners, seminars, meetings, lectures, and presentations.

ARRANGEMENT: Unarranged. FINDING AIDS: None. SPECIAL CONDITIONS: Use of this record unit requires prior arrangement with the Archives staff.

Office of Special Events, Woodrow Wilson International Center for Scholars, 1970-1978
Records (1.2 linear meters).

The earliest functions of the Woodrow Wilson International Center for Scholars were arranged by a staff secretary with the approval of the Director. As the number of dialogues and receptions increased, a Special Events Coordinator was needed to arrange for catering, invitations, and other details. Louise Platt served as Coordinator, 1975-   .

These records consist of invitations, guest and participant lists, seating plans, responses, menus, and occasional background papers of speakers.

ARRANGEMENT: Chronologic. FINDING AIDS: None. SPECIAL CONDITIONS: Use of this record unit requires prior arrangement with the Archives staff.

Hubert H. Humphrey Fellowship in Social and Political Thought, Woodrow Wilson International Center for Scholars, 1978-1979
Records (0.1 linear meter).

The Hubert H. Humphrey Fellowship in Social and Political Thought was administered by the Office of the Director, Woodrow Wilson International Center for Scholars (WWICS). It was established in 1978 by Congress to honor Hubert H. Humphrey, former Senator and Vice-President of the United States, who was also the first Chairman of the Board of Trustees of the Wilson Center. The Humphrey Fellow was to serve for one year, delivering a Hubert H. Humphrey Memorial Lecture and carrying out projects consistent with the Fellowship. Congress eventually chose not to fund the Fellowship, and the program has remained dormant.

These records document the establishment of the Fellowship by the WWICS. They include background materials on other similar prizes, copies of legislation, and notes on the selection process and on congressional testimony.

ARRANGEMENT: Unarranged. FINDING AIDS: None. SPECIAL CONDITIONS: Use of this record unit requires prior arrangement with the Archives staff.

Pelikan Committee Review of International Programs, Woodrow Wilson International Center for Scholars, 1981-1982
Records (0.4 linear meter).

In 1981 James H. Billington, Director of the Woodrow Wilson International Center for Scholars (WWICS), announced the undertaking of a "visiting committee" review of the international programs of the Wilson Center. The programs evaluated were to include the Latin American Program, the East Asia Program, the International Security Studies Program, and the Kennan Institute for Advanced Russian Studies. The review, which took its name from its Chairman, Professor Jaroslav Pelikan, was administered by Deputy Director Prosser Gifford.

These records consist of fairly extensive background materials for each of the WWICS programs reviewed by the Pelikan Committee, including lists of fellows and their topics, publications, seminars and dialogues, and evaluations. Also included are notes, apparently of Prosser Gifford. Although there are letters of evaluation from area scholars, there does not appear to be a copy of the final report of the Committee.

ARRANGEMENT: Unarranged. FINDING AIDS: None. SPECIAL CONDITIONS: Use of this record unit requires prior arrangement with the Archives staff.

AREA STUDIES, 1973-1992

(291)

Kennan Institute for Advanced Russian Studies, Woodrow Wilson International Center for Scholars, 1975-1980
Records (4.8 linear meters).

The Kennan Institute for Advanced Russian Studies was founded in 1974 as a division of the Woodrow Wilson International Center for Scholars. Through its fellowship program and special projects, the Institute helps to promote advanced research on Russia and the U.S.S.R. by scholars and qualified persons from government, industry, and the press. It is directed by an academic council which was established in 1975 under the chairmanship of George F. Kennan, former United States Ambassador to the Soviet Union. In 1975 S. Frederick Starr was appointed Secretary of the Institute and remained in the post until 1980. Abbott Gleason became the new Secretary at that time.

This record unit documents the development of the Kennan Institute and its initial programs and includes incoming and outgoing correspondence maintained by Starr, 1975-1980, and Gleason, 1980, concerning the operation of the Institute, Russian history, and professional activities; an unsuccessful fellowship applicants' file; and records regarding events and programs which the Institute sponsored or participated in.

ARRANGEMENT: (1) General correspondence, 1975-1980; (2) fellowship records, 1976-1980; (3) events file, 1975-1979. FINDING AIDS: None. SPECIAL CONDITIONS: Use of this record unit requires prior arrangement with the Archives staff.

(567)

Kennan Institute for Advanced Russian Studies, Woodrow Wilson International Center for Scholars, 1978-1984
Records (2.5 linear meters).

For an administrative history of the Kennan Institute for Advanced Russian Studies, see record unit 291.

Abbott Gleason served as Secretary of the Kennan Institute until 1982 when John Glad assumed the position. Glad was succeeded the following year by Herbert J. Ellison, who served 1983-   .

These records document the administrative and program activities of the Kennan Institute under Abbott Gleason and John Glad. They include some budget material, files of ongoing projects, correspondence, and files on events such as conferences and dialogues.

ARRANGEMENT: (1) Kennan Institute records, 1978-1984, accession number 85-192; (2) Kennan Institute records, 1979-1983, accession number 84-194. FINDING AIDS: Box list in control file. SPECIAL CONDITIONS: (1) Restricted; (2) use of this record unit requires prior arrangement with the Archives staff.

(571)
State and Local Government Program, Woodrow Wilson International Center for Scholars, 1973-1979
Records (1.6 linear meters).

The State and Local Government Program of the Woodrow Wilson International Center for Scholars (WWICS) was established in January 1974, with Elliott L. Richardson as Chairman of its Advisory Committee. It consisted of approximately six fellows committed to the study and discussion of problems and challenges facing American government at the local level. A large number of the Advisory Committee members consisted of city mayors, current and former state governors, and other officials engaged in public administration.

In its early years the State and Local Government Program was administered by the fellows and other support staff of the Wilson Center, such as the Special Events Coordinator. Official correspondence of the Program was signed by the WWICS Director. In 1975 Jeffrey L. Mayer was appointed Associate Scholar and then Staff Administrator of the Program. He served through 1976 when Robert B. Hawkins, Jr., who had been a fellow, became Program Coordinator and served 1977-   .

These records consist of the administrative and program files of the State and Local Government Program. They include correspondence concerning arrangements for dialogues and colloquia, fundraising material, mailing lists, fellowship correspondence, records of advisory committee meetings, texts of papers given at various events, and some correspondence and a manuscript for the journal *Publius.*

ARRANGEMENT: Unarranged. FINDING AIDS: None. SPECIAL CONDITIONS: Use of this record unit requires prior arrangement with the Archives staff.

(569)
United States Studies Program, Woodrow Wilson International Center for Scholars, 1979-1990
Records (4.1 linear meters).

The American Society and Politics Program was created in 1980 to study issues in American life. Michael J. Lacey served as Secretary of the program, 1980-   . In 1989 his title was changed to Program Director, and in 1990 the name of the program was changed to the United States Studies Program.

These records document the United States Studies Program under Michael J. Lacey and consist of material on conferences and projects, fellows and interns, administrative matters, and publications.

ARRANGEMENT: (1) United States Studies Program, 1979-1990, accession number 90-168; (2) United States Studies Program, 1982-1989, accession number 92-129. FINDING AIDS: Folder list in control file. SPECIAL CONDITIONS: (1) Restricted; (2) use of this record unit requires prior arrangement with the Archives staff.

(559)

West European Program, Woodrow Wilson International Center for Scholars, 1985-1992
Records (4.5 linear meters).

The West European Program of the Woodrow Wilson International Center for Scholars was created in 1985 and Michael H. Haltzel was appointed its Secretary. In 1988 his title changed to Program Secretary and in 1989, to Program Director. Since 1990, the job title has been Director. Haltzel served until 1992 when Samuel F. Wells, Jr., took over, serving 1992- .

These records document the West European Program and contain files concerning conferences sponsored by the Program; correspondence files; files on fellows, scholars, and interns; administrative matters; information on funding; and photographs of fellows and staff.

ARRANGEMENT: (1) West European Program, 1985-1991, accession number 92-128; (2) West European Program, 1985-1992, accession number 94-078; (3) West European Program, 1986-1991, accession number 93-013. FINDING AIDS: Folder list in control file. SPECIAL CONDITIONS: Use of this record unit requires prior arrangement with the Archives staff.

RADIO DIALOGUE, 1980-1990

(601)

Radio Dialogue, Woodrow Wilson International Center for Scholars, circa 1980-1986
Audiotapes and Records (4.5 linear meters).

In 1978 the Woodrow Wilson International Center for Scholars (WWICS) entered into a contract with the Longhorn Radio Network at the University of Texas to participate in a public affairs consortium series of radio programs called "Focus." The Wilson Center produced the broadcasts on a variety of timely topics concerned with politics and current issues.

This arrangement lasted until 1983, when the Wilson Center began to produce its own series of radio broadcasts called "Radio Dialogue." Occasionally, these programs were also broadcast by National Public Radio or Radio Smithsonian. Deputy Director Prosser

Gifford was the moderator, aided by Eugenie Beth Skarstrom, who served as Radio Coordinator, 1984- .

These records consist primarily of ten-inch audiotapes of "Radio Dialogue" programs, as well as some administrative files, including release forms by participants, schedules, biographical information on WWICS scholar participants, listener responses, and contracts with Longhorn Radio Network. Also included are a few "Focus" tapes and some cassettes of programs broadcast by Radio Smithsonian.

ARRANGEMENT: Audiotapes are arranged numerically; administrative files are unarranged. FINDING AIDS: Box list, title list, numbering sequence, and participant index in control file. SPECIAL CONDITIONS: Use of this record unit requires prior arrangement with the Archives staff.

(602)

Radio Dialogue, Woodrow Wilson International Center for Scholars, 1984-1986
Audiotapes and Records (4.1 linear meters).

For an administrative history of "Radio Dialogue, " see record unit 601.

These records consist of tapes and copies of tapes, in addition to a small amount of administrative material.

ARRANGEMENT: Numerical. FINDING AIDS: Box list, title list, numbering sequence, and participant index in control file. SPECIAL CONDITIONS: Use of this record unit requires prior arrangement with the Archives staff.

(603)

Radio Dialogue, Woodrow Wilson International Center for Scholars, 1988-1989
Audiotapes and Transcripts (4.5 linear meters).

For an administrative history of the "Radio Dialogue" series, see record unit 601.

George Liston Seay became moderator of the "Radio Dialogue" series in 1988. He served in this position, 1988- .

These records consist of audiotapes broadcast by National Public Radio and Longhorn Radio Network, as well as unedited masters of tapes for "Radio Dialogue." Also included are transcripts for some of the broadcasts.

ARRANGEMENT: Numerical. FINDING AIDS: Box list, title list, numbering sequence, and participant index in control file. SPECIAL CONDITIONS: Use of this record unit requires prior arrangement with the Archives staff.

(604)

Radio Dialogue, Woodrow Wilson International Center for Scholars, 1989-1990
Audiotapes and Transcripts (3.3 linear meters).

For an administrative history of the "Radio Dialogue" series see record units 601 and 603.

George Liston Seay was Moderator of the series until 1990, when his title changed to Director. At the same time the program's name changed to "Dialogue." Seay served, 1990- .

This record unit consists of audiotapes and transcripts from "Radio Dialogue" and "Dialogue." Some on these tapes were also broadcast on National Public Radio.

ARRANGEMENT: Numerical. FINDING AIDS: Box list in control file. SPECIAL CONDITIONS: Use of this record unit requires prior arrangement with the Archives staff.

THE WILSON QUARTERLY, 1975-1987

(578)

The Wilson Quarterly, Woodrow Wilson International Center for Scholars, circa 1975-1987
Editor's Files (1.2 linear meters).

For an administrative history of *The Wilson Quarterly,* see record units 572 and 573.

These records consist of general correspondence of the Editor, in addition to some files on fundraising. Also included is correspondence between Editor Peter Braestrup and Wilson Center Director James H. Billington.

ARRANGEMENT: Unarranged. FINDING AIDS: None. SPECIAL CONDITIONS: (1) Restricted; (2) use of this record unit requires prior arrangement with the Archives staff.

(572)

The Wilson Quarterly, Woodrow Wilson International Center for Scholars, circa 1976-1987
Records (2.5 linear meters).

For an administrative history of *The Wilson Quarterly,* see record unit 573. Peter Braestrup served as Editor, 1976-   .

These records consist of the general correspondence of the Office of the Editor, as well as correspondence with authors and readers.

ARRANGEMENT: (1) *The Wilson Quarterly,* records, 1976-1979, accession number 81-047; (2) *The Wilson Quarterly,* records, 1981-1987, accession number 89-034. FINDING AIDS: None. SPECIAL CONDITIONS: (1) Restricted; (2) use of this record unit requires prior arrangement with the Archives staff.

(573)

The Wilson Quarterly, Woodrow Wilson International Center for Scholars, 1977-1984
Records (1.6 linear meters).

The Wilson Quarterly, journal of the Woodrow Wilson International Center for Scholars, was first published in fall, 1976. Peter Braestrup served as Editor, 1976-   .

These records consist of administrative files documenting publication of the *Quarterly.* They include press releases, budget materials, annual reports, and correspondence with readers. Researchers should also consult record units 572 and 578 which contain the correspondence of the Editor.

ARRANGEMENT: (1) *The Wilson Quarterly,* records, 1977-1981, accession number 84-052; (2) *The Wilson Quarterly* records, 1977-1984, accession number 84-215. FINDING AIDS: None. SPECIAL CONDITIONS: (1) Restricted; (2) use of this record unit requires prior arrangement with the Archives staff.

OTHER SMITHSONIAN BUREAUS

SMITHSONIAN TROPICAL RESEARCH INSTITUTE, 1918-1964

(134)

Canal Zone Biological Area, 1918-1964
Records (1.7 linear meters).

In 1923 the Institute for Research in Tropical America, a group of private foundations and universities under the auspices of the National Research Council, first established a research laboratory on Barro Colorado Island, Panama Canal Zone, in order to investigate the flora and fauna of tropical America. In 1940 an act of Congress placed the facility under control of a board composed of the heads of certain executive departments and prominent scientists. In 1946 the operation was transferred to the Smithsonian Institution, which renamed it the Smithsonian Institution Tropical Research Institute in 1966.

Records document the creation and development of the Canal Zone Biological Area (CZBA), including preliminary discussions in 1918, the selection of a site on Barro Colorado Island in 1923, and subsequent development of the CZBA. Also included are papers of James Zetek, an entomologist on the staff of the United States Department of Agriculture and a director of the CZBA.

ARRANGEMENT: (1) Executive Committee correspondence, 1920-1930; (2) administrative records, 1918-1964; (3) scientific research reports, 1925-1953; (4) James Zetek Papers, 1919-1953; (5) publications; (6) photographs and maps, *circa* 1930-1960. FINDING AIDS: Description in control file. SPECIAL CONDITIONS: Use of this record unit requires prior arrangement with the Archives staff.

ARCHIVES OF AMERICAN ART, 1954-1992

(401)

Archives of American Art, 1954-1985, with related records from 1919
Records (10.3 linear meters).

The Archives of American Art (AAA) was founded as an independent non-profit corporation in 1954. Edgar P. Richardson, then Director of the Detroit Institute of Arts, and businessman and art collector Lawrence Fleishman were its founders. AAA originally focused on collecting and microfilming information documenting artists' lives and careers as reflected in the records of museums, galleries, family members, and collectors. Subsequently the Archives broadened its interests to include the visual arts in America from the eighteenth century to the present day.

From its founding in 1954 until 1960 the AAA operated from Detroit, headquartered at the Detroit Institute of Arts, but independently supported by gifts and grants. In 1960 the Archives moved its headquarters to New York City, retaining an office in Detroit. In 1963 the AAA opened a field office in Rome in order to tap the records of American artists' work in Rome and in Italy generally. In 1970 the AAA became a bureau of the Smithsonian Institution. In 1970-1971 field offices were established in Boston and San Francisco, and in 1984 in San Marino, California.

Edgar Richardson, the first Director, had many other commitments, especially to his work at Winterthur Museum in Delaware. Increasingly, most duties fell to the Assistant Director, William E. Woolfenden, who served in that capacity from 1960 until 1964, when he officially became Director. Woolfenden remained Director until 1983, when he was succeeded by Richard N. Murray.

Records include correspondence of Edgar P. Richardson, the first Director, 1954-1964; his successor, William E. Woolfenden, 1964-1983; Richard N. Murray, 1983- , and other staff members; minutes and records of the Board of Trustees; financial records; manuscripts, correspondence, and other records of the *Archives of American Art Journal;* and files of various projects in which the Archives participated. These include the correspondence of Sandra J. Levy, area director for the Texas project, 1979-1985; correspondence of Sharyn Udall, AAA representative, about the Southwest Project, 1969-1975; correspondence of Paul Cumming, Boston area office; and records related to the Treasury Relief Art Project and other Depression-era relief programs for artists, surveyed and filmed in 1963-1964. Correspondents include William E. Woolfenden, Edgar P. Richardson, Garnett McCoy, Sharyn Udall, Sandra J. Levy, Paul Cumming, Richard J. Nicastro, Sylvia Loomis, Gilbert H. Kenney, Regina Soria, and Eloise Spaeth.

ARRANGEMENT: Unarranged, with the following series apparent: (1) William E. Woolfenden files, 1954-1983; (2) Garnett McCoy files, 1960-1974, with related records, 1919-1929; (3) Texas Project files, 1979-1985; (4) Southwest Project Files, 1969-1975; (5) *Archives of American Art Journal* records, 1969, 1972-1983; (6) miscellaneous records, 1944, 1954-1982. FINDING AIDS: Box list in control file. SPECIAL CONDITIONS: (1) Restricted; (2) use of this record unit requires prior arrangement with the Archives staff.

(402)

Archives of American Art, circa 1954-1984
Records (22.9 linear meters).

For an administrative history of the Archives of American Art (AAA), see record unit 401.

These records document the development of the Archives of American Art, chiefly in the period since acquisition of AAA by the Smithsonian in 1970, though some records from its earlier history in Detroit and New York are also included.

These records include editorial files for the *Archives of American Art Journal;* records from the Director of the New England office, which includes correspondence, quarterly reports, and records pertaining to the Board of Trustees; New York office records, including budgetary information, special events, and curatorial activities; administrative records of the Washington, D.C., office concerning educational outreach, fundraising, Executive Committee meetings, and publications; AAA staff photographs; files on the New Deal arts project; records documenting the establishment of the Los Angeles office; information regarding the Detroit video project, "In Celebration"; Board of Trustees and Advisory Committee correspondence, minutes, and files; correspondence of the first two Directors, Edgar P. Richardson and William E. Woolfenden; and correspondence of Garnett McCoy, Deputy Director.

ARRANGEMENT: Unarranged, with the following series apparent: (1) Records of the Board of Trustees and the Advisory Committee, 1954-1977; (2) general and professional correspondence of the Director, 1954-1984; (3) correspondence with Area Centers, 1956-1983; (4) editorial records of *Archives of American Art Journal;* (5) special projects files, 1959-1972; (6) financial records and fundraising, 1961-1983; (7) membership programs, 1954-1979; (8) records of the curatorial office, 1954-1979; (9) records of the AAA microfilming program, 1954-1984; (10) photographs, 1954-1984. FINDING AIDS: Records survey report available in control file. SPECIAL CONDITIONS: Use of this record unit requires prior arrangement with the Archives staff.

(403)

Archives of American Art, circa 1960-1992
Records (12.7 linear meters).

For an administrative history of the Archives of American Art (AAA), see record unit 401.

These records focus almost exclusively on the operations of the Archives of American Art after its transfer to the Smithsonian Institution in 1970, with only a few inclusions from its earlier days. Records document the work of the central AAA office in Washington, D.C., and include records of Richard N. Murray, Director, 1983-1987; Richard J. Wattenmaker, Director, 1990-   ; and Susan A. Hamilton, Deputy Director, 1982-   , and Acting Director, 1988. Correspondents include Robert F. Brown, Director of the New England region, 1970-   ; William P. McNaught, Director of the New York region, 1976-1990; Sue Ann Kendall, Director of the Midwest Regional Center, 1984-1987; Paul J. Karlstrom, Director of the West Coast Regional Center, 1973-1992; and Stella Paul, Area Collector for the Southern California Center, 1984-1988.

The records also contain budgets, fundraising reports, information on AAA-sponsored tours, and minutes of the AAA's Board of Trustees as well as photographs and videotapes.

ARRANGEMENT: (1) Records, *circa* 1960-1992. FINDING AIDS: Description in control file. SPECIAL CONDITIONS: (1) Restricted; (2) use of this record unit requires prior arrangement with the Archives staff.

NATIONAL MUSEUM OF AFRICAN ART, 1964-1987

(634)

Office of the Director, National Museum of African Art, 1964-1984
Records (6.1 linear meters).

In 1964 a privately-funded Museum of African Art (MAA) was established by Warren H. Robbins, a former American foreign service officer, at the Frederick Douglass house in Washington, D.C. Robbins served as first Director of MAA, which mounted exhibitions of traditional African artwork and developed educational programs to foster public insight and appreciation of the cultures and artistic achievements of Africa. When MAA became a bureau of the Smithsonian Institution on August 13, 1979, its collections included some eight thousand objects of African sculpture, costumes, textiles, musical instruments, and jewelry; numerous books on African culture and history; early maps of Africa; educational materials; and photographs, slides, and film segments on African art, society, and environment bequeathed to the Museum by world-renowned photographer Eliot Elisofon.

In 1981 MAA was renamed the National Museum of African Art (NMAfA). The following year Robbins became Founding Director Emeritus and John E. Reinhardt assumed responsibility as Acting Director. Sylvia H. Williams was appointed Director of NMAfA in 1983.

Staff of NMAfA has included Warren H. Robbins, Director, 1964-1981, and Founding Director Emeritus, 1982-   ; John E. Reinhardt, Acting Director, 1981-1982; Sylvia H. Williams, Director, 1983-   ; Jean M. Salan, Assistant Director for Administration, 1979-1980, Assistant Deputy Director, 1981-1982, and Assistant Director, 1983-   ; Lydia Puccinelli, Curator of Collections, 1979-   ; Roy Sieber, Associate Director for Collections and Research, 1983-   ; Roslyn A. Walker, Research Curator, 1981-   ; and Edward Lifschitz, Academic Coordinator, 1979-1982, and Curator of Education, 1983-   .

These records consist mostly of the correspondence of Warren H. Robbins, which documents activities of NMAfA since its inception. Also included are some correspondence and memoranda of Jean M. Salan, John E. Reinhardt, and David L. Stratmon, an Associate Director of MAA during the 1970s. The correspondence is with government officials of African nations, African art dealers, agencies of the United States government, individual benefactors of NMAfA, African-American artists, university professors, and others, and concerns donations, specimen acquisition and loans, planning of exhibitions, conservation of permanent collections, grants, scholarly research, and publications.

ARRANGEMENT: Alphabetic. FINDING AIDS: Folder list in control file. SPECIAL CONDITIONS: Use of this record unit requires prior arrangement with the Archives staff.

Office of the Assistant Director, National Museum of African Art, 1979-1987
Records (0.8 linear meter).

For an administrative history of the National Museum of African Art, see record unit 634.

This record unit contains the files of Jean M. Salan, Assistant Director for Administration, 1979-1980, Assistant Deputy Director, 1981-1982, and Assistant Director, 1983-   , of the National Museum of African Art (NMAfA). The records primarily consist of memoranda, correspondence, and blueprints documenting the South Quadrangle Project; exhibition contracts; grants; information on Museum development; and NMAfA budgetary agendas.

ARRANGEMENT: Unarranged. FINDING AIDS: Folder list in control file. SPECIAL CONDITIONS: Use of this record unit requires prior arrangement with the Archives staff.

OFFICES AND SPECIAL PROJECTS

INTERNATIONAL AND ENVIRONMENTAL PROGRAMS, 1962-1992

The Office of International Activities (OIA) was established in March 1966, with William W. Warner, who had served as consultant to the Secretary for international matters from 1964, as Director. The role of OIA was to establish cooperative research programs with institutions of higher learning in other countries and to serve as the Smithsonian's point of liaison with United States government agencies and international organizations dealing with matters of interest to the Institution. The Smithsonian Foreign Currency Program (SFCP) and the International Liaison Program were established under the direction of OIA. Warner served as Director of OIA until 1968. He was succeeded by David Challinor, 1968-1971, and Kennedy B. Schmertz, 1971-1973.

The Office of Environmental Sciences (OES) was established in October 1970 to "make more visible the Smithsonian's broad spectrum of research projects in the environmental sciences and improve the opportunities for attracting financial support and scientific collaboration." The Smithsonian programs in oceanography and ecology, along with the Chesapeake Bay Center for Environmental Studies (CBCES), were joined under the direction of OES. Directors of OES included Irvin Eugene Wallen, 1970-1971, and William L. Eilers, 1971-1973.

In October 1973, OIA and OES were combined to form the Office of International and Environmental Programs (OIEP). Wymberley D. Coerr, former Ambassador to Ecuador and Uruguay, was appointed Director of the new Office and Eilers became Deputy Director. Programs under the direction of the former OIA and OES continued to receive support under OIEP. In May 1975, the Smithsonian decided to dissolve the environmental sciences component of OIEP. At that time, OIEP was renamed the Office of International Programs (OIP). Coerr continued as Director of OIP until 1976, when he was replaced by Kennedy B. Schmertz. OIP was abolished in 1978. The Office's International Liaison Section was renamed the Office of International Activities, with Schmertz as Director of the new Office. OIP's Foreign Currency Program was transferred to the Office of Fellowships and Grants.

Programs and offices under the direction of OIA, OES, OIEP and OIP included the Smithsonian's Foreign Currency Program; the International Liaison Program; the Oceanography and Limnology Program (before 1969, the Office of Oceanography and Limnology), which administered the Smithsonian Oceanographic Sorting Center and the Mediterranean Marine Sorting Center; the Ecology Program (before 1969, the Smithsonian Office of Ecology); the Chesapeake Bay Center for Environmental Studies; the Center for Short-Lived Phenomena; and the Smithsonian Institution-Peace Corps Environmental Program.

Office of International Activities, 1964-1967
Records (2.2 linear meters).

These records include correspondence, memoranda, and other information about the activities of the Office, which establishes cooperative research programs with institutions of higher learning in other countries and fosters programs for the international exchange of persons in those fields of science and humanities related to the Smithsonian's interests. Especially well documented are activities relating to preservation of the temples of Abu Simbel in Egypt, threatened in 1964 by waters of the Aswan Dam, and the establishment in 1968 of the Indian Ocean island of Aldabra as an international conservation area.

ARRANGEMENT: (1) Aldabra, 1967; (2) Abu Simbel, 1964; (3) general file. FINDING AIDS: Folder list in control file. SPECIAL CONDITIONS: Use of this record unit requires prior arrangement with the Archives staff.

Foreign Currency Program, Office of International Activities, 1965-1973
Grant Records (1 linear meter).

The Foreign Currency Program was initiated in FY 1966 when the Smithsonian received its first appropriation of excess foreign currencies deriving from the sale of agricultural surplus under Public Law 480. Originally, grants were given to American universities or museums for research in archeology and related disciplines in excess currency countries, including Ceylon, Egypt, India, Israel, Pakistan, Poland, Tunisia, and Yugoslavia. Congress later extended the scope of the program to include research in systematic and environmental biology, earth sciences, astrophysics, and museum programs. Staff of the Foreign Currency Program included Kennedy B. Schmertz, Director, 1965- , and Kenneth Whitehead, Deputy Director, 1967-1972.

Files include grant proposals and awards, project status reports, and correspondence.

ARRANGEMENT: Alphabetic by name of principal investigator. FINDING AIDS: Folder list in control file. SPECIAL CONDITIONS: Use of this record unit requires prior arrangement with the Archives staff.

Ecology Program, Office of Environmental Sciences, 1965-1973
Records (3 linear meters).

The Ecology Program of the Office of Environmental Sciences was begun in 1965 when a predecessor, the Smithsonian Office of Ecology (SOE) was created. SOE was to help expand research opportunities for Smithsonian scientists and coordinate institutional ecological work with other government agencies. Initially placed under the National Museum of Natural History, SOE was transferred to the Assistant Secretary for Science in 1966. In 1969, SOE became the Ecology Program of the new Office of Environmental Sciences, and in 1973 became an administrative unit of the Office of International and Environmental Programs (OIEP). The Ecology Program was terminated in 1975.

Offices and programs administered by the Ecology Program of OES or its predecessor, the SOE, included the Chesapeake Bay Center for Field Biology (after

1970, the Chesapeake Bay Center for Environmental Studies), 1965-1969; the Center for Natural Areas, 1972-1974; and the Smithsonian Institution-Peace Corps Environmental Program, 1972-1974.

Staff of the Ecology Program and its predecessor, the SOE, included Helmut Karl Buechner, Assistant Director for Ecology, 1965-1966, Head, 1966-1968, and Senior Scientist, 1969-1971; Irvin Eugene Wallen, Acting Head, 1969; Dale W. Jenkins, Director, 1970-1973; Lee Merriam Talbot, Research Biologist, 1965-1966, Field Representative, Ecology and Conservation, 1966-1967, Deputy Head and International Field Representative, 1968, Resident Ecologist, 1969-1971, and Deputy Director, 1972-1973; and Francis Raymond Fosberg, Special Assistant for Tropical Biology, 1965-1966.

This record unit consists of files documenting the operation of the Smithsonian Office of Ecology (SOE), 1965-1970, and its successor, the Ecology Program of the Office of Environmental Sciences (OES), 1970-1973. The records include organizational files, 1965-1973; administrative records, 1965-1973, including material on the development of the Chesapeake Bay Center for Environmental Studies and the Smithsonian Institution-Peace Corps Environmental Program; project files, 1965-1973, including records documenting projects conducted as part of the International Program in Ecology; and files of Lee Merriam Talbot, 1965-1971.

ARRANGEMENT: (1) Organizational files, 1965-1973; (2) administrative records, 1965-1973; (3) project files, 1965-1973; (4) Lee Merriam Talbot files, 1965-1971. FINDING AIDS: Description in control file. SPECIAL CONDITIONS: Use of this record unit requires prior arrangement with the Archives staff.

(218)

Office of International and Environmental Programs, 1962-1975
Records (8.8 linear meters).

These records document the general administrative activities of the Office of International and Environmental Programs, and in particular, the Office's environmental research programs. They include general administrative correspondence, contract files, agency reports, program files, case files, and project reports concerning the organizational structure of the Office; personnel requirements; legal information on contractual agreements and project specifications; fiscal information relating to the Foreign Currency Program; budgetary outlays and fund allocations; and environmental information relating to marine ecology, schistosomiasis, specific fauna, and other scientific projects.

ARRANGEMENT: (1) General files, 1964-1975; (2) case files, 1964-1974; (3) Agency for International Development task orders and related material, 1964-1974; (4) Smithsonian Institution organization records, 1971-1973; (5) audiovisual materials. FINDING AIDS: Description in control file. SPECIAL CONDITIONS: Use of this record unit requires prior arrangement with the Archives staff.

Office of International Programs, 1964-1976
Records (1.4 linear meters).

This record unit consists of files created primarily by the Office of Environmental Sciences (OES), 1970-1973, prior to its merger with the Office of International Activities, and by the resulting Office of International and Environmental Programs, 1973-1975. Files predating the creation of OES in October 1970 are those of Irvin Eugene Wallen, in his capacity as Assistant Director for Oceanography, National Museum of Natural History, and head of the Office of Oceanography and Limnology, 1964-1969. The records consist of correspondence and memoranda, project proposals and reports, and publications. Included are records documenting the administration and operation of the Center for Short-Lived Phenomena, a program reporting to OIP and its predecessors, 1967-1976, and general administrative records of the office, 1964-1975. These records are closely related to those in record unit 218, and may be part of the same file.

ARRANGEMENT: (1) Center for Short-Lived Phenomena files, 1967-1976; (2) administrative records, 1964-1975. FINDING AIDS: Description in control file. SPECIAL CONDITIONS: Use of this record unit requires prior arrangement with the Archives staff.

Oceanography and Limnology Programs, Office of International and Environmental Programs, 1962-1974, with related records to 1977
Records (8.8 linear meters).

The Oceanography and Limnology Program began in 1962 when Irvin Eugene Wallen was appointed Assistant Director for Oceanography in the National Museum of Natural History (NMNH). Duties of the Assistant Director for Oceanography included aiding NMNH scientists in marine research; maintaining liaison with ocean-going vessels and scientists in order to collect biological materials; representing the Smithsonian Institution on committees and councils concerned with oceanography; and developing and operating the Smithsonian Oceanographic Sorting Center (SOSC) for marine biological and geological specimens. In 1966 the position of Assistant Director for Oceanography was abolished and its duties were assumed by the newly created Office of Oceanography and Limnology. The Office, with Wallen as head, reported to the Assistant Secretary for Science and was administratively responsible for the SOSC and the Mediterranean Marine Sorting Center (MMSC), which was established in September 1966. In 1969, the Office became the Oceanography and Limnology Program (OLP) of the newly created Office of Environmental Sciences. In October 1973, OLP became an administrative unit of the newly created Office of International and Environmental Programs (OIEO). OLP was abolished in June 1974, and SOSC became an administrative unit of NMNH. At that time, Smithsonian environmental programs were merged to form the International Environmental Science Program (IESP) of OIEP. IESP and OIEP were terminated in 1975. At that time, SOSC became an administrative unit of NMNH.

Staff of OLP and its predecessors included Wallen, Assistant Director for Oceanography, NMNH, 1962-1966, Head, Office of Oceanography and Limnology,

1966-1969; William Aron, Deputy Head, 1967-1969, Director, 1969-1971; Robert P. Higgins, Oceanographer, 1968-1969, Director, 1971-1974; David W. Brown, Oceanographer, 1970-1972; David K. Young, Deputy Director, 1972-1974; and Catherine J. Kerby, Estuarine Biologist, 1973, Deputy Director, 1973-1974.

This record unit consists primarily of records documenting the scientific activities of OLP, 1970-1974, and its predecessors, the Assistant Director for Oceanography, NMNH, 1962-1966, and the Office of Oceanography and Limnology, 1966-1970. The records consist of incoming and outgoing correspondence, proposals, reports, fiscal materials, publications, photographs, and research data. They include an organizational file documenting OLP relations with oceanographic institutions, commissions, government agencies, and colleges and universities; a file concerning international activities and projects of OLP; a subject file, primarily concerning oceanographic matters; records providing comprehensive documentation of the nine-year history of MMSC; and files concerning projects conducted at Skadar Lake, Yugoslavia, and Nam Ngum, Laos.

ARRANGEMENT: (1) Organizational file, 1962-1977; (2) international oceanography files, 1962-1974; (3) subject file, 1963-1974; (4) Mediterranean Marine Sorting Center files, 1965-1976; (5) "Limnological Investigations of Skadar Lake, Yugoslavia," project files, 1971-1977; (6) "Post-Impoundment Assessment of the Ecological Effects of the Nam Ngum Dam and Reservoir, Laos," project files, 1973-1975. FINDING AIDS: Description in control file. SPECIAL CONDITIONS: Use of this record unit requires prior arrangement with the Archives staff.

(563)
Oceanography and Limnology Program, Office of International and Environmental Programs, 1962-1975
Records (1.6 linear meters).

For an administrative history of the Oceanography and Limnology Program (OLP), see record unit 273.

These records document the activities of the OLP, 1970-1975, and its predecessors, the Assistant Director for Oceanography, National Museum of Natural History, 1962-1966, and the Office of Oceanography and Limnology, 1966-1970. Most of the records were created by Irvin Eugene Wallen, William Aron, and Robert P. Higgins. They include correspondence, memoranda, budgets, proposals, contracts, reports, and publications primarily concerning OLP's administration of the Smithsonian Oceanographic Sorting Center and the Mediterranean Marine Sorting Center and OLP-sponsored research projects.

ARRANGEMENT: Unarranged. FINDING AIDS: Folder list in control file. SPECIAL CONDITIONS: Use of this record unit requires prior arrangement with the Archives staff.

(610)
Smithsonian Oceanographic Sorting Center, circa 1962-1992
Records (7 linear meters).

The Smithsonian Oceanographic Sorting Center (SOSC) was established in 1962 as a unit of the National Museum of Natural History (NMNH) reporting to the Assistant Director for Oceanography. In 1966, administrative responsibility for SOSC was transferred to the newly created Office of Oceanography and Limnology (OLP). OLP was abolished in June 1974, and SOSC again became an administrative unit of NMNH. SOSC was terminated in 1992.

The purpose of SOSC was to assist the international oceanographic effort by processing biological and geological specimens for scientists throughout the world. Other objectives of SOSC included environmental analyses of biological specimens and support services for field activities of the Smithsonian and other organizations. Directors of SOSC included H. Adair Fehlmann, 1962-1973; Betty J. Landrum, 1973-1978; Frank D. Ferrari, 1978-1981; Leslie W. Knapp, 1981-1988; and Ernani G. Menez, 1988-1992.

This record unit documents the administration and programs of the SOSC during its entire thirty-year history. Included are correspondence, memoranda, proposals, and reports documenting SOSC contracts with agencies of the federal government, especially the United States Arctic Research Program of the National Science Foundation and the National Marine Fisheries Service, United States Department of Commerce; correspondence of SOSC Directors; administrative records, including budget files; annual reports of the SOSC and the Mediterranean Marine Sorting Center; and correspondence with specialists studying SOSC geological and photograph collections.

ARRANGEMENT: Unarranged. FINDING AIDS: Box list in control file. SPECIAL CONDITIONS: Use of this record unit requires prior arrangement with the Archives staff.

(264)

Smithsonian Institution-Peace Corps Environmental Program, 1970-1979
Records (5.2 linear meters).

In 1970 the Smithsonian Institution contracted with the Peace Corps to assist it to establish an international environmental program, the Smithsonian Institution-Peace Corps Environmental Program (SI-PCEP). The program helped the Peace Corps to develop conservation, biological, and ecological projects in natural resource fields with principal focus on wildlife conservation and national park development. Through the Office of Environmental Sciences (later the Office of International and Environmental Programs), SI-PCEP recruited and placed qualified Peace Corps volunteers with advanced degrees or specialized skills, assisted in establishing training programs, and provided information and technical and scientific support to volunteers in the field. In May 1975, direction of the program was transferred to the Assistant Secretary for Science. The program was terminated in September 1978.

The SI-PCEP records fall into two main areas: those about the program in general and those about the various environmental projects. The administrative records provide a broad understanding of the scope of SI-PCEP, especially as revealed through the contract files. These administrative records document the creation and continued efforts to expand the funding and impact of the program. In addition, SI-PCEP is well documented through publications generated by the program, including recruiting leaflets, training manuals, skill availability booklets, and published articles. The individual projects are documented in the correspondence of program administrators Robert K. Poole, 1970-1975, and James A. Sherburne, 1975-1978, with host countries and host agencies, and the correspondence of individual volunteers and their project reports. Contracts, in addition to those between the Smithsonian Institution and the Peace

Corps, include those sought for technical support of projects from the National Park Service, National Wildlife Fund, and Rockefeller Brothers Fund.

ARRANGEMENT: (1) Peace Corps volunteers, 1971-1979; (2) administrative records, 1970-1979; (3) SI-PCEP publications, 1971-1978; (4) publications about the SI-PCEP, 1971-1977; (5) host organizations, 1970-1978; (6) host countries, *circa* 1977-1978; (7) Peace Corps volunteers' project reports, 1971-1978. FINDING AIDS: Description in control file. SPECIAL CONDITIONS: Use of this record unit requires prior arrangement with the Archives staff.

OTHER OFFICES AND SPECIAL PROJECTS

(102)

Office of Academic Programs, 1964-1970
Records (3.9 linear meters).

The Office of Academic Programs was created in 1964 as the Office of Education and Training. It came under the directorship of Charles Blitzer in July 1965. The purpose of this Office was to make the resources of the Smithsonian, its collections, and staff available to the scholarly community. The Office provides research opportunities for visiting professional researchers and graduate students and helps in the exhibits and public education function of the Smithsonian museums. When Charles Blitzer was appointed Assistant Secretary for History and Art in 1968, the Office of Education and Training was renamed the Office of Academic Programs, and Philip C. Ritterbush became its Director in February 1968.

The major portion of these records was created during the tenure of Philip Ritterbush. Also included is some material from Ritterbush's tenure as Special Assistant to the Secretary for Scientific Matters, 1964-1967, and as Assistant to the Secretary for Policy Analysis and Planning, 1967-1968. These items apparently were integrated into the records of the Office of Academic Programs.

ARRANGEMENT: (1) Office of Education and Training, 1964-1967; (2) Office of Academic Programs, 1968-1970. FINDING AIDS: (1) Ritterbush biography; (2) folder list in control file. SPECIAL CONDITIONS: Use of this record unit requires prior arrangement with the Archives staff.

(494)

Division of Seminars, Office of Academic Programs, 1964-1970
Records (2.5 linear meters).

The Division of Seminars was established within the Office of Academic Programs in 1969 and was directed by Wilton S. Dillon. For an administrative history of the Office of Academic Programs, see record unit 102.

This record unit documents the first four International Symposia sponsored by the Smithsonian Institution, with some documentation of the fifth. The first symposium celebrated the bicentennial of James Smithson's birth and was organized by Philip C. Ritterbush, Special Assistant to the Secretary. The records consist of correspondence, memoranda, background research material, invitations, brochures, resumes, photographs, grant information, publication contracts, symposia schedules, travel and accommodation arrangements, and other administrative records for the *Smithson Bicentennial* symposium, 1965; the *Quality of Man's Environment* symposium, 1967; *Man and Beast: A Symposium on Comparative Social Behavior,* 1969; *Cultural Styles and Social Identities: Interpretations of Protest and Change,* 1970; and a fifth international symposium concerning art and technology.

These records were created or maintained by Philip C. Ritterbush, Special Assistant to the Secretary for Scientific Matters and Director of the Office of Academic Programs after 1968; Nathaniel Dixon, Associate Director of the Office of Academic Programs; and Wilton S. Dillon, Director of the Division of Seminars after 1969.

ARRANGEMENT: By symposium. FINDING AIDS: None. SPECIAL CONDITIONS: Use of this record unit requires prior arrangement with the Archives staff.

(609)
Office of American Studies, 1962-1987
Records (11.5 linear meters).

The Office of American Studies (OAS) was created in 1970, with Wilcomb E. Washburn as its Director, and reported to the Assistant Secretary for History and Art. For an administrative history of the Office, see record unit 160.

These records document the operations of OAS. They also contain records from an organizational predecessor, the Department of American Studies, Museum of History and Technology, which had been chaired by Washburn. OAS records deal with the work of the Office and its involvement with other Smithsonian offices and bureaus; its work with numerous colleges and universities and with students interested in training in American material culture; and relations with outside scholarly organizations and foundations.

ARRANGEMENT: (1) Records, 1965-1970, accession number T89004; (2) records, 1962-1972, accession number T89005; (3) records, 1964-1987, accession number 90-082. FINDING AIDS: Folder list in control file. SPECIAL CONDITIONS: Use of this record unit requires prior arrangement with the Archives staff.

(160)
Office of American Studies, 1969-1973
Records (0.3 linear meter).

The Department of American Studies of the Museum of History and Technology (MHT) was established in 1965 with Wilcomb E. Washburn as Chairman. When Charles Blitzer was appointed Assistant Secretary for History and Art in 1968, responsibility for the program was transferred from MHT to his office. The Department became the Office of American Studies in 1970, and Washburn's title was changed to Director.

The Office of American Studies seeks to promote study of the material culture of the United States by sponsoring graduate studies in the field in cooperation with universities. In addition to its formal program, it also offers graduate students an opportunity to do supervised reading and research with Smithsonian staff members and to make use of the Institution's extensive collections.

These records consist of telephone books and log sheets.

ARRANGEMENT: Chronologic. FINDING AIDS: None. SPECIAL CONDITIONS: Use of this record unit requires prior arrangement with the Archives staff.

(7269)

Badianus Manuscript Project, 1930-1935
(0.1 linear meter).

In the early 1930s the Smithsonian Institution, in cooperation with Johns Hopkins University, undertook the project of reproducing the "Badianus Manuscript" located in the Vatican Library. The "Manuscript," an Aztec herbal, was composed in Aztec and Latin by Martin de la Cruz and Juannes Badianus in 1552. The Smithsonian withdrew from the project in 1937.

Materials consist of approximately 115 gouache copies by Marie-Therese Missonnier-Vuillemin of illustrations in the "Badianus Manuscript"; and a descriptive pamphlet by Emily Walcott Emmart, *Concerning the Badianus Manuscript, an Aztec Herbal,* "Codex Barberini, Latin 24" (Vatican Library), 1935. Additional documentation concerning the project exists in record unit 46 and at Johns Hopkins University.

ARRANGEMENT: Unarranged. FINDING AIDS: Description in control file. SPECIAL CONDITIONS: Use of this record unit requires prior arrangement with the Archives staff.

(157)

Buildings Management Department, 1881-1973
Records (11.7 linear meters).

The Buildings Management Department and its predecessors operated, maintained, and protected the Smithsonian's offices, museums, and research facilities in the Washington, D.C., area. They provided security for museum collections, and information, direction, and assistance to Smithsonian visitors. In performing these duties, the Department supplied engineering, design, fabrication, repair, communication, transportation, special mechanical, and safety services.

Henry Horan was the first Superintendent of Buildings, holding that position from 1880 to 1896. In 1896, J. Elfreth Watkins became Chief of the newly created Division of Buildings and Superintendence. Another reorganization in 1902 gave Watkins the title of Superintendent and James S. Goldsmith that of Supervisor of Construction. In 1904, the Division of Construction and Labor was created. The title was changed to Buildings and Labor in 1915, Buildings and Grounds in 1954, and Buildings Management Department in 1958. Goldsmith was Superintendent from 1904 to 1935; Royal H. Trembly held the position from 1935 to 1943; and Lawrence L. Oliver held it from 1943 to 1957. Oliver became Buildings Manager in 1958 and was succeeded by Andrew F. Michaels in 1959. In 1965 the title was changed to Director of Buildings Management Department and Michaels held the position until 1973. In 1973, the Buildings Management Department was reorganized into a number of newly created offices.

These records include records of the Buildings Management Department and its predecessors, including subject files, photographs, plans, reports, sketches, drawings, blueprints, memoranda, and correspondence concerning maintenance, financial matters, labor and supply costs, visitors, receptions, exhibitions, guard forces, and buildings maintained by the Department.

ARRANGEMENT: (1) General correspondence, 1881-1960; (2) annual reports, 1902-1946; (3) alphabetic subject file, 1937-1973. FINDING AIDS: Folder list in control file. SPECIAL CONDITIONS: Use of this record unit requires prior arrangement with the Archives staff.

(565)

Buildings Management Department, 1899-1958
Records (0.4 linear meter).

For an administrative history of the Buildings Management Department, see record unit 157.

These records contain correspondence, reports, proposals, estimates, and drawings concerning various aspects of the Smithsonian physical plant, with emphasis on early electrical, heating, and ventilating systems in the Smithsonian Institution Building, the Arts and Industries Building and the Natural History Building.

ARRANGEMENT: Unarranged. FINDING AIDS: Folder list in control file. SPECIAL CONDITIONS: Use of this record unit requires prior arrangment with the Archives staff.

(532)

Buildings Management Department, 1958-1972
Records (54.9 linear meters).

For an administrative history of the Buildings Management Department, see record unit 157. During the period documented in this record unit the Department was divided into four divisions, the Office of the Director, Protection Division, Mechanical Services Division, and Building Services Division. The Office of the Director included the Design and Review Office, Engineering and Construction Division, and Safety Management Office.

These records comprise the working files of the Engineering and Construction Division as well as the files of the building managers and resident engineers in the Building Services Division. The records of the Engineering and Construction Division were maintained by James M. Murphy and Roy O'Brien. They concern repairs and improvements to Smithsonian facilities including the Arts and Industries Building, Barney Studio House, Barro Colorado Island, the Renwick Gallery, the National Zoological Park, Adelaide Forbes Calhoun property, River House residence, the Freer Gallery of Art, the Smithsonian Institution Building, the Hirshhorn Museum and Sculpture Garden, the John F. Kennedy Center for the Performing Arts, and the Andrew Carnegie Building.

These records contain correspondence, contracts, specifications, and blueprints concerning work planned and performed. The records of the building managers and resident engineers include blueprints, specifications, correspondence, reports, transcripts, photographs, shop drawings, and daily inspection reports concerning the

History and Technology Building, the Natural History Building, and the Fine Arts and Portrait Galleries Buildings. Harold L. Haworth and Roy W. Johnson were the Resident Engineers of the History and Technology Building from 1958 to 1967. F. H. Mahlman was the Resident Engineer of the Natural History Building from 1961 to 1964. Hugh E. Yates was the Resident Engineer for the Fine Arts and Portrait Gallery Building from 1964 to 1966.

ARRANGEMENT: (1) Resident Engineer, History and Technology Building, 1958-1967; (2) Resident Engineer, Natural History Building, 1961-1964; (3) Engineering and Construction Division, James M. Murphy, 1958-1972; (4) Building Manager, Natural History Building, 1964-1967; (5) Engineering and Construction Division, Natural History Building, Roy O'Brien, 1964-1966; (6) Resident Engineer, Fine Arts and Portrait Gallery Building, 1964-1966; (7) unarranged blueprints, drawings, specifications; (8) photographs; (9) utility records, 1964; (10) miscellaneous records, 1968-1972. FINDING AIDS: Description in control file. SPECIAL CONDITIONS: Use of this record unit requires prior arrangement with the Archives staff.

(639)

Engineering and Construction Branch, Buildings Management Department, 1963-1974
Photographs (1.2 linear meters).

For an administrative history of the Buildings Management Department, see record unit 157.

This record unit consists of exterior construction progress photographs and some blueprints documenting construction of the Hirshhorn Museum and Sculpture Garden, the National Air and Space Museum, and the National Museum of History and Technology, as well as the renovation of the Patent Office and Natural History Buildings.

ARRANGEMENT: Unarranged. FINDING AIDS: None. SPECIAL CONDITIONS: Use of this record unit requires prior arrangement with the Archives staff.

(607)

Center for Short-Lived Phenomena, 1968-1973
Records (3 linear meters).

The Center for Short-Lived Phenomena (CSLP) was created in January 1968 to assist Smithsonian scientists in studying short-lived phenomena and to provide a reporting and information service for use by the scientific community. Its focus was on meteoritics, vulcanism, earthquakes, and sudden changes in biological and ecological systems. In 1971 and 1972 CSLP broadened its scope to include an information service for high school and college students. In 1973 the Center formed a new National Environmental Alert Program which became part of the United Nations Earthwatch Program.

Robert Citron was appointed Director of CSLP and served from 1968- . Policy was formulated by a committee of Smithsonian scientists, chaired by Sidney Galler, Assistant Secretary for Science. The Center was operated from the Smithsonian Astrophysical Observatory, Cambridge, Massachusetts.

These records document the operations of CSLP under Citron. They include budget and personnel records, applications for grants in support of CSLP projects, publicity, and event reports documenting specific short-lived phenomena. There are also some records dealing with the Smithsonian Environmental Alert Pilot Program in 1972.

For additional administrative and operational records of the Center for Short-Lived Phenomena, see Office of International Programs, record unit 274.

ARRANGEMENT: (1) Records, 1968-1972, accession number T89039; (2) records, 1972-1973, accession number T89036. FINDING AIDS: Folder list in control file. SPECIAL CONDITIONS: Use of this record unit requires prior arrangement with the Archives staff.

(64)

Chief Clerk, 1869-1905
Records (2.9 linear meters).

Records of the Chief Clerk's office consist mostly of records of Chief Clerk William Jones Rhees, 1869-1905. Rhees, who joined the Smithsonian staff in 1852, performed many functions over the years, including general correspondence supervision, distribution of scientific publications, supervision of Smithsonian publications, and archival duties. For the most part, Clerk's records are retained here while papers relating to Rhees's work on Smithsonian history and other projects remain in his personal papers, but some overlapping is unavoidable.

Some records among the incoming correspondence probably belong with secretarial records, and some records very similar to those retained here in the Clerk's series may be found among secretarial records. The paperwork system of the offices is not fully understood, a problem compounded by later rearrangements of the records.

The most valuable part of this record unit is the incoming correspondence from Spencer F. Baird, 1875-1887, and, to a lesser degree, incoming correspondence from Samuel P. Langley.

ARRANGEMENT: (1) Alphabetic name-subject file, 1869-1896; (2) incoming correspondence and memoranda from Baird and Langley, 1875-1892; (3) outgoing correspondence, several series, 1885-1905; (4) incoming correspondence, 1881-1902; (5) miscellaneous fragments. FINDING AIDS: (1) Indexes bound in most outgoing volumes; (2) index to Langley's correspondence and memoranda to Rhees, providing name and subject access, boxed with the collection. SPECIAL CONDITIONS: Use of this record unit requires prior arrangement with the Archives staff.

(67)

Chief Clerk, 1887-1941
Records (0.1 linear meter).

The provenance of this collection is uncertain.

ARRANGEMENT: Unarranged. Includes records of Storage in SI Safe. FINDING AIDS: None. SPECIAL CONDITIONS: Use of this record unit requires prior arrangement with the Archives staff.

(65)

Chief Clerk, 1846-1933
Forms, Circulars, Announcements (2.3 linear meters).

ARRANGEMENT: (1) Forms and circulars of the Secretary, 1846-1888; (2) forms and circulars of the National Museum, Exchanges, Ethnology, Correspondence Clerk, Disbursing Clerk, International Catalogue of Scientific Literature, Library, and National Zoological Park; (3) forms ordered, 1860-1933; (4) lists of

Smithsonian employees, 1846-1910, with salaries; (5) invitations to Smithsonian events, *circa* 1915-1925. FINDING AIDS: None. SPECIAL CONDITIONS: Use of this record unit requires prior arrangement with the Archives staff.

(66)

Chief Clerk, 1868-1918
Special Communications Received (0.1 linear meter).

These records consist of letters, patents, ideas for inventions, and other papers sent to the Smithsonian, usually with the provision that they be sealed.

ARRANGEMENT: Chronologic. FINDING AIDS: None. SPECIAL CONDITIONS: Use of this record unit requires prior arrangement with the Archives staff.

(576)

Conservation Analytical Laboratory, 1963-1983
Records (5.7 linear meters).

A Conservation Research Laboratory was first established in 1963 under the direction of the United States National Museum (USNM). In 1964 the Laboratory was moved to new quarters in the Museum of History and Technology (MHT). In 1966 the Laboratory acquired its present name. Charles H. Olin became the first Director, 1966-1967, and was succeeded by Robert M. Organ, formerly on the staff of the British Museum and the Royal Ontario Museum. Organ continued as Director until retiring in 1983. Other staff members during this period included Jacqueline S. Olin, who joined as a Research Chemist in 1971 and became Supervisory Archaeometrist, 1980-   , and Eleanor McMillan, who began as a Conservator in 1970 and became Chief Conservator, 1972-   .

The Conservation Analytical Laboratory (CAL) began its work by focusing narrowly on preservation and restoration. However, over time its focus has broadened so that it is now involved in study and treatment of collections; provides data for understanding museum collections; and supports training and education for Smithsonian and non-Smithsonian staff.

The Laboratory specializes in two scientific pursuits: conservation science, which analyzes objects and their materials to determine suitable conservation treatment; and archaeometry, which aims to integrate scientific analysis of objects with their anthropological, archaeological, art historical, and cultural backgrounds.

These records deal with CAL's work with Smithsonian curators and collections during the tenures of John H. Olin, Robert M. Organ, Jacqueline S. Olin, and Eleanor McMillan. They also document the Laboratory's extensive training programs and its wide contacts with other museums, both in the United States and abroad.

ARRANGEMENT: Conservation Analytical Laboratory, records, 1963-1983, accession number 92-011. FINDING AIDS: Folder list in control file. SPECIAL CONDITIONS: Use of this record unit requires prior arrangement with the Archives staff.

Contracts Office, 1953-1990
Records (26.2 linear meters).

The Contracts Office was authorized to negotiate contracts and grants on behalf of the Smithsonian Institution. The Office was established in 1964 and Elbridge O. Hurlbut was named Contracting Officer. He directed the Office until his retirement in 1988, when Joseph H. Shealy became Acting Director. Prior to 1964 Contracting Officers and Specialists had been attached to the Office of the Secretary.

The grants accepted by the Smithsonian supported a wide variety of research and educational projects throughout the Institution. The contracts were agreements entered into with vendors who wished to supply goods and services either directly to the Smithsonian Institution or to the public under the auspices of the Smithsonian.

The records contain proposals and drafts of contracts and grants, correspondence concerning their acceptance and implementation, budget information, reports about grant-sponsored activities, and information concerning the administration of the Office and the authority of the Contracting Officer.

ARRANGEMENT: (1) Contracts and grants, accession number 83-083; (2) contracts and grants, accession number 87-036; (3) records, accession number 88-069; (4) contracts and grants, accession number 88-092; (5) contracts and grants, accession number 88-101; (6) contracts and grants, accession number 89-025; (7) records, accession number 89-093; (8) contracts and grants, accession number 91-118. FINDING AIDS: Folder list in control file. SPECIAL CONDITIONS: Use of this record unit requires prior arrangement with the Archives staff.

Contracts Office, 1962-1979
Grants and Contracts (13 linear meters).

For an administrative history of the Office and a description of the records maintained by the Contracting Officer, see record units 141 and 470.

ARRANGEMENT: Unarranged. FINDING AIDS: Folder list in control file. SPECIAL CONDITIONS: Use of this record unit requires prior arrangement with the Archives staff.

Contracts Office, 1963-1974
Grants and Contracts (4 linear meters).

The Contracting Officer is authorized to negotiate federal and private grants and contracts for the Smithsonian, and his records contain information on formulation and administration of contracts that is especially useful for information about research conducted by Smithsonian staff. These records include copies of grants and contracts kept by the Contracting Officer.

ARRANGEMENT: (1) Alphabetic by name of grantee; (2) alphabetic by name of Smithsonian division. FINDING AIDS: Description in control file. SPECIAL CONDITIONS: Use of this record unit requires prior arrangement with the Archives staff.

Contracts Office, 1961-1966
Smithsonian Astrophysical Observatory Contracts (2.2 linear meters).

This record unit consists of correspondence, memoranda, contracts, bids and invitations, proposals, reports and related materials maintained by the Contracts Office concerning Smithsonian Astrophysical Observatory (SAO) projects, especially Project Celescope. Of special interest are materials documenting contracts with Electro-Mechanical Research, Inc., and Westinghouse Research Laboratories for the technical development of Celescope. Also included is similar material concerning SAO projects funded by contracts with the National Aeronautics and Space Administration, United States Air Force, National Science Foundation, Office of Naval Research, and Harvard University.

ARRANGEMENT: Unarranged. FINDING AIDS: Folder list in control file. SPECIAL CONDITIONS: Use of this record unit requires prior arrangement with the Archives staff.

Office of the Coordinator of Public Information, 1977-1984
Records (4.5 linear meters).

The Office of the Coordinator of Public Information was created in 1977 to manage public relations at the Institution. The Office of Public Affairs, the Office of Special Events, and the Office of Congressional Liaison were placed under its jurisdiction. Lawrence E. Taylor served as Coordinator of Public Information from 1977 until his retirement due to illness in 1984, when the office was abolished. During his tenure, Taylor established the Smithsonian News Service, which wrote and distributed stories to newspapers around the United States.

These records consist primarily of administrative files of Lawrence E. Taylor as Coordinator of Public Information, 1977-1984. Also included are copies of the minutes of the Board of Regents, 1977-1983.

ARRANGEMENT: (1) Office of the Coordinator of Public Information, 1977-1984, accession number 84-229; (2) Office of the Coordinator of Public Information, 1977-1984, accession number 85-061. FINDING AIDS: Description in control file. SPECIAL CONDITIONS: Use of this record unit requires prior arrangement with the Archives staff.

Documents Clerk, 1885-1892
Records (0.3 linear meter).

The Documents Clerk, who reported to the Chief Clerk, was responsible for receipt of Smithsonian publications from printers and for certain types of Smithsonian publications, apparently filling requests made individually to the Institution. The records of this activity are fragmentary.

ARRANGEMENT: (1) Smithsonian publications, stock account, 1885-1892; (2) publications stock, ledger accounts, 1885-1887; (3) outgoing correspondence, Documents Clerk, 1890-1892. FINDING AIDS: None. SPECIAL CONDITIONS: Use of this record unit requires prior arrangement with the Archives staff.

Senior Engineer, Office of Design and Construction, 1964-1985
Records (3.1 linear meters).

In 1981 the Office of Design and Construction (ODC) was created from the Office of Facilities Planning and Engineering Services (OFPES). OFPES was the successor organization to the Buildings Management Department (BMD). For an administrative history of ODC and its predecessors, see record units 157 and 562.

Phillip K. Reiss was Director, ODC, 1981- . The Office consisted of four branches: Planning, Design, Construction, and Visual Communications. In 1984 the Visual Communications branch was moved under the administration of the Office of Plant Services.

These records were maintained by James M. Murphy. He served as Chief Engineer, Engineering and Construction Branch, BMD, 1964-1974; Chief, Engineering and Design Branch, OFPES, 1974-1977; Chief, Facilities Data Branch, OFPES, 1978-1980; Supervisory Engineer, ODC, 1981; and Quality Control Senior Engineer, ODC, 1982- .

This record unit primarily documents the Arts and Industries Building renovation and restoration project, 1972-1976, of which Murphy was the supervisor. Materials include project memoranda, budget and cost analysis, progress reports, press information kits, blueprints, and photographs. Also included in this collection are administrative office memoranda, budgets, reading files, and a progress report on the 2324 Massachusetts Avenue house renovation project, 1964-1965.

ARRANGEMENT: By project number. FINDING AIDS: Box list in control file. SPECIAL CONDITIONS: Use of this record unit requires prior arrangement with the Archives staff.

Office of Design and Construction, 1965-1980
Project Files (46.3 linear meters).

For an administrative history of the Office of Design and Construction, see record units 157, 562, and 640.

This record unit consists of project files documenting the repairs, improvement, and renovation of existing Smithsonian buildings. The records include memoranda with Smithsonian offices, correspondence with contractors, blueprints, cost analyses, specifications, and photographs.

ARRANGEMENT: (1) Blueprints; (2) Design and Construction central files; (3) Office of Facilities Planning and Engineering Services central files; (4) estimating and planning files. FINDING AIDS: Box list in control file. SPECIAL CONDITIONS: Use of this record unit requires prior arrangement with the Archives staff.

Editorial and Publications Division, 1906-1965
Records (10 linear meters).

For many years, the Editorial and Publications Division administered public relations activities as well as publications. In 1966 a major reorganization established the

Smithsonian Institution Press, concerned with publications, and created other offices for public relations, radio programs, and the like.

These records represent most of the activities of the Editorial and Publications Division. Included are a range of fiscal and administrative records pertaining to Smithsonian publications, especially correspondence with National Museum publications authors and background records for *Annual Reports,* news releases and news clippings, materials pertaining to Smithsonian house publications, Smithsonian radio programs, and miscellaneous collections of photographs. Records, 1936-1942, pertaining to the radio program "The World Is Yours" are of special interest; they include radio scripts and related promotional literature and a file of collected information on other contemporary educational radio programs.

ARRANGEMENT: (1) Radio scripts and promotional literature, 1936-1942; (2) alphabetic research file on other contemporary radio programs, 1936-1938; (3) unarranged material. FINDING AIDS: Folder or box list in control file. SPECIAL CONDITIONS: (1) Arrangement will be substantially altered when the collection is processed; (2) use of this record unit requires prior arrangement with the Archives staff.

(87)

Ethnogeographic Board, 1942-1945
Records (4.4 linear meters).

The Ethnogeographic Board, with offices in the Smithsonian Institution Building, was under the joint sponsorship of the American Council of Learned Societies, the Social Science Research Council, the National Research Council, and the Smithsonian. Founded in 1942, the Board was headed by William Duncan Strong until 1944. The Board served as a clearinghouse between its supporting institutions, the armed services, and government war agencies for information about geography, languages, and cultures of non-European areas of the war, especially Africa, Japan, and Micronesia. The Board disseminated ethnogeographic information and helped locate and mobilize trained personnel, especially anthropologists. The Smithsonian War Committee preceded the Board, worked with it, and also served the war effort in other ways. After 1944 the Ethnogeographic Board's importance declined, and apparently it was terminated in mid-1945.

These records include fiscal information, minutes of board meetings, and other administrative documents; correspondence and information files on manpower available in selected fields; and some correspondence and compiled information that served as a central reference source.

ARRANGEMENT: Includes the following segments: correspondence, reports to sponsoring agencies, budgets, personnel recruitment including *curricula vitae,* and records of projects completed. FINDING AIDS: None. SPECIAL CONDITIONS: Use of this record unit requires prior arrangement with the Archives staff.

(58)

Collected Letters on Ethnology, circa 1876-1879
(0.1 linear meter).

On February 1, 1878, the Smithsonian Institution released Circular 316, "In Reference to American Archaeology," prepared by Otis Tufton Mason, then a Collaborator in

Ethnology at the Smithsonian Institution and later Curator of Ethnology and Anthropology, and distributed it under Joseph Henry's name. The Circular was designed to solicit information concerning the location and extent of the archaeological remains of American Indians in various parts of the country. This information was to provide the basis for an exhaustive work on American archaeology to be published by the Smithsonian. With this end in mind, the replies were apparently turned over to Mason and Charles Rau, also a Collaborator in Ethnology and later Curator of Archaeology in the United States National Museum.

This record unit includes correspondence, drawings, and maps regarding American archaeology. Most of the correspondence was probably sent to the Smithsonian in response to Circular 316, but some has no reference to the Circular. A small portion antedates its release and was probably included in the collection because of related subject matter.

Most of the letters are addressed to Spencer F. Baird, Joseph Henry, or the Smithsonian. A large number of the letters were abstracted by Mason in the *Annual Report of the Smithsonian Institution,* 1879, pages 428-448.

ARRANGEMENT: Alphabetic. FINDING AIDS: None. SPECIAL CONDITIONS: Use of this record unit requires prior arrangement with the Archives staff.

(503)

Office of Exhibits Central, 1954-1979
Records (12.3 linear meters and oversize).

For an administrative history of the Office of Exhibits Central and its predecessors, the Office of Exhibits and the Office of Exhibits Programs, see record unit 90.

These records were mostly created by the Office of Exhibits, 1954-1969; the Office of Exhibits Programs, 1969-1973; and the Office of Exhibits Central, 1973-1979. They document a period of intense exhibition activity at the Smithsonian Institution and its bureaus. Especially well represented are permanent and special exhibitions at the National Museum of Natural History (NMNH), the National Museum of History and Technology (NMHT), the National Air and Space Museum (before 1966, the National Air Museum), and the Arts and Industries Building.

The records include correspondence, memoranda, exhibit scripts, budgets, specifications for exhibit halls, plans, press releases, annual reports, installation schedules, progress reports, photographs and negatives, publications, and posters. Of special interest are records concerning the United States National Museum's Exhibits Modernization Program during the 1950s and 1960s; the creation and early history of the Insect Zoo at NMNH, *circa* 1971-1973; the proposed rain forest exhibition at NMNH, *circa* 1970-1973; the special Smithsonian exhibition, *Drugs,* 1972; the planning and installation of the initial exhibitions at NMHT, *circa* 1957-1968; the *Laser-10* exhibition at NMHT, 1969-1970; and the installation of the *By-Word* program at NMNH, *circa* 1967-1971.

ARRANGEMENT: Unarranged. FINDING AIDS: Folder list in control file. SPECIAL CONDITIONS: Use of this record unit requires prior arrangement with the Archives staff.

Exhibits Editors' Office, Office of Exhibits Central, 1948-1978
Exhibits Scripts, (12.2 linear meters).

Prior to World War II exhibits at the Smithsonian were given low priority in comparison to research by the National Museum staff and were seldom changed. The exhibits function was discharged by curators, preparators, and other staff members as time permitted. After World War II a committee of curators was formed to consider how to modernize and improve the Museum's exhibits. In 1950 this committee began to implement a new system of contracting out exhibit design work, under close supervision by divisional curator and preparators.

In 1955 an Office of Exhibits was created by consolidating personnel and other exhibits resources, with John Anglim as its head. This Office was responsible for the design and production of exhibits for permanent halls and of special and traveling exhibits for the National Museum and its successors. In 1969 a new function, training exhibits personnel from smaller museums around the country, led to a name change to the Office of Exhibits Programs. A 1973 reorganization created independent exhibits functions in several of the museums, and changed the name of this office to the Office of Exhibits Central. The Office of Exhibits Central prepares exhibits for bureaus which have no exhibits staff; performs specialized exhibits services, including motion picture production and audiovisual services, plastic and model-restoration work, preparing for special and traveling exhibits; and conducts exhibits training programs.

These records document the work of the Exhibits Editors' Office in the Office of Exhibits Central. Included are scripts, correspondence, photographs, brochures, and memoranda dealing with permanent exhibit halls at the National Museum of Natural History (NMNH), National Museum of History and Technology (NMHT), National Portrait Gallery (NPG), National Collection of Fine Arts (NCFA); as well as special exhibits and the work of the Smithsonian Institution Traveling Exhibition Service (SITES). For administrative records of the Office of Exhibits and the Office of Exhibits Programs, see record unit 190.

ARRANGEMENT: (1) Permanent halls, NMNH, 1957-1974; (2) permanent halls, NMHT, 1958-1972; (3) permanent halls, NPG and NCFA, 1948-1978; (4) special exhibits, 1948-1978; (5) SITES, 1948-1978. FINDING AIDS: Description in control file. SPECIAL CONDITIONS: Use of this record unit requires prior arrangement with the Archives staff.

Exposition Records of the Smithsonian Institution and the United States National Museum, 1867-1940
(13.1 linear meters and oversize).

The Smithsonian Institution made great contributions to the Centennial Exposition of 1876, under the personal supervision of Assistant Secretary Spencer F. Baird. From that time the Institution participated in many national and international expositions. These records comprise most of the extant documentation for that activity.

The Centennial Exposition itself is poorly represented here, but it is documented in Baird's official and personal papers. The preservation of other records has been uneven and is not proportional to the importance of the exposition. There are far more records for the Southern Exposition, Louisville, 1883; the Cincinnati Industrial Exposition, 1884; and the World's Industrial and Cotton Centennial Exposition, New Orleans, 1884-1885, than for the Philadelphia Centennial Exposition, for instance, though the latter was surely more noteworthy.

The most extensive exposition records in the Archives are those for the Louisville-Cincinnati-New Orleans Expositions, 1883 to 1885; the World's Columbian Exposition of 1892 to 1894 in Chicago; the Cotton States and International Exposition in Atlanta, 1895; the Pan-American Exposition at Buffalo, New York, 1901; the Louisiana Purchase Exposition at St. Louis, 1904; the Panama-Pacific International Exposition at San Francisco, 1915; and the Panama-California Exposition at San Diego, 1916. Among the less well documented expositions are the Philadelphia Centennial Exposition of 1876; the Tennessee Centennial at Nashville, 1897; the Omaha, Trans-Mississippi, and International Exposition, 1898; the Lewis and Clark Exposition, 1905, in Portland, Oregon; the Century of Progress Exposition in Chicago, 1933; the California Pacific International Exposition in San Diego, 1935; the Texas Centennial Exposition in Dallas, 1936; the Great Lakes Exposition in Cleveland, 1936-1937; the International Exposition of Art and Technique in Modern Life, Paris, 1937; the Golden Gate International Exposition, San Francisco, 1939; the Seventh World's Poultry Congress and Exposition, Cleveland, 1939; and the New York World's Fair, 1939.

The records of foreign expositions are less fully preserved than domestic ones. Exceptions are the Berlin International Fisheries Exposition of 1880 and, to a lesser degree, the London International Fisheries Exposition of 1883 and Columbian Historical Exposition at Madrid in 1892.

Several factors complicated these records, making them difficult to describe and to use. In fact, what is called the exposition series is not really homogeneous. Parts of it were clearly kept in a separate exposition file; just as certainly, parts of it were removed from other series. The records originated in several offices and were sometimes mixed as they were created. Moreover, the organization of the Institution itself led to some confusion in record-keeping. The Smithsonian Institution conceived the National Museum as a government bureau placed under Smithsonian care. As a rule, the Smithsonian and the National Museum each appointed the same representative to the expositions—the Assistant Secretary for the National Museum. But in spite of this unity at the top, assistants from the two branches participated in planning and creating exhibits; several different offices within the Museum and the Institution generated records for a single exposition. Most confusing of all, representatives of the Smithsonian carried letterhead stationery with them into the field, a practice which played havoc with the traditional division of incoming and outgoing correspondence. Sometimes copies from the same person are both outgoing to the field and incoming from the field in the same volume.

The expositions themselves were often closely related. The exhibits assembled for one exposition were frequently taken up en masse for another. Thus, the Philadelphia Centennial exhibits furnished much of the material for the Berlin International Fisheries Exposition in 1880, for the London International Fisheries Exposition in 1883, and for the Louisville-Cincinnati-New Orleans Expositions from 1883 to 1885. Similarly, the exhibits for the Lewis and Clark Exposition held in Portland, Oregon, during 1905 were drawn almost entirely from those previously created for the Louisiana Purchase Exposition at St. Louis in 1904.

These records document the fiscal and technical aspects of exposition planning and, to some extent, museum practice in the nineteenth century. The volume of records varies from exposition to exposition. In some cases it is possible to follow planning, development, and operation of an exhibition virtually from inception to closing. The records include incoming and outgoing correspondence between Washington and the field agent; negotiations with suppliers and shippers—including invoices, bills, and vouchers; plans, sketches, and photographs of exhibits; and publications. Many announcements, certificates, and photographs are in oversize.

Also included are Government Board records and Smithsonian Exposition records of William deC. Ravenel, who was Administrative Assistant at the Museum. Between 1907 and 1919 he served as the Smithsonian's official representative to six expositions. At the Panama-Pacific International Exposition in San Francisco in 1915 and the Panama-California International Exposition in San Diego in 1916, he also served as Secretary of the Government Board of Management.

ARRANGEMENT: (1) Exposition Records of the Smithsonian Institution, the United States National Museum, and the United States Fish Commission, chronologic by exposition, 1875-1940; (2) Government Board records and Smithsonian exposition records of William deC. Ravenel, chronologic by exposition, 1907-1919. FINDING AIDS: (1) Description in control file; (2) many outgoing letterpress volumes are indexed. SPECIAL CONDITIONS: Use of this record unit requires prior arrangement with the Archives staff.

(637)

Office of Facilities Planning and Engineering Services, 1965-1978, with records dating from 1899
Records (6.6 linear meters).

For an administrative history of the Office of Facilities Planning and Engineering Services (OFPES), see record units 157 and 562.

These records contain project files, blueprints, contract and work files, photographs, and correspondence related to several renovation projects. Included are renovation and restoration plans for the Arts and Industries Building, the Patent Office Building, and the Freer Gallery of Art. Also included are original blueprints, drawings, and renovation plans from the Carnegie Mansion located at 91st Street and 5th Avenue, New York City, which is now the home of the Cooper-Hewitt Museum.

ARRANGEMENT: By building. FINDING AIDS: Box list in control file. SPECIAL CONDITIONS: Use of this record unit requires prior arrangement with the Archives staff.

(562)

Office of Facilities Planning and Engineering Services, 1973-1980, with records dating from 1890
Records (1.2 linear meters).

The Office of Facilities Planning and Engineering Services was established in 1973. Prior to that its activities were incorporated in the Buildings Management Department.

For an administrative history of the Buildings Management Department, see record unit 157. Andrew F. Michaels directed the Office until 1975, when Phillip K. Reiss became Director, 1975- .

These records consist of photographs, reports, correspondence, contracts, and blueprints documenting Smithsonian buildings and construction projects. The buildings documented include the Smithsonian Institution Building, the Arts and Industries Building, the Army Medical Museum, the Natural History Building, the Hirshhorn Museum and Sculpture Garden, the National Zoological Park, the Museum Support Center at Silver Hill, the Adelaide Forbes Calhoun property, the Marjorie Merriweather Post estate of Hillwood, the Renwick Gallery, the Freer Gallery of Art, and the old Patent Office Building. There is substantial documentation of efforts to provide parking on the Mall. Photographs in the collection document a number of activities, including the laying of the cornerstone for the Natural History Building, the rotation of the Joseph Henry statue, the removal of Horatio Greenough's statue of George Washington from the Smithsonian Institution Building, the 1970 fire in the American History Building, and repairs and renovations of numerous interior spaces throughout the Smithsonian.

ARRANGEMENT: Unarranged. FINDING AIDS: Description in control file. SPECIAL CONDITIONS: Use of this record unit requires prior arrangement with the Archives staff.

(641)

Engineering and Design Branch, Office of Facilities Planning and Engineering Services, 1970-1975, with materials dating from 1961
Records (1.6 linear meters).

For an administrative history of the Office of Facilities Planning and Engineering Services (OFPES), see record units 157 and 562.

This record unit primarily documents the interior construction of the Hirshhorn Museum and Sculpture Garden. Included are correspondence with contractors and suppliers, blueprints, specifications, and photographs.

ARRANGEMENT: Unarranged. FINDING AIDS: None. SPECIAL CONDITIONS: Use of this record unit requires prior arrangement with the Archives staff.

(484)

Office of Grants and Risk Management, 1953-1980
Records (34.8 linear meters).

The Office of Grants and Risk Management administered grant and contract awards to the Smithsonian Institution and assessed and procured insurance for the Institution. These duties were performed by accountants in the Fiscal Division until 1966, when the Contracts and Grants Section of the Fiscal Division was established. In 1969 the Contracts and Grants Division was established. That Division was renamed the Grants and Insurance Administration Division in 1972, with Phillip H. Babcock as its Chief. In 1978 the Division became the Office of Grants and Risk Management.

These records document the fiscal administration of grants received by the Smithsonian Institution. They consist of correspondence, memoranda, budgets, and reports. Many of these records were kept by Phillip H. Babcock, who became an accountant in the Fiscal Division in 1964, Chief of the Contracts and Grants Section in 1966, Chief of the Contracts and Grants Division in 1969, Chief of the Grants and Insurance Administration Division in 1972, and Director of the Office of Grants and Risk Management in 1978.

ARRANGEMENT: (1) Records, *circa* 1959-1966, accession number T89106; (2) records, *circa* 1969-1976, accession number T89107; (3) records, 1973-1980, accession number 81-086; (4) records, 1968-1979, accession number 82-094; (5) records, 1953-*circa* 1967, accession number T89108. FINDING AIDS: None. SPECIAL CONDITIONS: Use of this record unit requires prior arrangement with the Archives staff.

(300)

Interdisciplinary Communications Program, 1968-1976
Records (34 linear meters).

The concept for the Interdisciplinary Communications Program (ICP) originated in 1931 when the Josiah Macy Junior Foundation sponsored a series of medical conferences that explored advances in the medical sciences. Information from the conferences was used in funding decisions made by the Foundation. Frank Fremont-Smith began the series; when he retired as the Foundation's Medical Director, he was encouraged to apply the concept to the field of the biological sciences in general.

In 1964 ICP became affiliated with the New York Academy of Sciences (NYAS), with Fremont-Smith continuing as Director. In early 1966, Fremont-Smith began conversations with Sidney R. Galler, Assistant Secretary (Science) of the Smithsonian Institution, seeking NYAS-Smithsonian support. After Smithsonian negotiations with the National Aeronautics and Space Administration (NASA), already a frequent sponsor of ICP conferences, NASA agreed to provide support through a contract for funding beginning in October 1966. The Smithsonian administered this contract and several extensions, until the contract was closed in 1974.

In 1971, ICP contracted with the Agency for International Development (AID), through the Smithsonian, to begin an International Program for Population Analysis (IPPA). This program was intended to provide for analysis and dissemination of knowledge about population policies and dynamics to decision-makers in less developed countries, chiefly through interdisciplinary workshops and seminars. AID terminated funding for IPPA in 1976, at which time ICP ceased to operate.

Frank Fremont-Smith directed ICP until 1968, based in New York City. In 1967 Moses C. Shelesnyak became ICP's Associate Director and opened an office in Washington, D.C. Shelesnyak became Director in 1968 and served until ICP was ended in 1976.

These records document the activities of ICP and include contract information and proposals with NASA and AID; conference files and reports for conferences on population carcinogenesis, space biosciences, and biology of hard tissue; IPPA-related workshops and seminars; program files; semi-annual and annual reports; memoranda and correspondence concerning ICP internal operations, workshops, and programs; and the IPPA publication, *Population Dynamics Quarterly.*

ARRANGEMENT: Unarranged. FINDING AIDS: Partial folder list in control file. SPECIAL CONDITIONS: Use of this record unit requires prior arrangement with the Archives staff.

Office of Interdisciplinary Studies, 1976-1992
Records (1.3 linear meters).

For an administrative history of the Office of Interdisciplinary Studies and its predecessors, see record unit 495.

Records consist of programs, correspondence, memoranda, fundraising material, brochures, invitations, reports, audiotapes, background materials, and schedules for the following symposia: *Kin and Communities: The Peopling of America; Completing the Food Chain; Constitutional Roots, Rights, and Responsibilities; World Food Prize; Canvas of Culture: Rediscovery of the Past as Adaptation for the Future; How Humans Adapt: A Biocultural Odyssey; Man and Beast Revisited; Road after 1984: High Technology and Human Freedom;* and *The United States in the World.* These records were created or maintained by Wilton S. Dillon and Carla M. Borden.

ARRANGEMENT: (1) Records, 1976-1992, accession number 93-139; (2) programs, 1976-1986, accession number 92-142; (3) records, 1976-1985, accession number 90-070. FINDING AIDS: None. SPECIAL CONDITIONS: Use of this record unit requires prior arrangement with the Archives staff.

Office of Interdisciplinary Studies, circa 1978-1991
Records (3.7 linear meters).

Smithsonian Institution seminars and symposia were organized by the Division of Seminars of the Office of Academic Programs until 1971, when the Division became the Office of Seminars. In 1974 that Office became the Office of Symposia and Seminars. In 1987 Symposia and Seminars became the Office of Interdisciplinary Studies. For additional records documenting Interdisciplinary Studies, see record unit 498.

The records include correspondence, memoranda, announcements, publication contracts, photographs, grant information, lecture agreements, reports, brochures, research materials, resumes, and publication information for the following symposia: *Kin and Communities: The Peopling of America; Constitutional Roots, Rights, and Responsibilities; World Food Prize; The Muses Flee Hitler; Man and Beast Revisited; Road after 1984: High Technology and Human Freedom;* and *The United States in the World.* The records were maintained by Wilton S. Dillon, Director of the Division of Seminars, 1969-1970; Director of the Office of Seminars, 1971-1974; Director of the Office of Symposia and Seminars, 1974-1987; and Director of the Office of Interdisciplinary Studies, 1987-1989. The records were also maintained by Carla M. Borden an assistant, specialist, Deputy Director, Associate Director, and Acting Director of the Office from 1976 to 1992.

ARRANGEMENT: Unarranged. FINDING AIDS: Description in control file. SPECIAL CONDITIONS: Use of this record unit requires prior arrangement with the Archives staff.

International Catalogue of Scientific Literature, 1893-1933
Records (1.6 linear meters).

The International Catalogue of Scientific Literature was established by three international conferences in London in 1896, 1898, and 1900. Data collection began in 1901, and publications were issued annually until 1916; some activities, although not publication, resumed again after the First World War. The Smithsonian became the United States Bureau of the Catalogue in 1901, at first funding it by private funds and, after 1906, by special federal appropriations. Cyrus Adler, Librarian of the Smithsonian, encouraged the Smithsonian's participation and directed the Bureau's activities in the early years; he was succeeded by Leonard C. Gunnell. The titles of the Bureau's directors varied over the years, from Assistant Secretary to Assistant-in-charge. The Smithsonian discontinued the Bureau in 1933.

These records contain correspondence about the formation of the International Catalogue, planning and operation of the reporting system, and the circumstances of the Catalogue's demise.

ARRANGEMENT: (1) Incoming and outgoing correspondence and memoranda, 1893-1933, including secretarial records; (2) letterpress outgoing correspondence, 1898-1907, including correspondence of Cyrus Adler, Librarian of the Institution, on other topics; (3) alphabetical list of authors; (4) list of publications; (5) receipts; (6) Leonard C. Gunnell records. FINDING AIDS: Incomplete card index, created when the records were received or created, boxed with the records. SPECIAL CONDITIONS: Use of this record unit requires prior arrangement with the Archives staff.

International Exchange Service, 1849-1857, 1873-1953
Records (9.4 linear meters).

The international exchange program was established in 1849 to provide communication between scientific and literary societies through exchange of publications. Also, by publishing lists of correspondents, participating learned societies, and periodicals received, libraries were given valuable information to assist their collection building. Beginning officially in 1867, the Smithsonian distributed United States government publications to foreign countries. In the 1880s several international agreements were made for exchange of official publications, in which the Smithsonian directed the program for the United States government. In 1881 the Smithsonian received its first federal appropriation for international exchanges. From the outset, the Smithsonian's primary purpose was to increase knowledge by exchange of publications, rather than to build its own library; nevertheless, exchanges have contributed greatly to the development of the Smithsonian Library.

These records contain information about receipt of publications for the Smithsonian Library, 1849-1857; distribution information, 1899-1953; and substantial correspondence documenting the operation of the Exchange Service, 1880-1907. See also record unit 27.

ARRANGEMENT: (1) Record of publications received for the Smithsonian Library, 1849-1857; (2) incoming correspondence, 1878-1880; (3) incoming correspondence, 1882-1900; (4) outgoing correspondence, 1887-1907; (5) distribution of publications, an alphabetical list; (6) addresses for Smithsonian publication distribution; (7) records of publications, 1880; (8) record of shipments abroad, 1899-1953; (9) publications received, 1884-1892; (10) day books and invoice books; (11) private log of Jerome H. Kidder; (12) registers of letters sent and received. FINDING AIDS: Indexes to outgoing correspondence bound in each volume. SPECIAL CONDITIONS: Use of this record unit requires prior arrangement with the Archives staff.

(509)

International Exchange Service, 1872-1985
Records (14.4 linear meters).

For an administrative history of the International Exchange Service, see record unit 61.

Records include correspondence, memoranda, reports, budgets, ledgers, day books, and other administrative materials concerning the operations of the Service. Also included is a card index of employees who served between the 1880s and the 1930s.

ARRANGEMENT: Correspondence is arranged by countries, individuals and institutions, and universities. FINDING AIDS: Description in control file. SPECIAL CONDITIONS: Use of this record unit requires prior arrangement with the Archives staff.

(502)

International Exchange Service, circa 1908-1971
Records (10.3 linear meters).

For an administrative history of the International Exchange Service, see record unit 61.

Records contain correspondence of the Director of the International Exchange Service along with invoices and shipping instructions. The bulk of the correspondence relates to the exchange of publications between parties in the United States and abroad.

ARRANGEMENT: (1) Domestic correspondence; (2) international correspondence. FINDING AIDS: Description in control file. SPECIAL CONDITIONS: Use of this record unit requires prior arrangement with the Archives staff.

(298)

Local Notes, 1916-1933
Newsletter (0.3 linear meter).

The first issue of *Local Notes* appeared May 9, 1916. The purpose of this weekly newsletter, as stated in that issue, was "to record the progress of the Institution's activities throughout its various branches from week to week and maintain a degree of familiarity on the part of its employees with both one another and with the fields of operations covered by the Institution as a whole."

Secretary Walcott urged employees to cooperate by submitting short reports of their activities. *Local Notes* appeared weekly from 1916 through 1917; not at all in 1918; and biweekly, beginning in 1919. In 1933 it was reduced to a single sheet for financial reasons.

Local Notes contains personal notes on deaths, illnesses, marriages, births, vacations, retirements, honors and awards in and out of the museums, notes on official travel, discoveries, accessions, promotions, organizational changes, and exhibits.

ARRANGEMENT: Chronologic. FINDING AIDS: None. SPECIAL CONDITIONS: Use of this record unit requires prior arrangement with the Archives staff.

Management Analysis Office, 1949-1991
Records (12.3 linear meters).

For an administrative history of this Office, see record unit 294. John G. Motheral continued as Director of the Office through 1992.

These records consist of "Smithsonian Announcements," "Office Memoranda," "Special Memoranda," "Staff Handbooks," and various forms used in Smithsonian offices. The records include correspondence, drafts, and other background materials surrounding the creation of these documents. The Announcements concern office name changes, reorganizations, personnel title and duty changes, and the appointment of office directors. The Office Memoranda and Special Memoranda detail new policies, rules, and guidelines implemented by the Institution. The Smithsonian Staff Handbooks describe procedures to be followed by Smithsonian employees. Many of these records were created while John G. Motheral was Director of the Office.

ARRANGEMENT: (1) Records, 1949-1978, accession number 85-115; (2) records, 1954-1991, accession number 92-098; (3) records, 1960-1980, accession number 91-113; (4) records, 1963-1984, accession number 86-067; (5) records, 1970-1981, accession number 87-128; (6) records, 1973-1985, accession number 89-026; (7) records, 1980-1983, accession number 89-135. FINDING AIDS: Description in control file. SPECIAL CONDITIONS: Use of this record unit requires prior arrangement with the Archives staff.

Management Analysis Office, 1960-1980, with related records from 1918
Records (29.3 linear meters).

These records for the most part date from 1960, when Ann S. Campbell became Supervisory Management Analyst in the Office of the Assistant Secretary for Administration.

In 1961, an organization and methods unit was created informally under the Assistant Secretary, with the Supervisory Management Analyst in charge. The unit was formally recognized as the Organization and Methods Division in 1964; became the Administrative Systems Division (ASD) in 1968; and the Management Analysis Office (MAO) in 1972. Ann S. Campbell was Chief, ASD, 1968-1972, and Director, MAO, 1972-1980. John G. Motheral became Director of MAO in 1980.

The primary responsibilities of the Office have included surveys of Smithsonian offices, focusing on their function, objectives, staffing, and procedures, and recommending and developing operational changes as requested. MAO coordinates, prepares, and issues Smithsonian directives, including Smithsonian Manuals, Office Memoranda, and Announcements. In addition, MAO provides assistance in preparing, drafting, and controlling the use of Smithsonian forms. The Office gathers Smithsonian-wide information for institutional reporting to federal agencies, such as preparing the Smithsonian entry for the *Catalog of Federal Domestic Assistance.*

These records include correspondence, organization charts, project reports, audit reports, directives (with background information), various task force minutes, MAO internal records, and informational files, reflecting the Office's role as a clearinghouse for Smithsonian administrative activities, policy surveys, and changes. Pre-1960 records include correspondence of John Enos Graf and John L. Keddy, Assistant Secretaries of the Smithsonian. Of importance is the Keddy survey of United States National Museum collection management activity, 1953.

ARRANGEMENT: (1) Subject files, A-Z, *circa* 1918-1976; (2) subject files, A-Z, 1951-1980; (3) project files, *circa* 1972-1980; (4) outgoing correspondence, 1960-1976; (5) correspondence logs, 1964-1977; (6) cancelled forms, *circa* 1949-1979; (7) *Catalog of Federal Domestic Assistance, circa* 1976-1980. FINDING AIDS: Transfer lists and subject index in control file. SPECIAL CONDITIONS: (1) Records may be subject to rearrangement when processed; (2) use of this record unit requires prior arrangement with the Archives staff.

(60)

Meteorological Project, 1849-1875, and related records from 1820
Records (2.5 linear meters).

Joseph Henry's first major project at the Smithsonian was his plan to obtain weather reports from a countrywide network of voluntary observers; his plan is detailed in the Institution's 1848 *Annual Report.* Voluminous reports, maps, tables, and charts were prepared and published on all phases of the work—rainfall, snowfall, temperatures, barometric pressure, storms, meteors, auroras, and other phenomena. In 1869, when Congress established the Weather Bureau of the United States Signal Service, the Smithsonian system of meteorological reports was turned over to the new bureau. The Smithsonian continued to work on the material collected up to the time of transfer, however, and over the next few years issued reports, tables, and maps. A part of this record unit was published in the 1873 *Annual Report,* pages 84-140, "Classified Record of Monthly Meteorological Reports Preserved in the Smithsonian Institution"; and other segments of this unit were published elsewhere. Incoming and outgoing meteorological correspondence is completely unpublished, however. Correspondents include Lorin Blodget, James Henry Coffin, James Pollard Espy, Arnold Henry Guyot, Joseph Henry, Elias Loomis, and Charles Anthony Schott. These records were created after 1850, but contain meteorological information dating back to 1820.

ARRANGEMENT: (1) Incoming correspondence, 1852-1861, 1868; (2) miscellaneous correspondence, notes, reports, 1853-1875; (3) Lorin Blodget's outgoing correspondence, 1853-1854; (4) manuscript copy of the "Classified Record of Monthly Meteorological Reports Preserved in the Smithsonian Institution," *Annual Report,* 1873, pp. 84-140; (5) records relating to studies of monthly and annual mean temperatures in the United States and elsewhere in the Americas, data for years 1820-1875; (6) records relating to monthly and annual rainfall in the United States and elsewhere in the Americas, data for years 1820-1875; (7) records relating to atmospheric pressure, data for years 1850-1873; (8) records of meteorological observers, 1856-1860, 1868-1873; records of instrument distribution, 1850-1870; list of publications on meteorology; (9) clippings on meteorology, 1853-1873, with gaps; (10) miscellaneous meteorological records; (11) oversize, published meteorological maps. FINDING AIDS: Description in control file. SPECIAL CONDITIONS: (1) Microfilm copies of incoming correspondence, 1852-1861, 1868, are available; (2) use of this record unit requires prior arrangement with the Archives staff.

(629)

Office of Museum Programs, 1967-1986
Records (12.3 linear meters).

In 1967 an Office of Special Museum Programs was set up under the direction of Frank A. Taylor. Taylor, after a long career in many responsible posts at the Smithsonian, was acting as a consultant to Secretary S. Dillon Ripley, considering ways that museums could better meet the various needs of their visitors. In 1971 Peter C. Welsh was formally appointed as the first Director of the Office of Museum Programs (OMP). Frederick Schmid succeeded him, serving from December 1971 to 1973. At this time the Office was made responsible for many of the Smithsonian's obligations under the National Museum Act. The directorship was vacant until the appointment of Jane R. Glaser as Director in 1975.

The objective of OMP is to serve as a resource for the museum community—local, national, and worldwide. The Office sponsors workshops in the United States and abroad designed to train and counsel museum professionals in all aspects of museum work. It began a Museum Reference Center, which was administered by the Smithsonian Institution Libraries after 1978, and creates videotape and audiotape programs on topics of interest to museologists, which are available for loan or sale to interested users.

These records document OMP's efforts to promote knowledge of museology and its techniques. Many of the records deal with daily operations of the Office and its programs, including a Workshop Series, 1978-1984, Conservation Information program, and the National American Museums Program. Other records are concerned with cooperative work with international and national museum organizations.

ARRANGEMENT: Records, 1967-1986, accession number 90-023. FINDING AIDS: Folder list in control file. SPECIAL CONDITIONS: (1) Restricted; (2) use of this record unit requires prior arrangement with the Archives staff.

(624)

Office of Museum Programs, 1974-1988
Records (2.9 linear meters).

For an administrative history of the Office of Museum Programs (OMP), see record unit 629.

These records mostly document activities dealing with the International Council on Museums, conservation issues, the American Association of Museums, the Anacostia Museum Training Program, and the Kellogg Project, funded by the Kellogg Foundation to expand the educational influence of museums.

ARRANGEMENT: Records, 1974-1988, accession number 90-157. FINDING AIDS: Folder list in control file. SPECIAL CONDITIONS: (1) Restricted; (2) use of this record unit requires prior arrangement with the Archives staff.

(631)

Office of Museum Programs, circa 1974-1989
Records (7.4 linear meters).

For an administrative history of the Office of Museum Programs (OMP), see record unit 629.

These records document the museological work of OMP among its various constituencies—international, national, and local. The records focus on training for smaller museums in all aspect of museum work, including security, registration, conservation, graphics, education, and development. Of special interest are files on the outreach efforts to American Indian tribal museums by the National American Museum Program.

ARRANGEMENT: Records, 1974-1989, accession number 90-077. FINDING AIDS: Folder list in control file. SPECIAL CONDITIONS: Use of this record unit requires prior arrangement with the Archives staff.

(625)

Office of Museum Programs, 1975-1989
Records (8.2 linear meters).

For an administrative history of the Office of Museum Programs (OMP), see record unit 629.

These records document the tenure of Jane R. Glaser as Director of OMP, 1976-1989. Topics of note include the Kellogg Foundation Project, workshops offered to museologists, the 1986 Conference on Women's Changing Roles in Museums, and scripts and files for the Conservation Information Program. Videotapes are also included.

ARRANGEMENT: Records, 1975-1989, accession number 91-073. FINDING AIDS: Folder list in control file. SPECIAL CONDITIONS: (1) Restricted; (2) use of this record unit requires prior arrangement with the Archives staff.

(630)

Office of Museum Programs, 1979-1988
Records (11.9 linear meters).

For an administrative history of the Office of Museum Programs (OMP), see record unit 629.

These records document the operations of OMP and its work in the museum community including the on-site Workshop Program, 1984-1986, and the Awards for Minority Museum Professionals, 1984-1988. Of special interest are records of the Kellogg Project, funded by the Kellogg Foundation in an effort to expand the educational influence of museums.

ARRANGEMENT: Records, 1979-1988, accession number 90-061. FINDING AIDS: Folder list in control file. SPECIAL CONDITIONS: (1) Restricted; (2) use of this record unit requires prior arrangement with the Archives staff.

(574)

National Museum Act, 1966-1986
Records (26.7 linear meters).

The National Museum Act of 1966 affirmed the Smithsonian Institution's traditional role of assisting other museums and authorized the Institution to strengthen its activities of service to them. Funds appropriated to the Smithsonian for the implementation of the National Museum Act were made available primarily by grants and contracts to museums of all disciplines, non-profit museum-related organizations and associations, academic institutions, and individuals employed or sponsored by eligible organizations, after review by the National Museum Act Advisory Council. The membership of the Advisory Council encompassed the principal museum disciplines of art, science, and history and was broadly representative of the various regions of the United States.

Under the direction of the Secretary, the Director of the United States National Museum (USNM) continued to carry out the directives of the National Museum Act of 1966. The Office of Special Museum Programs was created in 1967, and Frank A. Taylor was named Director General of Museums. From 1968 until his retirement in January 1971, Taylor served as Director General of Museums and Director, USNM. In August 1972, Paul Perrot became Assistant Secretary for Museum Programs (Director, USNM). The Assistant Secretary for Museum Programs assumed essentially the same duties and responsibilities performed by the Director General of Museums. Perrot remained in this position until his retirement in February 1984. In 1985, William N. Richards, Jr., assumed the position of Acting Assistant Secretary for Museum Programs. The Act remained unfunded from 1966 until FY 1972 when it received a first appropriation of $600,000. The program was abolished in 1986.

These records consist of approved grant applications, letters of award, final reports from recipients, published materials, photographs, slides, researcher's files, project proposals, progress reports, financial statements, administrative files, correspondence, budget material, and memoranda.

ARRANGEMENT: (1) National Museum Act, records, 1967-1979, accession number 89-077; (2) National Museum Act, accepted applications, 1971-1977, accession number 81-044; (3) National Museum Act, records, 1972-1986, accession number 87-100; (4) National Museum Act, accepted applications, 1978-1979, accession number 84-031; (5) National Museum Act, accepted proposals, 1979-1982, accession number 84-216; (6) National Museum Act, accepted grants, 1981-1985, accession number 86-074; (7) National Museum Act, accepted grant files, *circa* 1982-1984, accession number 87-020; (8) National Museum Act, accepted grant files, 1983-1986, accession number 87-065; (9) National Museum Act, accepted grant files, 1985-1986, accession number 90-114. FINDING AIDS: Folder list in control file. SPECIAL CONDITIONS: Use of this record unit requires prior arrangement with the Archives staff.

(68)

Polaris Expedition Records, 1871-1876
(0.9 linear meter).

The Polaris Expedition was undertaken for scientific observation in the Arctic during the period from 1871 to 1873, under the direction of the United States Navy. The Smithsonian was involved, especially in meteorological observations, and acquired part of the records with a view to publishing them.

This collection consists of the Polaris Expedition records along with the preparatory work of Emil Bessels, who oversaw their publication in Emil Bessels, editor, *Scientific Results of the United States Arctic Expedition,* 1876.

ARRANGEMENT: Unarranged. FINDING AIDS: None. Consult *Smithsonian Annual Reports* for 1871 and 1874 for information about the expedition and publication project. SPECIAL CONDITIONS: Use of this record unit requires prior arrangement with the Archives staff.

(369)

Director, Office of Public Affairs, circa 1965-1976
Records (5.3 linear meters).

The Office of Public Affairs had its origins in the Editorial and Publications Division of the Institution, which had long been disseminating news about Smithsonian events and exhibitions. In 1965 a separate Office of Information, reporting to the Secretary, was created, in part to deal with festivities and events surrounding the Smithson Bicentennial. B. Richard Berg was appointed Director and George J. Berklacy, Press Officer. The Office issued press releases, answered public inquiries, maintained a system of recorded telephone announcements, arranged for the production of films, and dealt with the media.

The Office of Public Affairs was established in 1968. It was charged with publicizing the programs of the Smithsonian through a broad range of methods of communication, from radio to films to special events. Initially the Office provided services including tours, visitors' booths, publications, recorded messages, news releases, information leaflets, and the answering of public inquiries.

Frederic M. Philips served as Director, 1968-1972. He was succeeded by Carl W. Larsen, who held the position 1972-   .

These records consist of alphabetic subject files of the Directors, documenting their relations with Smithsonian administrators and museums, and their direction of publications relating to public affairs activities. Major events of the period included the openings of the Hirshhorn Museum and Sculpture Garden, the National Collection of Fine Arts, the National Portrait Gallery, and the National Air and Space Museum, as well as the establishment of the annual Festival of American Folklife and the 1976 Bicentennial of the American Revolution.

ARRANGEMENT: (1) Director's files, 1965-1976, accession number T90076; (2) Director's files, 1966-1976, accession number T90077; (3) Director's files, 1976, accession number T90075. FINDING AIDS: Description in control file. SPECIAL CONDITIONS: Use of this record unit requires prior arrangement with the Archives staff.

(368)

Office of Public Affairs, circa 1965-1982
Records (2.1 linear meters).

For an administrative history of the Office of Public Affairs, see record units 369 and 420.

These records consist of administrative files of the Office of Public Affairs. They include correspondence, memoranda, some printed materials, and a few photographs relating to the work of the Office. Events documented in the records include the opening of the National Air and Space Museum in 1976, the 1977 presidential inauguration, and Pope John Paul II's visit of 1979.

These records, although incomplete, include correspondence, memoranda, some printed materials, and an occasional photograph of an event.

ARRANGEMENT: (1) Office of Public Affairs files, 1967, 1975-1979, accession number 83-006; (2) Office of Public Affairs files, circa 1965-1982, accession number T90073. FINDING AIDS: None. SPECIAL CONDITIONS: Use of this record unit requires prior arrangement with the Archives staff.

(420)

Office of Public Affairs, circa 1963-1988
Biographical Files (1.3 linear meters).

For an administrative history of the Office of Public Affairs, see record unit 369. Since 1972, the following staff served as Directors of the Office: Carl W. Larsen, 1972-1978; Alvin Rosenfeld, 1979-1986; and Madeleine Jacobs, 1987-   .

This record unit contains biographical information about Smithsonian staff, most of whom were employed or active in the 1960s, 1970s, and 1980s. The files were kept as an information resource by the Office of Public Affairs and used as needed for announcements, public statements, and publications. Staff covered in the files include regents, bureau directors, office heads, and various employees of interest. Occasional materials on docents, volunteers, and contributors to the museum collections were also saved. Much of the information in this record unit resulted from a single event or single newspaper article, but important figures, such as regents and museum directors, are quite well documented.

Records include newspaper clippings, magazine articles, articles from *The Torch,* press releases, biographical sketches, announcements, and some photographs.

ARRANGEMENT: Alphabetic. FINDING AIDS: Description in control file. SPECIAL CONDITIONS: Use of this record unit requires prior arrangement with the Archives staff.

(405)

Office of Public Affairs, 1958-1988
Calendar of Events (0.4 linear meter).

The *Calendar of Events* was originally published by the Smithsonian Museum Service, which was established in 1958 to provide non-technical information about exhibits, research, and events to the public. G. Carroll Lindsay was appointed Acting Curator of the service in 1958 and Curator in 1959. He served until 1966, when Meredith Johnson was named Acting Director. James R. Morris became Director in 1967 and served until 1968, when the Office of Public Affairs was formally established. For an administrative history of the Office of Public Affairs, see record unit 369.

The *Calendar* was at first sent only to staff members, but eventually they were sent to docents and volunteers and then to other interested persons. In recent years the *Calendar* has been published in several Washington newspapers.

The *Calendar of Events* was issued monthly to inform the public of dates, times, and places of exhibitions, lectures, films, special events, tours, and hours of operation. The *Calendar* consists of one page and is usually folded and adapted for use as a mailer.

ARRANGEMENT: Chronologic. FINDING AIDS: Description in control file. SPECIAL CONDITIONS: (1) The set is not complete; (2) use of this record unit requires prior arrangement with the Archives staff.

(372)

Office of Public Affairs, 1965-1991
News Clipping File (23.8 linear meters).

For an administrative history of the Office of Public Affairs, see record units 369 and 420.

These records consist entirely of newspaper clippings concerning the Smithsonian Institution. Information documenting the Johnson-Sea Link submersible accident, the Smithson Bicentennial, and, in recent years, the Festival of American Folklife, was kept separately, but has been combined here with the main body of the news clipping file.

Researchers should also consult record units 83 and 96 for earlier clippings.

ARRANGEMENT: Alphabetic within the non-subject series: (1) Clippings concerning the Johnson-Sea Link accident, 1973, accession number T90080; (2) clippings concerning the Smithson Bicentennial, 1965, accession number T90083; (3) clippings, 1960-1982, accession number 86-105; (4) clippings, 1983-1984, accession number 87-054; (5) clippings, 1985, accession number 88-148; (6) clippings, 1986, accession number 88-073; (7) clippings, 1987, accession number 89-138; (8) clippings, 1988, accession number 90-014; (9) clippings, 1989, accession number 91-032; (10) clippings, 1990, accession number 91-155; (11) clippings, 1991, accession number 93-065; (12) clippings documenting the Festival of American Folklife, 1990, accession number 91-170; (13) clippings documenting the Festival of American Folklife, 1989, accession number 91-171. FINDING AIDS: None. SPECIAL CONDITIONS: Use of this record unit requires prior arrangement with the Archives staff.

(82)

Office of Public Affairs, 1911-1917, 1932-1969
News Releases (1.4 linear meters).

Successor to the Office of Information, the Office of Public Affairs seeks to broadly inform and to communicate the Smithsonian's programs to the nation at large. For an administrative history of the Office of Information and the Office of Public Affairs, see record unit 369.

These records consist mostly of news releases, but in some instances background material and correspondence are also included.

ARRANGEMENT: Chronologic. FINDING AIDS: None. SPECIAL CONDITIONS: Use of this record unit requires prior arrangement with the Archives staff.

(370)

Office of Public Affairs, 1958-1990
News Releases (7.8 linear meters).

News releases were published by the Smithsonian Museum Service, 1958-1967. In 1968 the newly established Office of Public Affairs assumed that responsibility. For an administrative history of the Smithsonian Museum Service, see record unit 405. For an administrative history of the Office of Public Affairs, see record unit 369.

News releases have long been issued by the Smithsonian to communicate information to the public about Smithsonian events, important visitors, new exhibitions, lectures, and scholarly and administrative appointments. For earlier news releases, researchers should consult record unit 82.

ARRANGEMENT: (1) News releases, 1958-1979, accession number 88-029; (2) news releases, 1968-1974, accession number T90074; (3) news releases, 1975-1980, accession number 81-088; (4) news releases, 1980, accession number 92-150; (5) news releases, 1981-1982, accession number 93-070; (6) news releases, 1983, accession number 85-065; (7) news releases, 1984-1985, accession number 86-168; (8) news releases, 1986-1987, accession number 88-139; (9) news releases, 1988, accession number 90-003; (10) news releases, 1989, accession number 91-102; (11) news releases, 1990, accession number 92-051. FINDING AIDS: Description in control file. SPECIAL CONDITIONS: Use of this record unit requires prior arrangement with the Archives staff.

Office of Public Affairs, circa 1968-1983
Photographs of Smithsonian Staff and Subjects (0.8 linear meter).

For an administrative history of the Office of Public Affairs, see record units 369 and 420.

From 1977 until 1984, the Office of Public Affairs (OPA) reported to the Office of the Coordinator of Public Information. Carl W. Larsen served as Director of OPA, 1972-1978, before becoming a Special Assistant in the Office of the Coordinator. Late in 1978 Alvin Rosenfeld became Acting Director of OPA and, in 1979, Director, serving 1979-   .

This record unit consists of a small group of photographs collected by the Office of Public Affairs for its various publications. It includes Smithsonian staff as well as a small number of photographs of Smithsonian buildings or their construction, exhibits, events, and important visitors.

ARRANGEMENT: Unarranged. FINDING AIDS: Folder list in control file. SPECIAL CONDITIONS: Use of this record unit requires prior arrangement with the Archives staff.

Office of Public Affairs, circa 1965-1974, 1987
Publicity Records (2.1 linear meters).

For an administrative history of the Office of Public Affairs, see record unit 369.

These records consist primarily of extensive publicity materials relating to the building and opening of the Quadrangle complex. They include photographs at many stages of construction, fundraising booklets, donor lists, press kits, press releases, and interviews. Also included are publicity materials relating to the Smithson Bicentennial, including copies of speeches given, and the opening of the Hirshhorn Museum and Sculpture Garden. The Hirshhorn materials consist mainly of clippings and articles in binders.

ARRANGEMENT: (1) Quadrangle publicity materials, 1987, accession number 89-101; (2) Quadrangle press kits, 1987, accession number 92-016; (3) Smithson Bicentennial publicity materials, 1965, accession number T90071; (4) Hirshhorn Museum and Sculpture Garden publicity materials, 1966-1974, accession number T90072. FINDING AIDS: None. SPECIAL CONDITIONS: Use of this record unit requires prior arrangement with the Archives staff.

Office of Public Affairs, 1955-1960, 1965-1988
The Torch (2.1 linear meters).

The Torch, a newspaper for Smithsonian employees, was first published in 1955 by the Office of Information and later by its successor, the Office of Public Affairs. The publication appeared somewhat sporadically until 1960, when it stopped, to resume in 1965. Since that time, it has appeared monthly in a larger format. Occasional special issues mark events such as the opening of a major museum or a change in the administration of the Institution.

Articles in *The Torch* concern exhibitions, events, seasonal happenings, administrative changes, job moves, retirements, marriages, births, and deaths. Also included are features on individual staff members, concerning interesting aspects of their jobs, sports, or hobbies.

These records consist of two copies (when available) of each issue of *The Torch*. Issues since roughly 1972 also include prints of some of the photographs for that issue. Not every photograph is included—only those transferred with the records. In some instances, there is a notation that a photograph was returned to its owner. In others, there is no explanation.

ARRANGEMENT: Chronologic. FINDING AIDS: Description in control file. SPECIAL CONDITIONS: Use of this record unit requires prior arrangement with the Archives staff.

(568)

Office of the Registrar, 1974-1992, with related records from 1967
Records (9 linear meters).

For information concerning the functions of the Registrar prior to 1974, see record unit 305.

In the early 1970s, the role of the Registrar at the Smithsonian Institution began to be reconsidered. Richard H. Lytle was appointed Acting Registrar in 1974. Lytle oversaw the decentralization of the Registrar's duties and the establishment of separate Registrars' offices in the National Museum of Natural History and the National Museum of History and Technology in 1976. The reconstituted Office of the Registrar (OR) assumed responsibility for oversight of Institution-wide collection management issues. The OR reviewed policies developed by Smithsonian museums and assured compliance with those policies; monitored procedures used for accessioning, cataloging, and deaccessioning objects and specimens; and was involved with the inventory processes in the museums. The Smithsonian Registrar served as permanent chair for the Council of Registrars and the Collections Policy and Management Committee.

Lytle served as Acting Registrar until 1976, when Philip Leslie was appointed Registrar. Leslie retired in 1985 and the following year Mary E. Case became Director, OR. She remained in the position until the Office was abolished in 1993.

These records primarily document the activities of the Office of the Registrar under the direction of Richard H. Lytle, 1974-1976; Philip Leslie, 1976-1985; and Mary E. Case, 1986-1993. They include reports, minutes, and other records of the Council of Registrars and the Collection Policy and Management Committee; a subject file containing various materials on collection management issues; budget and other administrative files; records concerning collections inventories at Smithsonian museums; and extensive files documenting the OR's oversight of the Smithsonian's automated Collection Information System.

ARRANGEMENT: (1) Office of the Registrar, records, 1970-1983, accession number 88-036; (2) Office of the Registrar, records, 1971-1986, accession number 88-055; (3) Office of the Registrar, records, 1967-1985, accession number 88-134; (4) Office of the Registrar, records, 1986-1989, accession number 91-026; (5) Office of the Registrar, records, 1984-1992, accession number 93-017. FINDING AIDS: Folder list in control file. SPECIAL CONDITIONS: (1) Restricted; (2) use of this record unit requires prior arrangement with the Archives staff.

Research Group in Psychology and the Social Sciences, 1957-1963
Records (1 linear meter).

The Smithsonian established the Research Group in Psychology and the Social Sciences in 1959 under Defense contract NONR 1354(08) with the Office of the Director of Defense Research and Engineering for the purpose of advising the latter concerning long-range research plans and programs. The Research Group consisted of sixty-five leading United States psychologists and social scientists as consultants, with Charles W. Bray as the Special Research Director. Bray's office reported to the Smithsonian Secretary. The Scientific Officer for the contract was the Director of Defense Research and Engineering. The Research Group conducted research and research planning studies in the areas of psychological and social sciences, including design and use of man-machine systems; human performance capabilities and limitations; decision processes; team functions; persuasion and motivation; and adaptation of complex organizations to changing demands. The studies culminated in *Social Science Research and National Security,* published by the Office of Naval Research in 1963.

These records include Charles W. Bray's incoming and outgoing correspondence in his capacity as Special Research Director; drafts and final copies of reports written by the Research Group consultants; and bibliographies compiled for the reports. Some information files and planning records predate establishment of the Research Group.

ARRANGEMENT: Alphabetic by name and subject. FINDING AIDS: Folder list in control file. SPECIAL CONDITIONS: Use of this record unit requires prior arrangement with the Archives staff.

Smithsonian, 1970-
Publications (2.7 linear meters).

The *Smithsonian* magazine was created in 1970 with the aim of extending the Smithsonian Associates into a large national organization. As the chief benefit of membership in the National Associates, the magazine serves as a means of communication between the Institution and its constituency. Following the original instructions of the Secretary to publish material in areas in which the Institution is interested or might be interested, *Smithsonian* has covered a broad range of topics in science, art, and history. Circulation grew from 180,000 in 1970 to almost 2,000,000 in 1982. Edward K. Thompson served as Editor, 1970-1980, and as Publisher, 1974-1980. Joseph J. Bonsignore became Publisher in 1981 after serving as Acting Publisher in 1980. Donald B. Moser became Managing Editor in 1980 and Editor, 1981-   . Ronald C. Walker became Publisher in 1991, serving 1991-   .

This record unit consists of a record set of *Smithsonian* magazine.

ARRANGEMENT: Chronologic. FINDING AIDS: None. SPECIAL CONDITIONS: Use of this record unit requires prior arrangement with the Archives staff.

Smithsonian Archives, circa 1948-1982
Administrative Records (2.1 linear meters).

For an administrative history of the Smithsonian Archives, see record unit 94.

This record unit consists of administrative files of the Smithsonian Archives, primarily during the tenures of Samuel T. Surratt, Archivist, 1965-1968, and Richard H. Lytle, Archivist, 1969-1981. The records concern budgets, exhibitions, committees, equipment, microfilming, records management, professional organizations, workshops, and space needs. Of special interest are materials documenting the establishment of the Joseph Henry Papers Project, the Office of the Registrar microfilming project, the 1971 and 1978 *Guide* to the holdings of the Smithsonian Archives, and Lytle correspondence with the National Archives concerning Smithsonian records. Also included are Smithsonian Archives annual reports, 1969-1982, and Smithsonian records surveys undertaken by the National Archives, 1951, 1962, 1964, 1966-1968.

ARRANGEMENT: Alphabetic. FINDING AIDS: Folder list in control file. SPECIAL CONDITIONS: Use of this record unit requires prior arrangement with the Archives staff.

Office of the Smithsonian Chemist, 1880-1883
Records (0.1 linear meter).

The Office of the Smithsonian Chemist appears to have been officially created about 1876. Prior to that time, the Institution maintained informal relations with a number of chemists, who had use of the Smithsonian's facilities to carry out their own work as well as some done for the Institution. Most of this work dealt with composition of minerals or with queries from government departments. Frederick W. Taylor served as the Smithsonian's chemist from 1877 until 1884, when he resigned. The Office was abolished, and the United States Geological Survey performed chemical work in the Smithsonian as needed.

These records consist of one letterpress book recording Taylor's reports of chemical analysis to various inquirers.

ARRANGEMENT: Unarranged. FINDING AIDS: None. SPECIAL CONDITIONS: Use of this record unit requires prior arrangement with the Archives staff.

Smithsonian Half-Century Book Project, 1893-1897
Records (2.9 linear meters).

This collection consists of correspondence about the text and proofs for George Brown Goode, editor, *The Smithsonian Institution, 1846-1896, The History of its First Half-Century,* Washington, 1897. Goode died before the book was published.

The primary value of this record unit is that it contains information about the Smithsonian which does not appear in the book.

ARRANGEMENT: Temporary arrangement includes the following segments: correspondence, drafts, proofs for the book. Some of these records originated in the Assistant Secretary's office and merged into records of the

Editor's office after Goode's death. FINDING AIDS: Box list in control file. SPECIAL CONDITIONS: Use of this record unit requires prior arrangement with the Archives staff.

(299)

Smithsonian Institution Employees Federal Credit Union, 1936-1955
Newsletters (0.1 linear meter).

The Smithsonian Institution Employees Federal Credit Union was chartered June 11, 1935.

At the February 11, 1936, Board of Directors meeting, it was decided to issue a monthly newsletter "for the purpose of keeping all in touch with the affairs of the organization," informing people of ways credit unions could be used, why they were formed, and how they protected depositors' shares. The newsletter also kept people abreast of personnel changes within the organization.

ARRANGEMENT: Chronologic. FINDING AIDS: None. SPECIAL CONDITIONS: Use of this record unit requires prior arrangement with the Archives staff.

(217)

Smithsonian Institution Library, 1865-1951
Records (2.7 linear meters).

The Act organizing the Smithsonian Institution in 1846 provided for the "...gradual formation of a library, composed of valuable works pertaining to all departments of human knowledge." Charles C. Jewett became the first administrator of the Smithsonian Library in 1847. After Jewett's resignation in 1854, the position of Librarian remained vacant until the appointment of Frederick William True in 1881. During the interim, library affairs were administered by Secretary Joseph Henry and Assistant Secretary Spencer F. Baird. Administrative officers of the Smithsonian Library included True, 1881-1887; John Murdoch, 1887-1892; J. Elfreth Watkins, July-October, 1892; Cyrus Adler, 1892-1909, including the years 1905-1909 when he held the title of Assistant Secretary in charge of Library and Exchanges; F. W. True, 1911-1914, with the title Assistant Secretary in charge of Library and Exchanges; Paul Brockett, 1914-1924, with the title Assistant Librarian; William L. Corbin, 1925-1942; and Leila F. Clark, 1943-   .

These records contain material concerning both the Smithsonian and United States National Museum libraries and consist mostly of incoming and outgoing correspondence. Most of the correspondence is routine and deals with requests for publications, acknowledgements of publications received, the exchange of publications, employment inquiries, staff matters, and administrative policy.

Correspondents include Smithsonian and Museum administrative officers and staff, libraries, scientific institutions and societies, and the general public. Of special interest is correspondence regarding the evacuation of rare books, manuscripts, and archival material from the library during World War II. Other material includes ledgers, logbooks, and other records relating to books borrowed and lent, publications deposited in the Library of Congress, and the exchange of publications with other institutions; and records relating to the construction of book stacks in the main hall of the Smithsonian Institution Building, 1914-1915.

ARRANGEMENT: (1) General correspondence, 1878-1944; (2) outgoing correspondence, 1882-1885; (3) ledgers, logbooks, and other records concerning books borrowed and lent, publications deposited in the Library of Congress, and the exchange of publications with other institutions, 1865-1951; (4) correspondence, plans, specifications, and contracts relating to the construction of book stacks in the main hall of the Smithsonian Institution Building, 1914-1915. FINDING AIDS: Temporary box list in control file. SPECIAL CONDITIONS: Use of this record unit requires prior arrangement with the Archives staff.

(535)

Smithsonian Institution Press, circa 1940-1972
Records (3.4 linear meters).

Webster Prentiss True, who had previously served the Institution as Editor, 1919-1939, was given the title of Chief of the Editorial Division in 1940. A separate Publications Division was responsible for the actual reproduction of manuscripts. On True's retirement, Paul H. Oehser, who had been Editor for the United States National Museum since 1931, was appointed Chief and served from 1951 to 1953. In 1954 the two divisions were combined as the Editorial and Publications Division, with Oehser as Chief. He held this post through 1965. In 1966 the Division was renamed the Smithsonian Institution Press, with Anders Richter as Director. Richter held the position through 1970, when Gordon Hubel became Director, serving 1970-   .

These rather fragmentary records primarily document the work of the Editorial and Publications Division, precursor of the modern Smithsonian Press. A small amount of material dates from the tenure of Webster P. True as Chief of the Division and consists of correspondence concerning manuscripts considered for publication. Also included are several mockups for plates in the proposed 1941 Smithsonian Field Work and Exploration series.

A second, larger section of this record unit contains a portion of the correspondence and memoranda of Paul Oehser as Chief. The records include a small alphabetic correspondence file as well as folders relating to various proposed publications. Included are some records of the 1960 and 1962 Smithsonian annual reports, consisting of the scientific articles for the volume, Oehser's correspondence with the authors, and some graphs and photographs. In addition, there is a small amount of material concerning volumes 1 and 2 of *The Papers of Joseph Henry,* a proposed manuscript on the planning of the Smithson Bicentennial, and several folders concerning *World Power from Solar Radiation,* one of the final manuscripts of the fifth Secretary of the Institution, Charles G. Abbot.

Researchers should also consult record unit 83 for records of the Editorial and Publications Division.

ARRANGEMENT: (1) Records, *circa* 1940-1961, accession number T90045; (2) records, *circa* 1960-1972, accession number T90127. FINDING AIDS: None. SPECIAL CONDITIONS: Use of this record unit requires prior arrangement with the Archives staff.

Smithsonian Institution Relief Association, 1885-1944

Records (0.3 linear meter).

The Smithsonian Institution Relief Association was organized in 1885 to give assistance to its members, especially through payment of death benefits. The Association was disbanded in 1944 because of declining membership.

ARRANGEMENT: (1) Minutes of meetings of governing board; (2) membership lists. FINDING AIDS: None. SPECIAL CONDITIONS: Use of this record unit requires prior arrangement with the Archives staff.

Smithsonian Institution Traveling Exhibition Service, 1952-1981

Records (11.8 linear meters).

For the early history of the Smithsonian Institution Traveling Exhibition Service (SITES), see record unit 316. Annemarie H. Pope remained as Chief until 1963. Other heads of SITES have included Dorothy Van Arsdale, Acting Chief and Chief, 1964-1970; Dennis A. Gould, Chief, 1971-1973, and Director, 1974-1979; and Peggy A. Loar, Director, 1981-   . Eileen Rose served as Acting Director during 1971 and 1979-1980.

In 1976, the celebration of the Bicentennial of the American Revolution led to an increase in the size of staff and the number of SITES-organized traveling exhibitions. By 1981, when SITES celebrated its thirtieth anniversary, there were nearly 150 of its exhibitions circulating in the United States and abroad. Exhibitions are developed and organized by SITES and produced both by the Smithsonian's Office of Exhibits Central and by outside sources. Themes cover the fields of art, history, and science, as well as current events.

These records consist primarily of exhibition files, 1952-1981, on shows no longer traveling. The files, which contain varying amounts of documentation, include correspondence, scripts, photographs, insurance and shipping forms, and publicity materials such as press releases and clippings. Also included are cancelled rental agreements, records of refused shows, and photographs and negatives. Additional SITES material can be found in the records of the Office of Exhibits Central.

ARRANGEMENT: (1) Exhibition files, 1952-1981, arranged alphabetically; (2) cancelled rental agreements, alphabetic by state; (3) refused shows, alphabetic by state and unarranged; (4) photographs of exhibitions, unarranged; (5) negatives, unarranged. FINDING AIDS: None. SPECIAL CONDITIONS: Use of this record unit requires prior arrangement with the Archives staff.

Office of the Director, Smithsonian Institution Traveling Exhibition Service, 1980-1987

Records (0.8 linear meter).

For an administrative history of the Smithsonian Institution Traveling Exhibition Service (SITES), see record units 290 and 316.

Eileen Rose served as Acting Director, 1979-1980. In 1981 Peggy A. Loar became Director and served until 1986. In 1987, Eileen Rose was once again named Acting Director.

These records consist of administrative subject files, which include information on corporate and program development, public affairs, the CBS software project, International Council on Museums, exhibitions, education, general administration, and correspondence with the Assistant Secretary for Museum Programs, as well as general correspondence from foreign countries. In addition there are several interim and status reports to the Assistant Secretary for Museum Programs.

ARRANGEMENT: (1) Administrative subject files; (2) general correspondence with foreign countries; (3) reports to the Assistant Secretary for Museum Programs. FINDING AIDS: Box list in control file. SPECIAL CONDITIONS: (1) Restricted; (2) use of this record unit requires prior arrangement with the Archives staff.

(489)

Office of Public Relations, Smithsonian Institution Traveling Exhibition Service, 1975-1989, with related records, 1955-1956
Records (20 linear meters).

The Office of Public Relations of the Smithsonian Institution Traveling Exhibition Service (SITES) had its origin in 1975 when Eileen Harakal joined the staff as Public Affairs Officer, serving until 1983. The job was vacant until 1985 when Ronald Gaetz was named Public Information Officer. He was succeeded by Deborah Bennett, who served as Public Relations Director, 1986-1987. In 1989 Elizabeth Hill was named Public Relations Officer.

These records document the public relations aspects of the traveling exhibitions. They include press releases, clippings, photographs, and other publicity materials. One scrapbook contains clippings about early shows, 1955-1956. Researchers should also consult record units 90, 290, 316, 487, and 488 for additional documentation of SITES exhibitions.

ARRANGEMENT: (1) SITES public relations records, 1955-1956, 1975-1987, accession number 88-001; (2) SITES public relations records, 1975-1988, accession number 89-134; (3) SITES public relations records, 1979-1989, accession number 91-058; (4) SITES public relations records, 1981-1987, accession number 89-048; (5) SITES public relations records, 1983-1985, accession number 88-039. FINDING AIDS: Folder list in control file. SPECIAL CONDITIONS: (1) Permission to duplicate photographs should be obtained from the Director of the Office, as some restrictions may apply; (2) use of this record unit requires prior arrangement with the Archives staff.

(518)

Smithsonian Institution Traveling Exhibition Service, 1965-1982
Exhibition Catalogs (0.9 linear meter).

For an administrative history of the Smithsonian Institution Traveling Exhibition Service (SITES), see record units 290, 316, 487, and 488.

This record unit consists of exhibition catalogs of shows circulated by the Smithsonian Institution Traveling Exhibition Service.

ARRANGEMENT: Unarranged. FINDING AIDS: Folder list in control file. SPECIAL CONDITIONS: Use of this record unit requires prior arrangement with the Archives staff.

Smithsonian Institution Traveling Exhibition Service, circa 1969-1990
Exhibition Files (43 linear meters).

For an administrative history of the Smithsonian Institution Traveling Exhibition Service (SITES), see record units 290, 316, and 488. Anna R. Cohn served as Director of SITES, 1988- .

SITES continued to serve a wide variety of American regional and community museums during the 1980s, and was also given a broader mandate in the area of international exhibitions. By 1990 SITES was developing and circulating approximately seventy-five exhibitions annually.

These records consist of SITES exhibition files, arranged by exhibition. The files contain varying amounts of information, including itineraries, shipping and insurance papers, press releases, checklists of objects on display, correspondence with lenders, and occasional photographs.

ARRANGEMENT: (1) SITES exhibition files, accession number 85-199; (2) SITES exhibition files, accession number 85-008; (3) SITES exhibition files, accession number 85-075; (4) SITES exhibition files, accession number 86-071; (5) SITES exhibition files, accession number 84-169; (6) SITES exhibition files, accession number 88-022; (7) SITES exhibition files, accession number 88-115; (8) SITES exhibition files, accession number 94-083; (9) SITES exhibition files, accession number 88-111. FINDING AIDS: Folder list in control file. SPECIAL CONDITIONS: (1) Restricted; (2) use of this record unit requires prior arrangement with the Archives staff; (3) accession number 84-169 was interfiled with accession number 86-071 and renumbered as box 22.

Smithsonian Institution Traveling Exhibition Service, circa 1978-1987
Exhibition Posters (24 items).

For an administrative history of the Smithsonian Institution Traveling Exhibition Service (SITES), see record units 290, 316, 487, and 488.

The twenty-four posters in this record unit were created for SITES exhibitions.

ARRANGEMENT: (1) Miscellaneous SITES exhibition posters, *circa* 1978-1987, accession number 85-185; (2) SITES exhibition poster, 1980, accession number 85-196. FINDING AIDS: None. SPECIAL CONDITIONS: Use of this record unit requires prior arrangement with the Archives staff.

Smithsonian Institution Traveling Exhibition Service, 1952-1988
Publications (0.8 linear meter).

For an administrative history of the Smithsonian Institution Traveling Exhibition Service (SITES), see record units 290, 316, and 488. Files on the exhibitions themselves can also be found in record unit 487.

These records consist of publications produced by SITES, often in conjunction with the Smithsonian Institution Press, including brochures, posters, guides, and catalogs documenting traveling exhibitions. The set is probably not complete.

ARRANGEMENT: Unarranged. FINDING AIDS: Publication list in control file. SPECIAL CONDITIONS: Use of this record unit requires prior arrangement with the Archives staff.

Smithsonian Institution Women's Council, 1972-1983
Records (1.4 linear meters).

The Smithsonian Institution Women's Council (SIWC) was formally established by the Secretary of the Smithsonian on April 19, 1972. The Council is dedicated to the achievements of women employees, particularly in employment areas that were previously closed to them because of their sex. The goals of the SIWC are achieved through various training opportunities, employee benefit programs, lectures, and a newsletter called *Four Star*.

Membership on the Council is on a voluntary basis. The twenty individuals who receive the highest number of votes in the biennial elections comprise the Council; from 1973 to 1979, elections were held annually. The Council's Executive Committee consists of the Chairperson, Vice-Chairperson, Secretary, Treasurer, and Historian.

Chairs of the Council have included Edna Owens, 1972; Gretchen Gayle, 1973; Edith Mayo, 1974; Mary C. Quinn, 1975; Dianne G. Walker, 1976; Penelope A. Packard, 1977; Rosemary M. DeRosa, 1978; Charlene James, 1979; Audrey B. Davis, 1980; Margaret Santiago, 1981; Elizabeth Beuck, 1982; and Susan Kalcik, 1983-   .

The records of the Council consist of correspondence; memoranda; newsletters of the Council and related women's groups; SIWC's constitution with amendments and original charter; newsclippings; meeting agendas; photographs of Council members, Smithsonian officials, and special events; an architectural drawing and plans of a proposed site for a child care facility at the Smithsonian; and copies of publications related to the Council's activities. Included are files documenting the election of the Council; minutes, correspondence, and financial records from Council meetings; surveys, evaluations, and reviews of statistical data of women and minorities in the Smithsonian workforce; a 1983 report to the Smithsonian's Executive Committee discussing the Council's history, achievements, and areas of involvement; files of various committees including the *Four Star* newsletter, career development, child care plans for Smithsonian employees, training, and upward mobility; files on a proposed Smithsonian women's exhibit; and records of the SI Minority Women's Council, a group formed prior to the official establishment of the SIWC.

ARRANGEMENT: (1) Organizational files, 1972-1983; (2) meeting materials, 1972-1983; (3) committee files, 1972-1983; (4) exhibition, membership, photographs, organizations, and related material, 1972-1983; (5) *Four Star* working copy, 1980-1983. FINDING AIDS: Description in control file. SPECIAL CONDITIONS: (1) Working copies of *Four Star* are restricted; (2) use of this record unit requires prior arrangement with the Archives staff.

Smithsonian Institution Women's Council, 1980-1992, with related records, 1973-1979
Records (2.5 linear meters).

The Smithsonian Institution Women's Council (SIWC) is an assembly of Smithsonian employees formed to represent the concerns of women before the administration of the Smithsonian Institution. For an administrative history of the SIWC, see record unit 310.

In the period covered by these records, SIWC helped to establish the Smithsonian Early Enrichment Center, 1988, and the Infant Care Center, 1991, as well as creating the Child Care Advisory Board and the Women in Museums Network. It continued to publish the SIWC newsletter, *Four Star*. The Senior Advisory Group to the SIWC was formed in 1984 to act as advisor and advocate for the Council. Chairs of the Smithsonian Institution Women's Council since 1980 have included: Audrey B. Davis, 1980; Margaret A. Santiago, 1981; Elizabeth Beuck, 1982; Susan Kalcik, 1983-1985; Carolyn Jones, 1985-1987; Judith O'Sullivan, 1987-1989; Ellen V. Sprouls, 1989; Janice Kaplan, 1989-1991; and Joanne Gigliotti, 1991- .

These records of the Smithsonian Institution Women's Council consist of election materials; fiscal records; attendance records; correspondence; memoranda; agendas and minutes of monthly and committee meetings; materials on exhibits, conferences, and lectures sponsored and/or attended by Council members; and the revised Council's constitution and by-laws of 1987. In addition, this record unit contains a detailed record of the Council's fight for child care in the Smithsonian; files of the SIWC newsletter, *Four Star;* an extensive information file on benefits, alternative work strategies, and health and fitness; and photographs of special events. For related activities, see record unit 7443, the Smithsonian Early Enrichment Center, 1984-1992.

ARRANGEMENT: (1) Organizational files, 1978-1992; (2) meeting records, 1977-1978, 1981-1992 and undated; (3) committee files, 1973-1992; (4) organizations, events, and projects associated with SIWC, 1982-1989; (5) photographs, 1983-1984, 1988, 1990. FINDING AIDS: Folder list in control file. SPECIAL CONDITIONS: (1) Restricted; (2) use of this record unit requires prior arrangement with the Archives staff.

(557)

Smithsonian National Associates Program, circa 1975-1986
Records (6.1 linear meters).

The Smithsonian National Associates Program (SNAP) was established in 1970 in conjunction with *Smithsonian* magazine. Through *Smithsonian* magazine, and in cooperation with other Smithsonian Institution bureaus, SNAP provides educational and cultural activities for contributing members throughout the nation and around the world, in order to "increase their awareness of the Institution and encourage support for its work."

In 1975, Robert H. Angle was appointed General Manager of SNAP. The following year SNAP was composed of three units—the Regional Associates Program, the Contributing Membership Program, and the Associates Travel Program, each offering benefits directed toward increasing membership interaction with the Smithsonian. Regional Associates was renamed the Regional Events Program in 1978. Also that year a Selected Studies Program was established, and Angle's title was changed to Director. Angle served in this capacity until Jacqueline Austin, a Program Director of the Associates Travel Program, replaced him in 1982. The Regional Events Program eventually merged with Selected Studies, in 1985, to form the Lecture and Seminar Program.

Staff of SNAP has included Robert H. Angle, General Manager, 1975-1977, and Director, 1978-1981; Jacqueline Austin, Program Manager of Associates Travel, 1977-1981, and Director, 1982- ; Joseph Carper, Assistant Director, 1985- ; Charlene

James-Duguid, Program Coordinator of Regional Associates, 1976-1977, Program Manager of Regional Events, 1978-1983, and Program Manager of Lecture and Seminar, 1984- ; Jessie A. Brinkley, Program Assistant, 1976-1977, Program Coordinator, 1978, and Program Manager of Contributing Membership, 1979-1981; Fern Segerlind, Program Manager of Contributing Membership, 1986- ; Janet Fesler, Program Manager of Contributing Membership, 1982-1985; Nancy Starr, Program Manager of Selected Studies, 1978-1983, Program Assistant for Lectures and Seminars, 1984; Abby Whitenack, Administrative Coordinator, 1981, and Program Analyst, 1982-1983; and Prudence Clendenning, Program Coordinator of Associates Travel, 1976-1977, Deputy Program Manager, 1978-1981, and Program Manager, 1982- .

This record unit consists of SNAP administrative records which document program activities. The records include correspondence and memoranda with Smithsonian Institution offices and bureaus, corporations, members, and grant foundations; annual appeals, promotional material, bequests, accounting summaries, and special events files of the Contributing Membership Program; course curricula and publicity information of the Lecture and Seminar Program; operations manual and reports of the Regional Events Program; and brochures of the Selected Studies Program.

ARRANGEMENT: (1) Smithsonian National Associates Program, 1976-1984, accession number 87-172; (2) Smithsonian National Associates Program, 1975-1986, accession number 89-111. FINDING AIDS: Folder list in control file. SPECIAL CONDITIONS: (1) Restricted; (2) use of this record unit requires prior arrangement with the Archives staff.

(388)
Smithsonian Office of Educational Research, 1983-1985, with related records from 1975
Records (1.2 linear meters).

The Smithsonian Office of Educational Research (SOER) was established on October 1, 1983, to investigate and improve learning as it occurs outside the formal educational system. SOER reported to the Assistant Secretary for Science. John H. Falk, previously on the staff of the Chesapeake Bay Center for Environmental Studies (CBCES), was appointed Director. SOER was abolished on September 30, 1985.

These records document the work of SOER during its two-year history. The records consist of correspondence, memoranda, reports, and printed materials concerning SOER educational programs, office administration, and relations with other Smithsonian bureaus and offices. Records predating the establishment of SOER in 1983 were created by Falk during his work as Associate Director for Education Programs, CBCES.

ARRANGEMENT: Unarranged. FINDING AIDS: Folder list in control file. SPECIAL CONDITIONS: (1) Restricted; (2) use of this record unit requires prior arrangement with the Archives staff.

(626)
Director, Smithsonian Resident Associate Program, 1967-1991
Records (2.1 linear meters).

The Smithsonian Resident Associate Program was originally established in September 1965 as the Smithsonian Society of Associates, to raise funds for the Institution by involving members in its work and activities. Executive Secretary Elizabeth Knight managed the organization until her resignation in May 1966. In June, Lisa Suter took charge as Program Director, and in September 1966 the organization was renamed the Smithsonian Associates. Susan A. Hamilton replaced Suter in July 1969, and *Smithsonian* magazine was launched in April 1970. The organization was then divided into the National Program and the Resident Program, and Hamilton became the Director of the latter. In 1972 the two Programs were consolidated under the management of Executive Director Robert W. Mason, and in July, Janet Solinger replaced Hamilton as Director of the expanded and renamed Smithsonian Resident Associates Program, which became the Smithsonian Resident Associate Program (RAP) in 1974.

The records of the Director of the Smithsonian Resident Associate Program document the administration and operations of the organization. They contain correspondence and memoranda concerning the budget, fiscal planning, and fundraising, as well as lectures, seminars, and performances offered by RAP. The files also include contact sheets showing staff receptions and public events, scrapbooks of newspaper clippings, and promotional material. In addition, the records document planning for the 20th and 25th anniversaries of the Program.

ARRANGEMENT: (1) Administrative files; (2) scrapbooks. FINDING AIDS: Description in control file. SPECIAL CONDITIONS: Use of this record unit requires prior arrangement with the Archives staff.

(627)

Director, Smithsonian Resident Associate Program, 1973-1984
Records (6.6 linear meters).

For an administrative history of the Office of the Director, Smithsonian Resident Associate Program, see record unit 626.

These records document many aspects of the management and functions of the Smithsonian Resident Associate Program (RAP). Administrative records include budget files and documentation of registration, travel, security, and parking issues. Program records contain files on symposia, seminars, receptions, classes, and performances offered by RAP; events associated with exhibitions and commemorations; international activities; and publicity. In addition, the records describe the development of RAP publications such as catalogs, calendars, posters, and prints. This record unit also includes files on cooperative projects with the National Science Foundation.

ARRANGEMENT: Unarranged. FINDING AIDS: Folder list in control file. SPECIAL CONDITIONS: Use of this record unit requires prior arrangement with the Archives staff.

(632)

Office of Public Affairs, Smithsonian Resident Associate Program, 1974-1991
Records (11.9 linear meters).

The Smithsonian Resident Associate Program was established in 1965 by Secretary S. Dillon Ripley to provide residents of the greater Washington, D.C., area the opportunity to participate in the activities of the Smithsonian Institution. The Program was administered under the Assistant Secretary for Public Service from 1965 to 1977 and thereafter under the Office of Management and Development, 1978-1990, and the Office of External Affairs, 1991-   . Janet W. Solinger served as Director of the Resident Associate Program, 1973-   . Catherine Joan Cole was Publicist, 1983-   .

These records document the activities of the Publicist and include information on special events sponsored by the Resident Associate Program. They consist of events files, correspondence, staff memoranda, photographs and slides, brochures, press releases, and news clippings. Most records are dated from 1983 to 1991, with some historical files dating from 1974. Of note are records of Smithsonian Kite Festivals; the Resident Associate Program's 25th Anniversary, 1990; and selected files concerning the Young Associates.

ARRANGEMENT: (1) News clippings, 1974-1985, accession number 87-094; (2) special events files, news clippings, 1984-1985, accession number 87-157; (3) special events files, news clippings, 1986-1987, accession number 89-049; (4) subject files, 1986-1987, accession number 89-041; (5) special events files, news clippings, 1987-1988, accession number 90-016; (6) special events files, 25th anniversary files, 1990-1991, accession number 93-053. FINDING AIDS: Folder list in control file. SPECIAL CONDITIONS: (1) Restricted; (2) use of this record unit requires prior arrangement with the Archives staff.

(482)

Smithsonian Science Information Exchange, 1946-1981
Records (52.8 linear meters).

The Smithsonian Science Information Exchange (SSIE) was a clearinghouse for information concerning ongoing research supported by federal and private sources. Its purpose was to prevent redundant research by enabling research administrators to know of similar ongoing research projects. The exchange collected Notices of Research Projects and stored, indexed, and retrieved them for interested persons. The Exchange was created in 1949 as the Medical Sciences Information Exchange. In 1953 the Exchange was renamed the Bio-Sciences Information Exchange and came to the Smithsonian. In 1960 it became the Science Information Exchange, as physical and social sciences were included; and in 1972 it was incorporated as the Smithsonian Science Information Exchange. The Exchange was unable to support itself from its revenues, and in 1981 it was disbanded and its responsibilities transferred to the National Technical Information Service. The Exchange was directed by Stella L. Deignan from its inception until 1961. Monroe E. Freeman directed the organization until 1973, when David F. Hersey became its last director.

The records contain minutes of the meetings of the Board of Directors and correspondence of Stella L. Deignan, Monroe E. Freeman, and David F. Hersey, along with budget and statistical information, reports analyzing the efficiency and usefulness of SSIE, litigation records, contracts, grant proposals, audit information, records detailing internal operations, supporting documentation for the extensive computer programs used by SSIE, several computer tapes containing indexes to the reports, as well as microfiche and microfilm of the reports themselves.

ARRANGEMENT: (1) Records, 1946-1981, accession number 82-023; (2) records, 1971-1981, accession number 83-102. FINDING AIDS: Description in control file. SPECIAL CONDITIONS: Use of this record unit requires prior arrangement with the Archives staff.

Office of Symposia and Seminars, circa 1971-1984
Records (2.5 linear meters).

For an administrative history of the Office of Symposia and Seminars and its predecessors, see record unit 495.

Records include correspondence, memoranda, brochures, announcements, background materials, audiotapes, videotapes, grant contracts, program reports, reading files, schedules, photographs, and expense reports concerning the following symposia: *Kin and Communities: The Peopling of America; Family Policy Forum; Festival of India; Man and Beast Revisited; Road after 1984: High Technology and Human Freedom;* and *The Nature* of *Scientific Discovery.* This record unit also contains information about the High School Scholars at the Smithsonian program.

ARRANGEMENT: Unarranged. FINDING AIDS: Description in control file. SPECIAL CONDITIONS: Use of this record unit requires prior arrangement with the Archives staff.

Office of Symposia and Seminars, 1973-1979
Records (4.5 linear meters).

For an administrative history of the Office of Symposia and Seminars, see record unit 495. During the period 1973 to 1979, Wilton S. Dillon was Director of the Office of Symposia and Seminars.

These records, maintained by Wilton S. Dillon, consist of correspondence, memoranda, background research material, invitations, brochures, resumes, photographs, grant information, publication contracts, symposia schedules, and other administrative records for the following symposia: *The Nature of Scientific Discovery* celebrating the 500th anniversary of the birth of Copernicus; *Outlook for Space; The United States in the World; Kin and Communities: The Peopling of America;* and for a number of activities celebrating the centennial of the birth of Albert Einstein.

ARRANGEMENT: By event. FINDING AIDS: None. SPECIAL CONDITIONS: Use of this record unit requires prior arrangement with the Archives staff.

Office of Symposia and Seminars, 1978-1986
Records (1.6 linear meters).

For an administrative history of the Office of Symposia and Seminars and its predecessors, see record unit 495.

Records include correspondence, memoranda, purchase orders, budget reports, addresses, invitations, brochures, lectures, fundraising information, announcements, lecturer files, and program plans for the following symposia: *The Muses Flee Hitler; Man and Beast Revisited; Festival of India;* and *Road after 1984: High Technology and Human Freedom.*

ARRANGEMENT: Organized by symposium. FINDING AIDS: Description in control file. SPECIAL CONDITIONS: Use of this record unit requires prior arrangement with the Archives staff.

(499)

Office of Symposia and Seminars, 1987
Videotapes (0.8 linear meter).

For an administrative history of the Office of Symposia and Seminars, see record unit 495.

These records consist of videotapes documenting the 200th Anniversary of the Constitution of the United States. They were made in conjunction with the symposium *Constitutional Roots, Rights, and Responsibilities.*

ARRANGEMENT: Unarranged. FINDING AIDS: Description in control file. SPECIAL CONDITIONS: Use of this record unit requires prior arrangement with the Archives staff.

(586)

Office of Telecommunications, circa 1963-1988
Records (3.7 linear meters).

The Office of Telecommunications (OTC) was established on August 15, 1976, as a separate unit reporting directly to the Office of the Assistant Secretary for Public Service. Prior to the creation of OTC, coordination of Smithsonian telecommunication activities was a function of the Smithsonian Museum Service, 1958-1965; the Office of Public Information, 1965-1967; and the Office of Public Affairs, 1967-1976. OTC develops ideas for the production of programs and broadcast series for public and commercial television and radio, films, and related visual and audio materials, which bring a better understanding of the Smithsonian to American and foreign audiences. OTC is also the contact point for all interested outside producers of telecommunications projects relating to all Smithsonian bureaus.

OTC broadcast series have included "Radio Smithsonian," a national, weekly radio program providing information about the multi-disciplinary activities of the Institution which was in production from 1969 to 1990; "Smithsonian Galaxy," a series of short radio features highlighting the work of Smithsonian curators, scientists, and researchers broadcast from 1979 to 1987; and "Here at the Smithsonian," a series of short features for television, produced from 1982 to 1989. In addition, OTC produces films of special events of the Institution; provides archival recordings of conferences, symposia, and other programs; and produces films for Smithsonian exhibitions.

Nazaret Cherkezian was appointed Director of OTC in 1976. He retired in 1986 and was replaced by Assistant Director Paul B. Johnson who served as Acting Director, 1986-1988, and Director, 1988-   .

These records primarily document the activities of OTC under Director Nazaret Cherkezian. A small amount of records were created by Paul B. Johnson. There are also a few records created by OTC's predecessor offices. The records include correspondence, memoranda, proposals, contracts, budgets, reports, newspaper clippings, press releases, scripts, and related materials concerning OTC radio broadcasts "Radio Smithsonian" and "Smithsonian Galaxy"; television and film productions, especially "Smithsonian World" and the Emmy award-winning *The Smithsonian Institution with S. Dillon Ripley, Secretary;* production planning; facilities and equipment, including the construction of the OTC studio in the National Museum of History and Technology; and administrative records.

ARRANGEMENT: Unarranged. FINDING AIDS: Folder list in control file. SPECIAL CONDITIONS: (1) Restricted; (2) use of this record unit requires prior arrangement with the Archives staff.

(594)

Office of Telecommunications, circa 1985-1991
Records (8.2 linear meters).

For an administrative history of the Office of Telecommunications (OTC), see record unit 586.

In 1986, the Smithsonian Institution began planning two major educational television projects. "University of the Air," a joint project of the Smithsonian, WETA Television, and Adrian Malone Productions, proposed to investigate the lives of major twentieth-century intellectuals and the basic themes that connected their work. In 1988, the title of the project was changed to "Smithsonian Project Discovery." "The Buried Mirror" project was a proposed ten-part television series on the history and culture of Iberia and Latin America to be produced by Malone Gill Productions in association with the Smithsonian. Both projects were terminated because of funding difficulties.

These records primarily document the planning for "University of the Air" (after 1988 "Smithsonian Project Discovery") and "The Buried Mirror." Many of the records were created by Elizabeth S. Brownstein, Media Project Development Specialist, OTC. Also included are files of Adrian Malone, Production Chairman, and Edward W. Bastian, Project Manager and Director for "University of the Air." The records include correspondence, memoranda, proposals, prospectuses, reports, research information, budgets, illustrations, photographs, scripts, articles, newspaper clippings, audiotape recordings of music, and marketing information.

The record unit also includes information files maintained by OTC on Smithsonian museums, bureaus, staff, and miscellaneous topics.

ARRANGEMENT: Unarranged. FINDING AIDS: Folder list in control file. SPECIAL CONDITIONS: Use of this record unit requires prior arrangement with the Archives staff.

(296)

Office of Telecommunications, 1969-1979
Audiotapes (7 linear meters).

For an administrative history of the Office of Telecommunications, see record unit 586.

"Radio Smithsonian" began its weekly half-hour broadcasts in the summer of 1969. The program was carried by local radio stations in the metropolitan Washington, D.C., area and educational radio stations around the country and overseas. Broadcasts provided the public with information about the activities of the Smithsonian through discussions, interviews, lectures, music, and research activity reports. Programs featured Smithsonian staff as well as guest scientists, historians, politicians, artists, authors, and musicians.

"Smithsonian Galaxy," a series of 2 1/2-minute radio features about the work of the Institution's curatorial, scientific, and research staffs, began production in 1978. The program was broadcast throughout the United States and overseas.

This record unit consists of master audiotapes for "Radio Smithsonian" programs 1-481, 1969-1978, and "Smithsonian Galaxy" editions 1-25, 1978-1979.

ARRANGEMENT: Chronologic by broadcast series. FINDING AIDS: Transfer list containing a synopsis of each broadcast in control file. SPECIAL CONDITIONS: (1) Restricted; (2) use of this record unit requires prior arrangement with the Archives staff; (3) in the 1983 *Guide to the Smithsonian Archives,* this record unit had been assigned the title, "Radio Smithsonian."

(589)

Office of Telecommunications, 1969-1983
Audiotapes and Scripts (1.6 linear meters).

For an administrative history of the Office of Telecommunications and information on its programs, see record units 296 and 586.

This record unit consists of master audio tapes for "Smithsonian Galaxy" editions 77-125, 1981-1983, and "Radio Smithsonian" programs 534-574, 1980; and scripts of "Radio Smithsonian" programs 1-400.

ARRANGEMENT: Chronologic by broadcast series. FINDING AIDS: Transfer list containing a synopsis of each broadcast in control file. SPECIAL CONDITIONS: (1) Restricted; (2) use of this record unit requires prior arrangement with the Archives staff.

(592)

Office of Telecommunications, 1970-1978, with related materials from 1938
Audiotapes (4.1 linear meters).

For an administrative history of the Office of Telecommunications and information on its programs, see record units 296 and 586.

This record unit consists of audiotape recordings of Smithsonian special events including concerts, exhibitions, lectures, interviews, symposia, and openings. Of special interest are recordings of the *1876* exhibition opening, 1976; Festival of American Folklife events; Smithsonian National Associates Program events; and a few copies of "The World Is Yours" broadcasts, 1938-1942.

ARRANGEMENT: Unarranged. FINDING AIDS: Transfer list in control file. SPECIAL CONDITIONS: Use of this record unit requires prior arrangement with the Archives staff.

(591)

Office of Telecommunications, circa 1971-1991
Audiotapes and Scripts (18.9 linear meters).

For an administrative history of the Office of Telecommunications and information on its programs, see record units 296 and 586.

This record unit consists of master audiotapes for "Radio Smithsonian" programs 750-1098, 1984-1989; elements, or original, unedited tapes for "Radio Smithsonian" programs 837-1098, 1985-1989; audio elements for the television series "Here at the

Smithsonian," volumes 3-8, 1984-1989; master audiotapes for "Folk Masters" radio series, 1991; scripts of "Radio Smithsonian" programs 400-975, 1977-1988; and audiotapes of Smithsonian special events, lectures, concerts, interviews, symposia, and openings, *circa* 1971-1991.

ARRANGEMENT: Mostly chronologic by broadcast series. FINDING AIDS: Transfer list with a synopsis of most "Radio Smithsonian" broadcasts in control file. SPECIAL CONDITIONS: (1) Restricted; (2) use of this record unit requires prior arrangement with the Archives staff.

(588)

Office of Telecommunications, 1974-1983
Audiotapes (2.9 linear meters).

For an administrative history of the Office of Telecommunications and information on its programs, see record units 296 and 586.

This record unit consists of master audiotapes for "Radio Smithsonian" programs 482-533, 1979, and "Smithsonian Galaxy" editions 26-76, 1979-1981; and audiotapes of Smithsonian special events, concerts, lectures, interviews, symposia, and openings, 1974-1983.

ARRANGEMENT: Mostly chronologic by broadcast series. FINDING AIDS: Transfer list containing a synopsis of each "Radio Smithsonian" and "Smithsonian Galaxy" broadcast in control file. SPECIAL CONDITIONS: (1) Restricted; (2) use of this record unit requires prior arrangement with the Archives staff.

(590)

Office of Telecommunications, 1981-1987
Audiotapes (3.7 linear meters).

For an administrative history of the Office of Telecommunications and information on its programs, see record units 296 and 586.

This record unit consists of master audiotapes for "Smithsonian Galaxy" editions 126-186, 1983-1987, and "Radio Smithsonian" programs 600-749, 1981-1984; and elements, or original, unedited tapes for "Smithsonian Galaxy" editions 104-186, 1982-1987, and "Radio Smithsonian" programs 689-836, 1983-1985.

ARRANGEMENT: Chronologic by broadcast series. FINDING AIDS: Transfer list containing a synopsis of each broadcast in control file. SPECIAL CONDITIONS: (1) Restricted; (2) use of this record unit requires prior arrangement with the Archives staff.

(587)

Office of Telecommunications, circa 1963-1989
Motion Picture Films (6.6 linear meters).

For an administrative history of the Office of Telecommunications (OTC), see record unit 586.

This record unit consists of 16mm motion picture films produced by OTC and its predecessors, the Smithsonian Museum Service, the Office of Public Information, and the Office of Public Affairs. Also included are films created by outside producers in collaboration with OTC. Included are black and white and color films, workprints, and silent films. Of special interest are films of Smithsonian special events, bureaus, facilities, equipment, exhibitions, openings, and staff; films of politicians and celebrities at the Smithsonian including Lyndon Baines Johnson and Lady Bird Johnson, Richard M. Nixon, Hubert H. Humphrey, and Alan B. Shepard, Jr.; films from the 1966 National Broadcasting Corporation series "The Smithsonian"; films from the British Broadcasting Corporation series "The Ascent of Man"; and Smithsonian-produced films *The Leaf Thieves,* 1963, which documents the planning and fabrication of a proposed rain forest exhibition in the National Museum of Natural History (NMNH), and *The Smithsonian's Whale,* 1964, which concerns the construction of a 92-foot model blue whale in NMNH.

ARRANGEMENT: Unarranged. FINDING AIDS: Film list in control file. SPECIAL CONDITIONS: (1) Restricted; (2) use of this record unit requires prior arrangement with the Archives staff.

(593)

Office of Telecommunications, circa 1977 and undated
Photographs (0.1 linear meter).

For an administrative history of the Office of Telecommunications (OTC), see record unit 586.

This record unit consists of photographs of OTC Director, Nazaret Cherkezian, *circa* 1977; OTC staff member William C. Grayson, *circa* 1977; and Smithsonian Astrophysical Observatory staff member James C. Cornell, Jr., writer of the OTC film *Mirrors on the Universe: The MMT Story.* Also included are photographs of the Emmy award received by OTC for the television show *The Smithsonian Institution with S. Dillon Ripley, Secretary,* and images from the OTC film *Reunion: Memories of an American Experience.*

ARRANGEMENT: Unarranged. FINDING AIDS: Folder list in control file. SPECIAL CONDITIONS: Use of this record unit requires prior arrangement with the Archives staff.

(69)

Topographical Data Project—Walter L. Nicholson Papers, circa 1873-1882
(1.4 linear meters).

The Smithsonian Institution and the United States Coast and Geodetic Survey collaborated in collection of data of relative elevations over the surface of the continent of North America, intending ultimately to publish a hypsometrical map. The collection of data was entrusted to Walter L. Nicholson, topographer of the Post Office Department, but about 1882 the project and apparently most of the records were transferred to the Survey.

This record unit contains data accumulated by Nicholson and several railroad elevation maps. Dates of the records are uncertain.

ARRANGEMENT: Unarranged, with the following segments: altitudes; graphs; charts; maps; correspondence, mostly regarding observations along railroad lines; railroad elevation maps, oversize. FINDING AIDS: None. SPECIAL CONDITIONS: (1) Maps cannot be reproduced; (2) use of this record unit requires prior arrangement with the Archives staff.

United States Civil Service Commission Correspondence, 1893-1894, 1896-1907
(0.5 linear meter).

Smithsonian federal employees were placed under the regulations of the Civil Service Commission by order of the President on June 16, 1896. Special records, signed by the Secretary, the Acting Secretary, the Assistant Secretary, and the Chief Clerk, were created to record transactions with the Commission.

Correspondence consists of outgoing letterpress copies to the Commission, mostly for the years 1896-1907, chiefly concerning appointments, promotions, and regulations. There is some intra-Smithsonian correspondence concerning Civil Service appointments and annual reports to the Commission, 1896-1902.

ARRANGEMENT: Chronologic. FINDING AIDS: Indexes in volumes. SPECIAL CONDITIONS: Use of this record unit requires prior arrangement with the Archives staff.

Unpublished Papers, 1865-1896 and undated
(1.8 linear meters).

Publication of memoirs, or scientific papers, began in 1848 with the Smithsonian Contributions to Knowledge series.

The papers in this record unit, apparently unpublished, consist of memoirs sent to or requested by the Smithsonian, but for some reason not published. Many are undated, but nothing suggests that any of these papers predate the 1865 fire in the Smithsonian Building.

ARRANGEMENT: Alphabetic by author's name. FINDING AIDS: None. SPECIAL CONDITIONS: Use of this record unit requires prior arrangement with the Archives staff.

Visitor Information and Associates' Reception Center, 1972-1989
Records (7.4 linear meters).

In October 1971 Mary Grace Potter became the first Director of the Smithsonian Associates' Reception Center, which was established to accommodate members of the National Associate constituency that was created with the publication of *Smithsonian* magazine. Initial duties of the Center included reception and orientation services for National Associate members visiting the Institution, response to telephone and mail inquiries from members, membership sales, and management of the reduced rate membership and gift fulfillment program for employees and volunteers.

It soon became apparent that the organization provided services that would be valuable to the public as well as to National Associates, and by June 1975 it was renamed the Visitor Information and Associates' Reception Center (VIARC). The Center operated originally under the auspices of the National Program of the Smithsonian Associates, but by 1977 it had emerged as a separate entity reporting directly to the Assistant Secretary for Public Service. By 1989 the functions of VIARC were divided among five separate units: the Information Resources Division; Public Inquiry Mail and

Telephone Information Services unit; the Seven Day Information Service unit; the Staff, Volunteer, and Intern Services unit; and Support Services.

These records document many aspects of the development and operation of VIARC, especially the administration of the Center's two volunteer corps. The bulk of the material consists of the administrative files of Mary Grace Potter from 1972 to 1987, including general correspondence, memoranda, and budget reports. Of particular note are early planning materials for the Smithsonian Information Center, which opened in the Castle in November 1989. In addition, the records contain the files of the Seven Day Information Service and the Staff, Volunteer, and Intern Services units from 1980 to 1989. These materials include memoranda, correspondence, reports, and surveys generated and received by the units.

ARRANGEMENT: (1) Office of the Director, records, 1976-1989, accession number 93-098; (2) Visitor Information and Associates' Reception Center, records, 1972-1989, accession number 94-025. FINDING AIDS: Description in control file. SPECIAL CONDITIONS: (1) Restricted; (2) use of this record unit requires prior arrangement with the Archives staff.

(62)

Visitors Registers of the Smithsonian Institution and the United States National Museum, 1852-1913
(3.3 linear meters).

ARRANGEMENT: (1) Smithsonian Institution, chronologic; (2) National Museum, chronologic. FINDING AIDS: None. SPECIAL CONDITIONS: Use of this record unit requires prior arrangement with the Archives staff.

FISCAL AND PAYROLL RECORDS

(93)

Fiscal Records, Federal, 1847-1942
(19.6 linear meters).

When the government's natural history and ethnology collections were transferred to the care of the Smithsonian Institution in 1858, Congress provided an annual allowance of $4,000 for their support. The Smithsonian provided for any additional costs necessary to maintain, preserve, and document the collections from its private funds. From 1870 to 1871, Congress appropriated $10,000 annually for the maintenance of the collections, which became part of the United States National Museum (USNM). Beginning in 1872, Congress began appropriating funds for the "Preservation of Collections," which, along with later appropriations for "Furniture and Fixtures," and "Heating, Lighting, Telephonic and Electrical Service," constituted the major congressional appropriations for the United States National Museum. Other major congressional appropriations were made for "International Exchanges," "American Ethnology," "National Zoological Park," and "Astrophysical Observatory," as well as for exposition functions and other temporary needs of the Institution.

These records include ledgers, account books, bills, daybooks, journals, receipted vouchers, records of payment, requisitions, cash books, and other fiscal records documenting the Smithsonian's congressional appropriations. These records deal with the financial affairs of the following Smithsonian bureaus: United States National Museum, Astrophysical Observatory, Bureau of American Ethnology, National Zoological Park, United States National Herbarium, and the International Exchange Service. Other projects of the Institution and its bureaus, such as the International Catalogue of Scientific Literature, are also documented.

ARRANGEMENT: (1) General ledgers, 1912-1937; (2) allotment ledgers, 1905-1913; (3) disbursement of appropriations, 1906-1911; (4) disbursements, salaries, 1909-1912; (5) disbursements, Astrophysical Observatory, 1908-1912, 1915; (6) disbursements, 1907-1910, 1923-1924, 1937-1941; (7) Treasury account, 1926-1934; (8) bills received, 1870-1871, 1880; (9) postage account, 1903-1932; (10) transportation bills to Treasury, 1923-1936; (11) United States National Museum daybooks, Preservation of Collections, 1881-1906; daybook for Armory, 1881-1884, included; (12) USNM daybooks, Furniture and Fixtures, 1880-1882, 1889-1906; (13) USNM daybooks, Heating and Lighting, 1884-1906; daybook for Armory, 1884-1886, included; (14) USNM daybooks, Building and Repairs, 1883-1906, includes receipted vouchers; (15) USNM daybook, Building Sheds, 1898, and Purchase of Specimens, 1901-1904; (16) International Exchanges, daybook, 1883-1904; (17) USNM journals, Furniture and Fixtures, 1883-1890; (18) USNM journal, Preservation of Collections, 1872-1880; (19) Museum galleries, daybook, 1897-1902; (20) Museum galleries, receipted vouchers, 1898-1902; (21) Bureau of American Ethnology, record of vouchers paid, 1893-1895; (22) North American Ethnology, daybooks, 1890-1904; (23) North American Ethnology, journals, 1893-1906; (24) National Zoological Park, journals, 1890-1904; (25) Astrophysical Observatory, daybook, 1891-1899; (26) Astrophysical Observatory, journals, 1899-1904, 1906; includes International Catalogue of Scientific Literature material, 1907; (27) Disbursing Clerk, ledgers, 1888-1895; (28) USNM, ledgers, 1873-1906; (29) USNM, accounts ledger, 1892-1901; (30) USNM appropriations, 1889-1890; (31) federal appropriations deposited in the United States Treasury, 1888-1905; (32) USNM, journal, Rent of Workshops, 1894-1905; (33) United States National Herbarium, journal, printing and publishing *Contributions from the*

United States National Herbarium, 1903; (34) bills vouchered for printing and binding, 1923-1934; (35) payments on accounts of salaries, 1931-1934; (36) government voucher book, 1931, 1933; (37) USNM, balance sheets, 1924-1934; (38) disposition of salaries, 1904; (39) National Zoological Park, ledger, 1890-1892; (40) record of accounts, 1935-1942; (41) International Catalogue of Scientific Literature, 1909-1919; (42) allotment ledger, 1933; (43) requisitions, 1912-1927; (44) fire protection, daybook, 1896; (45) American Ethnology, record of payments, 1907-1910; (46) Treasury balance and appropriation balance, 1897-1905; (47) USNM, disbursement journals, 1888-1905, with separate bound indexes for the years 1888-1889, 1890, 1898; (48) North American Ethnology, Bureau of American Ethnology, disbursement journals, 1892-1908; (49) Astrophysical Observatory, disbursement journals, 1892-1900; (50) International Exchanges, disbursement journal, 1894-1900; (51) National Zoological Park, disbursement journals, 1890-1900; (52) Astrophysical Observatory, International Exchanges, and National Zoological Park, disbursement journals, 1901-1907; (53) transportation for Treasury settlement, disbursement journals, 1899-1905; (54) USNM, cash book, *circa* 1872-1874; (55) publications, 1909-1911; (56) USNM, ledger, small purchases, 1881-1887; (57) USNM, receipted vouchers, Preservation of Collections, 1872-1904; (58) USNM, receipted vouchers, Furniture and Fixtures, 1880-1903; (59) USNM, receipted vouchers, Heating, Lighting, Telephonic and Electrical Service, 1886-1903; (60) USNM, receipted vouchers, Purchase of Specimens, 1900-1903; (61) USNM, receipted vouchers, Building Repairs, 1894-1904; (62) USNM, receipted vouchers, Armory, 1876-1887; (63) indexes to receipted vouchers, Preservation of Collections, 1881, 1884, 1886, 1890-1900; (64) indexes to receipted vouchers, Furniture and Fixtures, 1890-1900; (65) indexes to receipted vouchers, Building Repairs, 1895-1900; (66) payroll records, 1882-1904; (67) payroll records for February, May, August, and November, 1901-1942; (68) payroll vouchers, alphabetic by payee, 1912-1933; (69) payroll vouchers, chronologic, 1912-1923; (70) payroll for personal services, 1924-1932; (71) requisitions, 1890-1892; (72) copies of bills, 1847-1898; (73) cost of publications, 1862-1895; (74) travel authorizations for ethnological studies, 1881-1882; (75) apparatus bills, 1882-1899; (76) time work record, 1887-1892, 1900-1901; (77) USNM, compensation of employees, 1889; (78) Comptroller, correspondence, 1890-1891; (79) property record, O and F account, 1898-1901; (80) work orders, 1869-1896; (81) electrical current used, 1902-1907; (82) record of car tickets, 1902-1909; (83) stable keys record, 1905-1907; (84) record of bills, 1899-1903; (85) cancelled checks, 1847-1863, 1867, 1870-1900; (86) daybook, cost of supplies, 1877-1880; (87) vouchers, 1907-1908. FINDING AIDS: (1) Some volumes are individually indexed; (2) volume list for part of the records in control file. SPECIAL CONDITIONS: (1) Provenance not known for all records, probably will be rearranged; (2) use of this record unit requires prior arrangement with the Archives staff.

(100)

Fiscal Records, Private, 1846-1959
Records (7.5 linear meters).

The private funds of the Smithsonian Institution are those which are derived from non-federal sources. Over the years, these sources have included the original bequest of James Smithson and numerous other bequests and gifts from other benefactors. Private funds are managed separately from congressional appropriations, although both funds may at times support the same activities.

These records include daybooks, ledgers, receipts, journals, registers, statements, and other financial records documenting the management of the private funds of the Smithsonian.

ARRANGEMENT: (1) Fund ledgers, 1905-1924, 1953-1954; (2) receipts and disbursements, 1905-1953; (3) cash receipts and disbursement journals, 1905-1953; (4) salaries and expense ledger, 1877-1878; (5) allotment ledger, 1904-1908; (6) allotments and commitments, 1908-1929; (7) allotments and commitments, Freer Gallery of Art, 1924-1939; (8) requisitions and allotments, 1929-1953; (9) account ledgers, International Catalogue of Scientific Literature (ICSL), 1901-1908; (10) cash receipts ledger, ICSL, 1905-1924, 1927; (11) disbursement ledger, ICSL, 1908-1913; (12) inventory ledger, ICSL, 1909-1920, 1927; (13) disbursement journals, Panama-California Exposition, 1912-1919; (14) petty cash book, 1922-1924; (15) receipts received by the Secretary's office, 1931-1953; (16) investment ledger, 1925-1929; (17) suppliers list,

1883-1884; (18) accounts receivable ledger, 1912-1926; (19) Treasury account, 1927-1947, see combined ledger in record unit 93, above; (20) voucher registers, 1916-1955; (21) cash receipts, 1905-1959; (22) cash disbursements, 1953-1959; (23) daybook, Museum expenditures, 1849-1872; (24) Smithsonian Institution expenditures, journals, 1856-1866; (25) ledgers, Smithsonian Institution, 1846-1900, 1906; (26) journal, Smithsonian Institution, 1886-1887; (27) daybook, Smithsonian Institution books, 1899-1906; (28) account book, receipts and expenditures of the Smithsonian Institution, 1872-1882; (29) annual statement, itemized disbursements of the Smithsonian Institution, 1889-1891; (30) record of Smithsonian Institution bills, 1871; (31) indexes to ledgers on books and periodicals, 1885, 1899-1900; (32) Secretary's Reserve Fund, 1901, 1906; (33) disbursement journals, Smithsonian Institution, 1890-1911; (34) daybooks, disbursements, 1846-1884. FINDING AIDS: (1) Some volumes are individually indexed; (2) volume listing for part of the records in control file. SPECIAL CONDITIONS: (1) Provenance not known for all records, probably will be rearranged; (2) use of this record unit requires prior arrangement with the Archives staff.

(165)

Disbursement Clerk, 1882-1907
Records (1.6 linear meters).

Records of the Disbursement Clerk include outgoing letterpress financial statements, most of which were signed by William W. Karr. Karr was appointed to the position of "factotum" in 1879. His assignment included time-keeping, keeping accounts of expenditures, and making out bills for payment for the contractors during the construction of the Arts and Industries Building. As a result of his efficiency, Karr was appointed to the United States National Museum (USNM) staff as a clerk, November 1880, although he was also called bookkeeper, assistant, and cashier. In 1884 he became Accountant for the Smithsonian. Karr became Disbursement Clerk in 1888, and from 1888 to 1905 he held the joint position of Accountant and Disbursement Clerk, with his salary coming from both Smithsonian private and Museum federal funds. In 1905 Karr was discharged from his duties on charges of embezzlement, and W. I. Adams was appointed to fill Karr's position.

Prior to 1873 all accounts for the National Museum were paid by the Smithsonian and audited by the Executive Committee. From 1873 until 1888, bills for the USNM were approved by the Secretary and disbursed by the disbursing agent at the Department of the Interior. In a similar fashion, beginning in 1874, the Secretary of the Treasury disbursed Smithsonian funds and made payment on checks signed by the Secretary. In 1888, funds for the Museum and International Exchange Service as well as those from the Treasury Department were turned over to the Disbursement Clerk for the Smithsonian. Funds appropriated for North American Ethnology were transferred to the Smithsonian Disbursement Clerk in 1892.

Records include copies of disbursement vouchers, statements, abstracts of disbursements, monthly disbursement statements, cash vouchers, and summary balance and debit statements, and correspondence regarding the history of the Disbursement Clerk position. Disbursement of funds included both the private and federal side of the Smithsonian, in particular, the operations of the USNM, National Zoological Park, and International Exchange Service. Form vouchers were also signed by Secretaries Spencer F. Baird and Samuel P. Langley.

ARRANGEMENT: (1) Letterpress copies of outgoing financial records and correspondence, 1882-1907; (2) incoming correspondence, 1898-1905. FINDING AIDS: (1) Most volumes are individually indexed; (2) folder list in control file. SPECIAL CONDITIONS: Use of this record unit requires prior arrangement with the Archives staff.

Payroll Records, Federal, 1880-1888
(0.8 linear meter).

For information and other records concerning federal funding of the Smithsonian Institution, see record unit 93.

These records consist of payroll sheets for Smithsonian and United States National Museum employees whose salaries were derived from federally appropriated funds for "Preservation of Collections," "Furniture and Fixtures," and "Heating and Lighting." Also included are records for employees paid from special funding for expositions and other needs.

ARRANGEMENT: Alphabetic. FINDING AIDS: None. SPECIAL CONDITIONS: Use of this record unit requires prior arrangement with the Archives staff.

Payroll Records, Private, 1920-1956
(1.2 linear meters).

For information on private fund records of the Smithsonian Institution, see record unit 100.

These records consist of payroll vouchers and receipts for employees whose salaries were derived from non-federal sources. Included are payroll records for employees paid from the Freer Gallery of Art Fund, the Hodgkins Fund, the John A. Roebling Solar Research Fund, the Charles D. and Mary Vaux Walcott Research Fund, and others.

ARRANGEMENT: Chronologic. FINDING AIDS: None. SPECIAL CONDITIONS: Use of this record unit requires prior arrangement with the Archives staff.

AUDIO-VISUAL AND INFORMATION FILES

(7098)

Biographical Information File
(1.4 linear meters).

The Biographical Information File contains biographies of individuals associated with the Smithsonian as either administrative officers, curators, collectors, donors, regents, or research associates. Occasionally biographies of individuals less closely associated with the Institution are included.

ARRANGEMENT: Alphabetic. FINDING AIDS: None. SPECIAL CONDITIONS: Use of this record unit requires prior arrangement with the Archives staff.

(95)

Photograph Collection, 1850s-
(18.2 linear meters and oversize).

The Smithsonian Archives maintains this record unit as a central file of photographs documenting the history of the Institution. It is a combination of reference files which were created by various administrative offices of the Smithsonian, and individual photographs which have come in separately from other records or manuscript collections. Photographs that come into the Archives as part of a record unit are generally kept in that record unit. See Appendix A, Index by Form, for a list of other record units containing photographs.

Included in this record unit are photographs of Smithsonian officials and staff, scientists, and political figures; buildings and facilities of the Institution, some documented from groundbreaking to the present; exhibits; Smithsonian activities, including ceremonies, presentations, and openings; expositions, especially those in which the Institution participated; insignia and medals of the Smithsonian; and Washington, D.C., and vicinity. The collection also contains some photographs of specimens held by the museums, but researchers should generally consult the appropriate curatorial office for specimen photographs. A small number of engravings and prints are also included in this collection.

Researchers are advised that photographs in this and other collections in the Archives are only a small part of the Institution's photographic resources.

ARRANGEMENT: (1) Individuals; (2) group portraits; (3) buildings and facilities; (4) exhibits; (5) specimens, artifacts, equipment; (6) events; (7) expositions; (8) Smithsonian insignia and medals; (9) Washington, D.C., and vicinity; (10) published plates; (11) slides; (12) negatives. FINDING AIDS: Description in control file. SPECIAL CONDITIONS: Use of this record unit requires prior arrangement with the Archives staff.

Prints and Drawings, 1840-
(65 oversize drawers).

The Archives contains lithographs, photographs, original architectural renderings, blueprints, plans, and survey maps of Smithsonian buildings, proposed buildings, monuments, and the Smithsonian grounds and Mall area. The original Smithsonian Institution Building is the best documented, from 1846 to the renovation in 1965, including original renderings by John Notman, Isaiah Rogers, and Owen G. Warren, 1846, James Renwick, Jr., 1846-1848, and Cluss and Schulze renovation plans, 1884-1887. Also included are blueprints and drawings related to the Mall from 1841, in particular, photostatic copies of Robert Mills' proposal for a National Institute building on the Mall, 1841, and the original survey of the Smithsonian grounds, 1847; floorplan of the National Institute in the old Patent Office Building, 1840; Arts and Industries renderings and blueprints, including proposed drawings by Cluss and Schulze, J. L. Smithmeyer, and Hornblower and Marshall; an original floor plan of the Freer Gallery of Art by Charles A. Platt, 1913; the Astrophysical Observatory; the Barney Studio House; the Hirshhorn Museum and Sculpture Garden; History and Technology Museum; copies of drawings for the proposed National Gallery of Art (never constructed) by Charles A. Platt, 1924; the Natural History Building, including reproductions of plans and renderings by Hornblower and Marshall, 1901-1910; the National Zoological Park; photographs of the old Patent Office Building, and blueprints regarding the renovation of the building, 1962 (now called the American Art and Portrait Gallery Building).

In addition there are original renderings of the proposed Smithsonian Gallery of Art, 1939 (never constructed), by Eero Saarinen, Percival Goodman, Philip L. Goodwin, Harry F. Manning, James A. Mitchell, G. Holmes Perkins, and Peter and Stubbins; copies of sketches for the proposed George Washington Memorial by Tracy and Swartwout (never constructed); competition drawings for a proposed Smithson Memorial, 1904-1905, by Totten and Rogers, and Hornblower and Marshall, including two Henry Bacon drawings, 1904; and Smithson crypt gate competition design drawings by Thomas G. Bredlow, J. Richard Cronin, Frank Turley, L. Brent Kington, Samuel Yellin Metalworkers, and Albert Paley, 1975.

ARRANGEMENT: By building or subject and chronologic thereunder. FINDING AIDS: (1) Inventory of drawings of the Smithsonian Institution Building, Arts and Industries Building, and partial inventory of drawings of the Natural History Building prepared by the Curator of the Smithsonian Institution Building. SPECIAL CONDITIONS: (1) Often cannot be reproduced for special order because of size; (2) use of this record unit requires prior arrangement with the Archives staff.

Office of Smithsonian Institution Archives, 1930-
Research Records (8.2 linear meters).

Although the first Secretary, Joseph Henry, had seen the need for an archives to preserve the records of the Institution, the Smithsonian Institution Archives had its real origins in 1891, when William Jones Rhees, who had been Chief Clerk since 1855, was given the title Keeper of the Archives. Rhees served until his death in 1907.

For the first half of the twentieth century, the administrative staff of the Office of the Secretary cared for the historical records while maintaining the current files. In 1958 John F. Jameson III was hired by the Secretary's Office to care for the archives of the Institution while also working with the current files. In 1960 Jameson was succeeded as Archivist by John DeGurse, Jr., who remained until 1964.

The mission of the Archives changed to a more research-oriented operation in 1965, when Samuel T. Suratt was appointed Smithsonian Archivist. His hiring was accompanied by the charge to engage in the "development of the Archives as a facility for historical research in American Science" by making the Archives' resources more readily accessible to historians through better identification, preservation, and cataloging of Smithsonian documents. Within two years the Smithsonian Institution Archives was no longer funded by the Office of the Secretary and became a separate line item in the Institution's budget. Suratt served until 1969 and was followed by Richard H. Lytle. Lytle held the position until 1981, when William A. Deiss was named Acting Archivist. In 1983 William W. Moss was appointed Director of the Smithsonian Institution Archives.

In 1992 a reorganization resulted in the creation of the Office of Smithsonian Institution Archives with Moss as Director. The new Office consisted of an Archives Division, directed by Alan L. Bain, and an Institutional History Division, directed by Pamela M. Henson. Also included in the new office was the National Collections Program, which had taken over some of the duties of the former Office of the Registrar. In 1993 Moss retired and was succeeded by Henson as Acting Director, 1993, and John F. Jameson III, who served as Acting Director in 1994. Ethel W. "Edie" Hedlin served as Director, 1994-   .

This record unit consists of records of significant research undertaken in the Archives holdings by Smithsonian staff or outside scholars. Each record includes the reference form, any correspondence, and notes on sources.

ARRANGEMENT: Alphabetic by name or topic. FINDING AIDS: None. SPECIAL CONDITIONS: Use of this record unit requires prior arrangement with the Archives staff.

(96)

Smithsonian News Clipping File, 1852-1968
(3.4 linear meters).

The clipping file consists of news clippings and magazine articles concerning persons and events in Smithsonian history.

ARRANGEMENT: Chronologic. FINDING AIDS: None. SPECIAL CONDITIONS: Use of this record unit requires prior arrangement with the Archives staff.

Tape Recordings, 1958-
(5.9 linear meters).

These records include tape recordings made or received by the Office of Public Affairs, usually of Smithsonian events or by Smithsonian staff. They also include tapes made of animal sounds for the National Museum of Natural History Audioguide and other tapes received by the Archives, regardless of origin.

ARRANGEMENT: (1) Dated and identified tapes, arranged chronologically by date of event, 1958-1972; (2) dated and identified tapes, arranged chronologically by date of accession to Archives, *circa* 1959-   ; (3) undated tapes, alphabetic by title; (4) unidentified tapes. FINDING AIDS: Tape list in control file. SPECIAL CONDITIONS: Use of this record unit requires prior arrangement with the Archives staff.

PART II
SPECIAL COLLECTIONS

PAPERS OF JAMES SMITHSON
AND SECRETARIES

(7000)

James Smithson Collection, 1796-1951
(0.9 linear meter).

James Smithson (*circa* 1765-1829) was an amateur chemist and mineralogist of some reputation in his own day. He was the illegitimate son of Sir Hugh Smithson, Bt. (later duke of Northumberland) and Elizabeth Hungerford Keate Macie, a gentlewoman. To posterity he is best known as the founder of the Smithsonian Institution, created by a residual bequest under his will. Smithson was born in France about 1765; was naturalized a British subject about 1775; and entered Pembroke College, Oxford, in 1782, graduating M.A. in 1786.

This collection contains the few original Smithson papers to survive a fire at the Smithsonian in 1865. It is, however, chiefly concerned with efforts to obtain the bequest; to trace the details of Smithson's own history; and to reinter him in the United States, which was accomplished in 1904. Notable among the actors in these pursuits were William Jones Rhees, the Institution's Chief Clerk; Samuel P. Langley, its third Secretary; and Alexander Graham Bell, long a Smithsonian Regent. The collection consists of correspondence, photographs, and publications.

ARRANGEMENT: (1) Original Smithson manuscripts and copies, 1796-1878; (2) documents related to securing the Smithson bequest and claims by would-be heirs, 1835-1892; (3) research and correspondence about Smithson's life and lineage, 1881-1951 and undated; (4) removal of Smithson's remains to America, 1903-1905; (5) photographs; (6) publications. FINDING AIDS: Description in control file. SPECIAL CONDITIONS: Use of this record unit requires prior arrangement with the Archives staff.

(7001)

Joseph Henry Collection, 1808, 1825-1878, and related papers to circa 1903
(8.6 linear meters and oversize).

Joseph Henry (1797-1878) had careers as scientist, teacher, promoter of research, and administrator, which are documented in depositories throughout the world. The majority of the documentation in the Smithsonian Archives consists of secretarial records dating from 1865 to 1878 and his collection of personal and professional papers.

This collection includes the full range of Henry's activities from 1825 through 1878, although the years after he became Secretary in 1846 are more fully represented than those before. Henry carried on correspondence with many of the great scientific men of his day, and the correspondence runs the gamut from details of scientific research to the broadest questions of scientific policy and the growth of professional scientific organizations. Henry's work in electromagnetism is documented, as is his role in the development of the telegraph; and the many papers and addresses he gave on scientific, educational, and other topics are an important resource. His work in meteorology can be studied here and in the Meteorological Project records. A considerable segment of the papers deals with the United States Lighthouse Board, to which Henry was appointed in 1852, and with the American Association for the Advancement of Science, the National Academy of Sciences, and the Philosophical Society of Washington. One of Henry's daughters, Mary A. Henry, compiled extensive information for a biography of her father, which is also included in the Henry collection.

A letterpress edition of Henry's papers is being produced by the Joseph Henry Papers, a cooperative editorial project located at the Smithsonian Institution. The Joseph Henry Papers holds no original documents, but it does have extensive information on the location of Henry documents which is utilized by the Smithsonian Archives in answering research inquiries.

ARRANGEMENT: (1) Incoming and outgoing correspondence, 1808, 1825-1878; (2) outgoing correspondence, letterpress, 1865-1878; (3) letters to and from James H. Coffin, 1842-1873; (4) diaries, 1835-1877; (5) research and lectures; (6) United States Lighthouse Board; (7) honors, invitations, awards; (8) publications by Joseph Henry; (9) oversize; (10) memorials; (11) Harriet Henry papers, 1825-1878; (12) Mary A. Henry papers, including her work on the projected biography of Joseph Henry; (13) family papers; (14) biographical material to the present; (15) copies of Alexander Dallas Bache and Henry letters from other depositories. FINDING AIDS: (1) Joseph Henry Papers computer index, providing name and subject access to part of the Henry Collection; (2) card index to letters in chronological series (Item 1 above); (3) shelf list of Henry items, 1971; (4) Michele Aldrich, *Calendar of the Unknowns,* a list of difficult-to-identify items; (5) pocket notebooks of Joseph Henry, control file; (6) calendar of Joseph Henry, miniature notebooks, control file; (7) Joseph Henry, honors and awards, control file; (8) Joseph Henry, invitations and notices, control file; (9) Henryana Abstract and Index to Abstract, an obsolete finding aid to the collection before present arrangement was imposed, sometimes useful. SPECIAL CONDITIONS: (1) Microfilm available for most of the collection; (2) other pieces may require special order microfilming or xeroxing; (3) all requests for permission to publish must be approved by the Joseph Henry Papers Project; (4) use of this record unit requires prior arrangement with the Archives staff.

(7002)

Spencer F. Baird Papers, 1833-1889
(9.6 linear meters and oversize).

The career of Spencer F. Baird (1823-1887) is fully documented in the Smithsonian Archives. Most letters between Baird and Louis Agassiz have been published in Elmer Charles Herber, editor, *Correspondence Between Spencer Fullerton Baird and Louis Agassiz—Two Pioneer American Naturalists* (Smithsonian Institution Press, 1963).

The Baird Papers begin about 1833 with family correspondence and early journals and include records of Baird's education and teaching career, the latter dating from 1846 to 1850. The period between 1843 and 1869 Baird devoted to investigation of the vertebrate fauna of North America, and throughout the forty years from 1840 to 1880 he contributed greatly to scientific literature in this and other areas of natural science. From 1850 to 1878 Baird was Assistant Secretary of the Smithsonian Institution, and from 1878 to his death he was Secretary. Baird was a prolific correspondent. He wrote most of the important naturalists of his day, and almost one-half of these papers consists of letters written or received by Baird. Although official correspondence theoretically was relegated to Smithsonian records, in practice Baird observed no boundaries between professional and official; thus, these papers contain drafts of Smithsonian reports and correspondence relating to official functions. From 1871 until his death, Baird served as

United States Fish Commissioner. Most of Baird's work as Commissioner is documented in this record unit. The extensive correspondence, here and in the Assistant Secretary's records, of Baird's work with the exploring expeditions, especially the Ringgold, Hudson Bay Territory, United States and Mexican Survey, and the Northern Pacific Railroad Route, is also important.

ARRANGEMENT: (1) Correspondence registers, 1850, 1868-1869; (2) incoming correspondence, 1833-1849; (3) incoming correspondence, 1850-1854; (4) incoming correspondence, 1855-1865; (5) incoming correspondence, family, 1844-1887; (6) incoming correspondence, 1844-1887; (7) outgoing correspondence, 1849-1887; (8) journals, 1839-1875; (9) diaries, 1851-1865; (10) miscellaneous diaries, 1861, 1870; (11) Smithsonian reports and Museum receipts, Baird's drafts; (12) correspondence and fiscal papers related to expeditions, 1852-1884, especially Ringgold, Hudson Bay Territory, United States and Mexican Survey, and Northern Pacific Railroad Route; (13) Fish Commission; (14) Addresses of Scientific Men, compiled, *circa* 1852; (15) research and publications, 1839-1887; (16) personal miscellany, especially accounts; (17) biographical data, including correspondence and notes of Lucy Baird and others, some postdating Baird; some of these may be removed to other collections; (18) oversize sketches, awards, certificates; (19) miscellaneous manuscripts and notes. FINDING AIDS: (1) Card index, prepared after the records were created, providing mostly proper name access; (2) index to incoming correspondence in control file; (3) descriptive finding aid to part of the collection, in control file; (4) published letters between Baird and Agassiz; (5) index to Baird-Agassiz letters; (6) most volumes indexed individually. SPECIAL CONDITIONS: (1) Some items cannot be reproduced because of legibility and bindings; (2) record unit partially microfilmed; (3) use of this record unit requires prior arrangement with the Archives staff.

(7003)

Samuel P. Langley Papers, 1867-1906
(9.5 linear meters and oversize).

Samuel P. Langley (1834-1906) was the third Secretary of the Smithsonian Institution. Apparently many of Langley's papers were accidentally burned after his death. Langley papers in the Smithsonian are housed in the Smithsonian Archives and the National Air and Space Museum (NASM). The Allegheny Observatory holds papers from Langley's years there, from which copies of Langley's correspondence, 1867-1887, have been made for this collection.

These papers document important aspects of Langley's scientific and administrative career. Most of the material documents the progress of his aeronautical research from his first flying model of 1891 through the failure of his Aerodrome A of 1903. Also, information files housed in the National Air and Space Museum Library include secondary accounts and photographs relating to Langley's aeronautical studies. Related materials in the NASM Library include the Stephen M. Balzer papers, 1898-1902, which consist of correspondence with Langley and his associate, Charles M. Manly, regarding Balzer's aerodrome engines.

ARRANGEMENT: (1) Publications, including a bound collection of writings, and original manuscripts of many of Langley's publications, 1869-1905; (2) diaries and shorthand notebooks, mostly kept by Langley's secretary, 1889-1905; (3) bolograph curve and line spectrum readings; (4) microfilm and photocopies of Langley's outgoing correspondence from the Allegheny Observatory, 1867-1887; (5) astrophysical research correspondence; (6) scrapbooks, 1890-1903; (7) aeronautical research, including correspondence, wastebooks, and notes of Langley and Manly and their assistants, E. C. Huffaker, L. C. Maltby, B. L. Rhinehart, and R. L. Reed; (8) oversize aerodrome drawings and bolometer readings. FINDING AIDS: None. SPECIAL CONDITIONS: (1) Check finding aid for location; (2) use of this record unit requires prior arrangement with the Archives staff.

Charles D. Walcott Collection, 1851-1940 and undated
(11.7 linear meters and oversize).

Charles D. Walcott (1850-1927), a geologist, was the fourth Secretary of the Smithsonian Institution. Walcott's professional career began in 1876 when he became an assistant in the New York State Geological Survey. In 1879 he joined the United States Geological Survey (USGS) as an Assistant Geologist. He served as Director of USGS from 1894 to 1907. In 1907 he became Secretary of the Smithsonian, a post which he held until his death in 1927.

During his tenure at USGS Walcott maintained an association with the United States National Museum (USNM). From 1882 to 1883 he was an Honorary Assistant Curator in the Department of Invertebrate Fossils. From 1883 to 1893 he was Honorary Curator in the Department of Invertebrate Fossils (Paleozoic). Subsequently, he served as Honorary Curator, Department of Paleontology, 1894-1897; Acting Assistant Secretary in Charge of the United States National Museum, 1897-1898; and Honorary Curator, 1897-1904, and Curator, 1905-1907, Division of Stratigraphic Paleontology.

This collection consists of personal, professional, and official papers of Walcott and his family; some of the papers postdate Walcott's death. Included are diaries, 1870-1927, which document many of Walcott's official, personal and family activities; personal correspondence which documents Walcott's participation on several governmental committees such as the National Advisory Committee for Aeronautics and the Committee on Organization of Government Scientific Work, as well as several private conservation groups, and his appointment as Director of the United States Geological Survey; family correspondence with relatives and his immediate family concerning their investments, the deaths of two of his sons and one of his wives; correspondence concerning the role of his son, B. Stuart Walcott, in World War I and plans for memorials for him and his flying corps, the Lafayette Escadrille; family legal documents and financial records; scrapbooks and newspaper clippings documenting the activities of Walcott and his family, especially concerning his appointment as Secretary of the Smithsonian; biographical materials prepared by Walcott as well as others, including correspondence and an unpublished biography of Walcott by Adele Jenny; degrees and honors; popular, scientific, and official speeches; correspondence documenting part of Walcott's tenure with the United States Geological Survey as well as reports of his USGS research and participation on several conservation committees and a government organization study committee; drafts of manuscripts, drawings of geologic formations, and field notes, including some by Charles Elmer Resser, Ray S. Bassler, and Edward Oscar Ulrich, documenting Walcott's research in geology; photographs of Walcott, his family, and geologic formations, with special emphasis on the Rocky Mountains; records, including correspondence, minutes of various boards and committees, and reports documenting Walcott's active role in the Carnegie Institution of Washington, the National Academy of Sciences, the National Research Council, the Washington Academy of Sciences, and the George Washington Memorial Association; publications of Walcott and related ones by other scientists; and correspondence, photographs, notes, and lists documenting Walcott's research on Cambrian and pre-Cambrian algae.

ARRANGEMENT: (1) Personal correspondence, 1873-1928 and undated; (2) family correspondence and related materials, 1851-1922 and undated; (3) correspondence and related materials concerning B. Stuart Walcott, 1916-1929 and undated; (4) legal documents and financial records, 1891-1926 and undated; (5) diaries, 1870-1927; (6) scrapbooks and newspaper clippings, 1873-1927; (7) biographies and obituaries, 1914-1928, 1934-1939 and undated; (8) degrees and honors, 1892-1927; (9) speeches, 1898-1925 and undated; (10) United States Geological Survey correspondence, reports, and related materials, 1879-1898, 1903-1904, 1909, 1916 and undated; (11) manuscripts, 1879-1883, 1892, 1908, 1920 and undated; (12) field notes and drawings, 1876-1930, 1934, 1940 and undated; (13) Carnegie Institution of Washington correspondence, minutes, reports, financial records, and related materials, 1901-1929 and undated; (14) National Academy of Sciences and National Research Council correspondence, minutes, and related materials, 1896, 1909-1911, 1921-1922 and undated; (15) Washington Academy of Sciences correspondence and related materials, 1897-1904; (16) United States National Museum, Washington Academy of Sciences, and National Academy of Sciences correspondence and related materials, 1884-1901, 1918 and undated; (17) George Washington Memorial Association correspondence and related materials, 1898-1924 and undated; (18) photographs, 1860, 1868, 1895-1925 and undated; (19) publications, 1875-1928 and undated; (20) add acquisition, 1881-1898, 1911-1912, 1921 and undated; (21) correspondence, photographs, notes, and lists on Cambrian and pre-Cambrian algae, 1906-1925. FINDING AIDS: (1) Description in control file; (2) index to diaries in control file; (3) index to photographs, see box 44, folder 14. SPECIAL CONDITIONS: Use of this record unit requires prior arrangement with the Archives staff.

(7005)

Charles G. Abbot Papers, 1889-1973, and Records of the Smithsonian Astrophysical Observatory

(30 linear meters and oversize).

Charles G. Abbot (1872-1973), the fifth Secretary of the Smithsonian Institution, came to the Institution in 1895 as an assistant to Secretary Samuel P. Langley in the Smithsonian Astrophysical Observatory. In 1907 he was named Director of the Astrophysical Observatory, a position which he held until his retirement in 1944. He became an Assistant Secretary of the Institution in 1918, and served as Secretary from 1928 to 1944. Most of Abbot's research centered around studies of solar radiation and attempts to determine the relationship between solar variations and the earth's weather.

These papers consist mainly of records of the Astrophysical Observatory under the directorships of Samuel P. Langley, Charles G. Abbot, and Loyal B. Aldrich.

ARRANGEMENT: (1) Astrophysical Observatory daybooks, 1889-1907; (2) energy spectrum books, *circa* 1882-1904; (3) Astrophysical Observatory waste books, 1890-1948; (4) charts of solar constant readings taken at Mount Montezuma, Chile, and Table Mountain, California, 1920-1948; (5) Astrophysical Observatory correspondence, 1920-1955; (6) bolographic plates—energy spectrum scans, *circa* 1927-1956; (7) reminiscences contributed to the Smithsonian Archives, 1970; (8) miscellaneous personal correspondence; (9) publications. FINDING AIDS: Preliminary inventory in control file. SPECIAL CONDITIONS: (1) Much of this material consists of records of the Astrophysical Observatory and will be removed from this record unit as it is processed; (2) series 4 partially microfilmed; (3) use of this record unit requires prior arrangement with the Archives staff.

(7006)

Alexander Wetmore Papers, circa 1848-1979 and undated

(30.8 linear meters).

Alexander Wetmore (1886-1978) was the sixth Secretary of the Smithsonian Institution. A well-known ornithologist and avian paleontologist, Wetmore served as Secretary from

1945 to 1952. Wetmore came to the Smithsonian in November 1924 as Superintendent of the National Zoological Park after a fourteen-year career with the Bureau of Biological Survey of the United States Department of Agriculture. In March 1925, he was appointed Assistant Secretary of the Smithsonian in charge of the United States National Museum (USNM), a post he held until his appointment as Secretary in 1945. Wetmore retired in 1952 and was made an honorary Research Associate of the Smithsonian, where he continued his study of recent and fossil birds until his death.

These papers provide comprehensive documentation of all aspects of Wetmore's professional career, with particular emphasis on his ornithological and paleornithological research, field work and expeditions, and his activities in professional organizations. They also illustrate, to a lesser degree, his personal affairs. Wetmore was a prolific correspondent and a large part of his papers consists of letters written and received between 1901 and 1977. The correspondence reflects all phases of Wetmore's work, particularly his research, the progress of his career in the federal government, and his relations with the scientific community.

An organizational file contains records relating to Wetmore's activities as an officer and member of scientific societies, professional organizations, conservation groups, inter-governmental committees, colleges and universities, and social groups, including the American Committee for International Wild Life Protection; the American Ornithologists' Union; the American Philosophical Society; the Eighth American Scientific Congress, 1940; the Inter-American Committee of Experts on Nature Protection and Wild Life Preservation; the International Ornithological Congresses; the National Association of Audubon Societies; the Gorgas Memorial Institute of Tropical and Preventive Medicine; the George Washington University; the National Geographic Society; the Washington Biologists' Field Club; the Explorers Club; and the Cosmos Club. Other materials dealing with his professional activities include files on meetings and conferences attended, and records from his service on the Committee on the Daniel Giraud Elliot Award Fund of the National Academy of Sciences.

Wetmore's career as a field worker and scientific expedition member before and during his service in the federal government is thoroughly illustrated. Included are field notes, diaries, specimen catalogs, correspondence, collecting permits, expense accounts, photographs, motion pictures, and related materials documenting field trips to Puerto Rico, the Hawaiian and other Pacific islands, Alaska and the Aleutian Islands, Central and South America (especially Panama) and all regions of the United States.

The papers also include files documenting his work as head of the USNM and Smithsonian; biographical, genealogical, and personal information on Wetmore and his family; manuscripts, lists, notes, and drawings from his research on recent and fossil birds; desk diaries and appointment books documenting his daily activities; extensive photographs, photograph albums, lantern slides, and 35mm color slides including images of Wetmore, family, friends, scientific colleagues, and events; manuscripts, correspondence, and related materials concerning his *Birds of the Republic of Panama;* diplomas and certificates received by Wetmore; and typescript copies of John Xantus letters compiled by Wetmore for the use of Harry Harris during his research on Xantus.

ARRANGEMENT: (1) General correspondence, 1901-1977 and undated, with related materials from 1879; (2) organizational file, 1901-1977 and undated; (3) Smithsonian Institution and United States National Museum files, 1924-1976 and undated; (4) biographical and personal files, 1897-1979 and undated, with related materials from 1848; (5) expense accounts, 1929-1974; (6) permits, 1902-1977 and undated; (7) field notes, catalogs, laboratory notes, and related records, 1894-1936 and undated; (8) field work and official travel files, 1910-1974; (9) Panama field work files, 1944-1966; (10) *Birds of the Republic of Panama* manuscripts, proofs, correspondence, and related materials, 1968-1969 and undated; (11) drawings of fossil birds, 1918-1956; (12) desk diaries and appointment books, 1917-1956; (13) photographic materials, 1901-1974 and undated, with related materials from 1868; (14) National Academy of Sciences, Daniel Giraud Elliot Award Fund Committee, Chairman's files, 1929-1963; (15) research files, *circa* 1911-1972 and undated; (16) diplomas, certificates, and awards, 1901-1970 and undated, with related materials from 1876; (17) typescript copies of John Xantus correspondence, *circa* 1930s. FINDING AIDS: Description in control file. SPECIAL CONDITIONS: Use of this record unit requires prior arrangement with the Archives staff.

(7007)

Leonard Carmichael Papers, 1952-1964
(0.3 linear meter).

Leonard Carmichael (1898-1973) was the seventh Secretary of the Smithsonian, serving from 1953 to 1964. Most of Carmichael's papers are at the American Philosophical Society. This material has been retained because it relates to his work at the Smithsonian Institution.

ARRANGEMENT: (1) Appointment calendars, 1957-1963; (2) speeches; (3) miscellaneous correspondence and notes; (4) letter from Waldo LaSalle Schmitt, 1952; (5) biography and bibliography; (6) material relating to Carmichael's appointment and retirement as Secretary; (7) appointment books, 1953-1964. FINDING AIDS: Description in control file. SPECIAL CONDITIONS: Use of this record unit requires prior arrangement with the Archives staff.

(7008)

S. Dillon Ripley Papers, 1913-1993 and undated, with related materials from 1807, 1871-1891
(50 linear meters).

S. Dillon Ripley (1913-   ), ornithologist and eighth Secretary of the Smithsonian Institution, developed an interest in natural history in his youth. He received the B.A. from Harvard University in 1936 and the Ph.D. from Yale University in 1943. From 1946 to 1963, he was on the faculty of Yale University and served as Director of its Peabody Museum of Natural History from 1959 to 1963. He conducted extensive field work, including trips to New Guinea in 1938, Sumatra in 1939, and India and Nepal from 1946 to 1949. He began a long-term research program on birds of Southeast Asia, working with Indian ornithologist, Salim Ali. Based on this research, they produced the multi-volume *Handbook of the Birds of India and Pakistan.* Working with the illustrator, J. Fenwick Lansdowne, in 1977 Ripley produced *Rails of the World.* Ripley was also an avid aviculturalist, rearing exotic birds and waterfowl at his home in Litchfield, Connecticut. In 1964, Ripley was appointed Secretary of the Smithsonian Institution. During his twenty-year tenure as Secretary, he oversaw the development of numerous museums, research institutes, and public programs. Ripley was also involved in many conservation organizations, including the Charles Darwin Foundation for the Galapagos Islands, International Council for Bird Preservation, and International Union for the Conservation of Nature.

These papers consist of correspondence with family, friends, and colleagues in such fields as aviculture, ornithology, conservation, and museology; files documenting Ripley's field work, research, and publications; calendars; files documenting professional associations and meetings; audio-visual materials, including photographs, audiotapes, and videotapes; and Ripley family memorabilia, including nineteenth-century materials.

ARRANGEMENT: (1) General correspondence, *circa* 1914-1992; (2) organizational correspondence, *circa* 1943-1986; (3) calendars, 1964-1984; (4) travel files, *circa* 1936-1984; (5) meetings and conference files, *circa* 1950-1985; (6) research files, *circa* 1940-1988; (7) audio-visual materials, *circa* 1914-1993; (8) memorabilia, *circa* 1807, 1871-1891, 1920, 1948, 1974-1983. FINDING AIDS: Description in control file. SPECIAL CONDITIONS: (1) Restricted; (2) use of this record unit requires prior arrangement with the Archives staff.

OTHER PAPERS AND RECORDS

(7116)

John Abbot Collection, undated
(0.3 linear meter).

John Abbot (1751-*circa* 1840), an Englishman, migrated to America in 1773, settling in Virginia. By 1776 he had migrated to Georgia, where he spent most of the remainder of his life. An ornithologist and entomologist, Abbot is best known for his drawings of birds and insects.

There are five sets of Abbot's drawings of birds in existence. Two sets are located in the United States, one at the Boston Society of Natural History and the other at the University of Georgia. Three sets are in England at the British Museum, the Manchester Library, and the Zoological Museum at Tring. There is some confusion on this matter, but evidently all three sets are technically in the possession of the British Museum.

This collection consists of 130 watercolor drawings of birds which probably comprise a sixth set of Abbot drawings. Presumably these drawings are of birds of Georgia. It is not known if these drawings duplicate any of the other sets known to be in existence; nor is it known how they came to be in the possession of the Smithsonian Institution.

ARRANGEMENT: The sketches are numbered 1-130 and arranged in that order. FINDING AIDS: Description in control file. SPECIAL CONDITIONS: Use of this record unit requires prior arrangement with the Archives staff.

(7117)

William Louis Abbott Papers, 1887-1923
(0.5 linear meter).

A native of Philadelphia, William Louis Abbott (1860-1936) was educated at the University of Pennsylvania (A.B., 1881; M.D., 1884). He continued his medical education in England, attaining Licentiates from the Royal College of Surgeons and the Royal College of Physicians. Upon receiving his inheritance, however, Abbott left the practice of medicine forever, and from then on indulged his avocation for travel and the study of natural history.

Abbott had already made collections of birds in Iowa and North Dakota in 1880, and in Cuba and Santo Domingo in 1883. His collection of the birds of Philadelphia and southern New Jersey had been received by the Academy of Natural Sciences of Philadelphia. His serious field work began in 1887 with a two-year exploration of the Taveita region near Mount Kilimanjaro in East Africa, the products of which were presented to the United States National Museum in 1890. The same year Abbott returned to Europe by way of Madagascar and the Seychelles, collecting specimens as he traveled through those regions. Abbott went to Kashmir, India, in 1891, and traveled and collected throughout Kashmir until 1894, leaving only for a six-month voyage to the Seychelles in June 1892 and an expedition through Turkestan during the winter of 1893-1894. In December 1894, Abbott left Kashmir for Madagascar in order to enlist with the native "Hova" army during the Malay resistance to the second French occupation of the island. The local suspicion of foreigners caused his resignation, but Abbott continued to travel through the island collecting until his return to Kashmir in September 1895. Abbott sailed to the Far East the next year, where he explored and collected for the Smithsonian along the Malay Peninsula and in lower Thailand until he contracted fever. Returning to Kashmir to recuperate in the healthy highlands, Abbott continued his collecting there and in Tibet until 1898.

The hostility between the United States and Spain caused Abbott's return in 1898, and he was wounded slightly while serving as a volunteer in Cuba.

Upon his recovery in the same year, Abbott returned to Southeast Asia where he was to remain for the next ten years. Initially he continued his work along the Malay Peninsula, but in 1899 he had his schooner *Terrapin* constructed. In her, with a few Malay sailors as crew, and the occasional company of Cecil Boden Kloss (whose *In the Andamans and Nicobars* constitutes the only published account of the explorations of Abbott during this period), Abbott visited virtually all of the Southeast Asian island groups within 600 miles of Singapore. Abbott's collecting extended beyond mammal and bird specimens to include ethnological artifacts found among the local inhabitants he encountered.

Abbott's activities in Asia were halted by eye disease of increasing severity, which forced him to sell the *Terrapin* and return to Europe for treatment in 1909. Smithsonian acquisitions from the region did not cease, as Abbott funded the Borneo expeditions of Henry C. Raven, who continued what Abbott had been forced to leave. Upon his recovery in 1910, Abbott returned to Kashmir, where, while unable to shoot, he trapped specimens until 1915.

Abbott left Kashmir for the last time in 1916 to take up exploring and collecting on the island of Hispaniola. In July 1916, he spent five months in the Dominican Republic, and in 1917 and 1918 fifteen months in Haiti, leaving only after a near fatal attack of dysentery. He returned to Santo Domingo in 1919, and in 1920 returned to Haiti in the company of Emery Clarence Leonard to collect botanical specimens. In 1921 Abbott returned to the highlands of the Dominican Republic, as he was to do for the next two years until he retired in 1923.

William Louis Abbott was, in the words of a contemporary, "one of the greatest field naturalists America has produced." Although he did not engage in taxonomic analysis, his collecting activities were unparalleled in extent and scope, making available for study by the Smithsonian naturalists plants, land shells, ethnological material, and vertebrates of all classes, but particularly birds and small mammals. Of the latter more than 10,000 were donated by Abbott. Species described as new number 462, and more than twenty bear his name. Perhaps no other single collector provided as much for the Smithsonian Institution.

The papers of William Louis Abbott consist of specimen lists and letters to Smithsonian curators, 1892-1917; letters to his mother and sister, 1887-1923; photographs taken by Abbott in the field, 1890-1923; and some miscellaneous material.

In describing the individual pieces of this collection particular attention was paid to material relating to the natural and social history of the regions Abbott visited, the activities and people associated with the Smithsonian Institution and similar bodies, and, to a lesser extent, material that illuminated the character of the man. No attempt was made to highlight the personal relationships of the Abbott family except where larger issues were involved. Material on these matters may, however, be found in virtually every manuscript.

ARRANGEMENT: (1) Letters to the Smithsonian and related materials, 1891-1917; (2) letters to the Abbott family, 1887-1923; (3) photographs, 1891-1923; (4) miscellany. FINDING AIDS: Description in control file. SPECIAL CONDITIONS: Use of this record unit requires prior arrangement with the Archives staff.

(7305)

John Merton Aldrich Papers, circa 1916-1930
(0.3 linear meter).

John Merton Aldrich (1866-1934) was born in Minnesota. After graduating from South Dakota State University, Aldrich worked briefly for the South Dakota State Agricultural Experiment Station, and then became the first Professor of Zoology at the University of Idaho in 1891. While at Idaho, he worked on many phases of economic entomology and also began work on his catalog of American Diptera, which was published in 1905. In 1913, Aldrich was appointed Entomological Assistant in the Bureau of Entomology, United States Department of Agriculture, and was assigned to the Cereal and Forage Crop Insects Section in Indiana. In 1919, he moved to Washington, D.C., where he worked in the United States National Museum as Custodian of Diptera and Associate Curator of Insects, positions he held until his death.

This collection consists of correspondence between Aldrich and other dipterists and includes considerable correspondence with Leland Ossian Howard and Charles Henry Tyler Townsend.

ARRANGEMENT: Unarranged. FINDING AIDS: None. SPECIAL CONDITIONS: Use of this record unit requires prior arrangement with the Archives staff.

(7059)

Charles Armistead Alexander Papers, 1840-1870
(0.1 linear meter).

Charles Armistead Alexander (? -*circa* 1869) translated many foreign scientific papers for the Smithsonian, beginning about 1858. Most of the translations were published in the Smithsonian Institution *Annual Report*. Alexander also lectured at the Alexandria Lyceum during the 1840s.

These papers include texts of lectures, most of which were delivered at the Alexandria Lyceum. One was printed in the *Alexandria Gazette* in 1840. Also included are lists of translations Alexander did for the Smithsonian Institution, 1866-1870.

ARRANGEMENT: (1) Texts of lectures; (2) newspaper article and lists of translations. FINDING AIDS: Description in control file. SPECIAL CONDITIONS: Use of this record unit requires prior arrangement with the Archives staff.

Charles P. Alexander Papers, circa 1870-1979
(16.3 linear meters).

Charles P. Alexander (1889-1981), entomologist and university professor, was an authority on the study of crane flies. He developed an early interest in natural history, and he published a paper on ornithology at the age of 13 in 1903. He was educated at Cornell University, receiving the Bachelor of Science degree in 1913 and the Ph.D. in 1918. Alexander's professional career began in 1917 when he accepted the position of Curator of the Snow Entomological Collection at the University of Kansas. From 1919 to 1922, he served as a Curator with the Illinois Natural History Survey. In 1922 Alexander was appointed Assistant Professor at the Massachusetts Agricultural College at Amherst (now the University of Massachusetts), where he remained as a faculty member and administrator for the rest of his career. On his retirement in 1959 the University awarded him an honorary Doctor of Science degree.

Alexander's research was almost exclusively focused on the study of the Tipulidae, the largest family of the order Diptera. He described close to 11,000 species of Diptera, over 10,000 of them belonging to the family Tipulidae. Alexander assembled a huge personal collection of crane flies which contained more than 10,500 species. He acquired many specimens on numerous field trips and collecting expeditions to the western United States, western Canada, Alaska, New England, the Great Smoky Mountains and the maritime provinces of Canada. The collection was purchased by the Smithsonian Institution in 1973. His bibliography includes 1,017 papers and books totaling over 20,000 pages, with 15,000 of his own illustrations.

Alexander was active within the entomological profession, and his achievements were widely recognized. He served as President of the Entomological Society of America (ESA) from 1941 to 1943 and was elected an Honorary Member of the Society in 1969. In 1976 he received the L. O. Howard Award for Distinguished Achievement in Entomology of the Eastern Branch of ESA. He was the recipient of the Bernardo O'Higgins Order of Merit of the government of Chile in 1952.

The papers of Charles P. Alexander provide comprehensive documentation of his professional career and personal affairs. They include a voluminous file of correspondence with entomologists, naturalists, field collectors, professional colleagues, friends and family; a file containing information on the history of entomology and biographical data on, and photographs of entomologists; field notes, journals, diaries, and notebooks, primarily documenting collecting trips; personal, biographical and family records; photographs of Alexander during all stages of his career and of his family; notes, specimen lists, locality data, drawings and related materials documenting his research on and collection of crane flies; diplomas and certificates awarded to Alexander; copies of lectures and examinations given by Alexander; a large file of 35mm color slides taken by Alexander, primarily documenting field work; correspondence and a notebook of the New Zealand insect collector, Thomas R. Harris; and photographs, correspondence and family papers of the entomologist, Jay R. Traver.

ARRANGEMENT: (1) General correspondence, 1906-1979 and undated; (2) entomological biography and history file; (3) field work file, 1926-1964; (4) field notes, diaries, and notebooks, 1903-1970 and undated; (5) personal, biographical and family records, 1903-1979 and undated; (6) photographs, *circa* 1870-1979 and undated; (7) Thomas R. Harris Papers, 1919-1957 and undated; (8) Jay R. Traver Papers, 1898-1949 and undated; (9) collection and research records; (10) diplomas and certificates, 1910-1971; (11) lectures and examinations, *circa* 1930-1968; (12) 35mm color slides, 1951-1975 and undated. FINDING AIDS: Published finding aid available. SPECIAL CONDITIONS: Use of this record unit requires prior arrangement with the Archives staff.

(7261)

Arthur R. Allen Papers, 1928-1964
(0.3 linear meter).

Arthur R. Allen (1880-1962), an amateur mineralogist, spent a large part of his adult life searching for meteorites in Colorado, New Mexico, Kansas, and Oklahoma. Allen corresponded with professionals and other amateurs throughout the world in the hope of obtaining new specimens for his meteorite collection. After his death, his collection was purchased by the Smithsonian Institution.

These papers contain correspondence with amateur and professional mineralogists, curators, and collectors concerning the examination, identification, purchase, and exchange of meteorites, as well as eyewitness accounts of falling meteorites, in particular, the Bird City, Kansas, Meteor, 1931. Also included are photographs of the Walsenburg Quadrangle, Roy S. Clarke, Jr., Edward P. Henderson, and J. Edgar Chenowith; and newspaper clippings concerning meteorites. Important correspondents include Oliver Cummings Farrington, William F. Foshag, John Enos Graf, Herbert M. Hale, Edward P. Henderson, Oscar Monnig, Harvey Harlow Nininger, Charles P. Olivier, and Alexander Wetmore.

ARRANGEMENT: (1) General correspondence, 1928-1964; (2) journals and notes, *circa* 1930-1938; (3) invoices, packing list and inventory lists, 1932-1940, 1963; (4) photographs, newspaper clippings and specimen labels, 1937, 1964 and undated. FINDING AIDS: Description in control file. SPECIAL CONDITIONS: Use of this record unit requires prior arrangement with the Archives staff.

(7450)

American Association of Museums, 1906-1985
Records (17.6 linear meters).

The American Association of Museums (AAM) was established in 1905 in order to promote the welfare of museums, to increase and diffuse knowledge of all matters relating to them, and to encourage helpful relations among museums and those interested in them. By the mid-1980s AAM was governed by a board of trustees, a president, an executive committee and a council. Committees of the Association included public relations, non-print media, curators, education, small museum, security, opportunities for minorities, credentials, and one concerned with the handicapped.

These records comprise the working files of the American Association of Museums. They include correspondence, memoranda, reports, minutes, proceedings, copies of *Museum News,* 1931-1962, copies of *Museum Work,* 1919-1925, and a large number of other publications and guides relating to museums in the United States and around the world. There are also records relating to the AAM Commission on Museums for a New Century, which sponsored a number of colloquia and educational projects for museum professionals in the early 1980s.

ARRANGEMENT: (1) General correspondence, 1960-1968; (2) minutes, 1906-1954; (3) Museums for a New Century, 1982-1985; (4) committee records, 1977-1985; (5) publications, 1910-1979; (6) miscellany. FINDING AIDS: Description in control file. SPECIAL CONDITIONS: (1) Restricted; (2) use of this record unit requires prior arrangement with the Archives staff.

(7057)

American Historical Society, 1835-1841
Proceedings (1 volume).

The American Historical Society was founded in 1835 in Washington, D.C., to "discover, procure, and preserve, whatever may relate to the Natural, Civil, Literary, and Ecclesiastical History of America in general, and the United States in particular." In 1840 the Society became the Department of American History and Antiquities of the National Institution for the Promotion of Science.

ARRANGEMENT: Chronologic. FINDING AIDS: None. SPECIAL CONDITIONS: Use of this record unit requires prior arrangement with the Archives staff.

(7440)

American Ornithologists' Union, 1871-1994, with related records from 1845
Records (13.3 linear meters).

For an administrative history of the American Ornithologists' Union, see record unit 7150.

These records supplement record unit 7150 by extending coverage in early records and providing records from the mid-1970s. Particularly noteworthy are early records of Presidents—especially Joel Asaph Allen, Jocelyn Van Tyne, and Ernst Mayr, as well as Presidents' and Secretaries' papers since the mid-1970s. Information about early committee work is found in Allen's and Van Tyne's papers. Photographs of individuals and group members were taken at scientific meetings and strongly supplement record unit 7150. Editorial files chiefly cover *Ornithological Monographs,* with some documentation pertaining to the *Checklist of North American Birds* and *The Auk.*

ARRANGEMENT: (1) Presidents' papers, 1877-1994; (2) Secretaries' papers, 1883-1994; (3) Treasurers' papers, 1903-1993; (4) Historians' papers, 1845, 1888-1993; (5) committee papers, 1912-1991; (6) meeting records, 1927-1992; (7) editors' papers and society publications, 1901-1994; (8) photographs, 1871-1993 and undated. FINDING AIDS: Description in control file. SPECIAL CONDITIONS: (1) Access to this record unit may require permission of the American Ornithologists' Union; (2) use of this record unit requires prior arrangement with the Archives staff.

(7150)

American Ornithologists' Union, 1883-1977
Records (12.5 linear meters and oversize).

The American Ornithologists' Union (AOU) was organized by three members of the Nuttall Ornithological Club, Joel Asaph Allen, William Brewster, and Elliott Coues, who wanted to establish an American society for ornithologists similar to the British Ornithologists' Union. They issued a call which was answered by twenty-three noted American ornithologists, later designated the founders, to meet on September 26, 1883, at the American Museum of Natural History in New York City. Formal incorporation occurred in 1888 in the District of Columbia. The aim of the AOU is the advancement of ornithological science through annual meetings, membership, committees, and publications. There are several classes of membership—Patron; Benefactor; Member; Elective Member, bestowed upon those members who have made contributions to ornithology; and Fellow, the highest class, which is bestowed upon Elective Members who have made the most significant contributions. Publications of the Union include its quarterly magazine, *The Auk;* the *Handbook of North American Birds;* the *Check-list of North American Birds;* and *Ornithological Monographs.* The affairs of the AOU are administered under a constitution and by-laws by elected officers and a council.

These records document the history, operation, and activities of the AOU, 1883-1977. The papers were scattered in the hands of various officers until 1969 when the Committee on Archives was established. In 1974 the collection was brought together at the Smithsonian. The records include correspondence, constitutions and by-laws, minutes, membership lists, nominations, fiscal records, contracts, manuscripts, reports, drawings, memorabilia, programs, abstracts, scrapbooks, and photographs.

ARRANGEMENT: (1) Materials relating to the establishment of the AOU, 1883-1899; (2) constitutions and by-laws, 1886-1975; (3) minutes, 1883-1976; (4) membership records, 1883-1977; (5) fiscal records, 1883-1976; (6) committee records, 1921-1977; (7) records of the Bird Collection Survey, 1966-1976; (8) publication records, 1884-1977; (9) correspondence of AOU presidents, 1932-1976; (10) correspondence of AOU secretaries, 1918-1977; (11) Hoyes Lloyd AOU correspondence, 1916-1976; (12) records concerning AOU awards, 1919-1977; (13) associations, 1962-1976; (14) annual meeting materials, 1889-1977; (15) scrapbooks and memorabilia; (16) photographs and drawings. FINDING AIDS: Description in control file. SPECIAL CONDITIONS: (1) Restricted; (2) use of this record unit requires prior arrangement with the Archives staff.

(7308)

American Ornithologists' Union, 1883-
Biographical files (0.9 linear meter).

In 1975, the American Ornithologists' Union (AOU) began a continuing project to amass up-to-date biographical and bibliographical files on its members. The Biography Committee prepared a form for members to complete. The modern entries generally consist of *curricula vitae,* the biographical forms, and, often, bibliographies. The Committee intends to ask for responses every five years.

This record unit consists of an alphabetic file of biographical information on past and present ornithologists and naturalists, not all of whom were members of the AOU. A number of the entries represent a much older part of the collection for which material is often limited, but can consist of clippings, memorials, press releases, obituaries, pamphlets, and reminiscences.

ARRANGEMENT: Alphabetic. FINDING AIDS: Description in control file. SPECIAL CONDITIONS: (1) Individual files may be restricted; (2) use of this record unit requires prior arrangement with the Archives staff.

American Society of Ichthyologists and Herpetologists, 1917-1971
Records (8.2 linear meters).

The American Society of Ichthyologists and Herpetologists (ASIH) originated in a Publication Committee established for the journal *Copeia,* on January 1, 1916. In February, the Committee met and created a society to advance the science of cold-blooded vertebrates, which was first called the American Society for the Study of Fish and Reptiles. When by-laws were adopted for the Society on March 2, 1916, it became the American Society of Ichthyologists and Herpetologists.

These records include fiscal records, files of several past officers of the Society, and records relating to *Copeia.* Coverage is thin up to about 1930.

ARRANGEMENT: Unarranged, with the following divisions apparent: (1) Secretary's correspondence, 1937-1957; (2) ASIH office files, 1930-1948; (3) Edward C. Raney correspondence, 1948-1952; (4) Treasurer's records, 1953-1965; (5) records related to *Copeia,* 1958-1968; (6) general correspondence, 1950-1970; (7) annual meetings, 1917-1971. FINDING AIDS: Description in control file. SPECIAL CONDITIONS: (1) The Smithsonian Archives has been designated as the official depository for the archives of the American Society of Ichthyologists and Herpetologists; (2) use of this record unit requires prior arrangement with the Archives staff.

American Society of Mammalogists, 1919-1993 and undated
Records (20.5 linear meters and oversize).

The American Society of Mammalogists was founded at the Smithsonian Institution on April 3-4, 1919, as the result of informal associations among members of the United States Bureau of Biological Survey, which was housed at the United States National Museum. Hartley H. T. Jackson of the Survey was a prime organizer, thinking that he and his colleagues "could make a success of a mammal society" after attending a 1910 meeting of the American Ornithologists' Union. Jackson served as Chair of the 1919 organizing committee. The Committee members represented the Survey, American museums and societies of natural history, and the National Zoological Park. The 1920 act of incorporation described the purpose of the Society as "the promotion of the study of mammalogy by the publication of a serial and other publications, by aiding research, and by engaging in such other activities as may be deemed expedient." C. Hart Merriam, Chief of the Biological Survey, served as the first President. The Society published the *Journal of Mammalogy* quarterly and several series on a less regular basis. The Society is the chief American society for the study of mammals, with international connections. Smithsonian mammalogists are strongly represented among its members and leaders.

For further information on the Society, see *Seventy-five Years of Mammalogy, 1919-1994,* edited by Elmer C. Birney and Jerry R. Choate, 1994.

This record unit documents the history and development of the American Society of Mammalogists from its inception through 1993. There is less documentation about the Society prior to the mid-1950s than more recent records, especially Presidents' papers. Particularly noteworthy is a record copy of the *Journal of Mammalogy* through 1991; record copies of other Society publications; a record copy of meeting programs, 1920-1992; and an autobiographical members' survey undertaken in 1987.

Related records may be found in record unit 7172, the Hartley H. T. Jackson Papers.

ARRANGEMENT: (1) Publication and editorial files, 1919-1991; (2) Secretaries' papers, 1919-1991; (3) Presidents' papers, 1926-1988; (4) meetings, 1920-1992; (5) Treasurers' papers, 1919-1972; (6) committee papers, 1931-1992; (7) Historians' papers, 1919-1992; (8) Historians' photographic collection, 1919-1993 and undated. FINDING AIDS: Description in control file. SPECIAL CONDITIONS: (1) Access to this record unit may require permission of the American Society of Mammalogists; (2) use of this record unit requires prior arrangement with the Archives staff.

(7351)

American Society of Zoologists, 1890-1992
Records (7.4 linear meters).

The American Society of Zoologists was founded in 1889 under the name of the American Morphological Society, a laboratory-based natural history research society. The organization's early membership and leadership came from the ranks of closely affiliated societies, the American Society of Naturalists and the American Physiological Society. To emphasize research on the whole organism, rather than strictly morphological study, in 1903 the Society changed to its present name. Organizationally it was still divided into two autonomous branches, eastern and central; their merger in 1914 marks the beginning of the modern Society. By the 1920s, the American Society of Zoologists was truly the nation's generalist biological society. It withstood subsequent pressure to splinter along sub-disciplinary lines both by sponsoring broad-based symposia on topics such as genetics and by adopting a divisional structure within the Society. This divisional structure, mostly along functional lines, was fully operational by 1962 and has been expanded since. The Society established its own journal, *American Zoologist,* in 1961. In the context of current biological science, the organization functions as an interdisciplinary society with an international scope.

These records document the American Society of Zoologists in the form of its predecessor organization, the American Morphological Society, and its autonomous eastern and central branches, back to 1890. Early records include scrapbooks, constitutions, lists of members and officers, meeting programs, and abstracts of presentations. Correspondence and committee files of secretaries and presidents are particularly rich from the mid-1950s. Divisional files provide records for the divisions of comparative endocrinology, from 1957; vertebrate morphology, from 1958; invertebrate zoology, from 1961; history and philosophy of biology, from 1977; and animal behavior, from 1986. A special series in this collection relates to the Carnegie Foundation funded project, "Science as a Way of Knowing," documenting projects in evolution, human ecology, genetics, developmental biology, form and function, cell and molecular biology, and neurobiology and behavior.

ARRANGEMENT: (1) Early papers, 1890-1918; (2) meetings, 1905-1960, and printed *Proceedings of the American Society of Zoologists,* 1916-1951; (3) Secretaries' papers, 1944-1984; (4) Presidents' papers, 1956-1984; (5) division papers, 1957-1989; (6) "Science as a Way of Knowing" project, 1983-1992; (7) photographs and audiocassettes, 1972-1987. FINDING AIDS: Description in control file. SPECIAL CONDITIONS: (1) Access to this record unit may require prior permission of the American Society of Zoologists; (2) use of this record unit requires prior arrangement with the Archives staff.

William Henry Anderson Papers, 1938-1957
(0.1 linear meter).

William Henry Anderson (1908-   ), an entomologist, was educated at the University of Maryland where he received the Ph.D. degree in 1936. That same year he joined the United States Department of Agriculture (USDA) as a Field Assistant with the Bureau of Entomology and Plant Quarantine. He was promoted to Assistant Entomologist in 1937, and Entomologist in 1939. In 1960, Anderson was appointed Chief of the Insect Identification and Parasite Introduction Research Branch, USDA. He remained in the position until his retirement in 1967. Anderson was a specialist on the larvae of Coleoptera.

This collection consists of incoming and outgoing correspondence documenting Anderson's research on coleopterous larvae. Most of the letters concern the identification of specimens.

ARRANGEMENT: Alphabetic. FINDING AIDS: None. SPECIAL CONDITIONS: Use of this record unit requires prior arrangement with the Archives staff.

Animal Behavior Society, 1948, 1954-1992
Records (9.4 linear meters).

The Animal Behavior Society was formally established as an independent organization during the 1964 annual meeting of the American Association for the Advancement of Science (AAAS) in Montreal, Canada, although its earliest records date from the work of predecessor organizations, beginning in 1948. The Society was an outgrowth of the Section of Animal Behavior and Sociobiology (established in 1956) of the Ecological Society of America (ESA), and the Division of Animal Behavior (established in 1958) of the American Society of Zoologists (ASZ). They in turn stemmed from the *ad hoc* Committee for the Study of Animal Societies Under Natural Conditions (CSASUNC) organized by John Paul Scott and colleagues (1947) following a postwar (1946) Bar Harbor conference on Genetics and Social Behavior, supported by a grant from the Rockefeller Foundation.

With the establishment of the Section of Animal Behavior and Sociobiology (SOABS) within the ESA, the eventual development into the Animal Behavior Society was virtually assured. The Section issued newsletters to its members on a regular basis, replacing occasional newsletters distributed by CSASUNC.

In 1958, the Division of Animal Behavior (DAB) was established within the ASZ. The ASZ Division and the ESA Section functioned as a single entity, with overlapping membership, a common set of by-laws, and a single slate of officers. The joint DAB/SOABS organization then joined forces, in 1958, with the British Association for the Study of Animal Behaviour to sponsor the journal, *Animal Behaviour*. David E. Davis was named American Associate Editor. Archives of the journal are not included in this collection; instead they are maintained at the University of Akron, Ohio.

By 1963-1964, it was clearly time to consider the establishment of a new and completely independent society. The final steps were taken at the winter (1964) AAAS meeting in Montreal, Canada; and the Animal Behavior Society was formally created.

These records include correspondence, documents, and committee records documenting the operations of the Society, its officers, and committees, as well as dealings with organizations in related scholarly disciplines and various learned societies. The collection also contains a photograph collection and some memorabilia of various officers and committees. A complete set of newsletters is included, as are spreadsheets and database compilations done by Society historians listing all the individuals who contributed much time and effort to the workings of the Society from 1956 to 1990.

ARRANGEMENT: (1) Secretary's records, 1954-1991; (2) Historian's records, 1948-1991; (3) President's records, 1957-1992; (4) committee records, 1965-1991; (5) Historian's photograph collection, 1956-1989; (6) newsletter, 1953-1992; (7) Program Officer's records, 1966-1992; (8) Treasurer's records, 1964-1987. FINDING AIDS: Description in control file. SPECIAL CONDITIONS: (1) Restricted; (2) the Smithsonian Archives has been designated as the official depository for the records of the Animal Behavior Society; (3) use of this record unit requires prior arrangement with the Archives staff.

(1050103)

Esther Richards Applin Papers, circa 1923-1968 and undated
(5.6 linear meters).

Esther Richards Applin (1895-1972), a micropaleontologist, was educated at the University of California at Berkeley. She pioneered in the use of microfossils to determine stratigraphic correlation. This new approach was an important breakthrough for the oil exploration industry. Applin's work was done primarily in California, Mexico, South Dakota, and the southeastern and western coasts of the Gulf of Mexico.

In 1919 she joined the Rio Bravo Oil Company as a paleontologist while also being retained by the East Coast Oil Company, Texas Company, and Gulf Oil Company. From 1927 to 1942 Applin was a consulting paleontologist and subsurface geologist in Ft. Worth, Texas. Later, from 1942 to 1945, she was an Assistant Professor of Geology at the University of Texas and consulting paleontologist for the Sun Oil Company. From 1944 to 1962 Applin was a geologist with the United States Geological Survey (USGS). Together with her husband, Paul L. Applin (1891- ?), also a USGS geologist, she studied regional stratigraphy based on micropaleontology.

This collection consists of lithic and final determinations for cores and cuttings of wells and correspondence concerning geologic parameters in the wells; general correspondence of Esther and Paul Applin; series files consisting of descriptions, depth readings, and photographs; miscellaneous files including correspondence, charts, plates, photographs, and reports; geophysical logs, including partial or complete lithologic descriptions and faunal occurrences, reports, and correspondence; plotted strip logs containing descriptions of rocks and wells; and electric logs showing geophysical properties of rocks.

ARRANGEMENT: (1) Lithic and final determinations of wells, *circa* 1938-1960; (2) general correspondence, 1926-1968; (3) series files, *circa* 1949-1961 and undated; (4) miscellaneous files, *circa* 1935-1964 and undated; (5) geophysical plotted strip and electric logs, *circa* 1923-1964. FINDING AIDS: Folder list in control file. SPECIAL CONDITIONS: Use of this record unit requires prior arrangement with the Archives staff.

William Andrew Archer Papers, circa 1918-1973
(0.8 linear meter).

William Andrew Archer (1894-1973) was a botanist and plant collector. After serving in France during World War I, Archer earned his Ph.D. from the University of Michigan in 1926. Most of his professional career was spent in various positions with the United States Department of Agriculture (USDA), including Curator of the National Arboretum Herbarium from 1938 to 1964. After his retirement from the USDA, Archer was appointed Research Associate in the Department of Botany, National Museum of Natural History (NMNH). Archer's career was marked by extensive collecting trips to Central and South America, and to Africa.

This collection consists mostly of correspondence documenting Archer's role as a Research Associate in the Department of Botany, NMNH, 1964-1973. Most of the letters concern his work organizing the Department's archival collections. Archer's collecting work is documented by photographs and photographic data from trips to Colombia, 1931; Central and South America, 1934-1935; and Ethiopia, 1951. Also included are photographs of Archer, including several taken during his World War I service; employment records from his USDA career; and various notes, lists, and newspaper clippings relating to his professional work.

ARRANGEMENT: Unarranged. FINDING AIDS: None. SPECIAL CONDITIONS: Use of this record unit requires prior arrangement with the Archives staff.

(7143)

Frank G. Ashbrook Papers, circa 1915-1965
(2.6 linear meters).

In 1924, the Bureau of Biological Survey of the United States Department of Agriculture established a Division of Fur Resources to coordinate and conduct investigations and gather statistics on fur farming. Frank G. Ashbrook was the first head of the Division. In 1939, the Division was transferred, along with the Bureau, to the Department of the Interior; and in 1947, the Division's functions related to breeding, producing, and marketing of domestically-raised, fur-bearing animals were transferred to the Animal Husbandry Research Division of the Department of Agriculture.

Frank G. Ashbrook (1892-   ) was appointed a Junior Animal Husbandman in the Department of Agriculture in 1914 and placed in charge of the fur animal experiment station at Saratoga Springs, New York, in 1923. While head of the Division of Fur Resources, Ashbrook also served as Commissioner General for the United States at the International Fur Trade Exposition and Congress in Leipzig, Germany, in 1930. Ashbrook remained with the Fish and Wildlife Service, successor to the Biological Survey, until 1957 as Civilian-in-charge of Wild Fur Animal Investigations.

These records are the files of Frank G. Ashbrook and include correspondence, statistics, journal articles, and newspaper clippings concerning the fur industry, fur farming, and fur resources; laws and tariffs concerning textiles and fur trading; correspondence concerning the China dog-skin case, 1934-1942; correspondence concerning the history of the fur trade and the Division of Fur Resources; material concerning the Reorganization Act of 1939 and the 1947 transfer of the Division of Fur Resources' functions regarding domestic fur animals to the Department of Agriculture; and reports by Ashbrook and other staff members on trips to fur animal experiment stations, wildlife refuges, private fur farms, and fur association meetings.

ARRANGEMENT: (1) Material on fur trade associations, 1924-1954; (2) fur trade statistics, 1924-1964; (3) material on fur trade history, 1921-1963; (4) information on furs; (5) fur storage experiments, 1927-1955; (6) statistics on Canada and Alaska, 1923-1960; (7) information on fur animals, arranged by species; (8) fur research records, 1924-1949; (9) beaver investigations; (10) reports, 1915-1957; (11) reorganization plans, publications, hearings, and court cases. FINDING AIDS: Description in control file. SPECIAL CONDITIONS: Use of this record unit requires prior arrangement with the Archives staff.

(7139)

William Harris Ashmead Papers, circa 1895-1906
(0.3 linear meter).

William Harris Ashmead (1855-1908), entomologist, began to make contributions to scholarly journals in 1879. In 1887 he became a special field agent for the United States Department of Agriculture and worked for the Department in various capacities until 1890, when he took leave to study in Berlin. In 1895 Ashmead joined the United States National Museum as Assistant Curator in the Division of Insects, where he remained until his death. His interests included the systematics, economic problems, and biological aspects of insects. Ashmead is perhaps best known for his monograph on the Chalcidoidea.

These papers consist of notes made by Ashmead, mostly as he undertook the generic classification of other families beyond the Proctotrypidae, some notes on the Cynipoidea, miscellaneous notes and drawings, and an article and report.

ARRANGEMENT: (1) Articles and reports; (2) research notes. FINDING AIDS: Description in control file. SPECIAL CONDITIONS: Use of this record unit requires prior arrangement with the Archives staff.

(7459)

Association of Systematics Collections, circa 1972-1988
Records (13.9 linear meters).

The Association of Systematics Collections (ASC) is an international, non-profit organization of institutions that maintain biological collections. It was established on July 7, 1972 "... to foster the care, management, preservation, and improvement of systematics collections and to facilitate their utilization in science and society." The ASC is responsible for coordinating development and implementation of plans to improve the condition and availability of biological collections. It fulfills its mission by providing representation for institutions housing systematics collections, encouraging interaction among those concerned with systematics collections and their use, and providing a forum for consideration of mutual problems. The ASC publishes a bimonthly *ASC Newsletter* and booklets on a variety of topical issues. It is governed by a Board of Directors and a permanent Secretariat.

These records document the establishment and programs of the ASC. They include records and audiotapes of annual meetings and Board of Directors meetings, *circa* 1972-1987; outgoing correspondence of the ASC Secretary and Executive Director, 1972-

1983, which contains extensive documentation on the founding of the organization; correspondence with member institutions; files concerning ASC committees and councils; records concerning an ASC sponsored survey of systematics collections, *circa* 1976-1977; files regarding the ASC project "Development of a Center for Biosystematics Resources," which was supported by a contract with the United States Department of Energy, *circa* 1978-1981; records documenting ASC participation in the Convention on International Trade in Endangered Species of Wild Fauna and Flora; records of ASC conferences and symposia; records of the ASC project *Checklist of Vertebrates of the United States and the United States Territories, circa* 1980; files regarding an ASC survey of endangered and protected species in the United States, *circa* 1978-1980; records documenting ASC projects under contracts with the United States Fish and Wildlife Service, National Park Service, National Science Foundation, Environmental Protection Agency, and other organizations; and copies of the *ASC Newsletter.*

ARRANGEMENT: Unarranged. FINDING AIDS: Box list in control file. SPECIAL CONDITIONS: (1) Restricted; (2) use of this record unit requires prior arrangement with the Archives staff.

(7391)

Wilbur Olin Atwater Papers, circa 1883-1889
(0.1 linear meter).

Wilbur Olin Atwater (1844-1907) served as Honorary Curator, Section of Foods, United States National Museum (USNM) from 1884 to 1892.

This collection consists of correspondence, notes, scripts, and labels from Atwater's work on a USNM exhibition on the chemical composition of foods.

ARRANGEMENT: Unarranged. FINDING AIDS: None. SPECIAL CONDITIONS: Use of this record unit requires prior arrangement with the Archives staff.

(7294)

Audubon Naturalist Society of the Central Atlantic States, Inc., 1893-1980 and undated
Records (6 linear meters).

The Audubon Society of the District of Columbia was founded on May 18, 1897, "...for the protection and study of birds...." The original by-laws placed governing authority for the Society in a fifteen-member Executive Committee which supervised the election of officers, appointed committees, managed finances, and arranged for publications and meetings. Officers of the Society included a president, honorary vice-presidents, a secretary, and a treasurer. When the Society was incorporated in 1947, new by-laws were instituted which abolished the Executive Committee and replaced it with an annually-elected Board of Directors. In December 1959, the name of the Society was changed to the Audubon Naturalist Society of the Central Atlantic States, Inc. (ANS). In 1969, the Society moved into its headquarters at Woodend, a thirty-room mansion on forty acres of land in Chevy Chase, Maryland, which was bequeathed to ANS by Mrs. Chester Wells. The *Atlantic Naturalist,* the Society's official organ, was published from 1950 to 1976. In 1976, *Audubon Naturalist News* became the primary ANS publication.

Although the Society was founded "for the protection and study of birds," it has been active in all areas of wildlife protection, the preservation of natural areas, and pollution control. The Society has lobbied for environmental legislation, promoted environmental education, and disseminated environmental information through its publication program. Conservation efforts of the Society have included blocking the construction of highways along the C & O Canal and through Rock Creek and Glover-Archbold Parks; the preservation of Dyke Marsh in Virginia; assistance in the formation of the Potomac Valley Conservation and Recreation Council; and the protection of bald and golden eagles.

These records document the history, operation, and activities of the ANS (before 1960, the Audubon Society of the District of Columbia). They also help to illustrate the evolution of the local and national conservation movement; environmental legislation and issues supported by ANS; the development of environmental education; and the natural history of Washington, D.C., and vicinity. The records include correspondence, scrapbooks, minutes, announcements, circulars, publications, reports, fiscal records, photographs, newspaper clippings, field notes, manuscripts, tape recordings, phonograph records, drawings, and memorabilia.

ARRANGEMENT: (1) Scrapbooks, 1897-1960; (2) minutes, 1901-1976; (3) Irston R. Barnes correspondence, 1946-1965 and undated; (4) general files, 1902-1978 and undated; (5) organizations file, 1959-1977 and undated; (6) exhibits file, 1953, 1965, 1969-1977; (7) committee files, 1937-1978; (8) fiscal records, 1964-1980; (9) Woodend files, 1967-1977 and undated; (10) *Atlantic Naturalist* files, 1948-1980; (11) photographs, 1918-1964 and undated; (12) newspaper clippings and obituaries, 1905-1916, 1940-1978 and undated; (13) Clarence R. Shoemaker papers, 1893-1943 and undated; (14) papers on the natural history of Washington, D.C., and vicinity, 1934-1936 and undated; (15) Shirley A. Briggs papers, 1948-1976 and undated; (16) miscellany, 1901-1978 and undated. FINDING AIDS: Description in control file. SPECIAL CONDITIONS: Use of this record unit requires prior arrangement with the Archives staff.

(7068)

Robert Stanton Avery Papers, 1855-1894
(1.1 linear meters).

Robert Stanton Avery (1808-1894) graduated from Harvard Divinity School in 1846, but soon turned his attention to mathematics and its application to the physical sciences. Avery taught at schools in the South, and in 1853, joined the United States Coast Survey (USCS), where he became Chief of the Tidal Division. His duties included receiving observer reports taken from tide gauges established on the coasts of the United States and computing tide estimates based on the data received. When Avery retired from the USCS in 1885, he devoted his remaining years to the development of the techniques of phonetic spelling.

These papers consist of correspondence with members of the United States Coast Survey chiefly concerning tide gauges; descriptions and drawings of working parts of clocks and tide gauges; mathematical equations and tables; records of data connected with Coast Survey work; office notes and vouchers; drafts for articles written and collected by Avery; USCS, mathematical, and scientific publications; and Avery's phonetic alphabet primers. Also included is correspondence concerning a proposal to print Avery's primers in Great Britain, and an obituary of Avery.

ARRANGEMENT: (1) Correspondence, 1856-1894; (2) records of data and computations; (3) mathematical equations and tables; (4) clocks and tide gauges; (5) office notes; (6) phonetic alphabet project; (7) handwritten article drafts and notes; (8) publications; (9) oversize. FINDING AIDS: Description in control file. SPECIAL CONDITIONS: (1) Knowledge of stenography will be helpful in researching the material; (2) use of this record unit requires prior arrangement with the Archives staff.

(7053)

Alexander Dallas Bache Papers, 1821-1869
(0.9 linear meter and oversize).

The papers of Alexander Dallas Bache (1806-1867) relate to his study of European education, his appointment as Superintendent of the United States Coast Survey, his professional intercourse with other scientists on a broad range of topics, his own research, and his work on the United States Lighthouse Board. They include diaries, 1836-1837, of his study of educational institutions in Britain; correspondence, 1821-1866, documenting his European trip, his work on education during the years 1839-1841, and his contact with the American scientific community; small collections of papers concerning the Coast Survey, the Lighthouse Board, and the Smithsonian Institution; letters to his wife, Nancy Clarke Fowler Bache; and a small collection of posthumous papers.

ARRANGEMENT: (1) Diaries, 1836-1837; (2) outgoing correspondence, 1836-1841; (3) incoming correspondence, 1821-1866; (4) incoming correspondence, 1849; (5) Coast Survey papers, 1849, 1853-1854; (6) Lighthouse Board papers, 1853-1864; (7) lectures, reports, papers; (8) Smithsonian Institution notes, *circa* 1847-1855; (9) letters of recommendation of Bache; (10) honors and appointments, 1821-1865; (11) correspondence of Nancy Bache, 1859-1869; (12) posthumous; (13) magnetic and meteorological observations at Girard College, 1840-1845. FINDING AIDS: Description in control file. SPECIAL CONDITIONS: Use of this record unit requires prior arrangement with the Archives staff.

(7417)

Florence Merriam Bailey Photograph Collection, circa 1892-1898 and undated
(0.1 linear meter).

Florence Merriam Bailey (1863-1948), amateur ornithologist and naturalist, was the author of many papers and books on birds.

This collection consists of personal and family photographs of Florence Merriam Bailey. Included are images of Mormon families in Farmington, Utah, and photographs taken on trips to Twin Oaks, California; Concord, Massachusetts; Summerville, South Carolina; and Mount Hood, Oregon.

ARRANGEMENT: Unarranged. FINDING AIDS: None. SPECIAL CONDITIONS: Use of this record unit requires prior arrangement with the Archives staff.

(7267)

Vernon Orlando Bailey Papers, 1889-1941 and undated
(0.9 linear meter).

Vernon Orlando Bailey (1864-1942) was born in Manchester, Michigan. At an early age his family moved to Elk River, Minnesota, where he developed an interest in natural history. Around 1885, Bailey began sending collections of birds and mammals to Clinton Hart Merriam, Chief of the newly created Division of Economic Ornithology and Mammalogy of the United States Department of Agriculture (in 1896 the name was changed to the Bureau of Biological Survey). In 1887, Bailey was appointed Special Field Agent for the Division of Economic Ornithology and Mammalogy. His title was changed to Chief Field Naturalist in 1890, and he remained with the Biological Survey until his retirement in 1933. Bailey's chief biological interest was the study of the life history and distribution of mammals. During his career with the Biological Survey, he made field investigations throughout the United States, Canada, and Mexico, including intensive biological surveys of Texas, New Mexico, North Dakota, and Oregon. His bibliography numbered 244 titles and included scientific monographs, as well as publications for the general reader.

This collection documents Bailey's career as a field naturalist and consists mostly of field notes and journals maintained on his many biological expeditions and field trips, 1889-1941. Also included is a small amount of correspondence with Bureau of Biological Survey staff and personal friends, 1913, 1922, 1927-1932; photographs, 1898 and undated; maps; publications; newspaper clippings; and manuscripts of monographs and articles by Bailey, 1921-1940 and undated.

ARRANGEMENT: (1) Field notes and journals, 1889-1941; (2) correspondence, photographs, maps, publications, and newspaper clippings, 1898-1932 and undated. FINDING AIDS: Description in control file. SPECIAL CONDITIONS: Use of this record unit requires prior arrangement with the Archives staff.

(7110)

Baird Ornithological Club of Washington, D.C., 1922-1949
Records (0.1 linear meter).

The Baird Ornithological Club was founded in 1922 by a group of Washington ornithologists for "the advancement of ornithological knowledge, and the furtherance of good fellowship among the members." The founders of the Club were: William Bonar Bell, Albert Kenrick Fisher, Henry Corbin Fuller, Edward Alphonso Goldman, Walter Cleaveland Henderson, Ned Hollister, Arthur H. Howell, Hartley H. T. Jackson, Edwin R. Kalmbach, Frederick C. Lincoln, Waldo Lee McAtee, Edward William Nelson, Harry Church Oberholser, Theodore Sherman Palmer, Edward Alexander Preble, Charles Wallace Richmond, Joseph H. Riley, Leonhard Stejneger, Bradshaw Hall Swales, Alexander Wetmore, and Robert White Williams.

These records include minutes of the Club's meetings which were held several times each year. Meetings of the Club were not just meetings of a board, but rather informal meetings of the membership. The minutes of the meetings often record discussions being carried on by members or guests.

ARRANGEMENT: (1) Minutes of meetings, 1922-1943, 1948-1949; (2) constitution and by-laws; (3) list of members, 1949; (4) reminiscences of Spencer F. Baird by Albert Kenrick Fisher, William H. Dall, Clinton Hart Merriam, and Leonhard Stejneger; (5) miscellaneous correspondence, 1928-1948; (6) photographs. FINDING AIDS: Description in control file. SPECIAL CONDITIONS: Use of this record unit requires prior arrangement with the Archives staff.

Charles Fuller Baker Papers, 1913-1927
(0.3 linear meter).

Charles Fuller Baker (1872-1927) spent most of his career as a teacher of agronomy and agriculture, but he maintained a steady interest in entomology. Trained at Michigan Agricultural College, he taught for several years in Colorado, Alabama, and Missouri before going to California, where, in 1903, he obtained the M.S. degree at Stanford. After a brief stay at Pomona College, Baker did further teaching and field work in Cuba and Brazil, returned to Pomona for several more years and, in 1913, became a Professor of Agriculture at the University of the Philippines. In 1918 he became Dean of that University's College of Agriculture, a post he retained until his death. Although Baker's entomological studies were avocational, he made a significant addition to the United States National Museum, to which his collection passed at his death.

These papers consist of correspondence with collaborators, focused largely on the central and south Pacific, southeast Asia, and Australia. There is little reference to Baker's official employment. Most material consists of extracts from the literature and other bibliographical items.

ARRANGEMENT: Alphabetic. FINDING AIDS: Description in control file. SPECIAL CONDITIONS: Use of this record unit requires prior arrangement with the Archives staff.

Elmer Darwin Ball Papers, 1915-1938
(0.7 linear meter).

Elmer Darwin Ball (1870-1943) was born in Vermont. After attending Iowa State College and Ohio State University, Ball became Dean of the Utah Agricultural College in 1907. In 1916, he became State Entomologist of Wisconsin and in 1918 joined the faculty of Iowa State University. While on leave from Iowa State, Ball served as Assistant Secretary of Agriculture in 1920 and 1921. He left Iowa State in 1921 to serve as Director of Scientific Work in the Department of Agriculture and held that position until 1925. While at the Department, he organized the Graduate School and served as its Director. From 1925 to 1928, Ball was in charge of an investigation of celery pests for the Florida State Plant Board. In 1928 he joined the University of Arizona as Dean of the College of Agriculture and later served as Professor of Zoology and Economic Entomologist.

These papers include correspondence between Elmer Darwin Ball and his colleagues including requests for specimen identification or specimen exchange for the 1920s and 1930s; requests for Ball's evaluation of papers about to be published; voluminous correspondence between Ball and Dwight Moore DeLong concerning their joint Thamnotettix project; and personal correspondence and professional gossip.

ARRANGEMENT: (1) Correspondence; (2) notes. FINDING AIDS: Description in control file. SPECIAL CONDITIONS: Use of this record unit requires prior arrangement with the Archives staff.

Herbert Spencer Barber Papers, 1903-1950
(2.1 linear meters).

Herbert Spencer Barber (1882-1950) was associated with entomology in the United States National Museum from 1898 until his death in 1950, for many years as an assistant to Eugene Amandus Schwarz. For most of this time, Barber was an employee of the Department of Agriculture.

These papers mostly concern Barber's professional work as an entomologist and administration of the work of the Department of Agriculture and the National Museum. His field notebooks include information on his trips to California, 1903; Texas, 1904 and 1918; Guatemala, 1906; and Arizona, 1914; and lists of photographs of specimens taken during the trips. In a series of outgoing correspondence, 1904-1909, family and other personal correspondence predominates, but in later correspondence, professional and museum matters assume priority. Some letters to and from Schwarz are included, probably a result of their close association. This latter correspondence is concerned with Museum and Department of Agriculture business, including acquisition of specimens, arrangements for study at the Museum, internal administration, acquisition and loan of specimens, and answers to questions and requests for determinations. A substantial proportion of the correspondence consists of professional communications between Barber and other entomologists concerning questions of taxonomy and biology of insects.

ARRANGEMENT: (1) Notebooks, 1903-1918; (2) outgoing correspondence, 1904-1909; (3) correspondence, 1906-*circa* 1939; (4) correspondence, *circa* 1938-1950; (5) notes and papers; (6) miscellaneous correspondence, notes, and papers, 1915-1942 and undated, accession number 89-014. FINDING AIDS: Description in control file. SPECIAL CONDITIONS: (1) Check finding aid for location; (2) use of this record unit requires prior arrangement with the Archives staff.

William Barnes Catalog, undated
(1.2 linear meters).

William Barnes (1860-1930), surgeon, was born in Illinois. He was an amateur lepidopterist and assembled the largest private collection of butterflies in the country. Although Barnes did little scientific work himself, he employed a number of assistants who studied the collections. In 1922, the collection was sold to the United States National Museum, with the proceeds going to the hospital which Barnes had helped found.

This collection consists of a manuscript catalog of the Lepidoptera of North America.

ARRANGEMENT: Manuscript catalog of Lepidoptera of North America. FINDING AIDS: None. SPECIAL CONDITIONS: Use of this record unit requires prior arrangement with the Archives staff.

Alice Pike Barney Papers and Related Materials, circa 1889-1995
(5.8 linear meters).

Alice Pike Barney (1857-1931), art patron and painter, is best remembered for her efforts to transform Washington, D.C., into the nation's cultural capital during the first quarter of the twentieth century. Daughter of Cincinnati multimillionaire and art patron Samuel Nathan Pike, Alice studied art in Paris in the 1890s under such well-known artists as Carolus-Duran, Jean Jacques Henner, and James McNeill Whistler. Barney returned to the United States intent on building a thriving arts center in Washington that would cater to every member of society, not just the social elite. She staged exhibitions of her works of art and took on a position of leadership in local art circles, serving as Vice-President of the Society of Washington Artists for the first time in 1901.

Alice Pike Barney's home during her residence in Washington, The Barney Studio House, by architect Waddy B. Wood, provided a gathering place for the District's fledgling artists' community. There Barney entertained the likes of Franklin Roosevelt, Sarah Bernhardt, President Taft, and visiting avant-garde artists with elaborate performances of her countless plays, mime dramas, ballets, and musical productions. Barney convinced Congress to fund the building of the National Sylvan Theater on the grounds of the Washington Monument in 1916.

Alice's daughters, Natalie Pike Barney (1876-1972), and Laura Clifford Dreyfuss-Barney (1879-1974), lived most of their lives in Paris. In 1960, the daughters gave Studio House to the Smithsonian Institution for use as an arts and cultural center. The building initially housed offices and visiting scholars and guests. After renovation in 1980, Studio House was opened to the public for tours and entertainment events, including restagings of several of Alice Barney's plays. In March 1995, the Smithsonian approved the pending sale of Barney Studio House, the proceeds to go toward the endowment fund for its National Museum of American Art.

The strength of the Alice Pike Barney Papers lies in its extensive holdings of Alice Pike Barney's plays, mime dramas, ballets, short stories, and novel-length works. Some of the manuscripts are present in multiple copies, in various stages of editing. They span Barney's life from *circa* 1904 to 1931. Also included are selected sections and roles from her plays, known as sides and parts, and accompanying musical scores. Many of the theatrical works were performed at various public theaters in Washington, D.C., or at Barney Studio House, and at Theatre Mart in Hollywood. Also included are manuscripts of plays by other authors, sent to Barney for review and for possible production at Theatre Mart. Theatre Mart contracts between playwrights and Barney are arranged in alphabetical order by playwright.

Autobiographical information for Alice Pike Barney consists of her fictionalized, unpublished autobiography, which focuses on her romance with British explorer Sir Henry Morton Stanley, a date book covering the year 1926 in Hollywood, California, and Barney family lineage information compiled in 1921 by a relative.

Laura Clifford Dreyfuss-Barney's papers consist of a childhood autograph book, diaries recording her correspondents from 1931 to 1939, 1951, and 1953 to 1963, and a travel journal in manuscript form. Her papers also contain a collection of her short stories and one play, Legion of Honor awards for her service in both World Wars, and a monogrammed handkerchief belonging to her father, Albert Clifford Barney. Finally, the Barney Collection includes records of Barney Studio House and other Barney residences, including blueprints, architectural drawings, a visitors' register, and newspaper clippings regarding the divestment of the Barney Studio House by the Smithsonian Institution.

ARRANGEMENT: (1) Alice Pike Barney autobiographical information, 1926-1927, 1948; (2) theatrical productions: scripts, 1904-1931; (3) theatrical productions: selected scenes and roles, 1925-1931; (4) non-theatrical literary manuscripts, undated; (5) musical scores and sheet music, *circa* 1915-1929; (6) Theatre Mart plays: contracts, 1928-1930; (7) Theatre Mart plays: scripts, 1919-1930; (8) Laura Clifford Dreyfuss-Barney Papers, 1890-1963; (9) Barney Studio House and other residences, 1889-1995. FINDING AIDS: Description in control file. SPECIAL CONDITIONS: Use of this record unit requires prior arrangement with the Archives staff.

(7089)

Paul Bartsch Papers, 1901-1963
(2.6 linear meters and oversize).

Paul Bartsch (1871-1960) was a zoologist with the United States National Museum, 1896-1946, Professor of Zoology at George Washington University, and Director of the Histological and Physiological Laboratory at the Medical School of Howard University. He was in charge of the pearl mussel inquiry, 1907; Smithsonian representative on the *Albatross* Philippine Expedition, 1907-1909; Director, *Tomas Barrera* expedition to Cuba, 1914; recipient of the Walter Rathbone Bacon Traveling Scholarship to explore the West Indies, 1928-1930; Director, first Johnson-Smithsonian Deep-Sea Expedition to the Puerto Rico Trench, 1933; and a member of the Smithsonian-Roebling Expedition, 1937.

These papers include Bartsch's field notes based on his ornithological investigations in Haiti, the Florida Keys, and the West Indies; field notes pertaining to the *Albatross* Philippine expedition; field notes regarding the *Tomas Barrera* expedition to Cuba; extensive field notes, manuscripts, financial accounts, and correspondence regarding his explorations to the West Indies on the Walter Rathbone Bacon Traveling Scholarship, and the first Johnson-Smithsonian Deep-Sea Expedition to the West Indies; papers relating to the Bartsch process for the preservation of wood and fibres; student theses and reports done under Bartsch's guidance; publications, draft articles, and monographs including the text of Bartsch and Carlos de la Torre y de la Huerta, *The Terrestrial Mollusks of the Family Urocoptidae in the Island of Cuba*, with two supplementary reports, 1943-1950, unpublished; photographs of Bartsch and de la Torre, as well as of birds, mollusks, and research activities in Florida and the Caribbean.

ARRANGEMENT: (1) Biographical materials, 1952-1963; (2) correspondence, 1907-1946; (3) field notes on birds, 1912-1927; (4) research expedition materials, 1907-1933; (5) bibliography and publications, 1904-1950; (6) draft articles and monographs; (7) notes, speeches, and specimen lists; (8) student theses, reports, and examinations, 1915-1936; (9) photographs and prints; (10) newspaper clippings, 1907-1909, 1933; (11) gazetteers of Cuba, Haiti, and the Dominican Republic; (12) field notes and journals, 1907-1937; (13) publications with card index, 1901-1955. FINDING AIDS: (1) Incomplete Bartsch bibliography, prepared by the Division of Mollusks; (2) description in control file. SPECIAL CONDITIONS: (1) Check finding aid for location; (2) use of this record unit requires prior arrangement with the Archives staff.

(7214)

Carl Barus Papers, 1891, 1893
(1 folder).

In March of 1893, Samuel P. Langley, Secretary of the Smithsonian Institution, asked Carl Barus (1856-1935), then with the United States Weather Bureau, to prepare a short article concerning the adoption of the international electrical standards proposed by the Great Britain Board of Trade in 1893.

These papers consist of a typescript of the article prepared by Barus and a copy of an 1891 report by the Great Britain Board of Trade Committee on the subject.

ARRANGEMENT: (1) "The Adoption of International Electrical Standards in the United States," by Carl Barus, 1893; (2) report of the Great Britain Board of Trade Committee on Electrical Standards, 1891. FINDING AIDS: None. SPECIAL CONDITIONS: Use of this record unit requires prior arrangement with the Archives staff.

(7234)

Ray S. Bassler Papers, 1875-1961 and undated
(1.2 linear meters).

Ray S. Bassler (1878-1961) was born in Philadelphia. Bassler spent his childhood in Cincinnati where he came into personal contact with some noted geologists, including Charles Schuchert, Carl Ludwig Rominger, and Edward Oscar Ulrich. While in high school, Bassler sold fossils for Ulrich.

In 1902, Bassler received a B.A. degree from the University of Cincinnati and received his M.S. and Ph.D. degrees in 1903 and 1905, respectively, from George Washington University. From 1904 to 1948 he was an Assistant Professor of Geology there.

Bassler joined the United States National Museum staff as Assistant Curator in the Department of Geology's Division of Stratigraphic Paleontology in 1904. Three years later he was promoted to Curator in the Department's Division of Invertebrate Paleontology. From 1910 to 1922 he was Curator of the Division of Paleontology, and from 1923 to 1928, Curator of the Division of Stratigraphic Paleontology. In 1929 he was appointed Head Curator of the Department of Geology, a position which he held until his retirement in 1948 when he was appointed Associate in Paleontology.

Bassler's main interest was with the Tertiary Polyzoa of the Atlantic and Gulf coasts. In this study, he collaborated with Ferdinand Canu of France from 1905 to 1931.

These papers consist of Bassler's incoming and outgoing correspondence and a manuscript on Australian Tertiary Bryozoa with plates created during his tenure at the United States National Museum; and photographs, primarily of his family. Correspondence documents the identification and exchange of specimens; publications of scientific articles; the administration of the Department of Geology; and the effects of World War II on European scientific research, libraries, and museum geological collections. For the earlier years, there are no copies of Bassler's outgoing correspondence. Also included is correspondence addressed to Edward Oscar Ulrich and Charles D. Walcott. The Tertiary Bryozoa manuscript with annotations and plates was written by Bassler and Ferdinand Canu of France.

ARRANGEMENT: (1) General correspondence, 1875-1961 and undated; (2) manuscript on Australian Tertiary Bryozoa, *circa* 1935; (3) photographs, 1890-1921 and undated. FINDING AIDS: Description in control file. SPECIAL CONDITIONS: Use of this record unit requires prior arrangement with the Archives staff.

Barton A. Bean Papers, circa 1892-1897, 1903-1908
(0.1 linear meter).

Barton A. Bean (1860-1947) was born in Pennsylvania and moved to Washington, D.C., where he joined the staff of the United States National Museum in 1881. At the Museum, he worked in the Division of Fishes under his brother, Tarleton Hoffman Bean, the noted ichthyologist and fisheries expert. In 1890, Barton Bean became Assistant Curator of the Division and he retained that title until his retirement in 1932. Bean also worked, on a number of occasions, as an investigator for the United States Fish Commission.

These papers include correspondence, notes, and notebooks of Barton A. Bean concerning his work with the Fish Commission in 1892 and 1897; trips to New York, Florida, and the Bahamas, 1894, and *circa* 1903-1908; and daily activities in Washington, D.C., 1895-1897. There is also a personal journal, apparently kept by a member of Bean's family, 1906-1907.

ARRANGEMENT: (1) Correspondence and notebooks, 1892, 1894-1897, 1903, 1905-1908; (2) miscellany, 1897 and undated. FINDING AIDS: Description in control file. SPECIAL CONDITIONS: Use of this record unit requires prior arrangement with the Archives staff.

Rolla Kent Beattie Papers, circa 1928-1947
(0.1 linear meter).

Rolla Kent Beattie (1875-1960), botanist and plant pathologist, was born in Ashland, Ohio. Beattie received his A.B. degree from Cotner University in 1895, and his B.S. and M.A. degrees from the University of Nebraska in 1896 and 1898, respectively. While at Nebraska, Beattie came under the influence of Charles Edwin Bessey, and remained a disciple of the Besseyan school of botany throughout his career.

Beattie taught high school in Colorado and Wyoming before becoming an instructor of botany at Washington State College in 1899. At Washington State he collaborated with Charles Vancouver Piper on researching the flora of Washington, Idaho, and the Northwest coast. In 1903 Beattie succeeded Piper as department head and botanist at the College's Agricultural Experiment Station.

Beattie began his studies on plant diseases while at Washington State. His studies eventually led to his working intermittently for the Federal Horticultural Board and the Bureau of Plant Industry, United States Department of Agriculture. While working for these federal agencies, Beattie helped establish inspection procedures for plants and undertook the task of solving the chestnut blight and Dutch elm disease.

Beattie retired in 1945 and began a study of David Douglas, pioneer plant explorer in the Pacific Northwest. Ill health prevented Beattie from completing his task.

These papers consist of correspondence from Mary Agnes Chase, William Ralph Maxon, and Egbert Hamilton Walker, Division of Plants, United States National Museum, concerning the receipt, examination, and determination of Beattie's Japanese ferns and grasses; correspondence concerning Merritt Lyndon Fernald's critical remarks about government scientists; field notes taken in Washington and Idaho, 1946; notes concerning botanical publications, bibliographies, and explorations in China, with a list of books shelved in the Hong Kong Herbarium Library, undated; and newspaper clippings regarding scientific research and explorations in China and the Far East, 1928-1932.

ARRANGEMENT: Unarranged. FINDING AIDS: Description in control file. SPECIAL CONDITIONS: Use of this record unit requires prior arrangement with the Archives staff.

(7105)

Gustav Wilhelm Belfrage Papers, 1866-1882
(0.1 linear meter).

Gustav Wilhelm Belfrage (1834-1882), born in Sweden, came to America in 1860 or 1861 and for the next twenty years made his living in large measure by selling insect specimens to entomologists throughout the world. He had known Carl Heinrich Boheman and Carl Stal in Sweden, and maintained contact with them after coming to America. Soon after arriving, he went to Chicago, and in 1866 he began his plan to collect in Texas. He corresponded with many American entomologists and with their encouragement and that of the Swedish Academy of Sciences, went on a collecting trip to Texas in 1867. Many of his specimens are in collections throughout the world, but his own collections, among which are most types of the new species of Hymenoptera described by Cresson, are in the National Museum of Natural History. He collected in many areas of Texas, especially in Bosque and McLennan counties.

These papers consist of letters from entomologists throughout the United States and Europe regarding purchase and exchange of specimens, especially insects of Texas, and include correspondence from Austria, England, France, Germany, Sweden, Russia, the United States, and Mexico; and a commission of 1866 from the Swedish Academy of Sciences for Belfrage's collecting in Texas.

ARRANGEMENT: Alphabetic. FINDING AIDS: Description in control file. SPECIAL CONDITIONS: Use of this record unit requires prior arrangement with the Archives staff.

(7381)

John N. Belkin Papers, circa 1930-1980
(4.9 linear meters).

John N. Belkin (1913-1980) was born in Petrograd, Russia, and became a naturalized United States citizen in 1938. That same year, he received his B.S. at Cornell University. He continued at Cornell, first as Assistant Entomologist for two years and then as Entomology Instructor until 1942. Belkin accepted a position as Junior Entomologist for the Tennessee Valley Authority in 1942, but soon afterward was commissioned in the United States Army Sanitary Corps.

Belkin was the Commanding Officer of the 420th Malaria Survey Detachment in the Solomon Islands from 1943 to 1945, where he conducted his extensive surveys and collecting of specimens that would later serve as the basis of his two-volume *The Mosquitoes of the South Pacific.* Belkin returned to Cornell in 1946 and received a Ph.D. in medical entomology. He then worked briefly at Rutgers University as an Assistant Specialist in Entomology, and from 1946 until 1949 was Associate Professor of Biology for the Associated Colleges of Upper New York.

405

Belkin moved to California in 1949 to take a position as Assistant Professor of Entomology at the University of California, Los Angeles (UCLA). He became an Associate Professor in 1952 and a full Professor of Entomology in 1958. In 1962, Belkin became Professor of Zoology at UCLA, a position he held until his death in 1980.

These papers consist of notes and collection information gathered about mosquitoes from all over the world, as well as field notebooks and data used for *The Mosquitoes of the South Pacific*. Also included is the typed manuscript, illustrations, and galley proofs of *The Mosquitoes of the South Pacific*, Belkin's professional correspondence documenting his career at UCLA, and photographs and slides taken at many different field locations.

ARRANGEMENT: (1) Alphabetic correspondence, *circa* 1946-1980; (2) color slides and photographs, *circa* 1950-1975; (3) notes and collection data, *circa* 1930-1975; (4) field notebooks, *circa* 1940-1945, 1961; (5) *The Mosquitoes of the South Pacific, circa* 1960. FINDING AIDS: None. SPECIAL CONDITIONS: Use of this record unit requires prior arrangement with the Archives staff.

(7394)

Charles Emil Bendire Papers, 1887-1894
(0.1 linear meter).

Charles Emil Bendire (1836-1897) was an Army surgeon and ornithologist. He served as Honorary Curator of the Department of Birds' Eggs, United States National Museum, from 1884 until his death. Bendire was the author of two volumes of *Life Histories of North American Birds* published by the Smithsonian Institution.

These papers consist of correspondence, notes, and lists accumulated during Bendire's work on the *Life Histories*.

ARRANGEMENT: (1) Correspondence, 1888-1893; (2) notes and lists, 1887-1894. FINDING AIDS: None. SPECIAL CONDITIONS: Use of this record unit requires prior arrangement with the Archives staff.

(7128)

Foster Hendrickson Benjamin Papers, circa 1927-1933
(0.1 linear meter).

Foster Hendrickson Benjamin (1895-1936), lepidopterist, was introduced to entomology by George P. Engelhardt and Jacob Doll. Following his graduation from Cornell in 1921, Benjamin worked for the Mississippi State Plant Board. In 1922, he became Curator of the William Barnes Museum at Decatur, Illinois, and in 1927 joined the United States Department of Agriculture, Bureau of Entomology. There he assisted in the investigations of the Mexican (Texas, 1927) and Mediterranean (Florida, 1929) fruit flies. In 1931 Benjamin transferred to the taxonomic staff of the Bureau of Entomology located in the United States National Museum, where he remained until his death.

These papers consist of a small quantity of records dealing with the various fruit fly studies and a larger number of taxonomic papers prepared by Benjamin. Some are incomplete, some were finished and in press, and others were approved for publication.

ARRANGEMENT: (1) Fruit fly investigation records; (2) manuscripts on taxonomy. FINDING AIDS: Description in control file. SPECIAL CONDITIONS: Use of this record unit requires prior arrangement with the Archives staff.

Marcus Benjamin Papers, 1886-1929

(0.7 linear meter).

Marcus Benjamin (1857-1932) was a chemist, sanitary engineer, and served as editor of several scientific publications. Benjamin was a contributor and staff member of Appleton's *Cyclopaedia of American Biography* from 1883 to 1902 and served as Editor of the United States National Museum from 1896 to 1931.

These papers relate to Benjamin's biographical information project as a staff member of Appleton's *Cyclopaedia of American Biography.* The contents consist mostly of questionnaires returned by subjects, or correspondence with subjects or relatives and friends of subjects, along with newspaper articles, printed works, and obituaries. Also included are page proofs.

Persons for whom there is more than the minimum biographical information are: Alexander Graham Bell, John Shaw Billings, Charles Frederick Chandler, Edward Drinker Cope, Elliott Coues, Charles H. Davis (includes Henry Cabot Lodge letters to Benjamin), Clarence Edward Dutton, William Gilson Forlow, George Gibbs, Asa Gray, Ferdinand Vandeveer Hayden, Samuel P. Langley, John Lawrence LeConte, Elias Loomis, Edward Sylvester Morse, Simon Newcomb, and John Wesley Powell.

Apparently, these papers resulted from a biographical project begun by Benjamin in 1887. Some letters included by Benjamin's correspondents predate 1887, however, and a few post-1891 items have been filed here by others. There is also some correspondence unrelated to the biographical information project pertaining to publication of articles and Smithsonian administration.

ARRANGEMENT: (1) Correspondence, 1913-1929; (2) biographical information. FINDING AIDS: Description in control file. SPECIAL CONDITIONS: Use of this record unit requires prior arrangement with the Archives staff.

Arthur Cleveland Bent Papers, circa 1910-1954

(2.9 linear meters).

Arthur Cleveland Bent (1866-1954) began his multi-volume *Life Histories of North American Birds* in 1910, and spent the remaining years of his life attempting to complete the project. A prominent businessman and citizen of Taunton, Massachusetts, Bent had been an amateur ornithologist since his childhood. In 1910 he offered to undertake, in collaboration with the Smithsonian Institution, and at his own expense, the completion of the *Life Histories of North American Birds,* begun in the 1890s by Charles Emil Bendire (1836-1897). Between 1910 and his death, Bent completed 20 volumes, one of which was published posthumously, and had accumulated notes for three other volumes, which were published in 1968 under the editorship of Oliver L. Austin, Jr.

Bent regarded the *Life Histories* as collaborative works, and he solicited information, data, notes, and photographs from hundreds of professional and amateur ornithologists throughout North America.

This collection includes notes, correspondence, information, and photographs accumulated by Bent while writing the *Life Histories.*

ARRANGEMENT: (1) Correspondence and notes, *circa* 1910-1954; (2) photographs; (3) miscellaneous photographs; (4) negative plates. FINDING AIDS: Description in control file. SPECIAL CONDITIONS: Use of this record unit requires prior arrangement with the Archives staff.

(7302)

Joseph Charles Bequaert Papers, circa 1922-1949
(1.7 linear meters).

Joseph Charles Bequaert (1886-1982), entomologist and botanist, spent most of his professional career as a faculty member of the Harvard Medical School and as Curator of Insects at the Museum of Comparative Zoology.

These papers consist mostly of manuscripts, drawings, research notes and bibliographical citations documenting Bequaert's study of wasps, especially the family Vespidae.

ARRANGEMENT: Unarranged. FINDING AIDS: None. SPECIAL CONDITIONS: Use of this record unit requires prior arrangement with the Archives staff.

(7194)

Carl H. Berendt Papers, circa 1875
(1 folder).

Carl H. Berendt (1817-1878) worked in Mexico and Central America on the ethnology and philology of the native tribes. His work was supported in part by the Smithsonian, the Philadelphia Academy of Science, and the Chicago Academy of Science.

These papers include a letter to Joseph Henry on existing manuscript sources for the history of Guatemala, April 2, 1875; manuscript notes on Central America; and other notes and letters, some in Spanish.

ARRANGEMENT: Unarranged. FINDING AIDS: None. SPECIAL CONDITIONS: Use of this record unit requires prior arrangement with the Archives staff.

(7052)

Jean Louis Berlandier Papers, 1826-1851, and related papers to 1886
(2.5 linear meters).

Jean Louis Berlandier (*circa* 1805-1851), anthropologist, geographer, historian, meteorologist and naturalist, was one of the earliest scientists to explore northeastern Mexico and southeastern Texas. A native of France, Berlandier studied pharmacy in Geneva and later studied botany under Auguste-Pyrame de Candolle at the Academy of Geneva. In November 1826, Berlandier was assigned by de Candolle to collect natural history specimens in the northeastern part of Mexico, including Texas. After arriving in Mexico, Berlandier was appointed botanist for the *Comision de Limites,* a scientific boundary survey financed by the Mexican government to survey the Mexican-United States border west of the Sabine River. Berlandier traveled with the *Comision de Limites* to southeastern Texas from November 1827 until May 1828, when he became ill with malaria. Berlandier then returned to Matamoros to recuperate. From the fall of 1828 until the end of 1829, Berlandier continued his excursions into Texas. After 1830, Berlandier resided permanently at Matamoros as a physician and pharmacist, but maintained his interest in natural history and the physical sciences. Berlandier maintained an extensive record of meteorological observations begun when he left France in 1826. In May 1851, Berlandier drowned while crossing a river south of Matamoros.

These papers are only a segment of Berlandier's papers which were purchased from Berlandier's widow by Lt. Darius Nash Couch in 1853. The Smithsonian Institution received Berlandier's meteorological records, mineral collections, and natural history specimens and manuscripts. The remainder of the papers were sold by Couch.

Between 1855 and 1886, various persons connected with the Smithsonian used these papers, particularly Berlandier's zoological and meteorological data, for research and editing. Their notations, abstracts, and other materials are part of this record unit. Included are Caleb Burwell Rowan Kennerly, who translated portions of Berlandier's zoological manuscripts; James Henry Coffin, who reduced the meteorological observation data, which Joseph Henry intended to publish; and Walter L. Nicholson and Cleveland Abbe, both of whom attempted to edit the works of Berlandier and Coffin, but were unable to complete the project.

These papers include Berlandier's correspondence; handwritten manuscripts on comparative anatomy, birds, botany, fishes, invertebrates, mammals, meteorology, reptiles and amphibians; four volumes on zoology; a geographical journal; astronomical, barometrical, cyanometrical, and meteorological data; air temperature, rainfall, and underground temperature data; sketches and watercolor paintings of birds, fishes, invertebrates, mammals, reptiles, and amphibians; photographs of some of the watercolor paintings; a handwritten manuscript on Indian mummies; *Memorias de la Comision de Limites a los ordenes del General Manuel Mier y Teran,* co-authored by Berlandier and General Mier; handwritten manuscripts collected by Berlandier, including a Spanish-Latin dictionary on medicinal plants; and catalogs kept by Berlandier of his manuscripts and scientific collections sent to Europe or kept by him. Also included are Walter L. Nicholson correspondence; drawings of Berlandier's medical office and pharmacy at Matamoros; maps; lists of American medical officials stationed at Fort Brown, Texas, 1846-1851, and 1869; James Henry Coffin's abstracts of Berlandier's meteorological observation data as arranged by Nicholson; printed materials collected by Berlandier and Nicholson; translations of Berlandier's meteorological manuscripts by Cleveland Abbe, Coffin, and Nicholson; translations of portions of Berlandier's zoological manuscripts by C. B. R. Kennerly; a catalog of Berlandier's manuscripts printed by the Smithsonian Institution in 1853; and notes concerning the Berlandier manuscripts at the Library of Congress and the United States National Museum Library.

Berlandier's manuscripts were written mostly in French, with some written in Spanish and Latin.

ARRANGEMENT: (1) Catalog of the Berlandier Manuscripts, and materials concerning Berlandier's manuscripts; (2) Jean Louis Berlandier correspondence, 1843, 1848; (3) astronomical, atmospherical, cyanometrical, and meteorological observation data taken or collected by Berlandier, 1826-1851; (4) Berlandier's manuscripts on anthropology, botany, and natural history; (5) Berlandier's manuscripts on meteorology and the physical sciences; (6) Berlandier's catalogs, inventories, and lists of collections and shipments; (7) Berlandier's watercolor paintings, drawings, and photographs taken of these works; (8) manuscripts collected by Berlandier; (9) printed materials kept by Berlandier; (10) Cleveland Abbe and Walter L. Nicholson's extracts and translations of Berlandier's manuscripts; (11) Caleb Burwell Rowan Kennerly's translations of Berlandier's zoological manuscripts; (12) Walter L. Nicholson and James Henry

Coffin correspondence, maps, drawings, meteorological abstracts, computations, and other materials. FINDING AIDS: Description in control file. SPECIAL CONDITIONS: Use of this record unit requires prior arrangement with the Archives staff.

(7335)

S. Stillman Berry Papers, 1880-1984
(6.1 linear meters).

S. Stillman Berry (1887-1984) was both a scientist and a businessman. Born in Unity, Maine, in 1887, he spent many of his early years traveling back and forth between the family homes in Maine, Montana, and Redlands, California. He received a B.S. in Zoology from Stanford University in 1909, an M.S. from Harvard University in 1910, and a Ph.D. from Stanford University in 1913. His field of special interest was malacology. He served as librarian and research assistant at Scripps Institution for Biological Research, 1913-1916. Although this was his first and last employment as a zoologist, he continued his malacological work the rest of his life, carrying out field investigations, being active in professional organizations, and publishing. His own personal publication, *Leaflets in Malacology,* appeared from 1946 until 1969. In 1917 Berry was elected President of the family business, the Winnecook Ranch Company, and held the position until his death. Berry was also a professional nurseryman. This began as a hobby because of his interest in genetics. His horticultural business centered on the hybridization of irises and daffodils, which provided Berry a welcome income during the years of the Great Depression.

The papers of S. Stillman Berry document his work in malacology, his brief career at Scripps, his horticultural business, his family relationships, and his college years. Much of the material consists of correspondence. Also included are diaries for parts of his life, as well as school notebooks, photographs, and memorabilia of his college years. Of special interest are photographs, clippings, and correspondence concerning the San Francisco Earthquake of 1906, which caused a great deal of damage at Stanford while Berry was there.

ARRANGEMENT: (1) Scientific correspondence and related materials, 1903-1984; (2) Scripps Institution for Biological Research, correspondence and related materials, 1913-1919; (3) horticultural correspondence and related materials, 1914-1956; (4) personal correspondence, 1896-1984; (5) family correspondence, 1880-1939; (6) university and organizational records, memorabilia, and related materials, 1906-1920, 1922, 1927, 1956; (7) diaries and related materials, 1904-1905, 1911-1925, 1931-1940; (8) photographs; (9) biographical materials. FINDING AIDS: Description in control file. SPECIAL CONDITIONS: Use of this record unit requires prior arrangement with the Archives staff.

(7185)

Biological Society of Washington, circa 1880-1972
Records (2 linear meters).

The Biological Society of Washington was founded on December 3, 1880. Its original purpose was the furtherance of biological scholarship by providing a forum for the presentation of scientific papers. Later modifications limited the purpose to the furtherance of taxonomic study and the diffusion of taxonomic knowledge, mainly through the publication of the *Proceedings of the Biological Society of Washington.* It was also one of the eight founding organizations of the Washington Academy of Sciences.

The governing council of the Society includes the elected officers and selected local members. The first president was George Brown Goode and the first recording secretary was Richard Rathbun. A number of other Smithsonian Institution and United States National Museum staff have been active members of the Society, as have staff from other federal government scientific agencies, particularly the Departments of Agriculture and Interior.

The records of the Society include mailing and membership lists, officers' reports, financial material, minutes of meetings, and official correspondence. There is a sizeable amount of correspondence and related material concerning the publication of manuscripts in the *Proceedings of the Biological Society of Washington.*

ARRANGEMENT: (1) Constitution, general correspondence, and reports, *circa* 1880-1909, 1940; (2) minutes of general meetings, 1894-1959; (3) minutes of Council meetings, 1880-1959; (4) records of the Secretary, *circa* 1902-1909, 1924-1972; (5) records of the Treasurer, 1904-1905, 1917-1972; (6) material concerning publication of *Proceedings of the Biological Society of Washington, circa* 1896-1918, 1924-1952, 1960, 1971. FINDING AIDS: Description in control file. SPECIAL CONDITIONS: (1) The Smithsonian Archives has been designated as the official depository for the archives of the Biological Society of Washington, and further material will be added periodically; (2) use of this record unit requires prior arrangement with the Archives staff.

(7171)

Bird and Mammal Laboratories, United States Fish and Wildlife Service, circa 1885-1971

Records (6.9 linear meters).

The Bird and Mammal Laboratories of the Fish and Wildlife Service are located in the Natural History Building of the Smithsonian Institution. Their main functions are to "determine the identity and distribution of species and populations of birds and mammals which are of concern" to the Fish and Wildlife Service and to "conduct the basic research necessary for the more critical and accurate identification of those specimens." In the process of carrying out these functions, the Labs have accumulated and maintained one of the world's largest specimen collections of birds and mammals. Directors of the Labs have included Stanley Paul Young, 1958-1959; Richard Hyde Manville, 1960-1970; and Richard Charles Banks, 1971-   . Chiefs of the Section of Birds have included Thomas Dearborn Burleigh, 1959-1963; Lester LeRoy Short, Jr., 1963-1966; and Richard Charles Banks, 1966-1971. Chiefs of the Section of Mammals have included Richard H. Manville, 1958-1959; Arthur Merwin Greenhall, 1963-1968; and Clyde J. Jones, 1970-   .

The Bird and Mammal Labs have their origin in the work of Clinton Hart Merriam and the Bureau of Biological Survey and its predecessors in the Department of Agriculture. The Bureau of Biological Survey remained within the Department of Agriculture until 1939 when it was transferred to the Department of Interior. The following year it was combined with the Bureau of Fisheries, which had been transferred to Interior from the Department of Commerce, to form the United States Fish and Wildlife Service. Merriam recognized the need for an extensive collection of specimens for the purpose of identification of species and their distribution. The collections he started became the foundation of the Bird and Mammal Laboratories. These collections became the basis for all the distributional, taxonomic, and identification studies conducted by the Biological Survey. Since 1889, the Smithsonian has served as the official repository for the collections gathered by the Bird and Mammal Labs and their predecessors.

These records include early correspondence of the Bureau of Biological Survey; general files of the Bird and Mammal Labs including correspondence, project reports, annual and quarterly reports, memoranda, material of various staff members, and material on the organization, history, and policy of the Labs; correspondence of the Bird Section and Mammal Section on specimens; and material concerning studies of fur-bearing animals, particularly the nutria.

ARRANGEMENT: (1) Correspondence, reports, and related materials pertaining to activities of the Bureau of Biological Survey, *circa* 1907-1939, 1943-1944; (2) general files of the Bird and Mammal Laboratories, *circa* 1885-1971; (3) correspondence and memoranda concerning the Bird Section, 1924-1969, 1971; (4) correspondence and memoranda concerning the Mammal Section, 1921-1964; (5) correspondence, notes, reports, and related materials concerning activities of Van T. Harris and Herbert L. Dozier in Louisiana and the nutria controversy, 1936-1967. FINDING AIDS: Description in control file. SPECIAL CONDITIONS: Use of this record unit requires prior arrangement with the Archives staff.

(7407)

Bird and Mammal Laboratories, United States Fish and Wildlife Service, circa 1954-1970
Records (1.2 linear meters).

For an administrative history of the Bird and Mammal Laboratories, United States Fish and Wildlife Service, see record unit 7171.

This record unit consists of files of Directors Stanley Paul Young, 1958-1959, and Richard Hyde Manville, 1960-1970, primarily concerning the Alaska sea-otter investigations of Karl Walton Kenyon. The records include correspondence, memoranda, reports, statistics, and photographs. Also included is a small amount of records documenting professional activities and publications of Manville. Records predating the establishment of the Bird and Mammal Laboratories in 1958 were primarily created by Young and Frank G. Ashbrook as staff members of the Section of Wild Fur Animal Investigations, Fish and Wildlife Service.

ARRANGEMENT: Unarranged. FINDING AIDS: None. SPECIAL CONDITIONS: Use of this record unit requires prior arrangement with the Archives staff.

(1070201)

Bird and Mammal Laboratories, United States Fish and Wildlife Service, 1881-1970
Collected Notes, Lists, and Catalogs on Mammals (4.7 linear meters).

For an administrative history of the Bird and Mammal Laboratories, United States Fish and Wildlife Service, see record unit 7171.

This collection contains manuscript notes, lists, and catalogs concerning mammal specimens. The catalogs are the primary documentation for many of the specimens of the Mammal Section of the Bird and Mammal Laboratories, United States Fish and Wildlife Service. Although they vary in content, as a general rule they contain specimen-related data including catalogs of specimens collected, dates, localities, tag numbers, measurements, and remarks on the specimens. Less frequently, they contain journal entries of the collector describing field activities, affairs of the day, anthropological observations, personal financial accounts, and other personal matters. Some material on bird specimens may also be included. There is also a visitors' register for the Laboratories, 1941-1970.

ARRANGEMENT: (1) Notes, lists, and catalogs, 1881-1949; (2) visitors' register, 1941-1970. FINDING AIDS: Partial description in control file. SPECIAL CONDITIONS: Use of this record unit requires prior arrangement with the Archives staff.

(1070101)

Bird and Mammal Laboratories, United States Fish and Wildlife Service, 1890-1953, 1964-1965
Collected Notes, Lists, Drawings, and Catalogs on Birds (0.9 linear meter).

For an administrative history of the Bird and Mammal Laboratories, United States Fish and Wildlife Service, see record unit 7171.

This collection contains manuscript notes, lists, drawings, and catalogs concerning bird specimens. The catalogs are the primary documentation for many of the specimens of the Bird Section of the Bird and Mammal Laboratories, United States Fish and Wildlife Service. Although they vary in content, as a general rule they contain specimen-related data including catalogs of specimens collected, dates, localities, tag numbers, measurements, and remarks on the specimens. Less frequently, they contain journal entries of the collector describing field activities, affairs of the day, anthropological observations, personal financial accounts, and other personal matters. Some material on mammals may also be included in these notebooks.

ARRANGEMENT: Alphabetic by author. FINDING AIDS: Partial description in control file. SPECIAL CONDITIONS: Use of this record unit requires prior arrangement with the Archives staff.

(7146)

Bird and Mammal Laboratories, United States Fish and Wildlife Service, 1935-1968
Fur Catch and Big Game Inventory Statistics (0.5 linear meter).

For an administrative history of the Bird and Mammal Laboratories, United States Fish and Wildlife Service, see record unit 7171.

These records pertain mostly to fur catch and big game inventory statistics compiled for the *Fur Catch in the United States* and *Big Game Inventory* published by the Fish and Wildlife Service. Prior to 1958, Frank G. Ashbrook compiled the statistics for the *Fur Catch* publication. Since then, the Bird and Mammal Laboratories, located in the National Museum of Natural History, have compiled figures for the report. Statistics for the *Big Game Inventory* are likewise compiled by the Laboratories.

ARRANGEMENT: (1) Statistics for fur catch and big game reports, 1935-1969; (2) information relating to big game and fur-bearing animals, 1949-1968. FINDING AIDS: Temporary folder list in control file. SPECIAL CONDITIONS: Use of this record unit requires prior arrangement with the Archives staff.

Maulsby Willett Blackman Papers, 1929-1943

(7366)

(0.1 linear meter).

Maulsby Willett Blackman (1876-1943), an entomologist, received the Ph.D. degree from Harvard University in 1905. From 1907 to 1929, he was on the faculty of the New York State College of Forestry at Syracuse. In 1929, he was appointed Senior Entomologist with the Bureau of Entomology, United States Department of Agriculture (USDA). He remained in the position until his death. Blackman's research specialty was forest entomology, especially the biology and taxonomy of Scolytidae.

These papers document Blackman's career at the USDA and consist of incoming and outgoing correspondence concerning the identification of specimens, the control of insects injurious to forests, and his research on Scolytidae.

ARRANGEMENT: Alphabetic. FINDING AIDS: None. SPECIAL CONDITIONS: Use of this record unit requires prior arrangement with the Archives staff.

Richard Eliot Blackwelder Field Notebooks, 1935-1938

(7156)

(2 volumes).

Richard Eliot Blackwelder (1909-   ) was awarded the Walter Rathbone Bacon Traveling Scholarship of the Smithsonian Institution from 1935 to 1938, following the completion of his doctorate in zoology at Stanford University in 1934. Blackwelder's research during the period he held the scholarship was concerned with a study of the Staphylinid beetles of the West Indies. In this connection, he made a number of field trips to the West Indies from 1935 to 1938.

This collection consists of two volumes of Blackwelder's field notes concerning his entomological observations and collecting activities in the West Indies.

ARRANGEMENT: Chronologic. FINDING AIDS: None. SPECIAL CONDITIONS: Use of this record unit requires prior arrangement with the Archives staff.

Doris Holmes Blake Papers, 1899-1978

(7310)

(4.8 linear meters).

Doris Holmes Blake (1892-1978) was an entomologist who specialized in the study of Chrysomelidae. She earned a B.A. in 1913 from Boston University and an M.A. in Zoology and Psychology from Radcliffe College in 1917. She married the botanist Sydney Fay Blake the next year and in 1919 went to work for the Bureau of Entomology of the United States Department of Agriculture (USDA) under Frank Hurlburt Chittenden. In 1928 she moved to the Department of Entomology, United States National Museum (USNM), where she worked under Eugene Amandus Schwarz until 1933, when she was forced from federal employment. She continued to study beetles at the Smithsonian as an unpaid Research Associate until her death. Over the course of her life she published ninety-seven articles in scholarly journals.

These papers contain the professional correspondence of Doris Holmes Blake, primarily concerning the exchange and identification of beetles. The papers also contain Blake's correspondence with family and friends, including many letters from her husband, Sydney Fay Blake. Doris Holmes Blake kept extensive diaries for seventy-five years recording mundane details and her most personal thoughts. To preserve her privacy, the diaries, while in English, were written in Old German script, making them difficult to decipher. Some of Blake's entomological and botanical sketches, as well as her non-academic writing, are also included. The papers also include a number of photographs of Blake and her family and of entomologists, both at the Smithsonian and at USDA.

ARRANGEMENT: (1) Professional correspondence and papers, *circa* 1918-1978; (2) private correspondence, 1905-1978; (3) family correspondence and papers, *circa* 1899-1977; (4) diaries, 1901-1978; (5) popular writings, undated; (6) miscellaneous papers and memorabilia; (7) photographs, *circa* 1905-1976. FINDING AIDS: Description in control file. SPECIAL CONDITIONS: Use of this record unit requires prior arrangement with the Archives staff.

(7430)

Sydney Fay Blake Papers, 1909-1960
(0.1 linear meter).

Sydney Fay Blake (1892-1959) was born in Stoughton, Massachusetts. He studied systematic botany at Harvard, receiving his B.A. in 1912, his M.A. in 1913, and his Ph.D. in Botany in 1917. He began work as a botanist at the Bureau of Plant Industry of the United States Department of Agriculture (USDA) in 1917 and worked there until his death. He published a number of botanical works and was writing the second volume of his *Flora of the World* at the time of his death.

These papers contain some of Blake's professional and personal correspondence. He corresponded mainly with botanists and collectors concerning the identification, naming, and exchange of specimens. These papers also contain administrative correspondence concerning Blake's position at USDA and substantial correspondence with family and friends.

ARRANGEMENT: Unarranged. FINDING AIDS: None. SPECIAL CONDITIONS: Use of this record unit requires prior arrangement with the Archives staff.

(7071)

George A. Boardman Papers, 1860-1899 and undated, with related papers to 1904
(0.1 linear meter).

George A. Boardman (1818-1901) was born in Newburyport, Massachusetts. He moved to Calais, Maine, with his family in 1828, and lived there for the remainder of his life. Boardman owned a lumber business for over 30 years, retiring in 1871. An amateur ornithologist, Boardman was acquainted with many prominent naturalists and corresponded extensively with Spencer F. Baird of the Smithsonian Institution. After his retirement from business, Boardman spent his winters in Florida collecting specimens, many of which were donated to the United States National Museum. His primary contribution to ornithological literature was the "Catalogue of the birds found in the vicinity of Calais, Me., and about the islands at the mouth of the Bay of Fundy" which appeared in the *Proceedings of the Boston Society of Natural History* in 1862.

These papers document George A. Boardman's work as an ornithologist, and consist primarily of incoming correspondence to Boardman from naturalists, including Spencer F. Baird, Joel Asaph Allen, Thomas Mayo Brewer, Elliott Coues, Henry Eeles Dresser, Daniel Giraud Elliot, Robert Ridgway, Addison Emery Verrill, and William Wood. Small amounts of outgoing correspondence are included and are noted in the folder list. Also included is correspondence documenting the deposit of the Boardman papers in the Smithsonian Institution. The correspondence is arranged alphabetically by correspondent.

ARRANGEMENT: Alphabetic. FINDING AIDS: Description in control file. SPECIAL CONDITIONS: Use of this record unit requires prior arrangement with the Archives staff.

(7259)

Botanical Society of Washington, 1876-1977
Records (2.1 linear meters).

The Botanical Society of Washington (BSW) was established on November 23, 1901, by a union of the Botanical Seminar and the Washington Botanical Club. The aim of the BSW is the promotion of botanical activity in the Washington, D.C., area. Most of its members are botanists of the United States Department of Agriculture, the Smithsonian Institution, local universities, and other government agencies. The Society holds eight meetings a year and is affiliated with the Washington Academy of Sciences.

John A. Stevenson was archivist of the BSW from 1939 until 1975, when the Society's records were given to the National Fungus Collections. In 1978 the collection came to the Smithsonian Archives. These records include constitutions and by-laws, materials from predecessor botanical groups, minutes, membership records, correspondence, financial papers, publications of members, records of special activities, and photographs, negatives, and lantern slides.

ARRANGEMENT: (1) Constitutions, by-laws, and related materials, 1910-1976; (2) materials from predecessor botanical groups, 1887-1913; (3) minutes, 1901-1976; (4) membership records, 1902-1977; (5) correspondence, 1898-1976; (6) financial records, 1901-1960; (7) notices of meetings, 1898-1977; (8) special activities and questionnaires, 1921-1976; (9) publications and addresses, 1876-1975; (10) photographs, lantern slides, and slides, *circa* 1885-1974; (11) negatives, *circa* 1885-1976. FINDING AIDS: Description in control file. SPECIAL CONDITIONS: Use of this record unit requires prior arrangement with the Archives staff.

(7119)

Adam Giede Boving Papers, 1908-1945
(1.6 linear meters).

Adam Giede Boving (1869-1957) was born in Denmark, where he served as Assistant Curator of Entomology in the Zoological Museum, Copenhagen, from 1902 to 1913. In 1913 he joined the staff of the Bureau of Entomology, United States Department of Agriculture (USDA). He was a specialist in the larvae of Coleoptera. Boving was a Research Associate of the Smithsonian from 1939, and he retired from the USDA in 1945. He was the author of a series of illustrated descriptions on the early stages of Coleoptera.

These papers concern entomology, especially the early stages of insect development and more particularly the larvae of Coleoptera. They include extensive correspondence with J. P. Kryger, 1936-1939, and data on Kryger's contributions to the national collection of insects. Other correspondence with a wide range of professional acquaintances concerns the acquisition and loan of specimens, determinations, and evaluation of papers for publication. Much of the correspondence is in Danish, German, and French.

ARRANGEMENT: (1) Correspondence, 1910-1945; (2) notes and papers; (3) plates and drawings; (4) oversize; (5) add acquisition, 1920-1945. FINDING AIDS: Description in control file. SPECIAL CONDITIONS: Use of this record unit requires prior arrangement with the Archives staff.

(7189)

William Dunlop Brackenridge Papers, circa 1838-1875
(0.1 linear meter).

William Dunlop Brackenridge (1810-1893) was a gardener and nurseryman from Scotland who came to the United States in 1837. When Asa Gray resigned his position as Botanist for the United States Exploring Expedition of 1838-1842, William Rich, the Assistant Botanist, took his place and Brackenridge was appointed to fill Rich's place. When the expedition returned in 1842, Brackenridge was entrusted with the care of the living plants and also with the report on ferns collected by the expedition. In 1855 he moved to the Baltimore area and spent the rest of his life there as a nurseryman and landscape architect.

These papers include a notebook of William Dunlop Brackenridge with daily entries from July 19 to August 31, 1841; two portraits of Brackenridge; and correspondence with John Torrey, Herbert Torrey, Asa Gray, Charles Wilkes, Charles Pickering, and others.

ARRANGEMENT: Unarranged. FINDING AIDS: None. SPECIAL CONDITIONS: Use of this record unit requires prior arrangement with the Archives staff.

(7140)

Emma Lucy Braun Photograph Album, circa 1932-1940
(1 volume).

Emma Lucy Braun (1889-1971), a specialist in forest ecology, spent her entire professional career at the University of Cincinnati. Her primary field of interest was deciduous forests of eastern North America, a subject on which she produced several publications.

This album contains photographs of Kentucky and Tennessee forests, many of which appeared in her published work. Also included are some photographs of individuals and groups, and a series of photographs of forests taken by Ralph W. Chaney in 1940. Most of the photographs are of virgin forests that have since been destroyed by lumbering and mining.

ARRANGEMENT: Mainly chronologic. FINDING AIDS: Most of the photographs are identified by locality and date. SPECIAL CONDITIONS: Use of this record unit requires prior arrangement with the Archives staff.

Robert Angus Brooks Papers, 1926-1976

(1.7 linear meters).

Robert Angus Brooks (1920-1976) was a scholar of classical philology and an administrator. He was educated at Harvard (A.B., 1940, A.M., 1941, Ph.D., 1949) and served in the Army Air Force, 1942-1946, and taught classics at Harvard until 1951. He was Vice-President, 1951-1965, and President, 1969-1971, of Harbridge House, a Boston consulting firm, and Assistant Secretary of the Army, 1965-1969. He joined the Smithsonian as Deputy Under Secretary in 1971. He became Assistant Secretary in 1972 and Under Secretary in 1973.

These papers consist primarily of notes and reports relating to Brooks's education and military service. Coverage of most of his career—years at Harbridge House, the Pentagon, and the Smithsonian—is spare. Also included are papers concerning professional memberships, speeches, articles, poetry, resumes, and obituaries. Correspondence makes up a small part of the collection.

ARRANGEMENT: (1) Personal correspondence, 1948-1976 and undated; (2) Dalhousie Castle School, 1926-1935, 1960; (3) Roxbury Latin School, 1933-1944; (4) Harvard University, 1936-1976; (5) papers relating to military service, 1942-1956; (6) Harbridge House, 1951-1975; (7) Assistant Secretary of the Army for Installations and Logistics, 1965-1971; (8) Smithsonian Institution, 1971-1976; (9) memberships; (10) drama productions, articles, speeches, and poetry; (11) miscellany. FINDING AIDS: Description in control file. SPECIAL CONDITIONS: Use of this record unit requires prior arrangement with the Archives staff.

James Templeman Brown Papers, circa 1883-1884

(0.1 linear meter).

James Templeman Brown (? -1886), an assistant in the Department of Arts and Industries of the United States National Museum, apparently prepared this manuscript in connection with his duties as preparator of the whaling exhibit of the United States Fish Commission at the London International Fisheries Exposition of 1883. A similar work by Brown appears in the "Bulletin of the United States National Museum," no. 27, Part E.

The papers consist of a manuscript concerning the various boats, harpoons, cutting tools, and other instruments used by the United States whaling fleets, *circa* 1883.

ARRANGEMENT: Manuscript entitled "Apparatus of the Whaling Industry" by James Templeman Brown, *circa* 1883-1884. FINDING AIDS: None. SPECIAL CONDITIONS: Use of this record unit requires prior arrangement with the Archives staff.

Roland Wilbur Brown Papers, 1930-1958, with related materials, 1876-1878

(0.4 linear meter).

Roland Wilbur Brown (1893-1961), a paleobotanist, received his Ph.D. from the Johns Hopkins University in 1926. He was appointed Geologist with the United States Geological Survey (USGS) in 1928, where he remained until his retirement in 1958. Brown also served as a Research Associate in the Department of Geology, United States

National Museum (USNM) from 1951 until his death. He specialized in the study of Mesozoic and Cenozoic plants.

These papers consist mostly of incoming and outgoing correspondence documenting Brown's career with the USGS, his work at the USNM, and his paleobotanical research. The correspondence concerns the acquisition, loan, and identification of fossil plant specimens; the publication and review of scientific papers; and professional activities. Also included are notes and lists from his research; photographs of Brown, the paleobotanist David White, and collecting localities; and three letters to the paleontologist William Morris Fontaine from Edward Drinker Cope, Samuel H. Scudder, and Charles Leo Lesquereux dated between 1876 and 1878.

ARRANGEMENT: Unarranged. FINDING AIDS: None. SPECIAL CONDITIONS: Use of this record unit requires prior arrangement with the Archives staff.

(7361)

Lee L. Buchanan Papers, 1917-1948 and undated
(0.1 linear meter).

Lee L. Buchanan (1893-1958) was an entomologist specializing in Coleoptera taxonomy. From 1917 to 1929 he was Assistant Biologist with the Bureau of Biological Survey, United States Department of Agriculture (USDA). In 1929 he was appointed Entomologist with the Bureau of Entomology and Plant Quarantine, USDA. He remained in the position until his retirement in 1949. Buchanan also served as honorary Specialist for the Casey Collection of Coleoptera, United States National Museum, 1926-1958.

This collection consists of field notes taken by Buchanan during a collecting trip in Iowa, 1917; an unpublished manuscript on West Indian Apion; and notes, correspondence, and related materials concerning his research on Coleoptera.

ARRANGEMENT: Unarranged. FINDING AIDS: None. SPECIAL CONDITIONS: Use of this record unit requires prior arrangement with the Archives staff.

(7279)

Helmut Karl Buechner Papers, 1939-1975
(11.7 linear meters and oversize).

Helmut Karl Buechner (1918-1975) was born in Scotia, New York, and received his B.A. from New York State College of Forestry, Syracuse University, in 1941. He subsequently received an M.A. from Texas A & M College in 1943, and a Ph.D. from Oklahoma A & M College in 1949. From 1948 to 1965 Buechner taught zoology and botany at Washington State College (now University). He joined the Smithsonian in 1965 as its first Director of the Office of Ecology. From 1969 to 1972, Buechner served as Senior Ecologist for the Office of Environmental Sciences and from 1972 to 1975, for the National Zoological Park.

These papers chiefly document Buechner's research interest in the ecology of terrestrial vertebrates, especially as applied to vegetation and social behavior. Significant subjects include Buechner's research on pronghorn antelopes in Texas; elk and deer of the Blue Mountains region of Washington; and bighorn sheep, notably

Buechner's *The Bighorn Sheep in the United States, Its Past, Present, and Future,* 1959. Also present is material from Buechner's research on elephants and the kob in Uganda at various times between 1956 and 1972. The records likewise document a study of Indian rhinoceros mating behavior at the National Zoological Park in 1972, which led to the first successful live birth of this species in the Western Hemisphere in 1974. Finally, the papers record aspects of Buechner's work as an ecological consultant in Switzerland (1961), Kenya (1965), and New Jersey (1966, 1970).

ARRANGEMENT: (1) School notes, exams, lectures, and term papers, 1939-1947; (2) correspondence, 1946-1975; (3) general office files, 1950-1975, arranged alphabetically; (4) research projects, 1946-1975; (5) theses by former students, collected by Buechner, arranged chronologically, 1951-1960; (6) abstracts, articles, and book reviews, 1941-1974; (7) lectures, seminars, and symposia, 1949-1974; (8) audio recordings, 1959-1972; (9) photographs, arranged by subjects; (10) diplomas and certificates; (11) oversize, observation and machine readable data on the kob; (12) notepads and diary, 1965, 1970-1971; (13) oversize maps, charts, and blueprints. FINDING AIDS: Description in control file. SPECIAL CONDITIONS: Use of this record unit requires prior arrangement with the Archives staff.

(7168)

Bureau of Biological Survey, United States Department of Interior, 1928-1940
Big Game Estimates and Inventories (0.1 linear meter).

By letter of September 26, 1923, the Chief of the Bureau of Biological Survey requested from the National Park Service yearly "information as to the number of the different kinds of big game animals in the various national parks, for use in reissuance of lists of national and state game and bird refuges." In 1937, the Biological Survey began annual inventories of big game throughout the country, compiling these statistics from estimates of the National Park Service, Forest Service, and its own field agents and cooperative units.

These papers include correspondence, statistics, and material generated and collected by the Biological Survey in its administration of the inventory from 1928 to 1940.

ARRANGEMENT: Chronologic. FINDING AIDS: Description in control file. SPECIAL CONDITIONS: Use of this record unit requires prior arrangement with the Archives staff.

(7184)

Bureau of Fisheries, United States Department of Commerce, circa 1877-1948
Records (4 linear meters and 5 microfilm reels).

The Office of the United States Commissioner of Fish and Fisheries was established in 1871, and Spencer F. Baird of the Smithsonian was appointed the first Commissioner. The Office was created to study the diminution of the fishes of the coastal waters of New England. The duties of the Commission were gradually expanded to include fish culture, further studies of fisheries and fishery industries, and studies in freshwater and marine biology. The Commission was transferred to the Department of Commerce and Labor in 1903 and its name changed to the Bureau of Fisheries. In 1939, the Bureau was transferred to the Department of Interior, and in 1940 was merged with the Bureau of Biological Survey to form the Fish and Wildlife Service.

The United States Fish Commission and its successors have always maintained close ties with the Smithsonian and the United States National Museum. Baird was Assistant

Secretary and Secretary of the Smithsonian while serving as Commissioner and often assigned Smithsonian staff to Fish Commission duties. In a number of cases, there was considerable overlap between Smithsonian and Commission work. A number of Commission staff, including Tarleton Hoffman Bean and Barton Warren Evermann, served as Honorary Curators for the Museum's Division of Fishes. The Division has also served as the depository for specimens collected by the Fish Commission and its successors.

These papers include original logbooks for the vessels of the Fish Commission and its successors, including the *Albatross, Fish Hawk, Grampus, Danglade, Halcyon,* and *Yvonne,* containing hydrographic and dredging records; transcribed records of data gathered by some of those vessels; material concerning specimens collected by the Commission and its successors; and material concerning oyster surveys conducted by the Commission.

ARRANGEMENT: (1) Original logbooks for vessels, *circa* 1877-1925; (2) transcribed records for vessels, *circa* 1883-1916; (3) material concerning specimen accessions and transmittals, ship stations, and expositions, 1880, 1883, 1900, 1903, *circa* 1911-1948; (4) letters of transmittal and acknowledgement, 1889, 1894, 1896-1915; (5) notes, lists, and reports concerning scientific work, 1882-1883, 1890-1891, 1901, 1911-1914; (6) logbooks, notes, and correspondence concerning oyster surveys, 1888, 1897-1898; (7) mussel accession books, *circa* 1899-1912; (8) distribution records of fishes, 1881-1887; (9) microfilm copies of logbooks, tag records, and catalogs. FINDING AIDS: Description in control file. SPECIAL CONDITIONS: Use of this record unit requires prior arrangement with the Archives staff.

(7438)

Bureau of Fisheries, United States Department of Commerce, circa 1883-1915
Records (0.5 linear meter).

For an administrative history of the Bureau of Fisheries see, record unit 7184.

This collection consists mostly of records created during scientific voyages of the Bureau of Fisheries vessel *Albatross.* Included are dredging records, meteorological observations, hydrographic sounding records, and water temperature and specific gravity readings. Also included are reports of *Albatross* naturalist, James E. Benedict, 1883-1885; records concerning collections transferred by the Bureau of Fisheries to the United States National Museum, 1888-1910; and a record of photographs made by the United States Fish Commission, 1887-1891.

ARRANGEMENT: Unarranged. FINDING AIDS: None. SPECIAL CONDITIONS: Use of this record unit requires prior arrangement with the Archives staff.

(7368)

Barnard D. Burks Papers, 1949-1974
(1.2 linear meters).

Barnard D. Burks (1909-1990) studied at the University of Illinois and received his B.A. in 1933, M.A. in 1934, and Ph.D in entomology in 1937. From 1935 until 1942, he worked for the State Natural History Survey in Urbana, Illinois, as Assistant Entomologist. During World War II, he worked for the United States Army Sanitary Corps from 1942 to 1946. He then returned to the State Natural History Survey in 1946 as Associate Taxonomist, but resigned three years later to accept a position as

Entomologist at the Division of Insect Identification, United States Department of Agriculture (USDA), located in the Natural History Building in Washington, D.C. After 1972, the Division became the Systematic Entomology Laboratory. In 1964, his title was changed to Collaborative Scientist, and he continued the study of parasitic Hymenoptera until his retirement from the USDA in 1974. Burks also served as Associate Editor of *American Midland Naturalist* from 1954 to 1967, reviewing entomology papers for the journal.

These papers consist of incoming and outgoing professional correspondence mostly concerned with the identification of entomological specimens. Also included is correspondence relating to Burks' term as Associate Editor for *American Midland Naturalist*.

ARRANGEMENT: (1) Correspondence, alphabetic, 1949-1974; (2) *American Midland Naturalist* correspondence, 1954-1967. FINDING AIDS: None. SPECIAL CONDITIONS: Use of this record unit requires prior arrangement with the Archives staff.

(7129)

August Busck Papers, 1902-1933
(0.1 linear meter).

August Busck (1870-1944) was born and educated in Denmark. In 1893 he came to the United States and settled in West Virginia, where he became an American citizen. After an interval as a florist, Busck began work for the United States Department of Agriculture in 1896, where he remained until his retirement in 1940. A friend and colleague of both Lord Walsingham and Edward Meyrick, Busck was himself a microlepidopterist of real distinction. He made numerous field trips on expeditions into various regions of the western hemisphere, as well as conducting field studies in the United States. While his knowledge of the Lepidoptera was extensive, Busck chose to restrict his main efforts to American fauna, especially the groups formerly known as the Tineira and Torticina.

These papers consist of professional correspondence between Busck and others on entomological subjects.

ARRANGEMENT: (1) Correspondence, 1902-1933; (2) August Busck's copy of Meyrick's *Microlepidoptera;* (3) rearing notebooks. FINDING AIDS: Description in control file. SPECIAL CONDITIONS: (1) Check finding aid for location; (2) use of this record unit requires prior arrangement with the Archives staff.

(7377)

Charles Butts Papers, circa 1905-1946
(1.6 linear meters).

Charles Butts (1863-1946) was a paleontologist and authority on the Paleozoic formations of the Appalachian region. He received the B.S. in 1899, and the M.S. in 1900 from Alfred University. Butts joined the United States Geological Survey (USGS) in 1901 as Assistant Geologist, and was promoted to Paleontologist in 1909 and Geologist in 1912. He remained with the USGS until his retirement from federal service in 1933. From 1933 until his death, Butts was employed by the Virginia Geological Survey (VGS) to conduct mapping of the Paleozoic formations of the Appalachian valley. During his career with the USGS, Butts conducted extensive geological surveys in Alabama, Kentucky, and Virginia.

The papers of Charles Butts document his careers with the USGS and the VGS and his research on Appalachian geology and paleontology. They include a large file of incoming and outgoing correspondence with academic, government, and economic geologists and paleontologists. The letters concern his geological surveys of the Appalachian region, the preparation of publications and maps, and professional activities. Also included are notes, manuscripts, maps, lists, and related materials concerning his research.

ARRANGEMENT: Unarranged. FINDING AIDS: None. SPECIAL CONDITIONS: Use of this record unit requires prior arrangement with the Archives staff.

(7452)

George W. Byers Photograph Collection, 1956-1993
(0.1 linear meter).

George W. Byers (1923-   ) is an entomologist specializing in the study of Diptera. Most of his professional career was spent at the University of Kansas, where he retired as Director of the Snow Entomological Museum in 1988.

This collection consists of black and white and color photographs taken by Byers of fellow entomologists. Many of the photographs were taken at national and international entomological conventions.

ARRANGEMENT: Unarranged. FINDING AIDS: Description in control file. SPECIAL CONDITIONS: Use of this record unit requires prior arrangement with the Archives staff.

(7362)

Frank L. Campbell Photograph Collection, 1930-1968 and undated
(0.1 linear meter).

Frank L. Campbell (1898-1979) served as an Entomologist with the Bureau of Entomology, United States Department of Agriculture, from 1927 to 1936. He also had careers as Editor of the *Scientific Monthly* of the American Association for the Advancement of Science, 1947-1953, and as Executive Secretary of the Biology and Agriculture Division of the National Academy of Sciences—National Research Council, 1953-1964.

This collection consists of photographs collected by Campbell during his professional career. Most of the photographs are of Campbell and colleagues, especially staff members of the Bureau of Entomology. Also included are photographs of *Scientific Monthly* and Bureau of Entomology offices and facilities.

ARRANGEMENT: Unarranged. FINDING AIDS: None. SPECIAL CONDITIONS: Use of this record unit requires prior arrangement with the Archives staff.

Hahn William Capps Papers, 1939-1964
(0.8 linear meter).

Hahn William Capps (1903-   ), an entomologist, received his B.S. degree from the University of Kansas in 1929. Capps joined the staff of the United States Department of Agriculture (USDA) in 1930 when he was appointed Plant Quarantine Inspector with the Bureau of Entomology and Plant Quarantine. He was made Assistant Entomologist in 1938, and Entomologist in 1940, a position he held until his retirement in 1964. Capps specialized in the study of Lepidoptera in both their larval and adult stages.

The papers of Hahn William Capps document his career with the USDA and his research on Lepidoptera. They include incoming and outgoing correspondence concerning the identification of specimens, publication of papers, and professional activities; notes, lists, manuscripts, and bibliographical references from his research; newsletters of The Lepidopterist's Society, 1959-1964; and annual reports which he submitted to the USDA, 1939-1952.

ARRANGEMENT: Unarranged. FINDING AIDS: None. SPECIAL CONDITIONS: Use of this record unit requires prior arrangement with the Archives staff.

Philip Pearsall Carpenter Manuscript, circa 1870s
(0.4 linear meter).

Philip Pearsall Carpenter (1819-1877) was a minister from Montreal, Canada. The Smithsonian Institution published several of his monographs on mollusks.

This collection consists of an unpublished, two volume manuscript on chitons by Carpenter. The manuscript was apparently intended for publication by the Smithsonian, but the project was abandoned after Carpenter's death. Parts of the manuscript are written in his personal shorthand and are virtually indecipherable.

ARRANGEMENT: Taxonomic. FINDING AIDS: None. SPECIAL CONDITIONS: Use of this record unit requires prior arrangement with the Archives staff.

Melbourne Armstrong Carriker, Jr., Papers, 1901, 1907, 1909-1910, 1918, 1929-1965
(0.8 linear meter).

Melbourne Armstrong Carriker, Jr., (1879-1965), ornithologist and entomologist, collected birds in Latin America for over 50 years. Carriker's primary scientific interest was the study of bird lice. His association with the Smithsonian Institution began in 1940, when he collected birds in Vera Cruz, Mexico, for the United States National Museum (USNM). From 1941 to 1952, Carriker conducted collecting expeditions to Colombia for the USNM. From 1953 until his death, Carriker held the honorary post of Collaborator in the Department of Entomology of the National Museum of Natural History.

These papers document Carriker's expeditions to Latin America for the USNM and other museums and his research on birds and bird lice. Included is correspondence with ornithologists, entomologists, and USNM officials; diaries kept on expeditions to Costa Rica, 1907; Colombia, 1918, 1942, 1951; Peru, 1932-1933; and Bolivia, 1936-1937; photographs taken on expeditions to Costa Rica, 1901; Venezuela, 1909-1910; Peru, 1930-1932; and Colombia, 1943; and research notes on, and photographs of, drawings of bird lice.

ARRANGEMENT: (1) General correspondence, *circa* 1929-1965; (2) research materials on bird lice; (3) diaries, 1907, 1918, 1932-1933, 1936-1937, 1942, 1951; (4) photographs, 1901, 1909-1910, 1930-1932, 1943. FINDING AIDS: Description in control file. SPECIAL CONDITIONS: Use of this record unit requires prior arrangement with the Archives staff.

(7338)

Oscar L. Cartwright Papers, 1929-1979 and undated
(2 linear meters).

Oscar L. Cartwright (1900-1983) was a coleopterist and specialist on the biology and taxonomy of scarab beetles. He was educated at Allegheny College (B.S., 1923) and Ohio State University (M.S., 1925). In 1925, Cartwright was appointed Assistant Entomologist at the South Carolina Agricultural Experiment Station at Clemson College. He remained at Clemson until 1948, except for the years 1945-1946 when he was employed by the United States Public Health Service to study mosquito and rat borne diseases in South Carolina and Tennessee. In 1948, Cartwright was appointed Associate Curator in the Division of Insects, United States National Museum (USNM). When the Department of Entomology was created in 1963, as part of a reorganization of the National Museum of Natural History (NMNH), Cartwright was appointed Curator and supervisor of the Division of Coleoptera. After his retirement in 1970, Cartwright continued his research as an Emeritus Entomologist at NMNH.

Cartwright was an authority on Western Hemisphere Aphodiinae, a subfamily of scarab beetles. He conducted field work in the southeastern United States, Costa Rica, El Salvador, Guatemala, and the Bahama Islands. His bibliography included over 80 titles in which 132 new taxa were described. Seventeen beetles were named in his honor.

This collection consists mostly of incoming and outgoing correspondence documenting Cartwright's research on Coleoptera. Also included are records concerning his curatorial work at the Division of Insects, USNM, and the Department of Entomology, NMNH; field work; and professional activities. Smaller amounts of correspondence were written during his pre-Smithsonian career. The collection also contains a few photographs and illustrations of beetles, and research notes.

ARRANGEMENT: Alphabetic. FINDING AIDS: Description in control file. SPECIAL CONDITIONS: Use of this record unit requires prior arrangement with the Archives staff.

Julius Victor Carus Photograph Album Collection, circa 1854-1902 and undated, with related materials to 1953
(0.8 linear meter).

The Julius Victor Carus Photograph Album contains the private collection of photographic portraits assembled by Carus, a German zoologist and editor. The album contains 127 portraits, primarily of European scientists in the fields of natural history, biology, comparative anatomy, physiology, embryology, and medicine. Scientists represented by photographs include Charles Darwin, Jean Louis Agassiz, Karl Ernst von Baer, Ernst Haeckel, Thomas Henry Huxley, Richard Owen, Herbert Spencer, and many more. Also included are a few photographs of natural history specimens. Most of the photographs are *cartes-de-visite,* which were commonly exchanged between professional people during the latter half of the 19th century. A small number of cabinet size photographs are included. The album was donated to the Smithsonian in 1953 by Harley J. Van Cleave.

Also included are prints of the original photographs; reprints of articles on the album and negatives of plates which appeared in the articles; index card files which contain information on the portraits; and a partial description of the album.

ARRANGEMENT: (1) Julius Victor Carus Photograph Album, *circa* 1854-1902 and undated; (2) copy prints; (3) reprints, articles, negatives, and card files, 1943, 1953 and undated. FINDING AIDS: Description in control file. SPECIAL CONDITIONS: Use of this record unit requires prior arrangement with the Archives staff.

Thomas Lincoln Casey Papers, 1870-1871, 1873, 1881-1897
(1.2 linear meters).

Thomas Lincoln Casey (1857-1925) graduated from the United States Military Academy in 1879 and went into the Corps of Engineers. In his early years in the military he was engaged in astronomy, but his interest later turned to entomology, and he became an intense student of the Coleoptera. His first paper appeared in 1884. At first his study was confined to North America, but after 1910 he studied the Coleoptera of Central and South America as well. His collection of specimens and his library were given to the United States National Museum after his death.

These papers concern Casey's work in entomology, especially the creation of his collection of Coleoptera. A fragment of the papers relates to Casey's earlier work in astronomy. Included in the papers are letters from Casey's father, 1870-1871; observations and computations made while accompanying Simon Newcomb on an expedition to observe the transit of Venus, 1882; letters received from entomologists, 1887-1897, regarding specimen identifications, purchase and exchange of Coleoptera specimens, and relating to the publication of Casey's papers; an autograph collection, mostly of public or military figures; and drawings of fossil Diatomaceae done by Casey in 1873.

ARRANGEMENT: (1) Diary and keys to locations, 1881-1885; (2) unidentified notes; (3) entomological notes and drafts of letters and papers; (4) incoming correspondence, 1887-1897; (5) letters from Casey's father, 1870-1871; (6) autograph cards; (7) drawings of fossil Diatomaceae, 1873. FINDING AIDS: Description in control file. SPECIAL CONDITIONS: (1) Check finding aid for location; (2) use of this record unit requires prior arrangement with the Archives staff.

(7162)

Andrew Nelson Caudell Papers, circa 1889-1935
(0.1 linear meter).

Andrew Nelson Caudell (1872-1936), orthopterist, joined the Division of Insects of the United States Department of Agriculture in 1898. He remained with the Department until his death and, also while there, served as custodian of the Orthoptera collection of the Division of Insects of the United States National Museum.

These papers consist of Caudell's notebooks, including entomological diaries, 1889, 1891-1892, 1914, 1916-1917, and 1920-1926. They contain daily entries concerning Caudell's personal affairs and scientific work; notes on breeding experiments with Orthoptera, 1922-1926; a loan record for books, 1914-1935; and a key to his insect collection. Also included is some correspondence of Caudell, especially with Morgan Hebard and P. Wytsman.

ARRANGEMENT: (1) Notebooks; (2) correspondence. FINDING AIDS: Partial description in control file. SPECIAL CONDITIONS: (1) Check finding aid for location; (2) use of this record unit requires prior arrangement with the Archives staff.

(7258)

Frederick M. Chamberlain Papers, 1899-1909
(0.1 linear meter).

Frederick M. Chamberlain (1867-1921) served as a Scientific Assistant and Naturalist for the United States Fish Commission and its successor, the United States Bureau of Fisheries. Much of his work was aboard the steamer *Albatross* during its various investigations of west coast fisheries.

This collection consists of bound letterpress books of outgoing correspondence, 1899-1908, and diaries kept by Chamberlain, 1900-1905. Most of the correspondence is official, with smaller amounts of personal material included. The letterpress books also contain correspondence, reports and notes on Chamberlain's work for the Fish Commission and Bureau of Fisheries, particularly his investigations of Alaskan salmon fisheries. The diaries document several official field trips including cruises to Alaska, 1901, 1903-1905; field work in Hawaii, 1902, and Arizona, 1904; and Chamberlain's participation on the third Agassiz-*Albatross* Expedition to the eastern tropical Pacific, 1904-1905.

ARRANGEMENT: (1) Outgoing correspondence, 1899-1909; (2) diaries, 1900-1905. FINDING AIDS: Description in control file. SPECIAL CONDITIONS: Use of this record unit requires prior arrangement with the Archives staff.

(7228)

Howard I. Chapelle Papers, 1969-1975
(0.8 linear meter).

Howard I. Chapelle (1901-1975), marine architect and historian, began his career as a marine apprentice and designer in 1919. He worked for a number of shipbuilders until he went into business for himself in 1936. During this period, Chapelle also served as head of the New England section of the Historic American Merchant Marine Survey, a Depression-era project to gather information on American maritime history and provide work for destitute marine architects.

Chapelle's business was interrupted by World War II, during which he served in the United States Army Transportation Corps ship and boatbuilding program. Following the war, he pursued his interest in the history of marine architecture, traveling to England in 1950 to study colonial ship design on a Guggenheim Fellowship. In 1956-1957, Chapelle went to Turkey under the auspices of the United Nations Food and Agricultural Organization to serve as a consultant to the Turkish government on fishing vessel construction and fitting.

Chapelle was appointed Curator in the Division of Transportation, National Museum of History and Technology, in 1957. He served in that position until 1967 when he became Senior Historian. While at the Museum, he directed the planning and construction of hundreds of ship models for the Hall of Merchant Shipping. Chapelle retired in 1971, becoming Historian Emeritus in the Museum. A prolific writer, Chapelle authored a number of books on maritime history and marine architecture.

These papers of Howard I. Chapelle consist of his professional correspondence while he was Senior Historian and Historian Emeritus. Very little is concerned with Museum or Division of Transportation affairs. The correspondence concerns the history of naval architecture, amateur boatbuilding, availability of ships' plans, the restoration of historic ships, and the publication of Chapelle's later works. Correspondents include museum curators, historians, naval architects, amateur boatbuilders, and model builders.

ARRANGEMENT: Alphabetic. FINDING AIDS: Description in control file. SPECIAL CONDITIONS: Use of this record unit requires prior arrangement with the Archives staff.

(7451)

Chesapeake Research Consortium, Inc., 1970-1981
Records (5.7 linear meters).

The Chesapeake Research Consortium, Inc. (CRC) was established in 1972 when the Virginia Institute of Marine Science, the Johns Hopkins University, the University of Maryland, and the Smithsonian Institution (through the Chesapeake Bay Center for Environmental Studies) joined to identify and conduct research on the principal environmental, marine, atmospheric, terrestrial, societal, and technological problems of the Chesapeake Bay and its contiguous regions. The CRC conducts scientific research and programs in information transfer, technology applications, and education and training. Initial funding for CRC was provided by the National Science Foundation. Directors of CRC included Robert H. Roy, 1972-1973; Theodore Chamberlain, 1973-1977; and L. Eugene Cronin, 1977-   .

These records document the establishment, administration, and research program of the Chesapeake Research Consortium, Inc. They include records concerning the incorporation of CRC in 1972; budget and fiscal records; correspondence of Directors Roy, Chamberlain, and Cronin; correspondence, reports, and other records of the CRC's Research Advisory and Interagency Advisory Committees; correspondence, proposals, and reports submitted by CRC to funding agencies including the National Science

Foundation, the Environmental Protection Agency, and the National Aeronautics and Space Administration; records concerning workshops and seminars sponsored by CRC; CRC annual reports; and correspondence, memoranda, reports, and publications documenting research programs on wetlands preservation, waste water management, the effects of hurricanes, and other topics relating to the Chesapeake Bay.

ARRANGEMENT: Unarranged. FINDING AIDS: Folder list in control file. SPECIAL CONDITIONS: Use of this record unit requires prior arrangement with the Archives staff.

(7131)

Frank Hurlburt Chittenden Notebooks, 1907-1928
(0.1 linear meter).

Frank Hurlburt Chittenden (1858-1929) joined the staff of the Bureau of Entomology, Department of Agriculture, in 1891, where he served until his death. He was a coleopterist and economic entomologist.

These notebooks contain specimen information which Chittenden collected or which was collected by others and numbered according to Chittenden's directions.

ARRANGEMENT: Numeric. FINDING AIDS: Brief description in control file. SPECIAL CONDITIONS: Use of this record unit requires prior arrangement with the Archives staff.

(7183)

Austin H. Clark Papers, 1883-1954 and undated
(3.1 linear meters).

Austin H. Clark (1880-1954) was born in Wellesley, Massachusetts. He received his A.B. from Harvard in 1903, and by 1906 his interests had focused on marine biology. From 1906 to 1907 he served as Acting Chief of the Scientific Staff of the United States Bureau of Fisheries Steamer, *Albatross.*

Clark joined the staff of the United States National Museum in 1908 as Honorary Collaborator in the Division of Marine Invertebrates and was appointed Assistant Curator of the Division in 1909. He was promoted to the position of Curator of the Division of Echinoderms in 1920 when the echinoderm collection was removed from the Division of Marine Invertebrates and made a separate division. Clark held the position of Curator until his retirement in 1950 at which time he was made an Honorary Associate in Zoology, a position he retained until his death.

Clark's principal research field was in the class Crinoidea, but he also did research in the areas of oceanography, marine biology, ornithology, and entomology. Clark was able to gain access to specimens collected on various international expeditions, including the Canadian Arctic Expedition and the *Siboga* Expedition, due to a reciprocal exchange agreement between the United States National Museum and foreign institutions.

Clark displayed a deep interest in scientific journalism and was one of the first to realize the applicability of radio and television to the dissemination of scientific news and ideas. He helped develop the weekly radio talks aired by the Smithsonian from 1923 to 1926 in cooperation with the Carnegie Institution of Washington and various government agencies. In 1925 Clark and the Smithsonian were instrumental in establishing a series of radio broadcasts in the Boston area. Clark was appointed Director of Press Service for the American Association for the Advancement of Science (AAAS) in 1928. He also served as Press Relations Officer for the Eighth Pan-American Scientific Congress, 1940, and the AAAS Centennial Celebration, 1948.

These papers include incoming and outgoing correspondence; papers documenting Clark's participation in organizations outside the Smithsonian; records relating to the administration of the Division of Echinoderms; descriptive notes on specimen collections; bibliographic references; Addison Emery Verrill material maintained by Clark; charts and diagrams depicting the comparative bathymetric distribution of crinoids in the Atlantic and Indo-Pacific Oceans; and a scrapbook containing postcards received by Clark in connection with a nomenclature question concerning *Enerinus*.

ARRANGEMENT: (1) Correspondence, 1907-1954; (2) papers documenting participation in outside organizations, 1911-1952; (3) Division of Echinoderms administration, undated; (4) specimen description notes, undated; (5) manuscripts, undated; (6) bibliographic references, undated; (7) Addison Emery Verrill material, *circa* 1883-1915; (8) comparative bathymetric distribution of crinoids, undated; (9) scrapbook of postcards, 1909. FINDING AIDS: Description in control file. SPECIAL CONDITIONS: Use of this record unit requires prior arrangement with the Archives staff.

(7080)

Frank Wigglesworth Clarke Papers, 1873-1921
(0.2 linear meter).

Frank Wigglesworth Clarke (1847-1931) was a geological chemist. Clarke taught chemistry and physics at Howard University in Washington, D.C., 1873-1874, and at the University of Cincinnati, 1874-1883. While teaching at Howard University and the University of Cincinnati, Clarke collaborated with the Smithsonian Institution on atomic weight research. In 1883, Clarke joined the United States Geological Survey and served as Chief Chemist until 1925. Clarke was also Honorary Curator in the Division of Mineralogy and Petrology, Department of Geology, United States National Museum, 1883-1931, where he organized the Museum's mineral and gem collection.

These papers consist chiefly of incoming correspondence from Joseph Henry, Spencer F. Baird, Samuel P. Langley, and other scientists concerning Clarke's Smithsonian publications; his appointment as Honorary Curator of Mineralogy and Petrology; the determination of atomic weights; publication of scientific findings on atomic weights; and the International Committee on Atomic Weights. Also included are computations and tables on the atomic weight of elements and compounds; a budget proposal for the United States Geological Survey; memorabilia; a photograph of Clarke; and an annotated copy of Clarke's "The Constants of Nature. Part I. A Table of Specific Gravity for Solids and Liquids," *Smithsonian Miscellaneous Collections,* Number 659, 1888.

ARRANGEMENT: (1) Correspondence, 1873-1921; (2) atomic weights and tables; (3) memorabilia; (4) photograph; (5) "The Constants of Nature. Part I. A Table of Specific Gravity for Solids and Liquids." FINDING AIDS: Description in control file. SPECIAL CONDITIONS: (1) Some of the correspondence is written in French and German; (2) use of this record unit requires prior arrangement with the Archives staff.

Joseph Ashmead Clay and John Randolph Clay Papers, 1841, 1859-1866 and undated

(0.1 linear meter).

John Randolph Clay (1808-1885) was a career American diplomat who served in Europe and Latin America in the period from 1830 to 1860. Joseph Ashmead Clay (1806-1881) was Randolph's older brother. He managed Randolph's affairs in Philadelphia and influenced his diplomatic appointments in Washington. Both brothers developed an interest in mineralogy in their youth and collected avidly throughout their lives.

These papers concern the mineralogical collections of Joseph Ashmead and John Randolph Clay and incidentally relate to family affairs and politics. They include letters between Joseph and Randolph, and his son, Harry Gibbs Clay, concerning specimens sent or received; detailed specimen lists; and accounts of specimens bought, sold, and exchanged.

ARRANGEMENT: (1) Joseph Ashmead Clay to John Randolph Clay, 1841, 1863-1864; (2) Joseph Ashmead Clay to John Randolph Clay, 1865; (3) John Randolph Clay to Joseph Ashmead Clay, 1859, 1863-1864; (4) John Randolph Clay to Harry Gibbs Clay, 1864-1865; (5) specimen lists, 1861-1865; (6) undated specimen lists. FINDING AIDS: Description in control file. SPECIAL CONDITIONS: Use of this record unit requires prior arrangement with the Archives staff.

Henry Helm Clayton Papers, 1877-1949 and undated

(1.6 linear meters and oversize).

Henry Helm Clayton (1861-1946) was a meteorologist and weather forecaster. He began his career in 1884 as an assistant at the University of Michigan's Astronomical Observatory. In 1885 he was appointed assistant at Harvard University's Astronomical Observatory, and from 1886 to 1891 served as an observer at Harvard's Blue Hill Meteorological Observatory. From 1891 to 1893 he worked as a local forecast official with the United States Weather Bureau. In 1894 Clayton returned to the Blue Hill Meteorological Observatory, where he served as a meteorologist until 1909. Clayton became Chief of the forecast division of the Argentine Weather Service in 1913. While in Argentina, Clayton pursued research on a system of weather forecasting based on solar heat changes and began corresponding with Charles G. Abbot of the Smithsonian Institution, who was also conducting research on solar variation. From 1923 to 1926 he conducted research in cooperation with the Smithsonian on the effect of solar variation on world weather patterns. Clayton directed a private weather forecasting service and served as a consulting meteorologist for business organizations from 1920 until his death.

The papers of Henry Helm Clayton document his career as a meteorologist and weather forecaster and his research on solar variation. They consist mainly of professional and personal correspondence, including a large amount with Charles G. Abbot concerning solar research. Also included are weather forecasts, meteorological data, photographs, newspaper clippings, manuscripts, and related materials on meteorology. The small amount of correspondence and meteorological data that postdates Clayton's death in 1946 was compiled by his daughter, Frances Lindley Clayton.

ARRANGEMENT: (1) General correspondence, 1886-1949 and undated; (2) weather forecasts, meteorological data, photographs, newspaper clippings, manuscripts, and related materials on meteorology, 1877-1949 and undated. FINDING AIDS: Description in control file. SPECIAL CONDITIONS: Use of this record unit requires prior arrangement with the Archives staff.

(7151)

Doris Mable Cochran Papers, circa 1891-1968
(1.6 linear meters).

Doris Mable Cochran (1898-1968) was born in North Girard, Pennsylvania, and came to Washington, D.C., when her father received a government position. In November 1919 she was appointed an Aid to Leonhard Stejneger in the Division of Reptiles and Amphibians of the United States National Museum. She advanced through the Division becoming Assistant Curator in 1927, Associate Curator in 1942, and Curator in 1956. As Stejneger grew older, more of the work of the Division fell to Cochran, and following Stejneger's death in 1943, she became acting head of the Division and supervised the Division alone until 1964, when James A. Peters was appointed Associate Curator. She retired from the Museum in 1968.

Cochran's principal areas of interest were the reptiles and amphibians of Central and South America and of the West Indies, especially Haiti. She made two field trips to the region, in 1935 and 1962-1963, where she worked with Adolpho Lutz and his daughter Bertha, noted Brazilian herpetologists. In addition to her professional work, Cochran published a large number of popular articles and books on herpetology. She also was an accomplished scientific illustrator.

These papers include manuscripts, notes, and data on herpetology; material concerning specimens received by the Division of Reptiles and Amphibians; photographs of reptiles and amphibians; personal material including clippings and photographs related to Cochran's education, her Ph.D. dissertation on the blue crab, and her Smithsonian career; personal correspondence; correspondence concerning publications; and material on Cochran's travels to Europe and South America.

ARRANGEMENT: (1) Manuscripts, notes, data, and related materials on scientific work, *circa* 1921-1968; (2) personal materials, correspondence, and travel materials, 1891, 1900, 1907, 1919-1968. FINDING AIDS: Description in control file. SPECIAL CONDITIONS: Use of this record unit requires prior arrangement with the Archives staff.

(1020008)

Theodore D. A. Cockerell Papers, circa 1924-1930
(0.8 linear meter).

This collection was erroneously described in the *Guide To The Smithsonian Archives,* 1983. It was transferred to the Archives in 1991 and found to be correspondence written by Theodore D. A. Cockerell to United States Department of Agriculture (USDA) entomologists primarily concerning the identification of specimens. Also included are copies of USDA letters to Cockerell.

The correspondence is now a part of record unit 7458, Insect Identification and Parasite Introduction Research Branch, United States Department of Agriculture, Records, 1907-1959.

(7060)

James Henry Coffin Papers, 1848-1884
(0.1 linear meter).

James Henry Coffin (1806-1873) was a mathematician and meteorologist who specialized in the study of wind velocity. Coffin graduated from Amherst College in 1828 and taught at various schools and colleges. Coffin began his meteorological studies in 1838. While at Williams College, 1840-1843, he installed an apparatus on Mount Greylock, New York, for automatically recording the direction and the velocity of the wind. From 1846 until his death, Coffin held a chair of mathematics and natural philosophy at Lafayette College. In 1846, he began his collaboration with the Smithsonian Institution in meteorology. Two of Coffin's studies, *Winds of the Northern Hemisphere* and *Winds of the Globe* were published by the Institution in 1853 and 1875, respectively.

These papers consist of correspondence concerning temperature, wind, and weather reports of the Hudson Bay region, 1848; resolutions of condolence to Coffin's son, Seldon J. Coffin, from students and alumni of Lafayette College after Coffin's death, 1873; newspaper articles; an illustration of James H. Coffin; and the original manuscript of *Winds of the Northern Hemisphere.* Additional correspondence of James Henry Coffin exists elsewhere in the Smithsonian Archives, especially in the Joseph Henry Collection, record unit 7001, and Meteorological Project Records, record unit 60.

ARRANGEMENT: (1) Correspondence and newspaper articles; (2) manuscripts. FINDING AIDS: Description in control file. SPECIAL CONDITIONS: Use of this record unit requires prior arrangement with the Archives staff.

(7244)

Leon J. Cole Photograph Collection, 1941
(0.3 linear meter).

Leon J. Cole (1877-1948) was born in Allegany, New York. He received degrees from the University of Michigan, A.B., 1901, and Harvard University, Ph.D., 1906. In 1906 and 1907, Cole served as Chief of the Division of Animal Breeding and Pathology at the Rhode Island Experiment Station. From 1907 to 1910, he served as an Instructor of Zoology at the Sheffield Scientific School of Yale University. In 1910, he became Associate Professor of Experimental Breeding in the College of Agriculture, University of Wisconsin, and was made Professor in 1914. His title was changed to Professor of Genetics in 1918 and he remained in that capacity until 1947. Cole was a member of the Harriman Alaska Expedition of 1899 and participated in zoological expeditions to Bermuda, 1903; the Yucatan, 1904; Tortugas, Florida, 1906; Europe, 1911 and 1924; and Alaska, 1941. He also served as an investigator for the United States Bureau of Fisheries during the summers from 1901 to 1906.

This collection consists of an album of photographs taken by Cole in Alaska in 1941. The album also contains memorabilia collected by Cole. The photographs are in chronological order and are labeled.

433

ARRANGEMENT: Chronologic. FINDING AIDS: None. SPECIAL CONDITIONS: Use of this record unit requires prior arrangement with the Archives staff.

(7106)

The Coleopterists' Society, 1968-1971
Records (0.1 linear meter).

The Coleopterists' Society was founded at Dallas, Texas, in 1968 by members of the Entomological Society of America, who were anxious to promote the study of Coleoptera.

These records document the formation and operation of the Society; efforts to transfer the *Coleopterists' Bulletin* from Purdue University to the Society; and production of the *Checklist of North American Coleoptera* and the *Coleopterists' Newsletter.*

ARRANGEMENT: (1) Constitution and by-laws, 1968-1969; (2) minutes of meetings, 1968-1970; (3) reports of officers and committees, 1968-1971; (4) history; (5) publications, 1969-1971. FINDING AIDS: Description in control file. SPECIAL CONDITIONS: (1) The Smithsonian Archives has been designated the official depository for the Society's records; (2) additions are expected; (3) use of this record unit requires prior arrangement with the Archives staff.

(7051)

Columbian Institute Records, 1816-1841 with related papers, 1791-1800
(0.5 linear meter).

The Columbian Institute was organized at Washington, D.C., in 1816, originally as the Metropolitan Society, for the purpose of reducing the United States' dependence on a purely European cultural heritage. Its principal goal was utilitarian; it concentrated on encouraging the diffusion of information about agriculture, manufacturing, and natural resources, mainly through correspondence, exchanges, and a program of publication. The Society became the Columbian Institute for the Promotion of the Arts and Sciences later in 1816, and in 1818 was incorporated by Congress under that name. Despite several reorganizations and other attempts to keep the Institute alive, it collapsed in 1838 and was absorbed by the National Institute in 1841.

ARRANGEMENT: (1) Minutes and committee reports; (2) correspondence; (3) papers submitted to the Institute; (4) Treasurer's records; (5) miscellany; (6) papers of Francois de Laporte, Count Castelneau de Laporte. FINDING AIDS: Description in control file. SPECIAL CONDITIONS: Use of this record unit requires prior arrangement with the Archives staff.

(7292)

Paul S. Conger Papers, 1913-1979
(2.7 linear meters).

Paul S. Conger (1897-1979) was a botanist who specialized in the study of diatoms, microscopic components of plankton. He was the protege of Albert Mann (1853-1935), Diatomist of the Carnegie Institution of Washington (CIW). Mann was employed by the CIW but maintained his office and laboratory at the United States National Museum (USNM) where he also held the title of Honorary Custodian of Diatoms, 1913-1935. In 1922 Conger joined the staff of the Carnegie Institution and worked as Mann's assistant in the lab at the USNM. After Mann's death, Conger retained his affiliation with the CIW, serving as Research Associate, 1935-1943. Concurrently he was named Honorary Custodian of Diatoms at the USNM, 1935-1943; then Associate Curator, 1944-1966; and Botanist Emeritus of Cryptogams, 1967-1979.

These records consist of the correspondence of both Conger and Mann with botanists, diatomists, and other colleagues. The files were apparently begun by Mann, and then used and retained by Conger, who continued many of the same associations. Correspondence concerns specimens, identifications, laboratory administration, equipment, publications, research projects and summer work at Woods Hole, Dry Tortugas, Trout Lake, and Solomons Island. Also included are notes, annual and other reports, articles and papers, and the notes and manuscript of Conger's "Thomas Christian and the Diatomists of Richmond."

ARRANGEMENT: (1) Correspondence, 1913-1979; (2) "Thomas Christian and the Diatomists of Richmond," 1950; (3) publications, 1922, 1954, 1957 and undated; (4) notes and reports, 1917-1977. FINDING AIDS: Description in control file. SPECIAL CONDITIONS: Use of this record unit requires prior arrangement with the Archives staff.

(7437)

Paul S. Conger Papers, 1926-1966
(2.9 linear meters).

For biographical information and additional papers documenting the careers of Paul S. Conger and his mentor, Albert Mann, see record unit 7292.

These papers were created by both Conger and Mann and document their research on diatoms. They include correspondence with colleagues concerning the identification of specimens, publications, and professional matters, *circa* 1929-1966; correspondence, notes, publications, newspaper clippings, and related materials regarding Conger's investigation of several *Synura* epidemics in the Washington, D.C., water system during the 1940s and 1950s; correspondence concerning a conference of cooperating microbiologists on fish food problems which was organized by Mann in 1926; correspondence concerning Conger's article on Wisconsin peat deposits, 1939-1941; photographs of Mann, *circa* 1920s-1930s; and glass plate negatives of diatoms, diatom habitats, collecting trips, collecting equipment, and general botanical subjects.

ARRANGEMENT: Unarranged. FINDING AIDS: Box list in control file. SPECIAL CONDITIONS: Use of this record unit requires prior arrangement with the Archives staff.

(7225)

Anthony J. Conway Collection, 1929-1970
(0.3 linear meter).

This collection consists of newspaper clippings concerning the National Zoological Park (NZP), including public relations information, donations to the NZP, and animal collecting expedition articles.

ARRANGEMENT: Chronologic. FINDING AIDS: None. SPECIAL CONDITIONS: Use of this record unit requires prior arrangement with the Archives staff.

Orator Fuller Cook Papers, 1894-1905, 1933, 1948
(0.1 linear meter).

Orator Fuller Cook (1867-1949) was born in Clyde, New York. He was educated at Syracuse University, receiving the Ph.B. degree in 1890. After graduation, Cook remained at Syracuse as an Instructor in the Biology Department. From 1891 to 1897, Cook made several trips to Liberia as an agent for the New York Colonization Society and at various times served as Professor of Natural Sciences at Liberia College. In 1895, Cook joined the staff of the United States National Museum (USNM), in an honorary capacity, as Custodian of the Section of Myripoda of the Department of Insects. In 1898, Cook was appointed to a salaried position, as Assistant Curator in the Division of Plants, USNM. He resigned the following year to join the United States Department of Agriculture's Bureau of Plant Industry, where he remained until his death. He continued his association with the USNM as Custodian of the Section of Myripoda and was made Honorary Assistant Curator of the Section of Cryptogamic Collections of the Division of Plants in 1899.

This collection contains a small amount of Cook's correspondence, concerning the identification of Myripoda. Correspondents include Otis Warren Barrett, Theodore D. A. Cockerell, Carl H. Eigenmann, Karl Kraepelin, and Karl A. Mobius. Correspondence is arranged alphabetically.

ARRANGEMENT: Alphabetic. FINDING AIDS: None. SPECIAL CONDITIONS: Use of this record unit requires prior arrangement with the Archives staff.

G. Arthur Cooper Papers, 1923-1993 and undated, with related material from 1878 to 1892
(4.8 linear meters and oversize).

G. Arthur Cooper (1902-   ) pursued a career in invertebrate paleontology at the National Museum of Natural History (NMNH). Cooper received the B.S. in 1924, and M.S. in 1926 from Colgate University, and the Ph.D. in 1929 from Yale University. He was appointed Assistant Curator, Division of Stratigraphic Paleontology, at the United States National Museum (USNM) in 1930 and remained at the NMNH until his retirement as Paleontologist Emeritus in 1987. He served as Head Curator of the Department of Geology from 1957 to 1963 and as Chairman of the Department of Paleobiology from 1963 to 1967.

Cooper focused his research on the taxonomy and stratigraphy of Paleozoic brachiopods. His major monographs include: *Ozarkian and Related Brachiopoda,* 1938, with Edward Oscar Ulrich; *Chazyan and Related Brachiopods,* 1956; *Morphology, Classification, and Life Habits of Productoids (Brachiopoda),* 1960, with Helen M. Muir-Wood; and *Permian Brachiopods of West Texas,* volumes 1-6, 1969-1977, with Richard E. Grant. Throughout his career, he conducted extensive field work in the United States, Canada, and Mexico, adding significantly to the national collections. Under his guidance, the Smithsonian established an acid-etching laboratory for work with silicified fossils.

These papers consist primarily of scientific correspondence relating to taxonomic identification and the loan and exchange of specimen material. Correspondents include Preston E. Cloud, Jr., Helen M. Muir-Wood, Charles Schuchert, Edward Oscar Ulrich, and Alwyn Williams. Also present is routine administrative correspondence documenting Cooper's tenure as Head Curator of the Department of Geology. Material compiled by his predecessors is also included. Of special interest is correspondence relating to bequests; nineteenth-century correspondence among brachiopod specialists; reports regarding the modernization of exhibits; and field notes and manuscripts of William F. Foshag, who preceded Cooper as Head Curator in the Department of Geology. Extensive field notes from the two major localities where Cooper collected, the Hamilton formation of New York State and the Glass Mountain region of West Texas, are present, as well as from expeditions to the eastern and central United States, Quebec, and New Brunswick. The field notes for some of this work are complemented by photographs. Also included are manuscripts of papers and speeches, Cooper's complete M.S. thesis, and an incomplete draft of his Ph.D. dissertation.

ARRANGEMENT: (1) Scientific correspondence, 1878-1892, 1923-1933, 1940-1987 and undated; (2) travel and grant files, 1927-1968 and undated; (3) administrative correspondence, 1933-1967 and undated; (4) manuscripts, 1925-1974 and undated; (5) field notes, 1926-1970 and undated; (6) photographs, *circa* 1924-1945; (7) oversize material, 1939, 1943 and undated. FINDING AIDS: Description in control file. SPECIAL CONDITIONS: Use of this record unit requires prior arrangement with the Archives staff.

(7067)

James G. Cooper Papers, 1853-1870 and undated
(0.1 linear meter).

Born and educated in New York City, James G. Cooper (1830-1902) was a naturalist and physician with Isaac Stevens' Pacific Railroad Survey expedition of 1853. One of the first to collect specimens in the Pacific Coast regions, he became an expert on the geological, biological, and zoological aspects of that area. He published material on the natural history of California and Oregon and wrote a chapter on zoology for *Natural Wealth of California,* edited by T. F. Cronise. After traveling extensively, he practiced medicine and lived in California until his death in 1902. The Cooper Ornithological Society was named in his honor.

These papers consist of journals and manuscripts containing Cooper's descriptions of his travels in Oregon and Washington territories, California, and his homeward trip through Panama, and as far north as Cape Hatteras. Included are observations made while he was a part of the Isaac Stevens survey. The journals and manuscripts contain descriptions of geological features, weather observations, and technical notes on the plant and animal life of the area. Also included are specimen lists, maps, and sketches of his route while on the Stevens survey.

ARRANGEMENT: (1) Journals, 1853-1856; (2) manuscripts, 1860, 1870 and undated. FINDING AIDS: Description in control file. SPECIAL CONDITIONS: Use of this record unit requires prior arrangement with the Archives staff.

Daniel William Coquillet Papers, 1885-1911 and undated
(1 folder).

Daniel William Coquillet (1856-1911), a dipterist, economic entomologist, and taxonomist, served as Honorary Curator of Diptera in the United States National Museum from 1895 to 1911.

These papers consist of incoming correspondence of Coquillet.

ARRANGEMENT: Chronologic. FINDING AIDS: None. SPECIAL CONDITIONS: Use of this record unit requires prior arrangement with the Archives staff.

Elliott Coues Papers, 1872-1880, 1896-1899 and undated
(0.1 linear meter).

Elliott Coues (1842-1899), a disciple of Spencer F. Baird, was probably the most influential American ornithologist of his generation. From about 1860 to 1881 Coues served in the United States Army as Assistant Surgeon and from 1877 to 1886 served as Professor of Anatomy at Columbian College (now The George Washington University). His major publications include *Key to North American Birds,* 1872; *Check List of North American Birds,* 1873, 1882; and *Field Ornithology,* 1874.

These papers consist of a "Book of Dates" compiled by Coues between 1896 and 1899, probably when he was preparing to write his memoirs. It includes genealogical information dating to 1686, and is probably the most important source of information on Coues' life. Also included are thirty-eight letters written by Coues to Winfrid Alden Stearns, who was seeking Coues' help in writing a manual of New England ornithology. Stearns' work was finally published in 1883 in two volumes under the title *New England Bird Life, Being a Manual of New England Ornithology,* with extensive revisions and editing by Coues. In addition, this record unit contains an undated manuscript written by Coues on the geographic distribution of mammals.

ARRANGEMENT: (1) Elliott Coues' "Book of Dates", 1896-1899; (2) letters written to Winfrid Alden Stearns, 1872-1880; (3) manuscript on the geographic distribution of mammals, undated. FINDING AIDS: None. SPECIAL CONDITIONS: Use of this record unit requires prior arrangement with the Archives staff.

Thomas Coulter Journal, 1824-1827
(0.1 linear meter).

Thomas Coulter (1793-1843) was an Irish physician and botanist who collected plants in Mexico and California, 1824-1834.

From 1824 to 1827 he traveled from London to Vera Cruz. This journal consists of daily meteorological observations taken by Coulter on this journey.

ARRANGEMENT: Chronologic. FINDING AIDS: None. SPECIAL CONDITIONS: Use of this record unit requires prior arrangement with the Archives staff.

Frederick Vernon Coville Papers, 1888-1936 and undated

(0.8 linear meter).

Frederick Vernon Coville (1867-1937), botanist and blueberry breeder, was born in New York and educated at Cornell University (B.A., 1887). His important field work included the Geological Survey of Arkansas, 1888; the Death Valley Expedition, 1891; and the Harriman Alaska Expedition, 1899. Most of his career was spent at the United States Department of Agriculture, where he served as Assistant Botanist, 1888-1893, and Botanist, 1893-1937. He was also Honorary Curator of the United States National Herbarium, 1893-1937, and was instrumental in the establishment of the National Arboretum in 1927.

These papers consist of a small amount of correspondence; material concerning the Medicinal Plants Survey, 1897-1898; notes concerning the revision of Coville's work on Death Valley plants, 1933-1936; and a small group of manuscript notes on currants and gooseberries, undated. Events and items of special interest which are documented in the correspondence include the explorations of Per Axel Rydberg in the Black Hills; the artistic work of Frederick A. Walpole; the acquisition of the Greene Herbarium; the botany exhibits at the World's Columbian Exposition, 1893; and the Mearns collection from the United States-Mexican International Boundary Survey, 1893.

ARRANGEMENT: (1) Correspondence, 1888-1921 and undated; (2) Medicinal Plants Survey, 1897-1898; (3) Death Valley material, 1933-1936; (4) manuscript notes on currants and gooseberries, undated. FINDING AIDS: Description in control file. SPECIAL CONDITIONS: Use of this record unit requires prior arrangement with the Archives staff.

Richard Sumner Cowan Papers, circa 1952-1985 and undated

(2.5 linear meters).

Richard Sumner Cowan (1921-   ), a systematic botanist specializing in neotropical flora, received his Ph.D. from Columbia University in 1952. From 1952 to 1957, he served as Assistant Curator at the New York Botanical Garden. Cowan joined the United States National Museum (USNM) in 1957 when he was appointed Associate Curator in the Department of Botany. In 1962, he was appointed Assistant Director of the National Museum of Natural History (NMNH), and, in 1965, Director. Cowan retired from administration in 1973 and resumed his research as a Senior Botanist at NMNH. He remained in the position until his retirement in 1985. Cowan's primary research interest is the systematics of legumes in tropical America.

This collection documents Cowan's career as a systematic botanist at the New York Botanical Garden, USNM, and NMNH. Included are incoming and outgoing correspondence concerning the identification of specimens, the preparation of scientific papers and monographs, and professional activities; a subject file mostly documenting his research; and files relating to his work as Secretary of the National Committee of the International Botanical Congress, 1969.

For additional materials documenting Cowan's botanical research and administrative career at NMNH, see record units 155, 197, and 9501.

ARRANGEMENT: (1) General correspondence, *circa* 1952-1981; (2) general correspondence, *circa* 1973-1985; (3) subject file, *circa* 1964-1981 and undated; (4) International Botanical Congress files, 1965-1971. FINDING AIDS: Box list in control file. SPECIAL CONDITIONS: Use of this record unit requires prior arrangement with the Archives staff.

(7114)

James Chamberlain Crawford Papers, 1901-1927
(0.1 linear meter).

James Chamberlain Crawford (1880-1950) graduated from the University of Nebraska and joined the Bureau of Entomology, United States Department of Agriculture, in 1904. From 1908 to 1917 he served as Assistant (later Associate) Curator, Division of Insects, United States National Museum, specializing in the taxonomy of Hymenoptera. After a time in private business, 1919-1923, Crawford worked for the North Carolina State Department of Agriculture. In 1930 he rejoined the Bureau of Entomology, where he remained until his retirement in 1950.

These papers consist of professional correspondence arranged alphabetically by correspondent, and reflect only a small part of Crawford's career.

ARRANGEMENT: Alphabetic. FINDING AIDS: Description in control file. SPECIAL CONDITIONS: Use of this record unit requires prior arrangement with the Archives staff.

(7197)

Bessie Nicholls Croffut Papers, undated
(1 folder).

Bessie Nicholls Croffut was the second wife of William Augustus Croffut (1835-1915), author and newspaperman. He served as executive officer of the United States Geological Survey from 1888 to 1894.

These papers consist of a manuscript of Bessie Nicholls Croffut, containing recollections of her life in Washington, D.C., with William Augustus Croffut. They also include a typescript of the work.

ARRANGEMENT: Manuscript of "Memories of William Augustus Croffut," by Bessie Nicholls Croffut, undated. FINDING AIDS: None. SPECIAL CONDITIONS: Use of this record unit requires prior arrangement with the Archives staff.

(1050101)

Joseph A. Cushman Papers, circa 1862-1977 and undated
(8 linear meters).

Joseph A. Cushman (1881-1949) received his undergraduate education from Bridgewater (Mass.) Normal School, 1897-1901, and Harvard's Lawrence Scientific School, 1901-1903. He also received his Ph.D. degree, 1909, and an honorary Doctor of Science degree, 1937, from Harvard.

From 1903 to 1923 Cushman was employed at the Boston Society of Natural History where he studied recent foraminifera collected by the United States Fish Commission Steamer *Albatross*. In 1912, he joined the United States Geological Survey (USGS) to study the coastal plain foraminifera with T. Wayland Vaughan of the USGS. In 1921, on leave from the USGS, Cushman was appointed consulting geologist for the Marland Oil Company, for which he spent several months in Mexico in field work. When he returned to his home in Sharon, Massachusetts, he built a laboratory which he called the Cushman Laboratory for Foraminiferal Research to continue his study of economic micropaleontology for Marland. In 1925 he severed his relationship with Marland and rejoined the USGS. In the meantime, his laboratory was opened to Boston area college students and to United States and foreign scientists for research on his foraminiferal collection. In 1926 a quarterly publication, *Contributions from the Cushman Laboratory for Foraminiferal Research* was begun, and in 1928 he began publishing *Special Publications of the Cushman Laboratory for Foraminiferal Research.* In 1927 and 1932, Cushman traveled to Europe as a representative of the Smithsonian Institution to study foraminifera in European museums. His close association with the Smithsonian and the USGS resulted in the bequest of his specimens, card catalog and library, and slide catalog to the United States National Museum.

These papers provide comprehensive documentation of Cushman's scientific career from around 1910 to 1949, with some records continued by his assistant, Ruth Todd, following his death. Included is correspondence with American and foreign scientists and students concerning the identification and exchange of specimens; use of the Cushman Laboratory for Research; his studies of European museum foraminiferal collections; his consulting work with the Marland Oil Company; his participation in professional societies, state geological surveys, international geological congresses, and geological expeditions; and the publishing of scientific journals. Also included are photographs of the Laboratory and prominent paleontologists; notebooks; scrapbooks of clippings, plates, notes, and tracings from published sources; and family correspondence, genealogies, reminiscences, paintings and sketches, photographs, and memorabilia.

There is no apparent logical arrangement to the papers, but there are several alphabetic correspondence series with similar subject matter and dates. It is unknown whether this is the order maintained by Cushman or whether the present order was established when the collection arrived at the United States National Museum. In some cases, folders are not identified so folder headings were added and enclosed in brackets.

ARRANGEMENT: (1) Private letter files, 1893, 1904-1977; (2) early files, 1875, 1889, 1904-1950; (3) correspondence file, A-Z, 1887, 1904-1950 and undated; (4) Marland Oil Company, 1921-1926 and undated; (5) photographs, notebooks, and memorabilia, *circa* 1862-1977 and undated. FINDING AIDS: Description in control file. SPECIAL CONDITIONS: Use of this record unit requires prior arrangement with the Archives staff.

(7073)

William H. Dall Papers, circa 1839-1858, 1862-1927
(10 linear meters).

Dean of Alaskan explorations, William H. Dall (1845-1927) began his scientific career as a member of the Scientific Corps of the Alaskan Western Union Telegraph Expedition in 1865. In 1871 he was appointed to the United States Coast Survey, where he continued his studies on Alaska and the northern Pacific Coast. Dall left the Coast Survey in 1884 to accept the rank of Paleontologist with the United States Geological Survey, a position he held until 1925. Having assembled and described some of the collections of mollusca and other organisms held by the United States National Museum since 1868, Dall served as Honorary Curator of the Museum's Division of Mollusks from 1880 until his death.

A prolific writer, Dall published more than five hundred scientific papers. Among Dall's more important larger works are *Alaska and its Resources,* 1870, and *Contributions to the Tertiary Fauna of Florida,* 6 volumes, 1890-1903, which is still considered the most important American publication on Cenozoic molluscan paleontology.

These papers provide comprehensive documentation of Dall's personal and scientific activities from 1865 to 1927, including diaries, scrapbooks, field notes, financial accounts, specimen collection notebooks, maps, and incoming and outgoing correspondence created during the Western Union Telegraph Expedition and pertaining to Alaskan towns, topography, mineral resources, flora and fauna of Alaska, and customs of Russian-Americans and Alaskan Indians; Robert Kennicott notes, correspondence, map, information concerning Kennicott's death, and description of the intrigue among members of the Expedition; diaries, correspondence, financial accounts, specimen collection notebooks, and field notes concerning Dall's explorations in Alaska, 1871-1876, 1879-1880, under the United States Coast Survey; material on Dall's explorations on the Pacific Coast and in Florida for the United States Geological Survey; reports to Secretary of State Thomas Francis Bayard regarding the Alaska-Canada boundary question, 1885, 1888; reports prepared for the Coast Survey, Geological Survey, and the National Museum's Division of Mollusks; correspondence with colleagues, administrators of scientific and educational organizations, editors, publishers, family members, friends, collectors of mollusca, and scientific societies, concerning membership and membership meetings, identification of fossil collections, publications and manuscripts, personal and family problems, student theses, appointment to the Geological Survey, honorary degrees, politics, economics, social conditions in Washington, D.C., and Dall's personal views regarding his professional competency and social status; diaries, 1865-1927; awards; photographs; publications; newspapers and newspaper clippings concerning Alaska; maps; poetry written by Dall's father; genealogy of Dall and his family; and autobiographical material.

A prolific correspondent, Dall received letters from leading naturalists, scientists, editors, and administrators including Louis and Alexander Agassiz, Spencer F. Baird, Franz Boas, Wendell Phillips Garrison, Joseph Henry, Julius Erasmus Hilgard, J. Gwyn Jeffreys, Samuel H. Scudder, William Stimpson, Addison Emery Verrill, and Oswald Garrison Villard.

ARRANGEMENT: (1) Publications, newspaper clippings, awards, photographs, and biographical and autobiographical material; (2) scrapbooks, 1839, 1843, 1853, 1855-1856, 1858, 1865-1872; (3) Department of Mollusks memoranda, 1880-1887, and correspondence, 1866-1926; (4) correspondence, 1865-1927; (5) registers of letters received and written, 1865-1878, 1882-1927; (6) diaries, 1865-1927; (7) Western Union Telegraph Expedition notebooks, 1865-1868; (8) United States Coast Survey, natural history, and bibliographic notebooks, 1871-1882; (9) United States Geological Survey and natural history notebooks, 1887-1910 and undated; (10) catalogs of specimens taken on expeditions, 1865-1880; (11) financial accounts, 1867-1911; (12) reports and other material on expeditions, 1861-1925; (13) notes, mollusk lists, manuscripts, and correspondence, 1862-*circa* 1923; (14) mollusk lists, manuscripts, Augustus Addison Gould drawings of fossils, and mollusk plates, undated; (15) mollusk plates; (16) outlines for a biography of Spencer F. Baird by George Brown Goode, *circa* 1890, and a manuscript of *Spencer Fullerton Baird, A Biography,* by Dall, 1915; (17) scrapbooks and newspaper clippings on Alaska, 1873-1905; (18) *The Alaskan,* 1886-1894; (19) articles and maps on Alaska; (20) photographs; (21) bibliography. FINDING AIDS: (1) Some letterpress books are individually indexed; (2) Kenneth J. Boss, Joseph Rosewater, and Florence A. Ruhoff, *The Zoological Taxa of William Healey Dall,* 1968; (3) description in control file. SPECIAL CONDITIONS: Use of this record unit requires prior arrangement with the Archives staff.

Stuart Taylor Danforth Collection, undated

(1.2 linear meters).

Stuart Taylor Danforth (1900-1938) received his B. S. degree in 1921 from Rutgers University and the Ph.D. in 1925 from Cornell. From 1925 to 1926 he was an instructor in biology at Temple University; and from 1926 until his death, he served as professor of zoology and entomology in the College of Agriculture and Mechanical Arts at Mayaguez, Puerto Rico. His main research interest was in the birds of the West Indies. Danforth's bird collection is now housed in the National Museum of Natural History.

This collection consists of nine boxes of 3 x 5 cards containing information on West Indian birds.

ARRANGEMENT: (1) Notes and references to literature, arranged by author; (2) notes and references to literature, arranged by species; (3) field notes and observations; (4) catalog of the "Bird Collection of Stuart T. Danforth." FINDING AIDS: None. SPECIAL CONDITIONS: Use of this record unit requires prior arrangement with the Archives staff.

Robert Tyler Davis Papers, 1918-1977 and undated

(4 linear meters).

Robert Tyler Davis (1904-1978) was a museum administrator and an educator in art and art history. He graduated from Harvard, A.B., 1926, A.M., 1928, and taught at the University of Rochester, 1929-1933, and at the Erskine School for Girls in Boston, 1933-1934. He was Director of Education at the Albright Gallery in Buffalo, New York, 1934-1939; Director of the Portland Museum of Art, 1939-1947; Director of the Montreal Museum of Fine Arts and Professor of Fine Arts at McGill University, 1947-1952; Director of Vizcaya, Dade County Art Museum, Miami, 1953-1957; Interim Director of the Lowe Gallery, University of Miami, 1955-1956; and Coordinator of Humanities and Professor of Art at the University of Miami, 1956-1959. Davis was a museum consultant for the French and Company art dealership, New York City, in 1960. In September 1968 he became Assistant Director of the National Collection of Fine Arts; was named Acting Director, June 1969-January 1970; and Special Assistant for the Collections, 1972-1975.

These papers document Robert Tyler Davis's education and career, 1918-1977. The majority of the documentation is dated from 1937 to 1977. Incoming correspondence illustrates Davis's personal life, and, to a lesser extent, his professional career. Materials concerning his career consist largely of photographs, newspaper clippings and research notes, and less often include official business papers and correspondence. Other materials include travel photographs and sketches by Davis.

ARRANGEMENT: (1) Correspondence, 1939-1940, 1947-1951, 1953-1977 and undated; (2) journals and daybooks, 1963-1977 and undated; (3) diplomas, almanacs, notes, notebooks, and lectures relating to Robert Tyler Davis's education and teaching career, 1918-1926, 1928, 1932-1934 and undated; (4) exhibition catalogs and photographs, notes, and Davis' publications relating to Albright Art Gallery, Buffalo, New York, 1937-1939 and undated; (5) reports, lecture notes, installation and collection photographs, exhibition catalogs, and museum publicity and policies relating to the Portland Museum of Art, 1939-1947; (6) correspondence, annual reports, lectures, notes, publicity information, exhibition photographs, and Davis' publications relating to the Montreal Museum of Fine Arts and McGill University, 1947-1952; (7) correspondence, policy committee meetings and agendas, memoranda, reports, financial statements, and photographs relating to Vizcaya, Dade County Art Museum, and the Lowe Art Gallery, Miami, 1934-1937, 1952-1957, 1959 and undated; (8) correspondence, photographs, and publicity information relating to French and Company, 1959-1960, 1962-1968 and undated; (9) correspondence, exhibition catalogs, reports, notes, Gellatly material, and course lectures relating to the National Collection of Fine Arts, Smithsonian Institution, 1968-1975; (10) personal and financial records, 1933, 1953, 1955-1977; (11) travels, 1949, 1974, 1976-1977; (12) sketches, paintings, prints, and photographs, 1928-1929, 1940, 1947, 1961-1962 and undated. FINDING AIDS: Description in control file. SPECIAL CONDITIONS: Use of this record unit requires prior arrangement with the Archives staff.

(7097)

E. Yale Dawson Papers, 1934-1966
(2.7 linear meters).

E. Yale Dawson (1918-1966) came to the Smithsonian Institution in 1965 to accept the newly established position of Curator of Cryptogamic Botany in the National Museum of Natural History. Dawson received his A.B. degree in 1940 from the University of California, and two years later he received his Ph.D. degree from the same institution. After a term of service in the United States Army, Dawson was a Research Associate at the Allan Hancock Foundation, University of Southern California (USC), from 1945 to 1955. In 1956 he was appointed Professor of Biology at USC, a position which he held with some interruptions, until 1964. From 1958 to 1962, he served as Research Director of the Beaudette Foundation for Biological Research; in 1964 he was Director of the San Diego Natural History Museum; and from 1964 until his death he served as Secretary of the Americas for the Charles Darwin Foundation for the Galapagos Islands. Dawson's research specialties included benthic marine algae, especially Rhodophyta of the tropical and subtropical Pacific, and Cactaceae. He published numerous books and papers on marine algae, cacti, and succulents. On June 22, 1966, Dawson drowned while diving for seaweed in the Red Sea.

This collection contains papers documenting the professional and personal life of E. Yale Dawson, with most of the collection consisting of correspondence with colleagues. There are, in addition, a few segments of field notes, manuscripts, and typescript copies, and drafts of some of his later publications. The collection generally does not include research and field notes, or publications.

ARRANGEMENT: (1) General correspondence, 1934-1966; (2) book drafts, unpublished typescripts, lecture notes, field notes, *circa* 1941-1966. FINDING AIDS: Description in control file. SPECIAL CONDITIONS: Use of this record unit requires prior arrangement with the Archives staff.

(7158)

William Lewis Dayton Scrapbook, 1864
(1 volume).

William Lewis Dayton (1807-1864) was a Regent of the Smithsonian Institution from 1861 to 1864. He also served as a member of the New Jersey legislature, 1837; Justice of the New Jersey Supreme Court, 1838-1841; United States Senator from New Jersey, 1842-1851; vice-presidential candidate for the Republican Party, 1856; Attorney-General of New Jersey, 1857-1861; and Minister to France, 1861-1864.

This scrapbook contains obituary notices from American and foreign newspapers on Dayton's death in Paris in 1864.

ARRANGEMENT: Unarranged clippings. FINDING AIDS: None. SPECIAL CONDITIONS: Use of this record unit requires prior arrangement with the Archives staff.

(7465)

Herbert Girton Deignan Papers, 1916-1970
(0.1 linear meter).

Herbert Girton Deignan (1906-1968), ornithologist and authority on the birds of Thailand, received the B.A. degree from Princeton University in 1928. That same year he took a position as Master in the Prince Royal College in Chiengmai, northern Siam. Deignan remained in Siam intermittently until 1937 and amassed a large collection of birds for the United States National Museum (USNM). In 1938, he was appointed Scientific Aid in the Division of Birds, USNM. He was promoted to Assistant Curator in 1940, Associate Curator in 1942, and Curator in 1959. Deignan retired in 1962.

During World War II, Deignan served in the Office of Strategic Services, 1944-1946, primarily in southern Asia. In 1948, he went to northern Australia as a member of the Commonwealth of Australia-National Geographic Society-Smithsonian Expedition to Arnhem Land. He also conducted field work for the USNM in Thailand, 1952-1953, and Madagascar, 1962.

These papers consist of photographs, including images of Deignan in Siam in the 1930s and on the 1948 Arnhem Land Expedition; letters written by Deignan to his mother from Siam, Central America, and Europe, 1931-1939; letters written by Deignan to family members, 1942-1948, including a few from Australia while serving on the Arnhem Land Expedition; official letters concerning his USNM career; certificates; and biographical materials on Deignan.

ARRANGEMENT: Unarranged. FINDING AIDS: None. SPECIAL CONDITIONS: Use of this record unit requires prior arrangement with the Archives staff.

(7195)

George Dimmock Papers, circa 1878-1915
(0.6 linear meter).

George Dimmock (1852-1930) specialized in anatomical studies of beetles. He also edited the entomological journal *Psyche* from 1877 to 1890.

In 1878 Dimmock began keeping a series of notebooks on his larval studies and his collections. Later he began calling the series "Entomological Notes." The notebooks contained observations, notes on collecting localities, and illustrations, many in color. The notebooks are arranged numerically by specimen number. An index to the notebooks is also included. In addition, there is a manuscript, apparently a translation of "Algunas Coccinellidae de Cuba" which appeared in *Estacion Central Agron. Annual* of 1906 in Cuba.

ARRANGEMENT: (1) Entomological notes, *circa* 1878-1915; (2) manuscript of "Some Cuban Coccinellidae," by George Dimmock, *circa* 1905-1906. FINDING AIDS: None. SPECIAL CONDITIONS: Use of this record unit requires prior arrangement with the Archives staff.

Richard P. Dow Papers, 1930-1939

(7457)

(0.1 linear meter).

Richard P. Dow (1907- ?), an entomologist, received his Ph.D. from Harvard University in 1935. From 1932 to 1941, he served as Curator of Insects at the Boston Society of Natural History. In 1947, he joined the staff of the Entomological Research Center, Florida Division of Health, where he remained until his retirement in 1972. Dow's research specialty was the taxonomy of Hymenoptera.

These papers consist mostly of correspondence received and written by Dow during graduate school and his tenure at the Boston Society of Natural History. The letters concern his research on the prey of wasps.

ARRANGEMENT: Alphabetic. FINDING AIDS: None. SPECIAL CONDITIONS: Use of this record unit requires prior arrangement with the Archives staff.

Carl John Drake Papers, 1930-1945

(7137)

(0.4 linear meter).

Carl John Drake (1885-1965) was born and educated in Ohio. He taught zoology and entomology at Ohio State University, 1913-1915; Syracuse University, 1915-1922; and became head of the Department of Zoology and Entomology at Iowa State University in 1922. There he also served as head of the Entomology Section of the Agricultural Experiment Station and as State Entomologist. His knowledge of farming helped him to solve many problems related to controlling the grasshopper, chinch bug, and other insect pests. Drake served on several national entomological organizations and headed the Tucara (grasshopper) Commission to Argentina in 1938-1939. In 1957 Drake joined the United States National Museum as an Honorary Research Associate, in which position he performed much valuable work, especially in tingid studies.

These papers consist of notebooks recording results of a pest mosquito and black fly control project in Iowa, 1933-1934 and fourteen reels of film documenting various features of Drake's work with grasshopper and chinch bug control programs in Iowa and Argentina.

ARRANGEMENT: (1) Still photographs and notebooks; (2) motion picture films. FINDING AIDS: Description in control file. SPECIAL CONDITIONS: Use of this record unit requires prior arrangement with the Archives staff.

Helen M. Duncan Papers, 1937-1966

(7397)

(2.1 linear meters).

Helen M. Duncan (1910-1971) received her B.A. (1934) and M.A. (1937) degrees from the University of Montana. She joined the United States Geological Survey (USGS) in 1942 as an editor, and later worked on a World War II fluorspar project. In 1945 Duncan was appointed Geologist in the Paleontology and Stratigraphy Branch of the USGS. She remained in the position until her death. Duncan specialized in the study of fossil Bryozoa.

The papers of Helen M. Duncan document her career with the USGS and her research on fossil Bryozoa. They include incoming and outgoing correspondence with colleagues, mostly concerning the identification of specimens; reports on specimens examined; and notes, lists, drafts of papers, and related materials from her research.

ARRANGEMENT: Unarranged. FINDING AIDS: None. SPECIAL CONDITIONS: Use of this record unit requires prior arrangement with the Archives staff.

(7101)

Harrison Gray Dyar Papers, 1882-1927
(0.8 linear meter).

Harrison Gray Dyar (1866-1929) was Honorary Custodian of the United States National Museum's collection of Lepidoptera for more than thirty years. His main research interests included the Lepidoptera, particularly their larvae; larvae of saw flies and mosquitoes; and bacteria. Dyar is especially noted for his work concerning mosquito-borne diseases. In addition to his research and curatorial duties, Dyar was proprietor and editor of *Insecutor Inscitiae Menstruus,* 1913-1927.

These papers include correspondence between Dyar and others regarding identification and exchange of specimens, comments on published papers, and other professional matters; Dyar's "Manuscript Notes on Lepidoptera," "Notes on Bombycidae of the United States," and material relating to his *List of North American Lepidoptera;* rearing records; a diary of field trips; and Dyar's catalog of Lepidoptera, a list of specimens which he placed in the national collection.

ARRANGEMENT: (1) Correspondence, 1887-1927; (2) *List of North American Lepidoptera;* (3) "Notes on Bombycidae of the United States;" (4) "Manuscript Notes on Lepidoptera;" (5) identifications, 1913-1925; (6) diary, 1905-1908; (7) rearing records, *circa* 1882; (8) catalog of Lepidoptera, *circa* 1885. FINDING AIDS: Description in control file. SPECIAL CONDITIONS: Use of this record unit requires prior arrangement with the Archives staff.

(7196)

R. Edward Earll Manuscript, circa 1880
(1 folder).

R. Edward Earll (1853-1896) joined the United States Fish Commission in 1877, following his graduation from Northwestern University. He served as a fish culturist for one year and then joined the scientific staff of the Commission. From 1879 to 1882, he engaged in special work for the Tenth United States Census and collected the statistics for fisheries in New England, Middle Atlantic, and Southern states. In 1883, Earll served as a member of the Commission staff for the London International Fisheries Exhibition. Upon his return, Earll was appointed Chief of the Division of Fisheries of the Fish Commission and an Honorary Curator of the United States National Museum. In 1888, he joined the Museum as a regular staff member and spent a good deal of his time working on the various expositions in which the Smithsonian and the National Museum participated. He also acted as editor of the *Proceedings* and the *Bulletin* of the Museum from 1893 to 1896.

This manuscript was probably prepared by Earll in connection with his work on the United States Census of 1880.

ARRANGEMENT: Manuscript of "Statistical Review of the Vessel Fisheries of the United States in 1880," by R. Edward Earll. FINDING AIDS: None. SPECIAL CONDITIONS: Use of this record unit requires prior arrangement with the Archives staff.

(7280)

Eastern Bird-Banding Association, 1923-1927, 1929-1936
Records (0.1 linear meter).

The Eastern Bird-Banding Association was founded in 1923 by a group of New York and Pennsylvania ornithologists to aid the Bureau of Biological Survey in the banding and study of migratory birds.

These records consist of a single bound volume which contains the Constitution of the Association and the correspondence of some of its officers and members. There appear to be gaps in the correspondence.

ARRANGEMENT: Chronologic and alphabetic thereunder. FINDING AIDS: None. SPECIAL CONDITIONS: Use of this record unit requires prior arrangement with the Archives staff.

(7468)

Egyptian Bombyliids Collection, 1930s
Watercolors (0.3 linear meter).

This collection consists of 84 watercolor paintings of Egyptian Bombyliids, or bee flies, executed by three Russian artists, Roman Strekalovsky, Nicholas Strekalovsky, and E. Kassessinoff. The paintings were done for a planned manuscript on the Bombyliids of Egypt by H. C. Efflatoun. Also included is a copy of Efflatoun's unpublished manuscript and photographs of the paintings.

This collection was previously described as record unit 1020011, R. Strekalovsky Drawings, *circa* 1940.

ARRANGEMENT: Unarranged. FINDING AIDS: List of paintings in control file. SPECIAL CONDITIONS: Use of this record unit requires prior arrangement with the Archives staff.

(7342)

James W. Eike Papers, 1927, 1950-1983
(0.8 linear meter).

James W. Eike (1911-1983), a native of Woodbridge, Virginia, joined the Virginia Society of Ornithology (VSO) in 1933, and was an active member and officer of the Society for the rest of his life. Eike was a lifelong observer of birds in and around northern Virginia, and he participated in numerous field trips and bird counts sponsored by the VSO and the Audubon Naturalist Society.

This collection consists of bird observation notes and sighting records, mainly in the form of field notes, although there are some compilations of his sightings.

ARRANGEMENT: Chronologic. FINDING AIDS: None. SPECIAL CONDITIONS: Use of this record unit requires prior arrangement with the Archives staff.

John F. Eisenberg Papers, circa 1960-1982 and undated
(7.4 linear meters).

John F. Eisenberg (1935-   ) received his B.S. from Washington State University in 1957, and his M.A. and Ph.D. degrees in zoology from the University of California, Berkeley, in 1959 and 1962, respectively. In 1962, he joined the staff of the University of British Columbia, Canada, as Assistant Professor of Zoology, a position he held until 1964. Eisenberg accepted an assistant professorship at the University of Maryland, College Park, in 1964, and was promoted to Research Associate Professor of Zoology the following year. He held this title until 1972, when he was promoted to Research Professor, a position he kept until 1982. Eisenberg was also an Associate of the Department of Mental Hygiene at Johns Hopkins University from 1973 to 1978.

In 1965, Eisenberg was also appointed Resident Scientist in the Department of Scientific Research at the National Zoological Park (NZP). He was made Acting Assistant Director for Zoological Programs in 1971, but when the office was abolished the following year, Eisenberg returned to his former title of Resident Scientist. He became Assistant Director for Animal Programs in 1979 and held that position until his resignation in 1982 to become Ordway Professor of Ecosystem Conservation at the University of Florida in Gainesville.

This collection primarily documents Eisenberg's tenure as Resident Scientist at NZP. Included are financial records, grant requests, progress reports, correspondence, photographs, and manuscripts relating to three long-term research projects under his direction: the Ceylon project on ecology and behavior of elephants (1967-1976) and primates (1968-1982); the Smithsonian-Venezuela Research Project on vertebrate behavior and ecology (1974-1982); and the Panama project on sloth and anteater research (1971-1977). Also included are general subject and correspondence files concerning research projects at NZP and abroad, as well as events and exhibits at NZP; correspondence and information about Eisenberg's publications and membership in numerous professional societies; and guidebooks, maps, and pamphlets from zoological parks that Eisenberg visited throughout the world.

ARRANGEMENT: Unarranged with the following collection divisions apparent: (1) research projects, 1967-1982; (2) alphabetic subject file, 1965-1982; (3) alphabetic correspondence file, 1960-1979; (4) publications, 1963-1977; (5) professional societies, 1963-1977; (6) foreign zoo guidebooks, 1962 and undated. FINDING AIDS: Folder list in control file. SPECIAL CONDITIONS: (1) Restricted; (2) use of this record unit requires prior arrangement with the Archives staff.

Farouk El-Baz Papers, circa 1965-1983
(32.8 linear meters).

Farouk El-Baz (1938-   ) was born in Zagazig, Egypt. He received a B.S. in chemistry and geology in 1958 from Ain Shams University, Cairo. In 1960 he came to the United States, where he earned an M.S. in geology at the Missouri School of Mines and Metallurgy in 1961 and a Ph.D. in geology at the University of Missouri in 1964. After teaching for a short period, he worked as an exploration geologist for the Pan American-United Arab Republic Oil Company, 1966-1967.

In 1967 he joined the staff of the Lunar Exploration Department of Bellcomm, Inc., and Bell Telephone Laboratories and in 1969 became supervisor of lunar science planning and lunar science operations. In that position, he worked directly with the United States space program on lunar data analysis, landing site selection, lunar exploration planning, and orbital science crew training. In 1969 he was named a member of the Apollo Program Science Support Team.

At Bellcomm El-Baz began pioneering work in remote sensing, examination of the surface of the earth or the moon from space. This work led him into the use of space photography to study the earth's deserts.

In 1973 El-Baz joined the staff of the Smithsonian's National Air and Space Museum, where he established the Center for Earth and Planetary Studies, which he directed until 1982. At the same time, he served as science advisor to President Anwar Sadat of Egypt, 1978-1981.

In 1982 El-Baz became Vice-President for International Development at Itek Optical Systems in Lexington, Massachusetts.

In addition to his work on remote sensing, El-Baz is also known for his participation in the International Astronomical Union's Task Group for Lunar Nomenclature, which was responsible for naming the features of the moon's surface geography.

These papers primarily document El-Baz's work at Bellcomm, his lunar studies and work with the United States Apollo program, and his participation in the *Apollo-Soyuz Test Program*, in which astronauts in space studied the earth's deserts. Also included is his *Desert Bibliography*. Papers include correspondence and memoranda, minutes of meetings, reports, charts, maps, printouts, logs, flight plans, press releases, and material relating to his book, *Apollo Over the Moon*. His participation in the lunar nomenclature committee, which is well represented, includes minutes of meetings, charts, and correspondence with committee members. There is also a copy of the master list of lunar names. For additional documentation of El-Baz's activities, see records of the Center for Earth and Planetary Studies, National Air and Space Museum, record unit 353.

ARRANGEMENT: (1) Farouk El-Baz Papers, *circa* 1970-1971, accession number 82-090; (2) Farouk El-Baz Papers, 1966-1982, accession number 82-091; (3) Farouk El-Baz Papers, 1968-1976, accession number 82-110; (4) Farouk El-Baz Papers, 1969-1981, accession number 82-097; (5) Farouk El-Baz Papers, *circa* 1965-1976, accession number 82-123; (6) Farouk El-Baz Papers, 1970-1978, accession number 83-011; (7) Farouk El-Baz Papers, *circa* 1980, accession number 83-064; (8) Farouk El-Baz Papers, 1976-1983, accession number 84-134. FINDING AIDS: Folder list in control file. SPECIAL CONDITIONS: (1) Restricted; (2) use of this record unit requires prior arrangement with the Archives staff.

(7369)

Henry W. Elliott Drawings, 1870
(0.1 linear meter).

Henry W. Elliott (1846-1930) was an artist, explorer, and conservationist. From 1869 to 1871 he served as an artist on the United States Geological and Geographical Surveys of the Territories under Ferdinand Vandeveer Hayden.

This collection consists of four pen-and-ink drawings of geological formations executed by Elliott while serving with the Hayden Survey in Wyoming in 1870.

ARRANGEMENT: Unarranged. FINDING AIDS: None. SPECIAL CONDITIONS: Use of this record unit requires prior arrangement with the Archives staff.

Douglas Ralph Emlong Papers, 1943-1980
(1 linear meter and oversize).

Douglas Ralph Emlong (1942-1980) was an amateur collector of marine mammal fossils. He amassed a large collection of fossils from the vicinity of his home on the Oregon coast and later sold them to the National Museum of Natural History (NMNH) in 1971. The collection included fifteen new species of marine mammals and two previously unknown families. He continued to collect for NMNH until his death, and for many years his work was supported by the Smithsonian Research Foundation. Emlong was also an amateur artist and lyricist.

These papers document Emlong's work as a collector of marine mammal fossils, his association with NMNH, and his personal life. Included is correspondence between Emlong and NMNH paleontologists A. Remington Kellogg and Clayton E. Ray documenting his early interest in fossil collecting and the development and sale of his collection; field notes and collecting records; photographs and slides of Emlong, his family, and his art work; manuscripts, mostly fictional, written by Emlong; tapes and sheet music of songs written and performed by Emlong; biographical information, newspaper clippings, and obituaries; high school papers; oversize oil paintings by Emlong; and a copy of the NMNH accession record for the Emlong collection.

See also record unit 9518 for a taped interview with Emlong.

ARRANGEMENT: Unarranged. FINDING AIDS: None. SPECIAL CONDITIONS: Use of this record unit requires prior arrangement with the Archives staff.

George Paul Engelhardt Papers, 1910-1942
(0.3 linear meter).

George Paul Engelhardt (1871-1942) was born and educated in Germany. In 1889 he emigrated to the United States and became a citizen. After various other employments, Engelhardt began in 1903 his association with the Brooklyn Museum, a connection which lasted until his retirement in 1930. Engelhardt's special interest was in the Aegeriidae, and he was acknowledged to be one of the world's greatest students and authorities in that area of entomology. His interest and knowledge were more than taxonomic. Engelhardt was particularly interested in assisting the careers of younger men in the field, and many entomologists who attained substantial standing owed their beginnings to his encouragement.

These papers include correspondence, chiefly for the period 1920-1942, with Engelhardt's professional colleagues, collaborators, and interested amateurs; and color drawings done by Mary Benson and Mrs. William Beutenmueller for United States National Museum Bulletin 190, *The North American Clear-Wing Moths of the Family Aegeriidae,* by George P. Engelhardt, published posthumously in 1946.

ARRANGEMENT: (1) Correspondence, 1910-1942; (2) color drawings for Bulletin 190. FINDING AIDS: Description in control file. SPECIAL CONDITIONS: Use of this record unit requires prior arrangement with the Archives staff.

Donald S. Erdman Papers, 1948
(0.1 linear meter).

Donald S. Erdman served as a Scientific Aid in the Division of Fishes, United States National Museum (USNM), from 1947 to 1950. In 1948, Erdman participated in a fisheries survey of the Persian Gulf and Red Sea under the auspices of the Arabian American Oil Company, on which he collected nearly 5,000 fishes for the USNM.

These papers document Erdman's field work in the Persian Gulf and Red Sea and include a journal and account book; notes, lists, and collection data; and photographs, color slides, and negatives.

ARRANGEMENT: Unarranged. FINDING AIDS: None. SPECIAL CONDITIONS: Use of this record unit requires prior arrangement with the Archives staff.

Wallace R. Ernst Papers, 1946-1971
(0.5 linear meter).

Wallace R. Ernst (1928-1971) came to the Smithsonian Institution in 1963 as Associate Curator of Phanerogams in the Botany Department of the United States National Museum. In 1970 he was appointed Curator of Phanerogams. Ernst's field of study was the taxonomy, morphology, and cytology of flowering plants, especially Papaveracae, Fumariaceae, and Loasaceae. In 1964 and 1965 Ernst journeyed to Dominica as a member of the Bredin-Archbold-Smithsonian Biological Survey of the Island. For two months in 1966 he participated in the archeological expedition to the Valley of Oaxaca, Mexico, under the leadership of Kent Flannery. Ernst also collaborated with Albert C. Smith on the latter's Flora of Fiji project financed by the National Science Foundation.

This collection contains papers documenting the professional and personal life of Ernst, especially during his tenure at the Smithsonian Institution. Included are field notebooks, 1956-1961, 1964-1966, documenting his collecting activities in California, Baja California, Dominica, Mexico, and research conducted in Europe in 1964; correspondence with colleagues regarding his work on Papaveracae, Eucnide, Loasaceae, and Fumariaceae; material documenting his collaboration with A. C. Smith on the Flora of Fiji project; correspondence documenting the Bredin-Archbold-Smithsonian Biological Survey of Dominica; and material concerning the internal affairs of the Department of Botany.

ARRANGEMENT: (1) General correspondence, 1956-1971; (2) field notebooks, 1956-1961; (3) additional acquisitions, 1946-1960s. FINDING AIDS: Description in control file. SPECIAL CONDITIONS: Use of this record unit requires prior arrangement with the Archives staff.

John Evans Papers, 1854-1856, 1860
(1 folder).

John Evans (1812-1861) joined David Dale Owen's survey of Wisconsin, Iowa, and Minnesota following his graduation from St. Louis Medical College, *circa* 1848. In

1851, he was appointed by the Secretary of the Interior to survey the Washington and Oregon territories, and in 1853 joined Isaac Stevens' Pacific Railroad Survey. He was also geologist to the Isthmus of Chiriqui Expedition to Central America in 1860.

These papers include a journal for Evans' tenure with the railroad survey, covering the period July to September 1854. They also include journals for Evans' journeys in the Port Orford region of Oregon in 1855-1856, and one page of Evans' journal for the Isthmus of Chiriqui Expedition of 1860.

ARRANGEMENT: Chronologic. FINDING AIDS: None. SPECIAL CONDITIONS: Use of this record unit requires prior arrangement with the Archives staff.

(7402)

Extinct and Vanishing Birds of the World, circa 1958
Drawings (0.1 linear meter).

This collection consists of original pen and ink drawings published in *Extinct and Vanishing Birds of the World* by James C. Greenway, Jr., 1958. All of the drawings were executed by D. M. Reid-Henry, except for one, which was drawn by Henry Seidel.

ARRANGEMENT: Unarranged. FINDING AIDS: None. SPECIAL CONDITIONS: Use of this record unit requires prior arrangement with the Archives staff.

(7286)

David Grandison Fairchild Journal, 1896-1897
(0.1 linear meter).

David Grandison Fairchild (1876-1954) was a botanist concerned with the search for valuable seeds and plants for introduction into the United States. He was appointed Pathologist at the United States Department of Agriculture in 1892. He eventually became head of the Section of Seed and Plant Introduction.

This journal was kept by Fairchild on a collecting trip to Java, 1896-1897. It includes descriptions of specimens, some loose notes on termites, and a small number of photographs of unidentified plants.

ARRANGEMENT: Chronologic. FINDING AIDS: None. SPECIAL CONDITIONS: Use of this record unit requires prior arrangement with the Archives staff.

(7446)

Augustus Fendler Papers, 1854, 1874, 1900 and undated
(0.1 linear meter).

Augustus Fendler (1813-1883), a natural history collector, was born in Prussia and spent one year at the technical school in Berlin. In 1836 he emigrated to Baltimore, and for the next eight years found irregular employment in trades in Philadelphia, New York, St. Louis, and New Orleans. He tried homesteading in Texas in 1839, and lived as a hermit on a Missouri River island in the winter of 1841-1842. A trip to Prussia in 1844 and a visit to Ernst Meyer, Professor of Botany at the University at Konigsberg, awakened him to the commercial possibilities of collecting botanical specimens. At first collecting in the Mississippi River valley, Fendler collaborated with botanist George Engelmann of St.

Louis in identifying specimens. At the outbreak of the Mexican War, through the help of Asa Gray, he was provided with free transportation with United States troops to Santa Fe, where he collected during the years 1846-1847. Gray's descriptions of these plants are classics in the field, and the Smithsonian purchased a set of his specimens. In 1849 Fendler attempted an unsuccessful expedition to the Great American Basin. Later collecting trips were to Panama, Arkansas, and Venezuela, where he lived for five years in the late 1850s. While in Venezuela, Fendler amassed a great collection of flora and became a meteorological correspondent of the Smithsonian. His travels continued in his later life as well, including Missouri, Prussia, Delaware (where he wrote *The Mechanism of the Universe),* and Trinidad, where he continued his botanical collecting until his death.

These papers were deposited with the Smithsonian along with manuscripts on botany, which form part of record unit 1010014. The present material consists chiefly of two possibly related series. One is the manuscript for his 1874 privately printed book, *The Mechanism of the Universe,* which was an attempt to find a coherent scheme to all motive powers in the universe, from physics to physiology. Included in this record unit are illustrations and an analytical table of contents that were not printed. The second series consists of notes, arranged by subject, on various aspects of natural science, including meteorology, climatology, geography, zoology, botany, and horticulture. These materials may have been intended to form the basis of a book, perhaps a companion to Fendler's *Mechanism,* as none of these topics are dealt with there. This record unit also includes a covering memorandum to the manuscript, dated June 16, 1900, from Randolph Iltyd Geare, Chief of Correspondence and Documents, to Richard Rathbun, Assistant Secretary; a letter from Fendler to Engelmann, April 22, 1854, written from Venezuela; and botanical illustrations.

ARRANGEMENT: (1) Correspondence, 1854; (2) materials concerning *The Mechanism of the Universe;* (3) notes on natural science; (4) botanical illustrations. FINDING AIDS: None. SPECIAL CONDITIONS: Use of this record unit requires prior arrangement with the Archives staff.

(7350)

Jesse Walter Fewkes Notebook, circa 1886
(0.1 linear meter).

Jesse Walter Fewkes (1850-1930) was born in Newton, Massachusetts. His scientific work is separated into two distinct periods, the first dealing with marine zoology and the second devoted to ethnology. Fewkes received his Ph.D. in marine zoology from Harvard University in 1877 and remained at the Museum of Comparative Zoology in charge of the lower invertebrates until 1887. While in California on a collecting trip, Fewkes became interested in the Pueblo Indians and their culture. During the next few years, he visited Hopi villages and made some of the first recordings of Hopi music, beginning his lifelong study of tribal ceremonies. In 1895, Fewkes began to conduct archeological explorations for the Bureau of American Ethnology of the Smithsonian Institution, and in 1918, he was appointed Chief of the Bureau. After his retirement in 1928, Fewkes continued his research as Associate Anthropologist until his death in 1930.

This notebook consists of observations and drawings of marine invertebrates in the area of Marblehead, Massachusetts, *circa* 1886. Included are observations of the fission of *Astrophyton* eggs, with drawings of the divisions, and an extended series of observations on *Hanonia cara.* Less detailed accounts list location, size, species, and abundance. Illustrations with proportional instructions were used to supplement the descriptions. Fewkes used Alexander Agassiz's prior work for reference and comparison. Also included is a sketch of Marblehead harbor from the water.

ARRANGEMENT: Notebook, circa, 1886. FINDING AIDS: Description in control file. SPECIAL CONDITIONS: Use of this record unit requires prior arrangement with the Archives staff.

(7463)

Edward L. Fireman Papers, circa 1950-1990
(10.3 linear meters).

Edward L. Fireman (1922-1990) was a physicist and authority on the analysis and dating of extraterrestrial materials. He received a doctorate from Princeton University in 1948 and in 1950 accepted a position as Physicist at the Brookhaven National Laboratory. In 1956, he was appointed Physicist with the Smithsonian Astrophysical Observatory (SAO) where he remained until his death.

Fireman's research interests included the analysis of returned meteorites, lunar samples, and recovered satellites; and investigations concerning cosmic rays, solar flares, muons, and neutrinos. He was also involved in developing methods for measuring the ages of ancient polar ice samples and using the information to refine the earth's climatic record. Fireman was a member of numerous professional societies and the author of some 200 scientific papers.

These papers mostly document Edward L. Fireman's scientific research program at the SAO, particularly his work on meteorites, lunar samples, satellite debris, and polar ice. They also concern his participation at conferences and symposia and other professional activities. They include incoming and outgoing correspondence with colleagues, research and professional organizations, and publishers; research and laboratory notebooks; notebooks and 35mm slides concerning his research on ice at Camp Century, Greenland, 1963-1966; and notes, lectures, manuscripts, proposals, reprints, data, 35mm and lantern slides, and related research materials.

ARRANGEMENT: (1) Edward L. Fireman Papers, 1963-1979, accession number 84-035; (2) Edward L. Fireman Papers, *circa* 1950-1990, accession number 90-144; (3) Edward L. Fireman Papers, *circa* 1950-1990, accession number 91-010. FINDING AIDS: Box list in control file. SPECIAL CONDITIONS: Use of this record unit requires prior arrangement with the Archives staff.

(7124)

Asa Fitch Notebooks, circa 1827-1872
(7 volumes).

Asa Fitch (1809-1879), the founder of economic entomology in America, was trained in medicine, which he practiced briefly. Fitch was largely self-taught in entomology. In 1838 he abandoned his medical practice and devoted himself to entomological studies, to such good effect that in 1854 he was appointed State Entomologist of New York. His appointment marked the first serious attention to be paid to insect damage in the United States. Fitch's studies, largely confined to New York, were extremely thorough and made a great impression on Charles Valentine Riley and other members of the generation of entomologists to follow Fitch.

This collection consists of five volumes of notes of observations, some rearing data, and information copied from other sources and researchers; a few illustrations; and some notes and marginalia by later users of the notebooks. The notebooks are arranged roughly by orders and families of insects; species are usually described separately, with dates of observation, anatomy, coloration, and habitats given. Dates of observation often vary widely within each volume, most often ranging between 1830 and 1860. Some specimens were supplied by correspondents. There are also occasional notes on practical remedies for insect pests.

ARRANGEMENT: Numeric by volume number. FINDING AIDS: Description in control file. SPECIAL CONDITIONS: Use of this record unit requires prior arrangement with the Archives staff.

(7242)

August F. Foerste Papers, 1887-1933 and undated
(1.2 linear meters).

August F. Foerste (1862-1936) was born in Dayton, Ohio. Foerste studied geology at Denison University, B.A., 1887, and Harvard University, M.A., 1888, and Ph.D., 1890. While at Harvard, he also served as a part-time assistant with the United States Geological Survey studying the stratigraphy and petrography of New England. Following his attendance at Harvard, Foerste studied for two years at Heidelberg University and the College de France. In 1893, he returned to Dayton and became a science teacher at a high school where he remained until his retirement in 1932.

Foerste's summer vacations were spent participating in geological surveys in Indiana, 1896, 1897, and 1899; Ohio, 1908 and 1919; Kentucky, 1904-1912; and Canada, 1911-1912. In 1920, Foerste began research in invertebrate paleontology at the United States National Museum (USNM) and was appointed Associate in Paleontology at the USNM in 1932.

Foerste's study of fossils centered on three areas: Ohio Valley Silurian stratigraphy and paleontology; Ordovician fossils of the United States and Canada; and lower Paleozoic cephalopods, particularly those of the Ozarkian-Canadian system with Edward Oscar Ulrich of the USNM.

These papers consist of Foerste's field, specimen, and miscellaneous notebooks; drafts of manuscripts on Ozarkian and Canadian cephalopods; and topographic maps.

ARRANGEMENT: (1) Notebooks, 1887-*circa* 1916 and undated; (2) drafts of manuscripts on Ozarkian and Canadian cephalopods, 1926-1933 and undated; (3) topographic maps, 1909-1914 and undated. FINDING AIDS: Description in control file. SPECIAL CONDITIONS: Use of this record unit requires prior arrangement with the Archives staff.

(7130)

Arnold Foerster Notebooks, 1843, 1864 and undated
(1 microfilm reel).

Arnold Foerster (1810-1884) was a German entomologist of distinction.

These notebooks contain keys and descriptions, mostly of genera of Hymenoptera, almost entirely the Ichneumonidae. The greater part of the notebooks have been published, but contain unpublished information. The notebooks are written in German, Greek, and Latin.

ARRANGEMENT: Chronologic. FINDING AIDS: Description in control file. SPECIAL CONDITIONS: Use of this record unit requires prior arrangement with the Archives staff.

(7216)

Edward R. Foreman Papers, circa 1868-1879
(0.1 linear meter).

Edward R. Foreman (1808-1885) was born in Baltimore, Maryland. After twelve years as an Assistant Professor at the University of Pennsylvania, he was appointed Assistant in the Smithsonian Institution in 1848. Foreman's duties with the Smithsonian included the organization of the meteorological reporting system initiated by Secretary Joseph Henry and the arrangement of scientific lectures. During his years at the Smithsonian, Foreman also served as Professor of Chemistry in the National Medical College. In 1852, he accepted the position of chief examiner in the Patent Office, a position he retained until 1860. Foreman returned to the Smithsonian in 1874 as a collaborator in Ethnology in the United States National Museum.

These papers include lectures and notes on chemistry, ethnology, and natural history, especially botany; a sketch of the geology of Arkansas; and various lists of specimens.

ARRANGEMENT: Unarranged. FINDING AIDS: None. SPECIAL CONDITIONS: Use of this record unit requires prior arrangement with the Archives staff.

(7281)

William F. Foshag Collection, 1923-1965 and undated
(2.5 linear meters).

William F. Foshag (1894-1956) joined the United States National Museum's Division of Mineralogy and Petrology as an Assistant Curator in 1919. From 1929 to 1941, he served as Curator of the Division of Physical and Chemical Geology (Systematic and Applied), and from 1929 to 1948 was also Curator of the Division of Mineralogy and Petrology. From 1948 to 1956, Foshag was Head Curator of the Department of Geology and Acting Curator of the Division of Mineralogy and Petrology.

Foshag's research was primarily devoted to the study of the geology and mineralogy of Mexico. Between 1926 and 1941, Foshag made several collecting trips to Mexico under the auspices of the Smithsonian's Roebling Fund. While serving as a representative of the United States Geological Survey in its cooperative work with the Mexican government, Foshag was able to study the eruption of the Paricutin Volcano in 1943. He made subsequent visits to Paricutin in 1944 and 1945 to observe the volcano. In 1946, he went to Japan to supervise the grading, classifying and appraising, for the United States government, of diamonds captured from the Japanese during World War II. In 1949, Foshag was commissioned by the Guatemalan government to survey ancient jade objects from Central America.

This collection consists mostly of materials documenting Foshag's research on Paricutin Volcano. Included are field notes recorded by Foshag, as well as notes and observations made by Jenaro Gonzalez and Gutierrez Celedonio; photographs, color slides, and glass plate negatives documenting the birth and subsequent activity of the volcano, research notes mostly concerning the analysis of lava and other materials erupted from Paricutin; manuscripts, reports, reprints, and publications concerning Paricutin and volcanology, and maps of Mexico, particularly the Paricutin region. Also included in the collection is general correspondence of Foshag, 1923, 1942-1965, including letters concerning his study of Paricutin Volcano and his survey of Central American jade objects, and photographs taken on several of Foshag's mineral collecting trips to Mexico, 1926-1934.

A collection of 151 photographic prints and corresponding negatives from his study of Paricutin Volcano were transferred by Foshag to the National Archives in 1951 (NARS Accession Inventory No. 451-111).

ARRANGEMENT: (1) General correspondence, 1923, 1942-1965; (2) photographs of Mexican field trips, 1926-1927, 1929, 1931, 1934; (3) field notes on Paricutin Volcano, 1943-1952; (4) photographs, slides, and glass plate negatives of Paricutin Volcano, 1943-1955 and undated; (5) manuscripts, reports, reprints, and publications on Paricutin Volcano, 1943-1954 and undated; (6) research notes on Paricutin Volcano, 1946-1950 and undated; (7) maps of Mexico. FINDING AIDS: Description in control file. SPECIAL CONDITIONS: Use of this record unit requires prior arrangement with the Archives staff.

(7180)

Henry Weed Fowler Papers, circa 1920, 1930-1941
(3.1 linear meters).

Henry Weed Fowler (1878-1965) was born in Holmesburg, Pennsylvania. His post-high school academic career was limited to two years, *circa* 1900, spent at Stanford University as a special student under David Starr Jordan. His entire professional life was spent in association with the Academy of Natural Sciences of Philadelphia, where he was employed as a museum assistant, 1903-1922; a museum fellow, 1922-1923; Associate Curator of Vertebrate Zoology, 1925-1934; Curator of Fishes and Reptiles, 1934-1940; and Curator of Fishes, 1940-1965. Although Fowler published papers on crustaceans, birds, reptiles, and amphibians, ichthyology was his main interest. He was a founder of the American Society of Ichthyologists and Herpetologists and Treasurer for seven years. He was also President of the Society in 1927.

Fowler's connection with the Smithsonian included two major projects. Around 1918, Barton A. Bean, Assistant Curator of Fishes at the United States National Museum, recommended that the fishes collected by the United States Exploring Expedition of 1838-1842 be sent to Fowler since they had never been properly identified. Fowler returned a manuscript of approximately 750 pages in 1920. This manuscript was never published, although Fowler did publish a summary of the paper in 1940 in the *Proceedings of the American Philosophical Society,* volume 82. Bean and Fowler also published a report on eighteen new species of fish in the United States Exploring Expedition collection in the *Proceedings of the United States National Museum,* volume 63.

In 1925, Fowler and Bean began a collaborative work on the fishes collected by the Bureau of Fisheries steamer *Albatross* in the Philippines from 1907 to 1910. Six volumes were published from 1928 to 1941 as parts 7-8 and 10-13 of *United States National Museum Bulletin 100.* The first three were jointly authored by Bean and Fowler and the latter three by Fowler alone. In addition, Fowler submitted six additional manuscripts which were never published.

These papers include Fowler's unpublished manuscript on the United States Exploring Expedition fishes and the last six unpublished parts of his work on the Philippine fishes.

ARRANGEMENT: (1) Unpublished manuscript entitled "The fishes obtained by the United States Exploring Expedition, 1838-1842, under the command of Capt. Charles Wilkes," *circa* 1920; (2) unpublished manuscript on the fishes of the Philippines, *circa* 1930-1940. FINDING AIDS: Description in control file. SPECIAL CONDITIONS: Use of this record unit requires prior arrangement with the Archives staff.

(7319)

Ira N. Gabrielson Collection, 1918-1987
(1.8 linear meters).

Ira N. Gabrielson (1889-1987) was a wildlife biologist and early promoter of wildlife conservation. He joined the Bureau of Biological Survey in 1915, specializing in rodent control and game management, with a particular interest in waterfowl. By 1935 he had become Chief of the Survey, and when it was merged with the Bureau of Fisheries in 1940 to become the United States Fish and Wildlife Service, he was named its first Director. During his tenure, 1940-1946, millions of acres were added to the National Wildlife Refuge System. From 1946 to 1970, he served as President of the Wildlife Management Institute and became Chairman of its Board of Directors in 1970. He was active in many national and international wildlife organizations and at home served as Chairman and Chairman Emeritus of the Northern Virginia Regional Park Authority until his death. He received many conservation awards, was an active participant in professional groups, and the writer of four books, many articles, and many speeches.

This collection is composed of four distinct parts. Records documenting the writing of *The Birds of Alaska,* which he co-authored with Frederick C. Lincoln, include correspondence, species notes, and drafts of chapters. The *Memoirs of Ira Noel Gabrielson and What Others Have Said About Him,* compiled by his son-in-law, Robert A. Nesbitt, contains obituaries, reminiscences, and an autobiography which Gabrielson began and never completed. Gabrielson's diaries, 1918-1977, range from a few notes on birds seen that day to substantial accounts of daily activities. The final section of the collection contains his articles and speeches, 1936-1968.

ARRANGEMENT: (1) Records relating to *The Birds of Alaska,* 1944-1958; (2) *Memoirs of Ira Noel Gabrielson and What Others Have Said About Him,* by Robert A. Nesbitt, 1987; (3) diaries, 1918-1977; (4) articles and speeches, 1936-1968. FINDING AIDS: Description in control file. SPECIAL CONDITIONS: Use of this record unit requires prior arrangement with the Archives staff.

(1020009)

Arthur Burton Gahan Notes, circa 1927
(1.2 linear meters).

Arthur Burton Gahan (1880-1960) was born and educated in Kansas. In 1904, he became an assistant in the Department of Entomology of the Maryland Agricultural College, where he started his studies of parasitic wasps. He was appointed Assistant Entomologist in the Bureau of Entomology of the United States Department of

Agriculture in 1913 and was assigned to the United States National Museum, where he continued his studies and became an authority on chalcid wasps.

This collection consists of notes on Chalcidoidae, taken by Gahan at European museums. Many of the specimens have since been destroyed by war.

ARRANGEMENT: By family of Chalcidoidae. FINDING AIDS: None. SPECIAL CONDITIONS: Use of this record unit requires prior arrangement with the Archives staff.

(7312)

Adelia Gates Collection, 1879-1898 and undated
(0.8 linear meter).

Adelia Gates (*circa* 1820-1912) was born in the Susquehanna Valley of New York State. At age sixteen she taught in a country school, and later worked in the cotton mills at Lowell, Massachusetts. Gates attended Antioch College when she was in her thirties, but had to leave after two years because of poor health. At the age of fifty, Gates was taught how to paint flowers by Madame Vouga in Geneva, Switzerland.

This collection consists of 327 watercolors of flowers painted by Adelia Gates. It represents a fragment of a collection of 502 Gates watercolors donated to the Smithsonian by Eleanor Lewis in 1913. Approximately 175 watercolors are missing. The paintings cover a wide range of native and exotic plants and a majority of the studies were made in California, Algeria, and Italy. Also included is an alphabetic index to the paintings, arranged by genus.

ARRANGEMENT: (1) Folio I, no. 4179.1 - no. 4179.23; (2) Folio II, no. 4180.1 - no. 4180.180; (3) Folio III, no. 4181.1 - no. 4181.124; (4) index arranged by genus. FINDING AIDS: None. SPECIAL CONDITIONS: Use of this record unit requires prior arrangement with the Archives staff.

(7314)

Charles Lewis Gazin Papers, 1901-1984 and undated
(6.5 linear meters).

Charles Lewis Gazin (1904-1995) was born in Colorado and educated at the California Institute of Technology where he earned his B.S. in 1927, his M.S. in 1928 and his Ph.D. in geology and paleontology in 1930. In 1930 Gazin began work for the United States Geological Survey. In 1932 he was named Assistant Curator in the Division of Vertebrate Paleontology at the United States National Museum (USNM). Gazin became Associate Curator in 1942 and Curator of the Division in 1946. In 1967 he was named Senior Paleobiologist, and when he retired in 1970 he became Paleobiologist Emeritus. In 1982 he was named Curator Emeritus. Gazin led field expeditions almost every summer between 1934 and 1969, except while he was in the United States Army Air Force during World War II. Gazin published ninety-nine works on vertebrate paleontology, many of them concerning mammalian paleontology. He served as President of the Society of Vertebrate Paleontology and Director of the American Geological Institute and was actively involved in other professional organizations.

These papers document Gazin's career at the Smithsonian as a vertebrate paleontologist, focusing on the Tertiary and Quaternary fossils of continental North America. They contain little record of his personal life. His curatorial responsibilities are documented through specimen loans, memoranda, inventories, and drawings relating to the design of exhibitions. Division activities are documented in the annual reports, which also contain thorough reports of Gazin's field work. Records concerning Gazin's grant-sponsored research and trips can be found in the National Science Foundation files. Notes, drafts, and manuscripts of his publications, as well as illustrations prepared for them, can be found in the papers. These papers also contain other photographs and drawings of specimens. There is a substantial amount of correspondence, memoranda, and minutes of meetings of the scientific organizations in which Gazin was involved, including the American Geological Institute, the Geological Society of America, the Washington Academy of Sciences, the National Science Foundation, the National Research Council, and the Society of Vertebrate Paleontology.

ARRANGEMENT: (1) Correspondence, 1911, 1930-1983 and undated; (2) subject files, 1906, 1918, 1932-1984; (3) research reports and annual reports, 1906-1908, 1910-1933, 1935-1971; (4) expeditions, field work, and study trips, 1934-1941, 1946-1969 and undated; (5) organizations, 1930-1984; (6) Society of Vertebrate Paleontology, 1935-1983 and undated; (7) National Research Council, 1930, 1947-1952, 1957-1967, 1974-1975; (8) National Science Foundation, 1958-1977; (9) exhibitions, 1940-1941, 1946, 1955-1968, 1975 and undated; (10) autobiographical data and bibliographies, 1956, 1960, 1964-1966 and undated; (11) notes, drafts, manuscripts, 1921-1976 and undated; (12) collected manuscripts, correspondence, and related materials, 1901, 1924, 1961 and undated; (13) illustrations and photographs, 1906, 1920, 1933-1971 and undated; (14) field notes, 1930-1942, 1946-1969; (15) general correspondence, 1933-1981, accession number 88-041; (16) notes, manuscripts, correspondence, and photographs, 1959-1979, accession number 89-104. FINDING AIDS: Description in control file. SPECIAL CONDITIONS: (1) Check finding aid for location; (2) use of this record unit requires prior arrangement with the Archives staff.

(7341)

Louis G. Gentner Papers, 1920-1979 and undated
(0.4 linear meter).

Louis G. Gentner (1892-1980) was a coleopterist and authority on the taxonomy of flea beetles. He spent most of his professional career as an entomologist at the Southern Oregon Experiment Station. Gentner amassed a large collection of flea beetles which he donated to the National Museum of Natural History in 1979.

This collection consists of incoming and outgoing correspondence documenting Gentner's research on flea beetles. Most of the letters concern the identification and acquisition of specimens. Also included are newspaper clippings concerning Gentner, a copy of his bibliography, and sample labels from his collection.

ARRANGEMENT: (1) General correspondence, 1920-1977; (2) newspaper clippings, bibliography, and specimen labels, 1979 and undated. FINDING AIDS: None. SPECIAL CONDITIONS: Use of this record unit requires prior arrangement with the Archives staff.

(7471)

George Washington Memorial Association, 1890-1922
Records (0.6 linear meter).

The George Washington Memorial Association (GWMA) was organized in 1898 for the purpose of establishing in Washington, D.C., an educational institution for the "promotion of science and literature" as described by George Washington in his messages to Congress and in his will. Early attempts to establish a National University were unsuccessful and by early 1904 the GWMA entered into an agreement with Columbian College to build a marble monument to George Washington in the form of an administration building and cultural center for its site at Constitution Avenue at 17th Street, N.W. Plans for a building on the site fell through (although Columbian College did rename itself George Washington University), and the Association then joined with the Smithsonian to build a multi-purpose structure on the Mall that would serve as a memorial to George Washington.

In 1914 a competition was held and New York architects Evarts Tracy and Edgerton Swartwout were chosen. By the time the cornerstone was laid in 1921, the building was called the George Washington Victory Memorial Building to honor World War I veterans as well. The structure was to include a military museum and archives. The concrete foundation and stairway were complete by 1924 and a fence was constructed around the site. For more than ten years, the GWMA, with the help of Secretaries Walcott and Abbot, attempted to raise funds to complete the building, but failed. The foundation and monumental stairway were razed in 1937 for the construction of the National Gallery of Art.

These records document the history and organization of the GWMA and the planning for the George Washington Memorial Building—first in conjunction with the establishment of a National University in Washington, the construction of an administrative building and cultural center for Columbian College, and finally, allied with the Smithsonian, as a victory memorial for World War I veterans. Included is documentation of the fundraising efforts by Secretaries Langley and Walcott needed to complete the project, including financial records, brochures and descriptive material, correspondence, newspaper articles, drawings by the prize-winning architects, and photographs.

ARRANGEMENT: (1) General correspondence and accounting records, 1890, 1898-1920; (2) publications, 1890-1921; (3) newspaper clippings, 1901-1904, 1922. FINDING AIDS: Folder list in control file. SPECIAL CONDITIONS: Use of this record unit requires prior arrangement with the Archives staff.

(7290)

Carl Andreas Geyer Journal, 1838
(0.1 linear meter).

Carl Andreas Geyer (1809-1853) was a German botanist who took part in a number of North American expeditions, 1835-1844.

This record unit consists of the botanical journal kept by Geyer on the Nicollet Expedition, 1838, organized to survey the Missouri and Mississippi river area. Also included is a transcript of the journal with an introduction and index to specimen numbers.

ARRANGEMENT: Chronologic. FINDING AIDS: None. SPECIAL CONDITIONS: (1) Journal available on microfilm; (2) use of this record unit requires prior arrangement with the Archives staff.

Riccardo Giacconi Papers, circa 1960-1992
(37.4 linear meters).

Riccardo Giacconi (1931-   ), an astrophysicist, was born in Genoa, Italy. He attended the University of Milan, receiving the Ph.D. in 1954. From 1954 to 1956 he served as an Assistant Professor of Physics at the University, then became Research Associate (Fulbright Fellow) at Indiana University. From 1958 to 1959 Giacconi was a Research Associate in the Cosmic Ray Laboratory at Princeton University. In 1959 he took the post of Senior Scientist, Vice-President in charge of the Space Research and System Division, at American Science and Engineering (ASE), a private research corporation in Cambridge, Massachusetts. He stayed at ASE, becoming Executive Vice-President and a member of the Board of Directors, until 1973, when he left to become Associate Director of the High Energy Astrophysics Division of the Center for Astrophysics (CFA) and Professor of Astronomy at Harvard University. Giacconi stayed at the CFA until 1981 when he was appointed first Director of the Space Telescope Science Institute (STSI) and Professor of Physics and Astronomy at Johns Hopkins University. In 1981 Giacconi became Director of the STSI, managed by the Association of Universities for Research in Astronomy for the National Aeronautics and Space Administration (NASA). When fully operational, the STSI was to be the center of operations and research for the Hubble Space Telescope, which was launched in 1990. From 1987 to 1988 Giacconi served as a consultant to Montedison, an Italian chemical conglomerate, as Chairman of the Board of Instituto Donegani, the research arm of the parent corporation. In 1991 he was also appointed Professor of Physics at the University of Milan.

Much of Giacconi's pioneering work in X-ray astronomy took place during his tenure at ASE, and he was a major force in the development of the company. In 1962 Giacconi's group succeeded in detecting the first extrasolar X-ray source. In 1963 the same group obtained the first solar X-ray picture by using an X-ray telescope which had been conceived, advocated, designed, and fabricated by them. In that same year Giacconi proposed an X-ray astronomy satellite, *Explorer.* The proposal led to a program of construction in 1966-1970, followed by a successful launch in 1970. The satellite became known as *Uhuru,* and represented a major qualitative step in X-ray astronomy's observational capability. Following this early work on solar X-ray studies, a major program, initiated in 1968, culminated in the flight of the SO-54 X-ray Telescope on the Apollo telescope mount's Skylab mission. In 1970 a program for construction of a 1.2 meter X-ray telescope for study of extrasolar sources was initiated. The program was modified in 1973, and finally led to the Einstein Observatory mission, successfully launched in 1978. Giacconi had responsibility for the scientific direction and administrative management of all these programs.

These records document nearly all of Giacconi's professional career, and consist mainly of professional papers documenting his scientific work. Administrative records from ASE and STSI, if any, are fragmentary. A significant body of such records exists for Giacconi's CFA work. There is extensive documentation of Giacconi's professional activities, including meetings attended, papers presented, his services as officer or board member of professional societies; grants, proposals, and contracts, mainly with NASA;

correspondence with colleagues; slides and photographs of many facilities with which Giacconi was associated, some unidentified; news clippings and press releases; a few appointment books and journals; and files documenting his association with Montedison. Major projects that are well-documented include the High Energy Astronomy Observatory, *Uhuru,* the X-ray Telescope, and the Einstein Observatory.

ARRANGEMENT: (1) Riccardo Giacconi papers, *circa* 1962-1973, accession number T89101; (2) Riccardo Giacconi papers, 1960-1983, accession number 84-077; (3) Riccardo Giacconi papers, 1962-1983, accession number 84-202; (4) Riccardo Giacconi papers, 1960-1982, accession number 85-113; (5) Riccardo Giacconi papers, 1960-1974, 1983, accession number 86-047; (6) Riccardo Giacconi papers, 1960-1992, accession number 93-058. FINDING AIDS: Description in control file. SPECIAL CONDITIONS: (1) Restricted; (2) use of this record unit requires prior arrangement with the Archives staff.

(7209)

George Gibbs Papers, circa 1850-1853, 1857-1862
(0.1 linear meter).

George Gibbs (1815-1873) was an ethnologist and expert on the language and culture of the Indians of the Pacific Northwest. A graduate of Harvard University, Gibbs moved west during the gold rush of 1848 and eventually secured the position of Collector of the Port of Astoria, Oregon Territory. From 1853 to 1855, he was a geologist and ethnologist on the Pacific Railroad Survey of the 47th and 49th parallels under the command of Isaac Stevens. In 1857, Gibbs joined the Northwest Boundary Survey and served as geologist and interpreter until 1862. The last decade of his life was spent in Washington, D.C., where he undertook studies of Indian languages under the auspices of the Smithsonian Institution.

This collection consists primarily of journals kept by Gibbs while in Oregon Territory, 1850-1853, and on the Northwest Boundary Survey, 1857-1862. The journals contain zoological and ethnological observations, accounts of collections made, and Indian vocabulary. Also included are notes on the forest growth of Washington Territory, *circa* 1860.

ARRANGEMENT: (1) Journals, 1850-1853, 1857-1862; (2) notes on the forest growth of Washington Territory, *circa* 1860. FINDING AIDS: None. SPECIAL CONDITIONS: Use of this record unit requires prior arrangement with the Archives staff.

(7122)

Robert H. Gibbs, Jr., Field Notebook, 1949-1960
(1 volume).

Robert H. Gibbs, Jr., (1929-1988) joined the Smithsonian as Associate Curator in the Division of Fishes in 1963 and became Curator in 1967. Prior to 1963, Gibbs taught at New York State Teachers College, 1955-1956, and Boston University, 1958-1963, and served as marine biologist at Woods Hole Oceanographic Institute, 1956-1958.

This notebook contains data on a collection of dragonflies made in the United States, Canada, and Mexico, but principally in the eastern United States. Some collecting was done in the south, southwest, and west. A complete record of habitat from which most specimens were taken and occasional notes of the chase for especially prized specimens are included in the notebook.

ARRANGEMENT: Chronologic. FINDING AIDS: None. SPECIAL CONDITIONS: Use of this record unit requires prior arrangement with the Archives staff.

(7324)

James W. Gidley Papers, 1903-1931 and undated
(0.4 linear meter).

James W. Gidley (1866-1931) began his career at the United States National Museum (USNM) in 1905 when he was appointed Preparator in the Section of Vertebrate Fossils. In 1908, he was promoted to Custodian of Fossil Mammals in the newly created Division of Vertebrate Paleontology. He was made Assistant Curator in 1912 and remained in that position until his death. Gidley's work at the USNM was marked by several field explorations to collect fossil mammals. Included were trips to Maryland, Indiana, and Arizona. In the mid-1920s, he began a series of explorations around Melbourne and Vero Beach, Florida, in search of Pleistocene man. Prior to his service with the USNM, Gidley led field trips that discovered the fossil horses *Equus scotti* and *Neohipparion.*

The papers of James W. Gidley document his research on fossil mammals and his work at the USNM. They include incoming and outgoing correspondence with professional colleagues and USNM associates concerning various research topics, field work, museum business, and the preparation of scientific papers. Also included are manuscripts, notes, photographs, and illustrations from his research.

ARRANGEMENT: (1) General correspondence, 1903-1931 and undated; (2) notes, manuscripts, photographs, and illustrations concerning fossil mammals, 1905-1931 and undated. FINDING AIDS: Description in control file. SPECIAL CONDITIONS: Use of this record unit requires prior arrangement with the Archives staff.

(7187)

Isaac Ginsburg Papers, circa 1911-1919, 1924-1958
(1 linear meter).

Isaac Ginsburg (1886-1975) was born in Lithuania and came to the United States as a young boy. He studied ichthyology at Cornell University and after graduating was employed as an Aid in the Division of Fishes, United States National Museum, for a short time in 1917. In 1922, he received an appointment with the Bureau of Fisheries and worked there as a systematic ichthyologist until his retirement in 1956.

Ginsburg's chief scientific interest was the marine fishes of the Gulf of Mexico. His other duties at the Bureau of Fisheries included handling of the scientific correspondence concerning marine fishes, and war work in connection with the coordination of fisheries in 1943-1944.

The papers of Isaac Ginsburg chiefly document his career with the Bureau of Fisheries from 1922 to 1956. There is extensive correspondence concerning the fishes of the Gulf coast and ichthyological nomenclature, and lesser amounts about his war work and Bureau affairs. The collection also contains materials concerning Bureau investigations that were probably sent to Ginsburg in connection with his research, including notes and logs of William W. Welsh and Samuel Frederick Hildebrand on their investigations in New England and the Gulf of Mexico, and photographs, probably relating to Hildebrand's work in Central America and the southern United States.

ARRANGEMENT: (1) Correspondence, 1925-1958; (2) material concerning Bureau of Fisheries investigations, 1911-1917, 1919, 1926-1927, 1930; (3) material concerning the Bureau of Fisheries work of William W. Welsh and Samuel F. Hildebrand, *circa* 1916-1917, 1924; (4) photographs, 1924-1925, 1933-1937. FINDING AIDS: Description in control file. SPECIAL CONDITIONS: Use of this record unit requires prior arrangement with the Archives staff.

(7190)

Charles Frederic Girard Papers, circa 1846-1860 and undated
(0.8 linear meter).

Charles Frederic Girard (1822-1895) was born in France. He became a student and assistant to Louis Agassiz in Switzerland and came to the United States with Agassiz in 1847. He worked in Cambridge with Agassiz until 1850 when he left to become Spencer F. Baird's principal assistant at the Smithsonian Institution. While at the Smithsonian, Girard published a number of works on herpetology and ichthyology, both alone and in collaboration with Baird. In 1860, he accepted a commission from the Confederacy to supply drugs and medical supplies and left for Paris. He made a brief trip to the Southern states in 1863. Following the war, he returned to Paris, where he spent the rest of his life in medical practice.

The papers of Charles Frederic Girard consist chiefly of manuscripts, research notes, and bibliographical data on natural history. Also included is a small amount of correspondence. Of particular interest is a manuscript concerning Girard's voyage to America with Louis Agassiz in 1846 and copies of correspondence and statements by Girard concerning a dispute with Agassiz. Much of the material is written in French.

ARRANGEMENT: (1) Manuscripts, speeches, correspondence, notes, and related materials, 1846-1854 and undated; (2) bibliography of natural history, *circa* 1850-1860. FINDING AIDS: Description in control file. SPECIAL CONDITIONS: Use of this record unit requires prior arrangement with the Archives staff.

(7329)

George Herbert Girty Papers, 1896-1948 and undated
(0.8 linear meter).

George Herbert Girty (1869-1939) was an invertebrate paleontologist specializing in the study of Carboniferous formations and fauna. He was educated at Yale University, receiving the A.B. in 1892 and the Ph.D. in 1894. After a postgraduate year at Stanford University, Girty was appointed Paleontologist with the United States Geological Survey (USGS) in 1895. He remained with the USGS for the remainder of his career, an association that lasted over 44 years. While best known for his research on Permian faunas, Girty was also an expert on Mississippian and Pennsylvanian invertebrates of the western United States.

This collection consists mostly of correspondence documenting Girty's paleontological research and his official duties with the USGS. A large file of general correspondence contains letters concerning his research on Carboniferous invertebrates; his USGS work, especially reports on specimens sent in for identification; field work of Girty and other USGS geologists and paleontologists; and the preparation, publication, and review of scientific manuscripts. The collection also includes a partial file of Girty's outgoing correspondence. These letters document his field work, 1913-1915, as well as his research and USGS affairs. A small amount of biographical and autobiographical information on Girty is included in the collection.

ARRANGEMENT: (1) General correspondence, 1896-1939 and undated, with related materials to 1948; (2) outgoing correspondence, 1897-1915; (3) biographical and autobiographical information on George Herbert Girty, 1923, 1939-1940 and undated. FINDING AIDS: Description in control file. SPECIAL CONDITIONS: Use of this record unit requires prior arrangement with the Archives staff.

(7257)

Steve A. Glassell Papers, 1932-1949 and undated
(0.1 linear meter).

Steve A. Glassell (? -1949) was an amateur carcinologist. His primary interest was the study of American pinnotherid crabs.

This collection consists mostly of correspondence between Glassell and fellow carcinologists concerning his research on American pinnotherid crabs and other crustacea. Also included is correspondence from United States National Museum (USNM) administrators concerning the transmission of specimens for study and USNM shipping invoices. Correspondents include Fenner A. Chace, Jr., W. Lee Chambers, John Enos Graf, Mary Jane Rathbun, Waldo LaSalle Schmitt, Clarence R. Shoemaker, and Alexander Wetmore. The correspondence is arranged alphabetically by correspondent.

ARRANGEMENT: Alphabetic. FINDING AIDS: Description in control file. SPECIAL CONDITIONS: Use of this record unit requires prior arrangement with the Archives staff.

(7126)

Townend Glover Notebooks, circa 1850-1878
(1.4 linear meters).

Townend Glover (1813-1883) was the first entomologist of the United States Department of Agriculture. In 1854 he received an appointment in the Bureau of Agriculture of the Patent Office to collect "statistics and other information on seeds, fruits, and insects." He remained in government service with one brief interruption until 1878. After many years of contemplating publication of his wealth of notes and drawings, he began to publish in 1871 and continued through 1878; their quality has been severely questioned. In 1872 he published an author's edition of the plates of Orthoptera. A publication on the Diptera appeared in 1874, entitled "Manuscript Notes from My Journal or Illustrations of Insects." In 1876 his edition of Hemiptera appeared in a format similar to that of Diptera. In these years he added to his plates in many orders, in the form of scrapbooks entitled "rough notes" and "prepared notes." In 1878 he issued his last publication, 12 copies of his entire set of 273 plates. All plates were named except Lepidoptera. He deposited most of his notes and plates in the National Museum before 1878, and the government purchased the set of his copper plates.

This collection contains notes taken and plates prepared for the following: Diptera, Heteroptera, Hemiptera, Orthoptera, Homoptera, Hymenoptera, Neuroptera, Coleoptera, and Lepidoptera, and to a lesser extent, Arachnida, Myriapoda, Crustacea, Annelida, and Entozoa. They include "rough notes," "prepared notes," and in some cases, lithographed final copies for Glover's projected publications, many of which were never printed.

ARRANGEMENT: Notebooks organized by insect order. FINDING AIDS: Description in control file. SPECIAL CONDITIONS: (1) Check finding aid for location; (2) use of this record unit requires prior arrangement with the Archives staff.

(7388)

Howard K. Gloyd Papers, 1914-1973

(4.1 linear meters).

Howard K. Gloyd (1902-1978) received his Bachelor of Science degree from Ottawa University in 1924 and an honorary Ph.D. in 1942. He earned his M.S. degree at Kansas State College, Manhattan in 1929, and his Ph.D. from the University of Michigan in 1937. After the completion of his doctorate, Gloyd became the Director of the Chicago Academy of Sciences where he remained until 1958 when he joined the faculty of the University of Arizona. Gloyd published in both the fields of ornithology and herpetology but he is best known as a herpetologist. His life's work became a monograph covering the genus *Agkistrodon* world-wide, on which he worked with Roger Conant.

These papers consist of professional correspondence to and from Gloyd. Also included are requests for publications and extensive communications with Conant.

ARRANGEMENT: Alphabetic. FINDING AIDS: None. SPECIAL CONDITIONS: Use of this record unit requires prior arrangement with the Archives staff.

(7090)

Robert H. Goddard Papers, 1917-1946

(1 linear meter).

Robert H. Goddard (1882-1945), a pioneer in modern rocket research, was aided by the Smithsonian at an early and crucial point in his work. This collection consists of copies of letters from Goddard to the Smithsonian Institution.

ARRANGEMENT: Chronologic. FINDING AIDS: None. SPECIAL CONDITIONS: (1) Record unit available on microfilm; (2) use of this record unit requires prior arrangement with the Archives staff.

(7050)

George Brown Goode Collection, circa 1814-1896 and undated, with related materials to 1925

(3.6 linear meters).

George Brown Goode (1851-1896), ichthyologist and museum administrator, received his B.S. degree from Wesleyan University in 1870. After a year of postgraduate study with Louis Agassiz at Harvard University, Goode returned to Wesleyan to direct the Judd Museum of Natural History. In 1872, Goode met Spencer F. Baird, Assistant Secretary of the Smithsonian Institution and United States Fish Commissioner. He quickly became Baird's chief pupil and assistant. In 1873, Goode was appointed Assistant Curator in the United States National Museum (USNM), a position he retained until 1877 when his title was changed to Curator. In 1881, when the new USNM building was completed, Goode was promoted to Assistant Director. On January 12, 1887, Goode was appointed Assistant Secretary in charge of the USNM, and he remained the chief administrative officer of the museum until his death.

Goode's primary scientific interest was ichthyology, and he published both specialized and popular works on fish and fisheries. In addition to his duties at the USNM, Goode also served in various capacities for the United States Commission of Fish and Fisheries. After Baird's death in 1887, Goode assumed the position of Fish Commissioner until January 1888.

Goode was regarded as the premier American museum administrator of his era. In 1881, he issued Circular No. 1 of the National Museum which set forth a comprehensive scheme of organization for the museum. Goode was involved in designing and installing Smithsonian and Fish Commission exhibits at many of the international expositions held during the latter half of the nineteenth century. Goode was also a historian, bibliographer, and genealogist, and he published several papers on the history of American science.

This collection provides partial documentation of Goode's professional career and personal life. The collection is strongest in documenting his research on fish and fisheries. Included is a large collection of autograph letters and signatures of scientists, government officials, diplomats, artists, literary figures, and socialites; incoming and outgoing correspondence documenting professional activities and research interests; correspondence, notes, manuscripts, and related records documenting his work on fish and fisheries; collected materials from the London International Fisheries Exposition of 1883; manuscripts and research materials from an unpublished ichthyological bibliography; an unpublished manuscript on the history of American science; scrapbooks and notebooks maintained during his childhood, college days, and early career; biographical materials on Goode; and various manuscripts, notes, photographs and drawings.

ARRANGEMENT: (1) Autograph letters, 1814-1895 and undated; (2) general correspondence, 1871-1896 and undated; (3) collected materials on fish and fisheries, 1875-1893 and undated; (4) collected materials on the London International Fisheries Exposition (1883), 1882-1883; (5) ichthyological bibliography, *circa* 1870s-1890s; (6) unpublished manuscript on the history of American science, *circa* 1896 and related materials to 1925; (7) notebooks and scrapbooks, *circa* 1865-1878 and undated; (8) biographical materials and publications, 1885-1903 and undated; (9) manuscripts, notes, photographs, drawings and miscellaneous materials, *circa* 1875-1892 and undated. FINDING AIDS: Description in control file. SPECIAL CONDITIONS: Use of this record unit requires prior arrangement with the Archives staff.

(7359)

Gordon Gordh Papers, 1974-1977
(0.5 linear meter).

Gordon Gordh (1945-   ) received his B.A. from the University of Colorado in 1967, his M.A. from the University of Kansas in 1972, and his Ph.D. from the University of California, Riverside in 1974. Gordh accepted a position in 1974 as a Research Entomologist at the United States Department of Agriculture (USDA), Systematic Entomology Laboratory, located at the National Museum of Natural History in Washington, D.C. He remained with the USDA until 1977, studying parasitic Hymenoptera from the super-family Chalcidoidea. In 1977, Gordh resigned from the

Systematic Entomology Laboratory to take a job as Assistant Professor of Entomology at the University of California, Riverside.

The papers of Gordon Gordh consist of correspondence and some subject files documenting Gordh's career at the USDA. Most of the material concerns the identification of specimens and also includes some reviews and corrections of professional papers sent to Gordh for comment.

ARRANGEMENT: Alphabetic. FINDING AIDS: None. SPECIAL CONDITIONS: Use of this record unit requires prior arrangement with the Archives staff.

(7148)

David Crockett Graham Papers, 1923-1936
(0.6 linear meter).

David Crockett Graham (1884-1961) was born in Green Forest, Michigan. He received a B.A. degree from Whitman College, Walla Walla, Washington, in 1908. Graham attended Rochester (New York) Theological Seminary (now Colgate Rochester Divinity School), from which he received his B.D. in 1916. In the fall of 1918, Graham attended the Divinity School at the University of Chicago for a year of postgraduate study, and, in 1926, for a year of doctoral study. Graham's Ph.D. dissertation, "Religion in Szechwan Province, China," was published by the Smithsonian Institution in 1928. During 1931 and 1932 Graham studied archeology, ethnology, and anthropology at the University of Chicago and Harvard University.

Graham was ordained to the Baptist ministry in 1911. Shortly afterward, Graham entered the service of the American Baptist Foreign Mission Society. Graham departed for China in the fall of 1911, and stayed briefly in Shanghai before traveling to the city of Suifu (now Yibin) in Szechwan Province, his post for twenty years. At Suifu, Graham was a missionary and studied the Chinese language and culture.

Beginning in 1919, Graham collected natural history specimens from Szechwan Province for the United States National Museum (USNM) during his summer vacations and spare time from missionary work. During the period from 1919 to 1939, Graham made fourteen summer expeditions in Szechwan Province, the Szechwan-Tibet region, and the Szechwan-Yunnan region, and several short trips in the vicinity of Suifu. The specimens he sent to the USNM were mostly mammals, birds, insects, snakes, and anthropological relics. In addition, he sent anthropological measurements of Chinese and Chinese aborigines common in Szechwan Province such as the Ch'uan Miao, Ch'iang, Lolo, and the Bolstoi people as well as their costumes and handicrafts.

In recognition of Graham's work, the USNM appointed Graham a Collaborator in Biology, an honorary title, in 1931. In 1932, Graham was transferred to Chengtu, the capital of Szechwan Province, where he was stationed until his retirement in 1948. He was made a curator of the West China Union University Museum of Archeology, Art, and Ethnology. During his retirement years, Graham prepared his books on the songs, stories, and folk religions of the Ch'uan Miao, and the Ch'iangs. These books were published by the Smithsonian.

This collection consists, for the most part, of diaries and photographs which document Graham's travels in Szechwan Province, China. The diaries contain information on Graham's day-to-day activities pertaining to the collection of specimens for the USNM.

Typewritten copies of the diaries are also included. The photographs consist of prints, most with annotations by Graham; lantern slides; and 609 negatives and their annotated wrapping papers. A microfilm copy of the 609 negatives has also been made. Also included in the collection are maps, hand-drawn by Graham, of several of Graham's summer expeditions; and correspondence with Alexander Wetmore, Director, USNM, and with William deC. Ravenel, Administrative Assistant, USNM, concerning shipment of specimens, diaries, and photographs.

ARRANGEMENT: (1) General correspondence, 1925-1936; (2) diaries, 1924, 1927-1930, 1932-1935; (3) maps, 1925, 1928-1930, 1933; (4) photographs and lantern slides, 1923-1929; (5) negatives, 1923-1930. FINDING AIDS: Description in control file. SPECIAL CONDITIONS: (1) Microfilm copy of photographs is available; (2) use of this record unit requires prior arrangement with the Archives staff.

(7307)

Frederick Atwood Greeley Papers, 1920-1979
(0.5 linear meter).

Frederick Atwood Greeley (1896-1980) served as bolometer assistant, station assistant director, and station director for the solar radiation observing stations established by the Smithsonian Astrophysical Observatory (SAO), 1920-1956. The SAO, under the direction of Charles G. Abbot, Director, 1907-1944, and Loyal B. Aldrich, Assistant Director, 1928-1944, and Director, 1944-1955, had established several solar radiation observing stations to determine the solar constant of radiation. Greeley was one of the staff members who manned these stations.

Greeley's duties as bolometer assistant and station assistant director included operating, reading, and maintaining the sensitive heat-measuring instruments; computations of the data obtained from the readings; and routine maintenance of the station's buildings and equipment. As station director he was fully responsible for the adjustment, repair, and operation of equipment, and the management of the station as a unit.

Greeley's tours of duty as bolometer assistant and station assistant director included service at the solar radiation observing stations at Mount Harqua Hala, Arizona, 1920-1923; Mount Montezuma, Chile, 1923-1926 and 1942-1943; Mount Brukkaros, South-West Africa, 1926-1929; Table Mountain, California, 1930-1933 and 1936-1941; and Mount Saint Katherine, Egypt, 1933-1936. Greeley's tours of duty as station director included service at Mount Montezuma Station, 1943-1946 and 1951-1955; Miami Station, Florida, 1947-1948; and Table Mountain Station, 1948-1951 and 1955-1956. Greeley retired from SAO in December 1956.

These papers document Greeley's career and experiences during his tours of duty at the solar radiation observing stations, usually located on high-elevation barren mountaintops in desert regions. These materials consist primarily of correspondence, diaries, notes, manuscripts, photographs, and personal documents.

The correspondence includes incoming and outgoing official correspondence, 1939-1955, mostly with Charles G. Abbot and Loyal B. Aldrich, concerning daily activities, equipment, station buildings, and financial reports; correspondence to family members, 1923-1952, in which Greeley described his experiences and travels; correspondence from Charles G. Abbot, 1964-1969, mostly concerning his activities and news of former

SAO staff; and correspondence from researchers interested in the study of the SAO's solar constant program, 1977-1978.

The manuscripts consist of Greeley's unpublished autobiography, "Following the Sun" (undated typed copies) and excerpts of correspondence to members of his family in which he described his daily life and experience at the stations and on travel, 1920-1936; and Douglas V. Hoyt's study, "Smithsonian Astrophysical Observatory Solar Constant Program," 1978, and a published version, 1979.

The diaries were written mainly by Greeley's wife, Olive A. Greeley, who also served as bolometer assistant at Mount Montezuma, 1943-1946. The entries document day-to-day activities at the various stations, mostly at Mount Montezuma, Miami, and Table Mountain, and entries by Greeley concerning traveling expense accounts, 1938, and 1940-1941.

The photographs consist of scenes taken by Greeley during his tours of duty. Also included in this collection are personal documents such as passports, automobile registrations, internal identification cards (Chile), and ship passenger lists; mathematical notes; instrument operation instructions; methods of data computation, issued by Abbot; newspaper articles about the Greeleys and the SAO's solar radiation observatories; radio interviews and speeches by the Greeleys about their experiences, and about Charles G. Abbot; and two 8mm motion pictures, one a black and white film, showing a panoramic view of the Sinai from Mount Zebir Gemir, *circa* 1934 and one in color showing a segment of the Rose Bowl Parade and snow scenes at Table Mountain, 1949.

ARRANGEMENT: (1) General correspondence, arranged alphabetically, 1923-1978; (2) official correspondence, arranged chronologically, 1921, 1939-1956; (3) diaries, 1936-1955; (4) manuscripts and notes; (5) speeches and radio interviews; (6) personal documents, 1923-1955; (7) newspaper and journal articles; (8) photographs, 1920-1955; (9) motion pictures *circa* 1934, 1949. FINDING AIDS: (1) Description in control file; (2) chronology of Greeley's SAO service, in control file. SPECIAL CONDITIONS: (1) Additional materials on the SAO solar constant program and Greeley's reports and correspondence can be found in record unit 85; (2) use of this record unit requires prior arrangement with the Archives staff.

(7354)

Charles Tull Greene Papers, 1912-1949
(0.1 linear meter).

Charles Tull Greene (1879-1958), an entomologist, joined the Bureau of Entomology, United States Department of Agriculture (USDA), in 1912 as an Agent in the Section of Forest Entomology. In 1919, he was transferred to the Bureau's taxonomic unit as a Diptera specialist to work under John M. Aldrich on the insect collections in the United States National Museum (USNM). He remained with the USDA until his retirement in 1949. He also served as Honorary Assistant Custodian of Diptera in the Division of Insects, USNM, from 1919 to 1949.

This collection consists primarily of incoming correspondence documenting Greene's work at the USDA and USNM, as well as his research on Diptera. Most of the letters concern the identification of specimens and the preparation of scientific papers.

ARRANGEMENT: Alphabetic. FINDING AIDS: Description in control file. SPECIAL CONDITIONS: Use of this record unit requires prior arrangement with the Archives staff.

Edward L. Greene Collection, 1897, 1936
(0.1 linear meter).

Edward L. Greene (1843-1915) was a Professor of Botany at the University of California, 1885-1895, and Catholic University, 1895-1904. He became an Associate in Botany at the Smithsonian in 1904 and retained that title until his death. Greene's work at the Smithsonian was primarily concerned with the history of botany, and he published "Landmarks of Botanical History, Part 1, Prior to 1562, A. D." as part of volume LIV of the "Smithsonian Miscellaneous Collections" in 1909.

This collection includes correspondence with Charles Russell Orcutt concerning Cactaceae, 1897; and a typescript for "Landmarks of Botanical History: A Study of Certain Epochs in the Development of the Science of Botany, Part 2, Prior to 1717 A. D.," 695 pages. This typescript is dated 1936 and apparently was typed from the manuscript which Greene was working on at the time of his death in 1915.

ARRANGEMENT: Chronologic. FINDING AIDS: Description in control file. SPECIAL CONDITIONS: (1) Check finding aid for location; (2) use of this record unit requires prior arrangement with the Archives staff.

David Griffiths Collection, circa 1900-1920
(14 linear meters).

David Griffiths (1867-1935), a botanist, received his Ph.D. from Columbia University in 1900. He joined the Bureau of Plant Industry, United States Department of Agriculture (USDA), in 1901 as an Assistant Agrostologist, and was promoted to Agriculturist in 1907 and Horticulturist in 1918. He remained with the USDA for his entire career. Griffiths was an authority on cacti, especially the genus *Opuntia.* His collection of cacti was donated to the United States National Museum in 1935.

This collection consists of glass plate negatives of cacti, primarily of the genus *Opuntia,* taken in their natural habitat. Also included are a few negatives of foreign publications on cacti.

ARRANGEMENT: By negative number. FINDING AIDS: List of negatives in control file. SPECIAL CONDITIONS: (1) Some negatives are broken; (2) use of this record unit requires prior arrangement with the Archives staff.

Arnold B. Grobman Papers, circa 1938-1991
(4.5 linear meters).

Arnold B. Grobman (1918-   ) was educated in the public schools of Newark, New Jersey, the University of Michigan (B.S., zoology, 1939) and the University of Rochester, where he received his Ph.D. in 1943. He remained at Rochester as an Instructor in the Department of Zoology, 1943-1944, and was a Research Associate on the Manhattan Project, 1944-1946, before moving to the University of Florida. He stayed at the University of Florida until 1959, serving as Assistant Professor, and later, Associate Professor of Biology, 1950-1952, and as Director of the Florida State Museum from 1952 to 1959. From 1959 to 1965 he was Director of the Biological

Sciences Curriculum Study at the University of Colorado. In 1965 he moved to Rutgers University, where he served as Dean of the College of Arts and Sciences, 1965-1967, and Dean of Rutgers College, 1967-1972. From 1972 to 1974 he was Vice-Chancellor of Academic Affairs at the Chicago Circle campus of the University of Illinois, and Special Assistant to the President from 1974 to 1975. From 1975 to 1985 he was Chancellor and Professor of Biology at the University of Missouri-St. Louis. He was named Chancellor Emeritus and Research Professor in 1986. He retired from the professorship in 1988, but remains Chancellor Emeritus.

Grobman's main scientific contributions have been in herpetology, but he has also published extensively on science education and academic administration. Grobman has held office in many professional organizations, including the American Association of Museums, the American Institute of Biological Sciences, and the American Society of Ichthyologists and Herpetologists (Secretary, 1952-1957, and President, 1964).

These papers document the professional career of Arnold B. Grobman. Included are correspondence with colleagues on scientific topics, professional societies business, and files documenting his activities on numerous boards and committees. As a general rule, his files as an academic administrator are not in these papers, nor are some files from offices he held in professional societies. His files as Secretary of the American Society of Ichthyologists and Herpetologists are in the Society's records housed in the Smithsonian Archives.

ARRANGEMENT: (1) Professional correspondence, 1938-1991; (2) publications of Arnold B. Grobman, 1930-1984. FINDING AIDS: Box list in control file. SPECIAL CONDITIONS: Use of this record unit requires prior arrangement with the Archives staff.

(7199)

Sven M. Gronberger Manuscript, circa 1916
(0.1 linear meter).

Sven M. Gronberger (1866-1916), born and educated in Sweden, moved to the United States and joined the library staff of the Smithsonian in 1907. He published a number of papers on ornithology and had almost completed the requirements for his Ph.D. in zoology and geology at the time of his death.

This manuscript was apparently Gronberger's doctoral dissertation on European and Asiatic species in Greenland from the eighteenth century until the date of writing.

ARRANGEMENT: Manuscript of "Birds of Palaearctic Distribution Occurring in Greenland and Adjoining Regions," *circa* 1916. FINDING AIDS: None. SPECIAL CONDITIONS: Use of this record unit requires prior arrangement with the Archives staff.

(7355)

Martin A. Gruber Photograph Collection, 1919-1924
(0.2 linear meter).

Martin A. Gruber (*circa* 1854-*circa* 1941), a native of Berks County, Pennsylvania, worked for the War Department in Washington, D.C., from 1891 until his retirement around 1929 at the age of 75. While in Washington, Gruber took many photographs of the local scenery.

The Martin A. Gruber Photograph Collection consists of black and white photographs taken by Gruber between 1919 and 1924. Subjects include buildings, bridges, monuments, and trees and flowers of the Washington, D.C., area, as well as views of the National Zoological Park.

ARRANGEMENT: (1) Buildings; (2) monuments; (3) bridges; (4) trees and flowers; (5) National Zoological Park. FINDING AIDS: None. SPECIAL CONDITIONS: Use of this record unit requires prior arrangement with the Archives staff.

(7300)

Ashley B. Gurney Papers, 1932-1978
(2.2 linear meters).

Ashley B. Gurney (1911-1988), an entomologist, began his career at the United States Department of Agriculture (USDA) in 1935 as a Field Agent with the Bureau of Entomology and Plant Quarantine. He remained at the Bureau until 1955, eventually achieving the title of Entomologist. In 1955, Gurney transferred to the Systematic Entomology Laboratory, USDA, where he served as an Entomologist until his retirement in 1975. At that time he was made a Cooperating Scientist at the Systematic Entomology Laboratory. Gurney was a member of the Entomological Society of America and served as Executive Secretary of the Society in 1954. His primary research interest was the study of orthopteroids, chiefly grasshoppers and cockroaches.

These papers document Gurney's professional career and consist of correspondence, primarily with entomologists, concerning USDA work; research on orthopteroids and other insects; and Entomological Society of America business.

ARRANGEMENT: Alphabetic. FINDING AIDS: Folder list in control file. SPECIAL CONDITIONS: Use of this record unit requires prior arrangement with the Archives staff.

(1010006)

Eduard Hackel Papers, 1903-1908
(47 items).

Eduard Hackel (1850-1926), botanist, was born in Haida, Bohemia. Hackel attended the Polytechnical School in Vienna from 1865 to 1869, and taught botany from 1869 to 1900. Hackel's botanical interests centered on grasses, especially the family Festuca and the taxonomy of Gramineae. He was the first botanist to discover the function of lociculae in flowering grasses.

These papers consist mostly of correspondence written by Juan V. Theodoro Stuckert to Hackel and photographs of botanical specimens.

ARRANGEMENT: Chronologic. FINDING AIDS: Description in control file. SPECIAL CONDITIONS: (1) Correspondence is written in German; (2) use of this record unit requires prior arrangement with the Archives staff.

J. Frank Hahn Scrapbooks, 1866-1870
(0.1 linear meter).

J. Frank Hahn was telegraph operator for the Banker's and Broker's Telegraph Company, Washington, D.C.

This record unit consists of scrapbooks of newspaper clippings on telegraphy, collected by Hahn.

ARRANGEMENT: Chronologic. FINDING AIDS: Index to each scrapbook by name of newspaper. SPECIAL CONDITIONS: Use of this record unit requires prior arrangement with the Archives staff.

Charles Hallock Papers, 1854, 1866-1868, 1873-1874, 1877-1913
(1 folder).

Charles Hallock (1834-1917), journalist, author, and naturalist, was a frequent correspondent of the Smithsonian, particularly in regard to his work with game preservation and his interests in natural history.

In 1912, Hallock gave a portion of his correspondence to the Smithsonian for preservation. This correspondence deals chiefly with Hallock's scientific and professional work.

ARRANGEMENT: Unarranged. FINDING AIDS: None. SPECIAL CONDITIONS: Use of this record unit requires prior arrangement with the Archives staff.

Alan Hardy Collection, 1986
Photographs of Entomologists (0.1 linear meter).

This collection consists of photographs of entomologists taken by Alan Hardy, a member of the Entomological Society of America, on December 10, 1986, during a Society meeting in Reno, Nevada. Included in this collection is a group photograph of the Chrysomelidae Interest Group.

ARRANGEMENT: By negative number. FINDING AIDS: List of photographs in control file. SPECIAL CONDITIONS: Use of this record unit requires prior arrangement with the Archives staff.

Thora M. Plitt Hardy Papers, 1940-1948
(0.1 linear meter).

During the Second World War, Thora M. Plitt Hardy (1902-   ) was a microanalyst for the Division of Wildlife Research, Fish and Wildlife Service, Department of Interior, in charge of fur hair projects at the Beltsville Research Center, Beltsville, Maryland. A good portion of the studies were in conjunction with requests from the War Production Board and the Quartermaster General's Office on the use of fur fibers for the armed forces. On June 30, 1946, Hardy was transferred to the Bureau of Animal Industry, United States Department of Agriculture. Hardy's files were transferred to the Bird and

Mammal Laboratories of the Fish and Wildlife Service located in the United States National Museum.

These papers include correspondence and articles for journals concerning research on fur fibers.

ARRANGEMENT: Alphabetic by subject. FINDING AIDS: Description in control file. SPECIAL CONDITIONS: Use of this record unit requires prior arrangement with the Archives staff.

(7243)

Harriman Alaska Expedition Collection, 1899
(0.1 linear meter).

The Harriman Alaska Expedition of 1899 was co-sponsored by Edward Henry Harriman, President of the Union Pacific Railroad, and the Washington Academy of Sciences. Originally conceived by Harriman as a big game hunt, it was transformed into a scientific exploring expedition on the advice of Clinton Hart Merriam, Chief of the Bureau of Biological Survey. Many prominent naturalists, scientists, and artists accompanied the expedition, including Merriam, Albert Kenrick Fisher, Grove Karl Gilbert, Frederick Vernon Coville, Bernhard E. Fernow, John Burroughs, John Muir, William H. Dall, Daniel Giraud Elliot, Robert Ridgway, Louis Agassiz Fuertes, Frederick Samuel Dellenbaugh, Frederick A. Walpole, Robert Swain Gifford, and Charles Robert Knight. Many of the specimens collected were deposited in the United States National Museum, including large collections of birds and mollusks secured by Ridgway and Dall. The expedition departed from Seattle, Washington, aboard the *George W. Elder,* on May 31, and returned on July 30, 1899.

This collection consists of photographs taken on the Harriman Alaska Expedition and prints of paintings made by artists accompanying the expedition.

ARRANGEMENT: (1) Photographs; (2) prints of paintings. FINDING AIDS: Description in control file. SPECIAL CONDITIONS: Use of this record unit requires prior arrangement with the Archives staff.

(7237)

Harry K. Harring Papers, 1910-1923, 1929 and undated
(0.3 linear meter).

Harry K. Harring (1871-1928) was born in Nykjobing, Denmark. He studied at the Technical School at Skanderborg, Denmark, and after graduation was employed in the design and manufacture of physical and chemical apparatus. He came to the United States in 1893 and shortly thereafter received appointment as Scientific Instrument Maker at the National Bureau of Standards, Washington, D.C. In his spare time, Harring developed an interest in fresh water microscopic organisms, especially the Rotatoria. His published works consist of 12 titles, including "Synopsis of the Rotatoria" (*United States National Museum Bulletin 81,* 1913). His most important work was "The Rotifers of Wisconsin," authored in collaboration with Frank Jacob Myers. On May 1, 1914, Harring was awarded the honorary title of Custodian of the Rotatoria in the Division of Marine Invertebrates of the United States National Museum (USNM). He was also editor for the section on Rotatoria, Gastrotricha, and Chaetognatha for *Biological Abstracts.*

The papers of Harry K. Harring include incoming correspondence, chiefly from Frank Jacob Myers, concerning the collection and identification of rotatoria and the monograph, "The Rotifers of Wisconsin." Correspondence with Frits Johansen concerns Harring's work on the rotatoria collected by the Canadian Arctic Expedition. Also included in the collection are field and research notes of Harring and field notes kept by Francis John Dyer while collecting rotatoria for the USNM in Honduras, 1915-1916.

ARRANGEMENT: (1) Incoming correspondence, 1914-1923, 1929; (2) field notes and research notes, 1910-1916 and undated. FINDING AIDS: Description in control file. SPECIAL CONDITIONS: Use of this record unit requires prior arrangement with the Archives staff.

(7365)

Wilbert Henry Hass Papers, 1945-1958
(0.1 linear meter).

Wilbert Henry Hass (1906-1959) was an invertebrate paleontologist specializing in the study of conodonts. He joined the Section of Paleontology and Stratigraphy, United States Geological Survey (USGS) in 1930 when he was appointed Junior Scientific Aid. He was promoted to the rank of Geologist in 1940 and remained with the USGS for the remainder of his life.

This collection consists of incoming and outgoing correspondence, mostly between Hass and USGS colleagues, concerning his research on conodonts.

ARRANGEMENT: Chronologic. FINDING AIDS: None. SPECIAL CONDITIONS: Use of this record unit requires prior arrangement with the Archives staff.

(7188)

Oliver Perry Hay Papers, 1911-1930
(0.5 linear meter).

In 1912, Oliver Perry Hay (1846-1930) was appointed research associate at the Carnegie Institution of Washington to pursue the study of the vertebrate animal life of the North American Pleistocene period. Hay was furnished with office space in the United States National Museum (USNM) to conduct his research. In addition, he assisted in working up and describing the USNM collections in vertebrate paleontology.

Hay's primary scientific interest was the study of the Pleistocene vertebrata of North America. His major contribution to the field of vertebrate paleontology was his *Bibliography and Catalogue of the Fossil Vertebrata of North America,* 1902, supplemented by the *Second Bibliography and Catalogue of Fossil Vertebrata of North America,* 2 vols., 1929-1930. Other important works include *The Fossil Turtles of North America,* 1908, and *The Pleistocene Geology of North America and its Vertebrated Animals,* 3 vols., 1923-1927.

The papers of Oliver Perry Hay consist of incoming correspondence, mostly concerning paleontological issues; and notes, drawings, bibliographies, photographs, and related material regarding Hay's research on the Pleistocene vertebrata of North America. Materials of special interest include correspondence concerning Pleistocene fossil discoveries at Vero Beach, Florida, 1917, and Frederick, Oklahoma, 1927.

ARRANGEMENT: (1) Incoming correspondence, 1911-1930; (2) notes, drawings, bibliographies, photographs, and related material regarding the Pleistocene vertebrata of North America. FINDING AIDS: None. SPECIAL CONDITIONS: (1) File may be incomplete; (2) use of this record unit requires prior arrangement with the Archives staff.

(7464)

Bruce C. Heezen Papers, circa 1947-1977
(52.5 linear meters and oversize).

Bruce C. Heezen (1924-1977), oceanographer and geologist, received the B.A. degree from Iowa State University in 1948 and his Ph.D. degree from Columbia University in 1952. Heezen's entire professional career was spent on the geology department faculty of Columbia University and as a scientist at the University's Lamont-Doherty Geological Observatory. He was Research Associate, 1955-1957; Senior Research Scientist, 1957-1960; Assistant Professor, 1960-1964; and Associate Professor, 1964-1977. Heezen was also a consultant with the United States Naval Oceanographic Office from 1968 until his death.

Heezen's interest in oceanography began in 1947 when as an undergraduate he was invited to join Maurice W. Ewing's expedition to study the Mid-Atlantic Ridge. His career was marked by constant seagoing voyages and submersible dives to support research on turbidity currents, abyssal plains, continental drift, and other aspects of the ocean floor. He was the author of over 300 scientific papers and several books including *The Face of the Deep,* with Charles D. Hollister in 1971. With his colleague Marie Tharp, Heezen created many maps and panoramas of the ocean floor. Several of the maps were published in *National Geographic* magazine. Heezen died in 1977 while working in the submersible NR-1 on the Reykjanes Ridge in the North Atlantic.

Heezen was a member and officer of numerous national and international organizations. He was the recipient of the Henry Bryant Bigelow Medal of the Woods Hole Oceanographic Institution, 1964; the Cullum Geographic Medal of the American Geographical Society, 1973; and the Gardiner Greene Hubbard Medal of the National Geographic Society, awarded posthumously in 1978.

The papers of Bruce C. Heezen primarily document his oceanographic and geological research and his career as a faculty member and scientist at Columbia University. To a lesser extent, they concern his personal affairs. They include incoming and outgoing correspondence with geologists, oceanographers, Columbia University colleagues, publishers and professional organizations; personal correspondence, memorabilia, and records from his college career; files on Heezen's professional activities including meetings, conferences, symposia, and lectures; correspondence, reports, proposals and related materials concerning contracts and grants received by Heezen; manuscripts and reprints of his published and unpublished scientific papers; classroom materials and teaching records; written and audio logs from oceanographic cruises and submersible dives; photographs, 35mm slides, videotapes, and motion pictures from research cruises and dives, including many underwater images; manuscripts, notes, and research materials from his book, *The Face of the Deep;* and maps of the ocean floor prepared by Heezen and Marie Tharp.

ARRANGEMENT: (1) Bruce C. Heezen Papers, *circa* 1947-1977, accession number 85-079; (2) Bruce C. Heezen Papers, *circa* 1951-1976, accession number 85-189; (3) Bruce C. Heezen Papers, *circa* 1950-1975, accession number 87-028; (4) Bruce C. Heezen Papers, *circa* 1961-1977, accession number T90002. FINDING AIDS: Box list in control file. SPECIAL CONDITIONS: Use of this record unit requires prior arrangement with the Archives staff.

(7125)

Carl Heinrich Field Notebooks, 1916-1919, 1927, 1929
(5 volumes).

Carl Heinrich (1880-1955) was born in New York and grew up in Nebraska. After studying Greek and drama at the University of Chicago, he moved to Washington, D.C., in 1902, where he worked in business. In 1908, he went to New York to study music. Heinrich moved back to Washington and in 1913 joined the United States Department of Agriculture. He first worked on applied entomology but later switched to the classification of Lepidoptera.

These notebooks document Carl Heinrich's field trips to New Mexico, 1916; Colorado, Texas, and Oklahoma, 1918; Texas, 1918-1919; Arizona, 1927; and expenses and collecting in Guatemala, 1929.

ARRANGEMENT: Chronologic. FINDING AIDS: Description in control file. SPECIAL CONDITIONS: Use of this record unit requires prior arrangement with the Archives staff.

(7179)

Edmund Heller Papers, circa 1898-1918
(1.8 linear meters).

Edmund Heller (1875-1939) was born in Freeport, Illinois, and later moved to California where he entered Stanford University in 1896. During his stay at Stanford, Heller collected natural history specimens in the Galapagos Islands and was employed by the Bureau of Biological Survey, United States Department of Agriculture, as an assistant in Alaska. Following his graduation, Heller joined the Field Columbian Museum as a field collector and worked the western United States and parts of Central America and Mexico. In 1907, he accompanied Carl Ethan Akeley on the Field Museum's African expedition. On his return, he was appointed Curator of Mammals at the Museum of Vertebrate Zoology of the University of California and participated in the 1908 Alexander Alaska Expedition.

Heller's connection with the Smithsonian began in 1909 when he was chosen as naturalist for large mammals on the Smithsonian African Expedition under the command of Colonel Theodore Roosevelt. On his return he co-authored *Life Histories of African Game Animals* with Roosevelt and also published many scientific papers. Heller also accompanied the Rainey African Expedition of 1911-1912 for the Smithsonian and led the Smithsonian Cape-to-Cairo Expedition of 1919-1920.

In addition to his Smithsonian expeditions, Heller also participated in explorations in Alaska with the Biological Survey, in Peru with Yale University and the National Geographic Society, in China with the American Museum of Natural History, and in Russia with Paul J. Rainey, official photographer to the Czech army in Siberia.

Following his return from the Cape-to-Cairo Expedition, Heller briefly worked for the Roosevelt Wild Life Experiment Station and was then appointed Assistant Curator of Mammals at the Field Museum. While there, he made collecting trips to Peru and Africa. Heller was Director of the Milwaukee Zoological Garden from 1928 to 1935 and Director of the Fleishhacker Zoo in San Francisco from 1935 until his death.

These papers primarily contain photographs as well as journals, notes, maps, manuscripts, and related material concerning Edmund Heller's collecting activities from 1908 to 1917. There are also some personal photographs and material as well as photographs of personnel and animals taken by Heller at the National Zoological Park.

ARRANGEMENT: (1) Personal materials; (2) materials, 1898-1908, related to expeditions to Galapagos Islands; Alberta, Canada; California and Oregon; Death Valley, California; Lower California, Mexico; Coahuila, Mexico; Guatemala; British East Africa; Louisiana; and Alaska; (3) materials concerning the Smithsonian African Expedition under the command of Colonel Theodore Roosevelt, 1909-1910; (4) materials concerning the Rainey African Expedition, 1911-1912; (5) materials concerning the Lincoln Ellsworth Expedition to Alberta and British Columbia, 1914; (6) materials concerning the National Geographic Society-Yale University Peruvian Expedition of 1915; (7) materials concerning the American Museum of Natural History China Expedition, 1916-1917; (8) photographs of animals and personnel at the National Zoological Park; (9) journal of Edmund Heller, 1918; (10) oversize photographs. FINDING AIDS: Description in control file. SPECIAL CONDITIONS: Use of this record unit requires prior arrangement with the Archives staff.

(7349)

Edward P. Henderson Papers, circa 1930-1987 and undated, with materials from 1859
(0.4 linear meter).

Edward P. Henderson (1898-1992), a chemist specializing in meteorites, received the B.S. and M.S. in chemistry from The George Washington University. From 1920 to 1929 he served as a chemist for the United States Geological Survey. In 1929, he was appointed Curator of Physical and Chemical Geology in the Department of Geology of the United States National Museum (USNM). He was named Curator of the Division of Meteorites, Department of Mineral Sciences, National Museum of Natural History (NMNH) in 1963. After his retirement in 1965, he continued his research as Curator Emeritus of the Division until 1988.

These papers consist of correspondence and photographs documenting Henderson's career at the USNM and NMNH, and his research on meteorites. Most of the material dates from the 1960s and 1970s when Henderson was Curator Emeritus. Also included is an 1859 letter from an ancestor of Henderson's, Charles Henderson, to Martha M. Henderson, chronicling his trip across the Plains from St. Joseph, Missouri, to the California gold rush.

ARRANGEMENT: (1) Correspondence, *circa* 1930-1987; (2) Charles Henderson letter, 1859. FINDING AIDS: None. SPECIAL CONDITIONS: Use of this record unit requires prior arrangement with the Archives staff.

(7075)

Henderson Family Papers, 1868-1923
(1.2 linear meters).

John Brooks Henderson (1826-1913), a lawyer and politician, served as United States Senator from Missouri from 1862 to 1869. In 1869, he returned to St. Louis where he practiced law and remained active in both local and national politics. In 1889, he retired from practice and moved to Washington, D.C. From 1892 to 1911, he served as a citizen member of the Smithsonian Institution Board of Regents.

Henderson's wife, Mary Foote Henderson (1841-1931), was involved in the suffrage and temperance movements. She was also a well-known socialite in Washington and a devotee of the arts, as well as an author of children's books and books on health.

John Brooks Henderson, Jr. (1870-1923), the son of John Brooks and Mary Foote Henderson, graduated from Harvard University in 1891 and Columbian Law School (now George Washington University) in 1893. From 1896 to 1897, Henderson was secretary to John W. Foster, a diplomatic advisor to the Chinese government. In 1897 he travelled with General Nelson A. Miles on a tour of Europe and the Ottoman Empire as a civilian observer of the armies of the great European powers. He was appointed a citizen member of the Smithsonian Institution Board of Regents in 1911 and retained that post until his death. Interested in shell collecting as a youth, Henderson later concentrated on the marine shell life of the West Indies and participated in several expeditions to the Caribbean. His collections were donated to the United States National Museum. He did volunteer work in the Division of Mollusks in his spare time, and wrote several articles for the *Proceedings of the United States National Museum* and *Bulletin of the United States National Museum.* He was also the author of *American Diplomatic Questions,* 1901, and *The Cruise of the Tomas Barrera,* 1916, based on his expedition to Cuba in 1914.

The Henderson Family Papers contain John Brooks Henderson, Jr.'s, correspondence, including many letters documenting his research on West Indian mollusks. Frequent correspondents include George H. Clapp, Charles Cleveland Nutting, Henry A. Pilsbry, and Charles Torrey Simpson. They also include his literary manuscripts; scientific notebooks; lists of shells from the Caribbean, Maine, and North Carolina; Henderson family correspondence, including John Brooks Henderson, Jr.'s, correspondence describing his travels; correspondence concerning the endorsement of Irving Fisher for Secretary of the Smithsonian Institution; cancelled checks; appointment calendars; medical and real estate records; notes; genealogy; Mary Foote Henderson's recipe and guest books; records from the United States Treasury Department on imports and exports; immigration and population statistics; federal expenditure statistics, 1892-1893; photographs, some of which were taken by Matthew Brady; blueprints; architectural drawings; newspapers; and journal articles.

ARRANGEMENT: (1) John Brooks Henderson, Jr., general correspondence, 1892-1923; (2) John Brooks Henderson, Jr., literary manuscripts and description of Haiti; (3) John Brooks Henderson, Jr., scientific notebooks, logbook, and manuscripts, 1899-1914; (4) Henderson family, general correspondence, 1868-1923; (5) Henderson family, genealogy, appointment calendars, medical reports, fiscal and real estate records, blueprints, and drawings; (6) Henderson family, guest books, recipe books, notes, pamphlets, journal, newspaper articles, and photographs; (7) John Brooks Henderson, Jr., correspondence on West Indian mollusks, 1898-1923. FINDING AIDS: Description in control file. SPECIAL CONDITIONS: Use of this record unit requires prior arrangement with the Archives staff.

Thomas R. Henry Papers, 1933-1966
(3.7 linear meters).

Thomas R. Henry (1893- ?), a science writer for the Washington *Evening Star,* also served as a press writer for the Smithsonian Institution from 1931 until the mid-1960s. During World War II he was a correspondent for the North American Newspaper Alliance serving in England, North Africa, Sicily, Italy, and France.

These papers document Henry's career in journalism and include manuscripts of articles and books on science; copies of press releases concerning the Smithsonian; newspaper articles; manuscripts; a typed copy of a journal; memorabilia from his career as a war correspondent; and scrapbooks containing his newspaper articles and columns.

ARRANGEMENT: Unarranged. FINDING AIDS: Box list in control file. SPECIAL CONDITIONS: Use of this record unit requires prior arrangement with the Archives staff.

Jon L. Herring Papers, 1962-1979
(0.3 linear meter).

Jon L. Herring (1922-1985) was born in Jacksonville, Florida. He attended the University of Florida at Gainesville, where he received his B.A. and M.A. After earning a Ph.D. in 1958 from the University of California, Berkeley, Herring was hired by the Government of American Samoa at Pago Pago as Staff Entomologist in charge of all entomological affairs.

In 1961, Herring returned from the South Pacific to take a job with the United States Department of Agriculture (USDA) in Beltsville, Maryland, working on the biological control of insects. By 1962, he had moved to the Natural History Building in Washington, D.C., to become the Heteropterist for the Insect Identification and Parasite Introduction Research Branch, USDA. After 1972, the Branch became the Systematic Entomology Laboratory.

The papers of Jon L. Herring document his career at the USDA from 1962 until his retirement in 1979. They consist of correspondence concerning his research in Hemiptera-Heteroptera, especially aquatic Heteroptera such as *Halobates.* Also included are research proposals that Herring reviewed for the National Science Foundation.

ARRANGEMENT: Alphabetic. FINDING AIDS: None. SPECIAL CONDITIONS: Use of this record unit requires prior arrangement with the Archives staff.

Brooke Hindle Papers, circa 1944-1985
(14.4 linear meters).

Brooke Hindle (1918-   ), historian, was born in Drexel Hill, Pennsylvania. He attended the Massachusetts Institute of Technology, 1936-1938, but completed his A.B., *magna cum laude,* at Brown University in 1940. Hindle received an M.A. (1942) and Ph.D.

(1949) from the University of Pennsylvania, and was a fellow at the Institute of Early American History and Culture, College of William and Mary, 1948-1950.

In 1950, Hindle joined the history faculty at New York University as Associate Professor and in 1961 became a Professor in the department. He was also Chairman of the history department, 1965-1967; Dean of the College of Arts and Science, 1967-1969; and Head of the history department, 1970-1974.

In 1974, Hindle succeeded Daniel J. Boorstin as Director of the National Museum of History and Technology (NMHT). He served until 1978, when he became Senior Historian. Hindle retired in 1985, but remained at the Smithsonian as Historian Emeritus.

Hindle belonged to numerous professional organizations, including the American Association for the Advancement of Science, History of Science Society, and Society for the History of Technology (SHOT), which he served as President, 1981-1982.

Hindle wrote and edited many articles and books on the history of science and technology in colonial America, including *The Pursuit of Science in Revolutionary America* (1956), *The Scientific Writings of David Rittenhouse* (1980), and *Emulation and Invention* (1981).

These papers document Hindle's teaching career; his tenure as an academic dean, historian, and professor of science and technology at New York University; his service as President of SHOT; and, to a lesser extent, his years as Director of the NMHT.

Papers consist of correspondence and memoranda with historical, scientific, and technological institutes and societies concerning research; correspondence and memoranda with prominent historians of science and technology, particularly Carl Bridenbaugh, Whitfield J. Bell, Jr., and A. Hunter Dupree; historical research proposals, manuscripts, publications, index cards, and related material; biographical information; slides and photographs of scientific illustrations and portraits of historic American figures; files concerning his presidency of SHOT and as a member of various visiting committees to review academic programs in the history of science and technology; and copies of course materials prepared during his teaching career at New York University.

ARRANGEMENT: (1) Correspondence and memoranda, 1944-1985; (2) publications and lectures, 1955-1984; (3) photographs and slides; (4) biographical information; (5) research manuscripts, 1955-1984; (6) course syllabi, 1966-1982; (7) index cards. FINDING AIDS: Folder list in control file. SPECIAL CONDITIONS: Use of this record unit requires prior arrangement with the Archives staff.

(7449)

Joseph H. Hirshhorn Papers, circa 1926-1982 and undated
(12.3 linear meters).

Joseph H. Hirshhorn was born in 1899 in Mitau, Latvia, the twelfth of thirteen children. His father died when Joseph was still an infant. In 1905 his mother immigrated with her children to the United States and settled the family in Brooklyn, New York, where she found work in a purse factory. Hirshhorn left school at the age of twelve to sell newspapers. By the age of fourteen, he was an office boy for the firm which later became the American Stock Exchange. In a short time, he became a chartist, charting stocks for an editor on Wall Street. In 1916 he took a small sum he had saved and launched himself as a broker, earning $168,000 the first year.

In 1924 Hirshhorn became a broker's broker, dealing with great success in bank stock and unlisted securities. In 1929 he distrusted the booming stock market and removed his capital of four million dollars just two months before the crash.

In the 1930s, Hirshhorn began to invest heavily in Canadian mining, discovering gold and then uranium. He secretly acquired mining rights to some 56,000 acres, which became two huge uranium mines. By the mid-1950s, his interests stretched across Canada and the United States, involving him in more than two dozen mining and oil companies. Shortly thereafter, he began to reduce his business interests.

Hirshhorn learned to love art and music as a child and began collecting paintings and sculpture as his fortune grew. Eventually his private collection numbered over 5,600 pieces. In the 1950s, he hired an art dealer, Abram Lerner, to curate the collection.

In 1966 President Lyndon B. Johnson announced that Hirshhorn would donate his entire art collection to the United States along with one million dollars to supplement the collection. A new museum would be constructed on the Mall as part of the Smithsonian Institution and would be named the Joseph H. Hirshhorn Museum and Sculpture Garden. The Museum opened in 1974 with Abram Lerner as its first Director. It was considered to be the most important art donation for the Capital since the Andrew Mellon gift of the National Gallery of Art.

Hirshhorn's collection includes an international range of sculpture by Henry Moore, Picasso, and others, but its paintings are primarily modern American, including works by Thomas Eakins, Jackson Pollock, and Stuart Davis.

Hirshhorn was married four times, lastly to Olga Cunningham, who shared his passion for art. He died in 1981.

These papers document Joseph Hirshhorn's relationships with artists and dealers, 1946-1981. Of particular interest is correspondence with artists Willem de Kooning, Georgia O'Keeffe, Alexander Calder, Marc Chagall, Pablo Picasso, George Rickey, Man Ray, David Hayes, and Henry Moore. There are smaller amounts of correspondence with other well-known artists including Robert Motherwell, Marcel Duchamp, Milton Avery, Josef Albers, Marino Marini, Louise Nevelson, Larry Rivers, and Niki de Saint-Phalle. Many of these files contain clippings, an occasional photograph, and greeting cards. Also included is Hirshhorn's general and social correspondence; Hirshhorn's speeches; awards, plaques and diplomas; personal newspaper clippings, 1955-1981; fan letters; some biographical material; a large number of photographs; and material regarding the Hirshhorn Museum and Sculpture Garden. These papers contain no material relating to Hirshhorn's business interests.

ARRANGEMENT: (1) Joseph H. Hirshhorn Papers, *circa* 1926-1982, accession number 91-104; (2) Joseph H. Hirshhorn Papers, *circa* 1969, 1973-1977, 1982 and undated, accession number 94-008. FINDING AIDS: Box list and index to artists' correspondence in control file. SPECIAL CONDITIONS: Use of this record unit requires prior arrangement with the Archives staff.

(7474)

History of Science Society, circa 1930-1993
Records (22.1 linear meters).

The History of Science Society (HSS) was established in 1924 to ensure the future of *Isis,* the international journal founded by George Sarton in 1912. The purpose of HSS is to promote interest in the history of science, to provide a forum for discussion, and to encourage original research in the field. The Society meets these goals by holding annual meetings and other programs; by issuing *Isis, Osiris,* and other publications; by awarding prizes and medals for exceptional contributions to the field; and by cooperating with other professional groups. HSS is governed by a Council consisting of the officers of the Society: a President, Vice-President, Executive Secretary, Treasurer, and Editor of *Isis;* the ex-presidents of the Society; and fifteen additional members elected from the membership of the Society.

These records provide partial documentation of the history of HSS, *circa* 1930-1993. They consist mostly of records maintained by HSS officers that concern annual meetings; membership; the work of HSS committees; the HSS Council; the publication of *Isis, Osiris,* and other HSS publications; elections of officers; HSS relations with other professional societies; financial matters; and prizes and awards granted by HSS. Also included are records concerning an HSS fundraising campaign started in 1983; files of the HSS Committee on Independent Scholars, 1986-1989; files of Nathan Reingold as Chairman of the Conference on Science Manuscripts, 1960, which was co-sponsored by HSS; and copies of the HSS *Newsletter.*

ARRANGEMENT: (1) Records of the Secretary, *circa* 1953-1979; (2) records of Robert P. Multhauf as President, 1979-1980, and as *Isis* Editor, 1964-1980; (3) records of President Dorothy Stimson, *circa* 1930s-1950s; (4) HSS Archives, *circa* 1930s-1960s; (5) records of Treasurer William Stahlman, 1956-1963; (6) records of President John C. Greene, 1973-1976; (7) records of Treasurers John G. Burke and Arthur L. Norberg, 1969-1977; (8) records of *Isis* Editors I. Bernard Cohen and Harry Woolf, 1947-1964; (9) records of Secretary Audrey B. Davis, 1983-1985; (10) records of Treasurers Seymour Mauskopf and Spencer Weart, 1979-1985; (11) HSS *Newsletters,* 1972-1982; (12) election records, 1984-1986; (13) records of Secretary Audrey B. Davis, 1983-1986; (14) records of Executive Secretary Michael Sokal, 1988-1992, and records of the *Isis* Editor and HSS Publications Office, 1959-1992; (15) records of the HSS Committee on Independent Scholars, 1986-1989; (16) records of Secretary Sally Gregory Kohlstedt, 1972-1988; (17) records of Executive Secretary Michael Sokal, 1982-1992; (18) fundraising campaign files, 1983-1993; (19) records of Executive Secretary Michael Sokal, 1988-1992; (20) records of President Sally Gregory Kohlstedt, 1992; (21) HSS Archives, *circa* 1985-1989; (22) records of Presidents Robert P. Multhauf, Frederic L. Holmes, and Gerald Holton, 1980-1989; (23) records of Secretary Sally Gregory Kohlstedt, 1980-1982; (24) records of Secretary Sally Gregory Kohlstedt, 1980-1982; (25) files of Nathan Reingold as Chairman of the Conference on Science Manuscripts, 1960. FINDING AIDS: Box list in control file. SPECIAL CONDITIONS: (1) Restricted; (2) use of this record unit requires prior arrangement with the Archives staff.

(7469)

Horton H. Hobbs, Jr., Papers, 1935-1993, with related material from 1900-1906
(4.9 linear meters).

Horton H. Hobbs, Jr., (1914-1994), an invertebrate zoologist, received his Ph.D. in biology from the University of Florida in 1940 and taught there from 1937 to 1946. He joined the faculty of the University of Virginia in 1946 and served as Director of its Mountain Lake Biological Station from 1956 to 1960. Hobbs joined the staff of the United States National Museum in 1962 as Head Curator of the Department of Zoology. In 1964 he was appointed Senior Scientist in the Department of Invertebrate Zoology, National Museum of Natural History (NMNH), a position he retained until his retirement in 1984. At that time, Hobbs was given the title of Emeritus Zoologist while continuing his research on the taxonomy, ecology, and geographic distribution of freshwater decapod crustaceans.

The papers of Horton H. Hobbs, Jr., consist of incoming and outgoing correspondence primarily documenting his research on crayfish. Most of the correspondence was created during his career at NMNH, with smaller amounts from his days at the University of Florida and the University of Virginia. The correspondence is largely with professional colleagues and concerns the identification of specimens, preparation of scientific publications, field work, and professional matters. Also included is correspondence between Hobbs and students conducting doctoral programs under his supervision. The papers also include a few letters of the invertebrate zoologist, William Perry Hay, 1900-1906.

For additional information, see record unit 9509, Horton H. Hobbs, Jr., Interview, 1976.

ARRANGEMENT: Alphabetic. FINDING AIDS: Box list in control file. SPECIAL CONDITIONS: Use of this record unit requires prior arrangement with the Archives staff.

(7392)

Ned Hollister Papers, 1916-1923
(0.1 linear meter).

Ned Hollister (1876-1924) began his career in 1904 as a Field Naturalist with the Bureau of Biological Survey, United States Department of Agriculture. From 1910 to 1916 he served as Assistant Curator in the Division of Mammals, United States National Museum. In 1916, Hollister was appointed Superintendent of the National Zoological Park (NZP) where he remained until his death.

This collection consists of correspondence, mostly concerning Hollister's selection as Superintendent of the NZP, and correspondence, lists, and notes documenting his research on the mammals of the Philippine Islands.

ARRANGEMENT: (1) Correspondence, 1916; (2) correspondence, notes, and lists on the mammals of the Philippine Islands, 1922-1923. FINDING AIDS: None. SPECIAL CONDITIONS: Use of this record unit requires prior arrangement with the Archives staff.

(7084)

William Henry Holmes Papers, 1870-1931
(1 linear meter).

William Henry Holmes (1846-1933) was an anthropologist, archeologist, artist, and geologist. Born near Cadiz, Ohio, Holmes graduated in 1870 from McNeely Normal School in Hopedale. After teaching for a brief period, Holmes left Ohio for Washington, D.C., where he studied art under Theodore Kauffman. In Washington, Holmes became acquainted with the Smithsonian and soon began sketching natural history specimens for staff members of the National Museum.

In 1872, Holmes was appointed artist-topographer to the United States Survey of the Territories under Ferdinand V. Hayden, and in 1874 was appointed Assistant Geologist. Holmes' survey in New Mexico and Arizona eventually led to his career in archeology and his interest in the cliff-dwellings of the Southwest.

Holmes joined the United States Geological Survey (USGS) in 1880 and remained with the Survey until 1889 when he transferred to the Bureau of American Ethnology

(BAE). Between 1882 and 1889, Holmes was also Honorary Curator of Aboriginal Ceramics, United States National Museum (USNM).

Holmes left the BAE to serve as Head Curator of Anthropology at the Field Columbian Museum in Chicago, 1894-1897, and subsequently held positions as Head Curator of the Department of Anthropology, USNM, 1897-1902, and Chief of the BAE, 1902-1909. Holmes served as Curator of the National Gallery of Art from 1907 to 1920, and as Head Curator of the Department of Anthropology from 1910 to 1920. When the National Gallery of Art (now known as the National Museum of American Art) became a separate bureau of the Smithsonian, Holmes severed his ties with the USNM and served as Director of the National Gallery from 1920 until his retirement in 1932.

These papers include Holmes' personal and professional correspondence, including correspondence between other scientists, which was collected by Holmes in connection with his research. The correspondence mainly documents Holmes' research in American ethnology and archeology; but also includes material dealing with international scientific meetings and professional conflicts. Also included are photographs; tracings and sketches; field notes; notes; biographical information; catalogs; published materials; book reviews; a list of Holmes' published works; and memorabilia. A microfilm copy of Holmes' *Random Records of a Lifetime,* volumes 1-16, is also available. Other material pertaining to Holmes may be found in the National Anthropological Archives and the American Art and Portrait Gallery Library.

ARRANGEMENT: (1) Correspondence, arranged alphabetically, 1882-1931; (2) correspondence, arranged numerically by Holmes, 1870-1931; (3) correspondence, arranged by subject; (4) memorabilia; (5) field notes, sketches, photographs, and a diary; (6) handwritten and printed drafts of articles; (7) biographical information; (8) published material; (9) microfilm copy of Holmes' *Random Records of a Lifetime,* volumes 1-16. FINDING AIDS: Description in control file. SPECIAL CONDITIONS: Use of this record unit requires prior arrangement with the Archives staff.

(7454)

Harry Hoogstraal Papers, circa 1940-1986
(48.4 linear meters and oversize).

Harry Hoogstraal (1917-1986) was an internationally renowned medical zoologist, entomologist, and specialist on ticks and tick-borne diseases. He received degrees from the University of Illinois (B.A., 1938 and M.S., 1942) and the London School of Hygiene and Tropical Medicine (Ph.D., 1959 and D.Sc., 1971). After service in the United States Army during World War II, Hoogstraal was appointed Head of the Medical Zoology Department, Naval Medical Research Unit No. 3 (NAMRU-3), Cairo, Egypt. He held his post with NAMRU-3 from 1949 until his death.

Hoogstraal participated in several scientific expeditions, mostly between the years 1938 and 1949. Field work was conducted in Mexico, New Guinea, the Philippines, and Africa. His research produced over 500 publications, an eight-volume bibliography of ticks and tick-borne diseases, and over 1,750 translated books and research articles, primarily from Russian. Hoogstraal amassed a large collection of ticks, which was acquired by the National Museum of Natural History. He was active within the profession of medical zoology and served as President of the American Society of Parasitologists, 1984, and President-Elect of the American Society of Tropical Medicine and Hygiene, 1986. Hoogstraal was the recipient of numerous awards including the

Henry Baldwin Ward Medal, American Society of Parasitologists, 1967; the Presidential Order of Merit, First Class, Arab Republic of Egypt, 1978; and the Walter Reed Medal, American Society of Tropical Medicine and Hygiene, 1978.

These papers document the professional career, and to a lesser extent, the personal affairs of Harry Hoogstraal. Most of the papers concern his work after he joined NAMRU-3 in 1949. There appears to be little documentation of his participation on scientific expeditions during the 1930s and 1940s. The papers primarily consist of a voluminous file of incoming and outgoing correspondence with medical zoologists, entomologists, physicians, museum personnel, NAMRU-3 colleagues, and personal friends concerning Hoogstraal's research on ticks and tick-borne diseases; NAMRU-3 business; the preparation and publication of scientific papers; the development of his tick collection; his translating work; and his activities as a member and officer of countless professional organizations. Also included are manuscripts and illustrations from scientific papers; records concerning the administration of NAMRU-3; and notes, lists and other data from Hoogstraal's research.

ARRANGEMENT: (1) Correspondence, *circa* 1940-1986; (2) manuscripts, *circa* 1950-1986; (3) NAMRU-3 administrative records, *circa* 1978-1986; (4) research data; (5) illustrations. FINDING AIDS: Box list in control file. SPECIAL CONDITIONS: Use of this record unit requires prior arrangement with the Archives staff.

(7061)

William Jervis Hough Papers, 1846-1847, 1896-1901
(0.1 linear meter).

William Jervis Hough (1795-1869), lawyer, served as a congressman from New York, 1845-1847. He was appointed a Regent of the Smithsonian Institution in August 1846. Hough attended the Board of Regents' first meeting in the fall of 1846, and served as Secretary of that body. Hough was also on the Smithsonian Building Committee. After his term as congressman ended, Hough returned to law practice in New York State.

These papers consist of Hough's correspondence with David Dale Owen concerning the selection of stones for the Smithsonian Building and an original proposal for the Smithsonian Building from the architect, William Archer; notes regarding the 1846 founding of the Smithsonian Institution; a report by the Smithsonian Building Committee; notes from contractors; and an 1863 newspaper article about the Smithsonian Building. Also included is later correspondence between William Jones Rhees and Charles E. Stevens, Hough's son-in-law, concerning the deeding of Hough's papers to the Smithsonian Institution.

ARRANGEMENT: (1) Correspondence; (2) notes, report, and newspaper article. FINDING AIDS: Description in control file. SPECIAL CONDITIONS: Use of this record unit requires prior arrangement with the Archives staff.

(7169)

Arthur Holmes Howell Papers, circa 1905-1940, 1967
(0.1 linear meter).

Arthur Holmes Howell (1872-1940) developed an interest in natural history, especially birds, as a boy in New York State. He later joined the Linnaean Society of New York and the American Ornithologists' Union. Through his membership in these groups, he came

489

to know many of the naturalists of the day, particularly Harry C. Oberholser, the ornithologist. On the advice of Oberholser, Vernon Bailey of the United States Department of Agriculture, Division of Ornithology and Mammalogy, later the Bureau of Biological Survey, gave Howell a temporary appointment in 1895 and took him on a western trip as a field assistant. Following a second temporary appointment in 1896, Howell became a permanent special assistant and was assigned work on the preparation of scientific study skins and the Bureau's mammal collection. Howell remained with the Biological Survey until his death and held the position of Senior Biologist in the Division of Wildlife Research, Fish and Wildlife Service, successor agency of the Bureau.

During his career, Howell became one of the leading American ornithologists and mammalogists. He was a charter member of the American Society of Mammalogists, a member of the Society's Board of Directors, 1935-1940, and Chairman of the editorial committee, 1938-1940. In addition, he was a Fellow of the American Ornithologists' Union and a member of the Baird Ornithological Club, the Cooper Ornithological Club, and the Biological Society of Washington. Howell's major publications dealt with the fauna of the southeastern United States, particularly birds and mammals.

ARRANGEMENT: (1) Correspondence and notes concerning the determination of life zones in the southeastern United States, particularly Alabama, *circa* 1909-1936; (2) correspondence and notes concerning the birds and mammals of Florida, *circa* 1905-1940; (3) bibliography of Arthur Holmes Howell, 1967. FINDING AIDS: Description in control file. SPECIAL CONDITIONS: Use of this record unit requires prior arrangement with the Archives staff.

(7405)

John Southgate Yeaton Hoyt and Sally Foresman Hoyt Papers, 1938-1964
(0.1 linear meter).

John Southgate Yeaton Hoyt (1913-1951), an ornithologist, received his Ph.D. from Cornell University in 1948. Most of his professional career was spent as an assistant to Arthur A. Allen at the Cornell University Laboratory of Ornithology.

Sally Foresman Hoyt (1914-   ), also known as Sally Hoyt Spofford, received her Ph.D. in ornithology from Cornell University in 1948. From 1955 to 1969, she was employed in various administrative posts at the Cornell University Laboratory of Ornithology.

These papers consist of correspondence, photographs, field notebooks, manuscripts, lists, notes, and newspaper clippings documenting the Hoyts' research on pileated woodpeckers.

ARRANGEMENT: Unarranged. FINDING AIDS: None. SPECIAL CONDITIONS: Use of this record unit requires prior arrangement with the Archives staff.

(7107)

Henry Guernsey Hubbard Papers, 1871-1899
(0.5 linear meter).

Henry Guernsey Hubbard (1850-1899) was a horticulturist and botanist as well as an entomologist. He attended Harvard University in the days of Louis Agassiz and Asa Gray, graduating in 1873. His interest in entomology was influenced by Hermann August

Hagen and Baron von Osten-Sacken. He also met Eugene Amandus Schwarz, who became his best personal and professional friend.

These papers concern the taxonomy and biology of insects, especially pests of cotton and orange trees, and incidentally relate to botany and horticulture. They include a collection of field notebooks, 1873-1898, for field work in Arizona, California, Colorado, Florida, Kentucky, Michigan, Virginia, and Jamaica; drawings, notes, and plates relating to Hubbard's publications; and correspondence with Theodore D. A. Cockerell, Hermann Hagen, Leland Ossian Howard, John Lawrence LeConte, Fritz Muller, and Eugene Amandus Schwarz.

ARRANGEMENT: (1) Notebooks, 1871-1899; (2) correspondence, 1876-1892; (3) notes and drawings. FINDING AIDS: Description in control file. SPECIAL CONDITIONS: Use of this record unit requires prior arrangement with the Archives staff.

(7398)

John W. Huddle Papers, 1968-1975
(0.4 linear meter).

John W. Huddle (1907-1975) received his Ph.D. in paleontology from Indiana University in 1934. He served on the faculty of the University of North Carolina from 1934 to 1949. Huddle was appointed Geologist with the United States Geological Survey (USGS) in 1950. He remained with the USGS until his death. Huddle's research specialty was conodont biostratigraphy.

These papers consist of correspondence, drafts, notes, lists and related materials, mostly concerning Huddle's research on conodonts from the Genesee Formation in western New York.

ARRANGEMENT: Unarranged. FINDING AIDS: None. SPECIAL CONDITIONS: Use of this record unit requires prior arrangement with the Archives staff.

(7311)

Paul D. Hurd, Jr., Papers, 1938-1982 and undated
(7.8 linear meters).

Paul D. Hurd, Jr. (1921-1982), entomologist and university professor, was an authority on the taxonomy and biology of bees. He was educated at the University of California, Berkeley, receiving the B.S. degree in 1947, the M.S. degree in 1948, and the Ph.D. degree in 1950. His professional career began in 1950 when he was appointed Senior Museum Entomologist at his alma mater. Hurd was eventually given teaching as well as research responsibilities, and by 1965 he had attained the rank of Professor of Entomology and Entomologist in the California Agricultural Experiment Station. During 1967-1968, he took a leave of absence from the University to join the National Science Foundation as Associate Program Director in the Division of Biological and Medical Sciences. In 1970, Hurd left Berkeley to accept appointment as Curator in the Department of Entomology, National Museum of Natural History (NMNH). From 1971 to 1976, he served as Chairman of the Department and in 1980 was appointed Senior Scientist.

Hurd's research interests were broad and he published on several of the families of the insect order Hymenoptera. However, most of his research was devoted to the bees of the superfamily Apoidea. He published over twenty papers and books on the carpenter bees (xylocopinae) and conducted extensive studies on the bee pollinators of squashes, gourds, and the creosote bush. Hurd's research at the NMNH was highlighted by his work as co-editor and an author of the revised *Catalog of Hymenoptera in America North of Mexico* which was published in 1979. He conducted field work in the western and southwestern United States, Mexico, South America, Central America, and Alaska. Hurd was a member of several professional organizations, and he served on the Governing Board of the Entomological Society of America and as editor of the *Pan-Pacific Entomologist,* journal of the Pacific Coast Entomological Society.

These papers document the professional career of Paul D. Hurd, Jr., between 1938 and 1982. Particularly well-represented in the papers is material concerning his research on the insect order Hymenoptera. They include a large file of correspondence, written and received by Hurd between 1942 and 1982, which illustrates all aspects of his career; correspondence, field notes, manuscripts, specimen lists, photographs, and notes documenting his research on carpenter bees and squash and gourd bees; records regarding Hurd's research project on the bee pollinators of the creosote bush and his work on the *Catalog of Hymenoptera in America North of Mexico;* an entomological subject file, primarily dealing with Hymenoptera; field notes, correspondence and reports documenting field research conducted in the western and southwestern United States, Mexico, and Alaska; desk diaries maintained by Hurd during his tenure as Chairman, Department of Entomology, NMNH; and correspondence, class and lecture notes, copies of examinations, and related materials illustrating Hurd's college days and his teaching career at the University of California, Berkeley.

ARRANGEMENT: (1) General correspondence, 1942-1982 and undated; (2) correspondence relating to carpenter bees research, 1951-1977; (3) carpenter bees research file, 1955-1981 and undated; (4) squash and gourd bees research file, 1968-1975 and undated; (5) larrea bees project file, 1968-1975 and undated; (6) *Catalog of Hymenoptera in America North of Mexico* file, 1971-1979 and undated; (7) field work file, 1938-1963; (8) desk diaries, 1972-1975; (9) entomological subject file, 1946-1980 and undated; (10) college and teaching file, 1946-1970. FINDING AIDS: Description in control file. SPECIAL CONDITIONS: Use of this record unit requires prior arrangement with the Archives staff.

(7248)

Louis W. Hutchins Papers, circa 1939-1957 and undated
(1 linear meter).

Louis W. Hutchins (1916-1957) was born in Washington, D.C. He was educated at Yale University, B.A., 1937 and Ph.D., 1941. Hutchins worked as a laboratory assistant at Yale from 1937 to 1938. During 1941 and 1942, he studied at Ohio State University as the recipient of the Mary S. Muellhaupt Scholarship. In 1942, he joined the staff of the Woods Hole Oceanographic Institution as an Assistant Marine Biologist. He was promoted to Associate Marine Biologist in 1943 and Marine Biologist in 1947. From 1949 to 1952, Hutchins served as Director of the Bermuda Biological Station for Research. In October 1957, Hutchins was drowned while on a field trip to Plummers Island in the Potomac River.

Hutchins' primary zoological interests were the studies of marine bryozoa and marine fouling. From 1943 to 1947, Hutchins served as Chief Biologist on a survey, sponsored by the United States Navy, to study the effect of marine fouling on buoys in the coastal waters of the United States. In 1945, he was engaged by the Lynn Gas and Electric Company of Lynn, Massachusetts, to investigate the fouling problem caused by mussels in their intake water tunnel. Hutchins also participated in the Woods Hole Oceanographic Institution's expedition to the Mid-Atlantic Ridge in 1948.

The papers of Louis W. Hutchins document his work on marine fouling and his study of marine bryozoa, and consist of correspondence, manuscripts and reprints, field notes, and research data.

ARRANGEMENT: (1) General correspondence, 1939-1957; (2) field notes, 1948; (3) manuscripts and reprints, 1940-1955 and undated; (4) research data, photographs, and miscellaneous notes, *circa* 1943-1957. FINDING AIDS: Description in control file. SPECIAL CONDITIONS: Use of this record unit requires prior arrangement with the Archives staff.

(7205)

Joseph Paxson Iddings Papers, 1914
(1 folder).

Joseph Paxson Iddings (1857-1920), geologist and petrologist, made a geological expedition to the South Pacific islands in 1914. These papers consist of carbon copies of letters written by Iddings while in the South Pacific, dated August 20 to October 30, 1914.

ARRANGEMENT: Chronologic. FINDING AIDS: None. SPECIAL CONDITIONS: Use of this record unit requires prior arrangement with the Archives staff.

(7380)

Ralph W. Imlay Papers, 1933-1984 and undated
(0.8 linear meter).

Ralph W. Imlay (1908-1989) was a paleontologist and authority on North American Jurassic and Lower Cretaceous invertebrate fauna. He received his Ph.D. from the University of Michigan in 1933. In 1940, Imlay joined the staff of the United States Geological Survey (USGS) as a Geologist. He remained with the USGS until his retirement in 1970. Imlay was a Research Associate in the Department of Paleobiology, National Museum of Natural History (NMNH), from 1967 until his death.

During his USGS career, Imlay conducted extensive field research in the western United States, Alaska, and Mexico where he collected many of the Jurassic fossils in the NMNH collection. He served as President of the Paleontological Society during 1964-1965.

This collection consists mostly of correspondence documenting Imlay's work at the USGS and the Department of Paleobiology, NMNH, and his research on invertebrate paleontology. The correspondence is with USGS, domestic, and foreign colleagues and concerns the identification of specimens, field work, publication of scientific papers, and professional matters. Also included are notes, lists, and illustrations from his research.

ARRANGEMENT: (1) General correspondence, 1933-1984; (2) notes, lists and illustrations, undated. FINDING AIDS: None. SPECIAL CONDITIONS: Use of this record unit requires prior arrangement with the Archives staff.

(7458)

Insect Identification and Parasite Introduction Research Branch, United States Department of Agriculture, 1907-1959
Records (0.7 linear meter).

For an administrative history of the Insect Identification and Parasite Introduction Research Branch, United States Department of Agriculture (USDA), and similar records, see record unit 7309.

These records consist of incoming and outgoing correspondence concerning the identification of specimens sent to the USDA for determination. Correspondents include J. Chester Bradley, Theodore D. A. Cockerell, Ezra Townsend Cresson, Jr., Henry Torsey Fernald, and Phil Rau.

ARRANGEMENT: Alphabetic. FINDING AIDS: Folder list in control file. SPECIAL CONDITIONS: Use of this record unit requires prior arrangement with the Archives staff.

(7141)

International Congress of Systematic and Evolutionary Biology, 1969-1973
Records (1.2 linear meters).

The First International Congress of Systematic and Evolutionary Biology (ICSEB) met in Boulder, Colorado, August 4-12, 1973. The idea for the meeting was conceived by Richard Sumner Cowan, National Museum of Natural History, and Frans Antonie Stafleu, University of Utrecht, Netherlands. The International Association for Plant Taxonomy and the Society of Systematic Zoology sponsored the meeting.

These records include steering committee minutes and correspondence, program development and plans, keynote speaker correspondence, symposia organizer correspondence, abstracts of contributed papers, and photographs of the steering committee members.

ARRANGEMENT: (1) General organization files, arranged by subject and mostly chronologic thereunder; (2) program files, arranged by subject and mostly chronologic thereunder. FINDING AIDS: (1) L. L. Short, "International Congress of Systematic and Evolutionary Biology: First Meeting a Success," article located in control file; (2) description in control file. SPECIAL CONDITIONS: Use of this record unit requires prior arrangement with the Archives staff.

(7145)

International Congress of Systematic and Evolutionary Biology, 1971-1973
Local Arrangements Records (0.7 linear meter).

For the most part, these records originated with Robert W. Pennak, executive committee and steering committee member of the International Congress of Systematic and Evolutionary Biology (ICSEB), and Doris Love, Chairman of the local arrangements committee, Boulder, Colorado. The first meeting of ICSEB was held on the University of Colorado campus in Boulder.

Records relate to local arrangements including financial matters, organization of field trips, providing room and board for participants, providing space and equipment for sessions, and other activities.

ARRANGEMENT: (1) Correspondence, alphabetic by subject; (2) Doris Love correspondence; (3) Robert W. Pennak correspondence; (4) David Rogers and Sam Shushan material. FINDING AIDS: Description in control file. SPECIAL CONDITIONS: Use of this record unit requires prior arrangement with the Archives staff.

(7109)

International Monetary Fund Collection, 1971
(0.1 linear meter).

The International Monetary Fund met at the Smithsonian Institution, December 17-18, 1971.

Material includes brochures on the Smithsonian Institution and Washington, D.C.; invitation; pamphlet containing names of the ministers of the "Ministerial Meeting of the Group of Ten"; parking permits; place setting and cards for the luncheon, December 18, 1971; and a photograph of Arthur F. Burns, Chairman of the Board of Governors of the Federal Reserve System.

ARRANGEMENT: Unarranged. FINDING AIDS: Description in control file. SPECIAL CONDITIONS: Use of this record unit requires prior arrangement with the Archives staff.

(7165)

International Whaling Conference and International Whaling Commission, 1930-1968
Records (3.6 linear meters).

The International Whaling Commission (IWC) was established in accordance with the International Convention for the Regulation of Whaling which was signed December 2, 1946, and which entered into force November 10, 1948. Signatories for the United States included A. Remington Kellogg, Ira N. Gabrielson, and William E. S. Flory.

These records are the files of Kellogg which he accumulated in connection with his duties relating to the regulation of whaling. Previously, Kellogg had been the United States delegate to the Berlin conference of experts on whaling matters held under the auspices of the League of Nations in 1930. Kellogg later was named the State Department representative to the 1937 International Conference on Whaling held in London. In 1946 Kellogg chaired the Washington Conference which formulated the International Convention providing for the establishment of the International Whaling Commission. From 1947 to 1967, Kellogg served as United States Commissioner on the IWC. From 1952 to 1954 he also served as Chairperson. Kellogg was succeeded as U. S. Commissioner by John Laurence McHugh.

These records document the participation of A. Remington Kellogg in various international whaling conferences, 1930-1946, as well as his participation in the IWC meetings, 1947-1967. Also included are reports on the IWC meetings made to the Secretary of State; copies of treaties; whaling statistics and reports; and correspondence relative to each meeting of the IWC.

ARRANGEMENT: (1) International Whaling Conference records, 1930-1953; (2) International Whaling Commission meetings, 1949-1966; (3) International Whaling Commission correspondence, 1949-1968; (4) reports to the Secretary of State by the United States Commissioner to the International Whaling Commission, 1949-1968. FINDING AIDS: Description in control file. SPECIAL CONDITIONS: Use of this record unit requires prior arrangement with the Archives staff.

(7282)

Imre G. Izsak Papers, 1961-1965
(0.1 linear meter).

Imre G. Izsak (1929-1965) joined the staff of the Smithsonian Astrophysical Observatory (SAO) in 1959 as a Celestial Mechanic in the Research and Analysis Section. In 1961, he was appointed Chief of the Research and Analysis Section. Izsak's primary fields of study were geodesy and celestial mechanics.

These papers consist of Izsak's professional correspondence and concern his research on geodesy and celestial mechanics; scientific conferences and symposia; and the publication of scientific manuscripts.

ARRANGEMENT: Alphabetic. FINDING AIDS: Description in control file. SPECIAL CONDITIONS: Use of this record unit requires prior arrangement with the Archives staff.

(7172)

Hartley H. T. Jackson Papers, circa 1883-1976
(3.1 linear meters).

Hartley H. T. Jackson (1881-1976) was born in Wisconsin. His early studies in zoology brought him into contact with Ludwig Kumlien, later his college professor, and Ned Hollister, then a Wisconsin naturalist. Following Jackson's graduation from Milton College in 1904, he taught school for several years before entering the University of Wisconsin. In 1910, the Bureau of Biological Survey of the United States Department of Agriculture offered Jackson a position on its staff, and he was placed in charge of the Bureau's mammal collection. In 1924, he became Chief of the Division of Biological Investigations and in 1936 was placed in charge of the Section of Wildlife Surveys, later Biological Surveys. He remained in that position until 1951 when the Section was merged with that of Distribution and Migration of Birds, and he became Mammalogist in the new Section of Distribution of Birds and Mammals. Jackson's primary research interests were the mammalogy of Wisconsin, the life zone concept of Clinton Hart Merriam, and the taxonomy and distribution of mammals.

Jackson was one of the founders of the American Society of Mammalogists and served as Chairman of its organizing committee in 1919. He also served the Society as Corresponding Secretary, 1919-1925; Editor of the *Journal of Mammalogy,* 1925-1929; and President, 1938-1940.

The papers of Jackson include correspondence and material concerning the American Society of Mammalogists, the War Production Board, the Baird Ornithological Club, and the Wisconsin Academy of Sciences; travel itineraries, bibliography, correspondence, and other materials concerning Jackson's official and scientific work including biological surveys of Wisconsin, evaluations of a project to eradicate malarial mosquitoes, distribution of mammals, Civil Service testing for biological positions, the

Bureau of Biological Survey's work in Alaska, and wildlife research; glass negatives of field trips and Alaska; photographs of Jackson, his family, and professional colleagues; publications of Jackson and materials relating to his *Mammals of Wisconsin;* biographical information on Jackson; memberships and awards; personal correspondence; and a diary, 1908.

ARRANGEMENT: (1) Material on organizations and committees, *circa* 1936-1949; (2) material on official and scientific work and publications, *circa* 1914-1967; (3) glass negatives, *circa* 1889-1929; (4) add acquisition, *circa* 1863-1976. FINDING AIDS: Description in control file. 1889-1929. FINDING AIDS: Description in control file. SPECIAL CONDITIONS: Use of this record unit requires prior arrangement with the Archives staff.

(7092)

J. Gwyn Jeffreys Papers, 1859-1883
(0.1 linear meter).

J. Gwyn Jeffreys (1809-1885) was an English naturalist who assembled a large collection of mollusk specimens which was purchased by the United States National Museum. This collection consists of miscellaneous papers and incoming correspondence concerning mollusks, together with sketches and plates.

ARRANGEMENT: Unarranged. FINDING AIDS: None. SPECIAL CONDITIONS: Use of this record unit requires prior arrangement with the Archives staff.

(7409)

Frank Morton Jones Papers, circa 1940-1959
(0.4 linear meter).

Frank Morton Jones (1869-1962), an entomologist, was President of the Natural History Society of Delaware from 1928 to 1943. Jones donated his personal collection of Psychid moths to the United States National Museum.

This collection consists mostly of newspaper clippings, articles, and other published materials concerning Jones' interests in entomology, insectivorous plants, the natural history of Delaware, and evolution. Also included is a small amount of correspondence, notes, and lists relating to his collection of Psychidae.

ARRANGEMENT: Unarranged. FINDING AIDS: None. SPECIAL CONDITIONS: Use of this record unit requires prior arrangement with the Archives staff.

(7333)

A. Myra Keen Papers, circa 1918-1985 and undated, with family material dating from 1839
(5.6 linear meters).

A. Myra Keen (1905-1986), an expert on the systematics of Cenozoic marine mollusks, was born in Colorado Springs, Colorado. She graduated from Colorado College in 1930, received her M.A. at Stanford in 1931, and her Ph.D. in psychology at the University of California at Berkeley in 1934. While working on her Ph.D., Keen volunteered to help Ida Shepard Oldroyd with her work on shells at Stanford University. Unable to find employment in her field when she graduated, Keen continued her volunteer work on the shell collection at Stanford. She soon came under the influence of Hubert Gregory Schenck, a paleontologist, who encouraged her to concentrate on malacology. Keen spent the remainder of her career at the University.

Keen was appointed Curator of Paleontology in 1936, Assistant Professor of Paleontology in 1954, Curator of Malacology in 1957, and Associate Professor and Professor of Paleontology in 1960 and 1965, respectively. In 1970 Keen became Professor of Paleontology Emeritus and Curator of Malacology Emeritus. Keen retired from Stanford in 1972, but continued her scholarship and interest in the work of her students and colleagues until her death.

Keen's specialty was Tertiary and recent molluscan faunas. As part of her research, Keen undertook extensive field work along the coast of California, traveling as far south as Peru. Her best known work, published in 1958, was *The Shells of Tropical West America: Marine Mollusks from Lower California To Colombia.*

Myra Keen was active in many professional societies and served as President of the American Malacological Union, 1948. She was one of the chief organizers of the Pacific Division of the American Malacological Union in 1948 and became its Chairman in 1964. In 1949 Keen was made Chairman of the Pacific Coast Section of the Paleontological Society and became a Fellow of the Society the same year. Keen was elected President of the Western Society of Malacologists in 1970 and was Chairman of the Committee on Nomenclature of the Society of Systematic Zoology. Keen was awarded a Guggenheim Fellowship in 1964 and, in 1979, was the first woman to receive the Fellows' Medal of the California Academy of Sciences. On his visit to the United States in 1975, Emperor Hirohito of Japan, a noted student of shells, met with Keen.

This record unit documents the professional career of Keen and also includes information about her personal interests. Documentation about Keen's professional work includes correspondence with colleagues and amateur shell collectors regarding research and identification of specimens, activities as a professor at Stanford, involvement with professional scientific organizations, and requests for her to become editor of numerous scientific journals. Of importance is Keen's correspondence regarding her involvement with the International Commission on Zoological Nomenclature, 1943-1983; Joint Committee on Zoological Nomenclature for Paleontology in America, 1945-1963; and her work with the Society of Systematic Zoology, Nomenclature Committee, 1953-1969. Also documenting Keen's professional work are her diaries and notebooks, which contain information about her shell collecting; research expeditions; and trip to the British Museum (Natural History) in 1967. There are drafts of published papers on mollusks; bound notes on nomenclature; anatomical drawings; specimen photographs and slides; photographs of scientists, including S. Stillman Berry and Henry A. Pilsbry; and group photographs of the American Malacologists Union, Pacific Division, and the Western Society of Malacologists.

These papers also include private correspondence with family members and friends documenting her interests in religion (in particular her relationship with the Religious Society of Friends), philosophy, current affairs, health, financial matters, and her concern over the death of her mother; correspondence and scrapbooks concerning Keen's visit from Emperor Hirohito of Japan; family photograph albums, dating back to around 1870; school annuals from Colorado Springs High School, 1923, and Colorado College,

1928-1931; awards, honors, and ribbons; an autobiography; and an oral history interview by Eugene V. Coan in September 1983.

ARRANGEMENT: (1) Personal correspondence, 1934-1985 and undated; (2) professional correspondence, 1935-1985 and undated; (3) diaries and notebooks, 1918-1985; (4) research files, 1935-1984; (5) diplomas and citations, 1923-1984; (6) family data and related materials, 1839-1985; (7) scrapbooks and collected materials, 1924-1985; (8) collected manuscripts, writings and publications, 1927-1985; (9) memorabilia and personal material, 1905-1984; (10) photographic materials, *circa* 1870-1985 and undated. FINDING AIDS: Description in control file. SPECIAL CONDITIONS: Use of this record unit requires prior arrangement with the Archives staff.

(7241)

Henry C. Kellers Photograph Collection, 1929-1930
(0.2 linear meter).

Henry C. Kellers (1874-1954) was born in Charleston, South Carolina. A graduate of the South Carolina Medical School, Kellers joined the United States Navy as a Hospital Steward in 1903. During the First World War he served as Assistant Surgeon with the Navy. He was promoted to Lieutenant in the Medical Corps in 1920 and to Lieutenant Commander in 1931. In 1938, he was placed on the Retired List of Officers of the Navy. He was recalled to active duty in 1939, serving until 1945 when he again retired. Kellers died in Oakland, California.

During his career in the Navy, Kellers participated in several scientific expeditions. He was a member of the United States Naval Observatory Eclipse Expeditions of 1925, 1927, 1929, and 1930 to Sumatra, Nicaragua, the Philippine Islands, and Nivafoou Island, respectively. On these expeditions, Kellers served as a representative of the Smithsonian Institution for the purpose of making biological collections. While in Nicaragua in 1927, he collected over 130 animals and birds for the National Zoological Park; and he secured over 10,000 zoological specimens from the Philippine Islands in 1929.

This collection consists of lantern slides, a photograph album, and loose photographs taken by Henry C. Kellers on the United States Naval Observatory Eclipse Expeditions to the Philippine Islands, 1929, and Nivafoou Island, 1930.

ARRANGEMENT: (1) Lantern slides; (2) photograph album and photographs. FINDING AIDS: Description in control file. SPECIAL CONDITIONS: Use of this record unit requires prior arrangement with the Archives staff.

(7170)

A. Remington Kellogg Papers, circa 1871-1969 and undated
(1.4 linear meters).

A. Remington Kellogg (1892-1969) was born in Davenport, Iowa. Kellogg studied mammalogy at the University of Kansas and later at the University of California, where he concentrated on the evolution of marine mammals. At California, Kellogg met John Campbell Merriam, later President of the Carnegie Institution of Washington, who was instrumental in supporting Kellogg's studies in cetology. In 1920, Kellogg joined the Bureau of Biological Survey of the United States Department of Agriculture as an Assistant Biologist. Kellogg also held a research appointment at the Carnegie from 1921 to 1943. He transferred from the Biological Survey to the United States National

Museum in 1928 to become Assistant Curator of Mammals, and became Curator in 1941 on Gerrit Smith Miller, Jr.'s, retirement. In 1948, Kellogg was named Director of the United States National Museum and held that post until his retirement in 1962. He was also an Assistant Secretary of the Smithsonian from 1958 to 1962. After his retirement, the Smithsonian appointed Kellogg to an honorary position in the Division of Vertebrate Paleontology where he continued his studies in evolutionary marine mammalogy until his death in 1969.

Kellogg was also extensively involved with the international regulation of whaling from 1930 to 1967. During this period, he served as delegate to the League of Nations whaling conference, 1930; State Department representative to the International Conference on Whaling at London, 1937; Chairman of the Washington Conference, 1946; United States Commissioner on the International Whaling Commission, 1947-1967; and Chairman of the International Whaling Commission, 1952-1954.

The main body of these papers consists of correspondence regarding research in zoology and marine geologic formations. Papers also document Kellogg's relationships with various institutions, notably the Bureau of Biological Survey, the Carnegie Institution of Washington, and the National Research Council. Also included are photographs, some Kellogg manuscripts, and a personal information file. For additional papers documenting Kellogg's career, see record units 7165 and 7434.

ARRANGEMENT: (1) Correspondence, 1916-1969; (2) correspondence with institutions, 1916-1943; (3) information file, *circa* 1871-1933 and undated; (4) photographs, *circa* 1930-1968; (5) divisional histories of the National Museum of Natural History, *circa* 1946. FINDING AIDS: Description in control file. SPECIAL CONDITIONS: Use of this record unit requires prior arrangement with the Archives staff.

(7434)

A. Remington Kellogg Papers, circa 1903-1969, with related papers to 1982
(4.5 linear meters and oversize).

For a biographical sketch and additional papers documenting the career of A. Remington Kellogg, see record units 7165 and 7170.

These papers document the professional career of A. Remington Kellogg, and to a lesser extent, his personal life. A small amount of material, which mostly post-dates Kellogg's death in 1969, was created by his wife, Marguerite H. Kellogg. The papers include incoming and outgoing correspondence concerning his research on recent and fossil marine mammals, *circa* 1921-1969; personal correspondence, especially with his wife, *circa* 1932-1963; photographs of Kellogg, colleagues, fossil whales, and American Society of Mammalogists meetings; reports and miscellaneous materials regarding the International Whaling Commission, 1956, 1964-1965; files documenting his work on the National Geographic Society's Committee for Research and Exploration, 1969; field notes, diaries, journals, account books, passports, address books, and expense accounts, *circa* 1903-1958; biographical information on Kellogg; a scrapbook containing personal photographs and memorabilia, *circa* 1930-1960; diplomas, certificates, and awards; class notes and papers from Kellogg's college days at the University of Kansas and University of California; official documents concerning appointments and ratings from his career in the federal government; files regarding the International Congress of Zoology, 1963; an oil painting of Kellogg; an information file on mammals which includes extensive correspondence and other records documenting Philip Hershkovitz's collecting work in South America, *circa* 1941-1943; and notes, lists, manuscripts, publications, newspaper clippings and related materials concerning Kellogg's research.

ARRANGEMENT: (1) A. Remington Kellogg Papers, *circa* 1903-1982, accession number 83-104; (2) A. Remington Kellogg Papers, *circa* 1913-1960, accession number 83-136; (3) A. Remington Kellogg Papers, *circa* 1928-1968, accession number 84-006; (4) A. Remington Kellogg Papers, *circa* 1940-1950, accession number 85-162. FINDING AIDS: Box list in control file. SPECIAL CONDITIONS: Use of this record unit requires prior arrangement with the Archives staff.

(7383)

Roman Kenk Papers, circa 1921-1987
(1.2 linear meters).

Roman Kenk (1898-1988) was an invertebrate zoologist and authority on the morphology, ecology, and taxonomy of freshwater flatworms. Born in Ljubljana, Yugoslavia, he received his Ph.D. in zoology from the University of Graz, Austria, in 1921. From 1921 to 1938, Kenk taught zoology at the University of Ljubljana, except for the years 1931-1932 when he was a Rockefeller Foundation Fellow at the University of Virginia. Kenk emigrated to Puerto Rico in 1938, and became a naturalized United States citizen in 1942. He served as Professor of Biology at the University of Puerto Rico from 1938 to 1948, before moving to Washington, D.C., to become a bibliographer at the Library of Congress. After his retirement in 1966, Kenk was appointed Research Associate in the Department of Invertebrate Zoology, National Museum of Natural History (NMNH), where he was placed in charge of building the flatworm specimen collection and library. He remained at NMNH until 1987.

Kenk published over forty papers on flatworms. Nine invertebrates were named in his honor, including a family of flatworms called Kenkiidae. He donated his personal collection of flatworms to NMNH.

The papers of Roman Kenk document his research on flatworms during all phases of his career. They include three series of correspondence covering the identification, acquisition, and exchange of specimens; the preparation and review of publications; and collecting work in Europe, Puerto Rico, and all regions of the United States. Also included are diaries documenting Kenk's daily activities as a Research Associate in the Department of Invertebrate Zoology, NMNH, from 1967 to 1987. The diaries also contain data from several collecting trips taken by Kenk.

ARRANGEMENT: (1) Correspondence, *circa* 1921-1966, arranged by correspondent; (2) correspondence, *circa* 1966-1987, arranged by correspondent; (3) correspondence, *circa* 1966-1987, arranged by state or country; (4) diaries, 1967-1987. FINDING AIDS: None. SPECIAL CONDITIONS: Use of this record unit requires prior arrangement with the Archives staff.

(7202)

Caleb Burwell Rowan Kennerly Papers, 1855-1860
(0.1 linear meter).

Caleb Burwell Rowan Kennerly (? -1861) served as surgeon and naturalist on the Pacific Railroad Survey of the 35th parallel, 1853-1855; United States-Mexican Boundary Survey, 1855-1857; and the Northwest Boundary Survey, 1857-1861.

These papers include journals, field books, memoranda books, and zoological notes kept by Kennerly while serving with the United States-Mexican Boundary Survey, 1855-1857, and the Northwest Boundary Survey, 1857-1860. Also included is a copy of a letter from G. Simpson to Joseph Henry, December 10, 1857, concerning arrangements for the transportation of specimens collected by the Northwest Boundary Survey. In a few instances, notes kept on both the United States-Mexican Boundary Survey and Northwest Boundary Survey appear in the same journal. Notes made by George Gibbs, geologist and interpreter for the Northwest Boundary Commission, are contained in a few of the journals.

ARRANGEMENT: Unarranged. FINDING AIDS: None. SPECIAL CONDITIONS: Use of this record unit requires prior arrangement with the Archives staff.

(7072)

Robert Kennicott Papers, 1863-1865
(3 letters, 22 pages).

These letters of Robert Kennicott (1835-1866) include two excellent letters to Roderick Ross MacFarlane of Winnipeg, in which Kennicott states his views on everything from the status of arctic zoology to the progress of the Civil War.

ARRANGEMENT: Chronologic. FINDING AIDS: None. SPECIAL CONDITIONS: Use of this record unit requires prior arrangement with the Archives staff.

(7360)

Porter M. Kier Papers, 1957-1985
(2.1 linear meters).

Porter M. Kier (1927-   ), an invertebrate paleontologist and museum administrator, received his Ph.D. degree from Cambridge University in 1954. He joined the staff of the United States National Museum in 1957 when he was appointed Associate Curator in the Department of Geology. In 1966, Kier was promoted to Curator in the Department of Paleobiology, National Museum of Natural History (NMNH), and from 1967 to 1972 served as Chairman of the Department. He was appointed Director of NMNH in 1973. Kier stepped down from administration in 1979 and resumed his research career as a Senior Scientist. He remained in the position until his retirement in 1985.

Kier was a leading authority on fossil and living echinoids. He served as President of the Paleontological Society of America (PSA), from 1971 to 1972, and as Editor of its publication, *Journal of Paleontology,* from 1965 to 1970.

This collection consists of incoming and outgoing correspondence documenting Kier's research and curatorial careers. The letters concern the identification, exchange, and acquisition of specimens; the publication of scientific papers; field work; and professional activities, especially his work for the PSA.

ARRANGEMENT: Alphabetic. FINDING AIDS: Box list in control file. SPECIAL CONDITIONS: Use of this record unit requires prior arrangement with the Archives staff.

Ellsworth Paine Killip Papers, 1914-1950
(0.8 linear meter).

Ellsworth Paine Killip (1890-1968), a botanist, was raised in upstate New York and received the A.B. degree from the University of Rochester in 1911. He joined the staff of the United States National Museum (USNM) in 1919 as an Aide in the Division of Plants. He was promoted to Assistant Curator in 1927, Associate Curator in 1928, and Curator in 1946. In 1947, Killip was appointed Head Curator of the newly established Department of Botany, USNM, a position he retained until his retirement in 1950. He was a Research Associate in the Department of Botany, USNM, from 1950 to 1965. Killip specialized in the taxonomy of South American plants.

This collection consists primarily of correspondence, lists, and notes relating to Killip's research on South American plants. Most of the records concern the identification of specimens. Also included are a journal and photographs from a 1914 camping trip in the Adirondack Mountains of New York.

ARRANGEMENT: Unarranged. FINDING AIDS: None. SPECIAL CONDITIONS: Use of this record unit requires prior arrangement with the Archives staff.

Robert Merrill King Papers, 1962-1971
(0.1 linear meter).

Robert Merrill King (1930-) was a Research Associate with the Department of Botany, National Museum of Natural History, from 1971 to 1972. King's botanical studies concerned Compositae.

These papers consist of incoming correspondence from botanists, directors of herbaria, colleagues, and friends concerning the identification and determination of botanical specimens; specimen collecting; purchasing specimens, especially from Southeast Asia and Mexico; nomenclature concerning African specimens; publications; scientific activities; and personal matters.

ARRANGEMENT: Alphabetic. FINDING AIDS: Description in control file. SPECIAL CONDITIONS: Use of this record unit requires prior arrangement with the Archives staff.

Edwin Kirk Papers, 1783-1893, 1905-1941 and undated
(0.1 linear meter).

Edwin Kirk (1884-1955) was educated at Columbia University where he received his Ph.D. degree in 1911. While at Columbia, Kirk was an Assistant to Amadeus W. Grabau, one of America's foremost teachers of geology and paleontology. In 1907, Kirk left Columbia to become an Assistant Paleontologist with the United States Geological Survey (USGS). In 1909, he was promoted to Junior Geologist, and subsequently held positions as Assistant Geologist, 1911-1913; Associate Geologist, 1913-1914; Paleontologist, 1914-1920; Associate Geologist, 1921-1952; and Geologist, 1952-1954.

In 1920, Kirk interrupted his service with the USGS to become a paleontologist with the Bolivia-Argentina Exploration Corporation.

When Kirk joined the USGS he was an Assistant to Edward Oscar Ulrich, studying Ordovician and Silurian sediments of the Appalachians. Later, Kirk made field trips to the Rocky Mountains, the Great Basin, and southeastern Alaska. Kirk also had an avocational interest in the history of science.

These papers consist of memoranda and correspondence concerning USGS publications, identification of specimens, and collection and field reports submitted to the USGS; miscellaneous writings; field and locality notes; a specimen list; and a small group of autograph letters of 18th and 19th century European scientists collected by Kirk.

ARRANGEMENT: (1) Correspondence and memoranda, 1905, 1915, 1920-1933, 1941 and undated; (2) miscellaneous writings, 1926 and undated; (3) notes and specimen list, 1905-1922 and undated; (4) autograph letters, 1783-1893 and undated. FINDING AIDS: Description in control file. SPECIAL CONDITIONS: Use of this record unit requires prior arrangement with the Archives staff.

(7466)

Margaret B. Klapthor Papers, circa 1952-1982
(2 linear meters).

Margaret B. Klapthor (1922-1994) was born in Henderson, Kentucky. She graduated from the University of Maryland, B.A., 1943, and shortly thereafter was employed by the Smithsonian Institution as a scientific aide in the Civil Section of the Division of History, United States National Museum. Klapthor was assigned to restoring the First Ladies' dresses, the collection of White House gowns, which eventually became the First Ladies Hall exhibition at the Museum of History and Technology in 1964. Her positions later included Assistant Curator, 1947-1948, in the Section of Civil History, Division of History; Assistant Curator, 1949-1951, and Associate Curator, 1952-1957, in the Division of Civil History; and Associate Curator, 1957-1970, Curator, 1971-1983, and Curator Emeritus, 1984-1994, in the Division of Political History. Klapthor published many articles and several books during her tenure, including *The Dresses of the First Ladies of the White House* and *Official White House China: 1789 to the Present.*

These papers consist of exhibition scripts for the Hall of Political History; correspondence pertaining to publications, lectures, educational activities, and planning of the First Ladies Hall; research notes and drafts to the publications *Official White House China: 1789 to the Present, First Ladies Cookbook,* and *The Dresses of the First Ladies of the White House;* photographs of Klapthor; annual reports for the Division of Political History; published articles by Klapthor; and biographical information on the First Ladies.

ARRANGEMENT: Unarranged. FINDING AIDS: Folder list in control file. SPECIAL CONDITIONS: Use of this record unit requires prior arrangement with the Archives staff.

Frederick Knab Papers, 1885-1891, 1903-1914
(0.1 linear meter).

Frederick Knab (1865-1918), born in Bavaria, emigrated to the United States in 1873 with his parents. He subsequently returned to Munich to study art for a time. Entomology was also one of Knab's early interests. Coupled with his artistic skill, this interest earned him a commission from Leland Ossian Howard to study the mosquitoes of New England as part of a larger study then in progress on the mosquitoes of North and Central America. In 1906 Knab joined the Bureau of Entomology of the United States Department of Agriculture, where he continued his studies of disease-bearing Diptera until his death.

These papers consist principally of family correspondence, 1885-1891 and 1903-1914, in English and German; a small quantity of professional correspondence; and a journal of part of Knab's trip up the Amazon River in 1885-1886.

ARRANGEMENT: (1) Family correspondence, 1885-1886, 1888-1891, 1903-1905, 1909-1914; (2) general correspondence; (3) Brazil trip, 1885; (4) notes, manuscripts, and photographs. FINDING AIDS: Description in control file. SPECIAL CONDITIONS: Use of this record unit requires prior arrangement with the Archives staff.

J. Brookes Knight Papers, circa 1928-1955 and undated
(1.4 linear meters).

J. Brookes Knight (1888-1960) was born in St. Louis, Missouri. He received his bachelor's degree at Princeton University, 1911, his master's degree at the University of Kansas, 1928, and his Ph.D. at Yale University, 1931. After graduating from Princeton, Knight returned to St. Louis to help in his family's business. During this time he studied fossils from the St. Louis area which were later used as the basis for his thesis at Kansas.

Following his graduation from Yale, Knight remained there for two years as a Research Associate and Sterling Senior Fellow at the Peabody Museum of Natural History. In 1933 he left the Peabody Museum and went to Occidental College in California where he was an Assistant Professor of Geology. From 1934 to 1935, he was in Europe on a Penrose Grant from The Geological Society of America to study Paleozoic gastropod collections in European museums. In 1936, he was appointed Lecturer and Curator of Paleozoic Invertebrate Paleontology at Princeton. During World War II, he also served as Instructor of Geology at Princeton's Army Special Training Program. During the summers of 1931, 1936, and 1938, Knight was an Assistant Geologist with the United States Geological Survey, assisting Philip B. King in studying the Permian fossils of Texas.

In 1945 Knight joined the staff of the United States National Museum (USNM) as a Research Associate in Paleontology, a position which he held until his retirement in 1956 when he was made an Honorary Research Associate. At the USNM Knight was in charge of the Paleozoic gastropods. As a result of his work with these fossils, Knight helped to prepare a section on Paleozoic gastropods for the *Index Fossils of North America* (1944) and the *Treatise on Invertebrate Paleontology* published by the Paleontological Society in 1960. He also helped prepare a study of Permian fossils, parts of which were published posthumously.

These papers consist of general correspondence with his family and amateur and professional paleontologists; unpublished manuscripts on gastropods and a typescript by F. M. Wadley of the United States Department of Agriculture; and drawings and a map of geological formations in central Texas. Correspondence concerns family financial matters; the administration of the USNM's Department of Geology; the review and publication of journal articles; state geological surveys; Knight's involvement in professional societies; and his research in Europe.

ARRANGEMENT: (1) General correspondence, 1928-1955 and undated; (2) unpublished manuscripts, *circa* 1934, 1950 and undated; (3) drawings and map from central Texas, undated. FINDING AIDS: Description in control file. SPECIAL CONDITIONS: Use of this record unit requires prior arrangement with the Archives staff.

(7274)

Walter Norman Koelz Itinerary, 1936-1941, 1948
(1 item).

Walter Norman Koelz (1895-), zoologist and botanist, was born in Waterloo, Michigan. He received an A.B. degree from Olivet College in 1915, and his A.M. and Ph.D. degrees from the University of Michigan in 1917 and 1920, respectively. In 1919, Koelz held the position of Curator of Fishes at the Museum of Zoology at Michigan. From 1919 to 1927, and again in 1930, Koelz worked for the United States Bureau of Fisheries. From 1935 to 1941, and from 1947 to 1949, Koelz was a plant explorer for the United States Department of Agriculture.

The itinerary, compiled in 1948, documents Koelz's plant explorations in Ceylon, India, Afghanistan, and Iran from 1936 to 1941.

ARRANGEMENT: Unarranged. FINDING AIDS: Description in control file. SPECIAL CONDITIONS: Use of this record unit requires prior arrangement with the Archives staff.

(7352)

James P. Kramer Papers, circa 1937-1987
(0.9 linear meter).

James P. Kramer (1928-), a United States Department of Agriculture (USDA) Research Entomologist, received his B.S. from Beloit College (1950), M.S. from the University of Missouri (1952), and his Ph.D. from the University of Illinois (1961). In 1957, Kramer joined the staff of the Insect Identification and Parasite Introduction Section, Entomology Research Branch, USDA, located in the United States National Museum. After 1972, the Branch became the Systematic Entomology Laboratory. Kramer remained with the USDA until his retirement in 1987, studying the Homoptera suborder Auchenorrhyncha, with special emphasis on New World leafhoppers (Cicadellidae) and planthoppers (Fulgoridae).

The papers of James P. Kramer consist of incoming and outgoing correspondence documenting his career at the USDA from 1957 to 1987. Most of the letters concern the identification of specimens, but reviews of scientific papers and information about professional meetings are also included. A small amount of earlier correspondence, from 1937 to mid-1957, was created by Kramer's predecessors, Paul Wilson Oman and David A. Young, Jr. All records concern research on Homoptera done at the USDA.

ARRANGEMENT: Alphabetic. FINDING AIDS: None. SPECIAL CONDITIONS: Use of this record unit requires prior arrangement with the Archives staff.

(7157)

Frederick Kreutzfeldt Journal, 1853
(1 volume).

Frederick Kreutzfeldt (? -1853) was a German botanist who accompanied John C. Fremont's survey of the 38th parallel, 1848, and Captain John W. Gunnison's 38th parallel expedition, 1853. Kreutzfeldt was killed in the massacre of the Gunnison party on October 26, 1853.

There are several copies of the journal: a handwritten German version, a handwritten English translation, a typescript in English prepared from the handwritten English translation, and an edited version of the typescript. Apparently none of these is the original. In addition, the translations cover the period from June 18 to October 23, 1853, while the German version contains no entries later than October 11, 1853.

ARRANGEMENT: Chronologic. FINDING AIDS: None. SPECIAL CONDITIONS: Use of this record unit requires prior arrangement with the Archives staff.

(7435)

Boris Alexander Krukoff Papers, circa 1929-1975
(8 linear meters).

Boris Alexander Krukoff (1898-1983) was a Consulting Forester and Economic Botanist with United States Rubber Company, Chicle Company, and Merck Company. He made a number of expeditions to South America and Africa, 1929-1955, where he collected botanical and wood specimens. He held the positions of Honorary Curator at the New York Botanical Garden and Consulting Botanist at Merck Sharp and Dohme Research Laboratory. His special interests were gum-yielding trees and botanical sources of crude drugs.

This record unit consists of Krukoff's personal files of correspondence, specimen lists, and reports relating to his collections. Also included are extensive files on cinchona and gum yielding trees.

These papers were previously described as record unit 1010013.

ARRANGEMENT: (1) File series A-AAA, expedition files, 1929-1955; (2) file series B, papers resulting from projects, *circa* 1938-1973; (3) file series C, papers relating to fish and snake collections, 1934-1940; (4) file series D-F, herbarium exchange files, *circa* 1931-1949; (5) file series G, trip made for United States Rubber Company, 1955; (6) file series H, material on gum yielding trees, *circa* 1930-1970; (7) literature files, *circa* 1930-1975. FINDING AIDS: (1) Box list in control file; (2) file plan in box 1. SPECIAL CONDITIONS: Use of this record unit requires prior arrangement with the Archives staff.

(1040101)

George Frederick Kunz Papers, circa 1880-1932 and undated
(0.3 linear meter).

George Frederick Kunz (1856-1932) was a mineralogist and an authority on gems. His professional career began in 1879 when he was hired as a gem expert by Tiffany &

Company of New York. He was made Vice-President in 1907 and remained with the company until his death. Kunz also served as a special agent for the United States Geological Survey, 1883-1909; worked as an agent at several International Expositions; and made a study of American pearls for the United States Fish Commission, 1892-1898. He was Research Curator of gems and precious stones for the American Museum of Natural History, 1904-1918, and a Research Associate from 1918 until his death. A prolific writer, Kunz produced both popular and scholarly works on gems. In 1903, the gem, Kunzite, was named in his honor.

These papers provide partial documentation of Kunz's professional career. They consist primarily of correspondence with geologists, mineralogists, gemologists, jewelers, museums, government agencies, and personal acquaintances. The correspondence concerns the identification, acquisition, and sale of gems and mineral specimens; mineralogical research, especially the effects of radiation on the color of gemstones; activities in professional societies; publications; expositions, particularly the World's Columbian Exposition, Chicago, 1893; his work with Tiffany & Company, the United States Geological Survey and the American Museum of Natural History; and personal matters. Also included is an address book kept by Kunz on a trip to Europe in 1881, statistics on American mining compiled by Kunz, manuscripts, and a few photographs.

ARRANGEMENT: Unarranged. FINDING AIDS: Folder list in control file. SPECIAL CONDITIONS: Use of this record unit requires prior arrangement with the Archives staff.

(7396)

Harry Stephen Ladd Papers, circa 1915-1982 and undated
(1.2 linear meters).

Harry Stephen Ladd (1899-1982) received his Ph.D. in geology from the University of Iowa in 1925. The initial part of his professional career was spent in faculty positions at his alma mater and the University of Virginia, as a geologist with the Gulf Oil Company in Venezuela, and studying fossils under Edward Oscar Ulrich at the United States National Museum. Ladd began his career with the United States Department of the Interior in 1936 when he was appointed Geologist with the National Park Service. In 1940, he joined the United States Geological Survey (USGS) as a Geologist. He remained with the USGS until his retirement in 1969. Ladd was a Research Associate in the Department of Paleobiology, National Museum of Natural History, from 1969 until his death.

Ladd was an authority on the geology of the islands of the Pacific Ocean. He conducted extensive field work in the Pacific Basin and supervised deep sea drilling on Eniwetok, Midway and other atolls. He was also a major contributor to Project Mohole, a plan for drilling deep into the earth's inner crust on the Pacific Ocean floor near Hawaii. During 1946-1947, Ladd was in charge of geological work on Crossroads Operation which conducted the scientific survey and resurvey of Bikini Atoll, the site of atomic bomb tests. Ladd was active professionally and was a Vice-President of the Geological Society of America, 1955, and the American Association for the Advancement of Science, 1965, and President of the Paleontological Society, 1954.

These papers document Ladd's career with the USGS and his research on the geology of Pacific Islands. They include incoming and outgoing correspondence documenting field work, USGS matters, research and the publication of papers, and professional activities; diaries and field notes, mostly documenting his investigations in the Pacific; scrapbooks documenting personal and professional affairs, but which are particularly strong in documenting his role in the Crossroads Operation and Project Mohole; photographs, slides, and motion pictures, mostly from his field work in the Pacific; an oral history interview of Ladd conducted in 1977; and various manuscripts, notes, and lists from his research.

ARRANGEMENT: Unarranged with the following apparent divisions: (1) general correspondence, *circa* 1924-1982; (2) outgoing correspondence, 1973-1979; (3) diaries and field notes, 1915, 1925-1926, 1934, 1938, 1964-1968, 1973; (4) scrapbooks, 1918-1960; (5) photographs, slides, and motion pictures, 1947, 1961, 1971 and undated; (6) oral history interview, 1977; (7) research materials, *circa* 1959-1980. FINDING AIDS: None. SPECIAL CONDITIONS: Use of this record unit requires prior arrangement with the Archives staff.

(7201)

Arthur Lakes Journals, 1877-1880
(3 items).

Arthur Lakes (1844-1917) was a Professor of Natural History at Jarvis College, Golden, Colorado, and served as a collector of fossil vertebrates for Othniel Charles Marsh of Yale University.

The journals of Arthur Lakes record his observations while exploring for saurian fossils at Morrison, Colorado, 1877; Como Station, Wyoming, 1879; and various other locations. The journals also contain lectures and notes on the discovery of fossil vertebrates.

ARRANGEMENT: Chronologic. FINDING AIDS: None. SPECIAL CONDITIONS: Use of this record unit requires prior arrangement with the Archives staff.

(7065)

Isaac Lea Papers, 1832-1876
(0.1 linear meter).

These records of the research of Isaac Lea (1792-1886) document only a small part of his career. The most useful items are an unexpurgated manuscript of his critique of Timothy Abbott Conrad's *Synopsis of the Family of Naiades of North America* and some original manuscript drawings, notes, and labels for his famous study of the Unionidae. Lea gave an important collection of Unionidae to the United States National Museum.

ARRANGEMENT: Unarranged with the following divisions apparent: (1) sketches and labels for shells and lists of shells submitted or given to Lea; (2) fragments of incoming correspondence from persons largely unidentified; (3) manuscript critique of T. A. Conrad, *Synopsis of the Family of Naiades of North America.* FINDING AIDS: None. SPECIAL CONDITIONS: (1) Sketches and labels of shells are separate from one another; (2) use of this record unit requires prior arrangement with the Archives staff.

William Harding Longley Papers, 1892-1904, 1913-1935 and undated

(0.1 linear meter).

William Harding Longley (1881-1937) was born in Nova Scotia and educated at Acadia University and Yale University. He spent most of his professional life as a Professor of Biology and Botany, 1911-1937, at Goucher College in Baltimore. Longley's major scientific work, on the role of color and pattern in the life of tropical reef fishes, was done in connection with the Dry Tortugas Laboratory of the Carnegie Institution of Washington, of which he served as Director from 1922 to 1937. Longley also studied the evolution and distribution of species using statistical methods.

These papers contain notebooks of William Harding Longley concerning field work in the Tortugas, Hawaii, Samoa, and the Pacific; examination of specimens in European and American museums; and the evolution and distribution of species, including notes on botanical species. There is also a notebook which is marked as Longley's, but appears to be an A. B. Alexander field journal for the North Pacific, 1892-1904.

ARRANGEMENT: (1) Notes on evolution and distribution of species, undated; (2) notes on specimens, field notes, 1913-1935; (3) A. B. Alexander field journal, 1892-1904. FINDING AIDS: Description in control file. SPECIAL CONDITIONS: Use of this record unit requires prior arrangement with the Archives staff.

John Alden Loring Papers, 1889-1897

(0.1 linear meter).

John Alden Loring (1871-1947) served as a field naturalist with the Bureau of Biological Survey, United States Department of Agriculture, from 1892 to 1897. During that time he conducted extensive field surveys in all regions of the United States, as well as in Canada and Mexico.

These papers document Loring's association with the Bureau of Biological Survey and consist primarily of correspondence received by him while in the field. Most of the letters were written by Bureau Chief Clinton Hart Merriam and contain instructions for field work and identifications of collections made by Loring. Also included are a few letters concerning Loring's initial interest in natural history and his application for employment with the Bureau.

ARRANGEMENT: Chronologic. FINDING AIDS: None. SPECIAL CONDITIONS: Use of this record unit requires prior arrangement with the Archives staff.

Philip K. Lundeberg Papers, 1962-1984

(2.9 linear meters).

Philip K. Lundeberg (1923-   ) received his B.A. from Duke University in 1944, and his Ph.D. from Harvard University in 1954. After serving in the Navy, he was an Assistant Professor at St. Olaf College from 1953 to 1955, and at the United States Naval Academy from 1955 to 1959. He came to the Smithsonian in January 1959 as a Consultant in the Department of Armed Forces History in the Museum of History and

Technology, and in June of that year was appointed Associate Curator in the Division of Naval History. From 1961 to 1984 Lundeberg was Curator of the Division in what became in 1980 the National Museum of American History (NMAH). He became a Curator in the NMAH Division of Transportation in 1984.

Lundeberg held positions in a number of national and international professional organizations. He was President of the American Military Institute, the Council of American Maritime Museums, and the United States Commission on Military History, as well as Chairman of the International Congress of Maritime Museums, Secretary of the International Committee on Museum Security of the International Council of Museums, and a member of the National Trust for Historic Preservation's Committee on Maritime Preservation.

Lundeberg's involvement with these organizations from 1962 to 1984 is documented in his papers. Included are correspondence with colleagues regarding governance, meetings, and publishing efforts of the organizations; papers presented at meetings by Lundeberg and his colleagues; and materials distributed at meetings or published by the groups. Documented in particular detail are the publication of the *Bibliography of the History of the Great Sea Routes* by the International Commission of Maritime History; Lundeberg's column, "The Museum Perspective" in *Military Affairs;* the International Commission of Military History (ICMH) Colloquy on Military History, held in Washington in July 1982 and sponsored by the U.S. Commission on Military History; and NMHT security and safety concerns, including his role as Chairman of the Museum's Security and Fire Prevention Committee from 1971 to 1979. An audio recording from the International Conference on the History of Cartography, held in Washington, D.C., in August 1977, is also included. Some scholarly papers and correspondence with foreign colleagues is in French or German.

ARRANGEMENT: (1) NMHT Security and Fire Prevention Committee, 1968-1982; (2) International Commission of Maritime History, 1962-1975; (3) American Military Institute, *Military Affairs,* 1968-1981; (4) Council of American Maritime Museums, Committee on Maritime Preservation, and International Congress of Maritime Museums, 1971-1984; (5) International Committee on Museum Security, 1975-1979; (6) ICMH Colloquy on Military History, Washington, D.C., 1974-1982; (7) U.S. Commission on Military History, 1973-1984. FINDING AIDS: None. SPECIAL CONDITIONS: Use of this record unit requires prior arrangement with the Archives staff.

(7207)

Roderick Ross MacFarlane Papers, 1889

(0.1 linear meter).

Roderick Ross MacFarlane (1833-1920) was born in Scotland, but joined the Hudson's Bay Company in 1852 and spent most of the rest of his life in Canada. MacFarlane had charge of a number of fur-trading posts in western and northwestern Canada between 1852 and 1894. These posts were the only settlements in these areas and, as a result, were used as headquarters by a number of naturalists who explored and collected in the region. In 1859, Spencer F. Baird sent Robert Kennicott to the Mackenzie River area to collect for the Smithsonian Institution. Kennicott's work there stimulated MacFarlane's interest in natural history, and MacFarlane began to collect specimens from the areas where he was stationed. He made a number of important collections for the Smithsonian in this manner, chiefly of birds and mammals. He also published a few works on the birds and mammals of western and northwestern Canada.

These papers consist of both a partial and a complete typewritten copy of MacFarlane's testimony before a Canadian Senatorial Committee on January 11, 1889, concerning the resources of the Mackenzie Basin, British Columbia.

ARRANGEMENT: (1) "Answers by R. MacFarlane to the Senatorial Queries, 11, Jany. 1889, 'The Great Mackenzie Basin';" (2) "From Testimony regarding the Resources of British America by R. MacFarlane, Made before a Canadian Senatorial Committee (1889?)." FINDING AIDS: Description in control file. SPECIAL CONDITIONS: Use of this record unit requires prior arrangement with the Archives staff.

(7254)

James O. Maloney Papers, 1925-1945
(0.1 linear meter).

James O. Maloney (1897- ?) was an Assistant Inspector for the State Plant Board of Mississippi. In 1923, Maloney was appointed Aid in the Division of Marine Invertebrates of the United States National Museum, a position he held until his resignation in 1945. Maloney's main zoological interest was the study of isopods.

This collection consists of a small amount of correspondence between Maloney and scientific colleagues including Kenneth Neff Dearolf, Ralph Warren Dexter, Stephen P. Hatchett, and Horton H. Hobbs, Jr. Most of the correspondence concerns Maloney's research on isopods.

ARRANGEMENT: Alphabetic. FINDING AIDS: None. SPECIAL CONDITIONS: Use of this record unit requires prior arrangement with the Archives staff.

(7293)

William M. Mann and Lucile Quarry Mann Papers, circa 1885-1981
(3.8 linear meters).

William M. Mann (1886-1960), entomologist and zoologist, was born in Helena, Montana. Mann received his B.A. degree from Stanford University in 1911 and his Sc.D. degree from Harvard University in 1915. Mann made several entomological collecting trips: as a member of the Stanford Expedition to Brazil (1911); to Haiti (1912); to Cuba and Mexico (1913); as a member of the Philip Expedition to the Middle East (1914); and as a Sheldon Traveling Fellow in Fiji and the Solomon Islands (1915-1916). Mann was an entomologist for the Bureau of Entomology, United States Department of Agriculture (USDA), 1916-1925; and served as an assistant director of the Mulford Biological Expedition to the Amazon Basin, 1921-1922.

Mann was appointed Superintendent of the National Zoological Park (NZP) in 1925, and served as Superintendent and Director of the Park until his retirement in 1956. Mann's major accomplishments at NZP included the Park's building program and his expeditions to collect live animals in order to increase the NZP population, notably: the Smithsonian-Chrysler Expedition to East Africa (1926); to British Guiana (1931); the National Geographic Society-Smithsonian Institution Expedition to the East Indies (1937); to Brazil and Argentina (1939); and the Smithsonian-Firestone Expedition to Liberia (1940). During World War II Mann served briefly as a Technical Observer for the Quartermaster Corps, United States Army, in the Pacific.

Lucile Quarry Mann (1897-1986) was born in Ann Arbor, Michigan, and received her B.A. from the University of Michigan in 1918. Lucile Quarry worked briefly for Military Intelligence; as an assistant editor for the Bureau of Entomology, USDA, in Washington, D.C.; and as an editor for *The Woman's Home Companion* in New York City. In 1926 Lucile Quarry married William Mann. As a zookeeper's wife, she traveled with her husband on his trips abroad, and helped raise many of the animals born at NZP in the Manns' apartment. From 1951 to 1971 Lucile Mann worked in the administrative offices of the NZP, and edited *Tiger Talk* and *Spots and Stripes*. A taped interview with Lucile Mann was made in 1977 as part of the Archives' Oral History Project. The tapes and transcript can be found in record unit 9513.

These papers document William Mann's early entomological collecting trips, as well as the Manns' experiences at the NZP, and on their travels abroad. Included are correspondence, photographs, motion picture film on Liberia (1940), typewritten manuscripts, printed materials, field notes and diaries, newspaper and journal articles, transcripts of radio talks and lectures, and William Mann's entomological monographs.

Also included in this collection is a report to the Quartermaster Corps when William Mann was Technical Observer; William Mann's collection of photographs of individuals, mostly entomologists; group photographs of the Manns with personal acquaintances; a scrapbook of newspaper articles on William Mann's autobiography, *Ant Hill Odyssey* (1948); and a photograph of Smithsonian officials and staff with President Calvin Coolidge, 1928.

ARRANGEMENT: (1) General correspondence, arranged alphabetically by correspondent, 1897-1972; (2) general correspondence, arranged alphabetically by subject, 1912-1972; (3) diaries and field notes, arranged chronologically, 1905-1940; (4) manuscripts; (5) personal documents; (6) lectures and radio talks, arranged by subject; (7) printed materials and book reviews written by or about the Manns; (8) printed materials collected by the Manns; (9) audiovisual materials. FINDING AIDS: Description in control file. SPECIAL CONDITIONS: Use of this record unit requires prior arrangement with the Archives staff.

(7086)

Otis Tufton Mason Papers, 1889-1900
(0.1 linear meter).

Otis Tufton Mason (1838-1908) was an ethnologist and museum expert. From 1884 he was Curator of Ethnology at the United States National Museum, and from 1902 he was Head Curator, Department of Anthropology.

These papers consist of copies of letters which Mason wrote back to the Smithsonian while on a trip in Europe to study museum practices, 1889; correspondence concerning his work on Central American ethnology, 1899-1900; and newspaper clippings collected by Mason concerning museums, 1890-1897.

ARRANGEMENT: Unarranged. FINDING AIDS: None. SPECIAL CONDITIONS: Use of this record unit requires prior arrangement with the Archives staff.

Rowland Robbins McElvare Papers, 1936-1967
(0.5 linear meter).

Rowland Robbins McElvare (1893-1976), an amateur lepidopterist, was born in Brooklyn, New York. He was graduated from Columbia College in 1913, and, after taking advanced degrees at Columbia University and Harvard, entered the banking profession in 1917. Two years later he married Lillian Adele Waring, with whom he spent the rest of his life. McElvare became prominent in the field of banking and finance, eventually rising to the position of Director of the Public National Bank and Trust Company of New York, as well as serving as President of the Savings and Loan Division of the American Banking Association. He was also a member of the faculty of the Graduate School of Banking.

McElvare's interest in lepidopterology had its beginnings early in his life under the guidance of George P. Englehardt of the Brooklyn Museum. In the mid-1930s, McElvare decided to focus his attention on the noctuid subfamily Heliothiinae, a day-flying moth, principally found in the Southwest, which hitherto had attracted little scholarly interest. He began compiling information on this variety of insect, a difficult task due to the lack of material. Few institutions held useful collections of Heliothiinae, and extensive field work was still needed to obtain complete specimen collections, as well as gathering data on the life cycle of Heliothids. McElvare, in the course of his studies, which were conducted after business hours until his retirement in 1953, assembled one of the most comprehensive collections of Heliothiinae extant, and in addition supplied type and paratype specimens to the United States National Museum and the British Museum (Natural History). During the period most heavily represented in this collection, 1940-1960, Rowland Robbins McElvare was the foremost American authority on Heliothiinae.

McElvare published numerous journal articles on his work, including several describing new species of Heliothiinae and on the synonymy of a species hitherto thought valid. The majority of his publications appeared in the *Journal of the Brooklyn Entomological Society,* of which he was President from 1945 to 1947.

This collection documents McElvare's activities in the field of lepidopterology. Of principal interest is the correspondence between McElvare and numerous amateur and professional lepidopterists, both in this country and abroad. These letters deal predominantly with insect collection and exchange, as well as the sharing of information on Heliothiinae and lepidopterology in general. McElvare took extensive notes on the species of Heliothiinae, drawn from personal examination of his collection, as well as his study of institutional collections throughout North America. These, and the transcripts of original descriptions of type insects found in classic works of lepidopterology, comprise the bulk of the remainder of the collection.

ARRANGEMENT: (1) Correspondence, 1936-1967; (2) notes on Heliothiinae; (3) publications, 1938-1966; (4) photographs. FINDING AIDS: Description in control file. SPECIAL CONDITIONS: Use of this record unit requires prior arrangement with the Archives staff.

Edgar Alexander Mearns Papers, circa 1871-1916, 1934 and undated
(3.5 linear meters).

Edgar Alexander Mearns (1856-1916) was an army surgeon and field naturalist. He developed an early interest in natural history, studying the flora and fauna around his home in Highland Falls, New York. Mearns was educated at Donald Highland Institute, Highland Falls, and in 1881 graduated from the College of Physicians and Surgeons of New York. In 1883, he was commissioned Assistant Surgeon in the Medical Corps of the U. S. Army and assigned to duty at Fort Verde, Arizona. He was transferred to Fort Snelling, Minnesota, in 1888. In 1891, Mearns was assigned to serve as Medical Officer with the survey conducted by the United States-Mexican International Boundary Commission. From 1892 to 1894, Mearns explored the boundary line from El Paso, Texas, to San Clemente Island and collected 30,000 specimens of flora and fauna which were deposited in the United States National Museum (USNM). From 1894 to 1903, Mearns continued his natural history investigations while stationed at Fort Myer, Virginia; Fort Clark, Texas; Fort Adams, Rhode Island; and Fort Yellowstone. He also conducted field research in the Catskill Mountains and Florida during this period. Between 1903 and 1907, Mearns served two separate tours of duty in the Philippine Islands. While in the Philippines he made natural history collections and participated in expeditions to the three highest mountains in the islands, Mount Apo, Grand Malindang, and Mount Halcon. After returning to the United States, Mearns served at Fort Totten, New York, until his retirement from the Army on January 1, 1909. Later that year, he was invited by Theodore Roosevelt to accompany the Smithsonian-Roosevelt African Expedition as naturalist. From 1909 to 1910, Mearns explored parts of British East Africa from Mount Kenya to the White Nile. Mearns' last expedition was in 1911, when he served as a naturalist with the Childs Frick Expedition to Africa.

Mearns' primary biological interests were ornithology and mammalogy. He was a founding member of the American Ornithologists' Union and in 1909 was appointed Honorary Associate in Zoology of the USNM.

This collection documents Mearns' career as a field naturalist and expedition member and consists of correspondence, 1898-1909, including copies of letters written by Mearns while he served on the Smithsonian-Roosevelt African Expedition of 1909; biographical material on Mearns and his family; field notes, research notes, specimen lists, photographs, and related materials concerning Mearns' field work, 1871-1911; correspondence, photographs, drawings, and research data regarding Mearns' work on the United States-Mexican International Boundary Survey, *circa* 1891-1907; and correspondence, notebooks, newspaper clippings, and research materials concerning his survey of the mammals of Rhode Island, *circa* 1899-1902.

ARRANGEMENT: (1) General correspondence, 1898-1909 and undated; (2) biographical material, 1879, 1885-1900, 1934; (3) field notes, research notes, specimen lists, manuscripts, and reprints, 1871-1911 and undated; (4) United States-Mexican International Boundary Survey, 1892-1894, correspondence, photographs, drawings, and research data on mammals, *circa* 1891-1907; (5) correspondence, notebooks, newspaper clippings, and research materials concerning the mammals of Rhode Island, *circa* 1899-1902; (6) field notes, *circa* 1872-1903. FINDING AIDS: Description in control file. SPECIAL CONDITIONS: (1) Check finding aid for location; (2) use of this record unit requires prior arrangement with the Archives staff.

Fielding B. Meek Papers, 1843-1877 and undated
(1.3 linear meters).

Fielding B. Meek (1817-1876), paleontologist, joined the staff of the Smithsonian in 1858 and was eventually made Resident Collaborator in Paleontology, a position he held until his death. While at the Smithsonian, he continued his earlier association with Ferdinand Vandeveer Hayden and other leading geologists and paleontologists.

These papers consist of correspondence, mostly incoming, concerning specimens and geological observations; notebooks and diaries resulting from field work; manuscripts and original plate illustrations; and miscellaneous personal papers.

ARRANGEMENT: (1) Incoming and outgoing correspondence, 1849-1876; (2) manuscripts and related papers, 1865-1876 and undated; (3) miscellany, 1843-1876 and undated; (4) notebooks and diaries, 1846-1875. FINDING AIDS: Description in control file. SPECIAL CONDITIONS: Use of this record unit requires prior arrangement with the Archives staff.

Axel Leonard Melander Notes and Manuscript, undated
(0.1 linear meter).

Axel Leonard Melander (1878-1962) was born in Illinois. He developed an interest in insects together with his friend, Charles T. Brues, and both studied entomology at the University of Texas. From 1904 to 1926, he taught entomology at the University of Washington and then moved to the College of the City of New York, where he remained until his retirement in 1943. Melander worked in both pure and applied entomology and gathered a large collection of Diptera, now in the Smithsonian.

This collection consists of notes and a preliminary manuscript on Empidid flies by Melander.

ARRANGEMENT: Notes and manuscript on Empidid flies. FINDING AIDS: None. SPECIAL CONDITIONS: Use of this record unit requires prior arrangement with the Archives staff.

Clinton Levi Merriam Papers, circa 1848-1899
(0.4 linear meter).

Clinton Levi Merriam (1824-1900) was born in Leyden, New York. After attending Copenhagen Academy in Copenhagen, New York, he entered business as a merchant in Utica, New York. In 1847 he moved to New York City and became an importer, and in 1860, entered banking. While in New York City, he married Caroline Hart in 1850. In 1864, Merriam returned to Leyden, having retired from business early. He had a mansion built in Locust Grove, Lewis County, New York; and it was here that his son, Clinton Hart Merriam, the naturalist, grew up and had his original medical practice. From 1871 to 1875, the elder Merriam served two terms in Congress as a Republican from New York. He died on a trip to Washington, D.C., February 18, 1900.

This record unit contains journals kept by Clinton Levi Merriam from 1848 to 1899. These journals contain diary entries, poems, copies of letters, speeches, political writings, expense accounts, and clippings from newspapers. In many cases, the clippings have been pasted over a written entry. The record unit also contains a photograph album containing prints of family members, associates, and reproductions of paintings.

ARRANGEMENT: Chronologic. FINDING AIDS: Description in control file. SPECIAL CONDITIONS: Use of this record unit requires prior arrangement with the Archives staff.

(7177)

George P. Merrill Collection, circa 1800-1930 and undated
(3.6 linear meters).

George P. Merrill (1854-1929) was Curator of Geology in the United States National Museum from 1897 until his death.

This collection of photographs and autographs was assembled by Merrill in connection with his two works on the history of American geology, "Contributions to the History of American Geology" (*Report of the United States National Museum for 1904,* pp. 189-733), and *The First One Hundred Years of American Geology,* 1924. Many of the photographs and portraits in this collection appear in one of those two works. In addition, the collection contains many photographs and portraits of Merrill's contemporaries in the Smithsonian Institution and the geological sciences. A number of autographs appear to have been removed from official Smithsonian files. The collection contains a great deal of correspondence to James Hall, Ferdinand Vandeveer Hayden, and George P. Merrill.

ARRANGEMENT: (1) Photographs and correspondence of individual geologists, scientists, and Smithsonian staff, *circa* 1800-1920; (2) group photographs, *circa* 1860-1930; (3) photographs of the United States Geological and Geographical Survey of the Territories, *circa* 1871-1877; (4) photographs of geology and natural history subjects; (5) photographs of Washington, D.C., buildings; (6) general correspondence, 1885-1929 and undated. FINDING AIDS: (1) Description in control file; (2) all autographs are indexed by author and recipient in Smithsonian Archives' computer index. SPECIAL CONDITIONS: Use of this record unit requires prior arrangement with the Archives staff.

(7064)

Metropolitan Mechanics Institute, 1852-1857
Minutes (0.1 linear meter).

The Metropolitan Mechanics Institute was founded in 1852 in Washington, D.C. The Institute held its meetings at the Smithsonian Institution.

ARRANGEMENT: Chronologic. FINDING AIDS: None. SPECIAL CONDITIONS: (1) Binding may prevent photocopying; (2) use of this record unit requires prior arrangement with the Archives staff.

(7173)

Gerrit Smith Miller, Jr., Papers, 1908-1940
(0.5 linear meter).

Gerrit Smith Miller, Jr., (1869-1956) was born in Peterboro, New York, and grew up on a large estate in central New York. In this relatively isolated setting and through the influence of his great uncle, an ornithologist, Miller developed an early interest in natural history. Following his graduation from Harvard in 1894, Miller joined the Biological Survey in the Department of Agriculture and worked under Clinton Hart Merriam. In

1898 he joined the United States National Museum as Assistant Curator of Mammals and in 1909 became Curator of that Division. He continued in that position until 1940 when he retired and remained as an Associate in biology at the Smithsonian Institution until his death.

Miller's major contributions to mammalogy were his series of checklists of North American mammals, 1901, 1912, and 1924; "The Families and Genera of Bats," 1907; and the *Catalogue of the Mammals of Western Europe in the collection of the British Museum,* 1912. He also was an early critic of the discovery of the Piltdown Man in England. He published several papers on the controversy and corresponded with many of the principal investigators. Another of his fields of interest was primate behavioral patterns and their possible influence on the beginnings of human social development.

Miller's papers include personal material concerning awards and his investigation of Christian Science; material on mammalogical research including extensive correspondence with Michael Rogers Oldfield Thomas of the British Museum; and material on Miller's research with primates, especially the Piltdown Man and primate behavioral patterns.

ARRANGEMENT: (1) Personal correspondence, photographs, and related material, 1914, 1918, 1922-1929, 1934; (2) correspondence and manuscripts concerning mammalogy, 1908-1924, 1927-1930, 1933; (3) correspondence, notes, photographs, manuscripts, and related materials concerning primates, 1914-1919, 1929-1940. FINDING AIDS: Description in control file. SPECIAL CONDITIONS: Use of this record unit requires prior arrangement with the Archives staff.

(7336)

John W. Mills Photograph Collection, circa 1904-1939
(0.1 linear meter).

John W. Mills (1876-1952) was chief engineer at the Marine Biological Laboratory of the Carnegie Institution of Washington at Tortugas, Florida, from 1904 to 1939.

This collection consists of photographs of the Laboratory and the Dry Tortugas Islands. Included are photographs of laboratory facilities, research vessels, Fort Jefferson, Bird Key, and Loggerhouse Lighthouse. Several of the photographs show the effects of a 1919 hurricane on laboratory facilities.

ARRANGEMENT: Unarranged. FINDING AIDS: None. SPECIAL CONDITIONS: Use of this record unit requires prior arrangement with the Archives staff.

(7386)

Carl W. Mitman Papers, 1937-1946, 1949
(0.3 linear meter).

Carl W. Mitman (1889-1958) received his B. A. from Lehigh University in 1909 and his M. A. from Princeton University in 1912. He joined the United States National Museum (USNM) in 1914 as an Aid in the Division of Mineral Technology. Mitman held a succession of curatorial positions at the USNM, culminating with his selection as Head Curator of the Department of Arts and Industries in 1932. From 1942 to 1944, he served as Chairman of the Smithsonian War Committee which was established to explore ways in which the Institution could make its scientific resources available to the military community. In 1948, Mitman was appointed Assistant to the Secretary for the National Air Museum where he remained until his retirement in 1952.

These papers primarily document Mitman's role as Chairman of the Smithsonian War Committee. They include correspondence, memoranda, meeting minutes, reports, and related materials concerning activities and projects of the Committee. Also included are papers documenting Mitman's involvement with several projects including the National Resources Committee, National Youth Administration, and Interdepartmental Committee on Cooperation with the American Republics; photographs of an exhibition on the Smithsonian and its work held in the Smithsonian Institution Building in 1941; and photographs of the Canal Zone Biological Area in 1949.

ARRANGEMENT: (1) Smithsonian War Committee files, 1942-1945; (2) subject files, 1937-1942, 1946, 1949. FINDING AIDS: Description in control file. SPECIAL CONDITIONS: Use of this record unit requires prior arrangement with the Archives staff.

(7345)

Basil Elwood Montgomery Papers, 1928-1955
(0.1 linear meter).

Basil Elwood Montgomery (1899-1983) was an entomologist and authority on dragonflies. He spent most of his professional career as a faculty member at Purdue University. Montgomery donated a large collection of dragonflies to the National Museum of Natural History.

This collection documents Montgomery's research on dragonflies and the building of his collection. Included is correspondence with entomologists and collectors, mostly concerning the acquisition of specimens; a catalog of his dragonfly collection; and notes from his research.

ARRANGEMENT: Unarranged. FINDING AIDS: None. SPECIAL CONDITIONS: Use of this record unit requires prior arrangement with the Archives staff.

(7265)

John Percy Moore Papers, 1888-1965 and undated
(1 linear meter).

John Percy Moore (1869-1965) was a university professor and world recognized authority on leeches. He was educated at the University of Pennsylvania, B.S., 1892, and Ph.D., 1896. His teaching career began in 1890, when he was appointed Assistant Instructor of Zoology at the University of Pennsylvania. He was promoted to Instructor in 1892, Assistant Professor in 1907, and Professor in 1912. In 1939 he became Emeritus Professor. Moore was also an Assistant Curator and Corresponding Secretary for the Academy of Natural Sciences of Philadelphia from 1902 to 1939 and a member of the Board of Trustees from 1938 to 1957. In 1957 he was made an Honorary Life Trustee of the Academy.

Moore's primary zoological interest was the study of leeches and their biological control. He conducted field research in India during 1930-1931 to study the life history of Indian land leeches. His association with the United States National Museum (USNM) began in the early 1900s when he started identifying specimens in the Museum's leech collection. In recognition of his work he was appointed Honorary Collaborator in the Division of Marine Invertebrates, USNM, in 1930. On his death in 1965, Moore's collection of leeches was donated to the USNM.

The papers of John Percy Moore document his research on leeches. They include correspondence concerning the identification of specimens, his field research on Indian land leeches, and his work on the biological control of leeches. Also included are research notes, photographs, field notes, drawings, specimen lists, and manuscripts from his study of leeches.

ARRANGEMENT: (1) General correspondence, 1906-1965 and undated; (2) research notes, field notes, drawings, photographs, and related materials on leeches, 1888-1916 and undated. FINDING AIDS: Description in control file. SPECIAL CONDITIONS: Use of this record unit requires prior arrangement with the Archives staff.

(7376)

Joseph P. E. Morrison Papers, 1923-1973 and undated
(0.4 linear meter).

Joseph P. E. Morrison (1906-1983), a malacologist, was born in South Bend, Indiana. He was interested in zoology from his early childhood and spent much of his spare time collecting animals near his home. He graduated from the University of Chicago in 1926 and earned his M.S. (1929) and Ph.D. (1931) from the University of Wisconsin. Before joining the Smithsonian, he worked as a researcher for the Illinois State Museum, the Mount Desert Island (Maine) Biological Survey, and the Wisconsin State Natural History Survey. He began his career with the Division of Mollusks, United States National Museum (USNM), in 1934 as a Senior Scientific Aid. He was made Assistant Curator in 1942 and Associate Curator in 1946, a post he retained until his retirement in 1975.

While at the USNM, Morrison also did research for the Army Chemical Warfare Service in San Jose, Panama, in 1944. He participated in both the Crossroads Operation and the Bikini Scientific Resurvey research of the atomic bomb test sites in the Marshall Islands in 1946 and 1947. He was a consultant on medical and veterinary issues for the United States Department of Agriculture, the National Institutes of Health and the United States Fish and Wildlife Service, as well as acting as an adviser to colleagues and students.

The largest portion of Morrison's papers consists of professional correspondence, written and received between 1923 and 1973. It documents his research interests and the extent of his influence as an adviser and research editor to students and colleagues worldwide in malacological matters. In addition there are small groups of letters, notes and other materials that relate to Morrison's expeditions and his special interest in specimen collecting equipment and methods. Also included are research notes and information he collected which show the breadth of his interests. Although some of Morrison's expeditions and advisory work are not completely documented, the papers are representative of most of his interests and expertise.

ARRANGEMENT: (1) General correspondence, 1923-1973 and undated; (2) publications and related materials, 1938-1940, 1945-1961, 1967-1972 and undated; (3) specimen collecting equipment records, 1944-1969; (4) expeditions, 1944-1966; (5) biographical information, 1927-1963; (6) research and professional materials, 1926, 1942-1973 and undated. FINDING AIDS: Description in control file. SPECIAL CONDITIONS: Use of this record unit requires prior arrangement with Archives staff.

Conrad Vernon Morton Papers, 1917-1972 and undated

(0.9 linear meter).

Conrad Vernon Morton (1905-1972), a botanist and authority on ferns, came to the Smithsonian in 1928 as an aide in the Division of Plants, United States National Museum (USNM). He was promoted to Assistant Curator in 1938 and Associate Curator in 1946. In 1948 he was appointed Curator of the newly established Division of Ferns, Department of Botany. Morton was made Senior Botanist in 1970, a position he retained until his death. He also served in several editorial positions for the *American Fern Journal.*

These papers document Morton's professional career and include correspondence regarding curatorial duties at the USNM, research on ferns, and editorial work for the *American Fern Journal;* records concerning field trips to Cuba, the West Indies, Honduras, and Europe; photographs of and biographical information on Morton; and manuscripts and research notes, especially documenting his work on the flora of Cuba.

ARRANGEMENT: (1) General correspondence, 1917-1972; (2) travel file, 1941-1964; (3) biographical file and photographs, 1939-1972 and undated; (4) manuscripts and research notes, undated. FINDING AIDS: None. SPECIAL CONDITIONS: Use of this record unit requires prior arrangement with the Archives staff.

Robert P. Multhauf Papers, circa 1957-1987

(2.9 linear meters).

Robert P. Multhauf (1919-), historian of science, was born in Sioux City, South Dakota. He graduated from Iowa State University, B.S., 1941, and received his M.A., 1950, and Ph.D., 1953, from the University of California at Berkeley. Multhauf was employed by the Smithsonian Institution as Associate Curator for the Division of Engineering, United States National Museum (USNM), in 1954. The following year he became Curator of the Division and in 1957 was appointed Head Curator of the Department of Engineering and Industries at USNM. When USNM was reorganized and the Museum of History and Technology (MHT) established in 1957, Multhauf became Head Curator for the Department of Science and Technology under MHT. He also served as Acting Curator of the Division of Physical Sciences within the Department.

In 1966, Multhauf was appointed Director of MHT and served in this capacity until 1969, the year MHT was renamed the National Museum of History and Technology (NMHT). Afterwards he became Senior Scientific Scholar of the Department of Science and Technology, 1970-1977, and for the Department of the History of Science, 1978-1979, at NMHT. Multhauf joined the staff of the Office of Senior Historians in 1980, when NMHT was renamed the National Museum of American History, and retired from the Smithsonian Institution in 1987.

These papers consist largely of correspondence documenting Multhauf's participation in various national and international organizations, most notably the American Council of Learned Societies, History of Science Society, International Union of the History and Philosophy of Science, National Air and Space Administration Historical Committee, Society for the History of Technology, and American Federation of Information Processing Societies. In addition there are manuscripts of published and unpublished articles; copies of major publications including *The Origins of Chemistry* and *A History of Common Salt;* research notes; photographs of Multhauf at symposiums; and records pertaining to *Isis,* for which Multhauf was Editor.

ARRANGEMENT: Alphabetic. FINDING AIDS: Folder list in control file. SPECIAL CONDITIONS: Use of this record unit requires prior arrangement with the Archives staff.

(7266)

William Roger Murchie Papers, 1954-1967 and undated
(0.4 linear meter).

William Roger Murchie (1920-1968) was a biology professor and authority on earthworms. He was educated at Marietta College, A.B., 1942, and the University of Michigan, M.A., 1948, and Ph.D., 1954. His teaching career began at Marietta College where he served as Instructor of Biology, 1946-1950. In 1954, he was appointed Associate Professor of Biology at Thiel College, where he remained until 1956 when he accepted the position of Assistant Professor of Biology at Flint College, University of Michigan. The rest of his career was spent at Flint College where he was promoted to Associate Professor in 1958 and Professor in 1962. Murchie specialized in the study of the ecology and systematics of earthworms. After his death in 1968, Murchie's collection of earthworms was given to the National Museum of Natural History.

These papers document Murchie's research on earthworms and include manuscripts and related materials regarding the preparation and publication of manuscripts and records concerning earthworm collections made by Murchie.

ARRANGEMENT: (1) Manuscripts and related materials, 1954-1967 and undated; (2) collecting records, 1954-1967. FINDING AIDS: Description in control file. SPECIAL CONDITIONS: Use of this record unit requires prior arrangement with the Archives staff.

(7203)

John Murdoch Journals, 1881-1883
(2 items).

John Murdoch (1852-1925) served as naturalist on the International Polar Expedition to Point Barrow, Alaska, 1881-1883. From 1887 to 1892, Murdoch served as Librarian of the Smithsonian Institution.

This collection consists of two journals containing data on natural history and ethnological collections made by the Point Barrow Polar Expedition, 1881-1883.

ARRANGEMENT: (1) Record of collections made by the Point Barrow Polar Expedition, 1881-1883; (2) catalog of fishes and mammals, Point Barrow Polar Expedition, 1881-1883. FINDING AIDS: None. SPECIAL CONDITIONS: Use of this record unit requires prior arrangement with the Archives staff.

(7432)

Museum Computer Network, 1967-1988
Records (11.5 linear meters).

The Museum Computer Network promotes the use of computer technology by museums. It was established in 1967 by a consortium of New York City museums. In its early years it focused on the development of an object-cataloging database system called *Griphos.* This system was designed to enable creation of a union catalog of museum objects. In 1972 the consortium was incorporated into the non-profit Museum Computer Network (MCN), headed by David Vance. Until 1978 MCN functioned as a *Griphos* users group, but by then *Griphos* had become obsolete and MCN opened itself up to users of other computer systems. In 1985 Ron Kley became President and Acting Executive Director. Kley held those positions until 1988, when Deirdre Stam became Executive Director.

These records contain the administrative files kept primarily by David Vance, Ron Kley, and Deirdre Stam. The records concern the daily operations of MCN including preparation of the journal *Spectra;* planning for annual conferences and workshops; correspondence; grant proposals; annual reports; materials concerning *Griphos,* membership surveys; and publications concerning computerization.

ARRANGEMENT: Unarranged. FINDING AIDS: Folder list in control file. SPECIAL CONDITIONS: Use of this record unit requires prior arrangement with the Archives staff.

(7295)

Museum Education Roundtable, 1970-1982
Records (1.3 linear meters).

Education personnel at the Smithsonian Institution founded the Museum Education Roundtable (MER) in 1970 as a consortium of local museum educators. Today MER is an independent, non-profit, educational corporation which seeks to promote communication between museum personnel and local educators, further the use of museums and cultural institutions as educational resources, and develop educational services in museums and other public institutions. Regular meetings supplemented by workshops are also concerned with the creation of cooperative museum-school projects, and improving communication between educators in museums and schools by keeping members informed of programs available in the area, as well as professional museum education staff development. As a volunteer organization, MER seeks financial support through subscriptions to its quarterly newsletter, *Roundtable Reports,* and membership dues. Initial funding came from National Endowment for the Arts and National Endowment for the Humanities grants.

An elected board of directors governs MER. Their responsibilities include transforming the organization's goals into programs and obtaining funding. Chairs of the MER board have included: Tom Radford, 1971-1973; Sue Hoth, 1973-1975; Donna Ari, 1975-1977; Barbara Fertig, 1977-1979; Kenneth Yellis, 1979-1981; Susan L. Nichols, 1981-1982; and Schroeder J. Cherry, 1982-   . Membership information and surveys, minutes of board meetings, and membership materials are included in these MER records, as are workshop materials and funding proposals.

The Museum Education Roundtable promotes communication between the museum and education communities both nationally and locally through its publications. Through *Roundtable Reports* MER provides its members and other subscribers with information about national trends in museum education, recent developments in the profession, and nationally available resources such as other museum education organizations and their seminars, workshops, and committees. A nearly complete set of *Roundtable Reports,*

1973, 1975-1980, is part of this record unit as are manuscripts, layouts, and paste-ups for recent issues.

Another MER publication, the *Directory of Educational Opportunities in the Washington Area,* has had three editions, 1971-1973. Through the *Directory* readers learn about field trips and educational resources in the District of Columbia area. Other flyers and brochures are also part of the MER archives.

ARRANGEMENT: (1) Meeting materials, 1970-1979; (2) publications, 1972-1982; (3) grants, 1973-1979. FINDING AIDS: Preliminary inventory in control file. SPECIAL CONDITIONS: (1) The Smithsonian Archives has been designated as the official depository for the archives of the Museum Education Roundtable; (2) use of this record unit requires prior arrangement with the Archives staff.

(7317)

George Sprague Myers Papers, circa 1903-1986 and undated
(9.5 linear meters).

George Sprague Myers (1905-1985), ichthyologist, herpetologist, and university professor, received his Ph.D. degree from Stanford University in 1933. The same year he began his professional career when he was appointed Assistant Curator in charge of the Division of Fishes, United States National Museum. In 1936, Myers returned to Stanford when he was appointed Associate Professor of Biology and Curator of Zoological Collections in the Natural History Museum. By 1938 he had been promoted to Professor. He remained in the position until his retirement in 1970.

Myers' primary research interest was systematic ichthyology. A prolific writer and editor, his bibliography included over six hundred titles concerning reptiles, biogeography, and the history of science, as well as fishes. Myers participated on several scientific expeditions including the 1947 Bikini Scientific Resurvey. He served as President of the American Society of Ichthyologists and Herpetologists (ASIH) from 1947 to 1949.

The papers of George Sprague Myers document his research career in ichthyology and herpetology; his teaching career at Stanford University; professional activities, especially with the ASIH; expeditions and field work; and his work as an author and editor. Included are a large file of incoming and outgoing correspondence relating to all aspects of his career; manuscripts and speeches (many of which are unpublished); notes, illustrations, and related materials generated during his research; correspondence, classroom materials, and administrative records from his teaching career; collected materials relating to his family history, education, professional career, and personal affairs; photographs of and collected by Myers; and diplomas, certificates, and awards presented to him.

ARRANGEMENT: (1) General correspondence, 1903, 1920-1984 and undated, with related materials to 1986; (2) published manuscripts, 1924-1978; (3) unpublished manuscripts and speeches, *circa* 1927-1980 and undated; (4) teaching and professional files, 1927-1970 and undated; (5) research materials, undated; (6) collected personal and professional materials, *circa* 1915-1970 and undated; (7) photographs, 1922-1970 and undated; (8) diplomas, certificates, and awards, 1930-1984 and undated; (9) add acquisition, 1912-1978 and undated. FINDING AIDS: Description in control file. SPECIAL CONDITIONS: Use of this record unit requires prior arrangement with the Archives staff.

National Academy of Sciences, 1863-1887
Records (0.1 linear meter).

The National Academy of Sciences, founded in Washington, D. C., in 1863, grew out of a desire for a body of scientists to give advice on scientific matters to the federal government. Joseph Henry, first Secretary of the Smithsonian, was a force behind its creation.

These records of the National Academy of Sciences include accounts of grants from the Bache Fund; general fund accounts; correspondence and other documents regarding the James Watson Fund; printed constitution and by-laws; a few lists of members and papers read; a small amount of material on research for the government by Academy members, especially the whiskey meter; and documents relating to major gifts to the Academy. This collection was retained with the Joseph Henry Papers until 1973.

ARRANGEMENT: Unarranged. FINDING AIDS: None. SPECIAL CONDITIONS: Use of this record unit requires prior arrangement with the Archives staff.

National Institute, 1839-1863 and undated
Records (2.4 linear meters).

The National Institute was first organized as the National Institution for the Promotion of Science at Washington, D. C., in 1840. It was chartered by Congress in 1842 and called the National Institute for the Promotion of Science thereafter until its dissolution in 1862.

The Institute was probably formed with a view to gaining control of the Smithson bequest. This hope was frustrated with the creation of the Smithsonian Institution in 1846, and the Institute never succeeded in getting government financing, even though it exercised an informal curatorship of various government scientific collections for a time in 1841 and 1842. Even though the Institute numbered such powerful figures as Joel Roberts Poinsett among its members and supporters, its case grew worse with passing years—no space, no money, few and indifferent members. After a flurry of activity in connection with organizing the United States' participation in the Great Exhibition at London in 1851, it sank into a final decline and gave up the remainder of its collections to the Smithsonian in 1862.

These records, mostly 1840-1844, concern the founding and operation of the National Institute by Joel Roberts Poinsett, Peter Force, John James Abert, Francis Markoe, Jr., and others. Efforts to obtain federal subsidies, to provide space for its collections, and to gather support from the general scientific community occupied most of this time. There are also some records dealing with the Institute's care for a part of the collections of the United States Exploring Expedition.

ARRANGEMENT: (1) Incoming correspondence, 1839-1863 and undated; (2) outgoing correspondence, 1840-1855, 1857 and undated; (3) minutes and reports, 1840-1856; (4) records of the United States Exploring Expedition, 1839-1854; (5) ledgers and account books, 1840-1858; (6) accessions, 1840-1848, 1853-1854, 1857 and undated; (7) bills, 1841, 1843-1845, 1851-1853, 1857; (8) miscellany; (9) publications; (10) oversize, 1843-1853. FINDING AIDS: Description in control file. SPECIAL CONDITIONS: Use of this record unit requires prior arrangement with the Archives staff.

Edward William Nelson and Edward Alphonso Goldman Collection, circa 1873-1946 and undated

(5.6 linear meters).

Edward William Nelson (1855-1934), explorer, naturalist, and science administrator, was born in Manchester, New Hampshire. His professional career began in 1877 when he was appointed weather observer in the Signal Corps of the United States Army. From June 1877 to June 1881 Nelson was stationed at St. Michael on the Bering Sea coast of Alaska, where he made several excursions around the region compiling data on the lives and customs of the native people, and making ethnological and natural history collections for the Smithsonian Institution. In June 1881, he accompanied the revenue steamer *Corwin* on its search for the missing arctic ship *Jeannette.* The expedition was the first to reach and explore Wrangell Island.

In 1890, Nelson began a career with the Bureau of Biological Survey of the United States Department of Agriculture when he accepted appointment as a Special Field Agent with the Death Valley Expedition under the direction of Clinton Hart Merriam. Most of the period from 1892 to 1906 was spent conducting biological investigations in Mexico with Edward Alphonso Goldman. The pair collected nearly 30,000 mammals and birds, and amassed an enormous wealth of information on the natural history of Mexico. After concluding his work in Mexico, Nelson's duties with the Bureau of Biological Survey gradually shifted from scientific to administrative. He was Chief Field Naturalist, 1907-1912; Assistant in Charge of Biological Investigations, 1913-1914; Assistant Chief, 1914-1916; Chief, 1916-1927; and Senior Biologist, 1927-1929. Nelson was also a Research Associate of the Smithsonian Institution from 1930 until his death.

Nelson was a prolific author and his bibliography included over 200 titles, mostly concerning birds and mammals. He was President of the American Ornithologists' Union, 1908-1909; the Biological Society of Washington, 1912-1913; and the American Society of Mammalogists, 1920-1923. Nelson received an honorary M.A. from Yale University in 1920, and an honorary Doctor of Science from The George Washington University in the same year. He was also an owner and director of fruit orchard businesses in California and Arizona.

Edward Alphonso Goldman (1873-1946), field naturalist and mammalogist, was born in Mount Carroll, Illinois, and moved with his family to Tulare County, California, in 1888. In 1892, he was hired by Edward William Nelson to assist his field investigations in California and Mexico. Thus, Goldman began a career with the Bureau of Biological Survey that would continue for the remainder of his life. He served in a variety of positions including Field Naturalist, 1902-1917; Biologist in Charge, Division of Biological Investigations, 1919-1925; Biologist in Charge, Game and Bird Reservations, 1925-1928; and Senior Biologist, Division of Biological Investigations, 1928-1943. His career was interrupted during World War I when he served as Major in the Sanitary Corps of the American Expeditionary Force, in charge of rodent control in France. Goldman also had an honorary position with the Smithsonian Institution as Associate in Zoology from 1928 to 1946.

Goldman's research was primarily on mammals, and his bibliography included more than 200 titles. He conducted faunal studies as part of the Biological Survey of Panama during construction of the canal in 1911-1912. In 1936, Goldman was chosen to assist the United States Government in negotiations with Mexico for the protection of migratory birds and game mammals.

This collection consists primarily of papers documenting the professional career and personal life of Edward William Nelson. A smaller amount of material was created by Edward Alphonso Goldman and relates to both professional and private matters. Nelson's papers are valuable in documenting his work as a field naturalist, particularly in Alaska and Mexico; his administrative career with the Bureau of Biological Survey; his research on birds and mammals; professional activities; and personal and business matters. They include a large file of incoming and outgoing correspondence which documents all aspects of his professional career; journals and notebooks maintained during field work and other official travel, especially his explorations in Alaska and Mexico; correspondence and related records concerning family and business matters, particularly his involvement in the fruit orchard business; and notes, lists, newspaper clippings, manuscripts, and photographs relating to his research and his interest in conservation issues of the era.

Goldman's papers found in this collection are just a fragment of those generated during his long career. They include journals from his field investigations in Mexico with Nelson; correspondence with Nelson and family members; and notes, lists, manuscripts, and related materials documenting his research on mammals.

The collection contains photographs, photograph albums, and glass plate negatives documenting the careers of both men. Included are photographs taken during their Mexico field work, portraits, photographs of colleagues, and images taken in France during Goldman's service in World War I. The collection also includes correspondence, manuscripts, photographs, and related materials of the conservationist Charles Sheldon, and an annotated manuscript by George Shiras III on wildlife photography.

ARRANGEMENT: (1) Professional correspondence of Edward William Nelson, 1878-1934 and undated; (2) journals and notebooks of Edward William Nelson, 1877-1933 and undated; (3) personal and business records of Edward William Nelson, 1886-1933 and undated; (4) research files of Edward William Nelson, 1893-1931 and undated; (5) journals and field notes of Edward Alphonso Goldman, 1891-1925; (6) correspondence of Edward Alphonso Goldman, 1906-1946; (7) research files of Edward Alphonso Goldman, 1912, 1940-1941 and undated; (8) photographic materials, *circa* 1873-1926 and undated; (9) Charles Sheldon Papers, 1905-1928 and undated; (10) George Shiras III manuscript, *circa* 1906-1931. FINDING AIDS: Description in control file. SPECIAL CONDITIONS: Use of this record unit requires prior arrangement with the Archives staff.

(7200)

New England Fishing Schooner Logbooks, 1852-1862
(0.8 linear meter).

This collection consists of 112 logbooks maintained by various New England fishing schooners during voyages conducted from 1852 to 1862. The logbooks contain data regarding weather conditions, number of fish caught, and, to a lesser degree, types of fish caught.

ARRANGEMENT: Chronologic. FINDING AIDS: None. SPECIAL CONDITIONS: Use of this record unit requires prior arrangement with the Archives staff.

New England Glaciation Collection, circa 1893
Glass Plate Negatives (0.1 linear meter).

This collection consists of glass plate negatives depicting various aspects of glaciation in New England states. The negatives were used in the United States National Museum's geology exhibition at the World's Columbian Exposition, Chicago, 1893. Apparently, they were taken by William Otis Crosby and Oliver Cummings Farrington and purchased by the USNM for exhibition at Chicago.

ARRANGEMENT: Unarranged. FINDING AIDS: None. SPECIAL CONDITIONS: Use of this record unit requires prior arrangement with the Archives staff.

North Pacific Exploring Expedition Collection, 1852-1861 and undated
(0.3 linear meter).

The North Pacific Exploring Expedition, 1853-1856, was organized by the United States Navy Department "...for prosecuting a survey and reconnaissance, for naval and commercial purposes, of such parts of Bering Straits, of the North Pacific Ocean and the China Seas, as are frequented by American whale ships and by trading vessels in their routes between the United States and China." Captain Cadwallader Ringgold was placed in command of the expedition, which departed from Norfolk, Virginia, in June 1853. After Ringgold was recalled to the United States in 1854, Captain John Rogers assumed command for the remainder of the expedition. The expedition explored along the coasts of China and Japan, Madeira Island, the California coast, and Tahiti before returning via the Cape of Good Hope in 1856. Extensive natural history collections were made on the expedition, mostly by William Stimpson, Chief Zoologist. Other naturalists serving on the expedition included Alfred H. Ames, Assistant Naturalist, and Charles Wright, Botanist.

This collection documents the natural history work of the North Pacific Exploring Expedition and consists of correspondence and notes, manuscripts, and drawings by William Stimpson on the crustacea collections made on the expedition. Also included is Stimpson's journal of the expedition.

ARRANGEMENT: (1) Correspondence, 1852-1861 and undated; (2) notes, manuscripts, and drawings on crustacea by William Stimpson; (3) "Journal of a cruise in the U. S. Ship *Vincennes* to the North Pacific Ocean, China Seas, Behring Sts., etc. by William Stimpson, 1853-1855." FINDING AIDS: Description in control file. SPECIAL CONDITIONS: Use of this record unit requires prior arrangement with the Archives staff.

Paul Wilson Oman Papers, circa 1930-1972
(1.2 linear meters).

Paul Wilson Oman (1908-   ), an entomologist and specialist on leafhopper taxonomy, was educated at the University of Kansas (A.B., 1930; A.M., 1935) and the George Washington University (Ph.D., 1941). In 1930, Oman joined the United States Department of Agriculture (USDA) as a Junior Entomologist with the Bureau of

Entomology and Plant Quarantine. He remained with the USDA, in various research and administrative posts, until 1967 when he retired to join the faculty of Oregon State University. Oman served in the United States Army during World War II and the Korean War, conducting studies on medical entomology and the biological control of insects.

These papers consist of incoming and outgoing correspondence mostly documenting Oman's career as a research entomologist at the USDA and his study of leafhopper systematics. Most of the letters were exchanged between Oman and professional colleagues and concern the identification of specimens. Correspondence after 1950 was created primarily by David A. Young, Jr., and James P. Kramer, two USDA Homopterists who assumed responsibility for taxonomic studies after Oman's work became more administrative in nature.

ARRANGEMENT: Alphabetic. FINDING AIDS: Box list in control file. SPECIAL CONDITIONS: Use of this record unit requires prior arrangement with the Archives staff.

(7088)

Charles Russell Orcutt Papers, 1926-1929
(0.1 linear meter).

Charles Russell Orcutt (1864-1929) was a collector of natural history specimens and publisher of scientific journals. Orcutt's primary biological interests were malacology and botany, and he participated on collecting excursions to Baja California, Mexico, Central America, and the Caribbean. From 1927 until his death in 1929, Orcutt collected for the United States National Museum (USNM) in Jamaica and Haiti.

These papers consist primarily of material documenting Orcutt's collecting activity in Jamaica, 1927-1929. Included is correspondence with USNM staff and others regarding specimens collected, notes on Jamaican flora and fauna, and maps of Jamaica drawn by Orcutt.

ARRANGEMENT: (1) General correspondence, 1926-1929; (2) Jamaica notes and maps, 1927-1929. FINDING AIDS: Description in control file. SPECIAL CONDITIONS: Use of this record unit requires prior arrangement with the Archives staff.

(7387)

Henry Leslie Osborn Manuscript, circa 1879-1881
(0.1 linear meter).

Henry Leslie Osborn (1857-1940) was born in Newark, New Jersey. He received his A.B. from Wesleyan University in 1878, and the next year he became an agent with the United States Fish Commission. In 1881, Osborn returned to the classroom, and in 1884 he received his Ph.D. in zoology from the Johns Hopkins University. For the remainder of his career Osborn devoted himself to college life, first as a Professor of Zoology at Purdue University and later as Professor, Dean of the Faculty, and eventually Acting President of Hamline University.

This collection consists of portions of a manuscript written by Osborn while on board the *Victor,* a fishing vessel owned by Joseph O. Proctor, Jr., as an observer in the summer of 1879. The schooner set out from Gloucester, Massachusetts, and continued up the coast to fish off the banks of Newfoundland, Canada. Seven sections document the activities of the crew during their passage including the nationality of the crew, the crew at home, the routine of daily life on board, the routine of daily life while fishing off the banks, pastimes on board ship, the routine of life at baiting stations, and superstitions of the fishermen. A table of contents and list of illustrations are included, but the illustrations themselves are not contained in this copy of the manuscript. The manuscript was later published in sections IV and V of *The Fisheries and Fishery Industries of the United States* (1887) with John Templeman Brown as Associate Author and George Brown Goode as Editor.

ARRANGEMENT: Manuscript, *circa* 1879-1881. FINDING AIDS: Description in control file. SPECIAL CONDITIONS: Use of this record unit requires prior arrangement with the Archives staff.

(7246)

Raymond Carroll Osburn Papers, 1905-1955 and undated
(0.4 linear meter).

Raymond Carroll Osburn (1872-1955) received his B.S. (1898) and M.S. (1900) degrees from Ohio State University and his Ph.D. degree in 1906 from Columbia University. In 1898 Osburn was appointed Instructor of Biology and Embryology at Starling Medical College, and from 1899 to 1902 he was Professor of Biology at Fargo College. After studying at Columbia on a fellowship from 1902 to 1903, he taught at the New York High School of Commerce for four years. His other academic appointments included Assistant Professor of Zoology, 1907-1910, and Professor of Biology, 1910-1915, at Barnard College; Professor of Biology, 1915-1917, at Connecticut College for Women; and Professor of Zoology and Entomology and Entomology Department Chairman, 1917-1942, at Ohio State. In addition, he was Associate Director, 1910-1915, of the New York Aquarium; summer Director, 1918-1937, of the Franz Theodore Stone Laboratory of Ohio State; and Research Associate on Bryozoa, 1945-1952, at the Allan Hancock Foundation of the University of Southern California.

These papers consist of a small amount of Osburn's correspondence, research notes and drafts of publications on bryozoans, and original pen drawings of bryozoans.

ARRANGEMENT: (1) Correspondence, 1915, 1921, 1936, 1939, 1946, 1949 and undated; (2) research notes and drafts of publications, 1905-1949, 1955 and undated; (3) original pen drawings of bryozoans, undated. FINDING AIDS: Description in control file. SPECIAL CONDITIONS: Use of this record unit requires prior arrangement with the Archives staff.

(7425)

Paleontology and Stratigraphy Branch, United States Geological Survey, circa 1900-1987
Records (9.8 linear meters).

Paleontological studies were a part of the United States Geological Survey's (USGS) mission from its creation in 1879. The act establishing the USGS declared that fossils collected by the Survey be deposited in the United States National Museum (USNM) when no longer needed for investigations. As a result, several USGS paleontologists were stationed at the USNM, as honorary curators, to study and care for the collections. The main purpose of early paleontological work at the USGS was the identification and correlation of geologic formations by their fossil remains to aid geologists in delineating formations and making geologic maps.

As a result of a reorganization of the Geologic Branch, USGS, in 1900 the Division of Paleontology was established, with Timothy William Stanton as Paleontologist in Charge. Its name was changed to the Section of Paleontology in 1902, Section of Paleontology and Stratigraphy in *circa* 1907, and Paleontology and Stratigraphy Branch (P&S Branch) in 1949. Stanton remained in charge of USGS paleontological work until 1932. Other section or branch chiefs have included John B. Reeside, Jr., 1932-1949; Preston E. Cloud, Jr., 1949-1959; Charles W. Merriam, 1959-1962; J. Thomas Dutro, Jr., 1962-1968; Norman F. Sohl, 1968-1973; Joseph E. Hazel, 1973-1978; William V. Sliter, 1978-1983; Michael E. Taylor, 1983-1985; and Richard Z. Poore, 1985-   .

These records are the official files of the Branch Chief, Paleontology and Stratigraphy Branch, USGS, and document its research program and administration from 1900 to 1987. Included is a large amount of correspondence of the first two Branch Chiefs, Stanton and Reeside, which concerns the identification of specimens, field work of USGS paleontologists, the publication of scientific papers, professional activities, and administrative matters. The records also include a smaller amount of correspondence of Branch Chiefs Cloud, Merriam, and Dutro; outgoing correspondence of P&S Branch scientists documenting their research programs and professional activities; annual work plans and monthly reports of P&S Branch scientists; and correspondence concerning manuscripts submitted to the P&S Branch for publication.

ARRANGEMENT: Unarranged. FINDING AIDS: Box list in control file. SPECIAL CONDITIONS: (1) Restricted; (2) use of this record unit requires prior arrangement with the Archives staff.

(7327)

Section of Paleontology and Stratigraphy, United States Geological Survey, 1894-1956 and undated
Records (1.7 linear meters).

In 1907 the United States Geological Survey (USGS) established the Subsection of Coastal Plain Investigations within its Geologic Branch. In 1913 the name was changed to Section of Coastal Plain Investigations. The Section was responsible for the general study of the geology of the Atlantic and Gulf coastal plains of the United States. Subjects of its investigations included physiography, stratigraphy, geologic structure, paleontology, sedimentology, and ground waters. In 1936, as a part of a reorganization of the USGS, the Section was merged with the Section of Paleontology and Stratigraphy under the latter name.

T. Wayland Vaughan (1870-1952) was appointed Geologist in charge of coastal plain investigations in 1907. He remained in charge of the Section until 1923. Lloyd William Stephenson (1876-1962), who had served as Vaughan's assistant, was promoted to succeed him as Section Chief. Stephenson remained in the post until 1936 when the Section was abolished. From 1936 until his retirement in 1947, he served as a Geologist in the Section of Paleontology and Stratigraphy where he conducted research on Cretaceous paleontology at the United States National Museum (USNM). After his retirement, Stephenson continued his research at the USNM on a voluntary basis. Other geologists on the staff of the Section of Coastal Plain Investigations included C. Wythe

Cooke, 1910-1936; Julia A. Gardner, 1920-1936; Watson H. Monroe, 1930-1936; and Wendell P. Woodring, 1919-1936.

These records primarily document the official work of the Section of Coastal Plain Investigations, USGS. Also included are papers documenting the paleontological research and professional activities of Stephenson and Vaughan, as well as smaller amounts of records created by other staff geologists. Most of the collection consists of several series of correspondence. Included is general correspondence which primarily documents Stephenson's official and professional activities, 1913-1956; correspondence with paleontologists, state geologists, and economic geologists concerning surveys and other work of the Section, 1907-1945; letters concerning Vaughan's research on fossil corals, 1912-1933; and correspondence with paleontologists, museums, and universities concerning specimen-related issues, 1913-1946. The collection also contains records documenting Stephenson's work on the geological map of Texas, files concerning the examination of specimens submitted by Texas oil companies, administrative records of the Section, manuscripts written and reviewed by Stephenson, and collected geological charts.

ARRANGEMENT: (1) General correspondence, 1913-1956 and undated; (2) correspondence concerning Atlantic and Gulf coast investigations, 1907-1945 and undated; (3) correspondence concerning coral research of T. Wayland Vaughan, 1912-1933; (4) specimen-related correspondence, 1913-1946; (5) Texas map project records, 1931-1935 and undated; (6) Texas well records, 1902-1939; (7) administrative records, 1894-1955 and undated; (8) manuscripts, undated; (9) geological charts, 1909 and undated. FINDING AIDS: Description in control file. SPECIAL CONDITIONS: Use of this record unit requires prior arrangement with the Archives staff.

(7442)

Edward Palmer Papers, circa 1861-1914

(0.1 linear meter).

Edward Palmer (1831-1913), a naturalist, had his greatest influence as a plant collector in the western United States and Mexico. He collected extensively for the United States Department of Agriculture and the United States National Museum between 1869 and 1910.

These papers include incoming correspondence, 1887-1901, mostly concerning Palmer's botanical collecting; notes from his collecting trips to the American west and Florida, *circa* 1861-1890; and a catalog of Palmer's papers, 1914.

ARRANGEMENT: Unarranged. FINDING AIDS: None. SPECIAL CONDITIONS: Use of this record unit requires prior arrangement with the Archives staff.

(7455)

Collected Glass Plate Negatives of Panama, circa 1927 and undated

(0.1 linear meter).

The photographer of the negatives is unknown, as is their provenance.

This collection consists of sixty-six glass plate negatives of plants, animals, and various sites in Panama. Included are many negatives of diseased palm trees and a few images of the San Blas Islands.

ARRANGEMENT: By negative number. FINDING AIDS: Item list in control file. SPECIAL CONDITIONS: Use of this record unit requires prior arrangement with the Archives staff.

Vernon Sennock Lyonesse-Liancour Pate Papers, circa 1935-1950

(0.5 linear meter).

Vernon Sennock Lyonesse-Liancour Pate (1903-1958) was born in Philadelphia and educated at Cornell. He was an Instructor in Taxonomy at Cornell from 1932 to 1947 and Assistant Professor from 1948 to 1952. His research specialty was the classification of wasps.

These papers consist largely of research notes on the crabonine and other wasps, and a few lectures delivered by Pate at Cornell.

ARRANGEMENT: (1) Notes on wasps; (2) lectures. FINDING AIDS: None. SPECIAL CONDITIONS: Use of this record unit requires prior arrangement with the Archives staff.

(7208)

Albert Charles Peale Papers, circa 1891

(1 folder).

Albert Charles Peale (1849-1914) joined Ferdinand Vandeveer Hayden on the United States Geological and Geographical Survey of the Territories in 1871. In 1898, the United States National Museum appointed Peale as aid in charge of the paleobotany section of the Department of Geology, and he held that position until his death.

These papers consist of Peale's manuscript biography and a bibliography of Ferdinand Vandeveer Hayden which apparently was meant to be published as a *Bulletin* of the United States National Museum, but never was.

ARRANGEMENT: "The Published Writings of Ferdinand Vandeveer Hayden, by Albert Charles Peale," 1891. FINDING AIDS: None. SPECIAL CONDITIONS: Use of this record unit requires prior arrangement with the Archives staff.

(7284)

Stuart H. Perry Papers, 1930-1954, with related materials to 1963

(0.1 linear meter).

Stuart H. Perry (1874-1957) was a newspaper publisher and authority on meteorites. He made extensive collections of meteorites and donated many specimens to the United States National Museum (USNM). In 1940, Perry became an Honorary Associate in Mineralogy, USNM, a title he held until his death.

These papers document Perry's work on meteorites and consist of incoming and outgoing correspondence with geologists, meteorite collectors and owners, and museums mostly concerning efforts by Perry to purchase meteorite specimens. Of special interest is a large amount of correspondence with Harvey Harlow Nininger. Also included is a small amount of correspondence regarding fiscal matters; photographs of meteorites; and newspaper clippings.

ARRANGEMENT: (1) General correspondence, 1930-1954; (2) photographs and newspaper clippings, 1933, 1963 and undated. FINDING AIDS: Description in control file. SPECIAL CONDITIONS: Use of this record unit requires prior arrangement with the Archives staff.

Watson M. Perrygo Papers, circa 1880s-1979
(0.9 linear meter).

Watson M. Perrygo (1906-1984) field collector, taxidermist, and exhibits specialist for the United States National Museum (USNM) began his career at the USNM in 1927 as a scientific aid in the Division of Mammals and the taxidermy studio. In addition to taxidermic and other collection-related work, Perrygo was sent on field trips to collect natural history specimens unrepresented in the USNM. His collecting activities included trips to Haiti, 1929, and again in 1930 (the Parish-Smithsonian Expedition); West Virginia, 1936; Tennessee, 1937; Kentucky, 1938; North Carolina, 1939; South Carolina, 1940; and Rampart Cave, Arizona, 1942. Perrygo also accompanied Alexander Wetmore, then Secretary of the Smithsonian Institution, to Panama to collect birds, 1946-1953.

Perrygo served as exhibits preparator and zoological exhibits worker in the Department of Zoology, USNM, 1952-1958, and as zoological exhibits worker in the Office of Exhibits, Museum of History and Technology (MHT), 1958-1960. He was in charge of taxidermy for MHT, 1960-1962, and for the Museum of Natural History (MNH), 1962 to 1964. Perrygo was also an important figure in the exhibitions modernization program at the USNM during the 1940s and 1950s.

These papers consist of correspondence concerning field trips, including letters of introduction, correspondence with state game and fisheries agencies, and authorizations for field work. Other materials include field trip reports, 1936-1940; expense accounts; specimen lists; materials on taxidermy techniques; newspaper articles; taxidermist addresses, *circa* 1880s; and labels for natural history exhibits, *circa* 1880s.

Also included are photographs of USNM taxidermists, *circa* 1930s to 1973; mounted mammal specimens and zoological exhibits assembled by the taxidermists; Smithsonian staff; selected art works at the National Gallery of Art; exhibits in the USNM; mammals; taxidermy studio at the MNH; and scenes from Perrygo's field trips, 1929 to 1942. The collection also includes color motion pictures taken during the Panama trips, 1950-1953; of Skyline Drive, Virginia; and of the USNM taxidermy studio.

ARRANGEMENT: (1) Correspondence, 1928-1973; (2) materials documenting field trips, 1929, 1936-1942, 1947-1948; (3) materials on taxidermy and exhibits; (4) newspaper articles; (5) photographs; (6) motion pictures, 1950-1953; (7) oversize materials. FINDING AIDS: Description in control file. SPECIAL CONDITIONS: Use of this record unit requires prior arrangement with the Archives staff.

James A. Peters Papers, 1927-1973, and Records of the Division of Reptiles and Amphibians, 1927-1966
(6.1 linear meters).

James A. Peters (1922-1972) was born in Iowa and educated at the University of Michigan. He held teaching positions at Brown University, 1952-1958; Universidad Centrale de Ecuador, Fulbright Lecturer, 1958-1959; Southern Illinois University, 1959; and San Fernando Valley State College, 1959-1964. In 1964 Peters joined the Division of Reptiles and Amphibians, United States National Museum, and served as Associate Curator, 1964-1967, and Curator, 1967-1972.

Peters' professional activities included membership in a number of scientific societies, notably the American Society of Ichthyologists and Herpetologists (ASIH). He served the ASIH as Secretary, 1960-1966; Vice-President, 1967; and President, 1970. In 1965, he inaugurated the Smithsonian Herpetological Information Services which distributed material to herpetological labs and individual herpetologists.

The main subjects of Peters' research were the herpetology and zoogeography of Latin America, especially Ecuador. The computer analysis of biogeographic data greatly enhanced Peters' study of systematics and ecology of reptiles and amphibians. He also employed computer technology in the identification of specimens.

These papers include both personal and professional correspondence and documents relating to Peters' academic and curatorial careers. Also included are files of the Division of Reptiles and Amphibians maintained by Peters' predecessor, Doris Mable Cochran.

ARRANGEMENT: (1) Correspondence, 1938-1972; (2) societies, meetings, congresses, and symposia, 1940-1972; (3) manuscripts, 1942-1972; (4) publishers, 1955-1969; (5) publication requests, 1946-1973; (6) research awards, 1950-1970; (7) computers and computer usage file, 1960-1973; (8) non-Smithsonian files, 1937-1966; (9) Smithsonian-related files, 1962-1971; (10) Peters' personal papers, 1935-1969; (11) Division of Reptiles and Amphibians, outgoing shipping invoices, *circa* 1938-1964; (12) Division of Reptiles and Amphibians, incoming shipping invoices, *circa* 1938-1966; (13) Division of Reptiles and Amphibians, records, 1927-1966; (14) note cards and slides, *circa* 1956-1964, unarranged. FINDING AIDS: Description in control file. SPECIAL CONDITIONS: Use of this record unit requires prior arrangement with the Archives staff.

(7054)

Philadelphia Museum Company, 1792, 1808-1842 and undated
(0.1 linear meter).

The Philadelphia Museum Company had its genesis in the collections of Charles Willson Peale (1741-1827), which he placed on view in his Philadelphia home as early as 1786. In 1792, seeking to turn his enterprise into a national museum, Peale formed a Society of Inspectors, including Thomas Jefferson and Edmund Randolph, in an unsuccessful effort to attract private and government support. In 1794, he obtained a ten-year lease to lodge his collections in the American Philosophical Society building on State House Square, and in 1802 the Pennsylvania legislature authorized the Museum to occupy quarters in the State House itself.

Peale's son, Rembrandt, attempted a museum in Baltimore that failed, and attempts by Rubens Peale and Linnaeus Peale to set up museums in New York also failed. The Philadelphia Museum was incorporated in 1821 as the Philadelphia Museum Company. Charles Willson Peale died in 1827, and his sons, chiefly Rubens and Franklin, continued the enterprise in the Philadelphia Arcade, where it remained until the construction of a new building in 1836. Caught in hard economic times and a growing schism between scientific natural history on the one hand and showmanship represented by P.T. Barnum on the other, the Museum went out of existence through sale of its collections in the 1850s.

This record unit contains minutes of meetings of Peale's Society of Inspectors for the period March-July 1792, and a second minute book has a good run of entries from June 1827, just after the elder Peale's death, to the end of 1840. The remainder of this surviving remnant of records of the Philadelphia Museum Company is less than three dozen items of correspondence and oddments related to the Philadelphia Museum and the

Philadelphia Museum Company. Items are scattered through the period 1808-1842. Correspondents include Charles Willson Peale, Rubens Peale, Rembrandt Peale, and Titian Ramsay Peale.

ARRANGEMENT: (1) Minute books, 1792, 1827-1840; (2) general correspondence, 1808-1842 and undated. FINDING AIDS: Folder list in control file. SPECIAL conditions: (1) Fragile items require careful handling; (2) use of this record unit requires prior arrangement with the Archives staff.

(7079)

Philosophical Society of Washington, 1871-1968 and undated
Records (6.2 linear meters).

The Philosophical Society of Washington was organized in 1871 by a group of men who wanted to establish an organization dedicated to the advancement of science in the nation's capital. The Society's stated goals are the promotion of science, the advancement of learning, and the free exchange of views among its members on scientific subjects. It has developed these goals chiefly through publication of its *Bulletin,* and through programs of lectures on scientific topics.

Records document the routine operations of the Society, including election of officers, selection of members, minutes of meetings, financial records, copies of lectures, and Society publications.

ARRANGEMENT: (1) Minutes of meetings, 1871-1965; (2) minutes of the General Committee, 1883-1965; (3) correspondence, 1871-1968; (4) fiscal records, 1871-1968; (5) administrative records, 1884-1968; (6) lectures, 1931-1968; (7) publications, 1871-1962; (8) photographs and negatives, undated. FINDING AIDS: Description in control file. SPECIAL CONDITIONS: (1) The Smithsonian Archives has been designated as the official depository for the archives of the Philosophical Society of Washington; (2) use of this record unit requires prior arrangement with the Archives staff.

(7210)

Potomac-Side Naturalists' Club, circa 1858-1866
Records (1 folder).

The Potomac-Side Naturalists' Club was founded by a group of Washington, D.C., area naturalists in 1858 to provide an informal organization for persons interested in natural history. The Club had no full set of officers, no regular meeting place, and no museum. Activities of the Club included meetings at members' homes, reading of papers, discussion of scientific matters, and occasional excursions. The Club disbanded in 1866 and was revived in 1873, only to be replaced by other Washington area scientific societies in the 1880s.

These records include membership lists, rules and regulations, and a committee report on the revision of the Club constitution.

ARRANGEMENT: Unarranged. FINDING AIDS: None. SPECIAL CONDITIONS: Use of this record unit requires prior arrangement with the Archives staff.

Potomac Valley Ornithological Club, 1892-1896
Records (0.1 linear meter).

The Potomac Valley Ornithological Club was founded in 1892 by several ornithologists resident in the Washington, D.C., area. The Club did not meet after 1896.

These records include minutes of the Club's meetings, which were informal gatherings. The minutes contain synopses of scientific papers presented as well as discussions of research being carried on by the members.

ARRANGEMENT: (1) Minutes of meetings, 1892-1896, including a list of papers given at meetings, 1894-1895; (2) list of the birds of Washington and vicinity, prepared by the members of the Potomac Valley Ornithological Club, begun January 1892. FINDING AIDS: Description in control file. SPECIAL CONDITIONS: Use of this record unit requires prior arrangement with the Archives staff.

Edward Alexander Preble Papers, 1887-1957 and undated
(2.2 linear meters).

Edward Alexander Preble (1871-1957) was a naturalist and conservationist who conducted major field investigations of the birds and mammals of the northwest regions of Canada and the United States. Preble was born in Somerville, Massachusetts, and developed a strong interest in natural history during his youth in Wilmington, Massachusetts, and Ossipee, New Hampshire. Through early contacts with Frank Harris Hitchcock, Preble was appointed a Field Naturalist with the Bureau of Biological Survey in 1892 under Clinton Hart Merriam. Preble was appointed Assistant Biologist in 1902, Biologist in 1924, and Senior Biologist in 1928. While in the field for the Bureau, Preble kept detailed field diaries and notebooks. In addition, Preble always recorded observations of the local flora, fauna, and physical surroundings near his Massachusetts, New Hampshire, and Washington, D.C., homes.

In his later years with the Bureau as Senior Biologist, Preble became very interested in wildlife management and conservation. In 1925 Preble was appointed Consulting Naturalist for *Nature Magazine,* the publication of the American Nature Association. In 1935 he retired from government service to become the Associate Editor and, until his death in 1957, he wrote, edited, and reviewed articles for *Nature Magazine.* Preble published extensively throughout his life and corresponded with many naturalists and conservationists.

These papers document Preble's personal life and careers with the Bureau of Biological Survey and the American Nature Association. They include general correspondence, primarily incoming; published and unpublished manuscripts for scientific and conservation work; addresses and reports by others; field notebooks, diaries, lists and checklists for his field investigations and local observations; research notes for his scientific publications on mammals and birds of the northwest; auction catalogs for skins; news clippings and photographs; and biographical information on Preble.

ARRANGEMENT: (1) General correspondence, 1888-1956 and undated; (2) manuscripts, 1909-1950 and undated; (3) addresses and reports by others, 1909-1938 and undated; (4) field notebooks, 1887-1945 and undated; (5) research notes, undated; (6) auction catalogs, 1891, 1896; (7) photographs and news clippings, 1900-1948 and undated; (8) biographical information on Edward Alexander Preble, 1935-1965. FINDING AIDS: Description in control file. SPECIAL CONDITIONS: Use of this record unit requires prior arrangement with the Archives staff.

(7250)

Constantine Samuel Rafinesque Papers, 1815-1834 and undated
(0.1 linear meter).

Constantine Samuel Rafinesque (1783-1840) was born near Constantinople. In 1792, he moved with his family to Leghorn, Italy, where he was educated by private tutors. Rafinesque showed an early enthusiasm for the study of nature, beginning the systematic collection of a herbarium when he was eleven years old. In 1802, he traveled to Philadelphia, where he became acquainted with several American scientists, including Benjamin Rush and William Bartram. During his three years in America, Rafinesque made several field trips, collecting botanical and zoological specimens. He returned to Italy in 1805 and for the next ten years resided in Sicily. While studying the ichthyology of Sicilian waters, Rafinesque worked as secretary and chancellor to the American Consul and as an exporter of squills and medicinal plants. A series of personal problems caused him to return to America in 1815. Surviving a shipwreck off Long Island, he settled in New York where he worked at times as a private tutor. From 1815 to 1818, he studied the flora and fauna of the Hudson Valley, Lake George, and Long Island. In 1819, Rafinesque was appointed Professor of Botany, Natural History, and Modern Languages at Transylvania University in Lexington, Kentucky, where he remained until 1826. From 1826 until his death, he lived in Philadelphia and continued to make field trips and study the flora and fauna of the region.

Rafinesque's chief interests were botany and ichthyology. Despite a peculiar personality that alienated many colleagues, he contributed significantly to nineteenth century scientific thought. He was one of the first American naturalists to depart from the Linnaean system of classification and adopt the emerging schemes of natural plant classification. Rafinesque was an early advocate of evolutionary theory and his ideas were acknowledged by Charles Darwin in *On the Origin of Species.*

This collection consists of notebooks kept by Rafinesque on his many trips, containing natural history notes and observations; ichthyological and botanical drawings; sketches of landscapes and places visited; itineraries; and trip journals. Some of the notebooks are in French.

ARRANGEMENT: Chronologic. FINDING AIDS: Description in control file. SPECIAL CONDITIONS: Use of this record unit requires prior arrangement with the Archives staff.

(7240)

Franco Dino Rasetti Papers, 1944-1965 and undated
(0.2 linear meter).

Franco Dino Rasetti (1901-   ) was born in Castiglione del Lago, Italy. He received his doctorate in physics from the University of Pisa, 1923, and honorary degrees from Laval University, Ph.D., 1948, and the University of Glasgow, LL.D., 1957. He came to the

United States in 1947 and became a naturalized citizen in 1952. In the early 1970s he returned to Italy.

Rasetti was an Assistant Professor of Physics at the University of Florence, 1923-1926, and the University of Rome, 1927-1930. He then became Professor of Physics at Rome, 1931-1938; Laval University, 1939-1947; and Johns Hopkins University, 1947-1970.

In addition to his academic appointments, Rasetti was a Rockefeller Foundation Fellow at the California Institute of Technology, 1928-1929; a fellow at Berlin's Kaiser Wilhelm Institute, 1931-1932; a Research Associate at Columbia University, 1936; a Visiting Professor at the University of Miami, 1958-1959; a Guggenheim Memorial Foundation Fellow, 1959; and a Consultant for the National Committee on Nuclear Research at Rome, 1959.

Although Rasetti was a nuclear physicist, his avocation was paleobiology with an emphasis on Cambrian stratigraphy and paleontology in the Appalachians and the American and Canadian Rockies. From 1964 to 1967, Rasetti was an Honorary Research Associate in Invertebrate Paleontology at the Smithsonian's National Museum of Natural History. He was a Fellow of the Geological Society of America and the Paleontological Society and received the National Academy of Science's Walcott Medal in 1952.

These papers consist of field notebooks and notes; a draft of a publication; and photographs of geologic formations.

ARRANGEMENT: (1) Notebooks and notes, 1947-1965 and undated; (2) draft of publication, 1961; (3) photographs, 1944 and undated. FINDING AIDS: Description in control file. SPECIAL CONDITIONS: Use of this record unit requires prior arrangement with the Archives staff.

(7256)

Mary Jane Rathbun Papers, 1886-1938 and undated
(1 linear meter).

Mary Jane Rathbun (1860-1943) was born in Buffalo, New York. Educated in the public schools of Buffalo, she became interested in zoology through her brother Richard. A staff member of the United States Fish Commission (and later an Assistant Secretary of the Smithsonian Institution), Richard Rathbun introduced his sister to the Commission and its work at Woods Hole, Massachusetts. She worked for the Fish Commission, on a voluntary basis, during the summers from 1881 to 1884. In 1884, she was appointed to a salaried position as clerk with the Fish Commission, where she remained until 1886, when she joined the staff of the United States National Museum (USNM) as Copyist in the Department of Marine Invertebrates. Rathbun was promoted to Aid in 1893, Second Assistant Curator in 1894, and Assistant Curator in 1907. She resigned in 1914, so that her salary could be used to hire another Assistant Curator. After her resignation, she was given the honorary title Associate in Zoology and continued her work on the invertebrate collections in the USNM. In 1916, Rathbun received an honorary M.A. degree from the University of Pittsburgh and the following year received an honorary doctorate from The George Washington University.

Rathbun's primary zoological interest was the study of crustacea, particularly the crabs, both recent and fossil. Her bibliography numbered 158 titles, with her most important works being four monographs on the grapsoid, spider, cancroid, and oxystomatous crabs of America, published as bulletins of the United States National Museum between 1918 and 1939.

The papers of Mary Jane Rathbun document her career as a carcinologist and consist of correspondence, 1894-1938; manuscripts; research material; photographs; and an autobiographical memoir.

ARRANGEMENT: (1) General correspondence, 1894-1938; (2) manuscripts, 1923-1937 and undated; (3) fossil crustacea research file; (4) photographs, 1886 and undated; (5) autobiographical memoir, undated. FINDING AIDS: Description in control file. SPECIAL CONDITIONS: Use of this record unit requires prior arrangement with the Archives staff.

(7078)

Richard Rathbun Papers, 1870-1918 and undated
(2.1 linear meters).

Richard Rathbun (1852-1918) was born in Buffalo, New York. He received his early education in the public schools of Buffalo and after graduation worked in his father's stone quarry business. Rathbun developed an early interest in the geology and paleontology of western New York, and by 1870 had deposited large collections of fossils in the Buffalo Society of Natural History. In 1871, Rathbun entered Cornell University on the advice of the distinguished Brazilian explorer, Charles F. Hartt. He left Cornell in 1873 to study the fossil collections at the Museum of Comparative Zoology. In 1874, he was appointed Assistant in Zoology in the Boston Society of Natural History. While serving in this position, Rathbun also worked as a volunteer assistant with the United States Fish Commission (USFC). In 1875, he became a Geologist with the Geological Commission of Brazil, under the direction of Hartt. He remained in Brazil until 1878, when he returned to the United States to accept the position of Scientific Assistant with the USFC. Rathbun remained on the staff of the USFC until 1896. His association with the Smithsonian Institution and United States National Museum began in 1881, when he was made Honorary Curator of the Department of Marine Invertebrates, a position he held until 1914. In 1897, Rathbun accepted the position of Assistant Secretary of the Smithsonian Institution, in charge of Office and Exchanges. In 1898, Rathbun's duties were expanded to include certain aspects of museum administration, and in 1901 his title was changed to Assistant Secretary, in charge of the National Museum, a position he held until his death in 1918.

The papers of Richard Rathbun document his early investigations in geology and paleontology; his college career at Cornell University, 1871-1872; his work as Geologist on the Geological Commission of Brazil, 1875-1878; and his scientific and administrative careers with the United States Fish Commission and United States National Museum. Of special interest are correspondence and other materials concerning Samuel P. Langley's aerodrome experiments of 1903. The papers consist of incoming and outgoing correspondence; notebooks; manuscripts and research material; notes and sketches; photographs and lantern slides; and a manuscript on architecture by Rathbun's son, Seward Hume Rathbun.

ARRANGEMENT: (1) General correspondence, 1871-1918 and undated; (2) letters of condolence on the death of Richard Rathbun, 1918; (3) outgoing correspondence, 1885-1889; (4) notebooks, 1870-1891 and undated;

(5) *United States National Museum Bulletin 101,* "The Columbian Institute for the Promotion of Arts and Sciences," 1917, notes, drafts, and research material; (6) notes, drafts, and related material concerning the National Institute, undated; (7) manuscript on architecture by Seward Hume Rathbun, undated; (8) notes and sketches, 1870-1878 and undated; (9) photographs and lantern slides, *circa* 1875-1895 and undated. FINDING AIDS: Description in control file. SPECIAL CONDITIONS: Use of this record unit requires prior arrangement with the Archives staff.

(7070)

Charles Rau Papers, 1859-1886
(0.1 linear meter and oversize).

Charles Rau (1826-1887), archeologist, was born in Belgium and attended the University of Heidelberg. In 1848, Rau emigrated to the United States, where he taught foreign languages at schools in Illinois and New York City. While teaching, he conducted anthropological research on aboriginal Americans. Rau was appointed Resident Collaborator in Ethnology, United States National Museum (USNM) in 1875, and was given the responsibility for setting up the Smithsonian's anthropological exhibits at the 1876 Philadelphia Centennial Exhibition. From 1881 until his death, Rau was Curator of the Department of Archeology, USNM. Rau wrote articles and books on native Americans and on archeology in general, and many of his works were printed in Smithsonian publications.

These papers consist of correspondence from Joseph Henry, Spencer F. Baird, and scientific organizations, colleges, and libraries concerning archeological specimens and Rau's articles sent to the Smithsonian for publication; membership certificates; acknowledgement for books sent; formal death notices; a memorandum of agreement between Rau and Harper and Brothers; and statutes of two European anthropological organizations. Oversize material consists of certificates, a pencil drawing, and two Oriental documents.

ARRANGEMENT: (1) Correspondence, 1859-1886; (2) memorandum of agreement, statutes, and miscellaneous; (3) oversize. FINDING AIDS: Description in control file. SPECIAL CONDITIONS: Use of this record unit requires prior arrangement with the Archives staff.

(7178)

Henry Cushier Raven Field Journal, 1912-1914
(0.1 linear meter).

Henry Cushier Raven (1889-1944) began his zoological career in the Department of Preparation of the American Museum of Natural History in 1907. While there he worked with Jesse D. Figgins and Herbert Lang, noted taxidermists. When Figgins moved to the Colorado Museum of Natural History in 1910, he took Raven with him.

In 1912, the Smithsonian Institution and William Louis Abbott were looking for a young collector and explorer to carry on Abbott's work in the East Indies. Hearing good reports regarding Raven, they hired him; and he spent most of the next six years in the islands. His travels in the Pacific took him to Borneo, the Celebes, and the Moluccas.

Raven entered Cornell as a special student in zoology in 1918 and also served as Curator of the zoology museum. In 1919, the Smithsonian again employed him as a field collector, this time for the Cape-to-Cairo African Expedition. Upon his return in 1920, he entered Columbia and there studied comparative anatomy under William King Gregory. From 1921 to his death, Raven was employed by the American Museum of Natural History as a collector and Curator of Comparative Anatomy. He also held appointments with New York University, 1924-1926; Columbia University, 1926-1944; Johns Hopkins University, 1936-1938; and the New York Zoological Park, 1921-1944. Raven's major research contributions dealt with the distribution of animals in East Asia, the sperm and beaked whales, and the comparative anatomy of primates, especially gorillas.

The collection consists of a field journal of Raven's kept in the East Indies from 1912 to 1914 and a field map of Borneo.

ARRANGEMENT: Chronologic. FINDING AIDS: Description in control file. SPECIAL CONDITIONS: Use of this record unit requires prior arrangement with the Archives staff.

(7393)

Louis L. Ray Papers, 1930, 1932, 1936-1939
(0.1 linear meter).

Louis L. Ray (1909-   ), a geologist, was educated at Washington University (A.B., 1930 and M.S., 1932) and Harvard University (M.A., 1937 and Ph.D., 1938). Most of his professional career was spent as a Geologist with the United States Geological Survey. During 1936 and 1937, Ray participated in a Bureau of American Ethnology (BAE) excavation of Folsom Man artifacts at the Lindenmeier site in northern Colorado.

This collection includes Ray's field notes taken during his work with the BAE excavation, 1936-1937. The field notes document Ray's studies to determine the geological antiquity of the Lindenmeier site. Also included are field notes taken by Ray during research in Missouri, 1932, and Colorado and New Mexico, 1938-1939, and notes from research on his Master's thesis, 1930.

ARRANGEMENT: Chronologic. FINDING AIDS: None. SPECIAL CONDITIONS: Use of this record unit requires prior arrangement with the Archives staff.

(7326)

John B. Reeside, Jr., Papers, 1916-1958 and undated
(0.7 linear meter).

John B. Reeside, Jr., (1889-1958) was a geologist specializing in the study of the Mesozoic stratigraphy and paleontology of the western United States. While receiving his education at the Johns Hopkins University (A.B., 1911; Ph.D., 1915), he joined the United States Geological Survey (USGS) in 1912 as a part-time assistant. Reeside remained with the USGS for his entire professional career. After serving in a variety of research positions, Reeside was appointed Chief of the Paleontology and Stratigraphy Branch in 1932. He remained in the post until 1949 when he retired to resume full-time research. Reeside served on the USGS Committee on Geological Names from 1929 to 1958, and acted as Chairman from 1947 to 1952. He was a Research Associate in the Department of Geology, United States National Museum from 1944 until his death.

Reeside was the author of over 70 scientific papers, almost evenly divided between stratigraphy and descriptive paleontology. He was active professionally and served as

President of the Geological Society of Washington, 1941; President of the Paleontological Society, 1943; and Vice-President of the Geological Society of America in 1935 and 1944. Reeside was also a member of the Board of Directors of the American Geological Institute, 1948-1949.

This collection consists of papers documenting Reeside's career at the USGS, his paleontological research, and his service in professional organizations. Included is incoming and outgoing correspondence concerning his research; the identification of specimens; the publication of scientific papers; and USGS business, particularly his work on the Committee on Geological Names. Also included are files documenting his work in professional organizations, especially the American Geological Institute and the Geological Society of America; personnel and administrative records generated during his career; and a brief autobiographical sketch.

ARRANGEMENT: (1) General correspondence, 1916-1958; (2) organizational files, 1943-1958; (3) biographical, personnel, and United States Geological Survey materials, 1916-1957 and undated. FINDING AIDS: Description in control file. SPECIAL CONDITIONS: Use of this record unit requires prior arrangement with the Archives staff.

(7470)

Nathan Reingold Papers, 1952-1991
(12.7 linear meters).

Nathan Reingold (1927-   ), historian of American science, received the B.A. (1947) and M.A. (1948) degrees from New York University and the Ph.D. (1951) from the University of Pennsylvania. He was on the staff of the National Archives and Records Service from 1951 to 1959 and at the Library of Congress from 1959 to 1966. In 1966 Reingold was appointed Editor of the Joseph Henry Papers at the Smithsonian Institution. He continued in the position until 1985, when he was appointed Senior Historian in the National Museum of American History (NMAH). After his retirement in 1993, Reingold became Historian Emeritus at NMAH.

Reingold has researched and published extensively on the history of science in the United States. He is the author of *Science in Nineteenth-Century America, A Documentary History,* 1964; *Science in America since 1820,* 1976; *Science in America, A Documentary History, 1900-1939,* 1981; and *Science American Style: Selected Writings of Nathan Reingold,* 1991.

The papers of Nathan Reingold document his research on the history of American science, his professional activities, and his careers at the National Archives and Records Service, Library of Congress, and Smithsonian Institution. Included is incoming and outgoing correspondence, 1952-1991, with colleagues, publishers, administrators, professional organizations, students, and personal acquaintances concerning research interests, letters of recommendation, the review of manuscripts and grant applications, the publication of articles and books, official duties, and professional activities; correspondence, memoranda, manuscripts, drafts, talks, reports, minutes, and published materials documenting Reingold's membership and activities in numerous professional organizations, and on various councils, committees, and advisory boards including the American Association for the Advancement of Science, *Isis* Editorial Advisory Board, Panel for the History and Philosophy of Science of the National Science Foundation, and

Rockefeller Archive Center Council; and correspondence, memoranda, notes, microfilm, drafts, manuscripts, and related materials from his research on the history of American science, particularly his books *Science in Nineteenth-Century America, a Documentary History,* 1964, and *Science in America, a Documentary History, 1900-1939,* 1981, and his studies of Joseph Henry, Alexander Dallas Bache, and science and public policy in nineteenth-century Great Britain.

Researchers should also consult record unit 9503, Nathan Reingold Interview, 1973.

ARRANGEMENT: (1) Nathan Reingold Papers, 1952-1978, accession number 82-061; (2) Nathan Reingold Papers, 1964-1983, accession number 85-140; (3) Nathan Reingold Papers, 1974-1985, accession number 86-003; (4) Nathan Reingold Papers, 1969-1987, accession number 88-058; (5) Nathan Reingold Papers, 1960-1988, accession number 90-027; (6) Nathan Reingold Papers, 1985-1991, accession number 92-094. FINDING AIDS: Folder list in control file. SPECIAL CONDITIONS: (1) Restricted; (2) use of this record unit requires prior arrangement with the Archives staff.

(7232)
Charles Elmer Resser Papers, 1912-1942 and undated
(1.7 linear meters).

Charles Elmer Resser (1889-1943), paleontologist, was born in East Berlin, Pennsylvania. He was educated at Pennsylvania State Teachers College, B. Ped., 1912; Franklin and Marshall College, B.A., 1913; Princeton University, M.A., 1915; and The George Washington University, Ph.D., 1917. Resser's interest in Cambrian fossils was developed while a student of H. Justin Roddy at Franklin and Marshall.

In 1914 Resser came to the United States National Museum as an assistant to Charles D. Walcott. In 1915 he was appointed Assistant Curator in the Division of Paleontology, and subsequently held positions as Assistant Curator, Division of Stratigraphic Paleontology, 1923; Associate Curator, Division of Stratigraphic Paleontology, 1924-1928; Curator, Division of Stratigraphic Paleontology, 1929-1940; and Curator, Division of Invertebrate Paleontology and Paleobotany, 1941-1943. Resser was also a part-time faculty member at The George Washington University, 1915-1932. Resser also taught geology at the University of Maryland for several years.

These papers consist of Resser's professional correspondence, 1912-1940 and undated; notebooks from field trips in the United States and museum collection study trips in Europe; a manuscript on Wisconsin localities at the Milwaukee Public Museum; and photographs from his field trips.

ARRANGEMENT: (1) General correspondence, 1912-1940 and undated; (2) field notebooks, diaries, account books, and miscellaneous notebooks, 1913-1942 and undated; (3) unpublished manuscript on Wisconsin localities; (4) photographs, 1923-1941. FINDING AIDS: Description in control file. SPECIAL CONDITIONS: Use of this record unit requires prior arrangement with the Archives staff.

(7081)
William Jones Rhees Collection, circa 1878-1907
(7.9 linear meters).

William Jones Rhees (1830-1907) was Chief Clerk of the Smithsonian from 1852 until the early 1890s, and served as archivist almost until his death in 1907. In addition to his responsibility for the Institution's records, Rhees was in charge of publications. Moreover, in his personal life he was an avid autograph and manuscript collector.

These activities as Chief Clerk, editor, publicist, archivist, and autograph collector have resulted in a very peculiar records arrangement. Rhees never hesitated to remove items from official files for an institutional or personal publications project, and most of the removed items never found their way back to their original home. Secretarial records and Chief Clerk records are often filed together with Rhees' notes on biography and proofs of texts of Smithsonian publications. Apparently Rhees himself never perfected his own system, and over the years his files have been both raided and expanded.

The papers which Rhees assembled did contain valuable materials, both personal papers of several prominent figures and Smithsonian archives; but the best of his material is now in the Huntington Library rather than the Smithsonian. These materials were sold by Rhees' widow to the Huntington many years after Rhees' death. The history of the Rhees papers is traced by Nathan Reingold in "The Anatomy of a Collection: The Rhees Papers," *American Archivist,* April 1964, pages 251-259.

The most useful of the Rhees papers in the Smithsonian Archives are the records of the Chief Clerk, record unit 64. In the present collection, the vast majority of the documents are useful for reference purposes only, consisting of extensive files which Rhees assembled, usually for Smithsonian publications, especially for the *Half Century Book,* record unit 76, and his own *The Smithsonian Institution: Documents Relative to its Origin and History, 1835-1899,* 2 volumes, Washington, 1901. But because Rhees habitually removed records during his projects and filed them here, these papers should always be examined for originals. Probably some materials date before 1878, most of which will be moved to the proper locations.

ARRANGEMENT: (1) Alphabetic by subject; (2) Smithsonian reports and correspondence; (3) Smithsonian history, alphabetic by subject; (4) legislation concerning the Smithsonian; (5) *The Smithsonian Institution: Documents Relative to its Origin and History, 1835-1899,* notes, drafts, proofs; (6) joint resolutions by the Regents and records of their attendance at meetings; (7) Bureau of American Ethnology history; (8) Archives of the Smithsonian, lists; (9) biography file, mostly proofs for Smithsonian publications and newspaper clippings. Microfilm copies from the Rhees Collection at the Huntington Library have been placed in the Henry Papers, record unit 7001. FINDING AIDS: Correspondence regarding the fate of the Rhees Collection is in the control file. SPECIAL CONDITIONS: (1) Segments of this collection will be returned to the places from which Rhees removed them; (2) use of this record unit requires prior arrangement with the Archives staff.

(7382)
Charles Wallace Richmond Library Catalog and Lists, 1906-1908 and undated
(0.1 linear meter).

Charles Wallace Richmond (1868-1932) was born in Kenosha, Wisconsin, and moved to Washington, D.C., in 1881 where he became a page at the House of Representatives. In 1888, he joined a United States Geological Survey expedition to Montana to pursue his ornithological interests, and later joined the staff of the United States Department of Agriculture as an ornithological clerk in the Division of Economic Ornithology and Mammalogy. After a collecting trip to Nicaragua, Richmond returned to Washington and became a night watchman at the United States National Museum (USNM). He was soon promoted to the position of Aid and then Assistant in the Section of Birds. In 1894, Richmond was appointed Assistant Curator of Birds, and in 1918 he became Associate

Curator of this division. In 1929, he was appointed Curator but was reappointed Associate Curator at his own suggestion to allow for the appointment of Herbert Friedmann as Curator in the same year.

Richmond's scientific work dealt largely with problems of ornithological nomenclature in which he was recognized as an international authority. One of Richmond's greatest contributions to the field was his card catalog of generic and specific names of birds which was consulted by ornithologists all over the world.

This catalog consists of a list of the contents of Richmond's personal library. The entries document the title, author, place and year of publication of over 200 publications and auction catalogs in German, Italian, French, Spanish, Latin, and English on various natural history topics. The dates of publication range from 1657 to 1906. The catalog also records transfer of the materials to four repositories: the United States National Museum, the Academy of Natural Sciences of Philadelphia, the Library of Congress, and the California Academy of Sciences. In addition, there are separate lists documenting donations to the USNM between 1906 and 1908 in five installments.

ARRANGEMENT: (1) Catalog, undated; (2) lists of publications transferred to the USNM, 1906-1908. FINDING AIDS: Description in control file. SPECIAL CONDITIONS: Use of this record unit requires prior arrangement with the Archives staff.

(7374)

Edward Avery Richmond Papers, 1914-1967
(0.1 linear meter).

Edward Avery Richmond (1887-1970) was an entomologist specializing in the taxonomy and biology of water beetles. He received his Ph.D. from Massachusetts State College in 1930. Richmond held a variety of research and teaching posts between 1913 and 1957. Included were two positions with the United States Department of Agriculture. He was an entomologist with the Japanese Beetle Laboratory from 1924 to 1929 and a foreign plant quarantine inspector from 1945 to 1957. During 1944-1945, Richmond was stationed on Horn Island, off the Gulf Coast of Mississippi, as a health officer with the United States Army. He continued to conduct studies of the flora and fauna of Horn Island as a Research Associate of the Gulf Coast Research Laboratory from 1959 until his death. Richmond's collection of Coleoptera was donated to the National Museum of Natural History in 1972.

This collection consists of papers documenting Richmond's career and includes correspondence with colleagues concerning his research on water beetles; correspondence and photographs relating to his Army work on Horn Island, Mississippi, and subsequent research on the natural history of the island; and rearing notes and other research materials on water beetles, especially the family Hydrophilidae.

ARRANGEMENT: (1) General correspondence, 1915-1953; (2) correspondence and photographs concerning Horn Island, Mississippi, 1944-1967; (3) research materials, 1914-1930. FINDING AIDS: None. SPECIAL CONDITIONS: Use of this record unit requires prior arrangement with the Archives staff.

John L. Ridgway Drawings, 1881-1882
(1 folder).

John L. Ridgway was brought to Washington, D.C., to work as a copyist and draughtsman for the United States National Museum by his brother Robert Ridgway, the ornithologist, in the early 1880s. He later joined the United States Geological Survey.

This collection consists of about 200 drawings of birds' eggs done by John L. Ridgway for Spencer F. Baird in 1881 and a list of those drawings.

ARRANGEMENT: Unarranged. FINDING AIDS: None. SPECIAL CONDITIONS: Use of this record unit requires prior arrangement with the Archives staff.

Robert Ridgway Papers, circa 1850s-1919
(2.9 linear meters).

Robert Ridgway (1850-1929) was born in Mount Carmel, Illinois. In 1864 he wrote to Spencer F. Baird, asking Baird to identify a bird that Ridgway had seen. Ridgway and Baird began corresponding, and, in effect, Baird became Ridgway's mentor. In 1867 Baird secured an appointment for Ridgway as zoologist on Clarence King's Geological Survey of the Fortieth Parallel. Upon his return to Washington in 1869, Ridgway was put to work by Baird to furnish the technical descriptions and certain of the drawings for a book on North American birds being prepared by Baird and Thomas Mayo Brewer. In 1874 Ridgway was appointed an ornithologist on the staff of the United States National Museum. In 1880 he was appointed Curator of the Department of Ornithology. Ridgway remained Curator until his death in 1929, although after 1915 he resided in Olney, Illinois.

These papers consist of Ridgway correspondence with Spencer F. Baird, drawings of birds, and material collected by Ridgway for his important work, *Color Standards and Nomenclature* (Washington, 1912).

ARRANGEMENT: (1) Correspondence with Spencer F. Baird, 1864-1866; (2) drawings and sketches of birds, *circa* 1850s-1880s; (3) color plates and pigment samples used in *Color Standards and Nomenclature* (Washington, 1912); (4) photograph of Mr. and Mrs. Ridgway, Larchmound, 1919. FINDING AIDS: Description in control file. SPECIAL CONDITIONS: Use of this record unit requires prior arrangement with the Archives staff.

Charles Valentine Riley Papers, 1866-1895 and undated, with information to 1915
(3.9 linear meters).

Charles Valentine Riley (1843-1895) was one of two or three key figures in the development of economic entomology in the United States. An Englishman by birth, he was a protege of Benjamin Dann Walsh and was the first entomologist of the State of Missouri from 1868 to 1871. Riley secured establishment of the United States Entomological Commission in 1877 and the next year was named Entomologist of the United States. Riley was also Honorary Curator of Insects in the United States National Museum, 1882-1895; and from his own collections and those of the Department of Agriculture grew the national collection of insects. Riley also published two journals, in cooperation with others, the *American Entomologist,* 1868, 1880; and *Insect Life,* 1889-1894.

These papers concern entomology, mostly economic, and include scrapbooks compiled by Riley and occasionally by others, 1872-1894, tracing the history of entomology in clippings from a wide variety of sources arranged topically and especially useful for tracing Riley's work as State Entomologist of Missouri; *Memorandum Entomologicum,* 1866-1879, consisting of descriptions, drawings, observations, and some rearing data on a wide variety of injurious insects; outgoing correspondence, 1866-1895, including letters from Riley to other entomologists; incoming correspondence, 1882-1883, relating to silk culture; notes and papers, mostly on Psyllidae; and notes and correspondence concerning Phengodes and Zarhipis.

ARRANGEMENT: (1) Scrapbooks, 1872-1894; (2) *Memorandum Entomologicum,* 1866-1879; (3) outgoing correspondence, 1886-1895; (4) incoming correspondence, 1882-1883; (5) notes and papers; (6) miscellaneous drawings, notes, and correspondence, 1875, 1887, 1915 and undated, accession 89-014; (7) miscellaneous memoranda and correspondence, 1876, 1881-1895 and undated, accession number T89064. FINDING AIDS: Description in control file. SPECIAL CONDITIONS: Use of this record unit requires prior arrangement with the Archives staff.

(7118)

Joseph Harvey Riley Papers, circa 1903, 1906, 1930s and undated
(0.4 linear meter).

Joseph Harvey Riley (1873-1941) first came to the Smithsonian Institution in 1896 on a temporary appointment as Aid to assist Charles Emil Bendire in arranging the collection of eggs of North American birds in the Division of Birds. In 1898 he was appointed Aid as a regular member of the staff. In 1928 he became Assistant Curator, and in 1932, Associate Curator of the Division of Birds, a title which he held until his death.

Riley's early research interests centered around the birds of the West Indies, but later he turned his attention to describing the avifauna of Asia, publishing many papers based on collections made for the United States National Museum by William Louis Abbott in Southeast Asia, Henry Cushier Raven in the Celebes, Joseph Francis Rock in China, F. R. Wulsin in Mongolia, and David Crockett Graham in China and Tibet.

These papers consist of unpublished studies of birds in some of the collections mentioned above, and notes and lists compiled during Riley's research on the avifauna of the West Indies.

ARRANGEMENT: (1) Unpublished papers on Asian birds, *circa* 1930s; (2) notes and lists on West Indian birds, *circa* 1903, 1906 and undated. FINDING AIDS: Description in control file. SPECIAL CONDITIONS: Use of this record unit requires prior arrangement with the Archives staff.

(7299)

Henry B. Roberts Papers, 1955-1973
(0.1 linear meter).

Henry B. Roberts (1910-1979) came to the Smithsonian Institution in 1956 as a Museum Aid in the Division of Invertebrate Paleontology and Paleobotany, Department of Geology, United States National Museum. In 1962 he transferred to the Division of

Marine Invertebrates (after 1965, the Division of Crustacea) where he worked as a Museum Specialist until his retirement in 1973.

These papers consist primarily of correspondence relating to Roberts' official duties with the Division of Invertebrate Paleontology and Paleobotany and the Division of Marine Invertebrates. Also included are letters documenting his research on recent and fossil decapod crustacea.

ARRANGEMENT: Unarranged. FINDING AIDS: None. SPECIAL CONDITIONS: Use of this record unit requires prior arrangement with the Archives staff.

(7160)

Richard Brooke Roberts Notebook, 1938-1939
(1 volume).

Richard Brooke Roberts (1910-1980), physicist and biophysicist, participated in the experiment in which the splitting of the uranium atom was first observed in 1939. At the time, he was a Fellow at the Carnegie Institution in Washington, D.C.

This notebook contains Roberts' laboratory data and notes for the period September 1938 to April 1939, including notes on the atom-splitting experiment. The volume also contains a letter from Roberts to his father, giving the background of the experiment.

ARRANGEMENT: Chronologic. FINDING AIDS: None. SPECIAL CONDITIONS: Use of this record unit requires prior arrangement with the Archives staff.

(7287)

Joseph Francis Rock Collection, 1922-1929
(0.5 linear meter).

Joseph Francis Rock (1884-1962) was a botanist who specialized in the flora of Hawaii and China. He directed many expeditions on which he collected zoological, ornithological, and botanical specimens.

This collection consists chiefly of photographs of landscapes and plants taken by Rock on collecting trips to China and Tibet, 1922-1929. The Rock Specimen Catalog, located in the Botany Library of the National Museum of Natural History, includes a list of plants collected, 1921-1924, and identification of plants taken, 1928-1929. Also in the Botany Department are manuscript maps prepared by Rock showing his itinerary, 1925-1927.

ARRANGEMENT: (1) Photographs, 1922-1923, 1925-1926, 1928-1929; (2) specimen catalog, 1921-1924, 1928-1929; (3) maps, 1925-1927. FINDING AIDS: None. SPECIAL CONDITIONS: Use of this record unit requires prior arrangement with the Archives staff.

(7152)

Washington A. Roebling Papers, 1885-1926
(0.1 linear meter).

Washington Roebling (1837-1926) was a civil engineer and industrialist. He assisted and succeeded his father, John A. Roebling, in the family firm and is probably best known for his completion of the Brooklyn Bridge. Roebling was an avid collector of minerals and left his collection of over 15,000 specimens to the Smithsonian Institution on his death.

These papers document Roebling's interest in mineralogy, and consist of correspondence with geologists and mineralogists including William F. Foshag, R. B. Gage, Samuel F. Gordon, William F. Hillebrand, George Frederick Kunz, Charles Palache, Samuel Lewis Penfield, Waldemar Theodore Schaller, Earl V. Shannon, Edgar Theodore Wherry, and Herbert Percy Whitlock. Most of the correspondence concerns the sale or acquisition of mineral specimens by Roebling. The correspondence is arranged alphabetically by correspondent.

ARRANGEMENT: Alphabetic. FINDING AIDS: Description in control file. SPECIAL CONDITIONS: Use of this record unit requires prior arrangement with the Archives staff.

(7390)

Henry J. Rogers Papers, 1844-1896
(0.2 linear meter).

Henry J. Rogers (1811-1879) was an inventor and a pioneer in the development of the telegraph.

These papers include correspondence with Samuel F. B. Morse, Alfred Vail, and Matthew Fontaine Maury. Also included are patent applications, material documenting his pioneering work in nautical signal systems, a "Historical Sketch of the Electric Telegraph" by Rogers, and a certificate signed by Joseph Henry and Alexander Dallas Bache attesting to the quality of Rogers' design for an insulated wire for submarine and subterranean telegraph lines.

ARRANGEMENT: Unarranged. FINDING AIDS: None. SPECIAL CONDITIONS: Use of this record unit requires prior arrangement with the Archives staff.

(7408)

Mary Dora Rogick Papers, circa 1934-1964
(0.8 linear meter).

Mary Dora Rogick (1906-1964), an invertebrate zoologist, received her Ph.D. from Ohio State University in 1934. In 1935, Rogick was appointed to the faculty of the College of New Rochelle in New York. She remained at New Rochelle her entire career, eventually rising to the rank of Professor. Rogick's research specialty was the taxonomy and ecology of marine Bryozoa.

These papers consist of classroom and laboratory notes, lists, and a bibliographic card index from Rogick's research on Bryozoa; biographical information on Rogick; and photographs of Rogick and colleagues, including Ray S. Bassler and Raymond Carroll Osburn.

ARRANGEMENT: Unarranged. FINDING AIDS: None. SPECIAL CONDITIONS: Use of this record unit requires prior arrangement with the Archives staff.

Theodore Roosevelt Collection, circa 1901-1928, 1933, 1936 and 1958
Newspaper Clippings (0.1 linear meter).

This collection was compiled chiefly by the Roosevelt Memorial Association, Inc., created in memory of Theodore Roosevelt shortly after his death in 1919. The Association's goals included perpetuating Roosevelt's ideals; developing and maintaining a memorial park at Oyster Bay, New York; and constructing a memorial to him.

This record unit consists of newspaper clippings and magazine and journal articles, which document Theodore Roosevelt's activities as a naturalist. Additional material contains reminiscences of Roosevelt's friends during their association with him.

The newspaper, magazine, and journal articles focus on Roosevelt's conservation activities. They highlight the 1909 Smithsonian-Roosevelt Expedition to Africa and the Roosevelt-Rondon South American Expedition in 1913.

In 1913, Roosevelt and his party sailed by boat along some of the Amazon River's tributaries, exploring and mapping parts of Paraguay and western Brazil. Among the tributaries Roosevelt and one of his companions, Candido Mariano da Silva Rondon, charted in detail was the River of Doubt, later named Rio Teodoro after Roosevelt.

Newspaper clippings and personal accounts of the 1913 expedition document malaria infections and the wound Roosevelt sustained when he plunged into the river, trying to save a capsized canoe. The newspaper clippings also include information about the specimens collected during the expedition for the American Museum of Natural History. For documentation on the Smithsonian-Roosevelt African Expedition, see record unit 7179.

ARRANGEMENT: Newspaper, magazine, and journal clippings, accession number T90094. FINDING AIDS: None. SPECIAL CONDITIONS: Use of this record unit requires prior arrangement with the Archives staff.

(7447)

Dorothy Rosenberg Papers, 1963-1984
(2.4 linear meters).

Dorothy Rosenberg was born on November 16, 1920. After graduating from high school, she worked in the retail business from 1938 to 1944, when she began a series of clerical jobs. In 1950, she began her federal career, working at the Department of the Interior in a variety of offices, including the Office of the Secretary.

She came to the Smithsonian Institution in 1959 as the Administrative Officer to Assistant Secretary James C. Bradley. She remained in that position until 1970, when Bradley became Under Secretary. She remained with Bradley, working as his Administrative Officer until 1971, when she became the Administrative Officer to Assistant Secretary Robert A. Brooks. Her duties under both Bradley and Brooks included acting as liaison to the Board of Regents, a duty which she brought with her to the position of Executive Assistant to Secretary S. Dillon Ripley in 1973. This job also included management of the Office of the Secretary. Rosenberg received the Secretary's Gold Medal for Exceptional Service in 1979 and retired in 1980.

After her retirement, she remained a part-time contract employee as a consultant to Secretaries Ripley and Robert McCormick Adams. Her major project was preparing a history of the Board of Regents, which was to include a summary of Board of Regents activities and a collection of biographical notes on the Regents. She was also engaged in other projects, mostly dealing with the history and administrative structure of the Institution. Although her work on the Board of Regents project formally ended in 1984, she remained a consultant to Secretary Adams until 1986 and a volunteer with the Smithsonian National Associates until the late 1980s.

The Dorothy Rosenberg Papers include materials collected by Rosenberg during her tenure as Executive Assistant to Secretary S. Dillon Ripley and as a consultant. The papers fall into two parts. The first consists of interviews with, and information files on, members of the Board of Regents. The information files vary greatly in depth. Some files contain only biographical information, while others include a record of all actions as a Smithsonian Regent. The second part of the papers consists of materials for preparing a general history of the Board of Regents and of Secretary Ripley's tenure. These papers include copies of Regents' meeting minutes; attendance and membership records; records of the Regents' role in the Smithsonian's financial activities; records of Regents' resolutions; copies of legislation dealing with the Smithsonian; a record of the changing policy toward art collections and bequests; records of the creation of buildings and programs; records of the changing structure of the Board of Regents and governance of the Smithsonian; records and reports concerning the benefits and compensation of Secretaries and other executive-level employees; and photographs of Smithsonian buildings, collections, and events. There are also records of other projects Rosenberg participated in during her time as a consultant, including reports on the relationship of the Smithsonian to the United States Civil Service and James C. Bradley's report of Smithsonian events during Ripley's administration. Much of the historical material consists of copies, and some of the materials date from the nineteenth century. Many of the notes are in shorthand.

ARRANGEMENT: (1) Board of Regents members, research files and interviews, 1983-1984; (2) Board of Regents financial activities, 1855-1979; (3) Board of Regents activities and history, 1826-1984; (4) Board of Regents actions during the Ripley administration, 1960-1981; (5) legislation affecting the Smithsonian Institution, 1907, late 1930s-1980; (6) structure of the Smithsonian Board of Regents, 1894-1981; (7) Secretaries and other executive-level positions: retirement, compensation, appointment, and honors, 1906-1907, 1945-1983; (8) materials from the Ripley administration not related to the Board of Regents, 1964-1982; (9) photographs, 1965 and undated. FINDING AIDS: Folder list in control file. SPECIAL CONDITIONS: (1) Restricted; (2) use of this record unit requires prior arrangement with the Archives staff; (3) many notes are in shorthand.

Joseph Rosewater Papers, circa 1957-1985

(7413)

(2.1 linear meters).

Joseph Rosewater (1928-1985), a malacologist, was educated at the University of New Hampshire (B.S., 1950; M.S., 1955) and Harvard University (Ph.D., 1960). In 1960, he joined the Division of Mollusks, United States National Museum (USNM), and served as Associate Curator, 1960-1965, Curator-in-Charge, 1965-1968, and Curator, 1968-1985. Rosewater's research specialty was the systematics and evolutionary biology of the mollusk family Littorinidae. He participated on several major collecting expeditions, mostly to the Indo-Pacific region. Rosewater served as President of the American Malacological Union in 1969.

These papers consist of correspondence, manuscripts, notes, photographs, and related materials documenting Rosewater's curatorial career at the USNM; malacological research; professional activities; and collecting expeditions, especially a trip to Eniwetok Atoll, 1963, the *Te Vega* Expedition to Malaysia, Thailand, and Indonesia, 1963, and the *Pele* Expedition to Indonesia, 1970.

ARRANGEMENT: Unarranged. FINDING AIDS: None. SPECIAL CONDITIONS: Use of this record unit requires prior arrangement with the Archives staff.

(7221)

Bernard Rogan Ross Notebook, circa 1860-1861
(1 item).

Bernard Rogan Ross (1827-1874) was chief trader for the Hudson's Bay Company in the Mackenzie River District of northwest Canada during the 1860s. In that position, he was able to lend substantial help to Robert Kennicott in his explorations in that area. Kennicott's activities provided a stimulus to Ross and other members of the Company, and Ross began to make collections of ethnological and natural history specimens, many of which he sent to the Smithsonian.

This notebook contains catalogs and lists of collections made by Bernard Rogan Ross for the Smithsonian Institution, the Royal Industrial Museum of Scotland, and the Geological Museum of Canada. It also contains ethnological notes, especially on the Tinneh Indians, and copies of some of Ross' outgoing correspondence.

ARRANGEMENT: Notebook of Bernard Rogan Ross, *circa* 1860-1861. FINDING AIDS: None. SPECIAL CONDITIONS: Use of this record unit requires prior arrangement with the Archives staff.

(7330)

Paul V. Roundy Papers, circa 1911-1937 and undated
(0.1 linear meter).

Paul V. Roundy (1884-1937) was educated at Syracuse University and George Washington University (A.B. 1912). He joined the staff of the United States Geological Survey (USGS) as Preparator of Fossils in 1909. He was promoted to Associate Geologist in 1919 and remained in that position until his death. Roundy's paleontological research focused on Carboniferous invertebrates, especially conodonts and ostracods.

These papers document Roundy's twenty-eight year career with the USGS. They consist of incoming and outgoing correspondence concerning the identification of fossil specimens; his field work in Kansas and Oklahoma, 1918; research on Carboniferous invertebrates; and professional activities.

ARRANGEMENT: Alphabetic. FINDING AIDS: Description in control file. SPECIAL CONDITIONS: Use of this record unit requires prior arrangement with the Archives staff.

William Edwin Safford Papers, 1894-1925

(7275)

(0.1 linear meter).

William Edwin Safford (1859-1926), botanist, was born in Chillicothe, Ohio. Safford graduated from the United States Naval Academy at Annapolis in 1880, and served in the United States Navy from 1880 to 1890. He undertook postgraduate work at Yale University, 1883-1885, Harvard University, 1885, and finally received his Ph.D. from George Washington University in 1920. While serving in the Spanish-American War, Safford collected specimens for the Division of Ethnology, United States National Museum.

In 1902, Safford accepted the position of assistant botanist, United States Department of Agriculture (USDA), and became an economic botanist for the Bureau of Plant Industry, USDA, in 1915.

These papers consist of correspondence regarding Jean Nicolas Nicollet's expedition to Minnesota in 1836, a note concerning the identification of lakes on Nicollet's map, an account of Nicollet's expeditions of 1836, 1838-1839, and of plants collected during 1839; correspondence concerning information on plants in Mexico, the Philippine Islands, and Palestine; and a manuscript translating Jean Louis Berlandier's account of botanizing at Tamaulipas, Mexico.

ARRANGEMENT: Alphabetic. FINDING AIDS: Description in control file. SPECIAL CONDITIONS: Use of this record unit requires prior arrangement with the Archives staff.

Reece Ivan Sailer Papers, 1931-1963

(7136)

(1.3 linear meters).

Reece Ivan Sailer (1915-   ) joined the United States Department of Agriculture's Bureau of Entomology and Plant Quarantine in 1942. He subsequently held many assignments in the Department, culminating in 1967, when he became Chief of the Insect Identification and Parasite Introduction Branch. His special interests are in the taxonomy of the subfamily Heteroptera and the biology of Alaskan biting Diptera.

These papers consist of Sailer's professional correspondence with colleagues about entomological and taxonomic matters, determinations, and a small quantity of research notes. Also included in these files are letters from some of Sailer's associates and successors, especially Peter Dunning Ashlock, Harry Gardner Barber, and Richard C. Froeschner.

ARRANGEMENT: (1) Correspondence; (2) notes and drawings. FINDING AIDS: Description in control file. SPECIAL CONDITIONS: Use of this record unit requires prior arrangement with the Archives staff.

Orestes Hawley St. John Papers, circa 1825-1892

(7154)

(0.5 linear meter).

Orestes Hawley St. John (1841-1921) was a geologist whose main scientific interest was fossil fishes of the Paleozoic Era. St. John aided Amos Henry Worthen in the early

Geological Survey of Illinois on an intermittent basis from the 1860s until *circa* 1883. In addition to his work with the Illinois Survey, St. John served as principal geological assistant to Charles Abiathar White in the Second Geological Survey of Iowa from 1862 to 1868. In 1873, St. John made an extensive visit to the Museum of Comparative Zoology at Cambridge, Massachusetts, where he studied and helped arrange the paleontological collections.

St. John also accompanied Ferdinand Vandeveer Hayden's 1877-1878 survey of Idaho, Montana, and Wyoming. In 1878 St. John led the party which surveyed the Wind River Mountains, portions of the Gros Ventre Range, the Wyoming Range, and the Snake River Valley.

These papers relate to Paleozoic fossil fish and include abstracted articles, specimen notes and notebooks, and original notes for publications of the Illinois Geological Survey.

ARRANGEMENT: (1) Abstracted articles on fossil fishes, *circa* 1825-1884; (2) specimen notes, 1870-1882; (3) notes and notebooks on fossil fishes, 1868-1882 and undated; (4) original notes for publications of Illinois Geological Survey, 1881-1883, arranged by volume; (5) miscellany, *circa* 1860-1892. FINDING AIDS: Description in control file. SPECIAL CONDITIONS: Use of this record unit requires prior arrangement with the Archives staff.

(7456)

Grace Sandhouse Papers, 1924-1940
(0.1 linear meter).

Grace Sandhouse (1896-1940) graduated from the University of Colorado in 1920, where she worked with Theodore D. A. Cockerell, who led her to the study of bees. She later earned her A.M. degree from the University of Colorado and the Ph.D. from Cornell University. In 1926, Sandhouse joined the United States Department of Agriculture as a Junior Entomologist in the Bureau of Entomology and Plant Quarantine. She remained with the USDA until her death, eventually reaching the rank of Associate Entomologist. Her specialty was the taxonomy of the order Hymenoptera, especially the superfamily *Apoidea.*

This collection consists of incoming and outgoing correspondence between Sandhouse and professional colleagues. Most of the correspondence concerns the identification of specimens and her research on insects of the order Hymenoptera.

ARRANGEMENT: Alphabetic. FINDING AIDS: None. SPECIAL CONDITIONS: Use of this record unit requires prior arrangement with the Archives staff.

(1020012)

Leslie Gale Saunders Papers, undated
(0.1 linear meter).

Leslie Gale Saunders (1895-1968) was a Canadian dipterist. After working as an orchard inspector for the Provincial Government of Nova Scotia from 1914 to 1917, he entered McGill University, receiving degrees in 1920 and 1921. After receiving his Ph.D. from Cambridge in 1924, Saunders joined the faculty of the University of Saskatchewan in 1925.

These papers include notes, field notes, and drawings of Leslie Gale Saunders dealing with the Ceratopogonidae family of Diptera.

ARRANGEMENT: By sub-genus or location. FINDING AIDS: None. SPECIAL CONDITIONS: Use of this record unit requires prior arrangement with the Archives staff.

(7056)

Joseph Saxton Papers, 1821-1856
(0.1 linear meter).

Joseph Saxton (1799-1873), a self-educated inventor and machinist, developed his skills in mechanics, etching, and watchmaking while working as a watchmaker in Philadelphia. In 1828, Saxton left for Great Britain in order to further his education. While there, he was employed by the Adelaide Gallery of Practical Science in London, where he became well known for building and exhibiting scientific novelties and machines. In 1837 he returned to the United States to work for the United States Mint in Philadelphia as Constructor and Curator of the standard weighing apparatus of the Mint. From 1843 until his death, Saxton was Superintendent of Weights and Measures at the United States Coast and Geodetic Survey in Washington, D.C.

These papers consist of notebooks and diaries in which Saxton wrote detailed information on his experiments and social life in London; an appointment book for 1838; a scientific sketchbook with notes, which include drawings and descriptions of some of Saxton's inventions; and a textbook. Other Joseph Saxton material may be found in the Joseph Henry Collection, record unit 7001.

ARRANGEMENT: Notebooks and textbook. FINDING AIDS: Description in control file. SPECIAL CONDITIONS: Use of this record unit requires prior arrangement with the Archives staff.

(7100)

William Schaus Papers, 1917-1939
(2 linear meters).

William Schaus (1858-1942) studied art and music in America and abroad in preparation for a career as an art dealer. He came under the influence of Henry Edwards, the lepidopterist, however, and turned to entomology. For many years, he pursued his interest privately, traveling extensively in Europe to broaden his knowledge of Lepidoptera, the family to which he devoted his attention most of his life. In 1919, Schaus joined the Bureau of Entomology of the United States Department of Agriculture, and in 1921, began a long association with the Smithsonian Institution as Honorary Curator of Insects in the United States National Museum.

These papers consist largely of Schaus' professional correspondence with his peers and with amateurs, mostly in his capacity as Honorary Curator. They also include fragmentary research notes, correspondence, catalogs, and news clippings relating to acquisition of the Paul Dognin Collection of Lepidoptera.

ARRANGEMENT: (1) Correspondence, 1920-1939; (2) correspondence and papers relating to the Paul Dognin Moth Collection, 1917-1928. FINDING AIDS: Description in control file. SPECIAL CONDITIONS: Use of this record unit requires prior arrangement with the Archives staff.

Waldo LaSalle Schmitt Papers, 1907-1978
(19.9 linear meters).

Waldo LaSalle Schmitt (1887-1977) was born in Washington, D.C. He developed an early interest in natural history, studying the flora and fauna of the District and nearby Maryland. He received the B.S. degree from George Washington University in 1913, the M.A. degree from the University of California in 1916, and his Ph.D. from George Washington University in 1922. In 1948, he was awarded an honorary Doctor of Science degree from the University of Southern California.

Schmitt began his career in government service in 1907 as an Aid in Economic Botany for the United States Department of Agriculture. He served in that position until 1910 when he was appointed Aid in the Division of Marine Invertebrates of the United States National Museum (USNM). At the USNM, he became acquainted with Mary Jane Rathbun and began to develop his interest in the study of crustacea. From 1911 to 1914, Schmitt served on the staff of the United States Bureau of Fisheries as Scientific Assistant and Naturalist aboard the *Albatross* during its cruises along the west coast of America and Alaska. Crustacean collections made on the *Albatross* surveys provided the material for Schmitt's M.A. thesis, "The Marine Decapod Crustacea of California." In 1915, Schmitt returned to the United States National Museum as Assistant Curator in the Division of Marine Invertebrates. From 1915 to 1920, he also served as part-time instructor of Zoology at George Washington University. In 1920, Schmitt was named Curator of the Division of Marine Invertebrates and remained in that capacity until 1943 when he was appointed Head Curator of the Department of Biology. The Department of Biology was split into the Departments of Zoology and Botany in 1947, with Schmitt as Head Curator of Zoology. Upon his retirement in 1957, Schmitt was named Honorary Research Associate and continued his association with the Smithsonian Institution until his death on August 5, 1977.

Schmitt participated in many biological expeditions and field trips during his career. Under the auspices of the United States Bureau of Fisheries, he spent the summer of 1918 studying the life history of the spiny lobster at the Scripps Institution, La Jolla, California. During the summers of 1924 and 1925, Schmitt was at the Carnegie Institution's Marine Laboratory at Tortugas, Florida, surveying the crustacean fauna of the area, identifying crustaceans found in the stomachs of fishes, and taking underwater photographs. He also participated in field work at Tortugas in the summers from 1930 to 1932. In 1925, Schmitt was awarded the Smithsonian's Walter Rathbone Bacon Traveling Scholarship "for the study of the fauna of countries other than the United States." The scholarship enabled him to collect marine invertebrates along the east coast of South America from August to December, 1925, and on the west coast from August 1926 to May 1927.

During the years 1933 to 1935, Schmitt was a member of three expeditions to the Galapagos Islands sponsored by G. Allan Hancock of Los Angeles, California. While on these trips, Schmitt became acquainted with a group of utopian colonists on Florena Island in the Galapagos, who attracted considerable attention in the world press by their intrigues and mysterious behavior. As a guest of G. Huntington Hartford, he explored and collected in the West Indies on the Smithsonian-Hartford West Indies Expedition of

1937. In 1938, Schmitt was chosen by the White House to accompany President Franklin D. Roosevelt as naturalist on the presidential cruise to Clipperton, Cocos, and the Galapagos Islands. In 1939, Schmitt was a member of the Hancock South America Expedition, and he served as the biologist in charge of field operations on the first United States Fish and Wildlife Service Alaska King Crab Investigation in 1940. During 1941 and 1942, Schmitt spent time on special detail with the United States Navy investigating the possibility of establishing a biological station in the Galapagos Islands. In 1943, he visited South America, under the auspices of the State Department, for the purpose of strengthening relations between the United States and Latin American scientists.

In 1955, the Smithsonian Institution began an association with J. Bruce Bredin of Wilmington, Delaware, that produced several scientific expeditions. In that year, Schmitt headed the Smithsonian-Bredin Belgian Congo Expedition. Schmitt led Bredin-sponsored expeditions in the Caribbean, 1956, 1958, and 1959; the Society Islands, 1957; and the Yucatan, 1960. Sponsored by a grant from the Office of Naval Research, Schmitt spent the summers of 1961 and 1962 with Harry Pederson photographing coral reef fauna of the Bahama Islands. Schmitt's last expedition was in 1962-1963, when he served as a member of the Palmer Peninsula (Antarctica) Survey of the United States Antarctic Research Program. During the survey, Schmitt collected over 29,000 specimens which were added to the collections of the National Museum of Natural History. In recognition of his contributions to the United States Antarctic Research Program, the Board of Geographic Names designated a thirty-mile ice-covered series of outcrops at the base of the Antarctic Peninsula, "Schmitt Mesa."

Schmitt's primary field of zoological investigation was carcinology, with special emphasis on the decapod crustaceans (the order that includes crabs, lobsters, and shrimp). His bibliography consists of more than 70 titles. A member of numerous professional organizations, Schmitt was active in the founding of the Society of Systematic Zoology and served as president in 1948. He was also president of the Washington Academy of Sciences in 1947. Schmitt was a trustee of the Bear's Bluff Laboratories, the International Oceanographic Foundation, and the Serological Museum of Rutgers University.

These papers document Schmitt's professional career and personal life and include correspondence; organizational files; diaries and miscellaneous notebooks; manuscripts, speeches, and records concerning publications; research material; material about Washington, D.C., traffic problems; biographical material on Mary Jane Rathbun; material concerning Robert A. Bartlett and the Bartlett Arctic Expeditions; a transcript of an oral history interview; expedition files; records concerning underwater photography field work with Harry Pederson; and photographs, slides, movies, lantern slides, tapes, awards, diplomas, and citations.

ARRANGEMENT: (1) General correspondence, 1907-1977; (2) organizational files, 1913-1977; (3) Antarctic Research Series files, 1962-1972; (4) Explorers Club files, 1923-1977; (5) Society of Systematic Zoology files, 1947-1976; (6) Committee on Polar Research files, 1958-1967; (7) diaries and miscellaneous notebooks, 1920-1971; (8) records concerning the publication of *Crustaceans,* 1960-1976; (9) *The American Commensal Crabs of the Family Pinnotheridae,* correspondence and research material, 1926-1971; (10) correspondence, newspaper articles, manuscripts, and related material concerning Washington, D.C., traffic problems, 1938-1965; (11) manuscripts, speeches, and publications, 1911-1964; (12) Mary Jane Rathbun biographical material, 1925-1973; (13) correspondence, manuscripts, photographs, newspaper clippings, and related material concerning Robert A. Bartlett and the Bartlett Arctic expeditions, 1928-1947; (14) oral history interview, 1976; (15) expedition files, 1911-1963; (16) records concerning underwater photography field work of Harry Pederson and Waldo LaSalle Schmitt, 1960-1966; (17) photographs, slides, movies, lantern slides, and tape recordings, *circa* 1924-1963; (18) awards, diplomas, and citations, 1926-1978. FINDING AIDS: (1) Description in control file; (2) published finding aid available. SPECIAL CONDITIONS: Use of this record unit requires prior arrangement with the Archives staff.

(7429)

Thomas J. M. Schopf Papers, circa 1963-1984
(9.6 linear meters).

Thomas J. M. Schopf (1939-1984) was born in Urbana, Illinois. He received his A.B. from Oberlin College in 1960 and his Ph.D. in paleontology from Ohio State University in 1964. While at Ohio State, Schopf served as an assistant at the Orton Museum. From 1964 to 1967, Schopf was a Fellow in the systematics-ecology program at the Marine Biological Laboratory, Woods Hole, Massachusetts. In 1967 and 1969 respectively, he became Assistant Professor and Associate Professor of Paleontology and Oceanography at Lehigh University. From 1978 to 1984 Schopf held the position of Professor of Paleobiology at the University of Chicago.

During these years Schopf held many concurrent positions including, Faculty Associate and Research Associate, Center for Graduate Studies, Field Museum of Natural History; Fellow and Instructor, Marine Biological Laboratory, Woods Hole, Massachusetts; Visiting Resident Associate, Department of Biology, California Institute of Technology; Visiting Professor, University of Hamburg; and Guggenheim fellow. He also founded the journal, *Paleobiology,* and edited the first volumes.

These papers consist primarily of Schopf's personal correspondence with professional colleagues and friends, as well as extensive research, laboratory, and field notes. Also included in these papers are documents regarding grant proposals, classes at Lehigh and Chicago, Schopf's involvement in professional societies, and administrative records and class notes from his years as a fellow and instructor at the Marine Biological Laboratory, Woods Hole, Massachusetts. Of special interest are drafts of manuscripts written and edited by Schopf including a copy of "Models in Paleobiology" and a number of manuscripts written in collaboration with Jim L. Gooch. Three 16mm motion picture films of Bryozoa are also worthy of note.

ARRANGEMENT: (1) Thomas J. M. Schopf Papers, *circa* 1963-1984, accession number 92-132; (2) Thomas J. M. Schopf Papers, *circa* 1965-1984, accession number 86-093. FINDING AIDS: Description in control file. SPECIAL CONDITIONS: (1) Restricted; (2) use of this record unit requires prior arrangement with the Archives staff.

(7406)

Anton Schrammen Collection, 1919-1920
(0.1 linear meter).

Anton Schrammen (1869- ?) was a German paleontologist. He unsuccessfully attempted to sell a collection of fossil sponges to the United States National Museum (USNM) in 1919.

This collection consists of a catalog of Schrammen's collection of fossil sponges and correspondence and copies of correspondence documenting his attempt to sell the specimens to the USNM.

ARRANGEMENT: Unarranged. FINDING AIDS: None. SPECIAL CONDITIONS: (1) Catalog and some of the correspondence written in German; (2) use of this record unit requires prior arrangement with the Archives staff.

(7233)

Charles Schuchert Papers, 1893-1904
(0.1 linear meter).

Charles Schuchert (1858-1942) was born in Cincinnati, Ohio. His formal education consisted only of bookkeeping and drawing courses. He did, however, receive honorary degrees from Yale, A.M., 1904, and Sc.D., 1930; New York University, LL.D., 1914; and Harvard, Sc.D., 1935.

Schuchert's introduction to paleontology resulted from his interest in the Cincinnati Society of Natural History, where he formed a relationship with the Society's curator of paleontology, Edward Oscar Ulrich. Between 1885 and 1888, Schuchert served as Ulrich's assistant in preparing lithographs for the state geological surveys of Illinois and Minnesota. In 1888, Schuchert was appointed as an assistant to James Hall, the New York Geological Survey Director, in Albany. In the summer of 1891, Schuchert joined Newton Horace Winchell in the study of Minnesota brachiopods. A year later, Charles Emerson Beecher, one of Hall's former assistants, hired Schuchert as preparator at Yale's Peabody Museum of Natural History; this work at Yale was later exhibited at the Columbian Exposition in Chicago in 1893. In 1893, he was hired by the United States Geological Survey (USGS), and in 1894, was appointed Assistant Curator of Invertebrate Paleontology at the United States National Museum. He remained there for ten years during which time he participated in Robert Peary's 1897 expedition to Greenland and represented the United States government at the International Geological Congress in Vienna in 1903.

In 1904, Schuchert succeeded Beecher as Curator of geological collections at the Peabody Museum and was appointed Professor of Historical Geology at Yale. From 1909 to 1921, he was Chairman of the Geology Department, Acting Dean of the Graduate School from 1914 to 1916, and administrative head of the Museum from 1912 to 1923. In 1925, he retired from teaching but continued to collect specimens for Peabody's collections.

These papers consist primarily of Schuchert's incoming correspondence, with some outgoing correspondence, while employed by the USGS and the United States National Museum. The correspondence concerns Schuchert's field work with the USGS and the examination and exchange of specimens.

ARRANGEMENT: Alphabetic. FINDING AIDS: Description in control file. SPECIAL CONDITIONS: Use of this record unit requires prior arrangement with the Archives staff.

Leonard Peter Schultz Papers, circa 1915-1970, with related papers from 1899
(4 linear meters).

Leonard Peter Schultz (1901-1986) was born in Michigan and educated at Albion College, the University of Michigan, and the University of Washington. He taught at Michigan, 1925-1927, and Washington, 1928-1936, before coming to the United States National Museum as Assistant Curator of the Division of Fishes in 1936. Schultz was made Curator in 1938 and retained that position until his retirement from administrative duties in 1965. He was Senior Zoologist from 1965 to 1968 and Zoologist Emeritus from 1968 until his death.

Schultz's research interests included the classification and taxonomy of fishes, sharks and shark attacks, and the life history of fishes. He participated in a number of expeditions, most notably the Navy Surveying Expedition to the Phoenix and Samoan Islands, 1939, and the zoological surveys prior to and following the Bikini Atoll atomic bomb tests.

These papers include correspondence, notes, research data, published material, illustrations, photographs, and related material documenting Schultz's ichthyological interests and his teaching, curatorial, and research careers. Of particular note is an extensive correspondence file maintained by Schultz as part of his duties as Secretary of the Shark Research Panel of the American Institute of Biological Sciences; notes and data regarding the Bikini surveys; and photographs from his work on the Navy Surveying Expedition to the Phoenix and Samoan Islands, 1939.

ARRANGEMENT: (1) Ichthyological research file, *circa* 1920-1968 and undated; (2) subject file, 1915-1916, *circa* 1922-1970; (3) shark research material, 1958-1969, with related data and material, 1899, 1913, *circa* 1919-1965; (4) Crossroads Operation, 1946-1955, with related material, 1924-1946; (5) Bikini Scientific Resurvey, 1946-1956; (6) published works by Schultz, 1926-1970; (7) Navy Surveying Expedition to the Phoenix and Samoan Islands, 1939. FINDING AIDS: Description in control file. SPECIAL CONDITIONS: Use of this record unit requires prior arrangement with the Archives staff.

Eugene Amandus Schwarz Papers, 1875-1928
(0.9 linear meter).

Eugene Amandus Schwarz (1844-1928) was born in Silesia, studied entomology in Europe, and first appeared in the United States in 1872 as a student of Hermann August Hagen at Harvard University. Later in the 1870s he made a collecting trip to the West with John Lawrence LeConte, and became a colleague of Charles Valentine Riley and other noted entomologists. In 1878 Schwarz accepted a position in the Department of Agriculture, where he remained, with a brief interruption, until his death in 1928. He became the senior scholar of entomology in the Agriculture Department and the National Museum, thus influencing several generations of entomologists. He was a prominent member of the Washington professional scene, including the Washington Entomological Society, the Washington Biologists' Field Club, and the Entomological Society of America. Schwarz had enormous impact on the national collection of insects, dating from his appointment as Custodian of Coleoptera in 1898. He introduced better standards of care and arrangement and personally secured numerous collections for the

National Museum, in addition to the one made by Henry Guernsey Hubbard and himself. He initiated the important collection of Coleoptera larvae. His field observations extended throughout all sections of the United States, and into Cuba, Guatemala, and Panama.

These papers concern the taxonomy and biology of insects, especially the Coleoptera, and include letters from Henry Guernsey Hubbard, 1896-1897, regarding Hubbard's trips to Arizona and California and containing substantial biographical information for the period; letters from John Lawrence LeConte, 1875-1880, regarding joint work of LeConte, Schwarz, and Hubbard, especially determinations of Texas, Florida, Virginia, and Michigan species, mostly Coleoptera, including some letters from LeConte and Hubbard; extensive correspondence from Raymond Corbett Shannon and his wife to Schwarz regarding Shannon's trips to Europe, 1924-1925, field work in Argentina, 1926-1927, and Peru, 1928; copies of letters from Schwarz to Leland Ossian Howard regarding fig trees and their pests in California, 1900; diaries of Schwarz for trips to Florida, 1876, 1919, Cuba, 1903-1904, Texas and Arizona, 1898 and 1901-1902, Guatemala, 1906, and Panama, 1911; diaries and detailed letters listing itineraries of Shannon; biographical information on Hubbard and Schwarz; notes and miscellaneous publications; and a card catalog produced by Schwarz to help him maintain the Coleoptera collection that he and Hubbard had developed.

ARRANGEMENT: (1) Notebooks, 1876-1921; (2) correspondence and notes, 1875-1928; (3) miscellaneous papers, correspondence, and catalogs, 1894-1927, accession number 89-014. FINDING AIDS: Description in control file. SPECIAL CONDITIONS: Use of this record unit requires prior arrangement with the Archives staff.

(7091)

Science Service, circa 1910-1963
Records (87.8 linear meters).

Science Service was established in 1920 through the efforts of E. W. Scripps in collaboration with the American Association for the Advancement of Science (AAAS), the National Academy of Sciences (NAS), and the National Research Council (NRC). In 1919 Scripps had established the American Society for the Dissemination of Science. Unknown to Scripps, the three major scientific organizations were trying to agree on a format and establish a popular science journal. In 1920 Scripps met with representatives of the AAAS, NAS, and NRC in an attempt to pool resources. Out of that meeting came Science Service, a news service designed to popularize science and to disseminate scientific knowledge.

Edwin E. Slosson (1865-1929), chemist, journalist, and editor of the *Independent,* was appointed first Editor of Science Service in 1921, a post he held until his death.

Watson Davis (1896-1967) was appointed Managing Editor of Science Service in 1921, and became Editor of the *Science News Letter* in 1922. After Slosson's death, Davis assumed the duties of Director, 1933- .

This record unit consists of records documenting the daily activities of Science Service and the professional activities Edwin E. Slosson and Watson Davis.

ARRANGEMENT: (1) Organization of Science Service, Board of Trustees and Executive Committee, 1919-1943; (2) Director's correspondence, 1921-1929; (3) Edwin E. Slosson biographical materials, personal files, writings, articles, and bibliography, 1902-1929; (4) Managing Editor's correspondence, 1922-1923; (5)

Watson Davis, News Editor and Managing Editor's files, *circa* 1923-1933; (6) editorial correspondence *circa* 1934-1963; (7) syndicated correspondence, 1954; (8) Watson Davis personal files, committees and organizations, writings, speeches, and publications; (9) CBS radio talks, *Advances in Science,* 1935-1939; (10) American Documentation Institute, *circa* 1938-1940; (11) National Inventor's Council, *circa* 1940-1948; (12) Latin American translations, *circa* 1940-1950; (13) UNESCO, 1948-1951; (14) Interlingua files; (15) Rockefeller Foundation Survey, 1938-1939; (16) Knud Rasmussen Expedition, 1925; (17) sampling of daily mail reports-science page, consisting of daily reports to newspapers that subscribed to Science Service. FINDING AIDS: Partial description in control file. SPECIAL CONDITIONS: (1) Arrangement may change; (2) use of this record unit requires prior arrangement with the Archives staff.

(7249)

Samuel H. Scudder Papers, 1879-1903 and undated

(0.1 linear meter).

Samuel H. Scudder (1837-1911) was born in Boston, Massachusetts. He studied entomology at Williams College from which he received an A.B. degree in 1857. Williams later awarded him A.M. and D.Sc. degrees in 1860 and 1890, respectively. He also received a B.S. degree in 1862 from Harvard's Lawrence Scientific School where he studied with Louis Agassiz.

Scudder remained at Harvard for two years as an assistant to Agassiz; from 1864 to 1870 he held various positions at the Boston Society of Natural History. From 1870 to 1879, Scudder held no salaried position except for the several months he spent with the Hayden Survey in 1877 in Colorado, Wyoming, and Utah. From 1879 to 1882 Scudder served as Assistant Librarian at Harvard University, and from 1883 to 1886 he was Editor of the magazine *Science.* From 1886 to 1892 Scudder was a paleontologist with the United States Geological Survey (USGS) where he specialized in fossil insects. While with the USGS he produced an index to the known fossil insects of the world. He was a leading authority on American Orthoptera.

These papers consist of correspondence concerning the transfer of Scudder's insect collection from the Hayden Survey to the United States National Museum; notebooks of Tertiary insect drawings; and a catalog and list of fossil insects, and notes.

ARRANGEMENT: (1) General correspondence, 1879, 1892-1895, 1898, 1902-1903; (2) notebooks, catalog, and notes, *circa* 1880, 1891 and undated. FINDING AIDS: Description in control file. SPECIAL CONDITIONS: Use of this record unit requires prior arrangement with the Archives staff.

(7288)

Viola Shelly Shantz Collection, 1961-1962 and undated

(0.1 linear meter).

Viola Shelly Shantz (1895-1977) served as a Biological Aide, Biologist, and Systematic Zoologist with the United States Fish and Wildlife Service and its predecessor, the Bureau of Biological Survey, from 1918 to 1961. During her career she served as Curator of the North American mammal collection of the Bird and Mammal Laboratories housed in the National Museum of Natural History.

This collection consists primarily of material concerning Schantz's retirement from the United States Fish and Wildlife Service including a citation for distinguished service presented to her by the Department of the Interior, 1962, and letters written to Schantz on her retirement in July 1961. Also included are photographs, including portraits and a group photograph taken at the annual meeting of the American Society of Mammalogists, 1962.

ARRANGEMENT: Unarranged. FINDING AIDS: Description in control file. SPECIAL CONDITIONS: Use of this record unit requires prior arrangement with the Archives staff.

(7283)

Charles Upham Shepard Papers, 1830, 1842-1894 and undated
(0.3 linear meter).

Charles Upham Shepard (1804-1886) was a mineralogist and authority on meteorites. Shepard was educated at Amherst College, graduating in 1824. After a short period as a school teacher in Boston, Shepard went to Yale College in 1827 as assistant to Benjamin Silliman. He remained at Yale until 1844 serving as Lecturer in Botany, 1830-1831; Director of the Brewster Scientific Institute, 1832-1833; and Lecturer in Natural History, 1833-1844. In 1844, he became lecturer in Natural History at Amherst College, where he remained until his retirement in 1877. From 1834 to 1869, Shepard served as Professor of Chemistry at the South Carolina Medical College (a position held concurrently with his lectureships at Yale and Amherst). Shepard made extensive collections of minerals and meteorites throughout his career. After his death in 1886, his meteorite collection (the largest in America at the time) was deposited in the United States National Museum (USNM) by his son, Charles Upham Shepard, Jr. The collection was officially bequeathed to the USNM in 1915.

This collection consists primarily of correspondence with mineralogists, collectors, and museums concerning Shepard's research on meteorites and the acquisition of specimens for his collection. Also included are notebooks, scrapbooks, catalogs, and lectures by Shepard; specimen lists; and newspaper clippings collected by Shepard mostly concerning meteorites. A small amount of correspondence of Shepard's son, Charles Upham Shepard, Jr., is contained in the collection, including correspondence with Frank Wigglesworth Clarke concerning the deposit of the Shepard Meteorite Collection in the USNM in 1886.

ARRANGEMENT: (1) General correspondence, 1830, 1842-1894 and undated; (2) notebooks, scrapbooks, catalogs, specimen lists, and newspaper clippings, 1845, 1859-1860, 1878, 1886 and undated. FINDING AIDS: Description in control file. SPECIAL CONDITIONS: Use of this record unit requires prior arrangement with the Archives staff.

(7296)

John D. Sherman, Jr., Papers, 1886-1960
(1.2 linear meters).

John D. Sherman, Jr., (1872-1960) was an entomologist and entomological book dealer. He lived in Mount Vernon, New York, and was a long-time member of the New York Entomological Society. For a time he served as President of the Society. Sherman sent specimens and reprints to the United States National Museum from 1893 to 1950.

These papers consist primarily of correspondence between Sherman and entomologists and other naturalists including Alexander Agassiz, William Harris

Ashmead, Samuel Henshaw, Leland Ossian Howard, John Lawrence LeConte, Clinton Hart Merriam, Alpheus Spring Packard, John Bernhard Smith, Robert Evans Snodgrass, Charles Henry Tyler Townsend, and James Zetek. Also included are diaries and notebooks which document his entomological studies, business records, and reprints.

ARRANGEMENT: (1) General correspondence, 1886-1960; (2) diaries and notebooks, 1881-1900; (3) business records, 1918-1957; (4) reprints. FINDING AIDS: None. SPECIAL CONDITIONS: Use of this record unit requires prior arrangement with the Archives staff.

(7082)

Bohumil Shimek Papers, 1878-1936
(2 linear meters).

Bohumil Shimek (1861-1937) studied civil engineering at the State University of Iowa (SUI), where he received a C.E. degree in 1883 and an M.S. degree in 1902. He served as railroad and county surveyor for Johnson County, Iowa, 1883-1885, and taught sciences at Iowa City High School, 1885-1888. From 1888 until 1890, Shimek was an instructor in zoology at the University of Nebraska. From 1890 to 1932, he taught botany at SUI and served as the head of the Department of Botany, 1914-1919. In 1914, Shimek was an exchange professor at Charles University in Prague. Shimek was also Curator of the Herbarium, SUI, 1895-1937; President of the Iowa State Academy of Sciences, 1904-1905; a geologist for the Iowa State Geological Survey, 1908-1929; and Director of the Lakeside Laboratory, Lake Okoboji, Iowa. Shimek's interest in the natural sciences and geology covered many areas, but he was mostly known for his study of loess, loess fossils, and fossil malacology in Iowa and the prairie states. He was the author of the term, "Nebraskan," which is used to describe the layer underneath the Aftonian interglacial deposits.

These papers consist of correspondence with conchologists, naturalists, and shell collectors pertaining to shell collections and exchanges, and responses to Shimek's questionnaires on *Pomatiopsis lapidarias* and other shells; notebooks listing personal names of those to whom Shimek sent his publications on loess, geology, and botany; a notebook containing names of Czech-Americans; a notebook containing personal names listed under the counties of Iowa; field notes and diaries documenting Shimek's scientific field explorations throughout the Midwest, the Atlantic coastal states, the South, the Southwest, and Nicaragua; photographs showing mostly geological features and flora; a scrapbook on the geology of several counties of Iowa; a class book kept by Shimek while he was an instructor at the University of Nebraska; maps of different localities in Iowa and Nebraska; bibliographical cards on geological formations, shells, loess, and botany, arranged by subject and alphabetically thereunder; newspaper clippings, journal articles, and speeches, probably on soil erosion and prevention, and on foreign immigration.

ARRANGEMENT: (1) Correspondence, 1878-1936; (2) classroom material, 1888-1889; (3) notebooks containing personal names; (4) field notebooks and diaries, specimen lists and catalog and other notes, 1878-1936; (5) newspaper clippings, journal articles, scrapbook, and speeches; (6) photographs; (7) maps; (8) bibliography cards. FINDING AIDS: Description in control file. SPECIAL CONDITIONS: Use of this record unit requires prior arrangement with the Archives staff.

Antonio Zeno Shindler Watercolors, circa 1887
(0.1 linear meter).

Antonio Zeno Shindler (? -1899) began his association with the Smithsonian Institution in 1876 when he was hired by Spencer F. Baird to paint casts of natural history specimens. He continued in various artistic positions with the United States National Museum (USNM) until his death.

This collection consists of four watercolor paintings of Funk Island by Shindler. The paintings were based on sketches by Captain Joseph William Collins, who led an 1887 voyage of the schooner *Grampus* to Funk Island, off the coast of Newfoundland, to collect skeletal remains of the Great Auk for the USNM.

ARRANGEMENT: Unarranged. FINDING AIDS: None. SPECIAL CONDITIONS: Use of this record unit requires prior arrangement with the Archives staff.

Robert E. Silberglied Papers, 1960-1982, with related materials to 1984
(7.5 linear meters).

Robert E. Silberglied (1946-1982) was an entomologist and university professor. He was educated at Cornell University (B.S., 1967; M.S., 1968) and Harvard University (Ph.D., 1973). He began his professional career in 1973 when he was appointed Assistant Professor of Biology at Harvard University and Assistant Curator of Lepidoptera at the Museum of Comparative Zoology (MCZ). He remained at Harvard until 1981, eventually receiving promotions to Associate Professor of Biology and Associate Curator of Lepidoptera. In 1976, a new dimension was added to Silberglied's career with his appointment as a biologist at the Smithsonian Tropical Research Institute (STRI). The position divided his research, teaching, and administrative responsibilities between Cambridge and Panama, as he began spending half of each year in the American tropics. He remained on the STRI staff as a Research Entomologist and Scientist-in-Charge of the Barro Colorado Island research station until his death.

Silberglied's entomological research was primarily focused on the Lepidoptera, and included studies of ultraviolet reflectance patterns of butterflies and flowers, insect vision, and insect behavior, especially with regard to courtship, mating, and reproductive isolation. His research was enhanced by a proficiency in photographic technique which led to new methods for the visualization and recording of ultraviolet reflection. He conducted extensive field research in many regions of North and Latin America, and was involved in conservation issues, especially those affecting the Galapagos Islands and Lignum Vitae Key in Florida.

The papers of Robert E. Silberglied provide extensive documentation of his academic, teaching, and research careers. They include a large file of correspondence which contains a continual exchange of ideas and information with scientific colleagues, family members, and friends; class notes, diaries, daily calendars, registration and admission records, and research materials relating to his academic training from high school through postgraduate work; correspondence, memoranda, classroom materials, administrative records, and research files generated during his careers at Harvard

University, MCZ and STRI; manuscripts, proposals, notes, data, photographs, films, reprints, lectures, speeches, and field notes which illustrate his efforts in the fields of lepidopterology, evolutionary theory, ultraviolet photography, and conservation; and various records and photographs documenting his personal affairs.

ARRANGEMENT: (1) General correspondence, 1964-1982 and undated; (2) student records, 1960-1973 and undated; (3) teaching records, 1968-1981 and undated; (4) Smithsonian Tropical Research Institute, records, 1976-1981 and undated; (5) research records and field notes, 1965-1981 and undated; (6) photographs, films, and photographic records, *circa* 1963-1979; (7) manuscripts, publications, and papers in progress, 1969-1984; (8) speeches and lectures, 1969-1981; (9) personal and biographical materials, 1946-1981 and undated. FINDING AIDS: Description in control file. SPECIAL CONDITIONS: Use of this record unit requires prior arrangement with the Archives staff.

(7414)

Gordon B. Small, Jr., Papers, circa 1972-1989
(0.8 linear meter).

Gordon B. Small, Jr., (1934-1989) received his B.A. degree from Bowdoin College in 1951 and his M.A. degree from Brown University in 1955. In 1962, he joined the Panama Canal Company as a mathematics instructor in their Department of Education in the Panama Canal Zone. Small remained in Panama until 1986, and he became an authority on the butterflies of the region. His butterfly collection of over 50,000 specimens was donated to the National Museum of Natural History.

These papers consist primarily of notes, data sheets, and check lists concerning Small's research on the butterflies of Panama and the development of his collection. Also included is correspondence with colleagues and a copy of a lecture on Panamanian butterflies.

ARRANGEMENT: Unarranged. FINDING AIDS: None. SPECIAL CONDITIONS: (1) Use of this record unit requires prior arrangement with the Archives staff; (2) some correspondence and notes are in Spanish.

(7206)

Charles W. Smiley and William V. Cox, Fishery Statistics, circa 1880
(5 bound volumes).

Charles W. Smiley (1846-1926) was educated at the Eastman National Business College and Wesleyan University, Middletown, Connecticut. He served as special agent in charge of fishery statistics for the Fisheries Division of the Tenth Census, 1879-1881, and as Editor for the United States Commission of Fish and Fisheries, 1881-1889.

William V. Cox (1852-1923) was appointed special agent for the Fisheries Division of the Tenth Census in 1879. Other positions held by Cox included Assistant for the International Fisheries Exhibition in London, 1883; Financial Clerk for the exposition work of the Smithsonian Institution, 1884-1885; and Chief Clerk of the United States National Museum, 1885-1902.

This collection consists of five bound volumes of statistics, compiled by Smiley and Cox, on the exportation and importation of fishery products, 1731-1880. Apparently these statistics were compiled for use by the Fisheries Division of the Tenth Census, 1880.

ARRANGEMENT: Bound in numeric sequence. FINDING AIDS: None. SPECIAL CONDITIONS: Use of this record unit requires prior arrangement with the Archives staff.

(7262)

Frank Smith Papers, 1893-1942 and undated
(0.4 linear meter).

Frank Smith (1857-1942) was a biology professor and authority on earthworms. He was educated at Hillsdale College (Michigan), Ph.B., 1885, and Harvard University, A.M., 1893. His first teaching job was at Hillsdale College where he served as Professor of Chemistry and Biology from 1886 to 1892. In 1893, Smith was appointed Instructor in Zoology at the University of Illinois. He was promoted to Assistant Professor in 1896, Associate Professor in 1900, and Professor in 1913. He retired in 1926 and was named Professor Emeritus. Smith also served as Curator of the University Museum of Natural History from 1900 to 1917. Smith's field experience included investigations at the University of Michigan Biological Station during the summers of 1911-1914 and 1919-1922, and a collecting trip to Colorado in 1916. For many years, Smith identified specimens and worked up collections of earthworms for the United States National Museum (USNM). In 1934, he donated his collection of earthworms to the USNM.

The papers of Frank Smith document his research on earthworms. They consist of correspondence with biologists and USNM administrators and staff, including Paul Bartsch, Nathan A. Cobb, Gordon Enoch Gates, Chancey Juday, James Arthur MacNab, John Percy Moore, Brayton Howard Ransom, Mary Jane Rathbun, Richard Rathbun, William deC. Ravenel, Waldo LaSalle Schmitt, and Paul Smith Welch; field notes; class notes kept by Smith at Harvard University, 1893; reprints; a bibliography; and research notes.

ARRANGEMENT: (1) General correspondence, 1895-1942 and undated; (2) field notes, class notes, bibliography, reprints, and research notes, 1893-1922 and undated. FINDING AIDS: Description in control file. SPECIAL CONDITIONS: Use of this record unit requires prior arrangement with the Archives staff.

(7276)

Lyman Bradford Smith Papers, 1959-circa 1970
(0.1 linear meter).

Lyman Bradford Smith (1904-   ), botanist, was born in Boston, Massachusetts. He attended Harvard University where he received an A.B. in 1925, an A.M. in 1929, and a Ph.D. in biology in 1930. From 1928 to 1929, Smith held a Sheldon traveling fellowship to Brazil. From 1931 to 1947, Smith was an Assistant Curator, Junior Curator, and Curator at the Gray Herbarium.

In 1947, Smith was appointed Associate Curator in the Division of Phanerogams, United States National Museum, and was made Curator of the Division in 1957. Smith retired from the Division in 1966 and has since held the position of Senior Botanist with the Department of Botany.

Smith has concentrated his studies on the taxonomy of flowering plants, especially those from Latin America, and the family Bromeliaceae.

These papers contain correspondence with botanists and directors of herbaria concerning the identification of specimens, collecting and exchanging botanical collections, especially those of South and Central America, and requests for publications and notes and a manuscript on a key to Tillandsia.

ARRANGEMENT: Mostly alphabetic. FINDING AIDS: Description in control file. SPECIAL CONDITIONS: Use of this record unit requires prior arrangement with the Archives staff.

(7443)

Smithsonian Early Enrichment Center, 1984-1994
Records (1.8 linear meters).

When the Smithsonian Institution Women's Council (SIWC) was formed in 1972, one of its most important aims was the establishment of a child care center at the Institution. The SIWC intensified its efforts in 1986: conducted surveys to determine the need and support for an on-site child care center, conducted feasibility studies for the various sites proposed, and obtained the professional advice of child care consultants. These efforts resulted in the appointment of a Child Care Advisory Board (CCAB) in January 1987. The mission of the CCAB was to investigate and report to Smithsonian management the prospective budget, policy, operations, facilities, and curriculum of a child care center at the Smithsonian. When the Advisory Board presented its business plan to the Smithsonian Institution Management Committee in May of 1987, the Committee gave its approval for setting up a center.

Although the Smithsonian generously offered to provide start-up funds and rent-free space and utilities, as well as other in-kind services, it was agreed that the child care center should be independently incorporated. In November 1987, the Smithsonian Child Care Advisory Board was formally incorporated as the Board of Directors for the Smithsonian Child Care Center. The first center opened in the National Museum of American History (NMAH) on October 3, 1988. The founding Board of Directors was replaced shortly thereafter by an elected, parent-majority board; and a Parents Association was established as a means of providing parent input and support for the Center and its Board. On January 1, 1989, the new Board changed the name of the child care center to the Smithsonian Early Enrichment Center.

Since 1989, the Board of Directors has devoted itself to oversight of the operations of the center, to further development of curriculum, and to expansion into other buildings. It also began a short-lived effort with IBM to create a computerized version of its "Museum Magic" curriculum and has also investigated publishing the curriculum. In January 1991, the Infant Care Center opened in the Arts and Industries Building.

These records were created by three women who were instrumental in bringing child care to the Smithsonian: Kathleen Baxter, Gretchen Gayle Ellsworth, and Katherine Sprague (Tkac). They consist of meeting minutes, agendas, and correspondence of the Smithsonian Institution Women's Council (SIWC) Child Care Committee, the Child Care Advisory Board (CCAB), the Smithsonian Early Enrichment Center Board of Directors, the Smithsonian Early Enrichment Center Parents Association, and the Infant Task Force; proposals, architectural drawings, and correspondence dealing with the selection and preparation of sites for the NMAH branch and the Arts and Industries Infant Care Center; personnel and financial records; materials dealing with the IBM/ SEEC curriculum project; and photographs of events at the NMAH center. For related records, see record units 310 and 507.

ARRANGEMENT: (1) Records of Kathleen Baxter, 1984-1989; (2) records of Gretchen Gayle Ellsworth, 1987-1988, with related records from 1985-1986; (3) records of Katherine Sprague (Tkac), 1981-1982, 1985-1990; (4) records of the Director, Smithsonian Early Enrichment Center, 1988-1994. FINDING AIDS: Folder list in control file. SPECIAL CONDITIONS: Use of this record unit requires prior arrangement with the Archives staff.

(7132)

Robert Evans Snodgrass Papers, 1924-1962
(3.1 linear meters).

Robert Evans Snodgrass (1875-1962) worked for the Bureau of Entomology and Plant Quarantine of the United States Department of Agriculture from 1906 to 1910 and from 1917 to 1945. His specialty was insect anatomy. He also taught entomology at the University of Maryland, 1924-1947, and was a Research Associate of the United States National Museum, 1953-1962.

These papers include materials concerning entomology and zoology; reviews of fellow scientists' manuscripts; identification of specimens; honors; requests for reprints; recommendations and personal appearances; photographs of specimens; and foreign correspondence, some in French and German.

ARRANGEMENT: (1) Correspondence, arranged alphabetically; (2) miscellaneous; (3) drawings and plates. FINDING AIDS: Description in control file. SPECIAL CONDITIONS: Use of this record unit requires prior arrangement with the Archives staff.

(7372)

Thomas Elliott Snyder Papers, circa 1944, 1955 and undated
(0.1 linear meter).

Thomas Elliott Snyder (1885-1970), an entomologist and authority on the taxonomy, biology, and control of termites, received his Ph.D. from the George Washington University in 1920. He joined the staff of the Division of Forest Insects, Bureau of Entomology, United States Department of Agriculture (USDA) in 1909. He remained with the USDA until his retirement in 1951. Snyder served as a Research Associate in the Department of Entomology, United States National Museum (USNM), from 1951 until his death. His collection of over 230,000 specimens was donated to the USNM.

These papers consist of Snyder's unpublished manuscript on entomology, *Insects, Man's Greatest Rivals* and photographs of Snyder and his family, as well as termite nests.

ARRANGEMENT: (1) *Insects, Man's Greatest Rivals,* 1944; (2) photographs, 1955 and undated. FINDING AIDS: None. SPECIAL CONDITIONS: Use of this record unit requires prior arrangement with the Archives staff.

(7419)

Paul J. Spangler Papers, 1962-1980, with related material from 1949
(0.4 linear meter).

Paul J. Spangler (1924-   ) received his B.A. from Lebanon Valley College in 1949, his M.S. from Ohio University in 1951, and his Ph.D in entomology from the University of Missouri in 1960. From 1951 to 1953, he worked as Museum Assistant in Entomology at the University of Kansas. Spangler then accepted a position at the University of

Missouri, where he worked as an Instructor in Entomology from 1953 to 1957. In 1957 he was stationed in Juneau, Alaska, as a Fishery Research Biologist with the United States Fish and Wildlife Service, a position he held until 1958.

In 1958, Spangler joined the staff of the Entomology Research Division, Agricultural Research Service, United States Department of Agriculture (USDA), located in the United States National Museum (USNM). He was a Systematic Entomologist with the USDA until 1962, when he took a job as an Associate Curator in the Division of Insects, USNM. When the Division of Coleoptera was created in 1963, Spangler became an Associate Curator with that division.

These papers consist mainly of professional correspondence documenting Spangler's work in the Division of Coleoptera and his research on aquatic beetles. Most of the material concerns the identification of entomological specimens. A small amount of correspondence predates Spangler's association with the USNM.

ARRANGEMENT: (1) Alphabetic correspondence, 1962-1980; (2) correspondence, 1949-1962. FINDING AIDS: None. SPECIAL CONDITIONS: Use of this record unit requires prior arrangement with the Archives staff.

(7325)

Timothy William Stanton Papers, 1885-1928, 1941 and undated
(0.7 linear meter).

Timothy William Stanton (1860-1953) was a paleontologist specializing in the study of Cretaceous invertebrates. His 46-year career with the United States Geological Survey (USGS) began in 1889 when he was appointed Assistant Paleontologist to support the work of Charles Abiathar White. By 1903 he had advanced to the position of Chief of the Section of Paleontology and Stratigraphy, USGS. In 1932 he became Chief Geologist, USGS, and remained in the position until his retirement in 1935. For many years, Stanton also acted as Chairman of the USGS Committee on Geologic Names. He also served as Custodian of Mesozoic Invertebrates, Department of Geology, United States National Museum (USNM) from 1894 to 1953.

Stanton's career with the USGS was marked by extensive field research, especially in the western and southwestern United States. He was active in the geological profession and served as President of the Paleontological Society in 1921. In the same year he served as Vice-President of the Geological Society of America.

The papers of Timothy William Stanton partially document his career with the USGS, his research on Cretaceous invertebrates, field expeditions, professional activities, and personal affairs. Included is incoming and outgoing correspondence which concerns USGS work, especially his service on the Committee on Geologic Names; his research at the USNM; and his work for the Paleontological Society and the Geological Society of America. The collection also includes outgoing correspondence written by Stanton and his predecessor, Charles Abiathar White, which mostly reports on fossils sent for identification; copies of letters written by Stanton while on field expeditions; and a copy of his autobiography, *Eighty Years of Joy and Gladness Mingled with some Work and Sadness,* 1941.

ARRANGEMENT: (1) General correspondence, 1921-1928 and undated; (2) outgoing correspondence, 1885-1916; (3) field letters, 1893-1928; (4) autobiography, 1941. FINDING AIDS: Description in control file. SPECIAL CONDITIONS: Use of this record unit requires prior arrangement with the Archives staff.

Arthur deC. Sowerby Papers, 1904-1954 and undated
(3.6 linear meters).

Arthur deC. Sowerby (1885-1954), naturalist, explorer, artist, and editor was born in Tai-yuan Fu, Shansi province, China, where his father served as a Baptist missionary. After a brief stay at Bristol University, England, Sowerby returned to China and began collecting specimens for the Natural History Museum in Tai-yuan Fu. In 1906, he was appointed to the staff of the Anglo-Chinese College at Tientsin as lecturer and curator of the Natural History Museum. He was a member of an expedition to the Ordos Desert in southern Mongolia in 1907, where he collected mammals for the British Museum (Natural History). In 1908, Sowerby joined American millionaire Robert Sterling Clark on an expedition into Shansi and Kansu provinces of north China. This began a long association with Clark, who financed several collecting trips by Sowerby. Many of the specimens collected by the Clark-Sowerby expeditions were deposited in the United States National Museum. During the Chinese Revolution of 1911, Sowerby led a relief mission to evacuate foreign missionaries in Shansi and Sianfu provinces. During World War I Sowerby served in France as Technical Officer in the Chinese Labour Corps. After the war, he settled in Shanghai and established *The China Journal of Science and Arts,* which he edited until the outbreak of World War II in 1941. During the war, Sowerby was interned by the Japanese army in Shanghai. He came to the United States in 1949 and spent the remainder of his life in Washington, D.C., pursuing genealogical research which resulted in a family history, "The Sowerby Saga."

These papers document the multi-faceted career of Arthur deC. Sowerby, especially his work as a naturalist and expedition member. They include correspondence, including a large amount with Robert Sterling Clark; fiscal records; material relating to his genealogical research and "The Sowerby Saga;" manuscripts, newspaper articles, and research notes written by Sowerby; photographs and lantern slides; the papers of his third wife, Alice Muriel Cowans Sowerby; paintings, sketches, and poetry; and a notebook, a diary, and an autobiographical memoir.

ARRANGEMENT: (1) General correspondence, 1908-1954; (2) fiscal records, 1931-1953; (3) correspondence, genealogical data, and related materials concerning "The Sowerby Saga," 1950-1954 and undated; (4) manuscripts, newspaper articles, and research notes written by Sowerby, 1922-1948 and undated; (5) photographs and lantern slides, 1908-1954 and undated; (6) Alice Muriel Cowans Sowerby papers, 1920-1954 and undated; (7) paintings, sketches, and poetry, 1904-1950 and undated; (8) notebook, diary, and autobiographical memoir, 1930, 1949 and undated. FINDING AIDS: Description in control file. SPECIAL CONDITIONS: Use of this record unit requires prior arrangement with the Archives staff.

John Mix Stanley Collection, 1852-1865, 1883-1886
(0.1 linear meter).

John Mix Stanley (1814-1872), a famous painter of Indians and Indian scenes, deposited 152 paintings with the Smithsonian Institution in 1852 with the intention of selling his collection to the government. Most of the paintings were destroyed in the Smithsonian fire of 1865. A list of the collection can be found in the Smithsonian catalog, *Portraits of North American Indians with Sketches of Scenery, etc.,* 1852.

This collection includes typewritten copies and original correspondence of Joseph Henry, Mary A. Henry, John Mix Stanley, and his family concerning the collection deposited with the Smithsonian; contract and correspondence concerning a loan made by Henry to Stanley; Henry's description of the attempts to save the paintings during the fire; contract between John R. Bartlett and Stanley concerning Bartlett's purchasing one-fourth interest in the collection; a list of the five surviving paintings; and three books printed for the Smithsonian Institution, including the catalog mentioned above, a *Guide to the Smithsonian Institution,* 1865, and a biography of John Mix Stanley by David I. Bushnell, Jr.

ARRANGEMENT: (1) Correspondence, 1858, 1864-1865, 1883-1886; (2) books, contracts, and list of paintings. FINDING AIDS: (1) Description in control file; (2) *Portraits of North American Indians with Sketches of Scenery, etc.,* 1852. SPECIAL CONDITIONS: Use of this record unit requires prior arrangement with the Archives staff.

(7077)

Robert Edwards Carter Stearns Papers, 1879-1909
(0.3 linear meter).

Robert Edwards Carter Stearns (1827-1909) was a public figure of some prominence whose careers included mining, publishing, and the natural sciences. A lover of nature since childhood, Stearns concentrated on conchology, mostly mollusks of the West Coast. Stearns was a researcher for the United States Commission of Fish and Fisheries, 1882-1884; an Assistant Curator, Department of Mollusks, United States National Museum (USNM); and a Paleontologist for the United States Geological Survey, 1884-1892.

These papers consist chiefly of incoming correspondence from the USNM, the Smithsonian Institution, and shell collectors; correspondence between scientists other than Stearns concerning publications, publication revision, and shell collections; scrapbooks containing correspondence, memoranda, labels, and cards collected while Stearns was an Assistant Curator; specimen labels donated to the USNM; handwritten and printed drafts for articles, including a preliminary report on the fossils at San Diego, and the original drawings and draft for "Anodontas of the West Coast"; and autobiographical materials.

ARRANGEMENT: (1) Correspondence, 1884-1909; (2) scrapbooks, 1879-1892; (3) handwritten and printed drafts for articles. FINDING AIDS: Description in control file. SPECIAL CONDITIONS: Use of this record unit requires prior arrangement with the Archives staff.

(7277)

Edward Strieby Steele Papers, 1903-1935
(0.4 linear meter).

Edward Strieby Steele (1850-1942) served as a botanical clerk for the United States Department of Agriculture (USDA) from 1891 to 1902. From 1902 to 1918, Steele was an editorial assistant for the Division of Plants, United States National Museum, and from 1918 to 1920 was an assistant botanist for the USDA.

These papers include correspondence mostly in regard to the collecting of *Liatris* specimens and a manuscript and correspondence concerning Steele's writing on wild blackberries and dewberries in the District of Columbia.

ARRANGEMENT: (1) Incoming correspondence, arranged alphabetically; (2) manuscript and correspondence concerning "Wild Blackberries and Dewberries in the District of Columbia and Vicinity"; (3) outgoing correspondence. FINDING AIDS: Description in control file. SPECIAL CONDITIONS: Use of this record unit requires prior arrangement with the Archives staff.

(7074)

Leonhard Stejneger Papers, 1753, 1867-1943

(6.1 linear meters and oversize).

Leonhard Stejneger (1851-1943) was born in Norway. In 1881 he left for the United States and arrived in Washington, D.C., where he soon began working with the birds of the New World at the Smithsonian Institution with particular interest in aquatic birds. In December 1884 he was appointed Assistant Curator in the Department of Birds under Robert Ridgway, Curator. In 1889 after the resignation of Henry Crecy Yarrow, Honorary Curator of the Department of Reptiles and Batrachians, Stejneger became the first full-time Curator for the Department. In 1903 he served as Acting Head Curator of the Department of Biology for several months, and in 1911 he was appointed Head Curator of the Department of Biology after Frederick William True vacated the post. From that time until his death Stejneger served both as Head Curator of the Department of Biology and Curator of the Division of Reptiles and Batrachians. He also chaired a Smithsonian committee which considered manuscripts for publication.

In addition to his herpetological and ornithological work, Stejneger was recognized as an authority on the fur seals of the North Pacific. He began his studies in this field when he was sent to the Commander Islands for the United States Signal Service in 1882, and made a number of trips to the area between then and 1922. In 1896, Stejneger was appointed to the International Fur Seal Commission by President Grover Cleveland. In connection with his fur seal work, Stejneger researched and published a biography of Georg Wilhelm Steller, 1936.

Stejneger also played an important role in international zoological meetings and was elected to the International Commission on Zoological Nomenclature in 1898.

The papers of Leonhard Stejneger consist of manuscripts on Japanese herpetology, Chinese herpetology, Puerto Rican and West Indian herpetology, North American herpetology, poisonous snakes, turtles, fur seals, ornithology, European fauna, and the study of life zones; manuscripts, general notes, bibliographic notes, and correspondence regarding the publication of Stejneger's biography of Georg Wilhelm Steller and a copy of Steller's *Ausfuhrliche Beschreibung von sonderbaren Meerthieren,* 1753; diaries, notebooks, and account books covering much of the time Stejneger spent at zoological congresses and on field trips; photographs of fur seals and natives of the North Pacific-Bering Sea area; photographs of mammal skulls and skeletons; scrapbooks; outgoing correspondence; and personal material.

ARRANGEMENT: (1) Manuscripts, notes, and related materials on herpetology, *circa* 1890-1943; (2) manuscripts, notes, and related materials on fur seals, 1882-1924; (3) manuscripts, notes, and related materials on ornithology, *circa* 1867-1905; (4) manuscripts, notes, and related materials on European fauna, *circa* 1904-1914; (5) manuscripts, notes, and related materials on Georg Wilhelm Steller, *circa* 1882-1941;

(6) diaries, notebooks, and account books, 1882-1913 and undated; (7) photographs, *circa* 1882-1916; (8) scrapbooks, undated; (9) outgoing correspondence, 1877-1882; (10) personal materials, honors, and genealogy, 1875-1932; (11) miscellany, 1902, 1904 and undated; (12) add acquisition, 1753, 1853-1945; (13) add acquisition, oversize, 1893-1935; (14) add acquisition, *circa* 1930-1941. FINDING AIDS: Description in control file. SPECIAL CONDITIONS: Use of this record unit requires prior arrangement with the Archives staff.

(7441)

Leonhard Stejneger and Georg Herman Baur Collection, circa 1850-1943
(1.6 linear meters).

For information on the life and career of Leonhard Stejneger, see record unit 7074.

Georg Herman Baur (1859-1898) was born and educated in Germany. He came to the United States in 1884 to be Othniel Charles Marsh's assistant at Yale University. He later held faculty positions at Clark University and the University of Chicago. Baur's primary fields of study were comparative osteology and paleontology. At the time of his death, Baur was preparing a monograph on the tortoises of North America which was to be published by the United States National Museum (USNM).

This collection consists of papers documenting the research of both Stejneger and Baur on tortoises. Much of the Baur material was created during his research for the planned USNM monograph on North American tortoises. The papers consist of correspondence, notes, manuscripts, lists, newspaper clippings, photographs, negatives, and drawings. Of special interest are color drawings executed by John H. Richard and Antonio Zeno Shindler.

ARRANGEMENT: Unarranged. FINDING AIDS: None. SPECIAL CONDITIONS: (1) The provenance of these records has been lost and the creator of some materials is unclear; (2) use of this record unit requires prior arrangement with the Archives staff.

(7379)

Arthur Wilson Stelfox Papers, 1904-1967
(1.6 linear meters).

Arthur Wilson Stelfox (1883-1972), Irish naturalist and entomologist, was born in Belfast and studied architecture in Ireland and England. While practicing that profession, Stelfox also pursued an interest in natural history and served as Secretary of the Belfast Naturalists Field Club. In 1920, he was appointed Assistant Naturalist at the National Museum of Ireland in Dublin, where he specialized in the Hymenoptera. Following his retirement in 1948, Stelfox continued to build his collections and donated them to the Smithsonian in 1966.

These papers document Stelfox's work as a naturalist in Great Britain and Ireland and the development of his collection of Hymenoptera. They include diaries concerning Hymenoptera and other insects collected, 1921-1965; lists of mollusks collected, 1904-1917; correspondence, primarily with A. Clive Jewitt, G. E. J. Nixon, and R. C. L. Perkins, concerning Stelfox's study of Hymenoptera; manuscripts sent to Stelfox for comment; published papers, with extensive marginalia; illustrations; and working notes.

ARRANGEMENT: (1) "Diary of Hymenoptera, other insects, plants, etc. seen or taken by A. W. Stelfox," 1921-1965, 32 volumes; (2) "Lists of land and freshwater mollusca and localities found in Great Britain and Ireland by A. W. Stelfox," 1904-1917, 3 volumes; (3) correspondence, 1932-1967; (4) manuscripts, illustrations, and notes. FINDING AIDS: Description in control file. SPECIAL CONDITIONS: (1) This record unit replaces previously numbered 1020013; (2) use of this record unit requires prior arrangement with the Archives staff.

(7373)

George C. Steyskal Papers, 1930, 1942-1990
(0.8 linear meter).

George C. Steyskal (1909-   ) was born and grew up in Detroit, Michigan, and graduated from the Henry Ford Trade School in Dearborn. After graduating in 1928, he worked at various tool and machine parts factories until 1962, all the while pursuing his interests as an amateur entomologist. In July 1962, Steyskal accepted a position as a Research Agriculturalist for the Insect Identification and Beneficial Insect Introduction Institute, United States Department of Agriculture (USDA), located in the Smithsonian's Natural History Building. After 1972, the Institute became the Systematic Entomology Laboratory, USDA. After his retirement in 1979, Steyskal continued to study the taxonomy and morphology of Diptera part time until he moved to Florida in 1990.

The papers of George C. Steyskal consist of incoming and outgoing correspondence mostly concerning the identification of specimens. Also included is a binder of personnel information and correspondence relating to Steyskal's hiring in 1962.

ARRANGEMENT: (1) Alphabetic correspondence, 1944-1990; (2) personnel information, 1930, 1942-1946, 1962-1990. FINDING AIDS: None. SPECIAL CONDITIONS: Use of this record unit requires prior arrangement with the Archives staff.

(7093)

William Stimpson Papers, 1852-1861
(0.3 linear meter).

Naturalist and zoologist, William Stimpson (1832-1872) spent four years as a naturalist with the North Pacific Exploring Expedition, 1852-1856. For nine years after the completion of the expedition, Stimpson utilized the facilities of the Smithsonian Institution while preparing a report based on the collections gathered during the expedition. While at the Smithsonian, he also helped classify and name specimens which the Smithsonian had been collecting. In 1865, Stimpson was called to Chicago by his friend Robert Kennicott in order to take over the directorship of the Chicago Academy of Sciences. At the Academy, Stimpson assembled probably the largest collection of specimens ever gathered up to that time, in preparation for a major work on invertebrates. It contained the Smithsonian specimens of American invertebrates and Stimpson's private collection, as well as loans from a number of other collections. This great collection, including all the manuscripts being prepared by Stimpson, was destroyed in the Chicago fire of 1871, an event from which Stimpson never fully recovered.

ARRANGEMENT: Unarranged with the following apparent divisions: (1) manuscripts; (2) catalog; (3) financial notebook, 1852-1857; (4) general correspondence and receipts regarding publications based on the North Pacific Exploring Expedition and Stimpson's manuscripts, 1858-1861. FINDING AIDS: None. SPECIAL CONDITIONS: Use of this record unit requires prior arrangement with the Archives staff.

Alan Stone Papers, circa 1931-1971
(2.5 linear meters).

Alan Stone (1904-   ), an entomologist specializing in the taxonomy of Diptera, was educated at Cornell University, receiving the B.S. degree in 1926 and the Ph.D. in 1929. In 1931, Stone was appointed Assistant Entomologist with the Bureau of Entomology and Plant Quarantine, United States Department of Agriculture (USDA). He was promoted to Entomologist in 1939 and remained with the USDA until his retirement in 1971. Stone was an authority on the Diptera families Culicidae, Tabanidae, and Simuliidae. His bibliography totaled over 105 titles including catalogs of the mosquitoes of the world, 1959, and the Diptera of North America, 1965.

The papers of Alan Stone consist of incoming and outgoing correspondence documenting his career at the USDA and his research on Diptera. Most of the letters concern the identification of specimens.

ARRANGEMENT: Alphabetic. FINDING AIDS: Box list in control file. SPECIAL CONDITIONS: Use of this record unit requires prior arrangement with the Archives staff.

Dayton Stoner Papers, 1914-1925
(0.1 linear meter).

Dayton Stoner (1883-1944) was educated at the State University of Iowa and served in a number of posts before becoming State Zoologist in the New York State Museum in 1932.

These papers consist of correspondence with professional colleagues, mainly regarding attempts to describe material collected by the State University of Iowa Expedition to Barbados and Antigua. Custody history of the correspondence is unknown.

ARRANGEMENT: Correspondence, 1914-1925. FINDING AIDS: Description in control file. SPECIAL CONDITIONS: Use of this record unit requires prior arrangement with the Archives staff.

Roman Strekalovsky Drawings, circa 1940
(79 items).

This collection consisting of 79 color plates of bee flies, drawn to accompany manuscripts of Professor Efflatoun, has been reassigned to record unit 7468.

These drawings were arranged by genus and were on loan to the National Museum of Natural History from the Egyptian Entomological Society.

George Suckley Papers, 1849-1861
(0.2 linear meter).

George Suckley (1830-1869) was born in New York City and graduated from the College of Physicians and Surgeons (now a part of Columbia University) in September 1851. In April 1853 Suckley was appointed assistant surgeon and naturalist to the Pacific

Railroad Survey of the 47th and 49th parallels between St. Paul, Minnesota, and Fort Vancouver, Washington Territory, under the command of Isaac I. Stevens. His work on the survey included a 1,049 mile, 53-day canoe trip down the Bitter Root, Clark's Fork, and Columbia Rivers to Fort Vancouver, during which he made extensive natural history collections. On December 2, 1853, Suckley was commissioned Assistant Surgeon, United States Army. He was ordered to duty at Fort Steilacoom, Washington Territory, where he remained until June 12, 1854, when he was transferred to Fort Dalles, Oregon Territory. In July 1854, Suckley obtained leave of absence for six months, which he partially spent collecting natural history specimens in Panama with James G. Cooper. Suckley resigned from the Army on October 3, 1856, and for the next five years pursued his interest in natural history. During this period, Suckley was assigned to write the reports on the mammals and salmonidae collected by the Northwest Boundary Survey of 1857. In 1859 he co-authored with James G. Cooper, *The Natural History of Washington Territory,* which was based primarily on data and observations made while serving with the Pacific Railroad Survey. On the outbreak of the Civil War, Suckley rejoined the Army and was commissioned Surgeon of Volunteers. He served for the duration of the war, resigning April 22, 1865. Suckley died July 30, 1869, in New York City.

The papers of George Suckley mostly concern his work on the Pacific Railroad Survey of the 47th and 49th parallels, 1853, and on the collections of the Northwest Boundary Survey of 1857. They include incoming and outgoing correspondence, mostly copies; journals, field books, notes, and related materials concerning the progress of the Railroad Survey, the canoe trip from Fort Owen to Fort Vancouver, Suckley's Panama trip with Cooper, and natural history observations and collecting work; fiscal matters; translation of Indian vocabulary; Suckley's monograph, *The Natural History of Washington Territory,* co-authored with Cooper; and manuscripts of Suckley's reports on the mammals and salmonidae collected on the Northwest Boundary Survey of 1857.

ARRANGEMENT: (1) Incoming and outgoing correspondence, 1853-1861; (2) journals, field books, and notes, 1849-1861; (3) manuscripts of reports on the mammals and salmonidae collected on the Northwest Boundary Survey of 1857, 1861. FINDING AIDS: Description in control file. SPECIAL CONDITIONS: Use of this record unit requires prior arrangement with the Archives staff.

(7142)

Systematic Biology Resource Management Project, 1971-1973
Records (0.8 linear meter).

In 1971, at the invitation of the Smithsonian, systematists and administrators representing seven scientific institutions, including the Smithsonian, convened to discuss a national program for systematics collections and their management. The participants recommended that further studies be undertaken and a report be presented to a national conference. Six committees were established and their findings presented to the Conference of Directors of Systematics Collections meeting at Gainesville, Florida, in April 1972. The meeting revised the reports and they were again reviewed in July 1972, at the Systematic Biology Symposium sponsored by the Smithsonian, the National Academy of Sciences, and the National Science Foundation. The findings were then turned over to a committee of systematists and administrators, meeting at the

Smithsonian's Belmont Conference Center, who were responsible for drafting a national plan for the coordination of national systematic resources. The Association of Systematics Collections, which replaced the Conference of Directors of Systematics Collections, received the draft and was charged with the responsibility to write, publish, and distribute the final report.

These records consist of materials of the Systematic Biology Symposium and the Belmont Conference concerning their discussion of the work of the six committees. They include general correspondence and the correspondence of the six committees; financial records; travel vouchers; position papers of the six committees; drafts of a national plan for systematics resources; a pre-publication draft of "America's Systematic Collections: A National Plan"; transcripts and tapes of the Systematic Biology Symposium; and correspondence, constitution, and by-laws of the Association of Systematics Collections.

ARRANGEMENT: By subject. FINDING AIDS: Description in control file. SPECIAL CONDITIONS: Use of this record unit requires prior arrangement with the Archives staff.

(7309)

Systematic Entomology Laboratory, United States Department of Agriculture, 1910-1973

General Correspondence (6.1 linear meters).

The Systematic Entomology Laboratory (SEL), United States Department of Agriculture (USDA), is responsible for the identification of insect specimens. Its work provides basic support for biological control projects, environmental studies, and research activities of federal and state agencies and other organizations. SEL scientists are also active in research focused upon insect groups of economic importance to American agriculture. SEL maintains offices at the National Museum of Natural History and at the Beltsville Agricultural Research Center, Beltsville, Maryland.

Taxonomic work in entomology at the USDA was given separate status in 1925 with the creation of the Division of Taxonomic Investigation. Sievert Allen Rohwer was placed in charge of the division. During its nearly sixty year history, the section responsible for entomological taxonomy at the USDA has undergone numerous administrative reorganizations and name changes. Over most of these years it has had four titles: Division of Taxonomic Investigation, 1925-1934; Division of Insect Identification, 1934-1952; Insect Identification and Parasite Introduction Research Branch, 1959-1972; and Systematic Entomology Laboratory, 1972- . USDA entomologists in charge of taxonomic work have included Rohwer, 1925-1927; Harold Morrison, 1927-1935; Carl Frederick William Muesebeck, 1935-1954; Paul Wilson Oman, 1954-1960; William Henry Anderson, 1960-1966; Reece I. Sailer, 1967-1972; and Richard H. Foote, 1972-1976.

This correspondence documents the work of the SEL and its predecessors, 1925-1973, and mostly concerns the identification of specimens sent to the USDA for determination. Correspondents include domestic and foreign entomologists, government scientists, university professors, and USDA staff. Correspondence before 1925 primarily documents the professional work of Sievert Allen Rohwer and includes letters relating to his duties as Custodian of Hymenoptera, Division of Insects, United States National Museum.

ARRANGEMENT: Alphabetic. FINDING AIDS: Description in control file. SPECIAL CONDITIONS: Use of this record unit requires prior arrangement with the Archives staff.

(7426)

Systematic Entomology Laboratory, United States Department of Agriculture, 1960-1988

Records (6.6 linear meters).

For an administrative history of the Systematic Entomology Laboratory, see record unit 7309.

These records primarily document the administration and research of the United States Department of Agriculture's Systematic Entomology Laboratory (SEL) under Chiefs Ronald William Hodges, 1976-1980, Paul Malcolm Marsh, 1980-1985, and Douglass R. Miller, 1985- . In 1985, the title Chief was changed to Research Leader.

This record unit contains information on administrative activities, curation of collections, publication of scientific manuscripts, cooperative research agreements with universities, budgets, staffing, committees, and grants. Incoming and outgoing correspondence, memoranda, research proposals, newsletters, and annual reports also document the activities of SEL. In addition, these records contain correspondence, memoranda, grant proposals, progress reports, publications, and related materials pertaining to foreign research projects of SEL funded by excess foreign currency. Of special interest in these records is information concerning the reorganization of the Agricultural Research Service and the Insect Identification and Parasite Introduction Research Branch, biographical data on various SEL entomologists, and photographs and slides of entomologists and scientific illustrators at work.

ARRANGEMENT: (1) Administrative files, 1968-1985, accession number 90-009; (2) foreign research files, 1960-1988, accession number 90-008; (3) outgoing correspondence, 1983-1985, accession number 87-092. FINDING AIDS: Folder list in control file. SPECIAL CONDITIONS: (1) Restricted; (2) use of this record unit requires prior arrangement with the Archives staff.

(7323)

Systematic Entomology Laboratory, United States Department of Agriculture, 1797-1988 and undated

Photographs and Biographical Information (2.7 linear meters).

For an administrative history of the Systematic Entomology Laboratory, United States Department of Agriculture (USDA), see record unit 7309.

This record unit was created by combining two separate accessions containing biographical information and photographs of entomologists. The biographical material is varied, and includes obituaries, magazine and newspaper articles, correspondence, bibliographies, photographs, handwriting samples, book reviews, and biographical sketches. Information on a number of entomological societies such as the Cambridge Entomological Club, the Entomological Society of America, and the Royal Entomological Society of London, is also included.

In addition, the collection contains photographs of entomologists collected for the most part by Eugene Amandus Schwarz and Herbert Spencer Barber, USDA entomologists associated with the United States National Museum. Included are formal portraits, casual photographs, photographs taken during field work, and group photographs. There are also photographs of field work sites from around the world.

This collection appeared as record units 1020002 and 1020003 in the 1983 *Guide to the Smithsonian Archives.*

ARRANGEMENT: (1) Biographical information primarily on dipterists, 1797-1988 and undated; (2) photographs of entomologists, 1878-1950 and undated. FINDING AIDS: Description in control file. SPECIAL CONDITIONS: Use of this record unit requires prior arrangement with the Archives staff.

(7226)

Society of Systematic Zoology, 1947-1975
Records (4.6 linear meters).

The Society of Systematic Zoology (SSZ) was organized at the Chicago meeting of the American Association for the Advancement of Science (AAAS) in 1947. Prior to the meeting, Waldo LaSalle Schmitt and George W. Wharton, Jr., had polled taxonomists about the founding of a systematics society; and the result was an organizational meeting on December 29, 1947. The first annual meeting of the SSZ was held in Washington in September 1948. Schmitt became its first president and Wharton its first secretary-treasurer. The government of the Society was vested in a council, with officers elected from nominees named by the Council. Original Council members were Alfred S. Romer, Carl Frederick William Muesebeck, Orlando Park, and Richard Eliot Blackwelder. A president and president-elect were elected to one-year terms.

A *News Letter* for the SSZ was first published in 1949 under the direction of Hobart Muir Smith, Chairman of the Publications Committee. In 1952 the *Journal of Systematic Zoology* was founded under the auspices of Richard Eliot Blackwelder. It gradually supplanted the *News Letter* which was discontinued in 1964. The quarterly *Journal* was considered the most important project of the SSZ; it was devoted to theoretical and philosophical considerations in systematics rather than the naming of new taxa.

Other projects of the Society have included the continuing publication of "List of Books on Zoology" and a *Directory of Zoological Taxonomists,* 1961.

The records include membership files, administrative files, reports, fiscal records, records related to the *Journal of Systematic Zoology* and copies of other SSZ publications, records related to the annual meetings, the Pacific Section of SSZ records, files on scientific societies, and the records of the Summer Institute in Systematics.

ARRANGEMENT: (1) Membership file, 1947-1974, alphabetic; (2) cancelled memberships, *circa* 1951-1971; (3) administrative files, 1952-1974, alphabetic; (4) reports, 1948-1969, chronologic; (5) fiscal records, 1948-1974, alphabetic; (6) records related to the publication and distribution of the *Journal of Systematic Zoology,* 1960-1975, alphabetic; (7) *News Letter* and pamphlets, 1949-1965, chronologic; (8) meetings of the SSZ, 1947-1971, chronologic; (9) SSZ Pacific Section records, 1951-1973, chronologic; (10) scientific societies, 1956-1975, alphabetic; (11) Summer Institute in Systematics, 1965-1970, chronologic. FINDING AIDS: Description in control file. SPECIAL CONDITIONS: (1) The Smithsonian Archives has been designated as the official depository for the archives of the Society of Systematic Zoology; (2) use of this record unit requires prior arrangement with the Archives staff.

Atanas Tasev Collection, 1949, 1952, 1956, 1976
(0.5 linear meter).

Atanas Tasev (1897-) was born in Sofia, Bulgaria, where he studied painting and had his first exhibition at age 23. He continued his education at the Academy in Prague and eventually made his home there for twenty-seven years, painting portraits, landscapes, and city street scenes. In 1946, he left Czechoslovakia for Sweden and came to the United States in 1948.

Tasev continued his portrait work in Washington, D.C., and in New York. Between 1948 and 1958, he frequently visited the National Zoological Park (NZP) in Washington and drew pencil sketches of the animals for relaxation. He was a good friend of William M. Mann, NZP Director from 1925 to 1956, and they often had tea together in Mann's Washington apartment.

These papers consist of three Tasev sketches of NZP animals drawn in 1949, 1952, and 1956. Also included is a 1976 book entitled *Washington Zoo,* a collection of Tasev's animal sketches.

ARRANGEMENT: (1) Drawings of zoo animals; (2) *Washington Zoo.* FINDING AIDS: Description in control file. SPECIAL CONDITIONS: Use of this record unit requires prior arrangement with the Archives staff.

Edward L. Todd Papers, circa 1952-1980
(0.7 linear meter).

Edward L. Todd (1922-1986) was born in Eureka, Kansas. He attended the University of Kansas in Lawrence, where he earned his B.A., M.A., and Ph.D. degrees. From 1945 until 1950, Todd was an Assistant and Laboratory Instructor in the entomology and general biology departments at the University. After receiving his Ph.D. in 1950, Todd worked from 1951 to 1952 as an entomologist for the Communicable Disease Center, United States Public Health Service, in Georgia.

In 1953, Todd became a Research Entomologist with the Division of Insect Identification, United States Department of Agriculture (USDA), located in the United States National Museum. In 1972, the Division became the Systematic Entomology Laboratory. Todd remained at the USDA until his retirement in 1979, working on the systematics and taxonomy of Lepidoptera (Noctuidae) and Hemiptera (Gelastocoridae).

The papers of Edward L. Todd consist of professional correspondence documenting his research in Lepidoptera and Hemiptera at the USDA. Also included are notes from professional meetings, research projects, and grant information.

ARRANGEMENT: (1) Correspondence, alphabetic, *circa* 1952-1974; (2) correspondence, unarranged, 1975-1980. FINDING AIDS: Description in control file. SPECIAL CONDITIONS: Use of this record unit requires prior arrangement with the Archives staff.

Ruel P. Tolman Collection, 1909-1964
(0.5 linear meter).

Ruel P. Tolman (1878-1954) was born in Brookfield, Vermont. After graduating from the University of California at Berkeley in 1902, he moved to Washington and attended the Corcoran School of Art. In 1906 he studied at the National Academy of Design and the Art Students League in New York. He taught classes at the Corcoran from 1906 until 1919.

Tolman's association with the Smithsonian began in 1912 when he joined the Division of Graphic Arts of the United States National Museum as a Preparator. He became an Aide in 1913, Assistant Curator in 1920, and Curator in 1932. From 1932 to 1946 Tolman also occupied the position of Acting Director of the National Collection of Fine Arts (known as the National Gallery of Art until 1937). Appointed Director in 1946, Tolman retired in 1948. His major work, *The Life and Work of Edward Greene Malbone, Miniature Painter,* was published in 1958 by the New York Historical Society, four years after Tolman's death.

Tolman was a practicing graphic artist, working in lithography, etching, mezzotint, drypoint, oil, and watercolor. He was active in the Washington art community and was nationally recognized as a painter of miniatures. He was founder and President of the Miniature Painters, Sculptors and Gravers Society of Washington. In 1909, he obtained a patent for an artist's wet-canvas carrier.

These papers consist of correspondence; biographical material; photocopies of prints, drawings and photographs; and four scrapbooks. One scrapbook documents a 1934 tour Tolman took of art galleries, museums and historical societies in the northeastern United States. Three scrapbooks contain photographs, dated 1934-1936, and 1944 taken by Tolman of Smithsonian staff, buildings, grounds, and exhibitions, and Washington scenes.

ARRANGEMENT: (1) Personal correspondence and related materials, 1909-1954, 1958-1962 and undated; (2) scrapbooks, 1934-1936, 1944; (3) prints, drawings and photographs, 1910-1945 and undated; (4) newspaper clippings, 1908-1952, 1964; (5) patent, 1909. FINDING AIDS: Description in control file. SPECIAL CONDITIONS: Use of this record unit requires prior arrangement with the Archives staff.

"Toward Our Third Century" Bicentennial Awards Program, 1975-1976
Prize Winning Entries (1 microfilm reel).

In 1975-1976 Wells Fargo Bank, in cooperation with the Smithsonian Institution, sponsored a bicentennial awards program. Contestants were to submit essays of no more than 3,500 words, or film or tape recordings not more than fifteen minutes in length on the theme "Toward Our Third Century."

Entrants were asked to look at the future of the United States and to suggest ideas for evaluating or coping with changes that will affect the nation in the years ahead. They were asked to address America's third century in terms of one of five themes: Individual Freedoms in Our Society; American Arts and Culture; Science, Technology, Energy, and the Environment; Family Life, Work and Leisure; and The United States and the World. Over 7,000 entries were received.

Initial judging of the entries was done by Smithsonian staff members, and final judging was done by a panel of nine distinguished Americans.

This record unit consists of one reel of microfilm containing the prize winning entries.

ARRANGEMENT: Unarranged. FINDING AIDS: None. SPECIAL CONDITIONS: Use of this record unit requires prior arrangement with the Archives staff.

Samuel Mills Tracy Papers, 1895-1914

(7278)

(17 items).

Samuel Mills Tracy (1847-1920), botanist, born in Hartford, Vermont, moved west with his parents, living first in Illinois and then Wisconsin. During the Civil War, Tracy served with the Wisconsin Volunteers for one hundred days. Upon returning home, he tried farming for one year and then enrolled at Michigan Agricultural College. Tracy received his B.S. in 1868 and his M.S. in 1871 from Michigan.

From 1871 to 1877, Tracy was involved with commercial horticulture work. In 1877 Tracy accepted the position of Professor of Botany at the University of Missouri, and left there to become the first Director of the Mississippi Experiment Station in 1887.

Tracy's botanic interests centered on the taxonomy of grasses, plant breeding, and the adaptation of forage plants to the southern states. Among numerous articles and books, Tracy wrote *Flora of Missouri* in 1886.

Papers consist of correspondence from colleagues and friends concerning the importation of cultivated plants to use for forage in the United States, botanizing in Alabama, receiving publications, and personal matters.

ARRANGEMENT: Alphabetic. FINDING AIDS: Description in control file. SPECIAL CONDITIONS: Use of this record unit requires prior arrangement with the Archives staff.

Gerard Troost Manuscript and Related Notes, Papers and Drawings, 1849-1904

(7301)

(0.1 linear meter).

Gerard Troost (1776-1850) was a Dutch paleontologist and geologist who came to America in 1810. In 1831 he became State Geologist of Tennessee. His special interest was the crinoid class of the echinoderms.

These papers include Troost's manuscript on the crinoids of Tennessee; diagrams, sketches, and notes on crinoids; and a small bit of correspondence concerning the history of the manuscript.

ARRANGEMENT: (1) "Monograph on Crinoids Discovered in the State of Tennessee," 1847; (2) diagrams of Troost's crinoids; (3) correspondence on Troost's manuscript; (4) notes and drawings. FINDING AIDS: None. SPECIAL CONDITIONS: Use of this record unit requires prior arrangement with the Archives staff.

Frederick William True Papers, circa 1886-1910
(0.4 linear meter).

Frederick William True (1858-1914) joined the Smithsonian Institution in 1881 as Librarian and Acting Curator of Mammals in the United States National Museum (USNM). He had previously served as a clerk for the United States Fish Commission, 1878-1881, and had charge of that agency's exhibition at the Berlin Fisheries Exposition of 1880. While with the Smithsonian, True held a number of positions including Curator of the Division of Mammals, 1883-1909; Curator of the Department of Comparative Anatomy, 1885-1890; Executive Curator of the United States National Museum, 1894-1897; Head Curator of the Department of Biology, 1897-1911; and Assistant Secretary in charge of the Library and International Exchange Service, 1911-1914. During this period, the Smithsonian was actively engaged in displaying exhibits at many expositions, and True was responsible for the preparation of a number of these exhibits.

True originally began his zoological studies with the invertebrates, but bad eyesight forced him to revise his plans and he turned to the study of mammals. His specialties were cetaceans and related groups. Later, he took up the study of fossil cetaceans and, in addition to publishing many important works in the field, helped build up the Museum's collections in this area.

These papers contain correspondence of Frederick William True with zoologists, naturalists, museum officials, Smithsonian administrators, and friends concerning specimens; publication of manuscripts; exhibitions; his trip to the Pribilof Islands, 1895; and USNM affairs. They also include files on USNM exhibits, fossil whales, and the Pribilof Islands; research and unpublished manuscript on antlers; lists of the genera of mammals and scientific publications at the Smithsonian Institution; and records created by True in his capacity as Executive Curator, 1894-1900.

ARRANGEMENT: (1) Correspondence, 1887-1900; (2) correspondence as Chairman of the Committee on Publications, 1894-1896; (3) correspondence, articles, clippings, memoranda, drawings, and related material concerning exhibits in the USNM, *circa* 1893-1910; (4) correspondence, notes, and related notebooks concerning trip to Pribilof Islands, 1895; (6) notes, drawings, photographs, and unpublished manuscript concerning antlers; (7) outgoing correspondence as Executive Curator, 1894-1900; (8) list of the genera of mammals, undated; (9) list of scientific periodicals held by the Smithsonian, undated. FINDING AIDS: Description in control file. SPECIAL CONDITIONS: Use of this record unit requires prior arrangement with the Archives staff.

Lucien M. Turner Papers, circa 1882-1884
(0.3 linear meter).

Lucien M. Turner (1848-1909), a member of the Army Signal Corps, collected natural history and ethnological specimens for the United States National Museum. From 1874 to 1877, he was a meteorological observer for the Signal Service at St. Michael, Alaska. He also trained voluntary observers for the Service in the Aleutians from 1878 to 1881. In 1882, Turner was sent to Fort Chimo, Labrador, as an observer and remained there until he returned to Washington in 1884. At each of his duty stations, Turner made extensive collections and sent them to the Smithsonian.

These papers include notes and manuscripts by Turner and by others concerning the collections he made, and photographs of the natives of Labrador.

ARRANGEMENT: (1) "Descriptive catalogue of Ethnological collections made by Lucien M. Turner in Ungava and Labrador, Hudson Bay Territory, June 24, 1882 to October 1884," Part 1 on Innuit, Part 2 on Indian specimens, by Lucien M. Turner, 1887; (2) "Contributions to the Natural History of Labrador and Ungava, Hudson Bay Territory," by Lucien M. Turner, 1886; (3) "Notes on the Mammals ascertained to occur in the Labrador, Ungava, East Main, Moose and Gulf Region," by Lucien M. Turner, undated; (4) manuscripts on the Turner natural history collections from Labrador including works on algae, by William Gilson Farlow; botany, by Turner; arachnids, by Turner and George Marx; moths, by Charles Henry Fernald; Lepidoptera, by William Henry Edwards; mollusks, by William H. Dall; crustacea, by Turner and Sidney Irving Smith; and fishes, apparently by Turner, undated. FINDING AIDS: None. SPECIAL CONDITIONS: Use of this record unit requires prior arrangement with the Archives staff.

(7424)

Ulke Family Papers, 1924, 1933, 1947 and undated
(0.1 linear meter).

Henry Ulke (1821-1910) was born in Prussia, but emigrated to the United States as a young man. A painter by profession, Ulke was also an amateur entomologist, and collected beetles avidly. Ulke amassed an impressive collection of insects, which he eventually donated to the Carnegie Museum in Pittsburgh. Ulke's son, Titus (1866-1961), shared his father's interest in entomology and often helped gather specimens for his father's collection.

These papers include two address books kept by Henry Ulke, with notes in German; a list of Coleoptera collected by Titus Ulke for his father in the Black Hills of South Dakota, with determinations made by Henry Ulke; a topographical map of the Maryland-Pennsylvania border; and newspaper clippings about Titus Ulke.

ARRANGEMENT: Unarranged. FINDING AIDS: None. SPECIAL CONDITIONS: Use of this record unit requires prior arrangement with the Archives staff.

(7332)

Edward Oscar Ulrich Papers, circa 1880-1938 and undated
(0.9 linear meter).

Edward Oscar Ulrich (1857-1944) was an invertebrate paleontologist and authority on Paleozoic fauna and formations. He developed an interest in fossils as a youth, collecting in the rich formations around his home in Covington, Kentucky. Ulrich attended German Wallace and Baldwin College at Berea, Ohio, and the Ohio Medical College at Cincinnati, but did not receive a degree from either. In 1877, he was appointed Curator of the Cincinnati Society of Natural History. After working many years as a freelance geologist and paleontologist on many of the state geological surveys, Ulrich accepted appointment with the United States Geological Survey (USGS) in 1897. He remained with the USGS until his retirement in 1932. He continued his paleontological studies as a Research Associate at the United States National Museum until his death.

Ulrich was an authority on Paleozoic invertebrates, especially the Bryozoa, Ostracoda, and conodonts. His bibliography included over 120 titles, with "Revision of the Paleozoic System" (1911), generally considered his classic work. He conducted extensive field work in the United States, England, and Europe. He was a Fellow of the Geological Society of America (GSA), President of the Paleontological Society, and a member of the National Academy of Sciences (NAS). He was the recipient of the Mary Clark Thompson Medal of the NAS in 1930, and the Penrose Medal of the GSA in 1932. Ulrich was awarded the honorary M.A. (1886) and D.Sc. (1892) from German Wallace and Baldwin College.

This collection documents the professional career and personal life of Edward Oscar Ulrich. It includes incoming and outgoing correspondence mostly concerning his paleontological research and professional activities after he joined the USGS in 1897. A small number of letters deal with family matters and personal affairs. The collection also includes photographs, many of which were taken at the 12th International Geological Congress held at Toronto in 1913, and during Ulrich's field work in England and Europe in 1925; manuscripts, notes, specimen lists, plates, charts, and related materials from his paleontological research; and various personal materials such as bank books, greeting cards, certificates and awards, notebooks, newspaper clippings, and memorabilia.

ARRANGEMENT: (1) General correspondence, 1880-1937 and undated; (2) photographs, *circa* 1913-1930 and undated; (3) research materials, *circa* 1905-1938 and undated; (4) personal materials, *circa* 1890-1933 and undated. FINDING AIDS: Description in control file. SPECIAL CONDITIONS: Use of this record unit requires prior arrangement with the Archives staff.

(7186)

United States Exploring Expedition Collection, 1838-1885
(0.8 linear meter).

The United States Exploring Expedition was authorized by an act of Congress in 1836 as "a surveying and exploring expedition to the Pacific Ocean and South Seas." Its commander was Lieutenant Charles Wilkes, USN. It was prompted by a desire to obtain information concerning an area which was rapidly becoming of interest to American traders and whalers. A contingent of scientists accompanied the expedition, including Charles Pickering, Titian Ramsay Peale, Joseph P. Couthouy, James Dwight Dana, William Rich, William Dunlop Brackenridge, and Horatio Hale. In addition to the scientists, two illustrators also accompanied the expedition, Joseph Drayton and Alfred T. Agate.

The expedition, also known as the Wilkes Expedition, sailed from Norfolk, Virginia, in August 1838. By the time it returned to New York in June 1842, it had visited and explored Madeira, both coasts of South America, Tierra del Fuego, the South Pacific islands, Australia, New Zealand, Antarctica, the Hawaiian Islands, Washington and Oregon territories, California, the Philippine Islands, Singapore, the Cape of Good Hope, and St. Helen. Wilkes's voyage along the Antarctic coast during the expedition established the existence of that continent.

During the voyage, the scientists gathered specimens and studied the flora and fauna of each place visited. At various points along the route, specimens were packed and sent back to the United States. Eventually, the specimens were placed in the custody of the National Institute in Washington, D.C., and installed in the Great Hall of the Patent Office. They remained there until their removal to the Smithsonian Institution in 1858.

These papers include manuscripts, notes, lists, catalogs of specimens, correspondence, and drawings relating to the United States Exploring Expedition of

1838-1842 and its scientific work. Of special interest are original drawings of fish and echinoderms done on the voyage; Peale's manuscript history of the expedition; original notebooks of the botanist; Jean Louis Agassiz's notes for his unpublished report on the fishes collected by the expedition; Charles Pickering's notes on fishes and echinoderms; and original specimen lists and catalogs kept by the members of the expedition.

ARRANGEMENT: (1) Correspondence, 1841; (2) Titian Ramsay Peale's manuscript on the United States Exploring Expedition, *circa* 1874; (3) catalogs, drawings, and other materials concerning the specimens collected by the United States Exploring Expedition, 1838-1863; (4) manuscripts on the fishes of the United States Exploring Expedition; (5) notes, lists and related materials concerning work done on fish and echinoderm specimens collected by the United States Exploring Expedition; (6) drawings and tracings of fishes, marked "rejected"; (7) drawings and tracings of fishes, marked "selected." FINDING AIDS: Description in control file. SPECIAL CONDITIONS: Use of this record unit requires prior arrangement with the Archives staff.

(7176)

United States Fish and Wildlife Service, 1860-1961
Field Reports (17.2 linear meters).

This collection consists of reports, notes, and biological data submitted to the Fish and Wildlife Service of the Department of Interior and its predecessor, the Bureau of Biological Survey of the Department of Agriculture, by naturalists conducting field research throughout the greater part of the Western Hemisphere. While the vast majority of the material concerns work conducted in the United States, a substantial amount of reports from Canada and Mexico is included. Reports from South and Central America, Africa, Europe, and Asia also exist in small quantities.

The bulk of the field reports fall into three categories: Special Reports, Physiography Reports, and Plant Reports. Bird and mammal notes are joined to comprise the Special Reports category and concern the identification, classification, distribution, and collection of specimens. The Physiography Reports consist of a general survey of the physical phenomena indigenous to the area of research including topography and climate. Data concerning the identification, classification, and distribution of plant life are recorded in the Plant Reports. In addition to these general notes, reports of a more specific nature appear throughout the collection.

ARRANGEMENT: (1) Field reports submitted by naturalists conducting field research in the United States; (2) field reports submitted by naturalists conducting field research in Canada, Mexico, and other foreign nations, and general field reports. FINDING AIDS: Description in control file. SPECIAL CONDITIONS: Use of this record unit requires prior arrangement with the Archives staff.

(7229)

United States Marine Mammal Program, circa 1967-1973 and undated
Records (1.4 linear meters).

The United States Marine Mammal Program was established in 1969 by the United States National Committee of the International Biological Program (USNC/IBP) and the International Marine Mammal Working Group of the International Biological Program.

In 1964 the International Council of Scientific Unions, a non-governmental organization, created a Special Committee for the International Biological Program (SCIBP) whose theme was the "Biological Basis for Productivity and Human Welfare."

Programs focusing on this theme were developed by SCIBP and were operational from 1967 to 1972, with a later extension to 1974. Participation by the United States government in the International Biological Program began in 1965 when a National Academy of Sciences *ad hoc* committee recommended the formation of USNC/IBP.

USNC/IBP's activities were coordinated by the National Science Foundation which also provided most of the funding. Support funds were also contributed by the Atomic Energy Commission, Department of Health, Education and Welfare, Department of Agriculture, Department of Defense, Smithsonian Institution, and private industry. In 1967, USNC/IBP began a study of marine mammals which finally resulted in the formation of the United States Marine Mammal Program.

The United States Marine Mammal Program was directed by an eleven-member Marine Mammal Council (MMC) appointed by the United States Marine Mammal Working Group. The Council, in turn, named a four-member Executive Committee to oversee daily operations; an office was set up in the Smithsonian Institution's National Museum of Natural History. Members of the Executive Committee included Program Director G. Carleton Ray of the Johns Hopkins University; Kenneth S. Norris of the Oceanic Institute, Hawaii; Charles O. Handley, Jr., of the Smithsonian Institution; and William E. Schevill of Woods Hole Oceanographic Institution. The Program Director also served as a member of the International Marine Mammal Working Group. As overseer of the Program, the MMC served as a catalyst for marine mammal studies by aiding in developing a Marine Mammal Study Center at the Smithsonian for the study of fossil and recent mammals; publishing *The Marine Mammal Newsletter;* sponsoring marine mammal conferences; cooperating with other phases of the United States International Biological Program; and coordinating existing and new research through its Integrated Research Program. By providing information needed for the rational international management of marine mammals, the Marine Mammal Program emphasized the opportunity for ecological studies rather than those having an economic or political basis. Other related activities of the Council included assisting and advising the United States Congress on marine mammal affairs following the introduction of bills and resolutions. Several Council members also testified before congressional committee hearings. On June 30, 1974, the United States' participation in the International Biological Program was officially terminated when funding from the National Science Foundation ceased.

These records consist of files maintained in the office of the Program Director of the United States Marine Mammal Program concerning the administration of the Program. Records include administrative files; handwritten notes by the Program Director; general correspondence; research proposals; records of an international conference; newsletters; reports; copies of legislation concerning marine mammal protection; and publications, newspaper clippings, and miscellany.

ARRANGEMENT: (1) Administrative files, 1969-1973; (2) G. Carleton Ray's notes, 1970-*circa* 1973; (3) general correspondence, 1967-1973; (4) IBP Component Program research proposals, 1971-1973 and undated; (5) International Conference on the Biology of Whales, 1970-1973; (6) newsletters, 1968-1973; (7) reports, 1967-1973; (8) legislation, 1971-1973; (9) publications, clippings, and miscellany, 1967, 1971-1973 and undated. FINDING AIDS: Description in control file. SPECIAL CONDITIONS: Use of this record unit requires prior arrangement with the Archives staff.

United States National Museum Bulletin 50 Collection, circa 1894-1950
(1 linear meter).

The first volume of Robert Ridgway's (1850-1929) work, *The Birds of North and Middle America,* appeared in 1901 as Part I, United States National Museum Bulletin 50. Part VIII, the last volume to appear during Ridgway's lifetime, was published in 1919. After Ridgway's death, his colleague in the Division of Birds, United States National Museum, Charles Wallace Richmond (1868-1932), gathered all of the notes that he had left behind and filed them for future use. Herbert Friedmann (1900-1987) was appointed Curator of the Division of Birds in 1929, and in 1933 he began working with Ridgway's notes in an effort to complete the project. Part IX of *The Birds of North and Middle America* was finally published in 1941, Part X in 1946, and Part XI in 1950. After about 1950, Friedmann stopped working on the project, and devoted his time to his own research.

This collection contains notes, drafts, and unpublished manuscripts for the projected, but never published, Parts XII and XIII of United States National Museum Bulletin 50: *The Birds of North and Middle America.* Included are notes of both Ridgway and Friedmann.

ARRANGEMENT: (1) Robert Ridgway notes and manuscripts, *circa* 1894-1929; (2) Herbert Friedmann notes and manuscripts, *circa* 1933-1950. FINDING AIDS: Description in control file. SPECIAL CONDITIONS: Use of this record unit requires prior arrangement with the Archives staff.

Vail Telegraph Collection, 1830-1898, 1912-1917
(2.2 linear meters).

This collection contains papers concerning the invention and development of the telegraph by Samuel F. B. Morse, Alfred Vail, and others, especially Vail's work with telegraph instruments and operation of telegraph stations, patent litigation, and Vail's publications concerning the telegraph. It also includes correspondence between Alfred and George Vail concerning their investment in the early telegraph enterprise and correspondence between Alfred Vail, Morse, Amos Kendall, and others, from 1837, relating to development of the telegraph, litigation and patents, administration of companies, especially the Magnetic Telegraph Company, the Morse-Joseph Henry dispute, and litigation between Morse, Francis O. J. Smith, and Henry O'Reilly. There is correspondence between Alfred Vail and many persons concerning construction of lines and training operators, with especially valuable information concerning construction of the Washington-Baltimore line. There are some Alfred Vail research notes and correspondence relating to insulation and insulators, receiving magnets and keys, and laying line in lead pipe. It includes account books, copies of contracts, agreements and assignments, and patent applications, extensive telegraph journals, data accumulated by Alfred Vail concerning rates and telegraph lines, correspondence, returned questionnaires, and other items relating to Vail's publications, especially *The Electro-Magnetic Telegraph,* and *The Register of Electro-Magnetic Telegraph Companies,* scrapbooks kept by Alfred Vail and his wife, Amanda, relating to the history of the telegraph. Also included is correspondence of Amanda Vail and of Alfred Vail's sons, Stephen and James Cummings Vail, and publications of the sons, all relating to Vail's role in telegraph development and to the Smithsonian's collection of Vail telegraph artifacts and its exhibition by the United States National Museum.

ARRANGEMENT: (1) Alfred Vail correspondence, 1830-1858; (2) Alfred Vail diaries and research notebooks, 1845-1849; (3) Alfred Vail telegraph journals, 1844-1851; (4) Alfred Vail accounts, 1845-1848; (5) Alfred Vail miscellaneous, 1837-1849; (6) George Vail correspondence, 1837-1858; (7) Amanda Vail correspondence and collected data, 1845-1849; (8) publications and photographs, 1845-1849; (9) scrapbooks, 1844-1858, 1896, 1912; (10) Stephen Vail correspondence, 1884-1892; James Cummings Vail correspondence, 1915-1917. FINDING AIDS: Description in control file. SPECIAL CONDITIONS: (1) Some items cannot be reproduced on special order due to bindings; (2) use of this record unit requires prior arrangement with the Archives staff.

(7063)

John Varden Papers, 1829-1863
(0.1 linear meter).

John Varden (? -1864) directed the Washington City Museum from 1829 until 1841. He then affiliated himself with the National Institute in some tenuous fashion. As the collections of the United States Exploring Expedition slipped away from the Institute's control during 1842, Varden also began to work under the direction of Captain Charles Wilkes. To these two jobs, he added an assignment in the National Gallery of the Patent Office. When the collections housed in the Patent Office were transferred to the Smithsonian in 1858, Varden accompanied them, working on museum specimens until his death in 1864.

These papers consist of a few pieces of incoming and outgoing correspondence, a daybook of the Washington City Museum from 1829 to 1841, a journal containing a listing of artifacts collected by the Museum, 1837-1841, a catalog of collections housed in the National Gallery of the Patent Office as of 1852, and Varden's diary, 1857-1863.

ARRANGEMENT: Chronologic. FINDING AIDS: None. SPECIAL CONDITIONS: Use of this record unit requires prior arrangement with the Archives staff.

(7087)

George Vasey Papers, 1889-1893
(0.1 linear meter).

George Vasey (1822-1893), a physician and botanist, was born near Scarborough, England. In 1828 his parents emigrated to the United States, settling in Oneida County, New York. Vasey became interested in botany as a youth, reading Almira Hart Lincoln's *Elements of Botany,* and meeting the German botanist, P. H. Kneiskern, who subsequently introduced him to John Torrey and Asa Gray.

Vasey graduated from Oneida Institute in 1841 and the Berkshire Medical Institute at Pittsfield, Massachusetts, in 1846. After spending a few weeks of training at the College of Physicians and Surgeons in New York City, Vasey left to practice medicine in New York and Illinois. Vasey collected botanical specimens while practicing medicine and helped form the Illinois Natural History Society. In 1864 he received an M.A. from Illinois Wesleyan University.

In 1872, Vasey was appointed Botanist of the United States Department of Agriculture (USDA) and Curator of the National Herbarium; and in 1889 he became Honorary Curator of the Department of Botany, United States National Museum. Vasey held these positions until his death. At the USDA, Vasey built up its collections of North American grasses, and was instrumental in establishing the Grass Experimental Station at Garden City, Kansas. Vasey's most important botanical study was on the agricultural grasses of the United States, published in 1884. In 1891 he began preparation of his work on North American grasses for publication. The first part of his work was issued in 1892, but he died before the second part could be published.

Vasey was a member of the Geographical Society of Washington; the Biological Society of Washington; a fellow of the American Association for the Advancement of Science; and an associate fellow of the American Academy of Arts and Sciences. In 1892 he was one of the vice-presidents at the Botanical Congress at Genoa, representing the USDA and the Smithsonian.

These papers consist of appointment letters to special posts and functions, and honors and awards. Official files of Vasey may be found in record unit 220.

ARRANGEMENT: Chronologic. FINDING AIDS: Description in control file. SPECIAL CONDITIONS: Use of this record unit requires prior arrangement with the Archives staff.

(1050102)

T. Wayland Vaughan Papers, 1908-1947 and undated
(3.2 linear meters).

T. Wayland Vaughan (1870-1952), geologist and oceanographer, was educated at Tulane University, B.S., 1889; and Harvard University, A.B., 1893, A.M., 1894, and Ph.D., 1903. He began collecting fossils when he was an Instructor at Mount Lebanon College, Tennessee, from 1889 to 1892. From 1894 to 1903, he was an Assistant Geologist with the United States Geological Survey (USGS). Between 1901 and 1923, Vaughan participated in several geological investigations of the West Indies and Puerto Rico which were sponsored by the USGS, the Smithsonian Institution, the Carnegie Institution of Washington, and the United States Navy. The USGS and the Carnegie Institution also helped to finance his investigations of the Atlantic and Gulf Coast states in cooperation with several state geological surveys, and his investigations of the corals and coral reefs of the Bahamas. In 1924, Vaughan became Director of the Scripps Institution of Oceanography, a position which he held until his retirement in 1936. In addition, he was an Associate in Marine Sediments, 1924-1942, and Associate in Paleontology, 1942-1952, at the United States National Museum.

Vaughan's research focused on three areas of science: the study of corals and coral reefs; the investigation of larger foraminifera; and oceanography. He was an authority on the corals of the United States, eastern Mexico, the West Indies, and Panama. As an oceanographer, Vaughan was interested in sedimentology and physical and chemical oceanography. With his work on oceanography, Vaughan served as Chairman, 1919 to 1923, of the Committee on Sedimentation of the National Research Council's Division of Geology and Geography; Chairman, 1926 to 1935, of the Pacific Science Association's International Committee on the Oceanography of the Pacific; and member of the National Academy of Sciences' Committee on Oceanography. This last committee was largely responsible for the founding of the Woods Hole Oceanographic Institution.

Vaughan held membership in numerous scientific and professional societies. In 1897, he was a delegate to the International Geological Congress in Russia, and between 1920 and 1936, he served as a delegate from the United States to six Pan-Pacific Science Congresses.

These papers consist of Vaughan's professional correspondence with American and foreign scientists concerning descriptions of fossil localities; the identification, description and exchange of specimens; research in corals, foraminifera, and oceanography; research conditions in Europe around the time of World War II; and the activities of scientific committees on which Vaughan served. Correspondence with detailed locality information has been flagged. Also included are writings, reports, correspondence, and notes by Vaughan and other scientists concerning specimen collections, analyses of core bottom samples, descriptions and lists of new species, and activities of the Committee of Sedimentation of the National Research Council; and field notebooks, including photographs, of corals of the Bahamas and the Pacific Ocean.

ARRANGEMENT: (1) General correspondence, 1912, 1920-1947 and undated; (2) writings and notes, 1913-1947 and undated; (3) notebooks, 1908-1923. FINDING AIDS: Description in control file. SPECIAL CONDITIONS: Use of this record unit requires prior arrangement with the Archives staff.

(7239)

John Paul Visscher Papers, circa 1922-1945 and undated
(0.5 linear meter).

John Paul Visscher (1895-1950) was born in Holland, Michigan. He received his A.B. degree from Hope College, Holland, Michigan, 1917, and his A.M. and Ph.D. degrees from Johns Hopkins University, 1920 and 1924. Visscher served with the United States Army during World War I, as Lieutenant in the Chemical Warfare Service. His first teaching position was at Washington University, St. Louis, where he served as Instructor of Zoology from 1920 to 1922. In 1924, he joined the staff of Western Reserve University as Assistant Professor of Biology. He was promoted to Associate Professor in 1926, Professor in 1931, and Head of the Biology Department in 1937. Visscher remained at Western Reserve University until his death in 1950.

Visscher's primary interest was protozoology. He also did extensive research on marine fouling of ships' bottoms. From 1922 to 1925, Visscher spent his summers as a special investigator for the United States Bureau of Fisheries, examining marine fouling on United States Navy and commercial ships. This research led to the publication of *The Nature and Extent of Fouling of Ships' Bottoms* in 1928. During 1935 and 1936, Visscher served as special investigator for the United States Navy's Division of Construction and Repair. In 1945 and 1946, he acted as a consultant at the Naval Research Laboratory in Washington, D.C.

These papers document Visscher's investigations on marine fouling of ship bottoms and include general correspondence, 1922-1945; photographs of ship fouling; manuscripts; and research notes and reports on ship fouling.

ARRANGEMENT: (1) General correspondence, 1922-1945; (2) photographs, *circa* 1922-1925; (3) manuscripts, 1928 and undated; (4) research notes and reports on ship fouling, *circa* 1922-1925. FINDING AIDS: Description in control file. SPECIAL CONDITIONS: Use of this record unit requires prior arrangement with the Archives staff.

The Vivarium Society, 1925-1930
Records (0.1 linear meter).

The Vivarium Society was founded in 1925 by a group of Washington area naturalists who were "actively interested in the study of natural history in the field, and in the maintenance of vivaria for scientific observations on living specimens." Activities centered around field trips and monthly meetings at which members or guests reported on their recent research.

ARRANGEMENT: (1) Constitution of the Vivarium Society; (2) minutes of meetings, 1925-1930; (3) correspondence; (4) newspaper clippings; (5) membership lists; (6) photographs, unidentified. FINDING AIDS: None. SPECIAL CONDITIONS: Use of this record unit requires prior arrangement with the Archives staff.

George B. Vogt Papers, circa 1933-1991
(1.6 linear meters).

George B. Vogt (1920-1991), an entomologist and authority on leaf beetles and longhorned beetles, was educated at the University of Maryland (B.S., 1941; M.S., 1949). His professional career began in 1942 when he joined the United States Public Health Service as an entomologist assigned to various World War II studies. In 1949, Vogt was appointed Entomologist with the Insect Detection and Identification Branch, United States Department of Agriculture (USDA), and assigned to taxonomic work at the United States National Museum. He remained with the Branch and its successor organization, the Systematic Entomology Laboratory (SEL) until 1972, when he was reassigned to the USDA's Southern Weed Science Lab (SWSL) in Stoneville, Mississippi. Vogt retired from the USDA in 1978, but continued his research at the SEL and SWSL until his death.

Vogt participated in several field expeditions during his career at the USDA. From 1950 to 1952, he was in Burma working on a mosquito survey. In 1956, Vogt explored Spain and southwest Asia for potential biological control agents for the weed *Halogeton,* and from 1960 to 1962, he traveled to South America to conduct investigations on the natural enemies of alligator weed.

The papers of George B. Vogt primarily document his entomological research and field work during his career with the USDA. They also concern, to a lesser extent, his work with the United States Public Health Service, 1942-1947, and entomological research before and after his career in federal service. They include correspondence and memoranda concerning the identification of specimens, publication of scientific papers, professional activities, and field work, especially his trips to Burma, Spain, southwestern Asia, and South America; field notes, 1933-1991, which contain information on specimens collected; and correspondence, notes, and drafts from his work on a chapter on Coleoptera which appeared in *Insects of Panama and Mesoamerica: Selected Studies,* 1992.

ARRANGEMENT: Unarranged, with the following divisions apparent: (1) correspondence and memoranda, *circa* 1942-1991; (2) field notes, 1933-1991; (3) correspondence, notes, and drafts concerning *Insects of Panama and Mesoamerica: Selected Studies* (1992), 1984-1990. FINDING AIDS: None. SPECIAL CONDITIONS: Use of this record unit requires prior arrangement with the Archives staff.

Wesley Wait Papers, 1921-1925
(0.1 linear meter and oversize).

Wesley Wait (1861-1949), dental surgeon and inventor, corresponded with the Smithsonian between 1921 and 1925 in regard to his research on "The Unity of the Universal Existence." Though most of this correspondence is presently missing, these papers contain a typescript of "The Unity of the Universal Existence" by Wait, 1901, and nineteen oversize drawings and charts which document Wait's theory.

ARRANGEMENT: (1) Typescript, 1901; (2) oversize, containing drawings and charts. FINDING AIDS: None. SPECIAL CONDITIONS: Use of this record unit requires prior arrangement with the Archives staff.

Egbert Hamilton Walker Papers, 1938-1961
(2.6 linear meters).

Egbert Hamilton Walker (1899-1991), botanist, was born in Chicago, Illinois. Walker received his B.A. from the University of Michigan in 1922, his M.S. from the University of Wisconsin in 1928, and his Ph.D. from Johns Hopkins University in 1940.

From 1922 to 1926, Walker was an instructor at the Canton Christian College, Canton, China. In 1928, Walker was appointed an Aid to the Division of Plants, United States National Museum. Walker was made an Assistant Curator in the Division in 1942, and an Associate Curator in 1947. When the Division was reorganized into the Department of Botany in 1947, Walker was assigned to the Division of Phanerogams. Walker resigned from the Division in 1959, and from 1959 to 1960 was a consultant with the American Institute of Biological Sciences in Washington, D.C. Walker was a Research Associate with the Department of Botany, National Museum of Natural History, from 1965 to 1987.

These papers include correspondence with Elmer Drew Merrill concerning Merrill's bibliographies on Polynesian and other Pacific plants, Merrill's joint effort with Walker on their *Bibliography of Eastern Asian Botany,* and Merrill's concern over Walker's attempt to provide a pocket manual on food plants for aviators downed in the South Pacific during World War II; correspondence with Harley Harris Bartlett concerning Bartlett's publications and botanical collections from the South Pacific; correspondence with Joseph Francis Rock regarding Rock's collecting activities; and general correspondence concerning Walker's work on the servicemen's collecting program, working conditions at the United States National Herbarium, Walker's travels and field work in the Pacific, and scientific meetings regarding Pacific projects. Also included are field notes, manuscripts, and reports.

ARRANGEMENT: (1) Correspondence with Elmer Drew Merrill and material related to the *Bibliography of Eastern Asian Botany,* arranged by subject; (2) correspondence with Harley Harris Bartlett and material concerning the servicemen's collecting program, arranged by subject; (3) correspondence with Joseph Francis Rock and general correspondence, A-Z. FINDING AIDS: Description in control file. SPECIAL CONDITIONS: Use of this record unit requires prior arrangement with the Archives staff.

Ernest Pillsbury Walker Papers, circa 1923-1956

(7161)

(8.1 linear meters).

Ernest Pillsbury Walker (1891-1969) served in a number of positions concerning game and wildlife management and preservation. He was fur game warden for the Territory of Alaska and the United States and did work for the Bureau of Biological Survey of the United States Department of Agriculture. From 1930 to 1956, Walker was Assistant Director of the National Zoological Park.

These papers include some correspondence and notes prior to Walker's tenure at the National Zoological Park, as well as working papers on mammalogy and some correspondence dating from his time at the National Zoo.

ARRANGEMENT: Unarranged. FINDING AIDS: None. SPECIAL CONDITIONS: Use of this record unit requires prior arrangement with the Archives staff.

Benjamin Dann Walsh Field Notebooks, 1860-1869

(7123)

(2 volumes).

Benjamin Dann Walsh (1808-1869) was born in Great Britain and educated at Oxford. Prepared for the Church, he instead became a writer and, after emigrating to the United States, a farmer, lumber dealer, and entomologist. Walsh became state entomologist of Illinois in 1867 and, with Charles Valentine Riley, founded the *American Entomologist* in 1868, a year before his death.

This collection consists of two field notebooks recording Walsh's observations of insect behavior and development in the vicinity of his home, Rock Island, Illinois. They also contain some clues to Walsh's reading habits and correspondents, as well as sketches and clippings from newspapers. The notebooks contain meticulous detail and show an evident interest in questions of economic entomology. The last pages of volume two contain an account of the founding of the Rock Island County branch of the Kansas Settlers Society of Chicago, June 12-25, 1856; Walsh was an officer and member of the Executive Committee of this body.

ARRANGEMENT: (1) Volume I, 1860-1868; (2) volume II, 1866-1869. FINDING AIDS: Description in control file. SPECIAL CONDITIONS: Use of this record unit requires prior arrangement with the Archives staff.

Henry Baldwin Ward Papers, 1888-1933 and undated

(7247)

(0.1 linear meter).

Henry Baldwin Ward (1865-1945) was born in Troy, New York. He received degrees from Williams College, Williamstown, Massachusetts, A.B., 1885 and Harvard University, A.M., Ph.D., 1892. From 1888 to 1890, Ward participated in postgraduate study in Europe at the universities of Gottingen, Freiburg, and Leipzig, and the biological stations at Naples, Heligoland, and Villefranche-sur-Mer. His first teaching job was at Troy High School, where he served as Instructor of Science from 1886 to 1888. In 1892, Ward accepted the position of Instructor of Morphology at the University of Michigan.

He was appointed Associate Professor of Zoology at the University of Nebraska in 1893, and was promoted to Professor in 1899 and Dean of the College of Medicine in 1902. Ward was named Professor of Zoology at the University of Illinois in 1909. In 1933, his title was changed to Emeritus Professor, and he remained at Illinois until his death.

This collection contains only a fragment of Ward's papers and consists mostly of photographs. A small amount of correspondence is also included.

ARRANGEMENT: (1) Photographs, 1888-1898 and undated; (2) correspondence, 1910, 1920, 1923, 1933 and undated. FINDING AIDS: Description in control file. SPECIAL CONDITIONS: Use of this record unit requires prior arrangement with the Archives staff.

(7321)

Lester Frank Ward Papers, 1882-1913, with related materials to circa 1965
(0.1 linear meter).

Lester Frank Ward (1841-1913) served as a geologist and paleontologist with the United States Geological Survey (USGS) from 1882 to 1905. In addition to his USGS career, Ward served as Honorary Curator of the Department of Fossil Plants in the United States National Museum (USNM) during the same span of years. In 1905, Ward accepted a faculty appointment at Brown University, where he remained until his death. Ward's paleobotanical research concentrated upon the relation of fossil plants to geology, and their value and importance in stratigraphic investigations. His scientific bibliography included over one hundred and fifty titles. Ward is probably best remembered for his pioneering work in sociology.

These papers consist primarily of incoming and outgoing correspondence documenting Ward's paleobotanical research and his curatorial work in the USNM. Also included are letters concerning his official duties with the USGS. The correspondence concerns the acquisition and identification of specimens, the preparation and publication of scientific manuscripts, and field work. Included is extensive correspondence with Charles Leo Lesquereux, John Strong Newberry, and Arthur Hollick. The papers also include a small amount of correspondence of Ward's assistant and colleague, Frank Hall Knowlton; a photograph of Ward taken in his USNM office in 1886; and a pencil sketch of Ward.

The papers do not concern Ward's sociological theories or writings. Researchers interested in that aspect of his career should consult Ward's papers deposited in the Library of Congress and Brown University.

ARRANGEMENT: (1) Lester Frank Ward correspondence, 1882-1905; (2) Frank Hall Knowlton correspondence, 1903-1926; (3) photographs and pencil sketch, 1886 and *circa* 1965. FINDING AIDS: Description in control file. SPECIAL CONDITIONS: Use of this record unit requires prior arrangement with the Archives staff.

(7099)

Washington Academy of Sciences, circa 1888-1972
Records (5.7 linear meters).

The Washington Academy of Sciences, incorporated February 18, 1898, serves as the federal head of thirty-five affiliated scientific societies in the Washington, D.C., area. Prior to incorporation of the Academy, a Joint Commission was set up in 1888 as an advisory body to the societies. The Joint Commission was dissolved in 1898 and the Board of Managers of the Academy took its place. The primary function of the Academy is promoting science through the publication of the *Journal of the Washington Academy of Sciences,* conducting science fairs, and sponsoring the Junior Academy of Sciences.

The records of the Academy include proceedings of the Joint Commission, minutes of general Academy and Board of Managers meetings, correspondence, membership applications, scrapbooks, photographs, and publications.

ARRANGEMENT: (1) Proceedings of the Joint Commission, 1888-1898; (2) minutes of Academy meetings, 1908-1936, minutes of the Board of Managers meetings, 1911-1960; (3) outgoing correspondence, 1900-1912; (4) correspondence, 1901-1968; (5) membership applications, 1898-1967; (6) scrapbooks, 1898-*circa* 1902; (7) photographs, 1898-1938, 1940-1944, 1946, 1948-1951, 1954; (8) publications, 1899-1972. FINDING AIDS: Description in control file. SPECIAL CONDITIONS: (1) The Washington Academy of Sciences has designated the Smithsonian Archives as the depository for its archives; (2) use of this record unit requires prior arrangement with the Archives staff.

(1020005)

Washington Biologists' Field Club, circa 1900-1966
Records (3.6 linear meters).

The Washington Biologists' Field Club was founded in 1900 by a group of Washington area naturalists to establish a base of field operations for working biologists. In that year, the Club rented property near Upper Marlboro, Maryland. In 1901, the members rented Plummer's Island, Maryland, located in the Potomac River and, in 1908, purchased the Island. In 1958, the United States government took possession of the Island through condemnation proceedings, but the Club has retained use of the Island through an agreement with the government.

The records of the Club include photograph albums; registers signed by members when visiting the Island; "Archives," including minutes, annual reports, correspondence, and legal documents; a card file compiled by members containing notes on bird species found on the Island; Treasurer's reports; a card catalog of Coleoptera on the Island; a card catalog of Diptera, vertebrates, and plants on the Island; and notes by Herbert Spencer Barber, mostly on beetles. The visitor registers also contain some observations on weather and other occurrences on the Island.

ARRANGEMENT: (1) Photograph albums, *circa* 1901-1961; (2) registers, 1901-1966; (3) "Archives," 1900-1960s; (4) bird notes; (5) Treasurer's reports, *circa* 1900-1966; (6) catalog of Coleoptera; (7) catalog of Diptera, vertebrates, and plants; (8) notes of Herbert Spencer Barber. FINDING AIDS: None. SPECIAL CONDITIONS: Use of this record unit requires prior arrangement with the Archives staff.

(7322)

C. Malcolm Watkins Papers, 1935-1979 and undated
(3.6 linear meters).

C. Malcolm Watkins (1911-   ) was born in Malden, Massachusetts, and received his Bachelor of Science degree from Harvard College in 1934. In 1936, he began to pursue his interest in early American culture through curatorial work at the Wells Historical Museum, the predecessor of Old Sturbridge Village, Sturbridge, Massachusetts. From 1942 to 1946, Watkins served in World War II in the United States Air Force. He returned to the Wells Historical Museum until 1948, when he accepted the position of Curator for the Department of Anthropology in the United States National Museum and then transferred to the Departments of Civil History and Cultural History at the National Museum of History and Technology, focusing on early American ceramics and glass. Watkins' research concentrated on early American life as seen through types of ceramics and their use. He was also instrumental in the development of the field of historic archeology, and he also studied pioneer life in California settlements.

These papers document Watkins' professional life, especially his research on early American culture and include correspondence, field notes from archeological digs, research notes, manuscripts, newspaper clippings, lists of artifacts, and photographs of archeological sites and finds. Also included are correspondence, 1941-1978; exhibition information; internal Smithsonian activities; documentation on the formation of the Society for Historical Archeology; papers on Watkins' sabbatical leave; and numerous photographs, mostly of research artifacts and acquisitions.

ARRANGEMENT: (1) General correspondence, 1941-1978 and undated; (2) subject files, 1949-1979 and undated; (3) museology, 1935-1976 and undated; (4) general Smithsonian, 1956-1978; (5) research correspondence, 1950-1970 and undated; (6) pottery research, 1960-1974 and undated; (7) California research, 1969-1975; (8) Marlborough research, 1953-1969; (9) *A Nation of Nations*, 1973-1978 and undated; (10) Society for Historical Archeology, 1967-1977. FINDING AIDS: Description in control file. SPECIAL CONDITIONS: Use of this record unit requires prior arrangement with the Archives staff.

(7268)

J. Elfreth Watkins Collection, 1869, 1881-1903, 1953, 1966 and undated
(0.3 linear meter).

J. Elfreth Watkins (1852-1903), a railroad employee and museum curator, was employed by the Delaware and Hudson Railroad Company as a mining engineer from 1871 to 1872. He then joined the Pennsylvania Railroad Company in 1872 as an Assistant Engineer of Construction. After a disabling accident in 1873, Watkins was employed as a Chief Clerk from 1874 to 1886 for the Pennsylvania Railroad and the Camden and Atlantic Railroad. In 1885, while still a railroad employee, Watkins was offered an honorary curatorial position in the Section of Steam Transportation, Department of Arts and Industries in the United States National Museum (USNM). In 1887 he was promoted to Curator of Transportation. Watkins returned to the Pennsylvania Railroad in 1892 to prepare its exhibit for the World's Columbian Exposition as Director of Industrial Arts. In 1895 he returned to the USNM as Curator of Technological Collections and in 1898 was named Curator of the Division of Technology (Modern Phases). He also served as Engineer of Property, 1888-1889, and Chief of Buildings and Superintendence, 1896-1903, for the USNM.

This collection consists of Watkins' official and personal correspondence concerning the efforts of the Smithsonian to obtain federal appropriations for the establishment of a section of steam transportation in the USNM, the construction of ship models for an exhibit at the Cotton States and International Exposition, and his various appointments at the Smithsonian; an annual report, 1892, for the Section of Transportation and Engineering; biographical material and newspaper clippings; photographs; a history of the Camden and Amboy Railroad, by Isaac L. Dripps; personal memorabilia;

correspondence and related documents concerning his research on the history of the Pennsylvania Railroad Company; and various publications by Watkins.

ARRANGEMENT: (1) General correspondence, 1869, 1881-1903; (2) annual report, biographical material, photographs, and other material, 1885-1900, 1953, 1966 and undated; (3) correspondence and related documents concerning the history of the Pennsylvania Railroad Company, 1892-1901, accession number 85-191; (4) publications, 1884-1890, accession number 89-082. FINDING AIDS: Partial description in control file. SPECIAL CONDITIONS: Use of this record unit requires prior arrangement with the Archives staff.

(7159)
Charles K. Wead Papers, circa 1893-1913
(1 folder).

Charles K. Wead (1848-1925) was an examiner for the United States Patent Office from 1892 to 1921. He also served as an officer of the Philosophical Society of Washington and filled the unexpired term of Simon Newcomb as President of that organization in 1909, after Newcomb's death.

These papers consist of Wead correspondence concerning personal matters and Philosophical Society of Washington affairs, particularly the memorial meeting for Simon Newcomb in 1909. Also included are two letters from Simon Newcomb to John A. Kasson, one concerning a committee of Congress to investigate the possibility of establishing the metric system in the United States.

ARRANGEMENT: Alphabetic. FINDING AIDS: None. SPECIAL CONDITIONS: Use of this record unit requires prior arrangement with the Archives staff.

(7400)
Donald M. Weisman Papers, 1965-1986
(0.1 linear meter).

Donald M. Weisman (1924-   ), an entomologist, received his B.A. degree from Miami University in 1950 and his M.Sc. degree from North Carolina State University in 1960. In 1961 he was appointed Entomologist with the Insect Identification and Parasite Introduction Research Branch, United States Department of Agriculture (USDA), and assigned to taxonomic work at the United States National Museum. He remained with the USDA until his retirement from the Systematic Entomology Laboratory in 1986. His research specialty was the taxonomy of immature Lepidoptera of economic importance.

These papers consist of incoming and outgoing correspondence with professional colleagues, mostly concerning the identification of specimens.

ARRANGEMENT: Unarranged. FINDING AIDS: None. SPECIAL CONDITIONS: Use of this record unit requires prior arrangement with the Archives staff.

(7127)
Lewis Hart Weld Papers, 1916, 1919-1963
(0.4 linear meter).

Lewis Hart Weld (1875-1964) studied entomology at the University of Rochester, Michigan, and Cornell, from which he went in 1904 to teach at Evanston Academy. While at Evanston, Weld began his lifelong study of cynipid gall wasps. During those years he also began a wide ranging series of field trips. In 1919 and again in 1923-1924 Weld worked for the Bureau of Entomology of the United States Department of Agriculture. In 1924 he resigned his official position, preferring to use his own independent means to pursue his interests at will, though he did remain a collaborator of the Department of Agriculture for more than 40 years.

These papers consist of a small quantity of personal correspondence, a somewhat larger amount of professional correspondence, and research notes. These papers document only a small part of Weld's career.

ARRANGEMENT: (1) Personal papers, 1916, 1927-1938; (2) professional correspondence, 1919-1963; (3) research notes and papers. FINDING AIDS: Description in control file. SPECIAL CONDITIONS: Use of this record unit requires prior arrangement with the Archives staff.

(7213)

Western Union Telegraph Expedition Collection, 1865-1867
(0.2 linear meter).

The Western Union Telegraph Expedition, 1865-1867, also known as the Russian-American Telegraph Expedition, was undertaken to study the possibility of setting up a communications system with Europe by way of Alaska, the Bering Straits, and Asia. The expedition was organized in three divisions, working in Canada, Russian-America (Alaska), and Asia. Robert Kennicott, the veteran Alaskan explorer, was placed in charge of the Russian-American division. Under the auspices of the Smithsonian Institution and the Chicago Academy of Sciences, a Scientific Corps was established, with Kennicott in command, to accompany the Russian-American division and make collections in natural history. Naturalists who served as members of the Scientific Corps included William H. Dall, Henry M. Bannister, and Henry W. Elliott. On the death of Kennicott on May 13, 1866, Dall became chief of the Scientific Corps until the expedition was terminated in July 1867 due to the successful laying of the Atlantic Cable.

This collection includes correspondence, mostly to Spencer F. Baird, from members of the Scientific Corps of the Western Union Telegraph Expedition, including Kennicott, Dall, Bannister, and Elliott; copies of reports submitted to divisional chiefs from expedition staff members; newspaper clippings concerning the expedition; copies of notes on natural history taken by Robert Kennicott; and a journal containing meteorological data recorded by Henry M. Bannister from March to August, 1866.

ARRANGEMENT: (1) Correspondence, 1865-1866; (2) copies of reports submitted to divisional chiefs from expedition staff members; (3) newspaper clippings, 1865-1867; (4) copies of notes on natural history taken by Robert Kennicott, undated; (5) meteorological journal of Henry M. Bannister, 1866. FINDING AIDS: None. SPECIAL CONDITIONS: (1) It appears that some of the material in this collection was removed from the official correspondence files of the Smithsonian; (2) use of this record unit requires prior arrangement with the Archives staff.

(7112)

John Obadiah Westwood Papers, 1816-1890
(0.4 linear meter and 4 reels of microfilm).

John Obadiah Westwood (1805-1893) was a naturalist, illustrator, paleographer, antiquarian, and the first Hope Professor of Zoology at Oxford University. One of the most important nineteenth-century British entomologists, Westwood wrote and illustrated many entomological monographs and also did illustrations of insects for the works of other entomologists.

In 1858, Westwood was appointed Keeper of the Hope entomological collection and library at Oxford. The collection and library were donated between 1847 and 1858 by Frederick William Hope. Westwood subsequently added his own entomological collection to Hope's. When Hope established the Hope Professorship in Zoology in 1861, Westwood was appointed to the chair. Westwood served as Professor of Zoology from 1861 to 1893.

These papers consist of correspondence to Westwood from entomologists including Alexander Henry Haliday, Sidney Smith Saunders, and George Henry Kendrick Thwaites on fig insects; and Thomas Whitmarsh on isosoma and gall flies; correspondence between Thwaites and Stanford Green concerning fig insects in Ceylon, 1877, collected by Westwood; letters and notes collected by Westwood as part of his collection of autographs of his entomological contemporaries, 1816-1837; and an autograph collection consisting of signatures only.

The manuscript collection, 1840-1890, consists of handwritten notes and drawings, some in color, mostly by Westwood (most were published); proof plates with notations by Westwood; correspondence concerning the disposition of Haliday's entomological collection after Haliday's death, 1882, and notes on the Haliday collection by Westwood; correspondence and drawings from Charles Robert Osten-Sacken and notes by Westwood concerning Diptera; and correspondence concerning corrections on manuscripts and proof plates to be sent for publication; handwritten manuscripts of a catalog of British insects by James Francis Stephens; entomological notes by Walter Elliot; and reprints. In addition, there are photographs of insects.

ARRANGEMENT: (1) Incoming correspondence, 1824-1888; (2) correspondence collected by John O. Westwood, 1816-1837, 1877; (3) autographs, signatures only; (4) handwritten manuscripts, drawings, proof plates, reprints, and photographs, 1840-1890. FINDING AIDS: Description in control file. SPECIAL CONDITIONS: (1) The John O. Westwood Papers were donated to Oxford University in May 1982; (2) the Archives retains a microfilm copy of the papers, and color transparencies of the color drawings; (3) use of this record unit requires prior arrangement with the Archives staff.

(7431)

Fred Lawrence Whipple Papers, circa 1927-1983
(9.8 linear meters).

Fred Lawrence Whipple (1906-), an astronomer, received the B.A. from the University of California at Los Angeles in 1927, and the Ph.D. from the University of California at Berkeley in 1931. In 1932, he joined the staff of Harvard University as an Instructor of Astronomy. By 1950, Whipple had become Professor and Chairman of the Department of Astronomy at Harvard. Whipple was appointed Director of the Smithsonian Astrophysical Observatory (SAO) when it moved to Cambridge, Massachusetts, in 1955. Since his retirement in 1973, Whipple has continued his research as a Senior Scientist at SAO.

During his tenure as Director, Whipple oversaw SAO research programs in stellar interiors, the upper atmosphere, meteorites, celestial mechanics, and geodesy studies. Major SAO projects under his direction included the Satellite Tracking Program, Project

Celescope, the Radio Meteor Project, and the Meteorite Photography and Recovery Project, also known as the Prairie Network. In the late 1960s, Whipple selected Mount Hopkins, Arizona, as the site for a new SAO astronomical facility. Renamed the Fred Lawrence Whipple Observatory in 1981, the facility houses the Multiple-Mirror Telescope (MMT), an innovative, low-cost telescope planned by Whipple and two colleagues.

Whipple is internationally recognized for his research on the moon, meteors, and comets. He has conducted pioneering research in photographically measuring the speeds and decelerations of meteors, computing the orbits of comets and asteroids, and describing the structure of comets. He is the author of more than 150 scientific books and papers; has served as editor of several publications; and has been a member and officer in numerous professional organizations. In 1975, the minor planet no. 1940 was named "Whipple" in recognition of his contributions to astronomy.

The papers of Fred Lawrence Whipple document his astronomical research; his professional work in the field of astronomy; his career as Director of the SAO; and, to a lesser extent, his activities as a faculty member of Harvard University. They include a large file of correspondence with professional colleagues, amateur astronomers, SAO staff scientists, Smithsonian Institution officials, scientific societies and professional groups, government agencies, and Harvard University staff and officials which concerns Whipple's research interests, scientific publications, and editorial work; SAO research projects, particularly the Satellite Tracking Program, Project Celescope, the Radio Meteor Project, and the Meteorite Photography and Recovery Project; Whipple's work for professional organizations and government agencies and committees including the International Astronomical Union, the Committee on Space Research, the Committee on Space and Astronautics of the United States House of Representatives, the National Aeronautics and Space Administration, the National Academy of Sciences, and the National Science Foundation; SAO relations with the Smithsonian Institution; and his activities at Harvard University and the Harvard College Observatory. Also included are college papers, notes, and a copy of his Ph.D. dissertation; manuscripts of articles, lectures, radio talks, reviews, and notes from his research; research notes on comets; correspondence, notes, reports, minutes and related materials from Whipple's work with professional groups and committees; files documenting the development of the MMT at Mount Hopkins, Arizona; and a set of Whipple's publications.

Researchers should also consult record unit 9520, Fred Lawrence Whipple Interviews, 1976.

ARRANGEMENT: (1) General correspondence, 1943-1983; (2) student papers, class notes, and Ph.D. dissertation, 1927-1931; (3) articles, lectures, reviews, and notes, *circa* 1931-1964; (4) notes on comets, 1928-1968; (5) professional activities, meetings, and committees, *circa* 1946-1970; (6) Multiple-Mirror Telescope files, 1966-1976; (7) Fred Lawrence Whipple publications, 1928-1971. FINDING AIDS: Folder list in control file. SPECIAL CONDITIONS: Use of this record unit requires prior arrangement with the Archives staff.

(7384)

John H. White, Jr., Papers, circa 1959-1989
(1.2 linear meters).

John H. White, Jr., (1933-   ), historian and museum curator, was born in Cincinnati, Ohio. He graduated with a B.A. in history from Miami University, Ohio, in 1958. Shortly after receiving his degree, White joined the staff of the Smithsonian Institution as Assistant Curator of the Division of Transportation, Department of Science and Technology, Museum of History and Technology. White later became Associate Curator of the Division, 1961-1966, Curator, 1967-1985, and Senior Historian, 1986-1989. White specialized in land transportation, particularly the history of railroads.

These papers consist mainly of correspondence documenting activities of John H. White, Jr., as Curator and Senior Historian of the Division of Transportation. Also included is some correspondence documenting White's work as editor of *Railroad History*.

ARRANGEMENT: (1) John H. White, Jr., Papers, 1971-1989, accession number 90-073; (2) John H. White, Jr., Papers, 1959-1989, accession number 90-106. FINDING AIDS: Folder list in control file. SPECIAL CONDITIONS: Use of this record unit requires prior arrangement with the Archives staff.

(7404)

Donald R. Whitehead Papers, 1972-1990
(0.8 linear meter).

Donald R. Whitehead (1938-1990) was an entomologist specializing in the systematics and biogeography of weevils. He received his B.S. from Rutgers University in 1961 and his Ph.D. from the University of Alberta in 1971. In 1976, Whitehead was appointed Research Entomologist in the Systematic Entomology Laboratory (SEL), United States Department of Agriculture, and assigned to taxonomic work at the National Museum of Natural History. He remained in the position until his death.

These papers document Whitehead's career at SEL and his research on weevils. They include correspondence and memoranda concerning the identification of specimens, publication of research papers, review of grant proposals and manuscripts, and SEL administration; notes, lists, and related research materials; and personnel records.

ARRANGEMENT: Unarranged. FINDING AIDS: None. SPECIAL CONDITIONS: Use of this record unit requires prior arrangement with the Archives staff.

(7238)

Henry Shaler Williams Papers, circa 1880-1916 and undated
(2.1 linear meters).

Henry Shaler Williams (1847-1918) was born in Ithaca, New York. He received degrees from Yale's Sheffield Scientific School, Ph.B., 1868, and Yale University, Ph.D., 1871.

In 1871, Williams went to Transylvania College, then known as Kentucky University, where he taught geology for a year. For the next several years he helped with his father's banking and mercantile enterprises in Ithaca. In 1879, Williams joined Cornell University as an Assistant Professor of Geology. He was later promoted to Professor of Paleontology, 1884, and Professor of Paleontology and Geology, 1886. Six years later Williams was selected by James Dwight Dana to succeed him as Silliman Professor of Geology at Yale where he remained until 1904. He returned to Cornell in 1904 as Professor of Geology and Director of the Geological Museum, a position which he held until his retirement in 1912. In addition to his academic appointments, Williams did research and field work for the United States Geological Survey.

Williams' paleontological interests were in the Devonian fossils of southern New York, Maine, Ohio, and Pennsylvania. Besides his contributions to research, Williams was one of the founders of the Sigma Xi honorary society, 1886, and the Geological Society of America, 1888.

These papers consist of a small amount of Williams' professional correspondence; field, office, and laboratory notebooks; notes from International Geological Congresses, 1885 and 1891; faunal notes and lists; drafts of writings; and illustrations and plates with accompanying explanations used in his publications. Most of this material was used in the preparation of Williams' publications on the fossils of the Watkins Glen-Catatonk Quadrangle, New York, and the Eastport Quadrangle, Maine.

ARRANGEMENT: (1) General correspondence, 1896, 1906-1907, 1914; (2) field, office, and laboratory notebooks, 1880-1916 and undated; (3) faunal notes and lists, *circa* 1884-1914 and undated; (4) drafts for publications, 1903-1916; (5) illustrations and plates for publications, 1912-1914. FINDING AIDS: Description in control file. SPECIAL CONDITIONS: Use of this record unit requires prior arrangement with the Archives staff.

(7328)

James Steele Williams Papers, circa 1918-1960 and undated
(1.3 linear meters).

James Steele Williams (1896-1957) was a specialist on Carboniferous and Permian paleontology and stratigraphy. He began his professional career as an Instructor of Geology at the University of Missouri in 1921. He continued his teaching career until 1930, eventually achieving the position of Associate Professor. In addition to his faculty post, Williams held appointment as Geologist on the staff of the Missouri Bureau of Mines and Geology. In 1930 he joined the United States Geological Survey (USGS) as assistant, and eventually successor, to George Herbert Girty, the USGS specialist on late Paleozoic marine fauna. Williams remained with the USGS for the remainder of his career, and at the time of his death he had risen to the position of Principal Geologist.

Williams' primary research interests were the Carboniferous and Permian invertebrates of the western United States (primarily the Rocky Mountain states) and Alaska. He spent several summers collecting fossils with USGS field parties detailed to the American West. During World War II, Williams was placed in charge of the USGS investigation of domestic fluorspar resources. Williams was active within the geological profession and served many organizations in elected or appointed capacities. In 1937, he was a United States delegate to the Seventeenth International Geological Congress in Russia. He traveled to Heerlen, Netherlands, in 1951, as USGS representative at the Third Congress of Carboniferous Stratigraphy and Geology.

The papers of James Steele Williams document his research on Carboniferous and Permian invertebrates; work on various USGS projects, especially the World War II era fluorspar investigations; field work in the western United States; and professional activities. Materials concerning Williams' teaching career at the University of Missouri and his concurrent duties with the Missouri Bureau of Mines and Geology are found in small amounts. The majority of the collection consists of incoming and outgoing correspondence exchanged between Williams and domestic and foreign paleontologists. The letters concern all aspects of his professional work, and are especially valuable in documenting day-to-day activities of the USGS Section of Paleontology. The papers also include notebooks, mostly from Williams' student days; unidentified and undated photographs of Williams; classroom materials used by Williams in courses taught at the University of Missouri; and a bibliography of Missouri geology maintained by Williams.

ARRANGEMENT: (1) Domestic correspondence, 1921-1960 and undated; (2) foreign correspondence, 1929-1956 and undated; (3) notebooks, 1918-1926 and undated; (4) photographs, undated; (5) teaching materials, *circa* 1921-1930 and undated; (6) bibliography of Missouri geology, *circa* 1918-1930 and undated. FINDING AIDS: Description in control file. SPECIAL CONDITIONS: Use of this record unit requires prior arrangement with the Archives staff.

(7285)

Archie F. Wilson Papers, 1949-1961
(1.4 linear meters).

Archie F. Wilson (1903-1960) was a wood enthusiast who assembled the foremost private wood collection in the United States. Although for most of his life he held managerial positions in the manufacturing industry, he devoted most of his free time to his avocation. During the 1950s he was a Research Associate in woods at the Chicago Natural History Museum (now the Field Museum of Natural History) and at various times between 1949 and 1960 he served as Editor, Secretary, Vice-President, and President of the International Wood Collectors Society (IWCS).

These papers consist primarily of correspondence, 1949-1961, which documents Wilson's activities in the IWCS, the growth of his collection, and his range of contacts with botanists, foresters, and other wood collectors around the world. Topics include collecting trips, specimens, and identifications, as well as IWCS business. Of special interest is Wilson's correspondence with William L. Stern, who became Curator of the Division of Woods at the Smithsonian in 1960. The long association of the two men resulted in Wilson's gift to the Institution, at his death in 1960, of his extensive wood collection. Also included are the constitution and by-laws of the IWCS, much taxonomic data, and specimen lists.

ARRANGEMENT: (1) Correspondence, 1949-1961; (2) miscellaneous correspondence, 1949-1961; (3) constitution and by-laws of the IWCS; (4) taxonomic data and specimen lists; (5) card file of information on collectors. FINDING AIDS: Description in control file. SPECIAL CONDITIONS: Use of this record unit requires prior arrangement with the Archives staff.

(7235)

Charles Branch Wilson Papers, 1894-1941 and undated
(1.3 linear meters).

Charles Branch Wilson (1861-1941) was born in Exeter, Maine. He received his A.B. and A.M. degrees from Colby College, Waterville, Maine, and the Ph.D. from Johns Hopkins University in 1910. While completing his A.M., Wilson worked as a tutor in Botany at Colby. In 1891, he was appointed Professor of Science at the State Normal School, Gorham, Maine. He became Professor of Natural Science at the State Normal School, Westfield, Massachusetts, in 1896 and the following year was made Professor of Biology and the Head of the Science Department. Wilson held the positions at Westfield until his retirement in 1932.

Wilson participated in several biological field trips during his career. He spent the summer of 1897 working at the Johns Hopkins University marine laboratory at Port Antonio, Jamaica. During the summer of 1899, Wilson worked at the United States Fish Commission's laboratory at Woods Hole, Massachusetts, where he undertook the investigation of parasitic copepods found in common foodfish. This began a long association between Wilson and the Fish Commission and its successor, the United States Bureau of Fisheries. Other work under the auspices of the Bureau of Fisheries included an economic survey of Lake Maxinkuckee, Indiana, in 1906; a survey of the fresh water mussels indigenous to the Mississippi River, 1907; and economic surveys of the Maumee River in 1908, the Kankakee River in 1909, and the Cumberland River in 1911. In 1912, he made a similar survey of the lakes of northern Minnesota. From 1913 to 1923, he served as an economic investigator for the Bureau of Fisheries at Fairport, Iowa. Wilson assisted in an economic survey of Lake Erie for New York State during 1928 and 1929.

Wilson's main zoological interest was the study of free swimming and parasitic copepods. His association with the United States National Museum (USNM) began in February 1901 when the entire USNM collection of parasitic copepods was turned over to him for identification. In recognition of his work on the USNM collections, Wilson was made Honorary Collaborator in Copepoda in 1933. His bibliography numbered more than 85 titles, with three of his major works being published posthumously. His most important work concerned the copepods collected by the Carnegie Institution's non-magnetic yacht, *Carnegie,* in 1928 and 1929. The study, for the first time in the history of oceanography, gave the directly comparable results of simultaneous three-level tows made in all oceans with identical gear, accompanied by full station data, including temperature, salinity, density, phosphates and hydrogen ion concentration.

These papers consist of incoming correspondence of Wilson, 1901-1941; research material, manuscripts, and miscellaneous writings, 1894-1941 and undated; and photographs of Jamaica taken while Wilson worked at the Johns Hopkins University marine laboratory at Port Antonio, 1897.

ARRANGEMENT: (1) Incoming correspondence, 1901-1941; (2) research material, manuscripts, and miscellaneous writings, 1894-1941 and undated; (3) photographs of Jamaica, 1897. FINDING AIDS: Description in control file. SPECIAL CONDITIONS: Use of this record unit requires prior arrangement with the Archives staff.

(7412)

Willis W. Wirth Papers, circa 1939-1984
(2.5 linear meters).

Willis W. Wirth (1916-1994), an entomologist, was educated at Iowa State College, B.S., 1940; Louisiana State University, M.S., 1947; and the University of California, Ph.D., 1950. From 1942 to 1947 he served as Senior Assistant Sanitarian with the United States Public Health Service. In 1949, Wirth was appointed Entomologist with the Division of Insect Identification, Bureau of Entomology and Plant Quarantine, United States Department of Agriculture (USDA), and assigned to taxonomic work at the United States National Museum. He remained with the USDA until 1984, when he retired from the Systematic Entomology Laboratory. Wirth's research specialty is the taxonomy of Diptera.

These papers consist of incoming and outgoing correspondence primarily documenting Wirth's career at the USDA and his research on Diptera. Also included are small amounts of correspondence concerning his work with the United States Public Health Service and his tenure as a Fulbright Research Scholar in Australia, 1956-1957. The correspondence concerns the identification of specimens, the preparation and publication of research papers, and the review of manuscripts and proposals.

ARRANGEMENT: Alphabetic and chronologic. FINDING AIDS: Box list in control file. SPECIAL CONDITIONS: Use of this record unit requires prior arrangement with the Archives staff.

(7385)

Philip W. Wolle Papers, 1883-1969
(0.8 linear meter).

Philip W. Wolle (1893-1969), a farmer from the Eastern Shore of Maryland, had an avocational interest in the study of algae. His paternal grandfather was the famous algologist, Rev. Francis Wolle.

These papers consist mostly of materials documenting Wolle's studies on algae. Included is a series of notebooks containing observations and drawings from his research, as well as information on his family; correspondence with Paul S. Conger, Ruth Patrick, Francis Drouet, and other algologists concerning a wide range of research topics; photographs of Wolle, his family, and his farm in Princess Anne, Maryland; a small amount of correspondence of his grandfather, Rev. Francis Wolle, written between 1883 and 1888; and biographical information on Wolle compiled by Conger.

ARRANGEMENT: Unarranged. FINDING AIDS: None. SPECIAL CONDITIONS: Use of this record unit requires prior arrangement with the Archives staff.

(7331)

A. Gilbert Wright Papers, circa 1936-1981 and undated
(0.5 linear meter).

A. Gilbert Wright (1909-1987) was a zoologist and exhibits curator. Born in Carthage, Illinois, he developed an interest in natural history, taxidermy, and museum curatorship in his youth. After receiving the B.A. in biology from Carthage College in 1932, Wright was appointed Zoologist at the Illinois State Museum (ISM) in 1933. He gained broad museum experience as a Rockefeller Foundation intern at the Buffalo Museum of Science in 1937-1938. Wright earned the M.S. degree in zoology from the University of Illinois at Urbana in 1946. In 1953, he left the ISM to accept the position of Curator of Exhibits at the Florida State Museum (FSM). During his tenure at FSM, Wright developed exhibits for the main museum, a "museumobile," and historical site museums throughout the state. In 1961, he was appointed Chief of the Museum Planning Branch of the National Park Service for the Jefferson National Expansion Memorial in St. Louis. In 1963, Wright joined the staff of the Office of Exhibits Programs at the Smithsonian Institution, as Assistant Chief with responsibilities for planning exhibits renovation in the National Museum of Natural History (NMNH). In 1971-1972, he was Assistant to the Director of the NMNH for exhibits planning and during this time developed the Insect Zoo. From 1972 until his retirement in 1975, Wright was a writer-editor in the Office of

Exhibits Central. In the early 1970s, Wright began teaching courses in museology at The George Washington University (GWU). After his retirement, he directed their new Museum Studies Program until 1978.

This collection documents most aspects of Wright's professional career and includes materials concerning his tenure as a Rockefeller Foundation intern at the Buffalo Museum of Science; his work at the Florida State Museum, the Jefferson National Expansion Memorial, and the Smithsonian Institution; and his teaching career at The George Washington University. The collection includes correspondence received and written by Wright which documents personal relationships, as well as most of his professional positions. Materials documenting Wright's professional work include his report on a tour of United States museums taken during the Rockefeller internship; teaching records from his GWU course on museology; publications written by or concerning him; and records concerning his work at the Smithsonian, especially the By-Word project at NMNH. The collection also includes photographs and slides, many of which were taken by Wright. Included are images of Wright; the muralist, Jay H. Matternes; and exhibits, research areas, laboratories, and personnel at the FSM and NMNH.

ARRANGEMENT: (1) General correspondence, 1936-1981; (2) collected professional materials, *circa* 1938-1978 and undated; (3) photographs and slides, *circa* 1936-1973 and undated. FINDING AIDS: Description in control file. SPECIAL CONDITIONS: Use of this record unit requires prior arrangement with the Archives staff.

(7212)

John Xantus Papers, 1857-1864
(0.1 linear meter).

A native of Hungary, John Xantus (1825-1894) came to the United States in 1850. In 1855, he entered the United States Army and served as a hospital steward at Fort Riley, Kansas Territory, 1855-1857, and Fort Tejon, California, 1857-1859. In January 1859, Xantus was appointed tidal observer for the United States Coast Survey stationed at Cape San Lucas, Lower California, where he remained until August 1861. After a short visit to Hungary, Xantus was appointed United States Consul at Manzanillo, Mexico, on November 25, 1862. In 1864, he returned to Hungary, where he spent the remainder of his life.

In 1857, Xantus began corresponding with Spencer F. Baird, and in subsequent years he made extensive collections for the Smithsonian Institution, especially in the field of ornithology.

These papers consist of correspondence from John Xantus to Spencer F. Baird, mostly concerning Xantus' collecting activities, 1857-1864. Also included are several letters (and copies of letters) from various individuals concerning Xantus, especially letters of recommendation for the position of U. S. Consul at Manzanillo, Mexico.

After entering the U. S. Army in 1855, Xantus began using the name Louis de Vesey. The letters in this collection for the years 1857-1858 are signed three different ways: "de Vesey," "L. X. de Vesey," and "L. Xantus de Vesey." By 1859, he had readopted his given name and letters are signed "J. Xantus."

ARRANGEMENT: Chronologic. FINDING AIDS: None. SPECIAL CONDITIONS: Use of this record unit requires prior arrangement with the Archives staff.

Henry Crecy Yarrow Papers, circa 1880-1890
(0.1 linear meter).

Henry Crecy Yarrow (1840-1929) served as the first Curator of Herpetology at the United States National Museum from 1878 to 1889. He had accompanied the United States Geographical and Geological Explorations and Surveys West of the 100th Meridian (the Wheeler Surveys) as a naturalist. An army surgeon, he was on duty at the Army Medical Library when Spencer Baird convinced him to take on the position of Honorary Curator on a part-time basis. He continued in this post until 1889 when he resigned.

Prior to his coming to the Museum, Yarrow wrote two herpetological reports concerning the Wheeler expeditions. While Curator, he prepared a "Check list of North American Reptilia and Batrachia, with catalogs of specimens in the U. S. National Museum," 1883.

ARRANGEMENT: (1) Material related to the history of the Department of Reptiles, 1887; (2) manuscripts of Henry Crecy Yarrow concerning reptiles, *circa* 1880-1890. FINDING AIDS: Description in control file. SPECIAL CONDITIONS: Use of this record unit requires prior arrangement with the Archives staff.

Stanley Paul Young Papers, 1921-1965
(1.3 linear meters).

Stanley Paul Young (1889-1969) was born in Astoria, Oregon, and grew up in that region. His outdoor interests led him to the University of Oregon where he received his B.A. in mining engineering in 1911. He went to the University of Michigan for graduate work in geology, but his interests changed and he completed his M.S. in biology.

In 1917, Young was hired as a ranger for the United States Forest Service. A few months later Young joined the Bureau of Biological Survey, United States Department of Agriculture, as a hunter, assigned to control predatory animals which were destroying the livestock of local ranchers.

In 1919, Young became Assistant Inspector for Arizona and New Mexico and, in 1921, agent-in-control of predatory animal work in the Colorado-Kansas district. He remained there until 1927 when he was assigned to Washington, D.C., as Assistant Head of the Division of Predatory Animal and Rodent Control. In Washington, Young filled a variety of positions in the Biological Survey: Chief of the Division of Economic Operations, 1928-1934; Chief of the Division of Game Management, 1934-1938; and Chief of the Division of Predator and Rodent Control, 1938-1939. When the Biological Survey was transferred to the Department of Interior in 1939, Young was made Senior Biologist in the Branch of Wildlife Research where he worked with Hartley H. T. Jackson. In 1957, when the Bird and Mammal Laboratories were made an independent research unit, Young was named the first Director and remained there until his retirement in 1959.

Young's chief research interests were the predatory mammals of the West: the wolf, coyote, puma, and bobcat.

The papers of Stanley Paul Young consist of records from his predatory animal control work; personal, official, and professional correspondence; material on his publications; and material on his professional career. Additional Young material can be found in record unit 7171, the Bird and Mammal Laboratories Records.

ARRANGEMENT: (1) Personal correspondence and related materials, 1938-1948, 1950, 1952-1960; (2) correspondence, reports, and photographs concerning official and professional work, 1927-1965; (3) correspondence, reports, and related materials concerning predatory animal and rodent control, 1921, 1923, 1925-1927, 1933-1939, 1946, 1954; (4) correspondence and notes concerning the publications of Stanley Paul Young, 1937-1957. FINDING AIDS: Description in control file. SPECIAL CONDITIONS: Use of this record unit requires prior arrangement with the Archives staff.

(7462)

James Zetek Papers, circa 1921-1951
(3.7 linear meters).

James Zetek (1886-1959) was an entomologist and authority on the natural history of Panama. From 1923 to 1956, he served as Resident Manager of the Canal Zone Biological Area on Barro Colorado Island in Panama. Zetek's primary research interest was the study of termites and termite control.

This collection consists primarily of an index card file documenting Zetek's research on the insects of Panama and his insect collection. The file contains information on insects collected, their identification, and their effect on native vegetation. Also included is a file of bibliography cards relating to the natural history of Panama.

ARRANGEMENT: (1) James Zetek Papers, *circa* 1921-1951, accession number 86-131; (2) James Zetek Papers, *circa* 1921-1936, accession number 90-126. FINDING AIDS: None. SPECIAL CONDITIONS: Use of this record unit requires prior arrangement with the Archives staff.

ORAL HISTORY COLLECTION

The Office of Smithsonian Institution Archives began its Oral History Program in 1973. Program staff conduct interviews with current and retired Smithsonian staff and others who have made significant contributions to the Institution. The purpose of the program is to supplement the written documentation of the Archives' record and manuscript collections, focusing on the history of the Institution, research by its scholars, and contributions of its staff. The Oral History Collection also contains interviews conducted by researchers or students on topics related to the history of the Smithsonian or the holdings of the Smithsonian Institution Archives. Interviews were recorded on audiotape or videotape, and transcripts are available for most interviews. Interviews in languages other than English have been transcribed into English. For additional interviews documenting the history of the Smithsonian, see the Videohistory Collection.

(9500)

Charles G. Abbot Interviews, 1973
(2 audiotapes).

Charles G. Abbot (1872-1973), astrophysicist, served as the fifth Secretary of the Smithsonian Institution from 1928 to 1944. Abbot came to the Smithsonian in 1895 to serve as an assistant to Secretary Samuel P. Langley in the Smithsonian Astrophysical Observatory. In 1906, he was named Director of the Observatory, a position he held until his retirement in 1944. He became Assistant Secretary in 1918 and Secretary in 1928. After his retirement in 1944, he was named Secretary Emeritus and continued research in astrophysics until his death. Abbot was known for his research on the solar constant and experiments with solar powered mechanisms.

These interviews of Abbot by Miriam S. Freilicher cover his scientific career, inventions, and role as a Smithsonian administrator, and include reminiscences of colleagues, notably Joseph G. Cannon, Robert H. Goddard, and Samuel P. Langley.

ARRANGEMENT: (1) Audiotapes, 2 hours; (2) transcript, 46 pages. FINDING AIDS: (1) Description in control file; (2) name index to transcript.

(9511)

John Warren Aldrich Interviews, 1975, 1977
(4 audiotapes).

John Warren Aldrich (1906-1995), an ornithologist affiliated with the National Museum of Natural History, first became interested in natural history in his youth through participation in bird walks and summer nature camps. After receiving the Ph.B. in biology from Brown University in 1928, Aldrich began his career at the Buffalo Museum of Science. In 1930, he joined the staff of the Cleveland Museum of Natural History as a Biological Assistant. Upon receipt of his Ph.D. in 1937 from Western Reserve University, Aldrich was appointed Curator of Ornithology at the Cleveland Museum. In 1941, Aldrich joined the staff of the Fish and Wildlife Service as a Biologist; in 1947, he was appointed Chief of the Section of Distribution and Migration of Birds; in 1957, Chief of the Section of Distribution of Birds and Mammals; and in 1957, Staff Specialist, Branch of Wildlife Research. During his tenure with the Fish and Wildlife Service, Aldrich was located in the National Museum of Natural History, Division of Birds, where he worked with the national collections. Because of his long association with the Division, Aldrich was appointed a Research Associate upon his retirement in 1973.

Aldrich's research interests included the taxonomy of North American birds, breeding bird population studies, bird banding, bird distribution studies, ecology, endangered species, and wildlife management. Aldrich was active in many professional organizations, including the Audubon Naturalist Society of the Central Atlantic States, Inc., American Ornithologists' Union, Baird Ornithological Club of Washington, D.C., Biological Society of Washington, Cosmos Club, International Council for Bird Preservation, Washington Biologists' Field Club, and Wilderness Society.

These interviews of Aldrich by Pamela M. Henson cover his early interests in natural history; education; career in ornithology at the Buffalo Museum of Science, Cleveland Museum of Natural History, Fish and Wildlife Service, and Division of Birds, National Museum of Natural History; research interests; and activities in professional organizations.

ARRANGEMENT: (1) Audiotapes, 3.5 hours; (2) transcript, 126 pages. FINDING AIDS: (1) Description in control file; (2) name index to transcript.

(9522)

Association of Curators Project, 1983
(2 audiotapes).

The Association of Curators of the National Museum of American History in 1983 sponsored a series of lectures by senior staff "On Being a Curator." Margaret B. Klapthor (1922-1994) was appointed Museum Aid in the Division of History of the United States National Museum in 1943. She advanced to Assistant Curator in 1952, Associate Curator in 1962 and Curator of the Division of Political History in 1970. After forty years at the Museum, she retired in 1983 and was appointed Curator Emeritus. J. Jefferson Miller II, (1925-   ) came to the Division of Ceramics and Glass in 1962 as an Assistant Curator. He served as Associate Curator from 1964 to 1969 and Curator from 1970 until his retirement in 1980.

Klapthor and Miller discussed their careers in the Divisions of Ceramics and Glass, History, and Political History at the National Museum of American History, focusing on curatorial methods and collecting policies.

ARRANGEMENT: (1) Audiotapes, 2 hours; (2) transcript, 71 pages. FINDING AIDS: (1) Description in control file; (2) name index to transcript.

(9556)

George V. Barton Reminiscences, 1982-1983
(3 audiotapes).

George V. Barton (1928-   ), marine electronics specialist and amateur astronomer, joined the staff of the Smithsonian Astrophysical Observatory (SAO) in 1957 to work on the Satellite Tracking Program (STP). Over the course of the next year, he set up Baker-Nunn cameras at satellite tracking stations in Las Cruces, New Mexico; Olifantsfontein, South Africa; San Fernando, Spain; Nainital, India; and Villa Dolores, Argentina.

Barton left the STP in 1958 to work on the Cateye Project from 1958 to 1963 and at the Naval Research Laboratory from 1964 to 1974. He then returned to the field of marine electronics.

These reminiscences by Barton cover his hiring, orientation to the Satellite Tracking Program, the launching of Sputnik, installation of Baker-Nunn cameras, and his technical innovations such as the Barton Scope and reels for winding film.

ARRANGEMENT: (1) Audiotapes, 4 hours; (2) transcript, 135 pages. FINDING AIDS: (1) Description in control file; (2) name index to transcript. SPECIAL CONDITIONS: Restricted.

(9563)

Charles F. Bennett, Jr., and Anna Carole Bennett Interview, 1975
(1 audiotape).

Charles F. Bennett, Jr., (1926-   ) received his B.A. in 1955 and Ph.D. in geography in 1960 from the University of California, Los Angeles, and in 1959 began his teaching career there. Charles and his wife, Anna Carole Bennett, first visited Barro Colorado Island (BCI) in 1952. The Barro Colorado Island Research Station, in the Panama Canal Zone, was a tropical biology field station established in 1923 and run by a consortium of universities and government agencies. Called the Canal Zone Biological Area (CZBA), it was transferred to the Smithsonian Institution in 1946 and was renamed the Smithsonian Tropical Research Institute (STRI) in 1966. The Bennetts returned in 1959 and 1961 and remained until 1964. During this time, they assisted the director, Martin Humphrey Moynihan, in organizing and cataloging the BCI library as well as collecting microclimatological data. Charles Bennett returned in 1965 to further study the evolution of neotropical forests. In 1966, Charles Bennett became an honorary Research Associate of STRI, providing advice and assistance in developing research projects and programs for the Institute.

This interview of Charles and Anna Bennett by Ira Rubinoff, Director of STRI, covers their first visit to BCI; how the station has changed; different directors' visions for the station, especially Martin Humphrey Moynihan; and STRI's outlook for the future.

ARRANGEMENT: (1) Audiotape, 1.5 hours; (2) transcript, 45 pages. FINDING AIDS: (1) Description in control file; (2) name index to transcript. SPECIAL CONDITIONS: Restricted.

(9526)

S. Stillman Berry Interviews, 1980-1982
(5 audiotapes).

S. Stillman Berry (1887-1984) was an independent researcher working in both malacology and horticulture. Educated at both Harvard University (M.A. 1910) and Stanford University (B.A. 1909, Ph.D. 1913), he concentrated his research on cephalopods, chitons, and land snails of California and the eastern Pacific. From 1913 to 1919, Berry worked as a Librarian at the Scripps Institution of Biological Research, developing the Institution's library holdings. Following his father's death in 1917, Berry took over as corporate president of his family's ranch in Montana, but remained in Redlands, California, to continue his scientific research independently. His varied work included describing 401 new taxa of mollusks, developing new varieties of irises and daffodils, amassing a significant shell and cephalopod collection, and compiling a private library of important and rare scientific works.

These interviews with S. Stillman Berry by Donald R. Shasky cover malacology; his work at Scripps; reminiscences of colleagues, especially Robert Edwards Carter Stearns, A. Myra Keen, and William M. Mann; and development of his private library.

ARRANGEMENT: (1) Audiotapes, 3.5 hours; (2) transcript, 71 pages. FINDING AIDS: (1) Description in control file; (2) name index to transcript.

(9517)

Richard Eliot Blackwelder Interview, 1978

(2 audiotapes).

Richard Eliot Blackwelder (1909-   ), a zoologist, specialized in entomology and the principles of zoology. Educated at Stanford University (B.A. 1931, Ph.D. 1934), he began his career with the Smithsonian's Walter Rathbone Bacon Traveling Scholarship from 1935 to 1938. He worked briefly for the Bureau of Entomology of the United States Department of Agriculture (USDA) before accepting an assistant curatorship at the American Museum of Natural History (AMNH) in 1938. From 1940 to 1954, Blackwelder was on the curatorial staff of the Division of Insects of the United States National Museum (USNM), specializing in the morphology, classification, and nomenclature of the Staphylinidae. Blackwelder was very active in the Society of Systematic Zoology (SSZ), notably as Editor of *Systematic Zoology*. In 1954, he began a study of the principles of zoology. From 1956 to 1958, he was an Associate Professor at St. John Fisher College, and in 1965 was appointed Professor of Zoology at Southern Illinois University.

This interview of Blackwelder by Pamela M. Henson covers his education; field work; career with the USDA, AMNH, USNM, St. John Fisher College, and Southern Illinois University; his research interests; the SSZ; and his colleagues. The interview focuses on his years in the Division of Insects, USNM; the SSZ; and his friend and colleague, Waldo LaSalle Schmitt, Head Curator of Biology in the USNM and a founder of the SSZ.

ARRANGEMENT: (1) Audiotapes, 2 hours; (2) transcript, 73 pages. FINDING AIDS: (1) Description in control file; (2) name index to transcript.

(9561)

Fausto Bocanegra Interviews, 1988

(0.1 linear meter).

Fausto Bocanegra (1926-   ) was born in Buenaventura, Colombia, and arrived on Barro Colorado Island (BCI) in Panama in 1952 at the age of twenty-six. The Barro Colorado Island Research Station, in the Panama Canal Zone, was a tropical biology field station, established in 1923 and run by a consortium of universities and government agencies. Called the Canal Zone Biological Area (CZBA), it was transferred to the Smithsonian Institution in 1946 and was renamed the Smithsonian Tropical Research

Institute (STRI) in 1966. Bocanegra first came to the island as a temporary construction worker, building a new laboratory building. Over the years, Bocanegra served as the principal caretaker for a large collection of live animals kept by STRI Director Martin Humphrey Moynihan; a knowledgeable guide to the island; and one of the unarmed game wardens, capturing poachers in a number of instances. He also operated the launches, carrying messages and transporting materials and visitors between the mainland and BCI; cleared trails for general use; and attended to general maintenance on the island. Bocanegra retired in 1988 after thirty-seven years on BCI.

These interviews of Bocanegra by Giselle Mora discuss his youth, over thirty years work on BCI, and reminiscences of fellow workers such as Martin Humphrey Moynihan, Oscar Dean Kidd, Carl B. Koford, James Zetek, Adela Gomez, and Francisco Vitola, *circa* 1952-1988. This collection consists of transcripts only. The interview transcript is available in both Spanish and English.

ARRANGEMENT: (1) Transcript, Spanish, 75 pages; (2) transcript, English, 89 pages. FINDING AIDS: (1) Description in control file; (2) name index to transcript. SPECIAL CONDITIONS: Restricted.

(9567)

Adrian M. Bouche Reminiscences, 1992
(1 audiotape).

Adrian M. Bouche (1923-   ), fossil preparator and amateur naturalist, was raised in the Panama Canal Zone and worked there until 1976 in a variety of occupations. After his retirement, he became a fossil preparator at Brigham Young University in Utah. He also revived plans begun by his grandfather to found a museum documenting the history of the Panama Canal Zone.

These reminiscences recorded by Bouche in 1992 discuss his family history, American scientists working in Panama, the Smithsonian Tropical Research Institute, plans for a scientific research center in Panama, his career as a fossil preparator, his plans for a museum of the Panama Canal Zone, and colleagues such as Graham Bell Fairchild and Robert L. Dressler.

ARRANGEMENT: (1) Audiotape, 1 hour; (2) transcript, 28 pages. FINDING AIDS: (1) Description in control file; (2) name index to transcript.

(9515)

James C. Bradley Interviews, 1974-1978
(26 audiotapes).

James C. Bradley (1910-1984) came to the Smithsonian in 1959 as Assistant to the Secretary, Leonard Carmichael. In 1960 he was appointed Assistant Secretary, and in 1970 was appointed Under Secretary of the Institution. After his retirement in 1972, he served as Consultant for Management and Planning to Secretary S. Dillon Ripley and as a Research Associate of the Institution.

These interviews of Bradley by Miriam S. Freilicher and Pamela M. Henson cover his responsibilities for administrative, fiscal, and legislative planning at the Smithsonian from 1959 to 1978, especially for program development and capital improvement of the Fine Arts and Portrait Galleries, the Hillwood Museum, Hirshhorn Museum and

Sculpture Garden, Museum Support Center, National Air and Space Museum, National Portrait Gallery, National Zoological Park, and Smithsonian Astrophysical Observatory; and his work with Secretaries Leonard Carmichael and S. Dillon Ripley.

ARRANGEMENT: (1) Audiotapes, 22.5 hours; (2) transcript, 363 pages. FINDING AIDS: (1) Description in control file; (2) name index to transcript.

(9514)

Fenner A. Chace, Jr., Interviews, 1977
(3 audiotapes).

Fenner A. Chace, Jr., (1908-   ) a carcinologist and Research Associate of the National Museum of Natural History (NMNH), specialized in the taxonomy, morphology, and distribution of decapod Crustacea. After receiving the Ph.D. in biology from Harvard University in 1934, Chace curated the crustacean collection of the Museum of Comparative Zoology (MCZ) until 1946. Chace was appointed Curator of the Division of Marine Invertebrates of the United States National Museum (USNM) in 1946 and, during his tenure, oversaw the growth of the Division, the move into the West Wing of the Natural History Building, and the modernization of exhibits. In 1963, Chace was appointed Senior Zoologist in the Department of Invertebrate Zoology, National Museum of Natural History (NMNH), and after his retirement in 1978, continued his work as a Research Associate of the Museum.

These interviews of Fenner Chace by Pamela M. Henson cover his youth and education, curatorial career at the MCZ, USNM, and NMNH, research interests in decapod Crustacea, service during World War II, and reminiscences about colleagues, especially Thomas Barbour, Horton H. Hobbs, Jr., and Alexander Wetmore.

ARRANGEMENT: (1) Audiotapes, 2.5 hours; (2) transcript, 72 pages. FINDING AIDS: (1) Description in control file; (2) name index to transcript.

(9541)

Nazaret Cherkezian Interview, 1986
(2 audiotapes).

Nazaret Cherkezian (1924-   ) began his career in 1946 as a journalist with the *New York Herald Tribune*. In 1949 he became Associate Director of Information Services at New York University, where he helped found the Office of Radio and Television and created the "Sunrise Semester" educational television series. In 1957, he was made producer of the WCBS-TV weekly series "Eye on New York," but two years later left commercial television for National Educational Television, where he became Executive Producer in 1965. In 1973, he came to Washington, D.C., to accept a post as Director of Programming for the National Public Affairs Center for Television.

Cherkezian's Smithsonian career began in 1974 when he became Telecommunications Coordinator for the Office of Public Affairs. Named Director of the Office of Telecommunications upon its creation in 1976, he was responsible for the Smithsonian's radio, television, and film productions until his retirement in 1986.

This interview with Nazaret Cherkezian by University of Maryland student John Peterson covers his education; experiences in television production and public affairs at

New York University, WCBS-TV, National Educational Television, and National Public Affairs Center for Television; and career as Director of the Office of Telecommunications at the Smithsonian.

ARRANGEMENT: (1) Audiotapes, 1.5 hours; (2) transcript, 35 pages. FINDING AIDS: (1) Description in control file; (2) name index to transcript.

(9555)
John Frederick Gates Clarke Interviews, 1986
(16 audiotapes).

John Frederick Gates Clarke (1905-1990) was a systematic entomologist specializing in Microlepidoptera. Clarke began collecting insects while growing up in Vancouver, British Columbia, and Bellingham, Washington. He worked briefly as a pharmacist but returned to school to pursue postgraduate studies in entomology at Washington State University and Cornell University. He began his career as a lepidopterist in 1936 when he joined the staff of the Bureau of Entomology, United States Department of Agriculture (USDA). Clarke was stationed in the United States National Museum (USNM) where he worked on the systematics of Macrolepidoptera and, later, Microlepidoptera. In 1954, he transferred to the Smithsonian payroll and was appointed Curator of Insects in the USNM. In 1963, he assumed the position of Chair of the newly created Department of Entomology until his appointment as Senior Entomologist in 1965. After his retirement from the NMNH in 1975, he continued his research as Curator Emeritus, until his death in 1990.

These interviews of Clarke by Pamela M. Henson cover his youth and education, career as an entomologist and administrator at the USDA and NMNH, and reminiscences of field work, life in the National Museum, and colleagues, notably August Busck, Carl Heinrich and Carl Frederick William Muesebeck.

ARRANGEMENT: (1) Audiotapes, 12.5 hours; (2) transcript, 366 pages. FINDING AIDS: (1) Description in control file; (2) name index to transcript.

(9528)
Henry Bascom Collins, Jr., Interviews, 1985
(7 audiotapes).

Henry Bascom Collins, Jr., (1899-1987) was an archeologist specializing in Eskimo prehistory. He worked at the Division of Ethnology of the United States National Museum from 1923 to 1938, Bureau of American Ethnology from 1939 to 1965, and the Department of Anthropology of the National Museum of Natural History from 1966 to 1987. During World War II, he served as Director of the Ethnogeographic Board, and after the war, participated in the founding of the Arctic Institute.

These interviews of Collins by Pamela M. Henson cover his youth, education, career in archeology at the Smithsonian, research interests and field work in Alaska, the Arctic, the Southeast and Southwest, directorship of the Ethnogeographic Board, work with the Arctic Institute and *Arctic Bibliography,* and reminiscences of colleagues, especially Ales Hrdlicka, Neil M. Judd, Thomas Dale Stewart, and Matthew William Stirling.

ARRANGEMENT: (1) Audiotapes, 7 hours; (2) transcript, 235 pages. FINDING AIDS: (1) Description in control file; (2) name index to transcript.

(9524)

G. Arthur Cooper Interviews, 1984

(6 audiotapes).

G. Arthur Cooper (1902-   ), a paleobiologist specializing in the classification and stratigraphy of Paleozoic brachiopods, was appointed Assistant Curator in the Division of Stratigraphic Paleontology of the United States National Museum (USNM) in 1930. He advanced to Curator of the Division of Invertebrate Paleontology in 1944. He assumed the Head Curatorship of the Department of Geology in 1957, oversaw its split in 1963, and continued as Chairman of the new Department of Paleobiology. In 1967, he was appointed Senior Paleobiologist, to devote his time completely to research, and continued as Paleobiologist Emeritus after his retirement in 1974.

These interviews of Cooper by Pamela M. Henson cover his youth and education; his career as Curator at the USNM, especially development of the collections, field work, research, and publications; his administrative responsibilities; and his reminiscences of colleagues at Yale University, the USNM, and the United States Geological Survey, including Charles Elmer Resser, Charles Schuchert, Edward Oscar Ulrich and Alexander Wetmore.

ARRANGEMENT: (1) Audiotapes, 5 hours; (2) transcript, 165 pages. FINDING AIDS: (1) Description in control file; (2) name index to transcript. SPECIAL CONDITIONS: Restricted.

(9501)

Richard Sumner Cowan Interviews, 1974

(4 audiotapes).

Richard Sumner Cowan (1921-   ), a systematic botanist specializing in neotropical flora, began his career in 1952 at the New York Botanical Garden. In 1957 he was appointed Associate Curator of the Department of Botany in the United States National Museum. Cowan was appointed Assistant Director of the National Museum of Natural History (NMNH) in 1962 and Director in 1965. He retired from administration in 1973, continuing his research as Senior Botanist until 1985.

These interviews with Cowan by Miriam S. Freilicher cover his education, research career in botany, and administration of NMNH.

ARRANGEMENT: (1) Audiotapes, 3.5 hours; (2) transcript, 136 pages. FINDING AIDS: (1) Description in control file; (2) name index to transcript.

(9570)

Wallace Joshan Dyar Interview, 1993

(4 audiotapes).

Wallace Joshan Dyar (1913-   ), philatelist, grew up in Washington, D.C., and at the Skyland Resort in the Shenandoah Mountains of Virginia. Son of Harrison Gray Dyar (1866-1929), a Smithsonian entomologist, and his second wife, Wellesca Pollock Allen

Dyar, he began work in 1933 at the Skyland Resort created by his uncle, George Freeman Pollock, and observed its development into the Shenandoah National Park. Dyar later worked as postmaster at Skyland and then for the United States Postal Service in Washington, D.C.

This interview of Dyar by Marc E. Epstein, Department of Entomology, National Museum of Natural History, and Pamela M. Henson, Institutional History Division, Office of Smithsonian Institution Archives, covers his family; youth; education in Washington, D.C.; careers at the Skyland Resort and United States Postal Service; reminiscences of his parents, including his father's entomological research at the Division of Insects, United States National Museum, his tunnel digging hobby, and their involvement in the Bahai faith; and the Pollock family's role in the development of kindergartens in the United States.

ARRANGEMENT: (1) Audiotapes, 2 hours; (2) transcript, 87 pages. FINDING AIDS: (1) Description in control file; (2) name index to transcript. SPECIAL CONDITIONS: Restricted.

(9571)

Dorothy Graham Edson Interviews, 1993
(12 audiotapes).

Dorothy Graham Edson was born in Suifu (now I-pin), Szechwan Province, China, on June 15, 1922. She lived there with her parents, Alicia Morey Graham and David Crockett Graham, missionaries for the American Baptist Foreign Mission Society stationed in Suifu and Chengtu for thirty-seven years. While stationed there, her father studied the culture and language of the Chinese, in addition to his missionary duties. Graham's Ph.D. dissertation, which he completed while on furlough at the University of Chicago, was published by the Smithsonian under the title "Religion in Szechuan Province" in 1928. Even though he was not officially connected with the Smithsonian, Graham made important natural history and anthropological collections for the Institution while in China, which are now housed in the National Museum of Natural History. Graham corresponded regularly with Smithsonian curators, and the Smithsonian also published a number of his articles in the Smithsonian Miscellaneous Collections series.

These interviews by Pamela M. Henson and William W. Moss III discuss travel and the daily routine in China; David Crockett Graham's work at the University of Chicago, including his work for the Museum of Art, Archeology, and Ethnology; Graham's collecting trips for the Smithsonian; the community of missionaries at the university; missionary duties; Graham's involvement with tribal cultures outside of city areas and his work recording Chinese stories and music of the Maio; the West China Border Research Society; and return to the United States after many years in the field, including his contact with the Smithsonian while residing in Washington, D.C.

ARRANGEMENT: (1) Audiotapes, 6 hours; (2) transcript, 268 pages. FINDING AIDS: (1) Description in control file; (2) name index to transcript. SPECIAL CONDITIONS: Restricted.

Jennie V. Emlong Interview, 1980
(2 audiotapes).

Jennie V. Emlong (1904-   ) is the mother of Douglas Ralph Emlong (1942-1980), an amateur field collector of fossils, especially marine mammals, in the Pacific Northwest. Douglas Emlong was self-taught and worked alone. However, he amassed a large collection of unique fossils which was purchased by the National Museum of Natural History (NMNH) and included fifteen new species of marine mammals and two previously unknown families. Emlong corresponded with A. Remington Kellogg, Curator of Mammals, who was interested in his fossil cetaceans, and was also supported and encouraged by Clayton E. Ray, Curator in the Department of Paleobiology.

Jennie Emlong was interviewed by Clayton Ray to provide a full picture of her talented and multi-faceted son. The interview covers his family background; childhood; education; development of interests in collecting; relationships with paleontologists, especially at the NMNH; major fossil finds; artistic activities; and personality.

ARRANGEMENT: (1) Audiotapes, 2 hours; (2) transcript, 52 pages. FINDING AIDS: (1) Description in control file; (2) name index to transcript. SPECIAL CONDITIONS: Restricted.

Robert K. Enders Interview, 1976
(2 audiotapes).

Robert Kendall Enders (1899-   ), a zoologist, was born in Essex, Iowa. After receiving his A.B. and Ph.D. in zoology from the University of Michigan in 1925 and 1927 respectively, he became an Assistant Professor of Biology at Union College. In 1928, he became an Assistant Professor at Missouri Valley College, and in 1932 was promoted to full Professor. He retired from Missouri Valley College in 1970. He was also appointed Emeritus Professor of Zoology at Swarthmore College in 1966.

Enders first visited Barro Colorado Island (BCI) in 1930 with a National Research Council Fellowship. The Barro Colorado Island Research Station, in the Panama Canal Zone, was a tropical biology field station established in 1923 and run by a consortium of universities and government agencies. Called the Canal Zone Biological Area (CZBA), it was transferred to the Smithsonian Institution in 1946 and was renamed the Smithsonian Tropical Research Institute (STRI) in 1966. In 1935, 1937, and 1941, Enders visited BCI again as a research fellow of the Academy of Natural Sciences of Philadelphia. As a professor, he continued his visits to Panama, bringing students to CZBA on field trips. While conducting research in mammalogy on BCI, he observed the development of the research station.

This interview of Enders by Neal G. Smith, a STRI biologist, discusses his introduction to BCI; subsequent research trips there; recollections of fellow scientists and staff on the island, including Frank Michler Chapman, Thomas Barbour, James Zetek, and Carl B. Koford; comparisons between the island then and now; and suggestions on how to improve the island for research purposes.

ARRANGEMENT: (1) Audiotapes, 2 hours; (2) transcript, 58 pages. FINDING AIDS: (1) Description in control file; (2) name index to transcript. SPECIAL CONDITIONS: Restricted.

John C. Ewers Interviews, 1974-1975

(9505)

(7 audiotapes).

John C. Ewers (1909-   ), an anthropologist specializing in the ethnology of the Plains Indians, began his career in 1935 as a field curator for the National Park Service, developing exhibits for park sites. From 1941 to 1944, he was Curator of the Museum of the Plains Indian, Bureau of Indian Affairs. In 1945, Ewers was appointed Associate Curator of the Division of Ethnology in the Department of Anthropology of the United States National Museum and developed the Museum's Exhibits Modernization Program. Ewers served as Planning Officer for the development of the National Museum of History and Technology (NMHT) from 1956 to 1959, as Assistant Director from 1959 to 1964, and as Director from 1964 to 1965. Ewers then returned to active research as Senior Ethnologist in the Department of Anthropology of the National Museum of Natural History until 1979, when he was appointed Ethnologist Emeritus.

These interviews of Ewers by Pamela M. Henson cover his education; early career with the National Park Service and the Museum of the Plains Indian; and his work at the Smithsonian, especially the Division of Ethnology, Exhibits Modernization Program, development of the NMHT, and ethnological research.

ARRANGEMENT: (1) Audiotapes, 5.5 hours; (2) transcript, 149 pages. FINDING AIDS: (1) Description in control file; (2) name index to transcript.

Graham Bell Fairchild Interview, 1989

(9559)

(2 audiotapes).

Graham Bell Fairchild was born in 1906 in Washington, D.C. He was introduced to tropical biology in his youth when he visited the Barro Colorado Island (BCI) research station of the Canal Zone Biological Area with his father, David Grandison Fairchild. He received the B.S., M.S., and Ph.D. in entomology from Harvard University, where he studied the collections at the Museum of Comparative Zoology (MCZ).

Fairchild began his career as an entomologist stationed in Brazil for the Yellow Fever Service of the Rockefeller Foundation from 1935 to 1937. He was an entomologist at the Gorgas Memorial Laboratory in Panama City, Panama, from 1938 to 1971, serving as Assistant Director from 1958 to 1971. At Gorgas, his research focused on the taxonomy of medically important insects, especially Tabanidae and Psychodidae. During his years in Panama, he observed the development of the BCI research station, first as a small university consortium and then under Smithsonian aegis as the Smithsonian Tropical Research Institute (STRI).

This interview of Fairchild by Joel B. Hagen, a Smithsonian Postdoctoral Fellow, discusses his reminiscences of BCI and the scientists who visited it; the development of STRI under Smithsonian administration; the faculty at Harvard and MCZ; and his career in medical entomology.

ARRANGEMENT: (1) Audiotapes, 1.5 hours; (2) transcript, 37 pages. FINDING AIDS: (1) Description in control file; (2) name index to transcript. SPECIAL CONDITIONS: Restricted.

Francis Raymond Fosberg Interviews, 1993
(22 audiotapes).

Francis Raymond Fosberg (1908-1993) was born in Spokane, Washington, and grew up in Turlock, California, with an early interest in natural history. He received his B.A. in botany from Pomona College in 1930. After graduation, he took a position at the Los Angeles County Museum researching plants of the desert Southwest and islands off the coast of California. This research led to his interests in island ecosystems, and in 1932 he moved to Honolulu to accept a position as an assistant at the University of Hawaii. While in Hawaii he was invited to participate in the Mangareva Expedition. He received his M.S. in botany from the University of Hawaii in 1937 and his Ph.D. from the University of Pennsylvania in 1939. Fosberg accepted a position at the United States Department of Agriculture (USDA) and was sent to Colombia to identify stands of *Cinchona* for quinine production for the war effort. After World War II, he participated in a survey of economic resources in the Micronesian Islands. Upon his return to the United States, he and his new assistant, Marie-Helene Sachet, began vegetation work for the newly formed Pacific Science Board under the National Research Council. Fosberg was also involved in the development of a joint program of the South Pacific Commission and the Pacific Science Board called the Coral Atoll Program, publishing papers twice a year.

Fosberg began his fifteen-year career at the United States Geological Survey (USGS) in 1951, mapping the military geology of islands in the Pacific. During his years there he also participated in many conferences, congresses, and scientific organizations such as the Pacific Science Association; United Nations Educational, Scientific, and Cultural Organization; the Pacific Science Board; and the American Association for the Advancement of Science. In 1966, Fosberg took a position at the Smithsonian's National Museum of Natural History (NMNH) in the tropical biology branch of the Ecology Program. Sachet was also appointed to the Program, allowing a continuation of their joint research. In 1968, with the demise of the Program, he and Sachet transferred to the Department of Botany, where Fosberg became Curator. He became Senior Botanist in 1976 and continued his career as Botanist Emeritus from 1978 to 1993.

These interviews of Fosberg by Pamela M. Henson cover his early life and influences; education and reminiscences of William Atwood Hilton and Philip Alexander Munz at Pomona, Harold St. John at Hawaii, and Jack Fogg at Pennsylvania; work on the Mangareva Expedition; his career at the USGS and USDA and work on the Colombian Cinchona Mission and the Marshall Islands and Micronesia surveys; work on *Cinchona* while on a Guggenheim Fellowship; career at the NMNH and reminiscences of Sachet; work in the international systematics community specifically on plant taxonomy and nomenclature, and work on the Pacific Science Congress; and his multidisciplinary, ecological view of science.

ARRANGEMENT: (1) Audiotapes, 11 hours; (2) transcript, 94 pages. FINDING AIDS: (1) Description in control file; (2) name index to transcript. SPECIAL CONDITIONS: Restricted.

Herbert Friedmann Interview, 1975

(3 audiotapes).

Herbert Friedmann (1900-1987), an ornithologist specializing in African and American parasitic birds, received the Ph.D. from Cornell University in 1923. He taught biology and ornithology at Brown University and Amherst College prior to being appointed Curator in the Division of Birds in the United States National Museum (USNM) in 1929. He also published on bird and animal symbolism in medieval and Renaissance art. In 1957, Friedmann was made Head Curator of the Department of Zoology in the USNM. He left the Institution in 1961 to become Director of the Los Angeles County Museum of Natural History, retiring from that position in 1970.

This interview of Friedmann by Pamela M. Henson covers his education, research interests, career and colleagues in the Division of Birds, administration of the Department of Zoology, USNM, and work in the Exhibits Modernization Program.

ARRANGEMENT: (1) Audiotapes, 2.5 hours; (2) transcript, 81 pages. FINDING AIDS: (1) Description in control file; (2) name index to transcript.

Edward P. Henderson Interviews, 1984-1985

(16 audiotapes).

Edward Porter Henderson (1898-1992) specialized in the study of meteorites for the United States National Museum (USNM). He received the B.S. and M.S. in chemistry from The George Washington University and was a chemist at the United States Geological Survey (USGS) from 1920 to 1929. In 1929, he was appointed Curator of Physical and Chemical Geology in the Department of Geology of the USNM, where he remained until his retirement as Curator of the Division of Meteorites in the Department of Mineral Sciences, in 1965. He continued as a Research Associate of the Division of Meteorites until 1988.

These interviews of Henderson by Pamela M. Henson cover his youth, education, career as a chemist at the USGS and a curator at the USNM, especially his development of the national collections, research techniques, field work, post-war work in Japan for the United States Army, and reminiscences of life in the Museum and colleagues, especially G. Arthur Cooper, William F. Foshag, and Stuart H. Perry.

ARRANGEMENT: (1) Audiotapes, 13 hours; (2) transcript, 492 pages. FINDING AIDS: (1) Description in control file; (2) name index to transcript.

Olga C. Hirshhorn Interviews, 1986-1988

(14 audiotapes).

Olga C. Hirshhorn (1920-   ), an art collector, was instrumental in the founding of the Hirshhorn Museum and Sculpture Garden. Born Olga Zatorsky, she was raised in Greenwich, Connecticut. She attended New York University and from 1939 to 1962 was married to John Cunningham. She established several of her own businesses, including a day care center and a business services firm, Services Unlimited. In 1964, she married financier and art collector, Joseph H. Hirshhorn (1900-1981), also a resident of Greenwich. She assisted her husband with his career and art avocation and began her own collection of modern art. The Hirshhorns were important figures in the art world and formed lasting friendships with many artists. In 1966, at the urging of Smithsonian Secretary S. Dillon Ripley, Joseph Hirshhorn donated his modern art collection to the Smithsonian Institution. In 1974, it opened as the Hirshhorn Museum and Sculpture Garden.

These interviews of Hirshhorn by Judith K. Zilczer, Curator, Hirshhorn Museum, and Pamela M. Henson, Smithsonian Institution Archives, discuss her youth; education; child-rearing years; careers in day care and business services; marriage to Joseph H. Hirshhorn; their travels, art collecting, meetings with S. Dillon Ripley, and the decision to donate the collection to the Smithsonian. Included are reminiscences of such art figures as Willem de Kooning, Henry Moore, Pablo Picasso, and Man Ray.

ARRANGEMENT: (1) Audiotapes, 12.5 hours; (2) transcript, 539 pages. FINDING AIDS: (1) Description in control file; (2) name index to transcript. SPECIAL CONDITIONS: Restricted.

(9509)

Horton H. Hobbs, Jr., Interview, 1976
(2 audiotapes).

Horton H. Hobbs, Jr., (1914-1994), specialized in the taxonomy, ecology, and geographic distribution of freshwater decapod crustaceans. Hobbs received his Ph.D. in biology from the University of Florida in 1940 and taught there until 1946. He joined the faculty of the University of Virginia in 1946 and served as Director of its Mountain Lake Biological Station from 1956 to 1960. In 1962, Hobbs was appointed Head Curator of the Department of Zoology, United States National Museum, serving as both an administrator and research scientist. In 1964, he retired from administration and was appointed Senior Scientist in the Department of Invertebrate Zoology. After his retirement in 1984, he continued as Zoologist Emeritus until 1994.

This interview of Hobbs by Pamela M. Henson covers his education and teaching at the University of Florida; career as a Professor of Zoology and Director of the Mountain Lakes Biological Station of the University of Virginia; research interests in crayfish; and role as Head Curator, Department of Zoology, United States National Museum, as Senior Scientist in the Department of Invertebrate Zoology, and as Director of the Archbold-Bredin-Smithsonian Biological Survey of Dominica.

ARRANGEMENT: (1) Audiotapes, 1.5 hours; (2) transcript, 55 pages. FINDING AIDS: (1) Description in control file; (2) name index to transcript.

(9525)

Phillip S. Hughes Interviews, 1985
(7 audiotapes).

Phillip S. Hughes (1917-), public administrator, was Under Secretary of the Smithsonian Institution from 1980 to 1985. Hughes served in a variety of administrative positions with the State of Washington, Veterans Administration, Bureau of the Budget,

General Accounting Office, and Department of Energy from 1938 to 1979. He was a consultant to the Audit and Review Committee of the Smithsonian Board of Regents in 1977, preparing the report, *Relations Between the Smithsonian and the Congress.* He returned to the Institution in 1980 to serve as Under Secretary until his retirement in 1985.

These interviews of Hughes by Pamela M. Henson cover his education, career in public administration, and interests in environmental conservation, but focus especially on his roles as consultant to the Board of Regents and as Under Secretary to Secretary S. Dillon Ripley.

ARRANGEMENT: (1) Audiotapes, 6.5 hours; (2) transcript, 185 pages. FINDING AIDS: (1) Description in control file; (2) name index to transcript.

(9558)

Louise Daniel Hutchinson Interviews, 1987
(4 audiotapes).

Louise Daniel Hutchinson (1928-   ) directed the Research Center at the Anacostia Museum (AM) from 1974 to 1986. Hutchinson began her museum career in 1971 when she joined the staff of the National Portrait Gallery (NPG) to conduct research on the William E. Harmon and Winold Reiss collections of portraits of African Americans. As an education specialist for the NPG, Hutchinson developed programs with the District of Columbia Public Schools and curriculum on the history of the District. In 1973, she moved to the National Park Service's site at the Frederick Douglass Home where she developed interpretive programs. In 1974, she returned to the Smithsonian to direct the Research Center at the AM. During her tenure, she conducted research in support of exhibits, developed an oral history program and the Anacostia Historical Society, and worked to establish collections and research expertise in African American history and culture at the AM.

These interviews of Hutchinson by University of Maryland graduate student Anne M. Rogers cover her childhood in Washington, D.C., education, reminiscences of segregation and community activism, her career as a researcher and educator for the NPG, Douglass Home and AM, and reminiscences of colleagues such as John R. Kinard and S. Dillon Ripley.

ARRANGEMENT: (1) Audiotapes, 3 hours; (2) transcript, 77 pages. FINDING AIDS: (1) Description in control file; (2) name index to transcript. SPECIAL CONDITIONS: Restricted.

(9573)

Meredith Leam Jones Interview, 1990
(11 audiotapes).

Meredith Leam Jones (1926-1996), invertebrate zoologist, received the B.A. in 1948, M.S. in 1952, and Ph.D. in 1956 from the University of California at Berkeley. From 1957 to 1960, he was an Assistant Professor at Florida State University. From 1960 to 1964, he was Assistant Curator in the Department of Living Invertebrates at the American Museum of Natural History (AMNH). In 1964, he accepted a position as Associate Curator in the Department of Invertebrate Zoology of the National Museum of

Natural History (NMNH). In 1970, he advanced to Curator in the Division of Worms, Department of Invertebrate Zoology, until his retirement in 1989. Jones' research focused on systematics of polycheate worms, especially those found at the hydrothermal vents in the eastern Pacific.

This interview of Jones by Pamela M. Henson discusses his education, his years at Florida State University and AMNH, his career at the NMNH, research on polycheate worms, especially the eastern Pacific hydrothermal rift fauna of giant tube worms, field work in the Caribbean and Pacific and at the Smithsonian Tropical Research Institute, and reminiscences of colleagues, notably Libby Henrietta Hyman, Ralph Smith, and Donald F. Squires.

ARRANGEMENT: (1) Audiotapes, 5.5 hours; (2) transcript, 168 pages. FINDING AIDS: (1) Description in control file; (2) name index to transcript. SPECIAL CONDITIONS: Restricted.

(9527)

A. Myra Keen Interview, 1983
(1 audiotape).

A. Myra Keen (1905-1986), was an invertebrate paleontologist and malacologist associated with the Stanford University Department of Geology for almost forty years. She received an A.B. from Colorado College in 1930, an M.A. from Stanford University in 1931, and a Ph.D. from the University of California at Berkeley in 1934. Educated primarily in psychology, Keen was a self-taught malacologist. Appointed Curator of Paleontology at Stanford in 1936, she began teaching during World War II, eventually advancing to Full Professor in 1965. Keen concentrated her research on molluscan systematics, but her studies ranged widely to include Recent marine mollusk fauna of the Panamic Province and marine molluscan Cenozoic paleontology, neontology, and zoogeography of western North America. She added to, cataloged, and systematically arranged the Cenozoic mollusk collections at Stanford. She advised advanced graduate students, several of whom have become leading malacologists.

This interview of Keen by Eugene V. Coan, malacologist and former student of Keen's, covers her education and early interests, career at Stanford University, research interests and fieldwork, and reminiscences about colleagues and students, notably Ida Shepard Oldroyd, Thomas Oldroyd, Paul Bartsch, and Robert Roberson.

ARRANGEMENT: (1) Audiotape, 1 hour; (2) transcript, 20 pages. FINDING AIDS: (1) Description in control file; (2) name index to transcript.

(9574)

Oscar Dean Kidd Interview, 1989
(4 audiotapes).

Oscar Dean Kidd (1907-   ) was born in Jamaica and migrated to Panama in 1909. He grew up in the Panama Canal Zone, eventually settling down in Frijoles, the train station used by scientists visiting Barro Colorado Island (BCI). The BCI Research Station was created in 1923 as a preserve for the study of tropical biology. In 1946, this Canal Zone Biological Area (CZBA) was transferred to the Smithsonian and in 1966 was renamed the Smithsonian Tropical Research Institute (STRI). As a motorboat operator, Kidd became acquainted with scientists visiting BCI, especially CZBA Director James Zetek.

This interview of Kidd by Pamela M. Henson, Patricia Escobar Paramo, and Elizabeth Stockwell covers his youth, work as a chauffeur and motorboat operator, and reminiscences of Barro Colorado Island and the scientists working there.

ARRANGEMENT: (1) Audiotapes, 4 hours; (2) transcript, 27 pages. FINDING AIDS: (1) Description in control file; (2) name index to transcript. SPECIAL CONDITIONS: Restricted.

(9538)

John R. Kinard Interview, 1987
(2 audiotapes).

John Robert Edward Kinard (1936-1989) was the Director of the Anacostia Museum from its founding in 1967 until his death. Kinard was born and raised in the Washington, D.C., area and came to the Smithsonian with a long background of service to his community, both locally and internationally.

The Anacostia Neighborhood Museum was developed as part of a broader plan to make museums more accessible to people in African American communities. In 1987, its name was changed to the Anacostia Museum to reflect its evolution beyond the neighborhood museum concept.

This interview with John Kinard by University of Maryland graduate student Anne M. Rogers covers his education, early work in community service, the founding of the Anacostia Neighborhood Museum, and his directorship. Topics include early exhibits, staff, and Kinard's vision for the Museum.

ARRANGEMENT: (1) Audiotapes, 1.5 hours; (2) transcript, 40 pages. FINDING AIDS: (1) Description in control file; (2) name index to transcript.

(9513)

Lucile Quarry Mann Interviews, 1977
(10 audiotapes).

Lucile Quarry Mann (1897-1986) was an editor and writer. After receiving the B.A. in English in 1919 from the University of Michigan, she pursued a career in editing and journalism. In 1926 she married William M. Mann (1886-1960), Director of the National Zoological Park (NZP). William Mann received the Sc.D. from Harvard University in 1915, and was an entomologist specializing in ants and termites. After eight years with the Bureau of Entomology of the United States Department of Agriculture, William Mann was appointed Director of the NZP in 1925. Both the Manns travelled extensively for the NZP, collecting animals and studying other zoological parks. Lucile Mann worked in the administrative offices of the NZP from 1951 to 1971, continuing after William Mann's retirement in 1956 and serving as editor for many zoo publications.

Many animals born at the NZP were raised in the Manns' home across the street from the zoo. Both the Manns published about their lives and interests, and had a wide circle of friends in many walks of life. William Mann was a circus fan as well as an opera enthusiast. Lucile Mann was a specialist in tropical aquarium fishes and wrote for the popular press on that topic.

These interviews of Lucile Mann by Pamela M. Henson cover her education; editorial and administrative careers with the Bureau of Entomology and the NZP; life as wife of the NZP Director; travels and expeditions for the zoo; animals raised in their home; famous residents of the Zoo; and reminiscences about famous scholars and personalities such as Austin H. Clark, Leonhard Stejneger, Noel Coward, and Alexander Woollcott.

ARRANGEMENT: (1) Audiotapes, 8.5 hours; (2) transcript, 250 pages. FINDING AIDS: (1) Description in control file; (2) name index to transcript.

(9575)

William W. Moss III Interview, 1993
(1 videotape).

William W. Moss III (1935-   ) received his B.A. from Haverford College in 1957. Moss began his federal service in the United States Navy in 1958. During nearly five years of active duty, he spent a year studying Chinese at the Army Language School in Monterey, California. From 1963 to 1964, he undertook graduate work in Chinese and public law and government at Columbia University, and was awarded the M.A. in 1965. He worked as an Intelligence Research Analyst in foreign language at the National Security Agency from 1964 through 1969. In 1969, he left to accept a position at the John F. Kennedy Library in Boston, Massachusetts, as Oral History Interviewer, and in 1970, became Chief of the Oral History Program. Moss became Senior Archivist for national security and foreign affairs materials at the Library in 1972 and Chief Archivist in 1975. In 1983, Moss came to the Smithsonian as Archivist of the Institution and Director of the Smithsonian Institution Archives. During his ten years at the Archives, he participated in the establishment of the Council of Information and Education Directors (CIED) and served as its head for two years. He also presided over the formation of the Smithsonian Institution Archives and Special Collections Council and served as chairman for three years. Moss retired in 1993 to accept a position teaching in the International Programs Office at the Foreign Affairs University in Beijing, China, and was named the first Archivist Emeritus.

This interview of Moss by Marc Pachter, Acting Assistant Secretary for External Affairs, covers his early life and education; naval career; graduate studies; work at the National Security Agency; career at the Kennedy Library and the Smithsonian Institution Archives, including interest in history at the Smithsonian, the space problem at the Archives, formation of CIED, and future directions for the Institution; oral history and archival practices; and interest in China and Chinese archives.

ARRANGEMENT: Videotape, 1.2 hours. FINDING AIDS: Description in control file. SPECIAL CONDITIONS: Restricted.

(9502)

Robert P. Multhauf Interviews, 1974
(3 audiotapes).

Robert P. Multhauf (1919-   ), historian of science, was appointed Curator of the Division of Engineering in the United States National Museum in 1955. From 1957 to 1966, he served as Head Curator of the Department of Science and Technology. In 1966,

Multhauf was appointed Director of the National Museum of History and Technology (NMHT), and, upon his retirement from administration in 1969, continued his research as Senior Historian until 1986. He also served as Editor of *Isis* from 1964 to 1978.

These interviews of Multhauf by Miriam S. Freilicher and Pamela M. Henson cover his education, career as a historian of science, work in the development of the NMHT, and his role as an administrator. They include reminiscences of colleagues such as Leonard Carmichael, Howard I. Chapelle, and Frank A. Taylor.

ARRANGEMENT: (1) Audiotapes, 3 hours; (2) transcript, 109 pages. FINDING AIDS: (1) Description in control file; (2) name index to transcript.

(9576)

Gilberto Ocana Interview, 1989

(2 audiotapes).

Gilberto Ocana (1931-   ), agronomist specializing in tropical flora, received the B.S. from the Ecole Nationale d'Agriculture in Alger, Algeria, in 1955. From 1955 to 1960, he served on the staff of the Servicio Interamericano de Cooperacion Agricola en Panama and taught at the Agricultural School of the University of Panama from 1961 to 1963. In 1967, he received the Ph.D. in plant pathology from the University of California at Riverside. He then returned to the University of Panama, serving as Dean as well as Professor of Agronomy. In 1980 he joined the staff of the Smithsonian Tropical Research Institute (STRI) as manager of the Barro Colorado Nature Monument, a nature preserve consisting of Barro Colorado Island and its surrounding peninsulas. While at STRI, he developed an experimental farm at Las Pavas on the Gigante Peninsula that would restore soils destroyed by cattle grazing and provide a comfortable income for small farmers. He retired from STRI in 1993.

This interview of Ocana by Pamela M. Henson discusses his family, education, work as an agronomist and professor in Panama, and career at STRI, especially his agriforestry project.

ARRANGEMENT: (1) Audiotapes, 2 hours; (2) transcript, 34 pages. FINDING AIDS: (1) Description in control file; (2) name index to transcript. SPECIAL CONDITIONS: Restricted.

(9507)

Paul H. Oehser Interviews, 1974-1975

(7 audiotapes).

Paul H. Oehser (1904-   ) began his career in 1925 as an editor for the United States Department of Agriculture, Bureau of Biological Survey. In 1931, he was appointed Editor for the United States National Museum and in 1950 assumed the position of Editor, Smithsonian Institution Editorial and Publications Division. Oehser also served as the Institution's Public Relations Officer from 1950 to 1966. Upon his retirement in 1966, Oehser was made a Research Associate of the Smithsonian Institution and became Editor of Research and Exploration Publications for the National Geographic Society. In addition to his editorial work at the Smithsonian, Oehser published poetry, books about the Smithsonian and its scientists, and was active in the conservation movement.

These interviews of Oehser by Pamela M. Henson cover his education, career as an editor for the Bureau of Biological Survey, Smithsonian and National Geographic Society, role as Public Relations Officer, and work as an author and conservationist.

ARRANGEMENT: (1) Audiotapes, 6 hours; (2) transcript, 173 pages. FINDING AIDS: (1) Description in control file; (2) name index to transcript.

(9540)

Ella B. Howard Pearis Interview, 1986
(1 audiotape).

Ella B. Howard Pearis is a fourth generation resident of Anacostia in Washington, D.C. She comes from a family of community activists and has carried on that tradition through her work for organizations such as the Anacostia Historical Society, of which she is a founding member.

This interview by University of Maryland history student Sabine K. Lovett covers Pearis' life in Anacostia, including her youth, education, work in day care and at the Bureau of Engraving and Printing, and her activities associated with the Anacostia Historical Society and the Smithsonian's Anacostia Museum.

ARRANGEMENT: (1) Audiotape, 1.5 hours; (2) transcript, 22 pages. FINDING AIDS: (1) Description in control file; (2) name index to transcript.

(9516)

Watson M. Perrygo Interviews, 1978
(26 audiotapes).

Watson M. Perrygo (1906-1984), a naturalist with broad interests in natural history, served as field collector and taxidermist for the United States National Museum (USNM). As a youth, Perrygo often visited the Museum and went on local field trips with Alexander Wetmore, then Director of the Museum. In 1927 he was appointed Scientific Aid to work with the collections of the Division of Mammals and to do taxidermy. During his long career at the Smithsonian, Perrygo advanced to Chief Taxidermist, was a key figure in the Exhibits Modernization Program, and conducted extensive field work in the United States and Central America. After his retirement in 1964, he was active in historic preservation as president of the Charles County, Maryland, Historical Society and a member of the board of the Maryland Historic Trust. He also directed the museum exhibits program of the Botanical Museum in Santo Domingo, Dominican Republic.

These interviews of Perrygo by Pamela M. Henson cover his youth, education, early associations at and impressions of the Museum; career at the USNM, especially his field trips and work on the Exhibits Modernization Program; recollections of colleagues, such as Alexander Wetmore and A. Remington Kellogg; interests in historic preservation; and the development of the Botanical Museum in Santo Domingo.

ARRANGEMENT: (1) Audiotapes, 26 hours; (2) transcript, 893 pages. FINDING AIDS: (1) Description in control file; (2) name index to transcript.

Forrest C. Pogue Interview, 1986
(1 audiotape).

Forrest C. Pogue (1912-   ), military historian, received the A.B. from Murray State College in 1931, M.A. from the University of Kentucky in 1932, and Ph.D. from Clark University in 1939. He taught for several years before joining the historical section of the United States Army during World War II. He pioneered the use of oral history interviews to compile battlefield histories. He was appointed Director of the George C. Marshall Research Center in 1956 and later directed the Marshall Library and Marshall Research Foundation until 1974. During this time, he began a four volume biography of General George C. Marshall. In 1974, Pogue was named Director of the newly established Eisenhower Institute for Military Research at the Smithsonian and continued in that position until his retirement in 1986.

This interview of Pogue by University of Maryland student James Tapley discusses his research on Marshall, career at the Marshall Research Center and Library, and at the Eisenhower Institute, the role of the Institute within the Smithsonian Institution and National Museum of American History, the history of the National Armed Forces Museum Advisory Board and his work with the International Commission for Military History.

ARRANGEMENT: (1) Audiotape, 1 hour; (2) transcript, 28 pages. FINDING AIDS: (1) Description in control file; (2) name index to transcript. SPECIAL CONDITIONS: Restricted.

Louis R. Purnell Interviews, 1993-1994
(24 audiotapes).

Louis R. Purnell (1920-   ) was born in Snow Hill, Maryland. Early in his life he was able to realize his dream of becoming a pilot when the Civilian Pilot Training Program (CPTP) was instituted on the campus of his undergraduate institution, Lincoln University. In 1942, he was accepted into the seventh class of African American Army Air Force aviation cadets stationed at the Tuskegee Army Air Field in Tuskegee, Alabama (the Tuskegee Airmen), and in 1943 joined the all-Black 99th Fighter Squadron. During World War II, he completed two tours of duty in North Africa and southern Italy with the 99th, and later the 332nd Fighter Group. After his return to the United States, Purnell worked with the Office of the Quartermaster General and the United States Book Exchange at the Library of Congress.

In 1961, Purnell joined the Division of Invertebrate Paleontology and Paleobotany in the National Museum of Natural History (NMNH) and remained there until 1968. During his career as a Technician in this Division, he published a catalog of type specimens of invertebrate fossils. In 1968, he moved to the Department of Astronautics of the National Air and Space Museum (NASM). During his career in the Astronautics Department (renamed the Department of Space Science and Exploration in 1980), he progressed through the ranks from Museum Specialist to Curator. Purnell taught classes on aviation and astronautics for the Smithsonian Resident Associates, managed the artifact loan program, and travelled all over the world in search of space artifacts. He remained with this Department until his retirement in January 1985.

Louis R. Purnell was interviewed by Terrica M. Gibson, Institutional History Division, Office of Smithsonian Institution Archives. These interviews cover Purnell's childhood in Wilmington, Delaware, and Cape May, New Jersey; his education; love of flying; service during World War II; reminiscences of prominent Army Air Corps personnel, including General Benjamin O. Davis, Jr.; work with the Office of the Quartermaster General, U.S. Book Exchange, NMNH and NASM; the circumstances surrounding the first lunar landing; the move of NASM from the Arts and Industries Building; relationship with the National Aeronautics and Space Administration; and reminiscences of colleagues including G. Arthur Cooper, S. Paul Johnston, and Michael Collins.

ARRANGEMENT: (1) Audiotapes, 12 hours; (2) transcript, 284 pages. FINDING AIDS: (1) Description in control file; (2) name index to transcript. SPECIAL CONDITIONS: Restricted.

(9579)

A. Stanley Rand Interviews, 1986, 1989-1990
(5 audiotapes).

A. Stanley Rand (1932-   ), a herpetologist specializing in frog communication, received the B.A. in zoology from DePauw University in 1955 and the Ph.D. in biology from Harvard University in 1961. From 1962 to 1964, he was a zoologist at the Departamento de Zoologia, Sao Paulo, Brazil. In 1964, he was appointed a Biologist at the Smithsonian Tropical Research Institute (STRI) in Panama. From 1974 to 1979, he served as Assistant Director at STRI, and in 1979 was named Senior Biologist. His research focused on the behavior and ecology of tropical reptiles and amphibians, especially the evolution of communication in anurans, and the ecology and behavior of iguanid lizards.

These interviews of Rand by University of Maryland student Daryl Jones and Pamela M. Henson, Smithsonian Institution Archives, cover his youth, education, career in Brazil and at STRI, his research on reptiles and amphibians, life for families stationed on Barro Colorado Island (BCI) in the 1960s and 1970s, his observations of changes at the BCI research station of STRI, and reminiscences of colleagues, including Martin Humphrey Moynihan, Neal G. Smith, and Dagmar Werner.

ARRANGEMENT: (1) Audiotapes, 3.5 hours; (2) transcript, 108 pages. FINDING AIDS: (1) Description in control file; (2) name index to transcript. SPECIAL CONDITIONS: Restricted.

(9568)

Theodore H. Reed Interviews, 1989-1994
(58 audiotapes).

Theodore H. Reed (1922-   ), veterinarian and zoo administrator, received the D.V.M. in 1945 from the School of Veterinary Medicine, Kansas State College. From 1946 to 1955, he practiced as a veterinarian in Oregon and Idaho. He gained experience with exotic animals while serving as a veterinarian to the Portland Zoological Park from 1951 to 1955. In 1955, Reed was appointed Veterinarian at the National Zoological Park (NZP). In 1956, he was named Acting Director after the retirement of William M. Mann, and in 1958, he advanced to Director. During his tenure, Reed oversaw a capital renovation of the NZP; development of the Conservation and Research Center (CRC) in Front Royal, Virginia, in 1974; a transition from display of exotic specimens to breeding of endangered species; and many advances in exotic animal care and medicine. Reed retired from administration in 1983 and from the NZP in 1984.

These interviews of Reed by Pamela M. Henson discuss his youth; education; veterinary practice; experiences at the Portland Zoo; and career at the NZP, including his tenure as Veterinarian and achievements as Director, especially renovation and modernization of facilities, development of the Cap-chur Gun, acquisition of such animals as the Giant Pandas, Komodo dragon, and white tigers, development of research and educational programs, creation of an endangered species program and the CRC, participation in the Species Survival Program, his role in the American Association of Zoological Parks and Aquariums and the International Union of Directors of Zoological Gardens; and reminiscences of such colleagues as William Mann, John Perry, and Leonard Carmichael.

ARRANGEMENT: (1) Audiotapes, 29 hours; (2) transcript, 650 pages. FINDING AIDS: (1) Description in control file; (2) name index to transcript. SPECIAL CONDITIONS: Restricted.

(9519)

Harald A. Rehder Interviews, 1976-1977
(6 audiotapes).

Harald A. Rehder (1907-   ), an invertebrate zoologist, specialized in systematic malacology. Rehder received the B.A. from Bowdoin College in 1929, M.A. from Harvard University in 1933, and Ph.D. in zoology from The George Washington University in 1934. He began his career at the United States National Museum (USNM) in 1932 as Senior Scientific Aid in the Division of Mollusks, advanced to Assistant Curator, Associate Curator, and then Curator in 1946. In 1965, he was appointed Senior Zoologist in the Division, and after his retirement in 1980 was named Zoologist Emeritus.

These interviews of Rehder by Pamela M. Henson cover his youth, education, early interests in natural history, career in the Division of Mollusks of the USNM, reminiscences of Paul Bartsch and other colleagues, field work, and research interests in the systematics and geographic distribution of mollusks, especially the marine mollusks of the Indo-Pacific region.

ARRANGEMENT: (1) Audiotapes, 6 hours; (2) transcript, 105 pages. FINDING AIDS: (1) Description in control file; (2) name index to transcript.

(9503)

Nathan Reingold Interview, 1973
(1 audiotape).

Nathan Reingold (1927-   ), historian of American science, received the Ph.D. from the University of Pennsylvania in 1951. He was on the staff of the National Archives from 1951 to 1959 and the Library of Congress from 1959 to 1966. In 1966, he was appointed Editor of the Joseph Henry Papers Project at the Smithsonian Institution. He continued his research as Senior Historian at the National Museum of American History from 1985 to 1993, when he was named Historian Emeritus.

This interview of Reingold by Miriam S. Freilicher covers background on the history of science at the Smithsonian, and potential issues and interviewees for the Oral History Program.

ARRANGEMENT: (1) Audiotape, 1 hour; (2) transcript, 34 pages. FINDING AIDS: (1) Description in control file; (2) name index to transcript.

(9569)

Ralph Rinzler Interview, 1993
(2 videotapes).

Ralph Rinzler (1934-1994) was born in Passaic, New Jersey, and was interested in music at an early age. He was given a collection of ethnographic recordings from the Archive of Folk Song of the Library of Congress by his uncle, Harvard University ballad scholar George Lyman Kittredge, and they soon became his favorites. He became actively involved in folk music while attending Swarthmore College, organizing an annual folk festival on campus. He received his B.A. in 1956, and did graduate work at Middlebury College and the Sorbonne in French literature and language. Upon his return to the United States, he played mandolin for four years with the Greenbriar Boys, touring with singer Joan Baez. During the 1960s, he also studied and worked with performers of traditional music, such as Doc Watson and Bill Monroe, both of whom gained international recognition in part through his efforts. In 1964, Rinzler accepted the position of Director of Field Programs at the Newport Folk Foundation.

Rinzler came to the Smithsonian in 1967 as the founding Director of what is now the Center for Folklife Programs and Cultural Studies, then in the Division of Performing Arts, to establish a center for research, publication, and presentation of programs in American subcultures. As Director, he also developed the annual Festival of American Folklife. After the summer-long festival of 1976, he initiated *Smithsonian Folklife Studies,* a publication series, and did research for the *Celebration* exhibit, which opened at the Renwick Gallery in 1982. Rinzler was appointed Assistant Secretary for Public Service in 1983 and Assistant Secretary Emeritus in 1990.

This interview of Rinzler by Marc Pachter, Acting Assistant Secretary for External Affairs, covers his early life and interest in music; involvement in the folk music scene at Swarthmore and organization of the festival there; time spent in London after graduate courses; life on the road with Joan Baez; work with Doc Watson, Bill Monroe, and others; field work for the Newport Foundation; beginnings of the Folklife Festival at the Smithsonian and his subsequent career at the Institution. It also includes reminiscences of many individuals at the Smithsonian and in the larger folklife community, including S. Dillon Ripley, Frank A. Taylor, Charles Blitzer, David Challinor, Robert McC. Adams, Michael Seeger, Peggy Seeger, and Alan Lomax; and discusses the rise of the folklife movement including the political and ethnological forces behind the movement.

ARRANGEMENT: Videotapes, 2.2 hours. FINDING AIDS: Description in control file. SPECIAL CONDITIONS: Restricted.

S. Dillon Ripley Interviews, 1977-1993
(50 audiotapes).

S. Dillon Ripley (1913-   ), ornithologist and eighth Secretary of the Smithsonian Institution, developed an interest in natural history in his youth. He received the B.A. from Harvard University in 1936 and the Ph.D. from Yale University in 1943. From 1946 to 1963, he was on the faculty of Yale University and served as Director of their Peabody Museum from 1959 to 1963. In 1964, he was appointed Secretary of the Smithsonian. During his twenty year tenure as Secretary, he oversaw the development of the Anacostia Museum, Cooper-Hewitt Museum, Festival of American Folklife, Hirshhorn Museum and Sculpture Garden, National Air and Space Museum, National Museum of African Art, Renwick Gallery, Arthur M. Sackler Gallery of Art, Smithsonian Associates, Smithsonian Environmental Research Center, and *Smithsonian* magazine. Ripley was also involved in numerous conservation organizations, including the Charles Darwin Foundation for the Galapagos Islands, International Council for Bird Preservation, and International Union for the Conservation of Nature. His interests in international affairs also led him to play a role in the foundation of the Woodrow Wilson International Center for Scholars.

These interviews of Ripley by Pamela M. Henson cover his youth, early interests in natural history, education, career on the faculty at Yale, field work and expeditions, tenure as Secretary of the Smithsonian, involvement in international conservation efforts, and reminiscences of individuals, including Salim Ali, August Heckscher, Joseph H. Hirshhorn, G. Evelyn Hutchinson, and Ralph Rinzler.

ARRANGEMENT: (1) Audiotapes, 38 hours; (2) transcript, *circa* 700 pages. FINDING AIDS: (1) Description in control file; (2) name index to transcript. SPECIAL CONDITIONS: Restricted.

Walter R. Roderick Interviews, 1986-1987
(4 audiotapes).

Walter R. Roderick (1935-   ), aircraft restoration specialist, served in the United States Air Force from 1952 to 1956. During these years, he gained experience in aircraft maintenance and repair. After three years with Capital Airlines, he joined the staff of the National Air and Space Museum (NASM) in 1959. His duties as an aircraft restoration specialist at NASM's Paul E. Garber Facility were to preserve, restore, and exhibit historic aircraft. Highlights of his career include the opening of the new NASM building in 1976 and the Silver Hill Museum in 1977. He retired as Chief of Production Operations at NASM in 1986.

Roderick was interviewed by Susan E. Ewing, a University of Maryland student and Technical Information Specialist for the NASM Archives. The interviews cover his youth; education; career in the Air Force, Capital Airlines, and NASM; restoration of such famous aircraft as the *Winnie Mae, Vin Fiz,* and Douglas *World Cruiser;* opening of NASM and Silver Hill Museum; and reminiscences of colleagues, including Edward B. Chalkley, Paul E. Garber, and Walter Male.

ARRANGEMENT: (1) Audiotapes, 3 hours; (2) transcript, 78 pages. FINDING AIDS: (1) Description in control file; (2) name index to transcript. SPECIAL CONDITIONS: Restricted.

(9581)

Pablo Rodriguez-Martinez Interview, 1990
(1 audiotape).

Pablo Rodriguez-Martinez (1936-   ) spent his early life in Montegrande, Penonome, in the Pajonal corregimiento of Panama before moving to Chorerra by Gatun Lake in 1950. The Barro Colorado Island Research Station (BCI), located in Gatun Lake in the Panama Canal Zone, was a tropical biology field station established in 1923 and run by a consortium of universities and government agencies. The Canal Zone Biological Area (CZBA) was transferred to the Smithsonian Institution in 1946 and was renamed the Smithsonian Tropical Research Institute (STRI) in 1966. Rodriguez-Martinez was first hired as a temporary general worker at Barro Colorado Island by Francisco Vitola in 1961. He became a permanent employee when he was hired in 1962 as a game warden to guard against poachers.

This interview by Pamela M. Henson covers Rodriguez-Martinez's career at STRI, including descriptions of patrol routines; arrest procedures and work schedules; reminiscences of fellow staff, such as Francisco Vitola and Fausto Bocanegra; and his views on improved working conditions and how the island has changed over the years. The interview is in Spanish. Transcripts are available in both Spanish and English.

ARRANGEMENT: (1) Audiotape, 0.5 hours; (2) transcript, Spanish, 16 pages; (3) transcript, English, 14 pages. FINDING AIDS: (1) Description in control file; (2) name index to transcript. SPECIAL CONDITIONS: Restricted.

(9582)

Ira Rubinoff Interviews, 1989-1990
(9 audiotapes).

Ira Rubinoff (1938-   ) received his B.S. from Queens College in 1959. He continued his education at Harvard University, receiving his A.M. in 1961 and Ph.D. in biology in 1963. In 1964, Rubinoff became Biologist and Assistant Director of marine biology at the Smithsonian Tropical Research Institute (STRI) where he conducted research on the evolution of fishes. The Barro Colorado Island Research Station (BCI), in the Panama Canal Zone, was a tropical biology field station established in 1923 and run by a consortium of universities and government agencies. This Canal Zone Biological Area (CZBA), was transferred to the Smithsonian Institution in 1946 and was renamed the Smithsonian Tropical Research Institute in 1966. Rubinoff became the Assistant Director for Science at STRI in 1970, and in 1973 he assumed the Directorship. Rubinoff also held many concurrent positions: member of the science advisory board for the Gorgas Memorial Institute, 1964-   ; Chairman for the board of fellowships and grants of the Smithsonian Institution, 1978-1979; and member of the board of directors for the Charles Darwin Foundation for the Galapagos Islands, 1977-   .

These interviews by Pamela M. Henson cover Rubinoff's education, how he came to STRI, establishment of the marine biology program at STRI, master planning for the island, reminiscences of STRI staff and influential visitors, development of an international mission statement for STRI, and the situation in Panama during the United States invasion in 1990.

ARRANGEMENT: (1) Audiotapes, 5.5 hours; (2) transcript, 182 pages. FINDING AIDS: (1) Description in control file; (2) name index to transcript. SPECIAL CONDITIONS: Restricted.

(9583)

Curtis W. Sabrosky Interviews, 1988
(10 audiotapes).

Curtis W. Sabrosky (1910-   ), an entomologist specializing in Diptera, received the A.B. in biology from Kalamazoo College in 1931, the M.S. in zoology from Kansas State College in 1933, and the Sc.D. from Kalamazoo College in 1966. He taught at Michigan State College from 1936 to 1944 and served in the Public Health Service during World War II. In 1946, he joined the staff of the United States Department of Agriculture, first with the Bureau of Entomology and later with its Systematic Entomology Laboratory (SEL) as a Research Entomologist, serving as Research Director from 1967 to 1973. From 1980 to 1988, he was a Cooperating Scientist at SEL, as well as a Research Associate of the Department of Entomology, National Museum of Natural History (NMNH). A specialist on issues of taxonomic nomenclature, from 1963 to 1985 he served as a member of the International Commission on Zoological Nomenclature (ICZN).

These interviews of Sabrosky by Pamela M. Henson cover his education; career at the USDA; work with the National Entomological Collection maintained by the NMNH; interests in issues of taxonomic nomenclature, especially his work with the ICZN; and reminiscences of colleagues, notably J. Chester Bradley, Roland Wilbur Brown, John Frederick Gates Clarke, and Carl Frederick William Muesebeck.

ARRANGEMENT: (1) Audiotapes, 5 hours; (2) transcript, 217 pages. FINDING AIDS: (1) Description in control file; (2) name index to transcript. SPECIAL CONDITIONS: Restricted.

(9510)

Leonard Peter Schultz Interview, 1976
(3 audiotapes).

Leonard Peter Schultz (1901-1986) began his career in ichthyology at Albion College, where he received his B.A. in 1924. Schultz received an M.S. in 1926 from the University of Michigan and a Ph.D. in ichthyology in 1932 from the University of Washington. From 1928 to 1936, Schultz taught at the College of Fisheries of the University of Washington. In 1936 Schultz was appointed Assistant Curator in charge of the Division of Fishes of the United States National Museum and in 1938 was appointed Curator of the Division. Upon his retirement in 1968, he was appointed a Research Associate of the Division of Fishes.

Research interests included life histories of fishes and revisions of genera and families. Schultz did much field work and collecting in the United States, especially in the western states, and participated in expeditions to the Phoenix and Samoan Islands in the Pacific and the Maracaibo Basin in Venezuela. Schultz was also a scientist with the Crossroads Operation, which conducted the scientific survey and resurvey of Bikini Atoll, the site of atomic bomb tests. He conducted a study of sharks and shark attacks for the Shark Research Panel of the American Institute of Biological Science.

This interview of Schultz by Pamela M. Henson covers his education; teaching career at the University of Washington; field work in Michigan, the western United States, Virginia, Phoenix and Samoan Islands, Venezuela and Bikini Atoll; research interests in life histories of fishes, tropical aquarium fishes, and sharks; and his career as Curator of the Division of Fishes.

ARRANGEMENT: (1) Audiotapes, 3 hours; (2) transcript, 101 pages. FINDING AIDS: (1) Description in control file; (2) name index to transcript.

(9508)

Senate of Scientists Interviews, 1975
(19 audiotapes).

The Senate of Scientists was formed in 1963 as the faculty senate for the professional research staff of the National Museum of Natural History.

These interviews of Richard S. Boardman, Martin A. Buzas, W. Donald Duckworth, Clifford Evans, Jr., Gordon D. Gibson, W. Duane Hope, Erle G. Kauffman, Porter M. Kier, and Saul H. Riesenberg by Pamela M. Henson document the formation of the Senate of Scientists and its early activities in the National Museum of Natural History.

ARRANGEMENT: (1) Audiotapes, 16.5 hours; (2) transcript, *circa* 612 pages. FINDING AIDS: (1) Description in control file; (2) name index to transcript. SPECIAL CONDITIONS: Restricted.

(9588)

Jean Chandler Smith Interview, 1986
(1 audiotape).

Jean Chandler Smith (1913-   ), librarian and bibliographer, received the A.B. from Bryn Mawr College in 1939, the M.S. from Yale University in 1953, and the M.L.S. from The Catholic University of America in 1973. She began her career as a reference librarian for the District of Columbia Public Library from 1939 to 1943. During the latter part of World War II, she worked as a translator in Panama and as a librarian in Hawaii. In 1944, she joined the staff of Yale University as a Librarian and Research Associate. In 1959, she accepted a position as Acting Chief of Acquisitions at the National Institutes of Health Library and moved to the Department of the Interior in 1963. She joined the staff of the Smithsonian Institution Libraries (SIL) in 1965. She served as Acting Director in 1972 and from 1977 to 1979. After her retirement in 1981, she continued her research as an SIL Research Associate.

This interview of Smith by University of Maryland student Linda Zindt covers her education and career at SIL, including staffing, technological advances, acquisition of the Dibner Library of the History of Science and Technology, and her role as an administrator.

ARRANGEMENT: (1) Audiotape, 1 hour; (2) transcript, 27 pages. FINDING AIDS: (1) Description in control file; (2) name index to transcript.

Neal Griffith Smith Interview, 1990
(5 audiotapes).

Neal G. Smith (1937-   ), an ornithologist and tropical biologist, received his B.A. from St. John's University in 1958, his M.A. in 1961, and Ph.D. in 1963 from Cornell University. He developed an interest in natural history in his youth and was encouraged as a volunteer at the American Museum of Natural History (AMNH) working under Eugene Eisenmann. Smith joined the staff of the Smithsonian Tropical Research Institute (STRI) immediately after graduation and began a long-term research program on the evolutionary biology of birds and insects.

This interview of Smith by Pamela M. Henson covers his youth; early interests in natural history at the AMNH; education; research on the evolutionary biology of birds and insects; career at STRI; and reminiscences of living on Barro Colorado Island in the 1960s and 1970s, and of colleagues, especially Eugene Eisenmann, Ernst Mayr, Robert H. MacArthur, Martin Humphrey Moynihan, and Robert Eric Ricklefs.

ARRANGEMENT: (1) Audiotapes, 2.5 hours; (2) transcript, 92 pages. FINDING AIDS: (1) Description in control file; (2) name index to transcript. SPECIAL CONDITIONS: Restricted.

Smithsonian Tropical Research Institute Group Interview, 1990
(2 audiotapes).

Many Smithsonian Tropical Research Institute (STRI) staff live on Barro Colorado Island (BCI). This group interview documents life on the island from the perspective of five residents, Brian C. Bock, A. Stanley Rand, Patricia Rand, Nicholas D. Smythe, and Tanis Smythe. The BCI Research Station, in the Panama Canal Zone, was a tropical biology field station established in 1923 and run by a consortium of universities and government agencies. Called the Canal Zone Biological Area (CZBA), it was transferred to the Smithsonian Institution in 1946 and was renamed the Smithsonian Tropical Research Institute (STRI) in 1966.

A. Stanley Rand received his Ph.D. in biology from Harvard University in 1961. After working with Harvard's Museum of Comparative Zoology and the Secretary of Agriculture in Brazil, he began working at STRI in 1964 as a herpetologist. From 1974 to 1979, Rand served as Assistant Director, and he was appointed Senior Biologist in 1979. His interest in the behavior and ecology of reptiles and amphibians led to pioneering studies of frog communications. Patricia Rand came to live on the island with her husband in 1964 and raised their family there. She has conducted research and prepared exhibits on the history of BCI.

Nicholas D. Smythe received his Ph.D. in biology from the University of Maryland in 1970. He began working at STRI the same year to develop baseline studies of the rainforest for the Environmental Sciences Program. His research interests have centered on frugivorous mammals, and during the 1980s Smythe began a successful domestication program for the paca, a species of cavy, which is an excellent source of protein and can be raised on forest by-products. Smythe's goal was a large scale paca industry which would prevent further destruction of the rainforest. Tanis Smythe took up residence on BCI with her husband in 1970.

Brian Bock, a herpetologist at the University of Tennessee, has been a visiting scientist in STRI's Biology Program and has worked at STRI with the iguana biology and management project.

This interview by Pamela M. Henson covers reminiscences of former colleagues, students, visitors, and staff at STRI from the late 1950s to 1990, including experiences with ants (Paraponera), snakes, food, beer, long-term residence on Barro Colorado Island, increasing institutional control of STRI, laundry, pets, and children.

ARRANGEMENT: (1) Audiotapes, 1 hour; (2) transcript, 40 pages. FINDING AIDS: (1) Description in control file; (2) name index to transcript. SPECIAL CONDITIONS: Restricted.

(9585)

Nicholas D. Smythe Interview, 1990
(4 audiotapes).

Nicholas D. Smythe (1934-   ), a biologist specializing in mammalian ecology and behavior, received his B.A. degree in psychology and zoology from the University of British Columbia in 1963 and his Ph.D. from the University of Maryland in 1970. He spent much of 1965-1967 at the Smithsonian Tropical Research Institute (STRI) in Panama on a predoctoral fellowship before returning there as a biologist in 1970. The Barro Colorado Island Research Station, in the Panama Canal Zone, was a tropical biology field station established in 1923 and run by a consortium of universities and government agencies. This Canal Zone Biological Area (CZBA) was transferred to the Smithsonian Institution in 1946 and was renamed the Smithsonian Tropical Research Institute in 1966. At STRI Smythe helped to develop baseline studies of the rainforest for the Environmental Sciences Program in the early 1970s, to negotiate an expansion of STRI and the Panamanian National Park system during the passage of the Panama Canal treaties in the late 1970s, and to develop a conservation education program in the early 1980s. During that decade he focused his research in tropical rodents on domesticating the paca (*Cuniculus paca*). In the 1980s, Smythe studied the seed dispersal relationships between frugivorous mammals, insects, and the palm *Astrocaryum standleyanum*. He retired in 1994.

This interview with Smythe by Pamela M. Henson covers his family background, education, early interest in mammals, and career at STRI, including his research and administrative activities. He also discusses changes occurring in the scientific intellectual community at large.

ARRANGEMENT: (1) Audiotapes, 2 hours; (2) transcript, 81 pages. FINDING AIDS: (1) Description in control file; (2) name index to transcript. SPECIAL CONDITIONS: Restricted.

(9521)

Thomas Dale Stewart Interviews, 1975, 1986
(14 audiotapes).

Thomas Dale Stewart (1901-   ), a physical anthropologist specializing in the diagnostic characteristics for human skeletons, began his career in 1927 as an Aid to Ales Hrdlicka in the Division of Physical Anthropology of the United States National Museum. He advanced to Curator of the Division in 1942 and to Head Curator of the Department of Anthropology in 1961. In 1963, he was appointed Director of the National Museum of Natural History and also served as Acting Assistant Secretary for Science in 1964. He retired from administration in 1966 to pursue his research as Senior Anthropologist. Upon his retirement in 1971, he was appointed Anthropologist Emeritus.

These interviews of Stewart by Pamela M. Henson cover his youth and education; his career as an Aid and Curator; his participation in the Exhibits Modernization Program; his anthropological and forensic research, especially his work on the Shanidar Neanderthal skeletons and ossuaries in Southern Maryland; reminiscences of the Bureau of American Ethnology and colleagues such as Ales Hrdlicka, Henry Bascom Collins, Jr., and Matthew Williams Stirling; and his role as a Smithsonian administrator.

ARRANGEMENT: (1) Audiotapes, 13.5 hours; (2) transcript, 341 pages. FINDING AIDS: (1) Description in control file; (2) name index to transcript. SPECIAL CONDITIONS: Restricted.

(9512)
Frank A. Taylor Interviews, 1974, 1979-1980, 1982
(23 audiotapes).

Frank A. Taylor (1903-   ) pursued a career in the history of science and technology and museum administration. Taylor began his career at the Smithsonian in 1922 as a Laboratory Apprentice in the Division of Mechanical Technology of the United States National Museum (USNM). After receiving his B.S. in mechanical engineering from Massachusetts Institute of Technology in 1928 and the J.D. from Georgetown University in 1934, he advanced to Head Curator of the Department of Engineering and Industries in 1948. During the 1950s, Taylor chaired the Exhibits Modernization Committee of the USNM. In 1955 he was appointed Assistant Director, USNM, with special responsibility for planning the new National Museum of History and Technology (NMHT), and in 1958 was appointed the first Director of the new museum. In 1962 Taylor became Director of the USNM with responsibility for both the National Museum of Natural History and National Museum of History and Technology, and in 1968 was appointed Director General of Museums.

Active in the international museum community, especially through the American Association of Museums and the International Council of Museums, Taylor worked on national legislation to support museums, notably the National Museum Act. After his retirement in 1971, Taylor continued to work at the Smithsonian as a Research Associate of the Smithsonian Institution Archives and as Consultant to the Secretary until 1984.

These interviews of Taylor by Miriam S. Freilicher and Pamela M. Henson cover his youth and education, career at the Smithsonian from Laboratory Apprentice to Director General of Museums, work on the Exhibits Modernization Program and museum legislation, development of the NMHT, role as an administrator, and work in the international museum community.

ARRANGEMENT: (1) Audiotapes, 19.5 hours; (2) transcript, 439 pages. FINDING AIDS: (1) Description in control file; (2) name index to transcript.

Tropical Rainforest Exhibit Interviews, 1992, 1994
(22 audiotapes and 1 videotape).

Museum exhibits are the result of a complex interplay between researchers, educators, and design specialists. Steven W. Allison, Smithsonian Predoctoral Fellow, from Cornell University, Department of Science and Technology Studies, conducted these interviews as a part of his doctoral research into the relationship between exhibition and research in natural history museums. He specifically focused on a case study of the evolution of a tropical rainforest life group at the National Museum of Natural History (NMNH) in the 1960s and 1970s, which first emerged as a Hall of Botany in 1960, was redefined as a Hall of Living Things in 1968, was eventually built for an exhibit on environmental issues called *It All Depends,* in 1974, and was later moved to the Hall of South American Anthropology in the Natural History Building.

The interviewees include: Stanwyn G. Shetler, Curator of Phanerogams, NMNH, member of the exhibit committee for the original Hall of Botany; Reginald "Bud" J. Sayre, Preparator, Natural History Laboratory, who participated in an expedition to Kaieteur Falls in British Guiana to collect specimens and make molds and drawings of the site for the rainforest part of the exhibit in NMNH; Sophy Burnham, former Assistant Curator of the Smithsonian Museum Service, who was instrumental in creating a film, *The Leaf Thieves,* which documents the creation of the exhibit; Richard Sumner Cowan, former Director, NMNH, who also participated in the Kaieteur Falls Expedition to collect materials for the original Hall of Botany; Joseph Shannon, former Designer, NMNH, who worked on the design of the Botany Hall and later the Hall of Living Things; Paul N. Perrot, former Assistant Secretary for Museum Programs, who was involved in providing support, recommendations, and facilitating the exhibit work, and who helped establish an Office of Exhibits Central at the Smithsonian; James A. Mahoney, former Chief of the Office of Exhibits Central, who worked on many aspects of the rainforest exhibit; David B. Lellinger, Curator of Ferns, NMNH, a member of the original exhibit committee and participant in several collecting field trips for the exhibit; and Thomas E. Lovejoy III, Counselor to the Secretary for Biodiversity and Evironmental Affairs, on the role of tropical rainforests as icons for the environmental movement.

These interviews cover the relationship between research and exhibition at the NMNH; the changes in meaning of the rainforest as it was reinterpreted for different exhibits; and the impact of trends in public education about science and the role of an icon, such as the rainforest, in discussions of the environment. Interviews of Sayre include both audiotaped and videotaped sessions and include many visuals from the exhibit.

ARRANGEMENT: (1) Audiotapes, 18 hours; (2) videotape, 0.40 hours; (3) transcript, 313 pages. FINDING AIDS: (1) Description in control file; (2) name index to transcript. SPECIAL CONDITIONS: Restricted.

C. Malcolm Watkins Interviews, 1992, 1994-1995
(22 audiotapes).

C. Malcolm Watkins (1911-), cultural historian, developed an early interest in American material culture through his parents, Charles H. and Lura Woodside Watkins, who collected glass and pottery. Watkins received the B.S. from Harvard College in 1934 and began his museum career as Curator for the Wells Historical Museum, predecessor of Old Sturbridge Village, in Massachusetts. In 1949, he was appointed Associate Curator in the Division of Ethnology, United States National Museum (USNM), where he was responsible for the collections documenting American technology and decorative arts. When a separate National Museum of History and Technology (NMHT) was created in 1958, Watkins assumed responsibility for a new Division of Cultural History in the Department of Civil History. In 1969, a separate Department of Cultural History was established, with Watkins as Chairman. In 1973, he was named Senior Curator in the Department, a position he held until his retirement in 1980; he continued his research as Curator Emeritus until 1984.

During his career at the USNM and NMHT, Watkins worked on numerous exhibits, including the Hall of Everyday Life in the American Past, *Growth of the United States,* and *A Nation of Nations.* He was responsible for the acquisition of many significant collections, including the Arthur and Edna Greenwood Collection of Americana, the Remensnyder Collection of American Stoneware, and the Morgenstern Collection of early American material culture. His major research projects included the Marlborough and Jamestown, Virginia, archeological sites, North Devon pottery export to America, and early California history. Watkins was a pioneer in the fields of material culture studies and historical archeology.

These interviews of C. Malcolm Watkins by Pamela M. Henson and Susan H. Myers discuss his family, youth, education, first job at Wells Historical Museum, curatorial career in the Division of Ethnology and Department of Cultural History, work on exhibits, research interests, role in the development of the fields of material culture studies and historical archeology, and reminiscences of such colleagues as Edna Greenwood, Herbert W. Krieger, Frank A. Taylor, George H. Watson, and Albert Wells.

ARRANGEMENT: (1) Audiotapes, 14.5 hours; (2) transcript, 181 pages. FINDING AIDS: (1) Description in control file; (2) name index to transcript. SPECIAL CONDITIONS: Restricted.

Helena M. Weiss Interviews, 1987
(16 audiotapes).

Helena M. Weiss (1909-), museum registrar and administrator, began her career as a stenographer for the Veterans Administration in 1930. In 1931, she was appointed Junior Clerk-Stenographer in the Office of Correspondence and Documents (renamed the Office of Correspondence and Records in 1947) of the United States National Museum (USNM) and in 1935 transferred to the Department of Geology. She returned to the Office of Correspondence and Records in 1948 as an Administrative Assistant and later that year advanced to Chief, after the retirement of Herbert S. Bryant. In 1956, her title was changed to Registrar and she remained in that position until her retirement in 1971.

As one of the first women managers at the Smithsonian, Weiss was responsible for the central filing system of the USNM, public inquiry mail, mail service, accession reports, loans and exchanges, shipping, foreign travel, customs regulations, insurance, and workman's compensation. She was involved in the acquisition of such famous museum specimens as the Wright Brothers' plane, *Kitty Hawk*, the Hope Diamond, and the Fenykovi elephant.

These interviews of Weiss by Pamela M. Henson discuss her work at the Veterans Administration and career at the Smithsonian, including her work as a stenographer for the Office of Correspondence and Documents and secretary for the Department of Geology, tenure as Registrar for the USNM, and role as one of the first women managers at the Smithsonian. Also included are reminiscences of many colleagues, notably Ray S. Bassler, Herbert S. Bryant, Louise M. Pearson, and Alexander Wetmore, and stories about her responsibilities for important artifacts and specimens.

ARRANGEMENT: (1) Audiotapes, 8 hours; (2) transcript, 357 pages. FINDING AIDS: (1) Description in control file; (2) name index to transcript. SPECIAL CONDITIONS: Restricted.

(9504)

Alexander Wetmore Interviews, 1974
(2 audiotapes).

Alexander Wetmore (1886-1978) began his career in systematic ornithology with the United States Department of Agriculture, Bureau of Biological Survey, in 1910. After working informally with the Smithsonian collections for many years, he was appointed Superintendent of the National Zoological Park (NZP) in 1924, and Assistant Secretary in charge of the United States National Museum (USNM) in 1925. In 1945, he was named Secretary and during his tenure oversaw the acquisition of the Canal Zone Biological Area (CZBA). After his retirement in 1952, he continued his study of North and South American birds as a Research Associate of the Institution.

These interviews of Alexander Wetmore by Miriam S. Freilicher cover his field work, expeditions for the Bureau of Biological Survey, duties at the NZP and USNM, administration of the Smithsonian, acquisition of the Canal Zone Biological Area, and reminiscences of colleagues, notably John L. Keddy, Louise M. Pearson, and James Zetek.

ARRANGEMENT: (1) Audiotapes, 2 hours; (2) transcript, 54 pages. FINDING AIDS: (1) Description in control file; (2) name index to transcript.

(9560)

George C. Wheeler Interview, 1989
(1 audiotape).

George Carlos Wheeler (1897-1992), an entomologist, specialized in the morphology and taxonomy of ants. He received the A.B. from the Rice Institute in Texas in 1918 and the M.S. in 1920 and Ph.D. in 1921 from Harvard University. From 1921 to 1926 he taught zoology at Syracuse University. He joined the faculty of the University of North

Dakota in 1926 and remained there until his retirement in 1967. He was then named University Emeritus Professor of Biology and was also named a research associate of the Desert Research Institute of the University of Nevada.

Wheeler was encouraged to visit the tropics by his advisor, William Morton Wheeler. Thus he spent the summer of 1924 studying ants on Barro Colorado Island in the Panama Canal. The Barro Colorado Research Station was established in 1923 as a reserve for scientific study in the tropics. The Smithsonian assumed responsibility for its management in 1946, and in 1966 it was renamed the Smithsonian Tropical Research Institute.

Wheeler was interviewed by Joel B. Hagen, a Smithsonian Postdoctoral Fellow, about his education and mentors at the Rice Institute and Harvard University, his career at the University of North Dakota, research on ants, and his reminiscences of Barro Colorado Island in 1924.

ARRANGEMENT: (1) Audiotape, 1 hour; (2) transcript, 20 pages. FINDING AIDS: (1) Description in control file; (2) name index to transcript. SPECIAL CONDITIONS: Restricted.

(9520)

Fred Lawrence Whipple Interviews, 1976
(4 audiotapes).

Fred Lawrence Whipple (1906-   ), an astronomer at the Smithsonian Astrophysical Observatory (SAO), was noted for his research and methodological innovations in studying the moon, meteors, and comets. The University of California, Los Angeles awarded him the B.A. in 1927 and the University of California, Berkeley the Ph.D. in 1931. After teaching at Stanford University in 1929, he joined the Harvard College Observatory staff in 1931. In 1955 he was appointed Director of the Smithsonian Astrophysical Observatory in Cambridge, Massachusetts. During his tenure, he established the Satellite Tracking Program (STP) which pioneered optical tracking systems utilized in geodesy and geophysics; oversaw SAO's research program in stellar interiors, upper atmosphere, meteorite, celestial mechanics, and geodesy studies; and its participation in Project Celescope. Whipple selected and developed an astronomical facility at Mount Hopkins, Arizona, named the Fred Lawrence Whipple Observatory in 1981. Now SAO's principal observation site, the facility houses the Multiple-Mirror Telescope (MMT), an innovative, low cost telescope planned by Whipple and two colleagues. After his retirement in 1973, he continued comet and meteor studies as Senior Scientist at SAO.

These interviews of Whipple by Pamela M. Henson cover his education; research interests; service during World War II; tenure as Director of SAO, especially development of the STP, Project Celescope, the Whipple Observatory, and MMT; and reminiscences of colleagues.

ARRANGEMENT: (1) Audiotapes, 3.5 hours; (2) transcript, 87 pages. FINDING AIDS: (1) Description in control file; (2) name index to transcript.

Frank C. Whitmore, Jr., Interview, 1989
(2 audiotapes).

Frank C. Whitmore, Jr., (1917-   ), research geologist for the Paleontology and Stratigraphy Branch of the United States Geological Survey (USGS) and Research Associate of the Department of Paleobiology, National Museum of Natural History (NMNH), specialized in the systematics of Tertiary Cetacea. Whitmore was also active in the Society of Vertebrate Paleontology (SVP) from its inception in 1940.

This interview of Whitmore by University of Maryland graduate student Joseph A. Cain discusses his education and career in vertebrate paleontology at the USGS and NMNH, focusing on his reminiscences of the history of the SVP.

ARRANGEMENT: (1) Audiotapes, 2 hours; (2) transcript, 55 pages. FINDING AIDS: (1) Description in control file; (2) name index to transcript.

A. Gilbert Wright Interviews, 1983
(9 audiotapes).

A. Gilbert Wright (1909-1987), zoologist and exhibits curator, began his career in 1933 as Zoologist for the Illinois State Museum. From 1953 to 1961, he was Curator of Exhibits at the Florida State Museum. In 1961, he was appointed by the National Park Service as Chief of the Museum Planning Branch for the Jefferson National Expansion Memorial in St. Louis, Missouri. When that project terminated in 1963, he transferred to the Smithsonian Institution. From 1963 to 1975, he served as Assistant Chief, Office of Exhibits Programs; Assistant to the Director for Exhibits Planning, National Museum of Natural History; and as Writer/Editor in the Exhibits Editor's Office. After his retirement in 1975, Wright directed the Museum Studies Program at The George Washington University until 1978.

These interviews of Wright by Pamela M. Henson discuss his youth, education, museum career with the Illinois State Museum, Florida State Museum, Jefferson National Expansion Memorial, and Smithsonian Institution, teaching, publications, and professional interests, and include reminiscences of colleagues such as Arthur Sterry Coggeshall, Ralph H. Lewis, Alexander Wetmore and John E. Anglim.

ARRANGEMENT: (1) Audiotapes, 7 hours; (2) transcript, 252 pages. FINDING AIDS: (1) Description in control file; (2) name index to transcript.

SMITHSONIAN VIDEOHISTORY
COLLECTION

In 1987, the Alfred P. Sloan Foundation awarded the Smithsonian Institution a grant to explore the use of videotape in historical research, specifically in the history of science and technology. With these funds, the Institution created the Smithsonian Videohistory Program (SVP). By the close of the Program in 1992 eighteen members of the research staff from the National Air and Space Museum, the National Museum of American History, the Smithsonian Astrophysical Observatory, and the Smithsonian Institution Archives had originated twenty-two projects, resulting in over 250 hours of tape, in diverse areas such as computers, robotics, space history, tropical biology, medical technology, and watch manufacturing. These projects make up the Smithsonian Videohistory Collection.

(9545)

Black Aviators Interviews, 1989-1990
(4 videotapes).

Throughout the 1930s, Black Americans struggled to overcome barriers in aeronautics and to gain the opportunity and right to fly airplanes. Despite widespread racism and sexism during that decade, their efforts resulted in a tenfold increase in the number of licensed black pilots, and led the federal government to sanction black male participation in aviation during World War II.

Theodore Robinson, National Air and Space Museum, conducted videotaped interviews with five black aviators on their experiences in the 1930s. C. Alfred Anderson, Janet Harmon Bragg, Cornelius Coffey, Harold Hurd, and Lewis A. Jackson explain how they obtained airplanes and training, publicized their aviation skills, and contended with social and institutional prejudices. Visual documentation includes group interaction and photographs.

ARRANGEMENT: (1) VHS tapes, 7 hours; (2) transcript, 200 pages. FINDING AIDS: (1) Description in control file; (2) name index to transcript.

(9534)

Classical Observation Techniques Interviews, 1988, 1991
(5 videotapes).

Developments in photography and non-visible radiation technology in the late twentieth century have rendered classical techniques of visual observation virtually obsolete. The United States Naval Observatory in Washington, D.C., one of the oldest continuously operating observatories in North America, has consistently upgraded the accuracy of its observations through the use of automated instrumentation.

David H. DeVorkin, National Air and Space Museum, conducted videotaped interviews with five astronomers at the Observatory to examine the increased automation of their field. Charles Worley combines nineteenth and twentieth-century technologies in his operation of the 26-inch telescope. He and the other members of the Observatory demonstrate the electronic operation of the 6-inch transit and the photographic zenith tube telescopes. Other interviewees include Thomas E. Corbin, Geoffrey Douglass, F. Stephen Gauss and Dennis Dean McCarthy. Visual documentation includes the operations, components and equipment associated with the telescopes, Worley's work areas, forms of information storage, Observatory buildings, and group interaction.

ARRANGEMENT: (1) VHS tapes, 7 hours; (2) transcript, 172 pages. FINDING AIDS: (1) Description in control file; (2) name index to transcript.

(9553)

Conservation of Endangered Species Interviews, 1990
(13 videotapes).

Efforts to preserve endangered species have focused on either maintenance of a controlled population that ensures genetic diversity or protection of habitat that ensures viability of a population in the wild. The Smithsonian Institution sponsors programs using both methods in the study and exhibition of the plant and animal kingdoms.

Pamela M. Henson, Office of Smithsonian Institution Archives, conducted videotaped interviews with researchers at the Smithsonian Tropical Research Institute (STRI) in Panama; the National Zoological Park (NZP), Washington, D.C.; and the Conservation and Research Center (CRC) of the NZP, located in Front Royal, Virginia.

Collection Division 1 (Sessions 1-11) contains interviews recorded in Panama with STRI staff and visiting researchers. Topics include research programs to study environmental issues relating to the tropical rainforest and marine environments in Panama. Interviewees at STRI included Nicholas D. Smythe, mammalogist, who demonstrated his project to domesticate pacas; marine biologist John H. Christy and his assistant, Todd Underwood, who demonstrated crab behavior studies; Brian D. Keller, marine biologist, who discussed studies of the impact of oil spills on coral reefs; Gilberto Ocana, an agronomist, who toured his experimental farm plot with Elias Gonzales, Arturo Cerezo and Juvencio Trujillo; Director Ira Rubinoff, who discussed the new Tupper Facility in Panama City; botanist Norman C. Duke who discussed his studies of the impact of oil spills on mangrove forests; biologist Donald M. Windsor who led a tour of the environmental monitoring station atop a tower in the Barro Colorado Island forest; botanist Alan P. Smith and his students, Kevin P. Hogan, Kaoru Kitajima Okada, and Mirna Samaniego, who demonstrated their research on plant uptake of energy from sunlight; herpetologist A. Stanley Rand who guided a tour of the facilities on Barro Colorado Island; and conservation biologist Robin Foster and his assistants, Zenith O. Batista, Rolando A. Perez, Dilia Santamaria, Eduardo Sierra, Hamilton W. Belton Santiago, and Ernesto Yallico, who demonstrated the survey techniques for the Tropical Forest Dynamics Project Fifty Hectare Plot. Visual documentation includes animals living and feeding in captivity, research on the flora and fauna of the tropical rainforest, and the various facilities and environments of STRI.

Collection Division 2 (Sessions 12-13) contains interviews recorded at the NZP and CRC, discussing and demonstrating their role in the conservation of endangered species through captive breeding and participation in the Species Survival Program. Participants explained the changes in institutional philosophy of research on endangered species over the past seventy-five years, their current approaches, and the application of those approaches to the animals and plants in their care. Visual documentation includes period photographs, animals living and feeding in captivity, and the various facilities and environments of the NZP and CRC. Interviewees at the NZP included former Director Theodore H. Reed; at the CRC, Reed, Larry R. Collins, Scott R. Derrickson, and Linwood Williamson.

ARRANGEMENT: (1) STRI: VHS tapes, 9 hours; transcript, 146 pages; (2) NZP: 4.5 hours; transcript, 79 pages. FINDING AIDS: (1) Description in control file; (2) name index to transcript.

(9549)
DNA Sequencing Interviews, 1989-1990
(5 videotapes).

In 1986, the California Institute of Technology (CIT) announced the development of a semi-automated machine for sequencing DNA. This machine significantly accelerated the process of mapping and sequencing genetic material, and has thus contributed to advanced scientific research projects like the on-going mapping of the human genome.

Ramunas A. Kondratas, National Museum of American History, conducted videotaped interviews with scientists and technicians at CIT, Applied Biosystems, and the National Institutes of Health. Interviewees explain and demonstrate the development of the DNA sequencer, the manufacturing process, and commercial and scientific applications. Interviewees include: Jeannine Gocayne, Leroy E. Hood, Michael Hunkapiller, Robert J. Kaiser, Lloyd M. Smith, J. Craig Venter, Kurt Becker, Kip Connell, Marilee Schaffer, Anthony R. Kerlavage, and W. Richard McCombie. Visual documentation at the three sites includes the prototype and commercial models of the sequencer, the manufacturing process and environment, development and medical laboratories, computer displays, instrument components, and group interaction.

ARRANGEMENT: (1) VHS tapes, 8.8 hours; (2) transcript, 176 pages. FINDING AIDS: (1) Description in control file; (2) name index to transcript. SPECIAL CONDITIONS: Restricted.

(9537)
Development of the Electrical Numerical Integrator and Computer (ENIAC) Interview, 1988
(2 videotapes).

The Electrical Numerical Integrator and Computer (ENIAC) was the largest and most powerful computer built during World War II. The United States Ordnance Department underwrote J. Presper Eckert and John W. Mauchly at the University of Pennsylvania as the principal designers of a device that computed one thousand times faster than any other machine at the time.

David Allison, National Museum of American History, conducted a videotaped interview with Eckert on his involvement with the ENIAC while the ENIAC was on display in the National Museum of American History in an exhibit on the history of computing. Eckert, while at the ENIAC exhibit, discussed his background, the use of calculators for ballistics experiments, materials testing, component design and assembly, and the differences between ENIAC and later computers. Visual documentation includes various components of ENIAC and their operation by Eckert.

ARRANGEMENT: (1) VHS tapes, 2.5 hours; (2) transcript, 55 pages. FINDING AIDS: (1) Description in control file; (2) name index to transcript.

(9546)

Video Portraits: Margaret J. Geller Interviews, 1989-1990
(4 videotapes).

Margaret J. Geller (1947-), Professor of Astrophysics, Harvard University, and astrophysicist, Smithsonian-Harvard Center for Astrophysics (CFA), is internationally regarded for her revolutionary research on the large-scale structure of the universe. Geller received her A.B. from the University of California at Berkeley in 1970. In 1972 she completed her M.A., followed by her Ph.D. in physics in 1975, both from Princeton University. Her professional experience includes a research fellowship in theoretical astrophysics at the Center for Astrophysics, 1974-1976. She was a senior visiting fellow at the Institute for Astronomy in Cambridge, England, 1978-1980, and also a research associate at the Harvard Observatory, 1978-1980. She has taught astrophysics and astronomy at Harvard University since 1980 and reached the rank of full professor in 1988. At the Smithsonian Astrophysical Observatory, Geller has conducted research and published her findings on the nature and history of galaxy distribution, the origin and evolution of galaxies, and x-ray astronomy. The discovery by Geller, John Huchra, and Valerie de Lapparant of the bubble structure of galaxies is arguably among the most important developments in twentieth-century astronomy.

Matthew Schneps, Smithsonian Astrophysical Observatory, and David H. DeVorkin, National Air and Space Museum, each conducted a videotaped interview with Geller at her home, office, and laboratory. Topics include family background, intellectual motivation, academic training, and present and future research interests at Harvard and the Center for Astrophysics. Visual documentation includes her working environment and the operation of computers used for galactic mapping.

ARRANGEMENT: (1) VHS tapes, 7 hours; (2) transcript, 199 pages. FINDING AIDS: (1) Description in control file; (2) name index to transcript. SPECIAL CONDITIONS: Restricted.

(9554)

The History of the Cell Sorter Interviews, 1991
(7 videotapes).

The cell sorter combines an array of optical, laser, electronic, and computer technologies to automatically separate and analyze both individual cells and related cell populations. After Mack Jett Fulwyler built a prototype at Los Alamos National Laboratory in 1965, Leonard A. Herzenberg of Stanford University developed the idea of using fluorescence to sort live cells for medical diagnosis and clinical research. He led the teams of biologists, biochemists, and engineers at Stanford and Becton Dickinson, Incorporated, in the late 1960s and early 1970s that converted the cell sorter into a commercial device.

Ramunas A. Kondratas, National Museum of American History, conducted videotaped interviews with Fulwyler, Herzenberg, and sixteen of the men and women with whom they worked on the development of the cell sorter at Los Alamos and Stanford. At sessions recorded in California, Rhode Island, and Washington, D.C., the participants discussed early cell sorting technology and its research applications, development of the Fluorescence Activated Cell Sorter (FACS) and its use in the study of Acquired Immune Deficiency Syndrome (AIDS), the history of Becton Dickinson and its commercial development of the FACS, operation of various models, and their clinical and research applications. Visual documentation includes close-ups of components; laboratory operation of various FACS machines; manufacture of FACS machines; and laboratory, manufacturing, and exhibition environments. Interviewees include: Mack Jett Fulwyler, Leonard A. Herzenberg, Bruce Allen Bach, Leonore A. Herzenberg, Mark A. Krasnow, Nagesh S. Mhatre, Monty Montano, Wayne A. Moore, Thomas Nozaki, Jr., Richard E. Owen, David R. Parks, Diether J. Recktenwald, Marcos Boris Rotman, Bernie Shoor, Richard T. Stovel, Richard G. Sweet, Marvin A. Van Dilla, and Nicholas Veizades.

ARRANGEMENT: (1) VHS tapes, 10.3 hours; (2) transcript, 203 pages. FINDING AIDS: (1) Description in control file; (2) name index to transcript. SPECIAL CONDITIONS: Restricted.

(9577)

History of the Polymerase Chain Reaction Interviews, 1992-1993
(11 videotapes).

The Polymerase Chain Reaction (PCR) technique was invented in 1985 by Kary B. Mullis, a chemist at the Cetus Corporation, a biotechnology firm in Emeryville, California. PCR allowed scientists to make millions of copies of a scarce sample of DNA. Although revolutionary, Mullis' technique proved to be slow and labor-intensive, and Cetus scientists soon automated the process with the creation of the first thermocycling machine, "Mr. Cycle." In 1985, Cetus formed a joint venture with the Perkin-Elmer Corporation in Norwalk, Connecticut, and introduced the DNA Thermal Cycler. On January 15, 1989, Cetus announced an agreement to collaborate with Hoffman-La Roche on the development and commercialization of *in vitro* human diagnostic products and services based on PCR technology. The PCR patent and associated technology was later purchased by Roche Molecular Systems.

Ramunas A. Kondratas, National Museum of American History, documented the discovery, development, commercialization, and applications of PCR technology. Interviewees included Kary B. Mullis, Norman Arnheim, John G. Atwood, Peter Barrett, Joseph L. DiCesare, Henry Anthony Erlich, Fred Faloona, David H. Gefland, Lawrence Allen Haff, David C. Jones, Elena D. Katz, Shirley Kwok, Richard Leath, Lynn H. Pasahow, Enrico Picozza, Riccardo Pigliucci, Randall K. Saiki, Donna Marie Seyfried, John J. Sninsky, Stephen Scharf, Robert Watson, Thomas J. White, Timothy M. Woudenberg, Joseph Widunas, Robert P. Regusa, Robert L. Grossman, and Lesley S. Kelley.

Topics discussed include the invention of the PCR technique, early applications, PCR patent rights, Perkin-Elmer's joint venture with Cetus, the design and engineering of commercial thermocyclers, marketing, and future applications.

ARRANGEMENT: (1) VHS tapes, 19 hours; (2) transcript, 346 pages. FINDING AIDS: (1) Description in control file; (2) name index to transcript. SPECIAL CONDITIONS: Restricted.

International Ultraviolet Explorer Interviews, 1990

(4 videotapes).

Launched in 1978 as a joint European, British, and American project, the *International Ultraviolet Explorer (IUE)* geosynchronous satellite carried the first orbiting astronomical telescope. The *IUE* was responsible for the discovery of sulfur in the nucleus of a comet and of the hot halo of gas surrounding the Earth's galaxy.

David H. DeVorkin, National Air and Space Museum, conducted videotaped interviews with a group of scientists about the origins, development, use, and administration of the *IUE*. Carol Armbruster, Albert Boggess, Yoji Kondo, and George Sonneborn discussed the cooperative nature of the enterprise, technical and engineering demands of the design process, and development and operation of data collection and analysis techniques. Visual documentation includes the operational facilities at the Goddard Space Flight Center, National Aeronautics and Space Administration, in Greenbelt, Maryland, during an observing session, and various components of an *IUE* model.

ARRANGEMENT: (1) VHS tapes, 6.7 hours; (2) transcript, 185 pages. FINDING AIDS: (1) Description in control file; (2) name index to transcript.

The Manhattan Project Interviews, 1987-1990

(26 videotapes).

The United States government established the Manhattan Project in 1942 to design, build, and deliver the world's first atomic bombs. The Project drew on academic, industrial, military, and human resources from across the United States and around the world.

Stanley Goldberg, National Museum of American History, conducted videotaped interviews with men and women from all phases of the Project, often at their wartime workplaces. Topics include how they became involved in the Project, what their jobs entailed, and how they reacted to the ultimate use of their work.

Collection Division 1 (Sessions 1-3) contains interviews with administrators and employees from the Hanford Engineering Works in the state of Washington. Frederic W. Albaugh, Richard F. Foster, Oswald H. Greager, Franklin T. Matthias, Lawrence Denton, Wilson A. Cease, Ralph K. Wahlen, Wakefield A. Wright, Vivian Russell Chapman, William P. McCue and Leonard F. Perkins, Sr., discuss operation of the nuclear reactors, chemical separation plants, and cooling systems; living conditions; and administration of the facility. Visual documentation includes group interaction and a reactor face, controls, and equipment at the Hanford facility.

Collection Division 2 (Sessions 4-8) contains interviews with line workers, engineers, and physicists at the Clinton Engineering Works in Oak Ridge, Tennessee. Dale F. Babcock, Edward C. Creutz, Alvin M. Weinberg, Eugene P. Wigner, Lyle F. Borst, Colleen Black, Connie Bolling, Jane W. Larson, Audrey B. Livingston, George M. Banic, Jr., Clarence E. Larson, Robert S. Livingston, John M. Googin, Chris P. Keim, Paul R. Vanstrum, James A. Parsons, and Paul Huber discuss development of fission theory and its application in reactor construction, living conditions, and technologies used in uranium isotope separation at the Y-12 and K-25 Plants. Visual documentation includes group interaction, the interiors of the plants, and period photographs of Oak Ridge.

Collection Division 3 (Sessions 9-12) contains interviews with physicists and their spouses who worked at the Los Alamos Scientific Laboratory in New Mexico. Kenneth T. Bainbridge, Donald Hornig, Philip Morrison, Robert Wilson, Robert Serber, Anthony French, David Frisch, Lillian Hornig, Rose Frisch, Alice Kimball Smith, Jane S. Wilson, Bernard T. Feld, and Cyril Smith discuss formation and organization of the laboratory, the Trinity atomic bomb test, and social life and community culture. Sessions were taped in a studio in Boston, Massachusetts; visual documentation includes group interaction and photographs.

Collection Division 4 (Sessions 13-16) contains interviews with physicists and administrators at the Los Alamos Scientific Laboratory and the Trinity test site at Alamogordo, New Mexico. Kenneth T. Bainbridge, Robert Wilson, Frederick Reines, Hans Bethe, J. Carson Mark, Robert Christy, Robert Bacher, Norris E. Bradbury, and David Hawkins cover subjects of Collection Division 3 from different perspectives. Visual documentation includes group interaction and sites at Alamogordo and contemporary Los Alamos.

Collection Division 5 (Sessions 17-18) contains interviews with members of the team that worked on Project Alberta, the delivery and detonation of the atomic bombs on Japan. Norman F. Ramsey, Jr., Harold M. Agnew, Frederick L. Ashworth, and Charles W. Sweeney discuss design of the bombs, flight training, preparation of Tinian Island airbase, and Hiroshima and Nagasaki missions. Visual documentation includes group interaction, production models of the "Fat Man" and "Little Boy" bombs, and the *Enola Gay* B-29 restoration project at the National Air and Space Museum's Paul E. Garber Facility in Suitland, Maryland.

ARRANGEMENT: (1) Hanford, *circa* 1943-1945: VHS tapes, 5.7 hours, transcript, 156 pages; (2) Oak Ridge, *circa* 1940-1945: VHS tapes, 12.3 hours, transcript, 374 pages; (3) Cambridge, *circa* 1943-1945: VHS tapes, 9.8 hours, transcript, 334 pages; (4) Los Alamos, *circa* 1943-1945: VHS tapes, 6.8 hours, transcript, 176 pages; (5) Alberta, *circa* 1944-1945: VHS tapes, 4.5 hours, transcript, 148 pages. FINDING AIDS: (1) Description in control file; (2) name index to transcript.

(9544)

Medical Imaging Interviews, 1989
(9 videotapes and 3 audiotapes).

The Automatic Computerized Transverse Axial (ACTA) scanner was introduced in 1973 and represented a major advance in medical imaging and diagnosis. As the first full-body Computer-assisted Tomography (CT) scanner, it permitted non-invasive, cross-sectional viewing of body tissues and revolutionized analyses of cancers, heart disease, and other soft tissue irregularities.

Ramunas A. Kondratas, National Museum of American History, conducted audiotaped and videotaped interviews with Robert S. Ledley, designer of the ACTA scanner, and his associates, David Griego, Seong Ki Mun, Homer Twigg, and Robert Zeman. They discussed the history of X-ray CT imaging and the development of the

ACTA scanner. Ledley also explained the activities and research projects at the National Biomedical Research Foundation (NBRF) at Georgetown University. In the audio interview Ledley reviewed his background and career. Visual documentation includes group interaction, two documentary films, components of early models of the ACTA scanner, facilities and equipment of the NBRF, and a complete CT scanning session with a patient.

ARRANGEMENT: (1) VHS tapes, 7.5 hours; (2) video transcript, Sessions 1 and 4 consist of the documentary films and were not transcribed, 154 pages; (3) audiotapes, 4.5 hours; (4) audio transcript, 96 pages. FINDING AIDS: Description in control file; (2) name index to transcript. SPECIAL CONDITIONS: Restricted.

(9533)

Minicomputers and Microcomputers Interview, 1987
(2 videotapes).

In the late 1970s a group of computer software designers organized "The Brotherhood," an informal assembly to exchange microcomputer programs. The graphic and game programs they produced influenced the development of more sophisticated computer systems.

Jon B. Eklund, National Museum of American History, conducted a videotaped interview with six members of The Brotherhood to discuss their activities. In an interview at the Broderbund Software office in San Rafael, California, on July 31, 1987, Douglas Carlston, Ken and Roberta Williams, Margot Comstock, Jerry Jewell, and Dave Albert discuss the creation, marketing, and distribution of microcomputer software in the late 1970s, and compare their techniques to similar efforts in the mid-1980s when the demand for personal computers leveled off. Visual documentation includes group interaction and demonstration of computer games.

ARRANGEMENT: (1) VHS tapes, 1.6 hours, session was recorded on two cameras, interview length, 1.6 hours; (2) transcript, 59 pages. FINDING AIDS: (1) Description in control file; (2) name index to transcript.

(9542)

Multiple-Mirror Telescope Interviews, 1989
(7 videotapes).

In the late 1970s, the Smithsonian Astrophysical Observatory and the University of Arizona joined together to construct the Multiple-Mirror Telescope (MMT) at the Fred Lawrence Whipple Observatory on Mt. Hopkins, Arizona. The MMT was the state of the art in telescope technology and represented a new scale of coordination within a scientific consortium created to build and operate the structure.

David H. DeVorkin, National Air and Space Museum, conducted videotaped interviews at the MMT and University of Arizona with some of the astronomers, engineers, and opticians responsible for the development and operation of the MMT. Nathaniel Carleton, Frederic H. Chaffee, Craig Foltz, Thomas E. Hoffman, Aden Meinel, Michael Reed, Robert R. Shannon, Ray J. Weymann, Joseph T. Williams and Fred Lawrence Whipple discuss the history of the MMT, the engineering involved in its design and construction, its capabilities, and its administration by the various institutions concerned with its operation. Visual documentation includes group interaction, designs and models, the proposed and final locations of the MMT, the main control rooms, and a demonstration of the MMT in operation.

ARRANGEMENT: (1) VHS tapes, 8.7 hours; (2) transcript, 257 pages. FINDING AIDS: (1) Description in control file; (2) name index to transcript.

(9539)

Naval Research Laboratory Space Science Interviews, 1986-1987
(8 videotapes).

The study of the upper atmosphere was a major research focus of the Naval Research Laboratory (NRL) in the years 1945 to 1987.

David H. DeVorkin, National Air and Space Museum, conducted videotaped interviews at the NRL with six scientists who pioneered the sciences of aeronomy and X-ray astronomy. They helped develop these hybrid fields by adapting extant technologies to research on the composition of the atmosphere and on the presence of solar and stellar radiation.

Collection Division 1 contains interviews with Edward T. Byram, Talbot A. Chubb, Herbert Friedman, and Robert Kreplin, all of whom worked on X-ray astronomy in the Electron Optics Branch of the NRL's Rocketry Division. Topics include development and application of radiation detection technologies and qualities of different rockets as experimental platforms. Visual documentation includes demonstration of the operation of contemporary and period laboratory equipment, X-ray astronomy instrumentation, and photographs.

Collection Division 2 contains interviews with Charles Y. Johnson and Julian C. Holmes, both of whom worked on aeronomy in the NRL's Rocketry Division. Topics include the development of laboratory equipment and the Aerobee rocket, and the process of data interpretation. Visual documentation includes the operation of lab equipment, aeronomy instrumentation, and documents.

ARRANGEMENT: (1) Early X-ray astronomy: VHS tapes, 9.7 hours; transcript, 266 pages; (2) NRL aeronomy: VHS tapes, 4.3 hours; transcript, 124 pages. FINDING AIDS: (1) Description in control file; (2) name index to transcript.

(9550)

New United Motor Manufacturing, Incorporated, Interviews, 1990
(3 videotapes).

In February 1983, General Motors Corporation (GM) signed an agreement with Toyota Motor Corporation of Japan to join forces as the New United Motor Manufacturing, Incorporated (NUMMI), to produce automobiles at the GM plant located in Fremont, California, one of the least efficient of the GM plants. Within five years the NUMMI plant, using Japanese managerial philosophy and an American labor force, rivaled Asian automobile factories in efficiency.

Peter Liebhold, National Museum of American History, conducted a videotaped tour of the NUMMI plant during which he interviewed seventeen workers and managers on their responses to changes in organization and labor relations. They explain job requirements and manufacturing processes, compare work at NUMMI with that of

American management, and discuss conflicting pressures for quality control and productivity. Among those interviewed were Michael Danner, Public Relations Officer, Gary Convis, Senior Vice-President for Manufacturing and Engineering, and George Nano, the NUMMI United Auto Workers Bargaining Committee Chairman.

ARRANGEMENT: (1) VHS tapes, 6 hours; (2) transcript, 109 pages. FINDING AIDS: (1) Description in control file; (2) name index to transcript.

(9536)

The Research and Development (RAND) Corporation Interviews, 1987-1990
(15 videotapes).

Initially underwritten by the United States Air Force (USAF) in 1946, the Research and Development Corporation of Santa Monica, California (RAND), represented one of the first "think tanks" dedicated to military and strategic policy.

Joseph Tatarewicz, Martin Collins, and Paul E. Ceruzzi, National Air and Space Museum (NASM), collaborated with Gustave Shubert, Willis Ware, and Robert Anderson of RAND to videotape interviews with former staff members on their experiences in three areas of research and development between 1945 and 1970.

Collection Division 1 (Sessions 1-3) contains interviews with Merton E. Davies, Amron H. Katz, and Walter Levison, who detail their roles at RAND in developing aerial reconnaissance photography for strategic purposes. Topics include developments in camera and aerial platform technology to the end of the 1950s, military and political consequences of those developments, the role RAND played between the government and corporate industry, and developments in photointerpretation from 1940 to 1970. Video documentation includes the duplex and HYAC cameras and photo interpretation tools. The sessions were shot at Katz's home in California and at NASM.

Collection Division 2 (Session 4) contains an interview at RAND headquarters with seven former division heads to discuss changes in the intellectual climate at RAND, especially as it related to the development of nuclear strategy in the 1950s. Bruno W. Augenstein, Edward J. Barlow, Burton H. Klein, Gustave Shubert, Robert D. Specht, Hans Speier, and Albert Wohlstetter discuss the relationship with the USAF, expansion of RAND's clientele, reasons why participants left RAND, and differences in RAND culture then and in 1989.

Collection Division 3 (Sessions 5-8) contains interviews at RAND headquarters with thirteen RAND staff members who worked on computer engineering and programming between 1945 and the 1960s, including Morton I. Bernstein, Edward C. DeLand, Irwin Greenwald, J. Clifford Shaw, Keith Uncapher, and Willis Ware. Topics include computer language and program design, computer and program applications, and problem-solving approaches at RAND compared to those on the East Coast. Video documentation consists of some computer hardware, mainly through photographs.

ARRANGEMENT: (1) Aerial photoreconnaissance: VHS tapes, 10 hours; transcript, 181 pages; (2) research and culture: VHS tapes, 4 hours; transcript, 99 pages; (3) early computing history: VHS tapes, 9 hours; transcript, 217 pages. FINDING AIDS: (1) Description in control file; (2) name index to transcripts.

Robotics Interviews, 1989-1990
(12 videotapes).

Robotics, the applied science of intelligent machines, poses significant design challenges to engineers. These interviews document the robotics development process in academic and corporate research environments.

Steven Lubar, National Museum of American History, conducted videotaped interviews with the field's practitioners at the University of Maryland at College Park; Carnegie-Mellon University, Pittsburgh, Pennsylvania; and Odetics, Incorporated, Anaheim, California. Professors, students, technicians, and engineers explained design and development processes, and operated their robots. Interviewees included: Lung-We Tsai, Jigien Chen, Shapour Azarm, Robert Drap, Joel Slutzkey, Armen Sivaslian, Steven Corley, Erik Krotkov, Kevin Dowling, Henning Pangels, John Bares, David Wettergreen, Regis Hoffman, William Whittaker, Peter S. Tanguy, James Albus and Thomas Wheatley. Visual documentation includes laboratories, group interaction, robot components, and robots in operation.

ARRANGEMENT: (1) VHS tapes, 22 hours; (2) transcript, 217 pages. FINDING AIDS: (1) Description in control file; (2) name index to transcript.

Smallpox Virus Sequencing Project Interviews, 1991
(2 videotapes).

In 1967, the World Health Organization (WHO) initiated a program of world-wide eradication of smallpox through mass immunization and the vigorous containment of outbreaks. The last naturally occurring case of smallpox was identified in Somalia in 1977, and after two additional years of worldwide surveillance, WHO announced the global eradication of smallpox. Strains of the virus were placed in storage at two authorized locations, and in May 1990 the United States Secretary of Health and Human Services announced that technological advances had made it possible to map the entire smallpox genome within three years. Scientists agreed that the first step toward the destruction of the virus was to determine its complete DNA sequence, thereby retaining the essential scientific information on what would soon become an extinct virus. In 1991, the National Institute for Neurological Disorders and Stroke (NINDS) at the National Institutes of Health (NIH) was chosen as the site for the sequencing of the *Bangladesh 1975* strain of the virus, a project sponsored jointly by the Centers for Disease Control (CDC) and NIH.

Ramunas A. Kondratas, National Museum of American History, documented the start of the project to sequence the smallpox virus genome at NINDS. Interviewees, who include NINDS employees Li-Ing Liu and J. Craig Venter, CDC scientist Brian Wilfred John Mahy, and researchers Teresa Utterback, Nicolay Selivanov, and Anthony R. Kerlavage, discuss the history of the smallpox sequencing project and demonstrate the process for sequencing the *Bangladesh 1975* strain of the virus.

ARRANGEMENT: (1) VHS tapes, 3 hours; (2) transcript, 44 pages. FINDING AIDS: (1) Description in control file; (2) name index to transcript. SPECIAL CONDITIONS: Restricted.

Smithsonian Institution Paleontology Interviews, 1987-1988
(5 videotapes).

G. Arthur Cooper (1902-   ), paleobiologist specializing in the classification and stratigraphy of Paleozoic brachiopods, was appointed Assistant Curator in the Division of Stratigraphic Paleontology of the United States National Museum (USNM) in 1930. He advanced to Associate Curator in 1941 and to Curator of the Division of Invertebrate Paleontology in 1944. He was named Head Curator of the Department of Geology in 1957, oversaw its division into two departments in 1963, and continued as Chairman of the new Department of Paleobiology. In 1967, he was appointed Senior Paleobiologist to devote his time to research, and continued as Paleobiologist Emeritus from 1974 to 1985. His research at the National Museum of Natural History (NMNH) included innovative techniques for the handling, processing, and interpretation of fossils.

Pamela M. Henson, Smithsonian Institution Archives, conducted videotaped interviews at the NMNH with Cooper and research associates J. Thomas Dutro, Jr., Richard E. Grant, and Ellis L. Yochelson. They discussed and demonstrated the methods used to collect, prepare, and analyze fossilized brachiopods. Visual documentation includes group interaction, Devonian and Permian era specimens, the acid etching process, and Cooper's laboratory.

ARRANGEMENT: (1) VHS tapes, 4.2 hours; (2) transcript, 117 pages. FINDING AIDS: (1) Description in control file; (2) name index to transcript.

Soviet Space Medicine Interviews, 1989
(6 videotapes and 1 audiotape).

The Institute for Biomedical Problems, Moscow, U.S.S.R, was founded in 1963 to undertake the study of space medicine.

Cathleen S. Lewis, National Air and Space Museum, interviewed Drs. Oleg Gazenko, Eugenii Shepelev, Abraham Genin, and technicians Irina Gireeva and Vladimir Magedov about research on high altitude and space medicine conducted since the 1950s. Visual documentation includes the Primate Space Flight Training Facility, the museum galleries and exteriors of the Institute, and group interaction.

ARRANGEMENT: (1) VHS tapes, 5.7 hours; (2) transcript, 86 pages, transcript has been translated into English; (3) audiotape, 1.25 hours; (4) transcript, 19 pages, transcript has been translated into English. FINDING AIDS: (1) Description in control file; (2) name index to transcript.

Twentieth Century Small Arms Development Interviews, 1988-1990
(14 videotapes).

Changes in technology and weapons procurement procedures in the past fifty years have made it increasingly difficult for an individual to develop and market a new weapon.

Edward Ezell, National Museum of American History, conducted videotaped interviews of Eugene M. Stoner of the United States and Mikhail T. Kalashnikov of the

Soviet Union, two of the world's most successful small arms designers. They discussed their careers since World War II and how they worked within their respective military-political systems.

Collection Division 1 (Sessions 1-6), recorded in Port Clinton, Ohio, contains an interview with Eugene M. Stoner. Topics include the design evolution of the M16 automatic rifle; his approach to weapons design; his relationship with the American military bureaucracy and other designers; and the development of various forms of ordnance and ammunition produced by his company, ARES Incorporated. Extensive visual documentation includes weapons discussed and the factory where some of them are manufactured.

Collection Division 2 (Sessions 7-11), recorded in the Soviet Union, contains an interview with Mikhail T. Kalashnikov. Topics include the design evolution of the AK47 automatic rifle, philosophic and technological trends toward simplicity and interchangeable parts, the RPK74 and PKM machine guns, and the collective nature of weapons development in the Soviet Union. There is extensive visual documentation of the weapons discussed.

Collection Division 3 (Session 12), recorded in western Virginia, features the first meeting between the two inventors. Stoner and Kalashnikov compare the design of the AK47 with that of the AR15, the prototype and commercial model of the M16. There is extensive visual documentation of both weapons.

ARRANGEMENT: (1) Eugene M. Stoner, *circa* 1955-1988: VHS tapes, 7.5 hours; transcript, 129 pages; (2) Mikhail T. Kalashnikov, *circa* 1942-1989: VHS tapes, 7.5 hours; transcript, 62 pages, Kalashnikov's responses have been translated into English for the transcript; (3) Stoner-Kalashnikov, *circa* 1946-1963: VHS tapes, 1.8 hours; transcript, 24 pages, Kalashnikov's conversation has been translated into English for the transcript. FINDING AIDS: (1) Description in control file; (2) name index to transcript. SPECIAL CONDITIONS: Restricted.

(9535)

Twenty-Fifth Anniversary of Mariner 2 Interview, 1987
(2 videotapes).

On December 14, 1962, the *Mariner 2* passed within 41,000 kilometers of Venus, returning important data on the conditions of the planet, as well as data on the electromagnetic and energetic particle environment of interplanetary space. This mission was the first successful encounter of a spacecraft with another planet.

On the twenty-fifth anniversary of the launch of the *Mariner 2,* Allan Needell, National Air and Space Museum, convened five of the scientists, engineers, and administrators associated with the spacecraft to discuss their experiences. Jack Albert, Albert R. Hibbs, Lewis D. Kaplan, Jack N. James, and Oran W. Nicks discussed the establishment of the Mariner program at the Jet Propulsion Laboratory of the University of California and the National Aeronautics and Space Administration, their individual contributions, teamwork, technical examination and operation of the mission itself, and tensions between military and civilian space interests. Visual documentation includes personal interaction, photographs, and models of the spacecraft.

ARRANGEMENT: (1) VHS tapes, 3 hours; (2) transcript, 61 pages. FINDING AIDS: (1) Description in control file; (2) name index to transcript.

Vermont Structural Slate Company Interviews, 1989

(3 videotapes).

As of 1989, the Vermont Structural Slate Company (VSS) in Fair Haven, Vermont, was one of only twenty slate-producing companies in the nation. The company operated several quarries, including the oldest active quarry in Vermont, the Eureka quarry, which opened for slate production in 1852. VSS was established in 1859, and it has continued to use nineteenth-century machinery for most quarrying and manufacturing operations, although the owners have attempted to upgrade the facility with more modern equipment.

William Worthington III, National Museum of American History, conducted a videotaped tour of the VSS quarry in Eureka to document remaining nineteenth-century techniques before the installation of modern equipment. Four employees explain and demonstrate old and new methods and technologies for extracting and processing slate. There is extensive visual documentation of the quarry, its operation, and environs. Interviewees included Brad Bauman, Everett Beayon, Joseph Root, and Raymond Cull.

ARRANGEMENT: (1) VHS tapes, 4 hours; (2) transcript, 63 pages. FINDING AIDS: (1) Description in control file; (2) name index to transcript.

Waltham Clock Company Interviews, 1989

(4 videotapes).

The Waltham Clock Company of Waltham, Massachusetts, the modern successor to the first American watch manufacturer, Waltham Watch Company, was founded in 1850. Waltham employees pioneered the machines and techniques necessary for the mass-production of pocket watches that made the company the dominant American watchmaking manufacturer in the nineteenth and early twentieth centuries. The electronics revolution of the 1970s made mechanical watches and watchmakers nearly obsolete. At the time of the video recording, Waltham Clock was the last firm in the United States still producing mechanical watches.

Carlene E. Stephens, National Museum of American History, visited Waltham, Massachusetts, and conducted a videotaped tour of the factory to document operating machinery and to record the process of making and testing mechanical watches. Interviews were conducted with employees who represented a range of factory operations, including Joseph "Chuck" Martin, Marie Bastarache, David Buccheri, Charlie Paradis, Vincent Rhoad, Richard Halstead, Edward Pitts, Stanford James, John Valmas, Bruce LeDoyt, Edward Murphy, Tam Thi Le, Richard Welch, and Savay Xayavong.

ARRANGEMENT: (1) VHS tapes, 5.7 hours; (2) transcript, 170 pages. FINDING AIDS: (1) Description in control file; (2) name index to transcript.

APPENDIX A

INDEX BY FORM

References are to page number, followed by record unit number, in brackets.

Audiotapes: data collection, 252 [RU 255]; 273 [RU 514]; 372 [RU 106]; 419 [RU 7279]; 479 [RU 7464]

Audiotapes: interviews, 214 [RU 454]; 214 [RU 455]; 271 [RU 469]; 359 [RU 296]; 360 [RU 589]; 360 [RU 591]; 360 [RU 592]; 361 [RU 588]; 361 [RU 590]; 372 [RU 106]; 387 [RU 7440]; 389 [RU 7357]; 390 [RU 7351]; 612 [RU 9500]; 612 [RU 9511]; 613 [RU 9556]; 614 [RU 9526]; 614 [RU 9563]; 615 [RU 9517]; 615 [RU 9561]; 616 [RU 9515]; 616 [RU 9567]; 617 [RU 9514]; 617 [RU 9541]; 618 [RU 9528]; 618 [RU 9555]; 619 [RU 9501]; 619 [RU 9524]; 619 [RU 9570]; 620 [RU 9571]; 621 [RU 9518]; 621 [RU 9562]; 622 [RU 9505]; 622 [RU 9559]; 623 [RU 9572]; 624 [RU 9506]; 624 [RU 9529]; 624 [RU 9566]; 625 [RU 9509]; 625 [RU 9525]; 626 [RU 9558]; 626 [RU 9573]; 627 [RU 9527]; 627 [RU 9574]; 628 [RU 9513]; 628 [RU 9538]; 629 [RU 9502]; 630 [RU 9507]; 630 [RU 9576]; 631 [RU 9516]; 631 [RU 9540]; 632 [RU 9578]; 632 [RU 9589]; 633 [RU 9568]; 633 [RU 9579]; 634 [RU 9503]; 634 [RU 9519]; 636 [RU 9590]; 636 [RU 9591]; 637 [RU 9581]; 637 [RU 9582]; 638 [RU 9510]; 638 [RU 9583]; 639 [RU 9508]; 639 [RU 9588]; 640 [RU 9580]; 640 [RU 9584]; 641 [RU 9521]; 641 [RU 9585]; 642 [RU 9512]; 643 [RU 9565]; 644 [RU 9586]; 644 [RU 9587]; 645 [RU 9504]; 645 [RU 9560]; 646 [RU 9520]; 647 [RU 9523]; 647 [RU 9557]; 654 [RU 9544]; 659 [RU 9551]

Audiotapes: music, 171 [RU 485]; 180 [RU 360]; 359 [RU 296]; 359 [RU 594]; 360 [RU 589]; 360 [RU 591]; 360 [RU 592]; 361 [RU 588]; 361 [RU 590]; 372 [RU 106]; 451 [RU 7348]

Audiotapes: special events, 67 [RU 416]; 111 [RU 428]; 180 [RU 360]; 228 [RU 554]; 244 [RU 520]; 271 [RU 469]; 272 [RU 481]; 273 [RU 514]; 297 [RU 585]; 301 [RU 601]; 302 [RU 602]; 302 [RU 603]; 332 [RU 498]; 357 [RU 496]; 359 [RU 296]; 360 [RU 589]; 360 [RU 591]; 360 [RU 592]; 361 [RU 588]; 361 [RU 590]; 372 [RU 106]; 380 [RU 7008]; 387 [RU 7440]; 394 [RU 7459]; 395 [RU 7294]; 557 [RU 7231]; 578 [RU 7142]; 613 [RU 9522]

Autographs, 99 [RU 1020001]; 114 [RU 237]; 400 [RU 7473]; 426 [RU 7134]; 468 [RU 7050]; 517 [RU 7177]; 601 [RU 7112]

Bound volumes, 107 [RU 272]

Bound volumes: account books, 70 [RU 431]; 87 [RU 433]; 389 [RU 7357]; 421 [RU 7438]; 452 [RU 7428]; 500 [RU 7434]; 501 [RU 7202]; 507 [RU 1040101]; 574 [RU 7074]; 576 [RU 7093]

Bound volumes: address books, 586 [RU 7424]

Bound volumes: diaries, 161 [RU 528]; 397 [RU 7053]; 400 [RU 7473]; 414 [RU 7310]; 424 [RU 7297]; 426 [RU 7134]; 427 [RU 7162]; 427 [RU 7258]; 441 [RU 7073]; 443 [RU 7439]; 452 [RU 7428]; 459 [RU 7319]; 468 [RU 7050]; 471 [RU 7307]; 487 [RU 7084]; 497 [RU 7333]; 500 [RU 7434]; 501 [RU 7202]; 501 [RU 7383]; 503 [RU 7375]; 505 [RU 7108]; 507 [RU 7157]; 508 [RU 7396]; 516 [RU 7062]; 516 [RU 7182]; 537 [RU 7252]; 564 [RU 7296]; 572 [RU 7263]; 575 [RU 7379]; 577 [RU 7191]; 590 [RU 7055]

Bound volumes: field notebooks, 82 [RU 7217]; 95 [RU 1030301]; 101 [RU 7135]; 101 [RU 7448]; 123 [RU 7264]; 123 [RU 1050401]; 131 [RU NAA06]; 436 [RU 7318]; 437 [RU 7067]; 441 [RU 7073]; 451 [RU 7348]; 452 [RU 7096]; 452 [RU 7428]; 456 [RU 7242]; 457 [RU 7281]; 460 [RU 7314]; 462 [RU 7290]; 464 [RU 7122]; 464 [RU 7209]; 477 [RU 7237]; 479 [RU 7464]; 480 [RU 7125]; 487 [RU 7084]; 490 [RU 7107]; 490 [RU 7405]; 491 [RU 7311]; 500 [RU 7434]; 501 [RU 7202]; 508 [RU 7396]; 510 [RU 7223]; 515 [RU 7083]; 516 [RU 7062]; 537 [RU 7252]; 538 [RU 7240]; 538 [RU 7250]; 541 [RU 7178]; 542 [RU 7393]; 544 [RU 7232]; 556 [RU 7056]; 565 [RU 7082]; 566 [RU 7316]; 568 [RU 7262]; 575 [RU 7379]; 577 [RU 7191]; 590 [RU 7055]; 601 [RU 7213]

Bound volumes: journals, 121 [RU 156]; 522 [RU 7203]

Bound volumes: laboratory notebooks, 549 [RU 7160]

Bound volumes: letterpress copybooks, 85 [RU 508]; 105 [RU 220]; 109 [RU 224]; 121 [RU 248]; 125 [RU NAA01]

Bound volumes: logbooks, 527 [RU 7200]

Bound volumes: notebooks, 427 [RU 7162]; 429 [RU 7131]; 564 [RU 7283]; 564 [RU 7296]; 572 [RU 7263]; 574 [RU 7074]

Bound volumes: photographic albums, 389 [RU 7357]

Bound volumes: scrapbooks, 112 [RU 229]; 144 [RU 84]; 286 [RU 289]; 341 [RU 372]; 390 [RU 7351]; 440 [RU 1050101]; 441 [RU 7073]; 468 [RU 7050]; 483 [RU 7347]; 497 [RU 7333]; 500 [RU 7434]; 508 [RU 7396]; 564 [RU 7283]; 565 [RU 7082]; 574 [RU 7074]; 583 [RU 7433]; 590 [RU 7055]

Cartographic materials: maps, 76 [RU 245]; 101 [RU 7448]; 109 [RU 226]; 128 [RU NAA05]; 131 [RU NAA06]; 189 [RU 74]; 194 [RU 365]; 239 [RU 353]; 256 [RU 478]; 304 [RU 134]; 325 [RU 58]; 336 [RU 60]; 362 [RU 69]; 370 [RU 92]; 397

[RU 7267]; 408 [RU 7052]; 419 [RU 7279]; 422 [RU 7377]; 437 [RU 7067]; 441 [RU 7073]; 449 [RU 7411]; 449 [RU 7415]; 456 [RU 7242]; 457 [RU 7281]; 470 [RU 7148]; 479 [RU 7464]; 480 [RU 7179]; 505 [RU 7251]; 529 [RU 7088]; 541 [RU 7178]; 549 [RU 7287]; 565 [RU 7082]; 586 [RU 7424]

Graphic illustrations, 443 [RU 7439]

Graphic illustrations: architectural, 7 [RU 31]; 12 [RU 171]; 49 [RU 71]; 50 [RU 81]; 123 [RU 328]; 135 [RU 276]; 177 [RU 580]; 244 [RU 358]; 256 [RU 478]; 264 [RU 4010003]; 281 [RU 492]; 282 [RU 545]; 288 [RU 287]; 294 [RU 544]; 308 [RU 635]; 317 [RU 157]; 318 [RU 532]; 319 [RU 639]; 321 [RU 576]; 324 [RU 638]; 324 [RU 640]; 329 [RU 637]; 330 [RU 641]; 352 [RU 310]; 370 [RU 92]; 400 [RU 7473]; 408 [RU 7052]; 461 [RU 7471]; 481 [RU 7075]

Graphic illustrations: artifacts, 151 [RU 397]; 155 [RU 471]; 212 [RU 452]; 256 [RU 478]; 258 [RU 522]; 325 [RU 58]; 351 [RU 536]; 487 [RU 7084]; 556 [RU 7056]; 585 [RU 7181]

Graphic illustrations: exhibitions and installations, 65 [RU 363]; 65 [RU 366]; 123 [RU 328]; 138 [RU 583]; 147 [RU 383]; 148 [RU 250]; 151 [RU 397]; 152 [RU 206]; 158 [RU 293]; 159 [RU 332]; 166 [RU 406]; 171 [RU 485]; 176 [RU 359]; 179 [RU 551]; 181 [RU 584]; 213 [RU 451]; 223 [RU 426]; 224 [RU 379]; 226 [RU 552]; 227 [RU 361]; 236 [RU 354]; 270 [RU 510]; 271 [RU 469]; 273 [RU 516]; 281 [RU 492]; 285 [RU 506]; 287 [RU 280]; 287 [RU 531]; 288 [RU 287]; 293 [RU 541]; 293 [RU 542]; 326 [RU 503]; 350 [RU 518]; 351 [RU 490]; 351 [RU 536]; 598 [RU 7322]

Graphic illustrations: flora and fauna, 80 [RU 7220]; 82 [RU 7217]; 89 [RU 7260]; 106 [RU 221]; 317 [RU 7269]; 382 [RU 7116]; 387 [RU 7150]; 394 [RU 7139]; 408 [RU 7052]; 408 [RU 7302]; 413 [RU 1070101]; 416 [RU 7119]; 426 [RU 7134]; 441 [RU 7073]; 451 [RU 7102]; 453 [RU 7402]; 453 [RU 7446]; 467 [RU 7126]; 478 [RU 7188]; 490 [RU 7107]; 497 [RU 7092]; 509 [RU 7065]; 515 [RU 7083]; 528 [RU 7253]; 530 [RU 7246]; 538 [RU 7250]; 540 [RU 7078]; 547 [RU 7076]; 547 [RU 7167]; 547 [RU 7211]; 554 [RU 7136]; 555 [RU 1020012]; 563 [RU 7249]; 570 [RU 7132]; 572 [RU 7263]; 573 [RU 7077]; 575 [RU 7379]; 584 [RU 7301]; 585 [RU 7181]; 587 [RU 7186]; 601 [RU 7112]

Graphic illustrations: landscape, 450 [RU 7369]; 566 [RU 7371]

Graphic illustrations: minerals and rocks, 377 [RU 7004]; 440 [RU 1050101]; 505 [RU 7251]; 604 [RU 7238]

Graphic illustrations: portraits, 286 [RU 289]; 597 [RU 7321]

Graphic illustrations: special events, 22 [RU 477]; 359 [RU 594]

Graphic illustrations: specimens, 80 [RU 7220]; 82 [RU 7217]; 85 [RU 7445]; 95 [RU 7218]; 95 [RU 7461]; 102 [RU 7422]; 123 [RU 7264]; 414 [RU 7310]; 425 [RU 7338]; 441 [RU 7073]; 454 [RU 7350]; 460 [RU 7314]; 465 [RU 7324]; 488 [RU 7454]; 490 [RU 7107]; 493 [RU 7380]; 519 [RU 7265]; 575 [RU 7379]; 575 [RU 7441]

Motion picture film footage, 22 [RU 281]; 151 [RU 397]; 180 [RU 360]; 195 [RU 395]; 252 [RU 255]; 361 [RU 587]; 378 [RU 7006]; 446 [RU 7137]; 471 [RU 7307]; 479 [RU 7464]; 512 [RU 7293]; 534 [RU 7306]; 557 [RU 7231]; 559 [RU 7429]; 566 [RU 7316]; 654 [RU 9544]

Paintings, 408 [RU 7052]; 440 [RU 1050101]; 443 [RU 7439]; 448 [RU 7468]; 451 [RU 7348]; 460 [RU 7312]; 500 [RU 7434]

Photographs, 7 [RU 31]; 89 [RU 307]; 100 [RU 1020003]; 112 [RU 229]; 197 [RU 311]; 220 [RU 316]; 252 [RU 255]; 266 [RU 286]; 281 [RU 267]; 288 [RU 287]; 312 [RU 273]; 324 [RU 83]; 376 [RU 7003]; 382 [RU 7117]; 385 [RU 7298]; 387 [RU 7150]; 392 [RU 1050103]; 395 [RU 7294]; 397 [RU 7267]; 398 [RU 7110]; 402 [RU 7089]; 407 [RU 7120]; 416 [RU 7259]; 417 [RU 7140]; 417 [RU 7189]; 419 [RU 7279]; 431 [RU 7153]; 432 [RU 7151]; 433 [RU 7244]; 441 [RU 7073]; 446 [RU 7137]; 449 [RU 7415]; 465 [RU 7187]; 468 [RU 7050]; 481 [RU 7075]; 487 [RU 7084]; 499 [RU 7170]; 505 [RU 7108]; 515 [RU 7083]; 534 [RU 7175]; 536 [RU 7079]; 537 [RU 7252]; 539 [RU 7256]; 540 [RU 7078]; 544 [RU 7232]; 546 [RU 7374]; 562 [RU 7091]; 572 [RU 7263]; 585 [RU 7181]; 585 [RU 7192]; 592 [RU 1050102]; 593 [RU 7239]; 594 [RU 7163]; 596 [RU 7247]; 597 [RU 7099]; 598 [RU 1020005]; 610 [RU 7174]

Photographs: architectural, 22 [RU 281]; 22 [RU 477]; 31 [RU 254]; 50 [RU 79]; 123 [RU 7264]; 135 [RU 276]; 139 [RU 285]; 149 [RU 297]; 176 [RU 359]; 224 [RU 379]; 253 [RU 262]; 256 [RU 478]; 264 [RU 4010003]; 317 [RU 157]; 318 [RU 532]; 319 [RU 639]; 324 [RU 638]; 324 [RU 640]; 329 [RU 637]; 330 [RU 641]; 343 [RU 549]; 369 [RU 95]; 370 [RU 92]; 423 [RU 7362]; 461 [RU 7471]; 474 [RU 7355]; 518 [RU 7336]; 518 [RU 7386]; 551 [RU 7447]; 583 [RU 7433]

Photographs: artifacts, 22 [RU 477]; 101 [RU 7448]; 138 [RU 583]; 147 [RU 383]; 148 [RU 250]; 151 [RU 397]; 155 [RU 396]; 159 [RU 332]; 161 [RU 528]; 165 [RU 331]; 171 [RU 485]; 184 [RU 581]; 262 [RU 4010001]; 267 [RU 412]; 271 [RU 469]; 272 [RU 481]; 273 [RU 516]; 285 [RU 506]; 287 [RU 531]; 290 [RU 284]; 293 [RU 541]; 293 [RU 542]; 321 [RU 576]; 343 [RU 371]; 369 [RU 95]; 370 [RU 92]; 408 [RU 7052]; 435 [RU 7437]; 463 [RU 7416]; 470 [RU 7148]; 551 [RU 7447]; 590 [RU 7055]; 598 [RU 7322]

Photographs: cityscape, 262 [RU 4010001]; 369 [RU 95]; 370 [RU 92]; 583 [RU 7433]

Photographs: exhibitions and installations, 22 [RU 281]; 22 [RU 477]; 65 [RU 363]; 65 [RU 366]; 67 [RU 416]; 94 [RU 7418]; 122 [RU 424]; 123 [RU 7264]; 135 [RU 276]; 137 [RU 278]; 138 [RU 583]; 139 [RU 285]; 147 [RU 383]; 148 [RU 250]; 149 [RU 297]; 152 [RU 206]; 153 [RU 413]; 155 [RU 396]; 155 [RU 471]; 158 [RU 293]; 159 [RU 332]; 166 [RU 406]; 171 [RU 485]; 176 [RU 359]; 177 [RU 580]; 179 [RU 551]; 180 [RU 360]; 181 [RU 584]; 182 [RU 595]; 198 [RU 312]; 206 [RU 315]; 208 [RU 465]; 211 [RU 314]; 211 [RU 449]; 213 [RU 451]; 217 [RU 321]; 223 [RU 426]; 224 [RU 379]; 226 [RU 552]; 227 [RU 361]; 228 [RU 554]; 243 [RU 409]; 264 [RU 4010004]; 270 [RU 510]; 271 [RU 469]; 272 [RU 481]; 273 [RU 514]; 273 [RU 516]; 275 [RU 515]; 281 [RU 492]; 286 [RU 289]; 287 [RU 280]; 287 [RU 531]; 293 [RU 541]; 304 [RU 401]; 305 [RU 402]; 306 [RU 403]; 326 [RU 503]; 327 [RU 70]; 327 [RU 90]; 338 [RU 574]; 343 [RU 371]; 343 [RU 549]; 349 [RU 290]; 350 [RU 489]; 351 [RU 487]; 369 [RU 95]; 370 [RU 92]; 443 [RU 7439]; 518 [RU 7386]; 583 [RU 7433]

Photographs: fine and decorative arts, 198 [RU 312]; 211 [RU 5000102]; 217 [RU 321]; 227 [RU 361]; 270 [RU 510]; 304 [RU 401]

Photographs: flora and fauna, 85 [RU 7445]; 101 [RU 7448]; 110 [RU 227]; 369 [RU 95]; 370 [RU 92]; 397 [RU 7417]; 474 [RU 7355]; 478 [RU 7188]; 490 [RU 7405]; 496 [RU 7172]; 532 [RU 7455]; 549 [RU 7287]; 565 [RU 7082]; 574 [RU 7074]; 575 [RU 7441]; 580 [RU 7323]

Photographs: landscapes, 76 [RU 245]; 101 [RU 7448]; 123 [RU 7264]; 369 [RU 95]; 370 [RU 92]; 436 [RU 7318]; 460 [RU 7314]; 471 [RU 7307]; 474 [RU 7355]; 477 [RU 7243]; 518 [RU 7336]; 518 [RU 7386]; 528 [RU 7460]; 532 [RU 7455]; 549 [RU 7287]; 580 [RU 7323]; 606 [RU 7235]

Photographs: minerals and rocks, 369 [RU 95]; 370 [RU 92]; 436 [RU 7318]; 528 [RU 7460]; 538 [RU 7240]

Photographs: portraits, 22 [RU 477]; 31 [RU 254]; 67 [RU 416]; 68 [RU 429]; 81 [RU 208]; 82 [RU 7320]; 94 [RU 7418]; 100 [RU 7401]; 101 [RU 7427]; 119 [RU 7230]; 120 [RU 7421]; 124 [RU 543]; 138 [RU 583]; 147 [RU 383]; 149 [RU 376]; 156 [RU 529]; 159 [RU 332]; 171 [RU 485]; 180 [RU 360]; 182 [RU 595]; 227 [RU 361]; 256 [RU 478]; 262 [RU 4010001]; 264 [RU 4010004]; 267

[RU 412]; 268 [RU 399]; 273 [RU 514]; 273 [RU 516]; 275 [RU 515]; 304 [RU 134]; 304 [RU 401]; 305 [RU 402]; 321 [RU 576]; 336 [RU 629]; 340 [RU 420]; 343 [RU 371]; 343 [RU 549]; 352 [RU 310]; 362 [RU 593]; 369 [RU 95]; 370 [RU 92]; 374 [RU 7000]; 377 [RU 7004]; 378 [RU 7006]; 380 [RU 7008]; 386 [RU 7261]; 387 [RU 7440]; 389 [RU 7357]; 390 [RU 7351]; 391 [RU 7334]; 397 [RU 7417]; 403 [RU 7234]; 414 [RU 7310]; 423 [RU 7362]; 423 [RU 7452]; 426 [RU 7315]; 430 [RU 7080]; 435 [RU 7437]; 436 [RU 7318]; 440 [RU 1050101]; 443 [RU 7439]; 445 [RU 7465]; 451 [RU 7348]; 460 [RU 7314]; 463 [RU 7416]; 470 [RU 7148]; 476 [RU 7436]; 480 [RU 7179]; 481 [RU 7349]; 484 [RU 7449]; 494 [RU 7141]; 495 [RU 7109]; 497 [RU 7333]; 500 [RU 7434]; 504 [RU 7466]; 508 [RU 7396]; 512 [RU 7293]; 516 [RU 7182]; 517 [RU 7177]; 521 [RU 7303]; 521 [RU 7467]; 526 [RU 7364]; 534 [RU 7306]; 547 [RU 7167]; 550 [RU 7408]; 551 [RU 7447]; 557 [RU 7231]; 563 [RU 7288]; 570 [RU 7372]; 574 [RU 7074]; 580 [RU 7323]; 580 [RU 7426]; 583 [RU 7433]; 590 [RU 7055]; 597 [RU 7321]; 599 [RU 7268]

Photographs: special events, 22 [RU 477]; 31 [RU 254]; 67 [RU 416]; 67 [RU 566]; 82 [RU 7320]; 94 [RU 7418]; 137 [RU 278]; 137 [RU 279]; 138 [RU 583]; 139 [RU 285]; 180 [RU 360]; 182 [RU 595]; 184 [RU 581]; 217 [RU 321]; 228 [RU 554]; 237 [RU 351]; 242 [RU 340]; 243 [RU 409]; 256 [RU 478]; 264 [RU 4010004]; 267 [RU 412]; 270 [RU 510]; 273 [RU 516]; 277 [RU 349]; 277 [RU 350]; 281 [RU 492]; 304 [RU 134]; 305 [RU 402]; 315 [RU 494]; 317 [RU 157]; 332 [RU 495]; 336 [RU 629]; 337 [RU 631]; 338 [RU 630]; 340 [RU 368]; 343 [RU 371]; 343 [RU 410]; 343 [RU 549]; 352 [RU 310]; 352 [RU 507]; 354 [RU 626]; 355 [RU 632]; 357 [RU 496]; 357 [RU 500]; 359 [RU 594]; 362 [RU 593]; 369 [RU 95]; 370 [RU 92]; 374 [RU 7000]; 377 [RU 7004]; 378 [RU 7006]; 380 [RU 7008]; 391 [RU 7334]; 403 [RU 7234]; 435 [RU 7437]; 440 [RU 1050101]; 443 [RU 7439]; 445 [RU 7465]; 452 [RU 7428]; 463 [RU 7416]; 476 [RU 7436]; 477 [RU 7243]; 497 [RU 7333]; 500 [RU 7434]; 503 [RU 7375]; 508 [RU 7396]; 512 [RU 7293]; 517 [RU 7177]; 518 [RU 7336]; 526 [RU 7364]; 534 [RU 7306]; 551 [RU 7447]; 557 [RU 7231]; 561 [RU 7222]; 563 [RU 7288]; 569 [RU 7443]; 583 [RU 7433]

Photographs: specimens, 76 [RU 245]; 85 [RU 7445]; 89 [RU 7260]; 95 [RU 1030301]; 102 [RU 7422]; 122 [RU 424]; 123 [RU 7264]; 128 [RU NAA05]; 131 [RU NAA06]; 139 [RU 285]; 254 [RU 304]; 256 [RU 301]; 304 [RU 134]; 326 [RU 503]; 369 [RU 95]; 370 [RU 92]; 377 [RU 7004]; 378 [RU 7005]; 378 [RU 7006]; 386 [RU 7261]; 397 [RU 7417]; 412 [RU 7407]; 414 [RU 7310]; 424 [RU 7297]; 425 [RU 7338]; 435 [RU 7437]; 449 [RU 7411]; 451 [RU 7348]; 452 [RU 7428]; 453 [RU 7286]; 455 [RU 7463]; 457 [RU 7281]; 460 [RU 7314]; 465 [RU 7324]; 473 [RU 7370]; 475 [RU 1010006]; 479 [RU 7464]; 480 [RU 7179]; 491 [RU 7311]; 492 [RU 7248]; 497 [RU 7333]; 499 [RU 7241]; 500 [RU 7434]; 514

[RU 7236]; 517 [RU 7173]; 519 [RU 7265]; 526 [RU 7364]; 533 [RU 7284]; 534 [RU 7306]; 552 [RU 7413]; 557 [RU 7231]; 565 [RU 7082]; 566 [RU 7316]; 570 [RU 7132]; 570 [RU 7372]; 574 [RU 7074]; 575 [RU 7441]

Videotapes: flora and fauna, 195 [RU 395]

Videotapes: interviews, 214 [RU 455]; 629 [RU 9575]; 635 [RU 9569]; 643 [RU 9565]; 648 [RU 9534]; 648 [RU 9545]; 649 [RU 9553]; 650 [RU 9537]; 650 [RU 9549]; 651 [RU 9546]; 651 [RU 9554]; 652 [RU 9577]; 653 [RU 9531]; 653 [RU 9543]; 654 [RU 9544]; 655 [RU 9533]; 655 [RU 9542]; 656 [RU 9539]; 656 [RU 9550]; 657 [RU 9536]; 658 [RU 9552]; 658 [RU 9564]; 659 [RU 9530]; 659 [RU 9532]; 659 [RU 9551]; 660 [RU 9535]; 661 [RU 9547]; 661 [RU 9548]

Videotapes: special events, 180 [RU 360]; 181 [RU 584]; 195 [RU 395]; 228 [RU 554]; 244 [RU 520]; 306 [RU 403]; 338 [RU 625]; 357 [RU 496]; 358 [RU 499]; 380 [RU 7008]

Videotapes: specimens, 479 [RU 7464]

APPENDIX B

INDEX BY DISCIPLINE

This index contains references to manuscript collections, described in this Guide, that relate to the listed fields of study. A list of record units containing records of non-Smithsonian organizations is also included. Record units containing official Smithsonian records are not included in this index. References are to page number, followed by record unit number in brackets.

Aeronautics, 376 [RU 7003]; 377 [RU 7004]; 468 [RU 7090]; 540 [RU 7078]; 632 [RU 9578]; 636 [RU 9590]; 636 [RU 9591]; 648 [RU 9545]

African American history, 615 [RU 9561]; 626 [RU 9558]; 627 [RU 9574]; 628 [RU 9538]; 631 [RU 9540]; 632 [RU 9578]; 648 [RU 9545]

Agronomy, 630 [RU 9576]

Anthropology, 382 [RU 7117]; 408 [RU 7052]; 408 [RU 7194]; 457 [RU 7216]; 464 [RU 7209]; 470 [RU 7148]; 487 [RU 7084]; 513 [RU 7086]; 522 [RU 7203]; 541 [RU 7070]; 553 [RU 7221]; 572 [RU 7066]; 577 [RU 7191]; 585 [RU 7192]; 587 [RU 7186]; 618 [RU 9528]; 620 [RU 9571]; 622 [RU 9505]; 641 [RU 9521]; 644 [RU 9586]

Archaeology, 487 [RU 7084]; 598 [RU 7322]

Architecture, 540 [RU 7078]

Archives, 629 [RU 9575]

Art, 382 [RU 7116]; 443 [RU 7439]; 484 [RU 7449]; 487 [RU 7084]; 572 [RU 7066]; 583 [RU 7433]; 624 [RU 9506]; 624 [RU 9566]; 626 [RU 9558]; 635 [RU 9569]; 636 [RU 9591]

Asian archives, 629 [RU 9575]

Astrogeology, 449 [RU 7415]

Astronautics, 449 [RU 7415]; 659 [RU 9551]

Astronomy, 463 [RU 7416]; 646 [RU 9520]

Astronomy and astrophysics, 376 [RU 7003]; 378 [RU 7005]; 408 [RU 7052]; 426 [RU 7134]; 496 [RU 7282]; 602 [RU 7431]; 613 [RU 9556]; 624 [RU 9529]; 648

[RU 9534]; 651 [RU 9546]; 653 [RU 9543]; 655 [RU 9542]; 656 [RU 9539]; 660 [RU 9535]

Astrophysics, 449 [RU 7415]; 455 [RU 7463]; 463 [RU 7416]; 471 [RU 7307]; 612 [RU 9500]; 646 [RU 9520]

Biography, 100 [RU 1020002]; 119 [RU 7230]; 369 [RU 7098]; 385 [RU 7298]; 407 [RU 7085]; 434 [RU 7292]; 444 [RU 7158]; 533 [RU 7208]; 544 [RU 7081]; 557 [RU 7231]; 580 [RU 7323]; 599 [RU 7268]

Biology, 650 [RU 9549]; 651 [RU 9554]; 652 [RU 9577]; 654 [RU 9544]; 658 [RU 9564]; 659 [RU 9551]

Botany, 317 [RU 7269]; 399 [RU 7113]; 404 [RU 7271]; 408 [RU 7052]; 415 [RU 7430]; 416 [RU 7259]; 417 [RU 7140]; 417 [RU 7189]; 434 [RU 7292]; 435 [RU 7437]; 439 [RU 7272]; 439 [RU 7356]; 444 [RU 7097]; 452 [RU 7096]; 453 [RU 7286]; 453 [RU 7446]; 457 [RU 7216]; 460 [RU 7312]; 462 [RU 7290]; 473 [RU 7155]; 473 [RU 7370]; 475 [RU 1010006]; 490 [RU 7107]; 503 [RU 7273]; 503 [RU 7375]; 506 [RU 7274]; 507 [RU 7157]; 507 [RU 7435]; 510 [RU 7223]; 521 [RU 7303]; 529 [RU 7088]; 532 [RU 7442]; 538 [RU 7250]; 549 [RU 7287]; 554 [RU 7275]; 565 [RU 7082]; 568 [RU 7276]; 573 [RU 7277]; 584 [RU 7278]; 587 [RU 7186]; 588 [RU 7176]; 591 [RU 7087]; 595 [RU 7270]; 606 [RU 7285]; 614 [RU 9563]; 619 [RU 9501]; 623 [RU 9572]; 643 [RU 9565]; 649 [RU 9553]

Chemistry, 430 [RU 7080]; 457 [RU 7216]; 521 [RU 7467]; 624 [RU 9529]

Communications, 617 [RU 9541]

Conservation, 377 [RU 7004]; 378 [RU 7006]; 380 [RU 7008]; 395 [RU 7294]; 619 [RU 9570]; 625 [RU 9525]; 630 [RU 9507]; 630 [RU 9576]; 633 [RU 9568]; 636 [RU 9591]; 637 [RU 9581]; 640 [RU 9580]; 641 [RU 9585]; 643 [RU 9565]; 649 [RU 9553]

Cultural history, 598 [RU 7322]

Ecology, 391 [RU 7334]; 417 [RU 7140]; 419 [RU 7279]; 428 [RU 7451]; 588 [RU 7176]; 623 [RU 9572]; 641 [RU 9585]; 643 [RU 9565]; 649 [RU 9553]

Education, 619 [RU 9570]; 626 [RU 9558]; 641 [RU 9585]

Electricity, 374 [RU 7001]; 402 [RU 7214]

Engineering, 656 [RU 9550]; 658 [RU 9552]; 659 [RU 9532]

Entomology, 99 [RU 1020001]; 100 [RU 1020002]; 100 [RU 1020003]; 384 [RU 7305]; 385 [RU 7298]; 394 [RU 7139]; 399 [RU 7113]; 399 [RU 7121]; 400 [RU 7103]; 400 [RU 1020006]; 405 [RU 7105]; 406 [RU 7128]; 408 [RU 7302]; 414

[RU 7156]; 414 [RU 7310]; 416 [RU 7119]; 419 [RU 7361]; 422 [RU 7129]; 423 [RU 7452]; 424 [RU 7297]; 426 [RU 7134]; 427 [RU 7162]; 429 [RU 7131]; 432 [RU 1020008]; 434 [RU 7106]; 436 [RU 7255]; 438 [RU 7164]; 440 [RU 7114]; 445 [RU 7195]; 446 [RU 7137]; 446 [RU 7457]; 447 [RU 7101]; 448 [RU 7468]; 451 [RU 7102]; 453 [RU 7286]; 455 [RU 7124]; 456 [RU 7130]; 459 [RU 1020009]; 461 [RU 7341]; 464 [RU 7122]; 467 [RU 7126]; 469 [RU 7359]; 472 [RU 7354]; 475 [RU 7300]; 476 [RU 7436]; 480 [RU 7125]; 483 [RU 7343]; 488 [RU 7454]; 490 [RU 7107]; 491 [RU 7311]; 494 [RU 7458]; 496 [RU 7172]; 497 [RU 7409]; 505 [RU 7108]; 506 [RU 7352]; 512 [RU 7293]; 514 [RU 7236]; 516 [RU 1020010]; 519 [RU 7345]; 528 [RU 7346]; 533 [RU 1020004]; 546 [RU 7374]; 547 [RU 7076]; 554 [RU 7136]; 555 [RU 7456]; 555 [RU 1020012]; 556 [RU 7100]; 561 [RU 7104]; 563 [RU 7249]; 564 [RU 7296]; 566 [RU 7316]; 567 [RU 7414]; 570 [RU 7132]; 570 [RU 7372]; 570 [RU 7419]; 575 [RU 7379]; 577 [RU 7340]; 577 [RU 1020011]; 579 [RU 7309]; 580 [RU 7323]; 580 [RU 7426]; 586 [RU 7424]; 596 [RU 7123]; 598 [RU 1020005]; 600 [RU 7127]; 600 [RU 7400]; 601 [RU 7112]; 607 [RU 7412]; 611 [RU 7462]; 615 [RU 9517]; 618 [RU 9555]; 619 [RU 9570]; 622 [RU 9559]; 628 [RU 9513]; 638 [RU 9583]; 640 [RU 9584]; 645 [RU 9560]; 647 [RU 9523]

Fisheries, 418 [RU 7193]; 421 [RU 7438]; 452 [RU 7428]

Folklife studies, 635 [RU 9569]; 636 [RU 9591]

Geography, 408 [RU 7052]; 453 [RU 7446]

Geology, 119 [RU 7230]; 120 [RU 7291]; 377 [RU 7004]; 392 [RU 1050103]; 403 [RU 7234]; 430 [RU 7080]; 436 [RU 7318]; 440 [RU 7197]; 440 [RU 1050101]; 452 [RU 7198]; 456 [RU 7242]; 457 [RU 7216]; 457 [RU 7281]; 479 [RU 7464]; 481 [RU 7349]; 487 [RU 7084]; 493 [RU 7205]; 501 [RU 7202]; 503 [RU 7245]; 505 [RU 7251]; 508 [RU 7396]; 517 [RU 7177]; 528 [RU 7460]; 538 [RU 7240]; 540 [RU 7078]; 542 [RU 7326]; 542 [RU 7393]; 544 [RU 7232]; 565 [RU 7082]; 584 [RU 7301]; 587 [RU 7186]; 592 [RU 1050102]; 604 [RU 7238]; 619 [RU 9524]; 623 [RU 9572]; 624 [RU 9529]; 644 [RU 9587]; 647 [RU 9557]; 659 [RU 9530]

Herpetology, 389 [RU 7149]; 432 [RU 7151]; 466 [RU 7190]; 468 [RU 7388]; 473 [RU 7389]; 534 [RU 7175]; 574 [RU 7074]; 575 [RU 7441]; 577 [RU 7191]; 594 [RU 7163]; 610 [RU 7166]; 633 [RU 9579]; 649 [RU 9553]

History, 387 [RU 7057]; 408 [RU 7052]; 427 [RU 7228]; 504 [RU 7466]; 544 [RU 7081]; 583 [RU 7433]; 613 [RU 9522]; 626 [RU 9558]; 628 [RU 9538]; 629 [RU 9575]; 631 [RU 9516]; 631 [RU 9540]; 632 [RU 9589]; 644 [RU 9586]

History of science and technology, 396 [RU 7068]; 402 [RU 7214]; 418 [RU 7193]; 427 [RU 7228]; 476 [RU 7475]; 503 [RU 7245]; 521 [RU 7467]; 543 [RU 7470]; 550 [RU 7390]; 556 [RU 7056]; 590 [RU 7055]; 599 [RU 7268]; 600 [RU 7159];

629 [RU 9502]; 632 [RU 9578]; 634 [RU 9503]; 639 [RU 9588]; 642 [RU 9512]; 644 [RU 9586]; 648 [RU 9534]; 648 [RU 9545]; 650 [RU 9537]; 650 [RU 9549]; 651 [RU 9546]; 651 [RU 9554]; 652 [RU 9577]; 653 [RU 9531]; 653 [RU 9543]; 654 [RU 9544]; 655 [RU 9533]; 655 [RU 9542]; 656 [RU 9539]; 656 [RU 9550]; 657 [RU 9536]; 658 [RU 9552]; 658 [RU 9564]; 659 [RU 9532]; 659 [RU 9551]; 660 [RU 9535]; 661 [RU 9547]; 661 [RU 9548]

Ichthyology, 375 [RU 7002]; 389 [RU 7149]; 404 [RU 7224]; 420 [RU 7184]; 421 [RU 7438]; 427 [RU 7258]; 447 [RU 7196]; 452 [RU 7428]; 458 [RU 7180]; 465 [RU 7187]; 466 [RU 7190]; 468 [RU 7050]; 510 [RU 7223]; 522 [RU 7203]; 527 [RU 7200]; 529 [RU 7387]; 538 [RU 7250]; 540 [RU 7078]; 554 [RU 7154]; 561 [RU 7222]; 567 [RU 7206]; 587 [RU 7186]; 637 [RU 9582]; 638 [RU 9510]

Invertebrate zoology, 89 [RU 7260]; 94 [RU 7418]; 95 [RU 7461]; 402 [RU 7089]; 420 [RU 7184]; 429 [RU 7183]; 441 [RU 7073]; 467 [RU 7257]; 477 [RU 7237]; 486 [RU 7469]; 492 [RU 7248]; 497 [RU 7092]; 497 [RU 7333]; 501 [RU 7383]; 509 [RU 7065]; 512 [RU 7254]; 519 [RU 7265]; 522 [RU 7266]; 528 [RU 7253]; 529 [RU 7088]; 530 [RU 7246]; 539 [RU 7256]; 540 [RU 7078]; 557 [RU 7231]; 565 [RU 7082]; 568 [RU 7262]; 573 [RU 7077]; 575 [RU 7379]; 576 [RU 7093]; 584 [RU 7301]; 587 [RU 7186]; 592 [RU 1050102]; 593 [RU 7239]; 606 [RU 7235]; 617 [RU 9514]; 625 [RU 9509]; 626 [RU 9573]; 627 [RU 9527]; 649 [RU 9553]

Latin American history, 615 [RU 9561]; 637 [RU 9581]

Libraries, 639 [RU 9588]

Lunar geophysics, 449 [RU 7415]

Malacology, 94 [RU 7418]; 497 [RU 7333]; 627 [RU 9527]; 634 [RU 9519]

Mammalogy, 389 [RU 7357]; 393 [RU 7143]; 397 [RU 7267]; 411 [RU 7171]; 412 [RU 1070201]; 413 [RU 7146]; 419 [RU 7279]; 420 [RU 7168]; 438 [RU 7344]; 476 [RU 7144]; 487 [RU 7392]; 489 [RU 7169]; 495 [RU 7165]; 496 [RU 7172]; 499 [RU 7170]; 500 [RU 7434]; 515 [RU 7083]; 517 [RU 7173]; 522 [RU 7203]; 526 [RU 7364]; 537 [RU 7252]; 563 [RU 7288]; 574 [RU 7074]; 577 [RU 7191]; 585 [RU 7181]; 588 [RU 7176]; 588 [RU 7229]; 596 [RU 7161]; 610 [RU 7174]; 621 [RU 9518]; 621 [RU 9562]; 631 [RU 9516]; 641 [RU 9585]; 649 [RU 9553]

Mathematics, 396 [RU 7068]

Medicine, 651 [RU 9554]; 654 [RU 9544]; 658 [RU 9564]; 659 [RU 9551]

Meteoritics, 624 [RU 9529]; 646 [RU 9520]

Meteorology, 374 [RU 7001]; 397 [RU 7053]; 408 [RU 7052]; 431 [RU 7153]; 433 [RU 7060]; 438 [RU 7289]; 453 [RU 7446]; 527 [RU 7200]; 598 [RU 1020005]

Military history, 632 [RU 9578]; 632 [RU 9589]; 648 [RU 9545]; 653 [RU 9531]; 657 [RU 9536]; 659 [RU 9532]

Mineralogy, 120 [RU 7291]; 386 [RU 7261]; 430 [RU 7080]; 431 [RU 7095]; 457 [RU 7281]; 507 [RU 1040101]; 533 [RU 7284]; 549 [RU 7152]; 564 [RU 7283]; 591 [RU 7063]; 624 [RU 9529]

Museology, 380 [RU 7008]; 513 [RU 7086]; 523 [RU 7295]; 540 [RU 7078]; 585 [RU 7181]; 598 [RU 7322]; 613 [RU 9522]; 622 [RU 9505]; 625 [RU 9525]; 631 [RU 9516]; 636 [RU 9591]; 642 [RU 9512]; 643 [RU 9565]; 644 [RU 9587]; 647 [RU 9523]

Music, 635 [RU 9569]

Natural history, 36 [RU 561]; 375 [RU 7002]; 380 [RU 7008]; 382 [RU 7117]; 390 [RU 7351]; 397 [RU 7267]; 408 [RU 7052]; 433 [RU 7244]; 437 [RU 7067]; 441 [RU 7073]; 453 [RU 7446]; 457 [RU 7216]; 464 [RU 7209]; 466 [RU 7190]; 470 [RU 7148]; 476 [RU 7204]; 477 [RU 7243]; 480 [RU 7179]; 496 [RU 7172]; 499 [RU 7241]; 501 [RU 7202]; 502 [RU 7072]; 507 [RU 7435]; 510 [RU 7420]; 511 [RU 7207]; 515 [RU 7083]; 517 [RU 7177]; 522 [RU 7203]; 525 [RU 7058]; 528 [RU 7253]; 529 [RU 7088]; 532 [RU 7455]; 535 [RU 7054]; 536 [RU 7210]; 538 [RU 7250]; 541 [RU 7178]; 553 [RU 7221]; 572 [RU 7263]; 574 [RU 7074]; 576 [RU 7093]; 577 [RU 7191]; 585 [RU 7192]; 587 [RU 7186]; 594 [RU 7163]; 598 [RU 1020005]; 601 [RU 7213]; 620 [RU 9571]; 636 [RU 9591]

Numismatics, 13 [RU 341]

Oceanography, 479 [RU 7464]; 592 [RU 1050102]; 606 [RU 7235]; 614 [RU 9526]; 626 [RU 9573]

Ornithology, 375 [RU 7002]; 378 [RU 7006]; 382 [RU 7116]; 387 [RU 7150]; 387 [RU 7440]; 395 [RU 7294]; 397 [RU 7417]; 398 [RU 7110]; 402 [RU 7089]; 407 [RU 7120]; 411 [RU 7171]; 413 [RU 1070101]; 415 [RU 7071]; 424 [RU 7297]; 437 [RU 7067]; 438 [RU 7344]; 443 [RU 1060105]; 445 [RU 7465]; 448 [RU 7280]; 448 [RU 7342]; 453 [RU 7402]; 459 [RU 7319]; 468 [RU 7388]; 474 [RU 7199]; 489 [RU 7169]; 490 [RU 7405]; 496 [RU 7172]; 515 [RU 7083]; 526 [RU 7364]; 537 [RU 7111]; 537 [RU 7252]; 545 [RU 7382]; 547 [RU 7167]; 547 [RU 7211]; 548 [RU 7118]; 574 [RU 7074]; 588 [RU 7176]; 590 [RU 7133]; 598 [RU 1020005]; 609 [RU 7212]; 612 [RU 9511]; 624 [RU 9506]; 636 [RU 9591]; 640 [RU 9584]; 645 [RU 9504]; 649 [RU 9553]

Paleontology, 377 [RU 7004]; 378 [RU 7006]; 392 [RU 1050103]; 403 [RU 7234]; 426 [RU 7134]; 436 [RU 7318]; 440 [RU 1050101]; 441 [RU 7073]; 446 [RU 7397]; 451 [RU 7348]; 456 [RU 7242]; 465 [RU 7324]; 466 [RU 7329]; 478 [RU 7188]; 478 [RU 7365]; 491 [RU 7398]; 493 [RU 7380]; 499 [RU 7170]; 500 [RU 7434]; 503 [RU 7245]; 505 [RU 7251]; 508 [RU 7396]; 509 [RU 7201]; 516 [RU

Women's history, 624 [RU 9566]; 639 [RU 9588]; 644 [RU 9587]; 648 [RU 9545]; 651 [RU 9546]; 653 [RU 9531]; 659 [RU 9551]

Zoological parks, 435 [RU 7225]; 480 [RU 7179]; 512 [RU 7293]; 628 [RU 9513]; 633 [RU 9568]; 649 [RU 9553]

Zoology, 390 [RU 7351]; 391 [RU 7334]; 402 [RU 7089]; 408 [RU 7052]; 410 [RU 7185]; 433 [RU 7244]; 449 [RU 7411]; 453 [RU 7446]; 454 [RU 7350]; 481 [RU 7075]; 512 [RU 7293]; 540 [RU 7078]; 550 [RU 7408]; 552 [RU 7413]; 557 [RU 7231]; 570 [RU 7132]; 576 [RU 7093]; 577 [RU 7138]; 596 [RU 7161]; 596 [RU 7247]; 614 [RU 9526]; 615 [RU 9517]; 615 [RU 9561]; 647 [RU 9523]; 649 [RU 9553]

APPENDIX C

DATE SPANS AND PAGE REFERENCES FOR SMITHSONIAN ARCHIVES RECORD UNITS

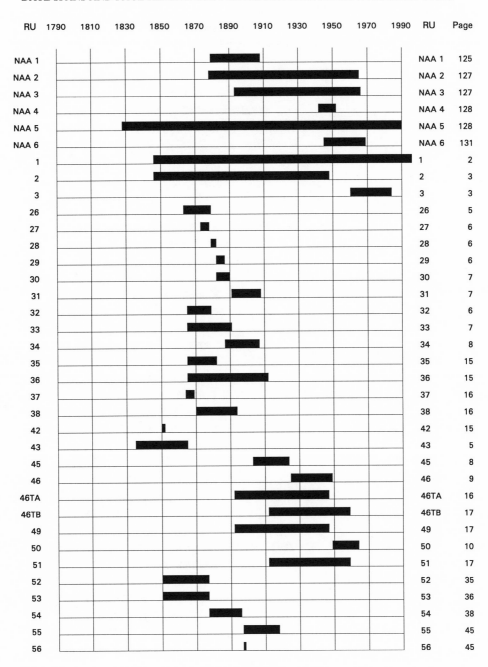

DATE SPANS AND PAGE REFERENCES FOR SMITHSONIAN ARCHIVES RECORD UNITS

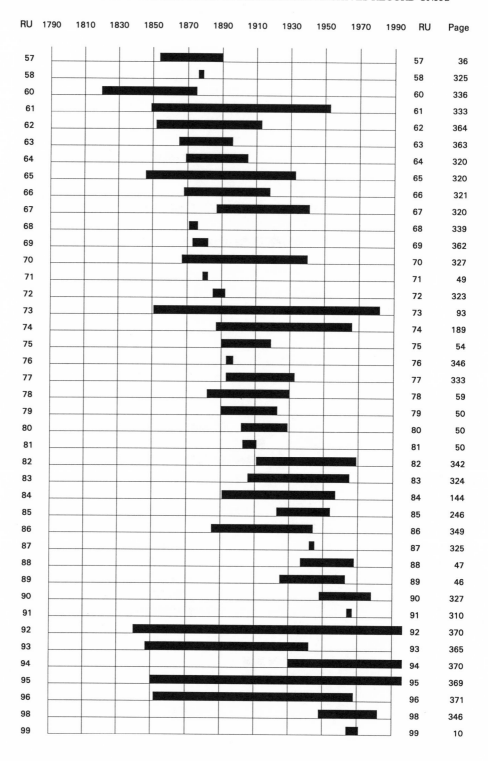

RU	1790	1810	1830	1850	1870	1890	1910	1930	1950	1970	1990	RU	Page
57												57	36
58												58	325
60												60	336
61												61	333
62												62	364
63												63	363
64												64	320
65												65	320
66												66	321
67												67	320
68												68	339
69												69	362
70												70	327
71												71	49
72												72	323
73												73	93
74												74	189
75												75	54
76												76	346
77												77	333
78												78	59
79												79	50
80												80	50
81												81	50
82												82	342
83												83	324
84												84	144
85												85	246
86												86	349
87												87	325
88												88	47
89												89	46
90												90	327
91												91	310
92												92	370
93												93	365
94												94	370
95												95	369
96												96	371
98												98	346
99												99	10

DATE SPANS AND PAGE REFERENCES FOR SMITHSONIAN ARCHIVES RECORD UNITS

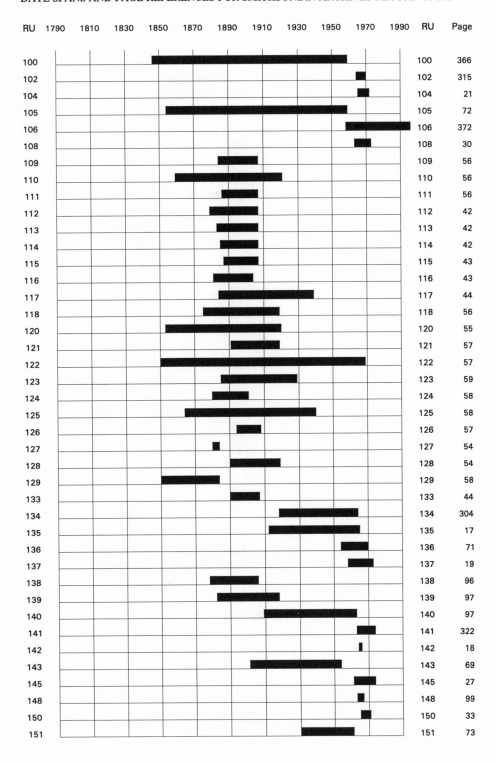

RU	1790	1810	1830	1850	1870	1890	1910	1930	1950	1970	1990	RU	Page
100												100	366
102												102	315
104												104	21
105												105	72
106												106	372
108												108	30
109												109	56
110												110	56
111												111	56
112												112	42
113												113	42
114												114	42
115												115	43
116												116	43
117												117	44
118												118	56
120												120	55
121												121	57
122												122	57
123												123	59
124												124	58
125												125	58
126												126	57
127												127	54
128												128	54
129												129	58
133												133	44
134												134	304
135												135	17
136												136	71
137												137	19
138												138	96
139												139	97
140												140	97
141												141	322
142												142	18
143												143	69
145												145	27
148												148	99
150												150	33
151												151	73

DATE SPANS AND PAGE REFERENCES FOR SMITHSONIAN ARCHIVES RECORD UNITS

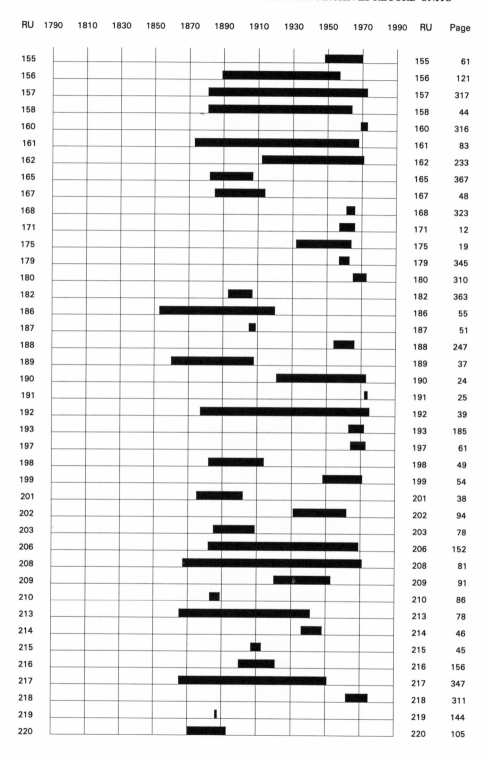

RU	Page
155	61
156	121
157	317
158	44
160	316
161	83
162	233
165	367
167	48
168	323
171	12
175	19
179	345
180	310
182	363
186	55
187	51
188	247
189	37
190	24
191	25
192	39
193	185
197	61
198	49
199	54
201	38
202	94
203	78
206	152
208	81
209	91
210	86
213	78
214	46
215	45
216	156
217	347
218	311
219	144
220	105

DATE SPANS AND PAGE REFERENCES FOR SMITHSONIAN ARCHIVES RECORD UNITS

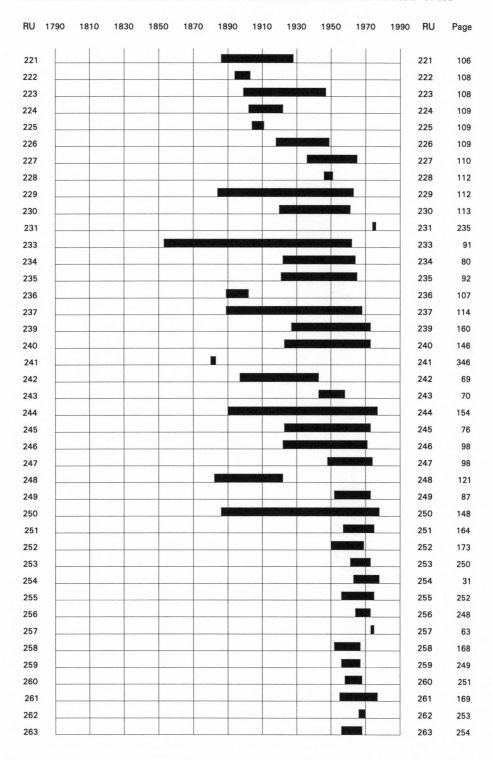

RU	1790	1810	1830	1850	1870	1890	1910	1930	1950	1970	1990	RU	Page
221												221	106
222												222	108
223												223	108
224												224	109
225												225	109
226												226	109
227												227	110
228												228	112
229												229	112
230												230	113
231												231	235
233												233	91
234												234	80
235												235	92
236												236	107
237												237	114
239												239	160
240												240	146
241												241	346
242												242	69
243												243	70
244												244	154
245												245	76
246												246	98
247												247	98
248												248	121
249												249	87
250												250	148
251												251	164
252												252	173
253												253	250
254												254	31
255												255	252
256												256	248
257												257	63
258												258	168
259												259	249
260												260	251
261												261	169
262												262	253
263												263	254

DATE SPANS AND PAGE REFERENCES FOR SMITHSONIAN ARCHIVES RECORD UNITS

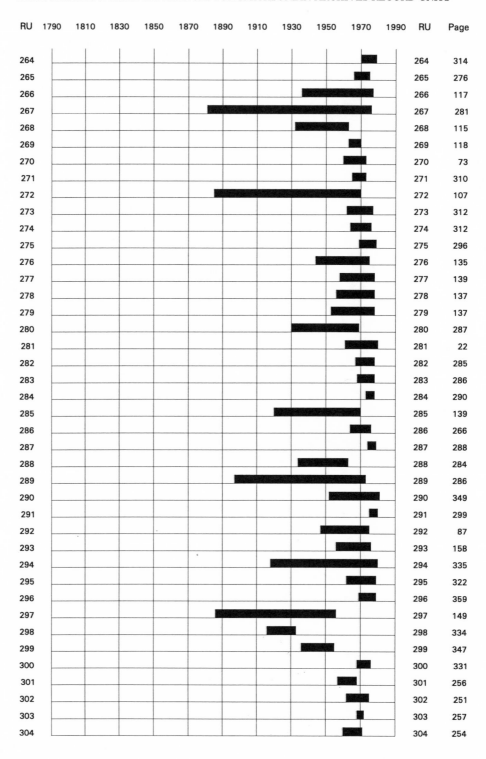

RU		Page
264		314
265		276
266		117
267		281
268		115
269		118
270		73
271		310
272		107
273		312
274		312
275		296
276		135
277		139
278		137
279		137
280		287
281		22
282		285
283		286
284		290
285		139
286		266
287		288
288		284
289		286
290		349
291		299
292		87
293		158
294		335
295		322
296		359
297		149
298		334
299		347
300		331
301		256
302		251
303		257
304		254

DATE SPANS AND PAGE REFERENCES FOR SMITHSONIAN ARCHIVES RECORD UNITS

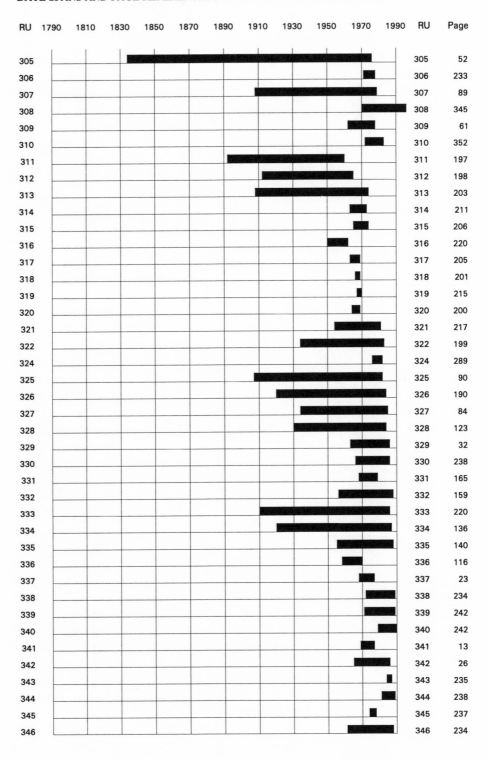

RU	1790	1810	1830	1850	1870	1890	1910	1930	1950	1970	1990	RU	Page
305												305	52
306												306	233
307												307	89
308												308	345
309												309	61
310												310	352
311												311	197
312												312	198
313												313	203
314												314	211
315												315	206
316												316	220
317												317	205
318												318	201
319												319	215
320												320	200
321												321	217
322												322	199
324												324	289
325												325	90
326												326	190
327												327	84
328												328	123
329												329	32
330												330	238
331												331	165
332												332	159
333												333	220
334												334	136
335												335	140
336												336	116
337												337	23
338												338	234
339												339	242
340												340	242
341												341	13
342												342	26
343												343	235
344												344	238
345												345	237
346												346	234

DATE SPANS AND PAGE REFERENCES FOR SMITHSONIAN ARCHIVES RECORD UNITS

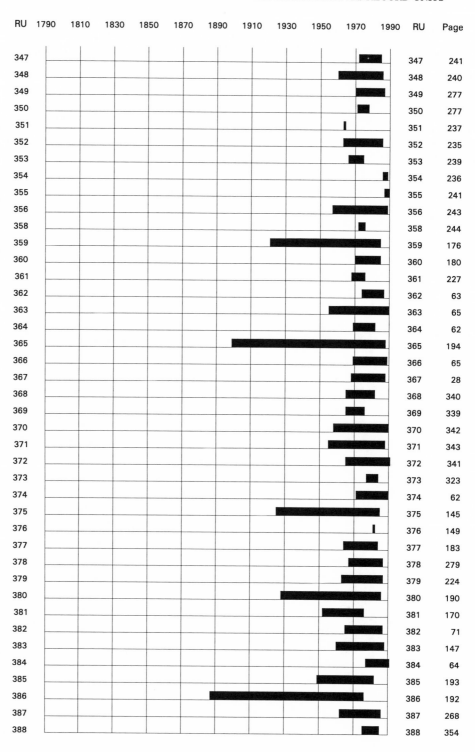

RU	1790	1810	1830	1850	1870	1890	1910	1930	1950	1970	1990	RU	Page
347												347	241
348												348	240
349												349	277
350												350	277
351												351	237
352												352	235
353												353	239
354												354	236
355												355	241
356												356	243
358												358	244
359												359	176
360												360	180
361												361	227
362												362	63
363												363	65
364												364	62
365												365	194
366												366	65
367												367	28
368												368	340
369												369	339
370												370	342
371												371	343
372												372	341
373												373	323
374												374	62
375												375	145
376												376	149
377												377	183
378												378	279
379												379	224
380												380	190
381												381	170
382												382	71
383												383	147
384												384	64
385												385	193
386												386	192
387												387	268
388												388	354

DATE SPANS AND PAGE REFERENCES FOR SMITHSONIAN ARCHIVES RECORD UNITS

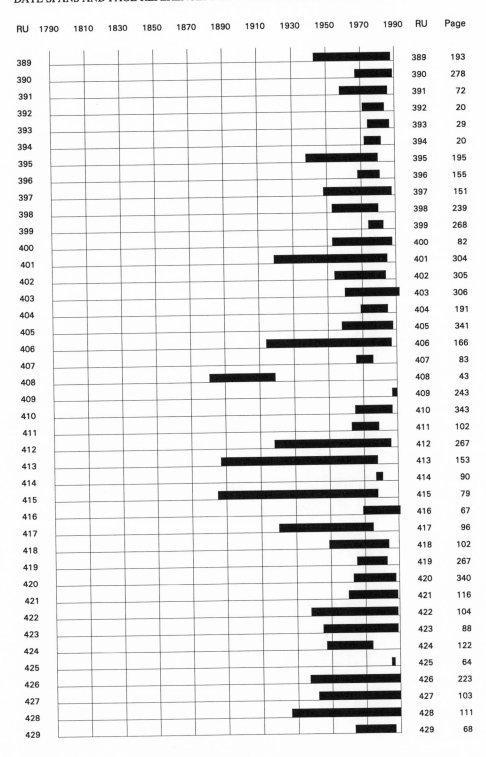

RU	Page
389	193
390	278
391	72
392	20
393	29
394	20
395	195
396	155
397	151
398	239
399	268
400	82
401	304
402	305
403	306
404	191
405	341
406	166
407	83
408	43
409	243
410	343
411	102
412	267
413	153
414	90
415	79
416	67
417	96
418	102
419	267
420	340
421	116
422	104
423	88
424	122
425	64
426	223
427	103
428	111
429	68

DATE SPANS AND PAGE REFERENCES FOR SMITHSONIAN ARCHIVES RECORD UNITS

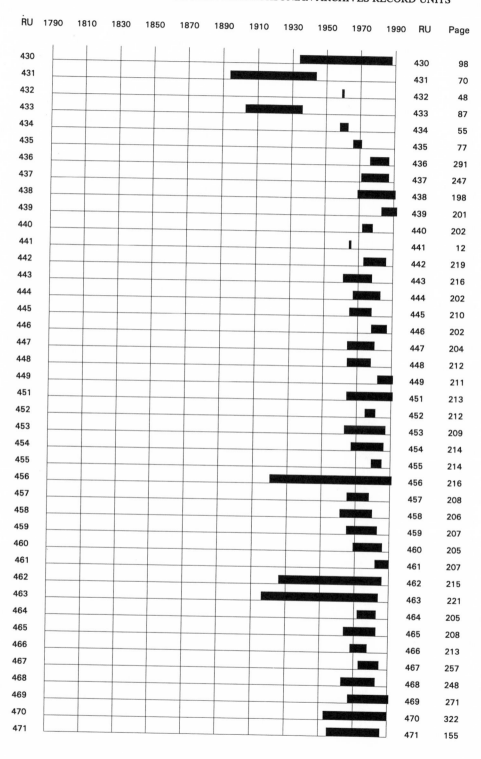

RU	1790	1810	1830	1850	1870	1890	1910	1930	1950	1970	1990	RU	Page
430												430	98
431												431	70
432												432	48
433												433	87
434												434	55
435												435	77
436												436	291
437												437	247
438												438	198
439												439	201
440												440	202
441												441	12
442												442	219
443												443	216
444												444	202
445												445	210
446												446	202
447												447	204
448												448	212
449												449	211
451												451	213
452												452	212
453												453	209
454												454	214
455												455	214
456												456	216
457												457	208
458												458	206
459												459	207
460												460	205
461												461	207
462												462	215
463												463	221
464												464	205
465												465	208
466												466	213
467												467	257
468												468	248
469												469	271
470												470	322
471												471	155

DATE SPANS AND PAGE REFERENCES FOR SMITHSONIAN ARCHIVES RECORD UNITS

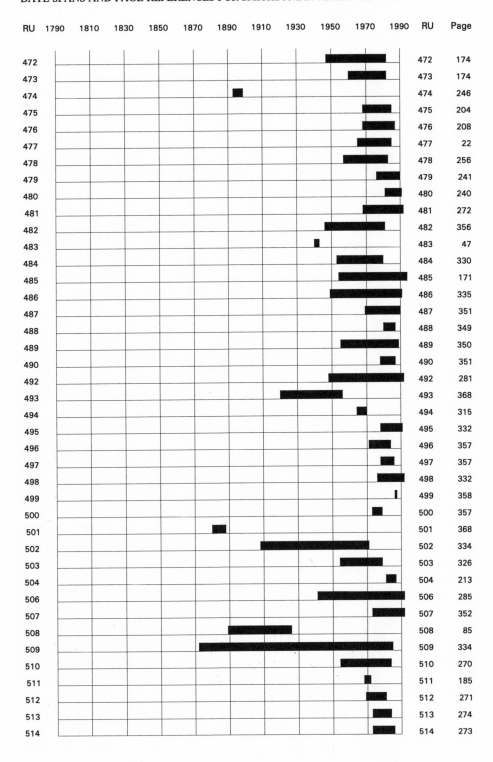

RU	1790	1810	1830	1850	1870	1890	1910	1930	1950	1970	1990	RU	Page
472												472	174
473												473	174
474												474	246
475												475	204
476												476	208
477												477	22
478												478	256
479												479	241
480												480	240
481												481	272
482												482	356
483												483	47
484												484	330
485												485	171
486												486	335
487												487	351
488												488	349
489												489	350
490												490	351
492												492	281
493												493	368
494												494	315
495												495	332
496												496	357
497												497	357
498												498	332
499												499	358
500												500	357
501												501	368
502												502	334
503												503	326
504												504	213
506												506	285
507												507	352
508												508	85
509												509	334
510												510	270
511												511	185
512												512	271
513												513	274
514												514	273

DATE SPANS AND PAGE REFERENCES FOR SMITHSONIAN ARCHIVES RECORD UNITS

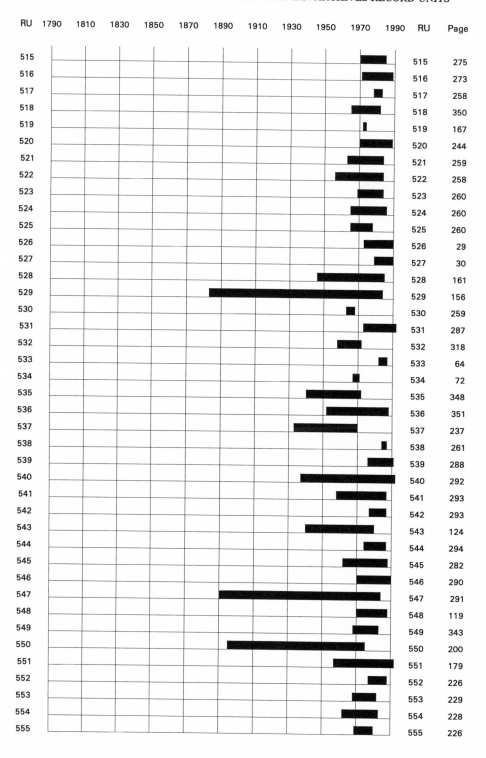

RU	Page
515	275
516	273
517	258
518	350
519	167
520	244
521	259
522	258
523	260
524	260
525	260
526	29
527	30
528	161
529	156
530	259
531	287
532	318
533	64
534	72
535	348
536	351
537	237
538	261
539	288
540	292
541	293
542	293
543	124
544	294
545	282
546	290
547	291
548	119
549	343
550	200
551	179
552	226
553	229
554	228
555	226

DATE SPANS AND PAGE REFERENCES FOR SMITHSONIAN ARCHIVES RECORD UNITS

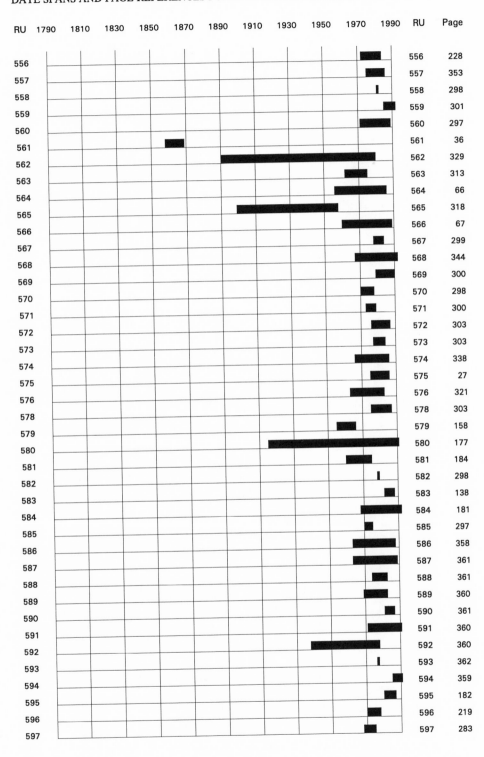

RU	Page
556	228
557	353
558	298
559	301
560	297
561	36
562	329
563	313
564	66
565	318
566	67
567	299
568	344
569	300
570	298
571	300
572	303
573	303
574	338
575	27
576	321
578	303
579	158
580	177
581	184
582	298
583	138
584	181
585	297
586	358
587	361
588	361
589	360
590	361
591	360
592	360
593	362
594	359
595	182
596	219
597	283

DATE SPANS AND PAGE REFERENCES FOR SMITHSONIAN ARCHIVES RECORD UNITS

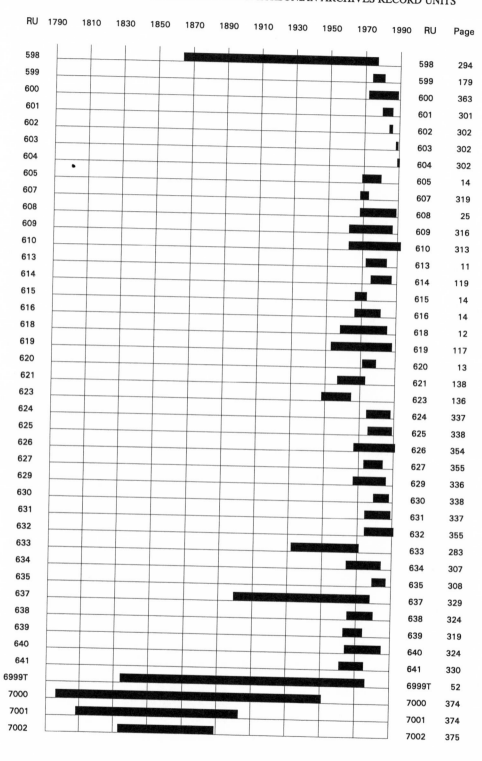

RU	1790	1810	1830	1850	1870	1890	1910	1930	1950	1970	1990	RU	Page
598												598	294
599												599	179
600												600	363
601												601	301
602												602	302
603												603	302
604												604	302
605												605	14
607												607	319
608												608	25
609												609	316
610												610	313
613												613	11
614												614	119
615												615	14
616												616	14
618												618	12
619												619	117
620												620	13
621												621	138
623												623	136
624												624	337
625												625	338
626												626	354
627												627	355
629												629	336
630												630	338
631												631	337
632												632	355
633												633	283
634												634	307
635												635	308
637												637	329
638												638	324
639												639	319
640												640	324
641												641	330
6999T												6999T	52
7000												7000	374
7001												7001	374
7002												7002	375

DATE SPANS AND PAGE REFERENCES FOR SMITHSONIAN ARCHIVES RECORD UNITS

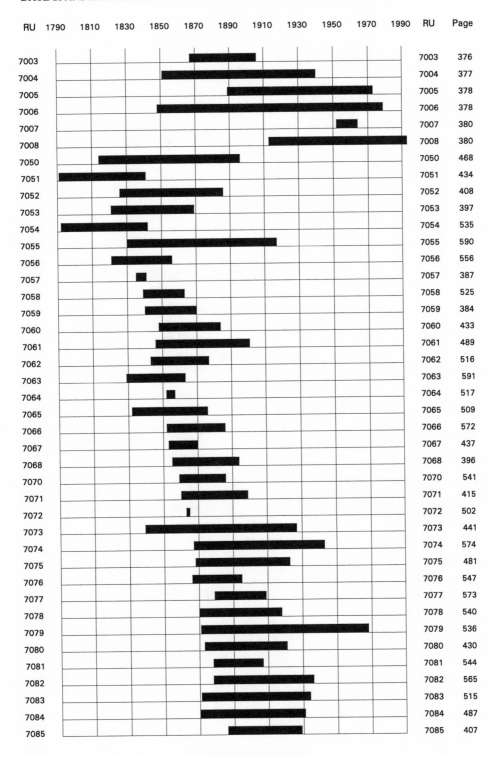

RU	Page
7003	376
7004	377
7005	378
7006	378
7007	380
7008	380
7050	468
7051	434
7052	408
7053	397
7054	535
7055	590
7056	556
7057	387
7058	525
7059	384
7060	433
7061	489
7062	516
7063	591
7064	517
7065	509
7066	572
7067	437
7068	396
7070	541
7071	415
7072	502
7073	441
7074	574
7075	481
7076	547
7077	573
7078	540
7079	536
7080	430
7081	544
7082	565
7083	515
7084	487
7085	407

DATE SPANS AND PAGE REFERENCES FOR SMITHSONIAN ARCHIVES RECORD UNITS

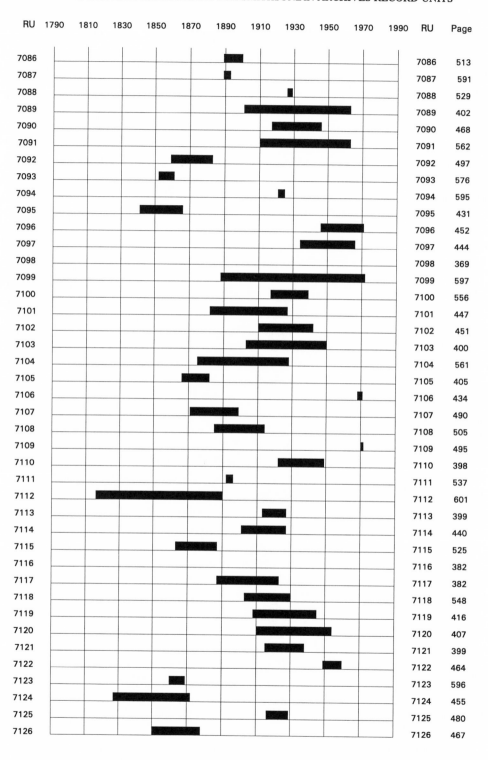

RU	Page
7086	513
7087	591
7088	529
7089	402
7090	468
7091	562
7092	497
7093	576
7094	595
7095	431
7096	452
7097	444
7098	369
7099	597
7100	556
7101	447
7102	451
7103	400
7104	561
7105	405
7106	434
7107	490
7108	505
7109	495
7110	398
7111	537
7112	601
7113	399
7114	440
7115	525
7116	382
7117	382
7118	548
7119	416
7120	407
7121	399
7122	464
7123	596
7124	455
7125	480
7126	467

DATE SPANS AND PAGE REFERENCES FOR SMITHSONIAN ARCHIVES RECORD UNITS

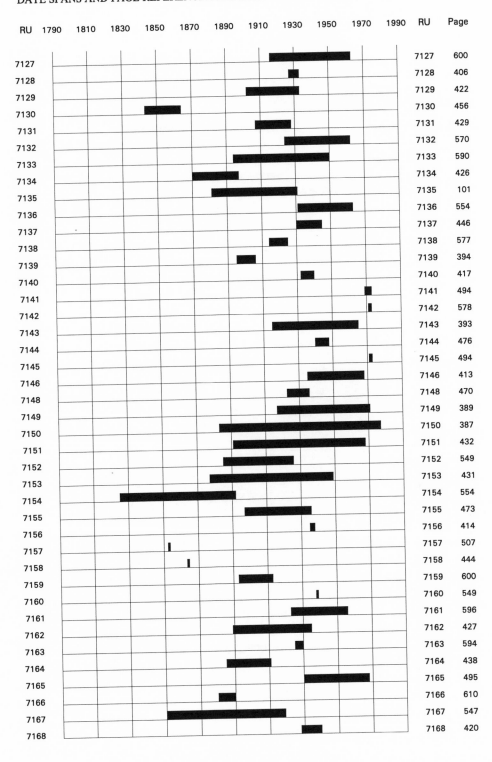

DATE SPANS AND PAGE REFERENCES FOR SMITHSONIAN ARCHIVES RECORD UNITS

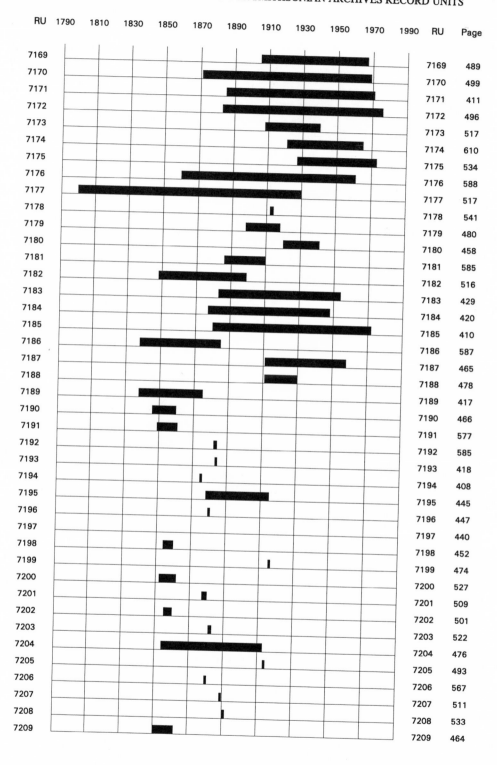

RU	Page
7169	489
7170	499
7171	411
7172	496
7173	517
7174	610
7175	534
7176	588
7177	517
7178	541
7179	480
7180	458
7181	585
7182	516
7183	429
7184	420
7185	410
7186	587
7187	465
7188	478
7189	417
7190	466
7191	577
7192	585
7193	418
7194	408
7195	445
7196	447
7197	440
7198	452
7199	474
7200	527
7201	509
7202	501
7203	522
7204	476
7205	493
7206	567
7207	511
7208	533
7209	464

DATE SPANS AND PAGE REFERENCES FOR SMITHSONIAN ARCHIVES RECORD UNITS

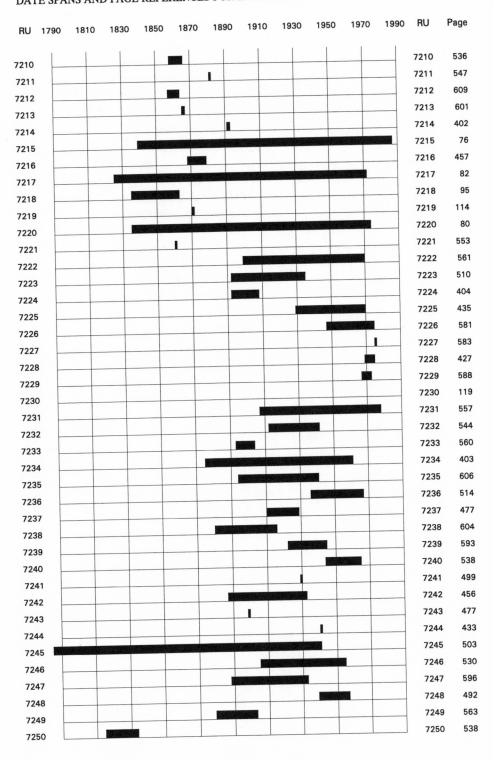

RU	Page
7210	536
7211	547
7212	609
7213	601
7214	402
7215	76
7216	457
7217	82
7218	95
7219	114
7220	80
7221	553
7222	561
7223	510
7224	404
7225	435
7226	581
7227	583
7228	427
7229	588
7230	119
7231	557
7232	544
7233	560
7234	403
7235	606
7236	514
7237	477
7238	604
7239	593
7240	538
7241	499
7242	456
7243	477
7244	433
7245	503
7246	530
7247	596
7248	492
7249	563
7250	538

DATE SPANS AND PAGE REFERENCES FOR SMITHSONIAN ARCHIVES RECORD UNITS

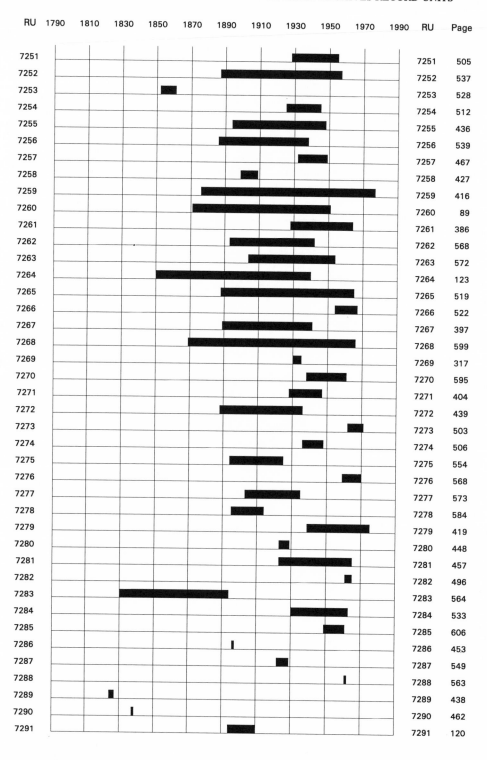

RU	Page
7251	505
7252	537
7253	528
7254	512
7255	436
7256	539
7257	467
7258	427
7259	416
7260	89
7261	386
7262	568
7263	572
7264	123
7265	519
7266	522
7267	397
7268	599
7269	317
7270	595
7271	404
7272	439
7273	503
7274	506
7275	554
7276	568
7277	573
7278	584
7279	419
7280	448
7281	457
7282	496
7283	564
7284	533
7285	606
7286	453
7287	549
7288	563
7289	438
7290	462
7291	120

DATE SPANS AND PAGE REFERENCES FOR SMITHSONIAN ARCHIVES RECORD UNITS

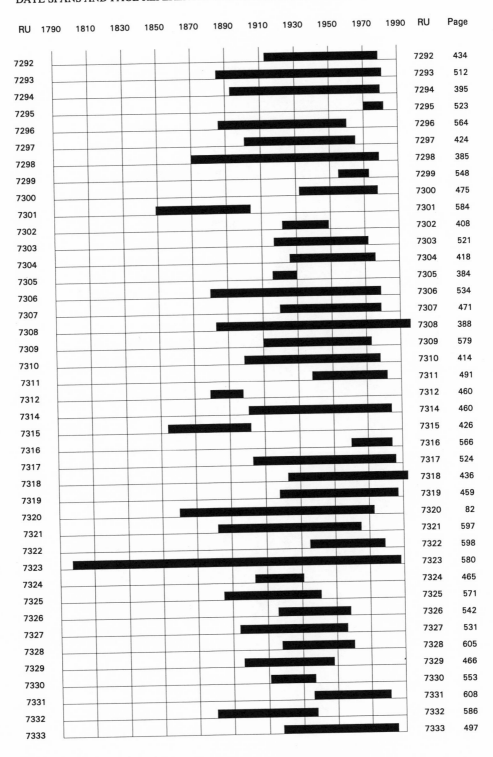

RU	Page
7292	434
7293	512
7294	395
7295	523
7296	564
7297	424
7298	385
7299	548
7300	475
7301	584
7302	408
7303	521
7304	418
7305	384
7306	534
7307	471
7308	388
7309	579
7310	414
7311	491
7312	460
7314	460
7315	426
7316	566
7317	524
7318	436
7319	459
7320	82
7321	597
7322	598
7323	580
7324	465
7325	571
7326	542
7327	531
7328	605
7329	466
7330	553
7331	608
7332	586
7333	497

DATE SPANS AND PAGE REFERENCES FOR SMITHSONIAN ARCHIVES RECORD UNITS

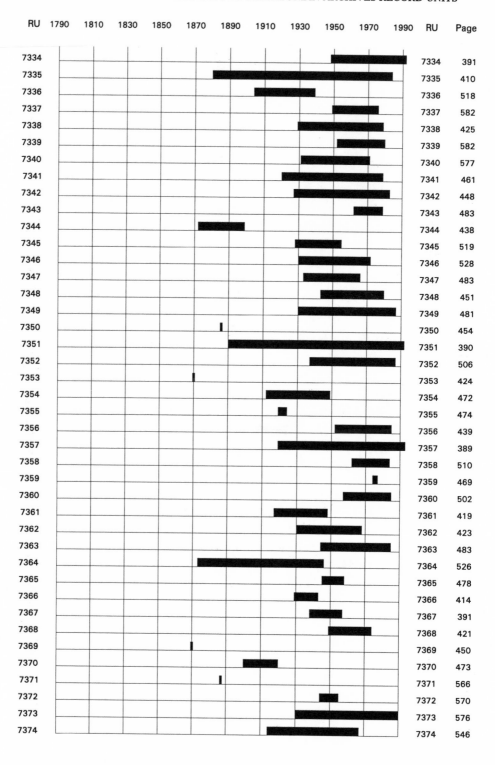

RU	1790	1810	1830	1850	1870	1890	1910	1930	1950	1970	1990	RU	Page
7334												7334	391
7335												7335	410
7336												7336	518
7337												7337	582
7338												7338	425
7339												7339	582
7340												7340	577
7341												7341	461
7342												7342	448
7343												7343	483
7344												7344	438
7345												7345	519
7346												7346	528
7347												7347	483
7348												7348	451
7349												7349	481
7350												7350	454
7351												7351	390
7352												7352	506
7353												7353	424
7354												7354	472
7355												7355	474
7356												7356	439
7357												7357	389
7358												7358	510
7359												7359	469
7360												7360	502
7361												7361	419
7362												7362	423
7363												7363	483
7364												7364	526
7365												7365	478
7366												7366	414
7367												7367	391
7368												7368	421
7369												7369	450
7370												7370	473
7371												7371	566
7372												7372	570
7373												7373	576
7374												7374	546

DATE SPANS AND PAGE REFERENCES FOR SMITHSONIAN ARCHIVES RECORD UNITS

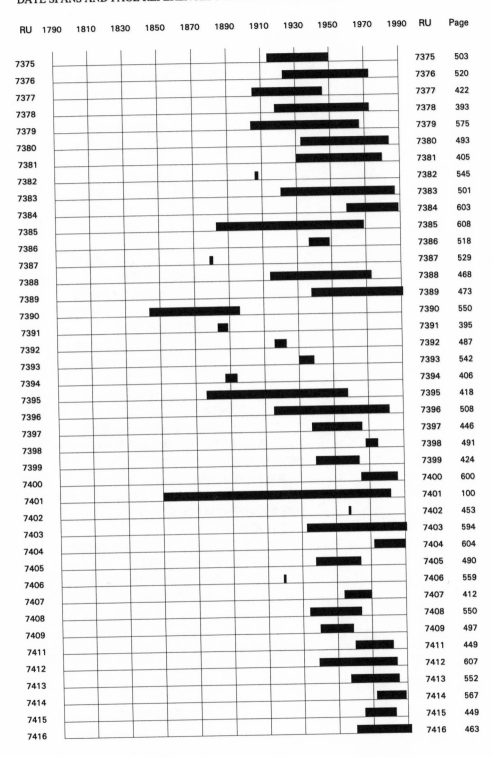

RU	Page
7375	503
7376	520
7377	422
7378	393
7379	575
7380	493
7381	405
7382	545
7383	501
7384	603
7385	608
7386	518
7387	529
7388	468
7389	473
7390	550
7391	395
7392	487
7393	542
7394	406
7395	418
7396	508
7397	446
7398	491
7399	424
7400	600
7401	100
7402	453
7403	594
7404	604
7405	490
7406	559
7407	412
7408	550
7409	497
7411	449
7412	607
7413	552
7414	567
7415	449
7416	463

DATE SPANS AND PAGE REFERENCES FOR SMITHSONIAN ARCHIVES RECORD UNITS

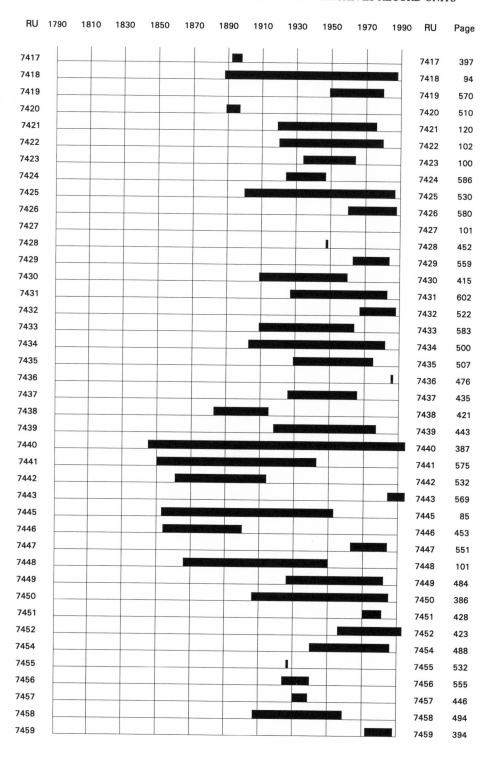

RU	1790	1810	1830	1850	1870	1890	1910	1930	1950	1970	1990	RU	Page
7417												7417	397
7418												7418	94
7419												7419	570
7420												7420	510
7421												7421	120
7422												7422	102
7423												7423	100
7424												7424	586
7425												7425	530
7426												7426	580
7427												7427	101
7428												7428	452
7429												7429	559
7430												7430	415
7431												7431	602
7432												7432	522
7433												7433	583
7434												7434	500
7435												7435	507
7436												7436	476
7437												7437	435
7438												7438	421
7439												7439	443
7440												7440	387
7441												7441	575
7442												7442	532
7443												7443	569
7445												7445	85
7446												7446	453
7447												7447	551
7448												7448	101
7449												7449	484
7450												7450	386
7451												7451	428
7452												7452	423
7454												7454	488
7455												7455	532
7456												7456	555
7457												7457	446
7458												7458	494
7459												7459	394

DATE SPANS AND PAGE REFERENCES FOR SMITHSONIAN ARCHIVES RECORD UNITS

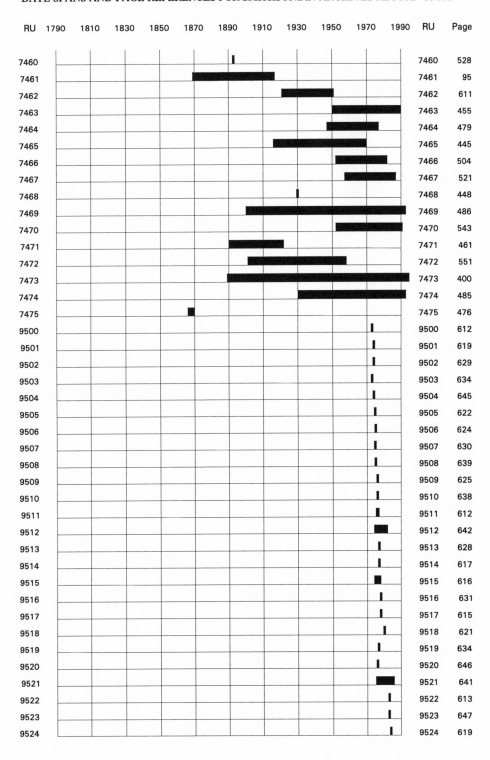

RU	1790	1810	1830	1850	1870	1890	1910	1930	1950	1970	1990	RU	Page
7460												7460	528
7461												7461	95
7462												7462	611
7463												7463	455
7464												7464	479
7465												7465	445
7466												7466	504
7467												7467	521
7468												7468	448
7469												7469	486
7470												7470	543
7471												7471	461
7472												7472	551
7473												7473	400
7474												7474	485
7475												7475	476
9500												9500	612
9501												9501	619
9502												9502	629
9503												9503	634
9504												9504	645
9505												9505	622
9506												9506	624
9507												9507	630
9508												9508	639
9509												9509	625
9510												9510	638
9511												9511	612
9512												9512	642
9513												9513	628
9514												9514	617
9515												9515	616
9516												9516	631
9517												9517	615
9518												9518	621
9519												9519	634
9520												9520	646
9521												9521	641
9522												9522	613
9523												9523	647
9524												9524	619

DATE SPANS AND PAGE REFERENCES FOR SMITHSONIAN ARCHIVES RECORD UNITS

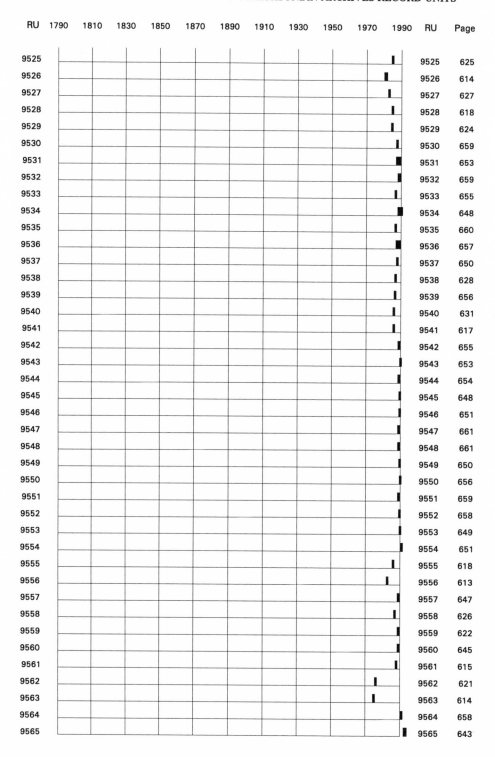

RU	1790	1810	1830	1850	1870	1890	1910	1930	1950	1970	1990	RU	Page
9525												9525	625
9526												9526	614
9527												9527	627
9528												9528	618
9529												9529	624
9530												9530	659
9531												9531	653
9532												9532	659
9533												9533	655
9534												9534	648
9535												9535	660
9536												9536	657
9537												9537	650
9538												9538	628
9539												9539	656
9540												9540	631
9541												9541	617
9542												9542	655
9543												9543	653
9544												9544	654
9545												9545	648
9546												9546	651
9547												9547	661
9548												9548	661
9549												9549	650
9550												9550	656
9551												9551	659
9552												9552	658
9553												9553	649
9554												9554	651
9555												9555	618
9556												9556	613
9557												9557	647
9558												9558	626
9559												9559	622
9560												9560	645
9561												9561	615
9562												9562	621
9563												9563	614
9564												9564	658
9565												9565	643

DATE SPANS AND PAGE REFERENCES FOR SMITHSONIAN ARCHIVES RECORD UNITS

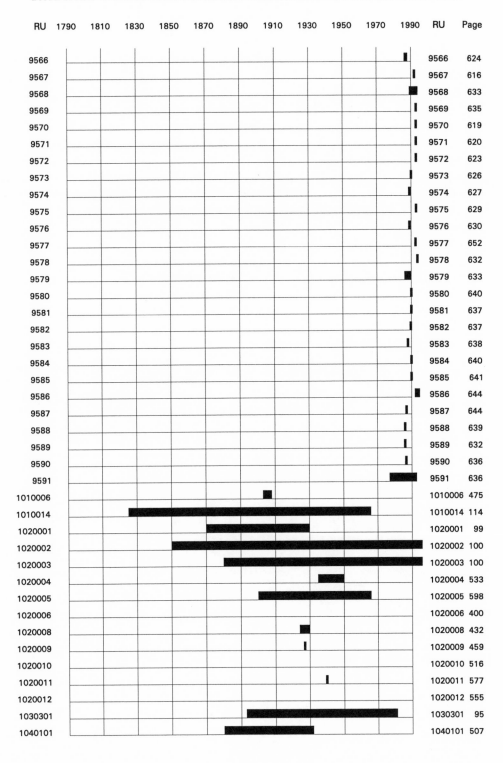

RU	1790	1810	1830	1850	1870	1890	1910	1930	1950	1970	1990	RU	Page
9566												9566	624
9567												9567	616
9568												9568	633
9569												9569	635
9570												9570	619
9571												9571	620
9572												9572	623
9573												9573	626
9574												9574	627
9575												9575	629
9576												9576	630
9577												9577	652
9578												9578	632
9579												9579	633
9580												9580	640
9581												9581	637
9582												9582	637
9583												9583	638
9584												9584	640
9585												9585	641
9586												9586	644
9587												9587	644
9588												9588	639
9589												9589	632
9590												9590	636
9591												9591	636
1010006												1010006	475
1010014												1010014	114
1020001												1020001	99
1020002												1020002	100
1020003												1020003	100
1020004												1020004	533
1020005												1020005	598
1020006												1020006	400
1020008												1020008	432
1020009												1020009	459
1020010												1020010	516
1020011												1020011	577
1020012												1020012	555
1030301												1030301	95
1040101												1040101	507

DATE SPANS AND PAGE REFERENCES FOR SMITHSONIAN ARCHIVES RECORD UNITS

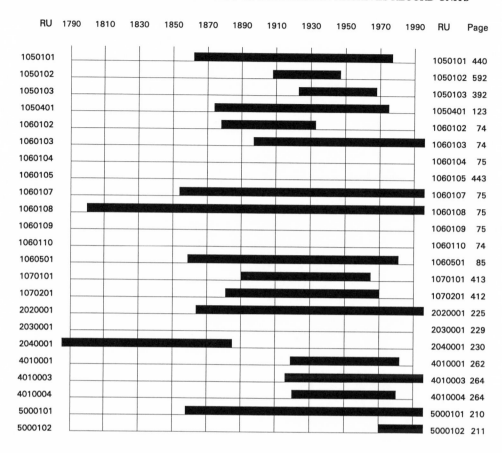

INDEX

This index contains references only to those selected personal, organizational, and other names which appear in the entries in this *Guide*; it does not cover all names that may appear in the records or special collections. The index does not contain references to subjects represented in the entries, although titles of Smithsonian departments, divisions, offices, and subheadings, as well as special collection headings, may be used as subject headings to institutional records and personal papers.

The section on the United States National Museum (USNM) contains central administrative records only. Index terms with (USNM) pertaining to curatorial departments and research projects will be found in other sections of this *Guide*. The National Museum of American History (NMAH), also known as the National Museum of History and Technology (NMHT) and the Museum of History and Technology has index terms referenced only to NMAH and NMHT. This is in keeping with the index practice used in the 1983 *Guide*.

As in the 1983 *Guide*, a thesaurus-like structure has been used to relate organizational units to one another. **BT** indicates an organizational unit to which the unit represented by the main entry is or was subordinate; conversely, **NT** indicates a unit which is or was subordinate to that represented by the main entry. **RT** indicates an unspecified relationship between the units; it is most frequently used to indicate a predecessor-successor relationship. **USE** references are simply references to preferred terms. The cross-references used in this index are a subset of the entire organizational thesaurus used by the Archives. Relationships which are obvious, redundant, or of no use to the reader have been dropped.

For brevity's sake, abbreviations have been used to cite Smithsonian and some non-Smithsonian bureaus and offices which appear frequently.

AM/ANM	-	Anacostia Museum/Anacostia Neighborhood Museum
CFA	-	Center for Astrophysics
CHM	-	Cooper-Hewitt Museum/Cooper-Hewitt Museum of Decorative Arts and Design
HMSG	-	Hirshhorn Museum and Sculpture Garden
NAA	-	National Anthropological Archives
NASM	-	National Air and Space Museum
NCFA	-	National Collection of Fine Arts
NMAA	-	National Museum of American Art
NMAH	-	National Museum of American History
NMHT	-	National Museum of History and Technology
NMNH	-	National Museum of Natural History
NPG	-	National Portrait Gallery
NZP	-	National Zoological Park
SAO	-	Smithsonian Astrophysical Observatory
SEEC	-	Smithsonian Early Enrichment Center
SNAP	-	Smithsonian National Associates Program
USDA	-	United States Department of Agriculture
USGS	-	United States Geological Survey
USNM	-	United States National Museum
WWICS	-	Woodrow Wilson International Center for Scholars

A

AAAS
USE: American Association for the Advancement of Science

Abbe, Cleveland, 408 [RU 7052]

Abbot, Charles G., 9 [RU 46]; 39 [RU 192]; 197 [RU 311]; 246 [RU 85]; 246 [RU 474]; 267 [RU 412]; 348 [RU 535]; 378 [RU 7005]; 431 [RU 7153]; 471 [RU 7307]

Abbot, John, 382 [RU 7116]

Abbott, R. Tucker, 93 [RU 73]; 94 [RU 7418]

Abbott, William Louis, 37 [RU 189]; 382 [RU 7117]

Abelson, Alison R., 214 [RU 455]

Abert, John James, 525 [RU 7058]

Abroad in America: Visitors to the New Nation, 1776-1914 (exhibition), 227 [RU 361]; 228 [RU 554]; 229 [RU 553]

Abu Simbel, temples of, 310 [RU 91]

Academic Programs, Office of, 315 [RU 494]; 315 [RU 102]
NT Seminars, Division of
RT Education and Training, Office of

Academic Studies, Office of, 10 [RU 99]; 21 [RU 104]

Academy of Natural Sciences of Philadelphia, 545 [RU 7382]

Academy: The Academic Tradition in American Art: Commemorating the 150th Anniversary of the National Academy of Design, 1975 (exhibition), 219 [RU 596]

Accession Acknowledgements (USNM), 56 [RU 109]
RT Registrar (USNM)

Accession Record Books (USNM), 56 [RU 110]
RT Registrar (USNM)

Accession Record Books, Temporary (USNM), 56 [RU 111]
RT Registrar (USNM)

Accession Records (USNM), 52 [RU 305]; 52 [RU 6999T]
RT Registrar
United States National Museum, Administrative Assistant

Accessions, Records Relating to (USNM), 56 [RU 118]
RT Registrar (USNM)

Acker, William R. B., 262 [RU 4010001]

Acquired Immune Deficiency Syndrome, 651 [RU 9554]

Adams, Robert McC., 551 [RU 7447]; 635 [RU 9569]

Adams, W. I., 367 [RU 165]

Addresses of Scientific Men, 375 [RU 7002]

Adelaide Forbes Calhoun property, 318 [RU 532]; 329 [RU 562]

Aditi (exhibition), 28 [RU 367]

Adler, Cyrus, 197 [RU 311]; 333 [RU 77]; 347 [RU 217]

Administration, Office of (NMAA), 204 [RU 475]
RT Administrative Services, Office of (NMAA)

Administration, Office of (NCFA), 204 [RU 447]

Administration and Museum Support Services, Department of (HMSG), 271 [RU 512]
BT Hirshhorn Museum and Sculpture Garden

Administration and Support Services, Department of (HMSG), 274 [RU 513]
NT Public Affairs, Office of (HMSG)

Administrative Assistant, United States National Museum
USE: United States National Museum, Administrative Assistant

Administrative Office (NPG), 224 [RU 379]

Administrative Services, Office of (NMAA), 204 [RU 475]
RT Administration, Office of (NMAA)

Administrative Systems Division, 335 [RU 294]
RT Management Analysis Office
Organization and Methods Division

"Adoption of International Electrical Standards in the United States, The," 402 [RU 7214]

Adrosko, Rita J., 174 [RU 472]

Advisory Committee on Printing and Publication, 8 [RU 34]

Advisory Council on Historic Preservation, 25 [RU 191]

Aerobee rocket, 656 [RU 9539]

Aerodynamical Laboratory, Langley, 8 [RU 45]

Aeronautics and Space Administration, National
USE: National Aeronautics and Space Administration

Aeronautics Board, Civil, 233 [RU 162]

Aeronautics, Department of (NASM), 136 [RU 344]; 238 [RU 330]

Aeronautics, Division of (USNM), 9 [RU 46]
RT National Air Museum

Aeronautics, National Advisory Committee for
USE: National Advisory Committee for Aeronautics

African American Museums Association, 67 [RU 566]; 277 [RU 349]

Afro-American Bicentennial Corporation, 277
[RU 349]
Agassiz, Alexander, 441 [RU 7073]; 454 [RU
7350]; 564 [RU 7296]
Agassiz, Jean Louis, 375 [RU 7002]; 426 [RU
7315]; 441 [RU 7073]; 466 [RU 7190]; 587
[RU 7186]
Agassiz-*Albatross* Expedition to the eastern
tropical Pacific, 1904-1905, 427 [RU 7258]
Agency for International Development, 311
[RU 218]; 331 [RU 300]
Agnew, Harold M., 653 [RU 9531]
Agricultural Experiment Station, Iowa, 446
[RU 7137]
Agricultural Industries, Section of (USNM),
146 [RU 240]
    BT Crafts and Industries, Division of
      (USNM)
    RT Agriculture and Wood Products,
      Division of (NMHT)
Agricultural Research Services (USDA), 580
[RU 7426]
Agriculture, Section of (NMHT), 146 [RU 240]
    BT Agriculture and Mining, Division of
      (NMHT)
    RT Agriculture and Forest Products,
      Division of (NMHT)
Agriculture, United States Department of
    USE: United States Department of
      Agriculture
Agriculture and Forest Products, Division of
(NMHT), 146 [RU 240]
    RT Agriculture and Mining, Division of
      (NMHT)
      Agriculture and Wood Products,
      Division of (NMHT)
      Agriculture, Section of (NMHT)
Agriculture and Mining, Division of (NMHT),
146 [RU 240]
    BT Industries, Department of (NMHT)
    NT Agriculture, Section of (NMHT)
    RT Agriculture and Forest Products,
      Division of (NMHT)
      Agriculture and Wood Products,
      Division of (NMHT)
Agriculture and Wood Products, Division of
(NMHT), 146 [RU 240]
    BT Science and Technology, Depart-
      ment of (NMHT)
    RT Agriculture and Forest Products,
      Division of (NMHT)
      Agriculture and Mining, Division of
      (NMHT)
Agrostology Section, Plant Industry, Bureau of
(USDA), 112 [RU 229]

Ahlborn, Richard E., 164 [RU 251]; 165 [RU
331]; 168 [RU 258]; 169 [RU 261]
Air and Space Bibliography (NASM), 235 [RU
343]
Air and Space Museum, National
    USE: National Air and Space Museum
Air Force, United States
    USE: United States Air Force
AK47 automatic rifle, 659 [RU 9532]
Akeley, Carl Ethan, 480 [RU 7179]
Alaska King Crab Investigation, 1940, 89 [RU
307]
Alaska King Crab Investigation, Fish and
    Wildlife Service, 557 [RU 7231]
Albatross (vessel), 420 [RU 7184]; 421 [RU
7438]; 427 [RU 7258]
Albatross Expedition to the eastern tropical
    Pacific, Agassiz-, 1904-1905, 427 [RU
7258]
Albatross, manuscript on fishes collected by,
458 [RU 7180]
Albatross Philippine expedition, 1907-1909,
402 [RU 7089]
Albaugh, Frederic W., 653 [RU 9531]
Albers, Harry, 254 [RU 263]
Albers, Josef, 484 [RU 7449]
Albert, Dave, 655 [RU 9533]
Albert Einstein Spacearium (NASM), 243 [RU
356]; 244 [RU 520]
    BT Interpretive Programs (NASM)
Albert, Jack, 660 [RU 9535]
Alberta, Project, 653 [RU 9531]
Alberto Giacometti 1901-1966 (exhibition),
272 [RU 481]
Albright Art Gallery (Buffalo, New York), 443
[RU 7439]
Albus, James, 658 [RU 9552]
Aldabra, 310 [RU 91]
Aldrich, John Merton, 97 [RU 140]; 384 [RU
7305]
Aldrich, John Warren, 612 [RU 9511]
Aldrich, Loyal B., 267 [RU 412]; 378 [RU
7005]; 471 [RU 7307]
Alexander, A. B., 510 [RU 7223]
Alexander, Carl A., 65 [RU 363]
Alexander, Charles Armistead, 384 [RU 7059]
Alexander, Charles P., 385 [RU 7298]
Alexander Alaska Expedition, 480 [RU 7179]
Alexandria Lyceum, 384 [RU 7059]
Alfred Duane Pell Collection, 8 [RU 45]; 166
[RU 406]
Ali, Salim, 380 [RU 7008]; 636 [RU 9591]
Allegheny Observatory, 376 [RU 7003]
Allen, Arthur R., 386 [RU 7261]

Allen, Joel Asaph, 387 [RU 7440]; 415 [RU 7071]

Allen Meteorite Collection, Arthur R., 118 [RU 269]

Allison, David, 650 [RU 9537]

Allison, Steven W., 643 [RU 9565]

Alva Studios, 262 [RU 4010001]

Amazon Ecosystem Research Program, 29 [RU 393]

    RT Neotropical Lowlands Research Program

America as Art, 1976 (exhibition), 199 [RU 322]; 202 [RU 440]; 206 [RU 458]; 212 [RU 448]

American Art Annual, 197 [RU 311]

American Art Forum, 198 [RU 438]

    BT National Museum of American Art

American Association for the Advancement of Science, 62 [RU 364]; 125 [RU NAA 1]; 374 [RU 7001]; 423 [RU 7362]; 429 [RU 7183]; 483 [RU 7363]; 543 [RU 7470]

American Association of Museums, 24 [RU 190]; 26 [RU 342]; 67 [RU 566]; 337 [RU 624]; 386 [RU 7450]; 473 [RU 7389]; 642 [RU 9512]

American Association of Zoological Parks and Aquariums, 190 [RU 326]; 191 [RU 404]; 633 [RU 9568]

American Committee for International Wild Life Protection, 378 [RU 7006]

American Costume, Hall of (NMAH), 174 [RU 473]

American Costume, Section of (NMHT), 173 [RU 252]; 174 [RU 473]

    BT Political History, Division of (NMHT)

American Council of Learned Societies, 521 [RU 7467]

American Documentation Institute, 562 [RU 7091]

American Ethnology, Bureau of, 7 [RU 31]; 10 [RU 50]; 125 [RU NAA 1]; 127 [RU NAA 2]; 127 [RU NAA 3]; 128 [RU NAA 4]; 128 [RU NAA 5]; 365 [RU 93]; 542 [RU 7393]; 544 [RU 7081]; 618 [RU 9528]; 641 [RU 9521]

    RT Anthropology, Department of (NMNH)

American Federation of Arts, 197 [RU 311]; 203 [RU 313]; 286 [RU 283]

American Federation of Information Processing Societies, 137 [RU 279]; 159 [RU 332]; 521 [RU 7467]

American Fern Journal, 108 [RU 223]; 521 [RU 7303]

American Fern Society, 108 [RU 223]

American Geological Institute, 460 [RU 7314]; 542 [RU 7326]

American Historical Society, 387 [RU 7057]

American History Building, 318 [RU 532]; 329 [RU 562]

    RT History and Technology Building

American Institute of Aeronautics and Astronautics, 240 [RU 348]

American Institute of Biological Sciences, 62 [RU 364]; 473 [RU 7389]; 561 [RU 7222]

    NT Shark Research Panel, American Institute of Biological Sciences

American Malacological Union, 93 [RU 73]; 94 [RU 7418]

American Malacological Union, Pacific Division, 497 [RU 7333]

American Maritime Enterprise, Hall of (NMAH), 161 [RU 528]

American Maritime Museums, Council of, 510 [RU 7358]

American Midland Naturalist, 421 [RU 7368]

American Military Institute, 510 [RU 7358]

American Morphological Society, 390 [RU 7351]

American Museum of Natural History, 507 [RU 1040101]; 551 [RU 7472]; 615 [RU 9517]; 626 [RU 9573]; 640 [RU 9584]

American Museum of Natural History China Expedition, 480 [RU 7179]

American Nature Association, 537 [RU 7252]

American Numismatic Association, 176 [RU 359]

American Ornithologists' Union, 378 [RU 7006]; 387 [RU 7150]; 387 [RU 7440]; 388 [RU 7308]

American Patent Centennial, 1891, 44 [RU 117]

American Philosophical Society, 378 [RU 7006]

American Physiological Society, 390 [RU 7351]

American Pieced Quilts, 1973-1975 (exhibition), 208 [RU 465]

American Portraits, Catalog of

    USE: Catalog of American Portraits

American Presidency in Cartoons, 1789-1977 (exhibition), 227 [RU 361]

American Revolution Bicentennial Coordinator, 13 [RU 341]

American School of Archeology in China, 8 [RU 45]

American School of Classical Studies in Athens, 12 [RU 618]

American Science and Engineering Corporation, 463 [RU 7416]
American Scientific Congress, Eighth, 1940, 9 [RU 46]; 378 [RU 7006]
American Self-Portraits, 1670-1972 (exhibition), 227 [RU 361]
American Society and Politics Program (WWICS), 300 [RU 569]
    RT United States Studies Program (WWICS)
American Society of Ichthyologists and Herpetologists, 389 [RU 7149]; 473 [RU 7389]; 524 [RU 7317]; 534 [RU 7175]
American Society of Mammalogists, 389 [RU 7357]; 496 [RU 7172]; 500 [RU 7434]
American Society of Naturalists, 390 [RU 7351]
American Society of Zoologists, 390 [RU 7351]
American Studies, Department of (NMHT), 316 [RU 160]; 316 [RU 609]
    RT American Studies, Office of (NMHT)
American Studies, Office of, 21 [RU 104]; 316 [RU 160]; 316 [RU 609]
    RT American Studies, Department of (NMHT)
American Zoologist, 390 [RU 7351]
Amphibians, Division of Reptiles and
    USE: Reptiles and Amphibians, Division of
Anacostia Coordinating Council, 277 [RU 349]
Anacostia Historical Society, 277 [RU 349]; 626 [RU 9558]; 631 [RU 9540]
Anacostia Museum, 22 [RU 477]; 276 [RU 265]; 278 [RU 390]; 626 [RU 9558]; 628 [RU 9538]; 631 [RU 9540]; 636 [RU 9591]
    NT Education Department (AM)
    RT Anacostia Neighborhood Museum
Anacostia Museum, Director, 277 [RU 349]; 628 [RU 9538]
Anacostia Museum Training Program, 337 [RU 624]
Anacostia Neighborhood Museum, 10 [RU 99]; 27 [RU 145]; 65 [RU 363]; 276 [RU 265]; 279 [RU 378]; 626 [RU 9558]; 628 [RU 9538]; 631 [RU 9540]
    NT Exhibits Department (ANM)
    RT Anacostia Museum
Anacostia Neighborhood Museum, Administrative Officer, 277 [RU 350]
Anacostia Neighborhood Museum, Director, 276 [RU 265]

Anderson, C. Alfred, 648 [RU 9545]
Anderson, Charles S., 82 [RU 7217]
Anderson, Dean W., 22 [RU 477]
Anderson, Robert, 657 [RU 9536]
Anderson, William Henry, 391 [RU 7367]; 579 [RU 7309]
Andrew Carnegie Building, 318 [RU 532]
Anglim, John E., 65 [RU 363]; 179 [RU 551]; 647 [RU 9523]
Animal Behavior Society, 391 [RU 7334]
Animal Department, (NZP), 193 [RU 385]
    RT Animal Management, Office of (NZP)
        Animal Programs, Office of (NZP)
        Living Vertebrates, Department of (NZP)
Animal Husbandry Research Division (USDA), 393 [RU 7143]; 400 [RU 7103]
Animal Management, Office of (NZP), 191 [RU 404]; 193 [RU 385]
    RT Animal Department, (NZP)
        Animal Programs, Office of (NZP)
        Living Vertebrates, Department of (NZP)
Animal Products, Section of, 128 [RU NAA 5]
Animal Programs, Office of (NZP), 191 [RU 404]; 192 [RU 386]; 193 [RU 385]
    RT Animal Department (NZP)
        Animal Management, Office of (NZP)
        Animal Records (NZP)
        Animal Registration Records (NZP)
        Living Vertebrates, Department of (NZP)
Animal Records (NZP), 192 [RU 386]; 193 [RU 389]; 194 [RU 365]
    RT Animal Programs, Office of (NZP)
        Animal Registration Records (NZP)
Animal Registration Records (NZP), 192 [RU 386]
    RT Animal Programs, Office of (NZP)
        Animal Records (NZP)
Annual Reports of
    USE: name of reporting organization
Anthropology, Department of (NMNH), 128 [RU NAA 5]; 598 [RU 7322]; 618 [RU 9528]; 622 [RU 9505]; 641 [RU 9521]
    NT Ethnology, Division of (NMNH)
    RT American Ethnology, Bureau of Smithsonian Office of Anthropology (NMNH)
Anthropology, Department of (USNM), 128 [RU NAA 5]

Anthropology, Division of (NMNH), 128 [RU NAA 5]
    RT Anthropology, Department of (NMNH)
Anthropology and Geography, Inter-American Society of, 128 [RU NAA 4]
Anthropology Laboratory (NMNH), 128 [RU NAA 5]
    BT Anthropology, Department of (NMNH)
Apollo Over the Moon, 449 [RU 7415]
Apollo Program Science Support Team, 449 [RU 7415]
Apollo-Soyuz Test Project, 239 [RU 353]; 449 [RU 7415]
"Apparatus of the Whaling Industry," 418 [RU 7193]
Appleman, Daniel E., 116 [RU 421]
Appleton's *Cyclopaedia of American Biography* (biographical information for), 407 [RU 7085]
Applied Arts, Department of (NMHT), 153 [RU 413]
    NT Graphic Arts, Division of (NMHT)
    Graphic Arts and Photography, Division of (NMHT)
Applied Biosystems, Incorporated, 650 [RU 9549]
Applin, Esther Richards, 392 [RU 1050103]
Applin, Paul L., 392 [RU 1050103]
AR15 automatic rifle, 659 [RU 9532]
Archaeological Institute of America, 12 [RU 618]
Archbold-Bredin-Smithsonian Biological Survey of Dominica, 452 [RU 7096]; 625 [RU 9509]
Archeology in China, American School of, 8 [RU 45]
Archer, Audrey, 277 [RU 350]
Archer, William, 489 [RU 7061]
Archer, William Andrew, 393 [RU 7378]
Archive of Folk Song, Library of Congress, 635 [RU 9569]
Archives of American Art, 21 [RU 104]; 22 [RU 477]; 203 [RU 313]; 304 [RU 401]; 305 [RU 402]; 306 [RU 403]
Archives of American Art Journal, 304 [RU 401]; 305 [RU 402]
Arctic Bibliography, 618 [RU 9528]
Arctic Institute, 618 [RU 9528]
Arctic Research Laboratory, 10 [RU 50]
A. Remington Kellogg Memorial Fund, 123 [RU 328]
Arem, Joel E., 116 [RU 421]
ARES Incorporated, 659 [RU 9532]

Ari, Donna, 523 [RU 7295]
Armbruster, Carol, 653 [RU 9543]
Armed Forces History, Department of (NMHT), 170 [RU 381]
Armed Forces History, Division of (NMAH), 147 [RU 383]
    BT History of Science and Technology, Department of the (NMAH)
    RT Naval History, Division of (NMAH)
    Military History, Division of (NMAH)
Armed Forces Museum Advisory Board, National
    USE: National Armed Forces Museum Advisory Board
Army Air Corps, 632 [RU 9578]
Army Language School (Monterey, California), 629 [RU 9575]
Army Medical Museum, 329 [RU 562]
Army, United States
    USE: United States Army
Arnheim, Norman, 652 [RU 9577]
Aron, William, 312 [RU 273]; 313 [RU 563]
Ars Islamica, 262 [RU 4010001]
Ars Orientalis, 262 [RU 4010001]
Art and Archeology of Vietnam, The (exhibition), 198 [RU 312]
Art, Archives of American
    USE: Archives of American Art
Art, Arthur M. Sackler Gallery of
    USE: Arthur M. Sackler Gallery of Art
Art, Department of Contemporary (NCFA), 206 [RU 315]
Art, Freer Gallery of
    USE: Freer Gallery of Art
Art, National Gallery of
    USE: National Gallery of Art
Art, National Museum of American
    USE: National Museum of American Art
Art, Smithsonian Gallery of
    USE: Smithsonian Gallery of Art
Art Commission, Smithsonian
    USE: Smithsonian Art Commission
Art in America: A Bibliography, 23 [RU 337]
Art Institute of Chicago, 262 [RU 4010001]
Art of Paul Manship, The, 1989 (exhibition), 207 [RU 461]
Art of the Arab World, 1975 (exhibition), 264 [RU 4010004]
Art Program, International
    USE: International Art Program
Art Program, White House, 203 [RU 313]
Arthur and Edna Greenwood Collection of Americana, 644 [RU 9586]

Arthur M. Sackler Collection of Oriental Art, 11 [RU 613]

Arthur M. Sackler Gallery of Art, 22 [RU 477]; 636 [RU 9591]
    BT Center for Asian Art
    RT Freer Gallery of Art

Artistic Collaboration in the Twentieth Century (exhibition), 272 [RU 481]

Arts, American Federation of
    USE: American Federation of Arts

Arts and Industries, Department of (USNM), 43 [RU 408]; 144 [RU 84]; 144 [RU 219]; 149 [RU 297]
    NT Engineering, Division of (USNM)
        Graphic Arts, Division of (USNM)
        Medicine, Division of (USNM)
        Mineral and Mechanical Technology, Divisions of (USNM)
        Preparator, Arts and Industries, Department of (USNM)
        Textiles, Division of (USNM)
    RT Engineering and Industries, Department of (USNM)
        National Museum of History and Technology

Arts and Industries, Department of, Preparator (USNM), 43 [RU 408]

Arts and Industries Building, 26 [RU 342]; 37 [RU 189]; 65 [RU 363]; 264 [RU 4010003]; 318 [RU 532]; 318 [RU 565]; 324 [RU 640]; 326 [RU 503]; 329 [RU 562]; 329 [RU 637]; 370 [RU 92]; 632 [RU 9578]

Arts and Industries Building, construction, 49 [RU 71]

Artyfacts, 215 [RU 319]

ASC Newsletter, 394 [RU 7459]

"Ascent of Man, The" (television broadcast), 361 [RU 587]

Ashbrook, Frank G., 393 [RU 7143]; 412 [RU 7407]; 413 [RU 7146]

Ashlock, Peter Dunning, 554 [RU 7136]

Ashmead, William Harris, 96 [RU 138]; 97 [RU 139]; 394 [RU 7139]; 564 [RU 7296]

Ashworth, Frederick L., 653 [RU 9531]

Assistant Director
    USE: name of organizational unit

Assistant Secretary, 19 [RU 175]; 35 [RU 52]; 36 [RU 53]; 36 [RU 57]; 36 [RU 561]; 42 [RU 112]; 46 [RU 89]; 47 [RU 88]; 616 [RU 9515]
    RT United States National Museum, Director

Assistant Secretary, Acting, 45 [RU 56]

Assistant Secretary (Administration), 19 [RU 175]; 335 [RU 294]
    NT Administrative Systems Division
        Organization and Methods Division
    RT Under Secretary

Assistant Secretary for Administration, 20 [RU 394]
    RT Under Secretary, Office of the

Assistant Secretary for History and Art, 21 [RU 104]; 22 [RU 281]; 22 [RU 477]; 23 [RU 337]; 27 [RU 145]

Assistant Secretary for Museum Programs, 24 [RU 190]; 25 [RU 191]; 25 [RU 608]; 26 [RU 342]; 27 [RU 575]
    RT Director General of Museums

Assistant Secretary for Museum Programs, Acting, 25 [RU 608]; 26 [RU 342]

Assistant Secretary for Museums, 25 [RU 608]

Assistant Secretary for Public Service, 27 [RU 145]; 28 [RU 367]; 635 [RU 9569]

Assistant Secretary for Research, 29 [RU 393]; 29 [RU 526]; 32 [RU 329]
    RT Assistant Secretary for Science

Assistant Secretary for Science, 29 [RU 526]; 30 [RU 108]; 31 [RU 254]; 32 [RU 329]; 33 [RU 150]; 63 [RU 362]
    RT Assistant Secretary for Research

Assistant Secretary for Science, Acting, 641 [RU 9521]

Assistant Secretary in charge of the United States National Museum, 37 [RU 189]; 38 [RU 54]; 38 [RU 201]; 42 [RU 112]; 42 [RU 113]; 43 [RU 116]; 44 [RU 117]; 45 [RU 55]; 46 [RU 214]; 50 [RU 79]; 645 [RU 9504]
    RT United States National Museum, Director

Assistant Secretary in charge of the United States National Museum, Reports on Inspected Specimens, 42 [RU 114]
    RT United States National Museum, Director

Assistant Secretary in charge of the United States National Museum, Transmission of Specimens, 43 [RU 115]
    RT United States National Museum, Director

Assistant to the Secretary, 12 [RU 171]

Assistant to the Secretary for Policy Analysis and Planning, 315 [RU 102]

Associate Director
    USE: name of organizational unit

Associates, Smithsonian
    USE: Smithsonian Associates

Association of Curators (NMAH), 613 [RU 9522]
    BT National Museum of American History
Association of Meiobenthologists, 96 [RU 417]
Association of Systematics Collections, 62 [RU 364]; 394 [RU 7459]; 578 [RU 7142]
Astronautics, Department of (NASM), 233 [RU 162]; 239 [RU 398]; 240 [RU 348]; 241 [RU 347]; 632 [RU 9578]
    BT National Air and Space Museum
    RT Space History, Department of (NASM)
        Space Science and Exploration, Department of (NASM)
Astrophysical Observatory
    USE: Smithsonian Astrophysical Observatory
Atil, Esin, 262 [RU 4010001]; 264 [RU 4010004]
Atlantic Naturalist, 395 [RU 7294]
Atomic and Molecular Physics Division (SAO), 247 [RU 437]
    BT Smithsonian Astrophysical Observatory
Atomic Energy Commission, 9 [RU 46]; 137 [RU 279]; 267 [RU 412]
Atomic Weights, International Committee on, 430 [RU 7080]
Atoms for Peace (exhibition), 137 [RU 279]
Atwater, Wilbur Olin, 37 [RU 189]; 395 [RU 7391]
Atwood, John G., 652 [RU 9577]
Audioguide (NMNH), 372 [RU 106]
    BT National Museum of Natural History
Audubon Naturalist Society of the Central Atlantic States, Inc., 395 [RU 7294]; 612 [RU 9511]
Audubon Society of the District of Columbia, 395 [RU 7294]
Augenstein, Bruno W., 657 [RU 9536]
Augustus Saint-Gaudens: The Portrait Relief (exhibition), 227 [RU 361]
Australia, Commonwealth of-National Geographic Society-Smithsonian Expedition to Arnhem Land, 1948, 80 [RU 234]; 445 [RU 7465]
Automatic Computerized Transverse Axial Scanner, 654 [RU 9544]
Avery, Milton, 484 [RU 7449]
Avery, Robert Stanton, 396 [RU 7068]
Ayensu, Edward S., 111 [RU 428]
Ayres, Waldemar A., 170 [RU 381]
Azarm, Shapour, 658 [RU 9552]

B

Babcock, Dale F., 653 [RU 9531]
Babcock, Phillip H., 330 [RU 484]
Baber, B. B., 102 [RU 7422]
Baby, Francis A., 235 [RU 352]
Bach, Bruce Allen, 651 [RU 9554]
Bache, Alexander Dallas, 374 [RU 7001]; 397 [RU 7053]; 543 [RU 7470]; 550 [RU 7390]
Bache, Nancy Clarke Fowler, 397 [RU 7053]
Bache Fund, 525 [RU 7115]
Bacher, Robert, 653 [RU 9531]
Bachmann, Konstanze, 294 [RU 544]
Bacon, Henry, 370 [RU 92]
"Badianus Manuscript," 317 [RU 7269]
Baez, Joan, 635 [RU 9569]
Bahai faith, 619 [RU 9570]
Bahr, A. W., 262 [RU 4010001]
Bailey, Florence Merriam, 397 [RU 7417]
Bailey, Vernon Orlando, 397 [RU 7267]
Bainbridge, Kenneth T., 653 [RU 9531]
Baird, Lucy H., 375 [RU 7002]
Baird, Spencer F., 5 [RU 26]; 6 [RU 28]; 6 [RU 29]; 7 [RU 30]; 7 [RU 33]; 16 [RU 38]; 35 [RU 52]; 36 [RU 53]; 36 [RU 561]; 38 [RU 54]; 38 [RU 201]; 39 [RU 192]; 49 [RU 71]; 54 [RU 127]; 55 [RU 120]; 72 [RU 105]; 78 [RU 213]; 81 [RU 208]; 83 [RU 161]; 85 [RU 7445]; 320 [RU 64]; 325 [RU 58]; 347 [RU 217]; 367 [RU 165]; 375 [RU 7002]; 398 [RU 7110]; 415 [RU 7071]; 430 [RU 7080]; 441 [RU 7073]; 541 [RU 7070]; 547 [RU 7167]; 601 [RU 7213]; 609 [RU 7212]
Baird Ornithological Club of Washington, D.C., 398 [RU 7110]; 496 [RU 7172]; 612 [RU 9511]
Baker, Charles Fuller, 39 [RU 192]; 399 [RU 7113]
Baker, Frank, 78 [RU 203]; 189 [RU 74]
Baker-Nunn camera, 613 [RU 9556]
Ball, Elmer Darwin, 399 [RU 7121]
Ball Herbarium, 37 [RU 189]
Balzer, Stephen M., 376 [RU 7003]
Banic, George M., Jr., 653 [RU 9531]
Banks, Harold H., Jr., 119 [RU 614]
Banks, Richard Charles, 411 [RU 7171]
Bannister, Henry M., 601 [RU 7213]
Barbehenn, Kyle R., 266 [RU 286]; 267 [RU 419]
Barbely, Charles G., 243 [RU 356]
Barber, Harry Gardner, 554 [RU 7136]
Barber, Herbert Spencer, 101 [RU 7448]; 400 [RU 7103]; 598 [RU 1020005]

Barbour, Thomas, 17 [RU 135]; 617 [RU 9514]; 621 [RU 9562]
Bares, John, 658 [RU 9552]
Barlow, Edward J., 657 [RU 9536]
Barnard, J. Laurens, 89 [RU 307]; 90 [RU 414]
Barnes, Irston R., 395 [RU 7294]
Barnes, William, 400 [RU 1020006]
Barnett, Frank M., 125 [RU NAA 1]
Barney, Alice Pike, 400 [RU 7473]
Barney Neighborhood House, 370 [RU 92]
Barney Studio House, 22 [RU 477]; 203 [RU 313]; 318 [RU 532]; 400 [RU 7473]
    BT National Museum of American Art
Barnston, George, 36 [RU 561]
Barnum, Phineas T., 39 [RU 192]
Barrett, Otis Warren, 436 [RU 7255]
Barrett, Peter, 652 [RU 9577]
Barro Colorado Island, 318 [RU 532]; 614 [RU 9563]; 615 [RU 9561]; 621 [RU 9562]; 622 [RU 9559]; 627 [RU 9574]; 630 [RU 9576]; 633 [RU 9579]; 637 [RU 9581]; 637 [RU 9582]; 640 [RU 9580]; 640 [RU 9584]; 641 [RU 9585]; 645 [RU 9560]; 649 [RU 9553]
    BT Canal Zone Biological Area
        Smithsonian Tropical Research
        Institute
Barro Colorado Island Research Station, 627 [RU 9574]
Barro Colorado Nature Monument, 630 [RU 9576]
Bartlett, Harley Harris, 595 [RU 7270]
Bartlett, John R., 572 [RU 7066]
Bartlett, Robert A., 89 [RU 307]; 557 [RU 7231]
Bartlett Arctic Expeditions, 1928-1947, 557 [RU 7231]
Bartnik, Robert V., 248 [RU 256]; 248 [RU 468]
Barton, George V., 613 [RU 9556]
Barton Scope, 613 [RU 9556]
Bartsch, Paul, 93 [RU 73]; 94 [RU 202]; 94 [RU 7418]; 402 [RU 7089]; 568 [RU 7262]; 627 [RU 9527]; 634 [RU 9519]
Barus, Carl, 402 [RU 7214]
Bassler, Ray S., 124 [RU 543]; 377 [RU 7004]; 403 [RU 7234]; 550 [RU 7408]; 644 [RU 9587]
Bastarache, Marie, 661 [RU 9548]
Bastian, Edward W., 359 [RU 594]
Batista, Zenith O., 649 [RU 9553]
Batrachians, Department of Reptiles and (NMNH)
    USE: Reptiles and Batrachians,
        Department of (NMNH)

Batrachians, Division of Reptiles and (NMNH)
    USE: Reptiles and Batrachians,
        Division of (NMNH)
Battison, Edwin A., 151 [RU 397]
Bauman, Brad, 661 [RU 9547]
Baumann, Richard W., 104 [RU 422]
Baur, Georg Herman, 39 [RU 192]; 575 [RU 7441]
Baxter, Kathleen T., 569 [RU 7443]
Bayard, Thomas Francis, 441 [RU 7073]
Bayer, Frederick Merkle, 89 [RU 307]; 90 [RU 325]
Beach Anglo-Egyptian Sudan Expedition, 1928, 82 [RU 7320]
Beach-Webb Alaskan Expedition, 1937, 82 [RU 7320]
Bean, Barton A., 78 [RU 213]; 404 [RU 7224]
Bean, Tarleton Hoffman, 78 [RU 213]
Beattie, Rolla Kent, 404 [RU 7271]
Beaudette, Susan B., 182 [RU 595]
Beaudette Foundation for Biological Research, 444 [RU 7097]
Beayon, Everett, 661 [RU 9547]
Becker, Kurt, 650 [RU 9549]
Becker, Ronald E., 140 [RU 335]
Becton Dickinson, Inc., 651 [RU 9554]
Bedini, Silvio A., 139 [RU 277]; 159 [RU 332]
Bedno, Edward, 235 [RU 352]
Beecher, Charles E., 121 [RU 248]
Beer, Alice Baldwin, 288 [RU 539]
Beeson, Loring W., 156 [RU 529]
Beets, Virginia, 140 [RU 335]
Beggs, Thomas M., 12 [RU 441]; 197 [RU 311]; 198 [RU 312]; 220 [RU 316]
Behlen, Eugene F., 65 [RU 363]
Belem Ecological Project, 72 [RU 534]
Belfrage, Gustav Wilhelm, 405 [RU 7105]
Belgian Gunmaking and American History (exhibition), 155 [RU 396]
Belkin, John N., 405 [RU 7381]
Bell, Alexander Graham, 148 [RU 250]; 374 [RU 7000]; 407 [RU 7085]
Bell, Whitfield J., Jr., 483 [RU 7363]
Bell Telephone Laboratories, 449 [RU 7415]
Belmont Conference, National Science Foundation, 1969-1970, 24 [RU 190]
Belmont Conference Center, 27 [RU 145]
Belote, Theodore T., 176 [RU 359]
Belton Santiago, Hamilton W., 649 [RU 9553]
Bendire, Charles Emil, 74 [RU 1060102]; 406 [RU 7394]
Benedict, James E., 69 [RU 242]; 91 [RU 233]; 421 [RU 7438]
Benjamin, Foster Hendrickson, 406 [RU 7128]

Benjamin, Marcus, 407 [RU 7085]
Bennett, Anna Carole, 614 [RU 9563]
Bennett, Charles F., Jr., 614 [RU 9563]
Bennett, Deborah, 350 [RU 489]
Benson, Mary, 451 [RU 7102]
Bent, Arthur Cleveland, 407 [RU 7120]
Bequaert, Joseph Charles, 408 [RU 7302]
Berendt, Carl H., 408 [RU 7194]
Berg, B. Richard, 339 [RU 369]
Berkebile, Donald H., 160 [RU 239]; 161 [RU
    528]
Berklacy, George J., 339 [RU 369]
Berlandier, Jean Louis, 408 [RU 7052]; 554
    [RU 7275]
Berlin International Fisheries Exposition,
    1880, 58 [RU 124]; 327 [RU 70]
Bermingham, Peter, 216 [RU 443]; 216 [RU
    456]
Bermuda Biological Station, 39 [RU 192]
Bernadou, John B., 39 [RU 192]
Bernstein, Morton I., 657 [RU 9536]
Berry, S. Stillman, 410 [RU 7335]; 497 [RU
    7333]; 614 [RU 9526]
Berthelot, Sabin, 95 [RU 7218]
Bertrand (ship), 170 [RU 381]
Bertrand Committee, 170 [RU 381]
Bessels, Emil, 339 [RU 68]
Bethe, Hans, 653 [RU 9531]
Beuck, Elizabeth, 352 [RU 507]
Beutenmueller, Mrs. William, 451 [RU 7102]
Beyond the Limits, 1987 (exhibition), 236 [RU
    354]; 241 [RU 479]
*Bibliography of the History of the Great Sea
    Routes,* 510 [RU 7358]
Bicentennial Coordinator's Office, 22 [RU
    281]; 23 [RU 337]
Bicentennial Inventory of American Paintings,
    203 [RU 313]
Bicentennial of the American Revolution, 22
    [RU 281]; 23 [RU 337]; 139 [RU 277]; 199
    [RU 322]; 339 [RU 369]; 583 [RU 7227]
Bicentennial of the birth of James Smithson
    USE: Smithson Bicentennial
Bicentennial Outdoor Museum Park, 184 [RU
    581]
Biennale of Paris (Sixth), 1969, 214 [RU 454]
Big Dish Radio Telescope (SAO), 250 [RU
    253]
*Bighorn Sheep in the United States, Its Past,
    Present, and Future, The,* 419 [RU 7279]
Bikini Scientific Resurvey, 1947, 80 [RU 234];
    520 [RU 7376]; 524 [RU 7317]; 561 [RU
    7222]
Bikini Scientific Survey, 1946, 80 [RU 234];
    561 [RU 7222]

Billings, John Shaw, 407 [RU 7085]
Billington, James H., 296 [RU 275]; 298 [RU
    558]; 303 [RU 578]
Bingham, Lois A., 217 [RU 321]
Biographical Information File, 369 [RU 7098]
Biological Conservation, Office of, 32 [RU
    329]
Biological Diversity Program (NMNH), 62
    [RU 374]
Biological Research, Beaudette Foundation for,
    444 [RU 7097]
Biological Sciences, American Institute of
    USE: American Institute of Biological
        Sciences
Biological Society of Washington, 410 [RU
    7185]; 612 [RU 9511]
Biological Survey, Bureau of (USDA) 8 [RU
    45]; 397 [RU 7267]; 411 [RU 7171]; 420
    [RU 7168]; 496 [RU 7172]; 499 [RU 7170];
    510 [RU 7420]; 526 [RU 7364]; 537 [RU
    7252]; 588 [RU 7176]; 610 [RU 7174]; 630
    [RU 9507]; 645 [RU 9504]
    BT United States Department of the
        Interior
    NT Fur Resources, Division of, Bureau
        of Biological Survey
    RT Bird and Mammal Laboratories
        Fish and Wildlife Service
        Fisheries, Bureau of
        United States Fish Commission
Biological Survey of the Panama Canal Zone,
    1911-1912, 8 [RU 45]; 39 [RU 192]
Biology, Department of (NMNH), 70 [RU
    243]; 83 [RU 161]; 557 [RU 7231]; 638
    [RU 9510]
    NT Fishes, Division of (NMNH)
        Reptiles and Batrachians, Division
        of (NMNH)
Biology, Department of (USNM), 69 [RU 143];
    69 [RU 242]; 70 [RU 431]
    NT Birds, Division of (USNM)
        Comparative Anatomy, Division of
        (USNM)
        Fishes, Division of (USNM)
        Insects, Division of (USNM)
        Mammals, Division of (USNM)
    NT Plants, Division of (USNM)
        Reptiles and Batrachians, Division
        of (USNM)
    RT Botany, Department of (USNM)
        Entomology, Department of
        (USNM)
        Zoology, Department of (USNM)

Bio-Sciences Information Exchange, 356 [RU 482]
    RT Medical Sciences Information Exchange
        Science Information Exchange
Bird and Mammal Laboratories, 411 [RU 7171]; 412 [RU 7407]; 412 [RU 1070201]; 413 [RU 7146]; 413 [RU 1070101]; 610 [RU 7174]
    BT Fish and Wildlife Service
        United States Department of the Interior
    RT Biological Survey, Bureau of
        Fisheries, Bureau of
        United States Fish Commission
        Wild Fur Animal Investigations, Section of (Fish and Wildlife Service)
Bird-Banding Association, Eastern, 448 [RU 7280]
Birds, Collected Notes, Lists, and Catalogs on, 76 [RU 7215]
Birds, Division of (NMNH), 72 [RU 105]; 72 [RU 391]; 73 [RU 151]; 73 [RU 270]; 74 [RU 1060103]; 74 [RU 1060110]; 75 [RU 1060104]; 75 [RU 1060107]; 75 [RU 1060108]; 75 [RU 1060109]; 76 [RU 245]; 612 [RU 9511]; 624 [RU 9506]
    BT Biology, Department of (NMNH)
        Vertebrate Zoology, Department of (NMNH)
        Zoology, Department of (NMNH)
    RT Ornithology, Department of (USNM)
        Pacific Ocean Biological Survey Program
Birds, Division of (USNM), 74 [RU 1060102]
    BT Biology, Department of (USNM)
Birds' Nests and Eggs, Data on, 74 [RU 1060102]
Birds of Alaska, The, 459 [RU 7319]
Birds of North and Middle America, The, Bulletin 50, United States National Museum, 590 [RU 7133]
"Birds of Palaearctic Distribution Occurring in Greenland and Adjoining Regions," 474 [RU 7199]
Birds of the Republic of Panama, 378 [RU 7006]
Bishop, Carl W., 262 [RU 4010001]
Bishop, Herbert R., 39 [RU 192]
Black, Colleen, 653 [RU 9531]
Black American History, Program in (NMAH), 181 [RU 584]

Black Presence in the Era of the American Revolution, 1770-1800, The (exhibition), 228 [RU 554]; 229 [RU 553]
Blackman, Maulsby Willett, 414 [RU 7366]
Blackwelder, Mary, 292 [RU 540]
Blackwelder, Richard Eliot, 414 [RU 7156]; 615 [RU 9517]
Blake, Doris Holmes, 414 [RU 7310]
Blake, John B., 154 [RU 244]
Blake, Sydney Fay, 414 [RU 7310]; 415 [RU 7430]
Blitzer, Charles, 21 [RU 104]; 22 [RU 281]; 22 [RU 477]; 27 [RU 145]; 315 [RU 102]; 635 [RU 9569]
Blodget, Lorin, 336 [RU 60]
Board of Directors (SEEC), 569 [RU 7443]
Board of Regents, 2 [RU 1]; 3 [RU 3]; 481 [RU 7075]; 489 [RU 7061]; 544 [RU 7081]; 551 [RU 7447]; 625 [RU 9525]
Board of Regents Audit and Review Committee, 625 [RU 9525]
Board of Regents Executive Committee, 3 [RU 2]
Board of Regents Permanent Committee, 3 [RU 2]
Boardman, George A., 415 [RU 7071]
Boardman, Richard S., 68 [RU 429]; 100 [RU 366]; 123 [RU 328]; 639 [RU 9508]
Boas, Franz, 441 [RU 7073]
Bocanegra, Fausto, 615 [RU 9561]; 637 [RU 9581]
Bock, Brian C., 640 [RU 9580]
Boggess, Albert, 653 [RU 9543]
Bolling, Connie, 653 [RU 9531]
Book-of-the-Month Club, 281 [RU 492]
Boorstin, Daniel J., 135 [RU 276]; 136 [RU 334]; 138 [RU 621]
Borden, Carla M., 332 [RU 495]; 332 [RU 498]
Borst, Lyle F., 653 [RU 9531]
Botanical Museum, Santo Domingo, Dominican Republic, 631 [RU 9516]
Botanical Society of Washington, 416 [RU 7259]
Botanical Station, Cinchona, Jamaica, 8 [RU 45]
Botany, Collected Notes and Lists on, 114 [RU 7219]
Botany, Department of (NMNH), 107 [RU 272]; 110 [RU 227]; 111 [RU 428]; 114 [RU 237]; 393 [RU 7378]; 439 [RU 7356]; 452 [RU 7096]; 619 [RU 9501]; 623 [RU 9572]
    NT Herbarium Services Unit (NMNH)

Building the Brooklyn Bridge: The Design and Construction (exhibition), 145 [RU 375]; 151 [RU 397]

Buildings, Smithsonian
    USE: Smithsonian Buildings

Buildings, Superintendent of, 317 [RU 157]

Buildings and Grounds, Division of, 317 [RU 157]
    RT Buildings and Labor, Division of
        Buildings and Superintendence, Division of
        Buildings Management Department
        Construction and Labor, Division of

Buildings and Labor, Division of, 317 [RU 157]
    RT Buildings and Grounds, Division of
        Buildings and Superintendence, Division of
        Buildings Management Department
        Construction and Labor, Division of

Buildings and Superintendence, Division of, 317 [RU 157]
    RT Buildings and Grounds, Division of
        Buildings and Labor, Division of
        Buildings Management Department
        Construction and Labor, Division of

Buildings Management Department, 317 [RU 157]; 318 [RU 532]; 318 [RU 565]; 319 [RU 639]; 324 [RU 638]; 324 [RU 640]; 329 [RU 562]; 329 [RU 637]; 330 [RU 641]
    NT Engineering and Construction Branch
    RT Buildings and Grounds, Division of
        Buildings and Labor, Division of
        Buildings and Superintendence, Division of
        Construction and Labor, Division of
        Design and Construction, Office of
        Facilities Planning and Engineering Services, Office of

Bureau of
    USE: name of bureau

"Buried Mirror, The" (proposed television production), 359 [RU 594]

Burke, John G., 485 [RU 7474]

Burke, John J., 251 [RU 260]; 253 [RU 262]

Burks, Barnard D., 421 [RU 7368]

Burleigh, Thomas Dearborn, 411 [RU 7171]

Burnham, Sophy, 643 [RU 9565]

Burns, Arthur F., 495 [RU 7109]

Busck, August, 101 [RU 7427]; 422 [RU 7129]; 618 [RU 9555]

Bush, Nancy F., 228 [RU 554]

Bushnell, David I., Jr., 572 [RU 7066]

Butts, Charles, 422 [RU 7377]

Buzas, Martin A., 68 [RU 429]; 123 [RU 328]; 639 [RU 9508]

By-Word, 326 [RU 503]; 608 [RU 7331]

Byers, George W., 423 [RU 7452]

Byers, Margery A., 214 [RU 454]

Byram, Edward T., 656 [RU 9539]

Byrd, Richard E., 39 [RU 192]; 252 [RU 255]; 273 [RU 514]; 372 [RU 106]; 419 [RU 7279]; 479 [RU 7464]

C

Cage, Xenia, 286 [RU 283]

Cahill, James F., 264 [RU 4010004]

Cain, Joseph A., 647 [RU 9557]

Calder, Alexander, 203 [RU 313]; 484 [RU 7449]

Calendar (NMNH), 63 [RU 362]

Calendar of Events, 341 [RU 405]

Calhoun property, Adelaide Forbes, 318 [RU 532]; 329 [RU 562]

California Academy of Sciences, 545 [RU 7382]

California Institute of Technology, 650 [RU 9549]

California Pacific International Exposition, San Diego, 1935, 327 [RU 70]

Calkins, C. G., 37 [RU 189]

Callen, Thomas H., II, 243 [RU 356]

Cambridge Entomological Club (Massachusetts), 580 [RU 7323]

Cambridge Radio Observatory Committee, 248 [RU 256]

Camden and Amboy Railroad, 599 [RU 7268]

Cammon, C. A., 105 [RU 220]

Camp, John H., 37 [RU 189]

Campbell, Ann S., 335 [RU 294]

Campbell, Frank L., 423 [RU 7362]

Campbell, Leon, Jr., 248 [RU 256]; 252 [RU 255]

Canadian Arctic Expedition, 1913-1916, 477 [RU 7237]

Canal Zone Biological Area, 9 [RU 46]; 10 [RU 50]; 17 [RU 135]; 304 [RU 134]; 518 [RU 7386]; 611 [RU 7462]; 614 [RU 9563]; 615 [RU 9561]; 621 [RU 9562]; 622 [RU 9559]; 627 [RU 9574]; 637 [RU 9581]; 637 [RU 9582]; 641 [RU 9585]; 645 [RU 9504]; 645 [RU 9560]
    NT Barro Colorado Island
    RT Smithsonian Tropical Research Institute

Canfield Mineral Collection, Frederick A., 120 [RU 7291]

Cannon, Faye (Walter F.), 145 [RU 375]; 158 [RU 293]; 185 [RU 193]
Cannon, Joseph G., 612 [RU 9500]
Cannonball, Project (SAO)
    USE: Earth Physics Satellite (Cannonball) (SAO)
Canu, Ferdinand, 403 [RU 7234]
Canvas of Culture: Rediscovery of the Past as Adaptation for the Future (symposium), 332 [RU 498]
Cap-chur Gun, 633 [RU 9568]
Capital Airlines, 636 [RU 9590]
Capps, Hahn William, 424 [RU 7399]
Capron, Horace, 37 [RU 189]
Carbon-Dating Laboratory, 267 [RU 412]; 268 [RU 387]
    BT Radiation and Organisms, Division of
        Radiation Biology Laboratory
        Smithsonian Environmental Research Center
Cardwell collection of Egyptian antiquities, 10 [RU 50]; 37 [RU 189]
Caribbean Coral Reef Ecosystems Program, 63 [RU 362]
Caribbean Research Institute, 170 [RU 381]
Carleton, Michael D., 82 [RU 400]
Carleton, Nathaniel, 655 [RU 9542]
Carlston, Douglas, 655 [RU 9533]
Carmichael, Leonard, 39 [RU 192]; 380 [RU 7007]; 616 [RU 9515]; 629 [RU 9502]; 633 [RU 9568]
Carnegie Foundation, 390 [RU 7351]
Carnegie Institution of Washington, 8 [RU 45]; 9 [RU 46]; 377 [RU 7004]; 429 [RU 7183]; 499 [RU 7170]
Carnegie Mansion (New York), 22 [RU 281]; 290 [RU 284]; 329 [RU 637]
Carnegie-Mellon University (Pittsburgh, Pennsylvania), 658 [RU 9552]
Carolina Art Association, 197 [RU 311]
Carpenter, Philip Pearsall, 424 [RU 7353]
Carrigan, J. Michael, 179 [RU 551]; 228 [RU 556]
Carriker, Melbourne Armstrong, Jr., 424 [RU 7297]
Carter, Jimmy, 340 [RU 368]
Cartwright, Oscar L., 102 [RU 411]; 425 [RU 7338]
Carus, Julius Victor, 426 [RU 7315]
Case, Mary E., 344 [RU 568]
Casey, Louis S., 238 [RU 330]
Casey, Thomas Lincoln, 426 [RU 7134]

Catalog of American Portraits (NPG), 223 [RU 426]; 224 [RU 379]; 228 [RU 556]; 229 [RU 2030001]
    BT Historian, Office of the (NPG)
Catalog of Federal Domestic Assistance, 335 [RU 294]
Catalog of Hymenoptera in America North of Mexico, 491 [RU 7311]
Cathcart, Ellen W., 107 [RU 236]
Caudell, Andrew Nelson, 427 [RU 7162]
CBS software project, 349 [RU 488]
Cease, Wilson A., 653 [RU 9531]
Celebrations, 1982, (exhibition), 635 [RU 9569]
Celedonio, Gutierrez, 457 [RU 7281]
Celescope, Project (SAO), 248 [RU 256]; 249 [RU 259]; 250 [RU 253]; 251 [RU 260]; 258 [RU 522]; 323 [RU 168]; 602 [RU 7431]; 646 [RU 9520]
    BT Flight Operations, Department of (SAO)
Census of 1880, 447 [RU 7196]; 567 [RU 7206]
Centennial Exposition, Philadelphia, 1876, 327 [RU 70]
Centennial of the Smithsonian Institution, 10 [RU 50]
Center for African, Near Eastern and Asian Cultures, 11 [RU 613]
Center for Asian Art, 22 [RU 477]
    NT Arthur M. Sackler Gallery of Art
        Freer Gallery of Art
Center for Astrophysics, 11 [RU 613]; 247 [RU 437]; 463 [RU 7416]; 651 [RU 9546]
    NT High Energy Astrophysics Division (CFA)
    RT Harvard-Smithsonian Joint Center for Astrophysics
        Smithsonian Astrophysical Observatory
Center for Earth and Planetary Studies (NASM), 239 [RU 353]; 240 [RU 480]; 449 [RU 7415]
Center for Folklife Programs and Cultural Studies, 635 [RU 9569]
Center for Natural Areas, 31 [RU 254]
    BT Ecology Program, Office of Environmental Sciences
        Ecology Program, Office of International and Environmental Programs
Center for Short-Lived Phenomena, 31 [RU 254]; 312 [RU 274]; 319 [RU 607]

BT Environmental Sciences, Office of
International and Environmental
Programs, Office of
International Programs, Office of
RT International Programs, Office of
Center for the Study of Man, 30 [RU 108]; 31
[RU 254]; 32 [RU 329]
Centers for Disease Control, 658 [RU 9564]
Central Bureau for Astronomical Telegrams
(SAO), 250 [RU 253]
Central Market, Washington, D.C., 264 [RU
4010003]
Century of Progress Exposition, Chicago,
1933, 39 [RU 192]; 327 [RU 70]
Century 21 Exposition, Seattle, 1962, 10 [RU
50]
Ceramics, Section of (USNM), 166 [RU 406]
BT Ethnology, Division of (USNM)
Ceramics and Glass, Division of (NMAH), 166
[RU 406]; 613 [RU 9522]
BT Social and Cultural History,
Department of (NMAH)
Ceramics and Glass, Division of (NMHT), 166
[RU 406]
BT Cultural History, Department of
(NMHT)
Industries, Department of (NMHT)
Ceramics and Glass, Section of (USNM), 166
[RU 406]
RT Ceramics and Glass, Division of
(NMHT)
Cerezo, Arturo, 649 [RU 9553]
Ceruzzi, Paul E., 241 [RU 479]; 657 [RU
9536]
Cetus Corporation, 652 [RU 9577]
Ceylon elephant research project, 1967-1976,
449 [RU 7411]
Ceylon primates research project, 1968-1982,
449 [RU 7411]
Chace, Fenner A., Jr., 87 [RU 249]; 89 [RU
307]; 91 [RU 233]; 467 [RU 7257]; 617
[RU 9514]
Chaffee, Frederic H., 655 [RU 9542]
Chagall, Marc, 484 [RU 7449]
Chaille-Long, Charles, 37 [RU 189]
Chalkley, Edward B., 636 [RU 9590]
Challinor, David, 29 [RU 393]; 29 [RU 526];
30 [RU 108]; 31 [RU 254]; 32 [RU 329];
635 [RU 9569]
Chalmers, James D. S., 39 [RU 192]
Chamberlain, Frances Lea, 37 [RU 189]
Chamberlain, Frederick M., 427 [RU 7258]
Chamberlain, Theodore, 428 [RU 7451]
Chamberlain, Von Del, 243 [RU 356]

Chambers, W. Lee, 467 [RU 7257]
Chandler, B. F., 39 [RU 192]
Chandler, Charles Frederick, 407 [RU 7085]
Chaney, Ralph W., 417 [RU 7140]
Chapelle, Howard I., 160 [RU 239]; 161 [RU
528]; 427 [RU 7228]; 629 [RU 9502]
Chapin, Edward Albert, 97 [RU 140]
Chapin, James Paul, 39 [RU 192]
Chapman, Frank Michler, 621 [RU 9562]
Chapman, Vivian Russell, 653 [RU 9531]
Charles County, Maryland, Historical Society,
631 [RU 9516]
Charles D. and Mary Vaux Walcott Research
Fund, 8 [RU 45]; 368 [RU 493]
Charles Darwin Foundation for the Galapagos
Islands, 63 [RU 362]; 380 [RU 7008]; 444
[RU 7097]; 636 [RU 9591]
Charles Frederich: The Washington Years,
1837-1848 (exhibition), 227 [RU 361]
Charles Willson Peale Papers (NPG), 223 [RU
426]; 224 [RU 379]; 230 [RU 2040001]
RT Peale Family Papers
Chase, Mary Agnes, 110 [RU 227]; 112 [RU
229]; 404 [RU 7271]
Chase Fund, Mary Agnes, 112 [RU 229]
Chatelain, Heli, 37 [RU 189]
Chemical Industries, Section of (USNM), 146
[RU 240]
Chemical Technology, Section of (USNM),
146 [RU 240]
Chemist, Office of the Smithsonian, 346 [RU
241]
Chemistry, Hall of (NMAH), 145 [RU 375]
Chemistry, Hall of (NMHT), 158 [RU 579]
Chen, Jigien, 658 [RU 9552]
Chenowith, J. Edgar, 386 [RU 7261]
Cherkasky, Shirley E., 181 [RU 584]
Cherkezian, Nazaret, 358 [RU 586]; 362 [RU
593]; 617 [RU 9541]
Cherry, Schroeder J., 523 [RU 7295]
Chesapeake Bay Center for Environmental
Studies, 10 [RU 99]; 31 [RU 254]; 32 [RU
329]; 266 [RU 286]; 267 [RU 412]; 267
[RU 419]; 268 [RU 399]; 310 [RU 271];
428 [RU 7451]
BT Environmental Sciences, Office of
RT Chesapeake Research Consortium
Chesapeake Research Consortium,
Inc.
Radiation and Organisms, Division
of
Radiation Biology Laboratory
Smithsonian Environmental Research
Center

Chesapeake Bay Center for Environmental
Studies, Associate Director for Education
Programs, 268 [RU 399]; 354 [RU 388]
Chesapeake Bay Center for Environmental
Studies, Office of the Director, 266 [RU
286]; 267 [RU 419]
Chesapeake Bay Center for Field Biology, 266
[RU 286]
    BT Smithsonian Office of Ecology
Chesapeake Research Consortium, 267 [RU
419]
    RT Chesapeake Bay Center for Environ-
        mental Studies
Chesapeake Research Consortium, Inc., 266
[RU 286]; 428 [RU 7451]
    RT Chesapeake Bay Center for Environ-
        mental Studies
Chief Clerk, 6 [RU 27]; 48 [RU 167]; 320 [RU
64]; 320 [RU 65]; 320 [RU 67]; 321 [RU
66]
    NT Documents Clerk
    RT United States National Museum
Child, C. Allan, 90 [RU 414]
Child, Robert C., 246 [RU 474]
Child Care Advisory Board, 352 [RU 507]; 569
[RU 7443]
Child Care Center, Arts and Industries
Building, 569 [RU 7443]
Child Care Center (NMAH), 569 [RU 7443]
Children's Room of the Smithsonian Institu-
tion Building, 45 [RU 55]
Chin, Cecilia H., 221 [RU 463]
China, Szechwan Province, 1911-1948, 470
[RU 7148]
Chinese Civil War, 262 [RU 4010001]
Chittenden, Frank Hurlburt, 429 [RU 7131]
Christian, Thomas, 434 [RU 7292]
*Christian Gallager: Portrait Painter to
Federal America* (exhibition), 227 [RU
361]
Christy, John H., 649 [RU 9553]
Christy, Robert, 653 [RU 9531]
*Chronicle of the Museum for the Arts of
Decoration of the Cooper Union,* 294 [RU
598]
Chrysomelidae Interest Group, 1986, 476 [RU
7436]
Chubb, Talbot A., 656 [RU 9539]
Cinchona Botanical Station, Jamaica, 8 [RU
45]
Cincinnati Industrial Exposition, 1884, 58 [RU
124]; 327 [RU 70]
Cities, 281 [RU 492]
Citron, Robert L., 319 [RU 607]
Civil Aeronautics Board, 233 [RU 162]

Civil History, Department of (NMHT), 12 [RU
618]; 164 [RU 251]; 173 [RU 252]; 598
[RU 7322]
    NT Cultural History, Division of
        (NMHT)
        Musical Instruments, Division of
        (NMHT)
        Numismatics, Division of (NMHT)
        Philately and Postal History,
        Division of (NMHT)
        Political History, Division of
        (NMHT)
    RT Cultural History, Department of
        (NMHT)
Civil History, Division of (USNM), 173 [RU
252]; 174 [RU 473]
    BT History, Department of (USNM)
    RT Political History, Division of
        (NMHT)
Civil Service Commission, United States, 91
[RU 209]; 363 [RU 182]
Civilian Pilot Training Program, 632 [RU
9578]
Clain-Stefanelli, Elvira Eliza, 176 [RU 359]
Clain-Stefanelli, Vladimir, 176 [RU 359]
Clapp, George H., 481 [RU 7075]
Clapp, Rebecca B., 180 [RU 360]
Clark, Austin H., 429 [RU 7183]; 628 [RU
9513]
Clark, Jane, 289 [RU 324]
Clark, Leila F., 347 [RU 217]
Clark, Robert Sterling, 572 [RU 7263]
Clarke, Arthur C., 239 [RU 398]
Clarke, Arthur H., 93 [RU 73]
Clarke, Frank Wigglesworth, 430 [RU 7080];
564 [RU 7283]
Clarke, John Frederick Gates, 97 [RU 140]; 98
[RU 247]; 98 [RU 430]; 99 [RU 148]; 103
[RU 427]; 618 [RU 9555]; 638 [RU 9583]
Clarke, Laurence, Jr., 36 [RU 561]
Clarke, Roy S., Jr., 68 [RU 429]; 115 [RU
268]; 118 [RU 269]; 119 [RU 548]; 386
[RU 7261]
Clay, Harry Gibbs, 431 [RU 7095]
Clay, John Randolph, 431 [RU 7095]
Clay, Joseph Ashmead, 431 [RU 7095]
Clay and Color: The Ceramics of Picasso
(exhibition), 293 [RU 541]
Clayton, Frances Lindley, 431 [RU 7153]
Clayton, Henry Helm, 431 [RU 7153]
Clerk
    USE: Chief Clerk
        Disbursement Clerk
        Documents Clerk

NT Public Information Office (CHM)
  Registrar, Office of the (CHM)
  Textiles, Department of (CHM)
Cooper-Hewitt Museum, Administrator, 282
  [RU 545]
Cooper-Hewitt Museum, Director, 281 [RU
  492]
Cooper-Hewitt Museum of Decorative Arts and
  Design, 11 [RU 613]
Cooper, James G., 437 [RU 7067]; 577 [RU
  7191]
Cooper Union for the Advancement of Science
  and Art, 281 [RU 267]; 283 [RU 633]; 286
  [RU 289]; 294 [RU 598]
Cooper Union, Friends of the Museum of the,
  284 [RU 288]
Cooper Union Museum, 203 [RU 313]
Cooper Union Museum, Committee to Save
  the, 283 [RU 633]
Cooper Union Museum, Council for the, 294
  [RU 598]
Cooper Union Museum for the Arts of
  Decoration, 281[RU 267]; 283 [RU 633];
  286 [RU 289]; 294 [RU 598]
    NT Exhibitions, Department of (Cooper
      Union Museum)
    RT Cooper-Hewitt Museum
Cooper, William, 121 [RU 248]
Cooperative Programs, Office of (NASM), 241
  [RU 355]
Coordinator of Public Information, Office of,
  323 [RU 373]
    NT Congressional Liaison, Office of
      Public Affairs, Office of
      Special Events, Office of
Cope, Edward Drinker, 407 [RU 7085]; 418
  [RU 7395]
Copeia, 389 [RU 7149]
Copernicus (symposium), 357 [RU 500]
Coquillet, Daniel William, 438 [RU 7164]
Coral Atoll Program, 623 [RU 9572]
Corals, Section of (NMNH), 94 [RU 202]
    BT Marine Invertebrates, Department of
      (NMNH)
      Marine Invertebrates, Division of
      (NMNH)
      Mollusks, Division of (NMNH)
Corbin, Thomas E., 648 [RU 9534]
Corbin, William L., 347 [RU 217]
Corley, Steven, 658 [RU 9552]
Cornell, James C., Jr., 362 [RU 593]
Cornell University, 533 [RU 1020004]; 540
  [RU 7078]

Correspondence and Documents, Division of
  . (USNM), 44 [RU 133]; 45 [RU 215]; 52
  [RU 305]
Correspondence and Documents, Office of
  (USNM), 644 [RU 9587]
    RT Correspondence and Records, Office
      of (USNM)
Correspondence and Records, Office of
  (USNM), 644 [RU 9587]
    RT Correspondence and Documents,
      Office of (USNM)
Cosmos Club, 378 [RU 7006]; 612 [RU 9511]
Costume and Furnishings, Division of
  (NMHT), 167 [RU 519]; 169 [RU 261]
    BT Cultural History, Department of
      (NMHT)
    RT Cultural History, Division of
      (NMHT)
      Domestic Life, Division of (NMHT)
Cotton States and International Exposition,
  Atlanta, 1895, 327 [RU 70]; 599 [RU 7268]
Cottrell, Frederic G., 17 [RU 46TB]; 17 [RU
  51]
Coues, Elliott, 36 [RU 561]; 81 [RU 208]; 407
  [RU 7085]; 415 [RU 7071]; 438 [RU 7344]
Coulter, Thomas, 438 [RU 7289]
Council for the Cooper Union Museum, 294
  [RU 598]
Council of American Maritime Museums, 510
  [RU 7358]
Council of Information and Education Direc-
  tors, 629 [RU 9575]
Council of Registrars, 292 [RU 540]; 344 [RU
  568]
    RT Registrarial Council of the
      Smithsonian Institution
      Smithsonian Institution Registrar's
      Council
Country Music Program (NMAH), 181 [RU
  584]
Coville, Frederick Vernon, 105 [RU 220]; 107
  [RU 236]; 108 [RU 223]; 439 [RU 7272]
Cowan, Richard Sumner, 61 [RU 155]; 61 [RU
  197]; 62 [RU 364]; 439 [RU 7356]; 619
  [RU 9501]; 643 [RU 9565]
Coward, Noel, 628 [RU 9513]
Cox, Beverly J., 227 [RU 361]; 228 [RU 556]
Cox, Marsha S.
    USE: Sitnik, Marsha E.
Cox, William V., 48 [RU 167]; 567 [RU 7206]
Crafts and Industries, Division of (USNM),
  146 [RU 240]
    BT Engineering and Industries,
      Department of (USNM)

NT Agricultural Industries, Section of
   (USNM)
Crawford, James Chamberlain, 97 [RU 139];
   97 [RU 140]; 440 [RU 7114]
Crawford, Richard D., 235 [RU 352]; 243 [RU
   356]
Credit Union Newsletter, Smithsonian
   Institution Employees Federal, 347 [RU
   299]
Cressey, Roger F., Jr., 88 [RU 423]; 89 [RU
   307]; 90 [RU 414]
Cresson, Ezra Townsend, Jr., 494 [RU 7458]
Creutz, Edward C., 653 [RU 9531]
Croffut, Bessie Nicholls, 440 [RU 7197]
Croffut, William Augustus, 440 [RU 7197]
Cronin, J. Richard, 370 [RU 92]
Cronin, L. Eugene, 428 [RU 7451]
Crosby, William Otis, 528 [RU 7460]
Crossroads Operation, 1946-1955, 508 [RU
   7396]; 520 [RU 7376]; 561 [RU 7222]; 638
   [RU 9510]
Crustacea, Division of (NMNH), 89 [RU 307];
   90 [RU 414]
      BT Invertebrate Zoology, Department of
         (NMNH)
      RT Marine Invertebrates, Division of
         (NMNH)
Crustacean Society, The, 90 [RU 414]
Cruz, Martin de la, 317 [RU 7269]
Cryptogams, Division of (USNM), 112 [RU
   228]
      BT Botany, Department of (USNM)
Cull, Raymond, 661 [RU 9547]
Cultural Anthropology, Division of (NMNH),
   128 [RU NAA 5]
      BT Anthropology, Department of
         (NMNH)
Cultural History, Department of (NMHT), 164
   [RU 251]; 165 [RU 331]; 169 [RU 261];
   598 [RU 7322]; 644 [RU 9586]
      NT Ceramics and Glass, Division of
         (NMHT)
         Costume and Furnishings, Division
            of (NMHT)
         Domestic Life, Division of (NMHT)
         Ethnic and Western Cultural
            History, Division of (NMHT)
         Graphic Arts, Division of (NMHT)
         Growth of the United States
            (NMHT)
         Musical Instruments, Division of
            (NMHT)
         Preindustrial Cultural History,
            Division of (NMHT)

      RT Civil History, Department of
         (NMHT)
Cultural History, Division of (NMHT), 168
   [RU 258]; 169 [RU 261]; 644 [RU 9586]
      BT Civil History, Department of
         (NMHT)
      NT Musical Instruments, Section of
         (NMHT)
      RT Costume and Furnishings, Division
         of (NMHT)
         Domestic Life, Division of (NMHT)
         Ethnology, Division of (USNM)
         Musical Instruments, Division of
            (NMHT)
*Cultural Styles and Social Identities: Interpre-
   tations of Protest and Change* (sympo-
   sium), 315 [RU 494]
Cumming, Paul, 304 [RU 401]
Curatorial Department (NMAA), 207 [RU 461]
      RT Painting and Sculpture, Department
         of (NMAA)
Curatorial Departments (NPG), 225 [RU
   2020001]
"Currants and Gooseberries," 439 [RU 7272]
Cushing, Frank Hamilton, 125 [RU NAA 1]
Cushman, Joseph A., 440 [RU 1050101]
Cushman Laboratory for Foraminiferal
   Research, 440 [RU 1050101]
Cutler, Carol, 228 [RU 554]
Cutress, Charles E., Jr., 89 [RU 307]
Cyclopaedia of American Biography,
   Appleton's (biographical information for),
   407 [RU 7085]

D

Dade County Art Museum (Miami), 443 [RU
   7439]
Dahlgreen, Charles W., 153 [RU 413]
Dall, William H., 93 [RU 73]; 94 [RU 7418];
   398 [RU 7110]; 441 [RU 7073]; 585 [RU
   7192]; 601 [RU 7213]
Danforth, Stuart Taylor, 443 [RU 1060105]
Danglade (vessel), 420 [RU 7184]
Daniel Giraud Elliot Fund, 8 [RU 45]; 9 [RU
   46]; 374 [RU 7001]; 378 [RU 7006]; 525
   [RU 7115]
      BT National Academy of Sciences
Danner, Michael, 656 [RU 9550]
Darton, Nelson Horatio, 121 [RU 248]
Darwin, Charles, 426 [RU 7315]

Darwin Foundation for the Galapagos Islands, Charles
    USE: Charles Darwin Foundation for the Galapagos Islands
Davies, Merton E., 657 [RU 9536]
Davis, Audrey B., 154 [RU 244]; 155 [RU 471]; 352 [RU 507]; 485 [RU 7474]
Davis, Benjamin O., Jr., 632 [RU 9578]
Davis, Charles H., 407 [RU 7085]
Davis, Donald R., 98 [RU 430]; 103 [RU 427]
Davis, Robert T., 251 [RU 260]
Davis, Robert Tyler, 203 [RU 313]; 204 [RU 447]; 208 [RU 465]; 443 [RU 7439]
Davis, Watson, 562 [RU 7091]
Dawson, E. Yale, 111 [RU 428]; 444 [RU 7097]
Dayton, William Lewis, 444 [RU 7158]
Dearborn, Mona, 228 [RU 556]
Dearolf, Kenneth Neff, 512 [RU 7254]
Death Valley plants, 1933-1936, 439 [RU 7272]
Decorative Arts, Department of (CHM), 285 [RU 282]; 285 [RU 506]
    BT Cooper-Hewitt Museum
Decorative Arts Association, 285 [RU 506]
Dee, Elaine Evans, 286 [RU 283]
Defense Research and Engineering, Office of the Director, 345 [RU 179]
Deignan, Herbert Girton, 39 [RU 192]; 72 [RU 105]; 73 [RU 270]; 445 [RU 7465]
Deignan, Stella L., 356 [RU 482]
de Kooning, Willem, 484 [RU 7449]; 624 [RU 9566]
DeLand, Edward C., 657 [RU 9536]
de Lapparant, Valerie, 651 [RU 9546]
DeLong, Dwight Moore, 399 [RU 7121]
Denton, Lawrence, 653 [RU 9531]
Dentzel Carousel, 26 [RU 342]
Department of
    USE: name of department
Deputy Assistant Secretary for Research, 30 [RU 527]
Deputy Director
    USE: name of organizational unit
Derrickson, Scott R., 649 [RU 9553]
de Saint-Memin, C. B. J. F., 223 [RU 426]
De Saint-Phalle, Niki, 484 [RU 7449]
Desautels, Paul E., 116 [RU 336]; 116 [RU 421]; 117 [RU 266]; 120 [RU 7421]
Deschamps, Emile, 37 [RU 189]
Desert Bibliography, 449 [RU 7415]
Design and Construction, Office of, 324 [RU 638]; 324 [RU 640]

    RT Buildings Management Department
        Facilities Planning and Engineering Services, Office of
Design and Production, Department of (NMAA), 213 [RU 451]
    RT Exhibition and Design, Office of (NMAA)
Design and Production, Department of (NPG), 226 [RU 552]
Detroit Trust Company, 262 [RU 4010001]
Development Office (CHM), 290 [RU 546]
Development Office (NMNH), 64 [RU 425]
    BT National Museum of Natural History, Special Assistant to the Director
DeVorkin, David H., 240 [RU 348]; 648 [RU 9534]; 651 [RU 9546]; 653 [RU 9543]; 655 [RU 9542]; 656 [RU 9539]
Dewey, Lyster Hoxie, 105 [RU 220]
Dexter, Ralph Warren, 512 [RU 7254]
"Dialogue" (WWICS) (radio broadcast), 302 [RU 604]
    RT "Radio Dialogue" (WWICS) (radio broadcast)
Dibner Library of the History of Science and Technology, 639 [RU 9588]
DiCesare, Joseph L., 652 [RU 9577]
Dickey, George, 484 [RU 7449]
Dietlein, Donald R., 193 [RU 385]
Different Drummers (exhibition), 272 [RU 481]
Dillon, Wilton S., 315 [RU 494]; 332 [RU 495]; 332 [RU 498]; 357 [RU 500]
Dimmock, George, 445 [RU 7195]
Diptera, Division of (NMNH), 104 [RU 422]
    BT Entomology, Department of (NMNH)
Director
    USE: name of organizational unit
Director General of Museums, 24 [RU 190]; 26 [RU 342]; 642 [RU 9512]
    RT Assistant Secretary for Museum Programs
        United States National Museum, Director
Dirks, Kathrine, 174 [RU 472]
Disbursement Clerk, 367 [RU 165]
    RT United States National Museum
Diving Board (NMNH), 63 [RU 362]
Division of
    USE: name of division
Dixon, Nathaniel, 315 [RU 494]
DNA sequencer, 650 [RU 9549]
DNA Thermal Cycler, 652 [RU 9577]

Editorial Division, 348 [RU 535]
    RT Editorial and Publications Division
        Smithsonian Institution Press
Editorial Office (NCFA), 215 [RU 319]
    RT Publication Editor (NCFA)
Edmonson, Julia Ellen, 102 [RU 7422]
Edson, Dorothy Graham, 620 [RU 9571]
Education, Department of (HMSG), 273 [RU 514]
Education, Department of (NCFA), 216 [RU 443]
Education, Department of (NPG), 226 [RU 555]
Education, Office of (NZP), 195 [RU 395]
Education, Office of Elementary and Secondary, 27 [RU 145]
Education Aide Program (NPG), 226 [RU 555]
Education and Information, Department of (NASM), 233 [RU 162]
Education and Training, Office of, 22 [RU 281]; 27 [RU 145]; 315 [RU 102]
Education and Visitor Information, Division of (NMAH), 179 [RU 599]
    RT Public Information and Education, Division of (NMHT)
Education Department (AM), 278 [RU 390]
    NT Outreach Services Branch (AM)
        Youth Advisory Council (AM)
Educational Programs, Office of (NMAA), 216 [RU 456]
    RT Museum Programs, Office of (NMAA)
Educational Research, Smithsonian Office of, 354 [RU 388]
Edward L. Greene Herbarium, 439 [RU 7272]
Edward W. Browning Achievement Award, 31 [RU 254]
Edwards, William Henry, 585 [RU 7192]
Efflatoun, H. C., 448 [RU 7468]; 577 [RU 1020011]
Eigenmann, Carl H., 436 [RU 7255]
1876: A Centennial Exhibition (exhibition), 174 [RU 473]; 360 [RU 592]
Eighteenth and Nineteenth Century Painting and Sculpture, Department of (NMAA), 205 [RU 460]; 207 [RU 459]
    RT Painting and Sculpture, Department of (NMAA)
Eighteenth-Century Agriculture, Symposium on, 146 [RU 240]
Eighth American Scientific Congress, 1940, 9 [RU 46]; 378 [RU 7006]
Eike, James W., 448 [RU 7342]
Einstein, Albert (centennial events), 357 [RU 500]

Einstein Observatory, 463 [RU 7416]
Einstein Spacearium, Albert (NASM), 243 [RU 356]; 244 [RU 520]
Eisenberg, John F., 191 [RU 404]; 193 [RU 385]; 449 [RU 7411]
Eisenhower Institute for Military History, 632 [RU 9589]
Eisenmann, Eugene, 640 [RU 9584]
Eklund, Jon B., 158 [RU 293]; 655 [RU 9533]
El-Baz, Farouk, 239 [RU 353]; 240 [RU 480]; 449 [RU 7415]
Eldredge, Charles C., 198 [RU 438]
Electrical Numerical Integrator and Computer (ENIAC), 650 [RU 9537]
Electrical Standards, Great Britain Board of Trade Committee on, 402 [RU 7214]
Electricity, Division of (NMHT), 148 [RU 250]
    BT Science and Technology, Department of (NMHT)
    RT Electricity and Modern Physics, Division of (NMHT)
        Electricity and Nuclear Energy, Division of (NMHT)
Electricity, Hall of (NMHT), 148 [RU 250]
Electricity, Section of (USNM), 148 [RU 250]
    BT Engineering, Division of (USNM)
    RT Electricity, Division of (NMHT)
Electricity and Modern Physics, Division of (NMHT), 148 [RU 250]
    BT History of Science, Department of (NMHT)
    RT Electricity and Nuclear Energy, Division of (NMHT)
        Electricity, Division of (NMHT)
Electricity and Nuclear Energy, Division of (NMHT), 148 [RU 250]
    BT Science and Technology, Department of (NMHT)
    RT Electricity and Modern Physics, Division of (NMHT)
        Electricity, Division of (NMHT)
Electro-Mechanical Research, Inc., 251 [RU 260]; 323 [RU 168]
Electron Optics Branch, Naval Research Laboratory, 656 [RU 9539]
Elementary and Secondary Education, Office of, 27 [RU 145]
Elias, James J., 275 [RU 515]
Elisha Kent Kane (exhibition), 227 [RU 361]
Elliot, Daniel Giraud, 415 [RU 7071]
Elliot Fund, Daniel Giraud
    USE: Daniel Giraud Elliot Fund
Elliot, Walter, 601 [RU 7112]
Elliott, Henry W., 450 [RU 7369]; 601 [RU 7213]

Ellsworth Expedition to Alberta and British Columbia, 1914, 480 [RU 7179]
Ellsworth, Gretchen Gayle, 569 [RU 7443]
Ellsworth, Lincoln, 480 [RU 7179]
Emlong, Douglas Ralph, 124 [RU 543]; 451 [RU 7348]; 621 [RU 9518]
Emlong, Jennie V., 621 [RU 9518]
Emmart, Emily Walcott, 317 [RU 7269]
Emmett, Rowland, 236 [RU 354]
Emry, Robert J., 122 [RU 424]
Emulation and Invention, 483 [RU 7363]
Endangered Species Scientific Authority, 32 [RU 329]
Enders, Robert K., 621 [RU 9562]
Energy, United States Department of
    USE: United States Department of Energy
Engelhardt, George Paul, 451 [RU 7102]
Engelmann, George, 453 [RU 7446]
Engineering, Division of (NMHT), 629 [RU 9502]
    BT Science and Technology, Department of (NMHT)
Engineering, Division of (USNM), 149 [RU 297]; 151 [RU 397]
    BT Arts and Industries, Department of (USNM)
        Engineering and Industries, Department of (USNM)
    RT Mechanical and Civil Engineering, Division of (NMHT)
Engineering and Construction Branch, 319 [RU 639]
    BT Buildings Management Department
Engineering and Design Branch (OFPES), 330 [RU 641]
    BT Facilities Planning and Engineering Services, Office of
Engineering and Industries, Department of (USNM), 144 [RU 84]; 149 [RU 297]; 153 [RU 413]; 642 [RU 9512]
    NT Crafts and Industries, Division of (USNM)
        Engineering, Division of (USNM)
        Graphic Arts, Division of (USNM)
        Medicine and Public Health, Division of (USNM)
    RT Arts and Industries, Department of (USNM)
        National Museum of History and Technology
Engineering and Industry, Division of (NMAH), 151 [RU 397]
    BT History of Science and Technology, Department of the (NMAH)
    RT Mechanical and Civil Engineering, Division of (NMAH)
        Mechanisms, Division of (NMAH)
Engineering and Industry, National Museum of, 39 [RU 192]; 149 [RU 297]
Engineering and Transportation, Section of (USNM)
    USE: Transportation and Engineering, Section of (USNM)
English Speaking Union, 13 [RU 341]
English Yellow-Glazed Earthenware, 166 [RU 406]
Engraving and Printing, Bureau of, 631 [RU 9540]
ENIAC
    USE: Electrical Numerical Integrator and Computer
Eniwetok Atoll Expedition, 1963, 552 [RU 7413]
Enola Gay (airplane), 653 [RU 9531]
Entomological Society of America, 475 [RU 7300]; 580 [RU 7323]
Entomological Society of America, 1986, 476 [RU 7436]
Entomologists, Collected Notebooks of, 101 [RU 7135]
Entomology, Bureau of (USDA), 406 [RU 7128]; 414 [RU 7310]; 414 [RU 7366]; 423 [RU 7362]; 472 [RU 7354]; 615 [RU 9517]; 618 [RU 9555]; 628 [RU 9513]; 638 [RU 9583]
    BT United States Department of Agriculture
Entomology, Collected Records and Papers on, 101 [RU 7448]
Entomology, Department of (NMNH), 97 [RU 140]; 98 [RU 246]; 98 [RU 247]; 98 [RU 430]; 99 [RU 148]; 100 [RU 7401]; 100 [RU 7423]; 100 [RU 1020002]; 100 [RU 1020003]; 101 [RU 7427]; 102 [RU 411]; 102 [RU 418];102 [RU 7422]; 103 [RU 427]; 104 [RU 422]; 414 [RU 7310]; 425 [RU 7338]; 491 [RU 7311]; 570 [RU 7419]; 618 [RU 9555]; 638 [RU 9583]
    NT Coleoptera, Division of (NMNH)
        Hemiptera, Division of (NMNH)
        Hemiptera and Hymenoptera, Division of (NMNH)
        Insects, Division of (NMNH)
        Lepidoptera, Division of (NMNH)
        Neuropteroids and Diptera, Division of (NMNH)
    RT Insects, Division of (NMNH)

Entomology, Department of (USNM), 99 [RU 1020001]
    BT United States National Museum
Entomology and Plant Quarantine, Bureau of (USDA), 104 [RU 422]; 391 [RU 7367]; 424 [RU 7399]; 475 [RU 7300]; 528 [RU 7346]; 577 [RU 7340]; 607 [RU 7412]
    NT Insect Identification, Division of (USDA)
        Insect Identification, Division of, Bureau of Entomology and Plant Quarantine (USDA)
Entomology Laboratory, Systematic (USDA)
    USE: Systematic Entomology Laboratory (USDA)
Environmental Programs, Office of, 31 [RU 254]
Environmental Protection Agency, 394 [RU 7459]; 428 [RU 7451]
Environmental Sciences, Office of, 30 [RU 108]; 31 [RU 254]; 312 [RU 274]
    NT Chesapeake Bay Center for Environmental Studies
        Ecology Program, Office of Environmental Sciences
        Oceanography and Limnology Program
    RT International Activities, Office of
Environmental Sciences Program, 32 [RU 329]; 248 [RU 256]; 641 [RU 9585]
Eppley Foundation, 267 [RU 412]
Epstein, Marc E., 619 [RU 9570]
Erdman, Donald S., 80 [RU 234]; 452 [RU 7428]
Erlich, Henry Anthony, 652 [RU 9577]
Ernst, Wallace R., 452 [RU 7096]
Erwin, Terry L., 102 [RU 411]
Escobar Paramo, Patricia, 627 [RU 9574]
Espy, James Pollard, 336 [RU 60]
Ethnic and Western Cultural History, Division of (NMHT), 164 [RU 251]
    BT Cultural History, Department of (NMHT)
Ethnogeographic Board, 9 [RU 46]; 325 [RU 87]; 618 [RU 9528]
Ethnology, Bureau of American
    USE: American Ethnology, Bureau of
Ethnology, Collected Letters on, 325 [RU 58]
Ethnology, Division of (NMNH), 128 [RU NAA 5]; 618 [RU 9528]; 622 [RU 9505]
    BT Anthropology, Department of (NMNH)
Ethnology, Division of (USNM), 168 [RU 258]; 644 [RU 9586]

    RT Cultural History, Division of (NMHT)
Ettinghausen, Richard, 262 [RU 4010001]; 264 [RU 4010004]
Euell, Julian T., 27 [RU 145]; 28 [RU 367]
Evans, Clifford, Jr., 29 [RU 393]; 39 [RU 192]; 68 [RU 429]; 128 [RU NAA 5]; 639 [RU 9508]
Evans, John, 452 [RU 7198]
Evans Gallery
    USE: Thomas M. Evans Special Exhibition Gallery
Evelyn, Douglas E., 138 [RU 583]
Evermann, Barton Warren, 78 [RU 213]
Everyday Life in the American Past, Hall of (NMHT), 165 [RU 331]; 644 [RU 9586]
Ewers, John C., 135 [RU 276]; 136 [RU 334]; 138 [RU 621]; 139 [RU 277]; 622 [RU 9505]
Ewing, Susan E., 636 [RU 9590]
Examinations and Reports, 57 [RU 121]
    RT Registrar (USNM)
Exchange Service, International
    USE: International Exchange Service
Executive Committee of the Board of Regents, 3 [RU 2]
Executive Officer
    USE: name of organizational unit
Exhibition
    USE: *Abroad in America: Visitors to the New Nation, 1776-1914*
        Academy: The Academic Tradition in American Art: Commemorating the 150th Anniversary of the National Academy of Design, 1975
        Aditi
        Alberto Giacometti 1901-1966
        America as Art, 1976
        American Pieced Quilts, 1973-1975
        American Presidency in Cartoons, 1789-1977
        American Self-Portraits, 1670-1972
        Art and Archeology of Vietnam, The
        Art of Paul Manship, The, 1989
        Art of the Arab World, 1975
        Artistic Collaboration in the Twentieth Century
        Atoms for Peace
        Augustus Saint-Gaudens: The Portrait Relief

USE: *Victory at Yorktown*
 Von Steuben
 Washington: From Banneker to
  Douglass, 1791-1870
 Washington in the New Era, 1870-
  1970
 We the People
 We Were But a Handful
 Wedgewood Portraits and the
  American Revolution
 Why Not A Woman
 Women in Science
 Woodenworks, 1972-1975
 Zoo to Art, 1985
Exhibition and Design, Office of (NCFA), 211
 [RU 314]; 212 [RU 448]
Exhibition and Design, Office of (NMAA), 212
 [RU 452]; 213 [RU 451]
 RT Design and Production, Department
  of (NMAA)
Exhibitions Abroad, Office of (NCFA), 217
 [RU 321]
 RT International Art Program
  Program Support, Office of (NMAA)
Exhibitions Coordinator (NMAA), 211 [RU
 449]
Exhibitions Department (CHM), 287 [RU 531]
Exhibitions, Department of (Cooper Union
 Museum for the Arts of Decoration), 287
 [RU 280]
Exhibitions, Office of (NPG), 227 [RU 361]
Exhibits, Department of (NMAH), 179 [RU
 551]
 RT Exhibits, Office of
  Exhibits Programs, Office of
   (NMAH)
Exhibits, Office of, 24 [RU 190]; 65 [RU 363];
 179 [RU 551]; 326 [RU 503]
 RT Exhibits Central, Office of
  Exhibits, Department of (NMAH)
  Exhibits, Office of (NMNH)
  Exhibits Program, Office of
  Exhibits Programs, Office of
Exhibits, Office of (NMNH), 65 [RU 363]; 66
 [RU 564]
 BT National Museum of Natural History
 RT Exhibits, Office of
  Exhibits Programs, Office of
Exhibits and Design, Department of (HMSG),
 273 [RU 516]
Exhibits Central, Office of, 26 [RU 342]; 326
 [RU 503]; 327 [RU 90]; 608 [RU 7331];
 643 [RU 9565]
 NT Exhibits Editors' Office

 RT Exhibits, Office of
  Exhibits Program, Office of
Exhibits Committee (NMNH), 65 [RU 363];
 65 [RU 366]
Exhibits Department (ANM), 279 [RU 378]
 NT Exhibits Design and Production
  Laboratory (ANM)
  Exhibits Training Program (ANM)
Exhibits Design and Production Laboratory
 (ANM), 277 [RU 350]; 279 [RU 378]
 BT Exhibits Department (ANM)
Exhibits Editors' Office, 327 [RU 90]
 BT Exhibits Central, Office of
Exhibits Editor's Office (NMNH), 647 [RU
 9523]
Exhibits Modernization Committee, United
 States National Museum, 24 [RU 190]; 642
 [RU 9512]
Exhibits Modernization Program, United
 States National Museum, 123 [RU 328];
 326 [RU 503]; 622 [RU 9505]; 624 [RU
 9506]; 631 [RU 9516]; 641 [RU 9521]; 642
 [RU 9512]
Exhibits Program, Office of, 326 [RU 503]
 RT Exhibits, Office of
Exhibits Programs, Office of, 24 [RU 190]; 65
 [RU 363]; 179 [RU 551]; 326 [RU 503];
 608 [RU 7331]
 RT Exhibits Central, Office of
  Exhibits, Department of (NMAH)
  Exhibits, Office of
  Exhibits, Office of (NMNH)
Exhibits Programs, Office of (NMNH), 647
 [RU 9523]
Exhibits Training Program (ANM), 277 [RU
 350]; 279 [RU 378]
 BT Exhibits Department (ANM)
Expedition
 RT Survey
 USE: Agassiz-*Albatross* Expedition to
  the eastern tropical Pacific,
  1904-1905
  Albatross Philippine expedition,
   1907-1909
  Alexander Alaska Expedition
  American Museum of Natural
   History China Expedition
  Bartlett Arctic Expeditions, 1928-
   1947
  Beach Anglo-Egyptian Sudan
   Expedition, 1928
  Beach-Webb Alaskan Expedition,
   1937
  Canadian Arctic Expedition, 1913-
   1916

USE: Commonwealth of Australia-
National Geographic Society-
Smithsonian Institution
Expedition to Arnhem Land,
1948

Eniwetok Atoll Expedition, 1963

Field Museum's African Expedition, 1907

Finn Ronn Antarctic Research
Expedition, 1946-1948

Firestone-Smithsonian Expedition
to Liberia, 1940

Greely Relief Expedition, 1884

Hancock Pacific-Galapagos
Expeditions, 1933-1935

Hancock South American Expedition, 1939

Harriman Alaska Expedition, 1899

Henderson Island Expedition,
1987

Hudson Bay Territory expeditions

Illustrated American Expedition to
Southern Utah and Northern
New Mexico

International Polar Expedition to
Point Barrow, Alaska, 1881-
1883

Isthmus of Chiriqui Expedition,
1860

Johnson-Smithsonian Deep-Sea
Expedition to the Puerto Rico
Trench, 1933

Johnson-Smithsonian Deep-Sea
Expedition to the West Indies,
1933

Knud Rasmussen Expedition,
1920

Koren Expedition to Siberia, 1914

Lincoln Ellsworth Expedition to
Alberta and British Columbia,
1914

Mangareva Expedition

Marsh-Darien expedition, 1924

Metropolitan Museum of Art
Expedition to Egypt, 1909

National Geographic Society-
Smithsonian Archeological
Expedition to Vera Cruz,
Mexico, 1938-1939

National Geographic Society-
Smithsonian Institution
Expedition to the Dutch East
Indies, 1937

National Geographic Society-
University of Virginia Expedition to the South Pacific Islands,
1939

National Geographic Society-Yale
University expedition to Peru

Navy Surveying Expedition to the
Phoenix and Samoan Islands,
1939

Nicollet Expedition, 1838

Northern Pacific Railroad Route
Expedition

Palmer Peninsula (Antarctica)
Survey, 1962-1963

Parish-Smithsonian Expedition,
1930

Pele Expedition, 1967

Pele Expedition to Indonesia, 1970

Rainey African Expedition, 1911-
1912

Roosevelt-Rondon South American
Expedition

Russian-American Telegraph
Expedition

Smithsonian Archeological
Expedition to Mexico

Smithsonian-Bredin Belgian Congo
Expedition, 1955

Smithsonian-Bredin Caribbean
Expeditions, 1956-1959

Smithsonian-Bredin Expedition to
Yucatan, 1960

Smithsonian-Bredin Society Islands
Expedition, 1957

Smithsonian-Chrysler Expedition
to East Africa, 1926

Smithsonian-Chrysler Expedition

Smithsonian-Firestone Expedition
to Liberia, 1940

Smithsonian-Hartford West Indies
Expedition, 1937

Smithsonian-Harvard Expedition to
Altai Mountains, Siberia, 1912

Smithsonian-Roosevelt African
Expedition, 1909

Smithsonian-Universal Film
Manufacturing Company African
Expedition, 1920

State University of Iowa Expedition to Barbados and Antigua

Te Vega Expedition to Malaysia,
Thailand, and Indonesia, 1963

Tomas Barrera expedition to
Cuba, 1914

USE: United States Exploring Expedition, 1838-1842
United States Naval Observatory Eclipse Expedition to Nivafoou Island, 1930
United States Naval Observatory Eclipse Expedition to the Philippine Islands, 1929
United States Navy Expedition to Guam, 1899
United States Navy Galapagos Expedition, 1941-1942
United States North Pacific Exploring Expedition
University of Pennsylvania expedition to Babylonia, 1887-1888
Walter Rathbone Bacon Traveling Scholarship expedition to the West Indies, 1928-1930
Western Union Telegraph Expedition

Explorer (satellite), 463 [RU 7416]

Explorers Club, 378 [RU 7006]; 557 [RU 7231]

Explorers Research Corporation, 170 [RU 381]

Exposition

USE: Berlin International Fisheries Exposition, 1880
California Pacific International Exposition, San Diego, 1935
Centennial Exposition, Philadelphia, 1876
Century of Progress Exposition, Chicago, 1933
Century 21 Exposition, Seattle, 1962
Cincinnati Industrial Exposition, 1884
Columbian Historical Exposition, Madrid, Spain, 1892
Cotton States and International Exposition, Atlanta, 1895
Golden Gate International Exposition, San Francisco, 1939
Great Lakes Exposition, Cleveland, 1936
Greater Texas and Pan American Exposition, 1937
International Exposition, Seville, Spain, 1927
International Exposition of Art and Technique in Modern Life, Paris, 1937
International Fur Trade Exposition and Congress, Leipzig, 1930
International Photographic Exposition, Dresden, 1909
International Silk Exposition, New York, 1921
Jamestown (Virginia) Tercentenary Exposition, 1907
Lewis and Clark Centennial Exposition, Portland, 1905
London International Fisheries Exposition, 1883
Louisiana Purchase Exposition, St. Louis, 1904
Louisville International Exposition, 1884
New York World's Fair, 1939
Ohio Valley and Central States Exposition, Cincinnati, 1888
Omaha, Trans-Mississippi, and International Exposition, 1898
Pageant of Progress Exposition, Chicago, 1922
Pan-American Exposition, Buffalo, New York, 1901
Panama-California Exposition, San Diego, 1916
Panama-Pacific International Exposition, San Francisco, 1915
Port-au-Prince Bicentennial Exposition, Haiti, 1949
Progress Exposition, New Haven, 1926
Sesquicentennial Exposition, Philadelphia, 1926
South Carolina Interstate and West Indian Exposition, Charleston, 1901-1902
Tennessee Centennial Exposition, Nashville, 1897
Texas Centennial Exposition, Dallas, 1936
World's Columbian Exposition, Chicago, 1893
World's Industrial and Cotton Centennial Exposition, New Orleans, 1884-1885
World's Poultry and Congress Exposition (Seventh), Cleveland, 1939

Exposition Records of the Smithsonian Institution and the United States National Museum, 327 [RU 70]

Exposition Shipping Records, 58 [RU 124]
    RT Registrar (USNM)
Extinct and Vanishing Birds of the World, 453 [RU 7402]
Eyde, Richard H., 68 [RU 429]; 111 [RU 428]
Ezell, Edward, 659 [RU 9532]

F

Face of the Deep, The, 479 [RU 7464]
Facilities Planning and Engineering Services, Office of, 324 [RU 638]; 324 [RU 640]; 329 [RU 562]; 329 [RU 637]; 330 [RU 641]
    NT Engineering and Design Branch (OFPES)
    RT Buildings Management Department
        Design and Construction, Office of
Fairchild, David Grandison, 453 [RU 7286]; 622 [RU 9559]
Fairchild, Graham Bell, 616 [RU 9567]; 622 [RU 9559]
Falk, John H., 29 [RU 393]; 268 [RU 399]; 354 [RU 388]
Faloona, Fred, 652 [RU 9577]
Family Policy Forum (symposium), 357 [RU 496]
Farber, Eduard, 158 [RU 579]
Farlow, William Gilson, 585 [RU 7192]
Farrington, Oliver Cummings, 386 [RU 7261]; 528 [RU 7460]
Fat Man (bomb), 653 [RU 9531]
FDR: The Intimate Presidency (exhibition), 149 [RU 376]
Federal Antiquities Act, 128 [RU NAA 5]
Federal City, The: Plans and Realities (exhibition), 23 [RU 337]
Feld, Bernard T., 653 [RU 9531]
Felhmann, H. Adair, 313 [RU 610]
Fellowes, Lucy, 287 [RU 531]; 288 [RU 287]
Fellowships and Grants, Office of, 29 [RU 526]; 32 [RU 329]
Fenykovi elephant, 82 [RU 7320]; 644 [RU 9587]
Fern, Alan M., 223 [RU 426]; 228 [RU 554]
Fern Journal, American
    USE: *American Fern Journal*
Fern Society, American, 108 [RU 223]
Fernald, Charles Henry, 585 [RU 7192]
Fernald, Henry Torsey, 494 [RU 7458]
Fernald, Merritt Lyndon, 404 [RU 7271]
Fernando Botero (exhibition), 272 [RU 481]
Ferrari, Frank D., 313 [RU 610]
Ferris, Jean Leon Gerome, 39 [RU 192]
Fertig, Barbara, 523 [RU 7295]

Fesperman, John T., Jr., 168 [RU 258]; 171 [RU 485]
Festival of American Folklife, 10 [RU 99]; 19 [RU 137]; 181 [RU 584]; 339 [RU 369]; 341 [RU 372]; 360 [RU 592]; 635 [RU 9569]; 636 [RU 9591]
Festival of India (exhibition), 28 [RU 367]
Festival of India (symposium), 357 [RU 496]; 357 [RU 497]
Fewkes, Jesse Walter, 454 [RU 7350]
Field, George B., 247 [RU 437]
Field, William D., 103 [RU 427]
Field Museum's African Expedition, 1907, 480 [RU 7179]
Fine Arts and Portrait Galleries, 370 [RU 92]; 616 [RU 9515]
    RT Patent Office Building
Fine Arts and Portrait Galleries Building, 203 [RU 313]; 318 [RU 532]
    RT Patent Office Building
Fine Arts Lending Program (NCFA), 210 [RU 445]
Fink, Eleanor E., 219 [RU 442]
Fink, Lois M., 219 [RU 596]
Finley, David E., 199 [RU 322]
Finn, Bernard S., 145 [RU 375]; 148 [RU 250]; 185 [RU 511]
Finn Ronn Antarctic Research Expedition, 1946-1948, 39 [RU 192]
Fireman, Edward L., 455 [RU 7463]
Firestone-Smithsonian Expedition to Liberia, 1940, 189 [RU 74]; 512 [RU 7293]
First Ladies Cookbook, 504 [RU 7466]
First Ladies Hall (NMAH), 174 [RU 473]; 504 [RU 7466]
First Ladies Hall (NMHT), 173 [RU 252]
Fiscal Division, 330 [RU 484]
    RT Contracts and Grants Division
        Contracts and Grants Section, Fiscal Division
        Grants and Insurance Administrative Division
        Grants and Risk Management, Office of
Fiscal Records, Federal, 365 [RU 93]
Fiscal Records, Private, 366 [RU 100]
Fish, Marie Poland, 80 [RU 234]
Fish and Wildlife Service, 394 [RU 7459]; 411 [RU 7171]; 412 [RU 7407]; 412 [RU 1070201]; 413 [RU 7146]; 413 [RU 1070101]; 420 [RU 7184]; 588 [RU 7176]; 612 [RU 9511]
    BT United States Department of the Interior

NT Alaska King Crab Investigation, Fish and Wildlife Service
Bird and Mammal Laboratories
Wild Fur Animal Investigation, Section of (Fish and Wildlife Service)
Wildlife Research, Branch of, Fish and Wildlife Service
RT Biological Survey, Bureau of
Fisheries, Bureau of
United States Fish Commission

Fish and Wildlife Survey of Guatemala, 1946-1947, 80 [RU 234]

Fish Commission, United States
USE: United States Fish Commission

Fish Hawk (vessel), 420 [RU 7184]

Fisher, Albert Kenrick, 398 [RU 7110]

Fisher, Irving, 481 [RU 7075]

Fisheries, Bureau of, 420 [RU 7184]; 421 [RU 7438]; 427 [RU 7258]; 465 [RU 7187]
RT Biological Survey, Bureau of
Bird and Mammal Laboratories
Fish and Wildlife Service
United States Fish Commission

Fisheries, Section of (USNM), 144 [RU 84]

Fisheries Division, Census of 1880, 567 [RU 7206]

Fisheries Exposition, Berlin International, 1880
USE: Berlin International Fisheries Exposition, 1880

Fishes, Collected Notes, Lists, Catalogs, Illustrations, and Records on, 80 [RU 7220]

Fishes, Division of (NMNH), 79 [RU 415]; 80 [RU 234]; 452 [RU 7428]; 524 [RU 7317]; 638 [RU 9510]
BT Biology, Department of (NMNH)

Fishes, Division of (USNM), 78 [RU 213]
BT Biology, Department of (USNM)
Zoology, Department of (USNM)
RT United States Fish Commission

"Fishes obtained by the United States Exploring Expedition, 1838-1842, under the command of Capt. Charles Wilkes," 458 [RU 7180]

Fishing schooner logbooks, New England, 527 [RU 7200]

Fiske, Richard S., 62 [RU 364]; 62 [RU 374]; 65 [RU 366]; 119 [RU 614]

Fitch, Asa, 455 [RU 7124]

Fite, Eugene J., 152 [RU 206]

Fitzhugh, William W., 128 [RU NAA 5]

Fleischman, Lawrence, 304 [RU 401]

Flentrop, D. A., 171 [RU 485]

Flentrop in America, 171 [RU 485]

Flight Operations, Department of (SAO), 251 [RU 260]
NT Celescope, Project (SAO)

Flint, James M., 154 [RU 244]

Flint, Janet L., 208 [RU 476]

Flint, Oliver S., Jr., 104 [RU 422]

Flora of Alaska, 439 [RU 7272]

Flora of America Commission, Medicinal, 37 [RU 189]

Flora of Fiji project, 452 [RU 7096]

Flora of North America Project, 61 [RU 197]

Florida State Museum, 608 [RU 7331]; 647 [RU 9523]

Florida State University, 626 [RU 9573]

Fluid Research Fund, 260 [RU 524]

Fluorescence Activated Cell Sorter, 651 [RU 9554]

Fluorspar investigations, United States Geological Survey, 605 [RU 7328]

"Focus" (WWICS) (radio broadcast), 301 [RU 601]

Foerste, August F., 456 [RU 7242]

Foerster, Arnold, 456 [RU 7130]

Fogg, Jack, 623 [RU 9572]

"Folk Masters" (radio broadcast), 360 [RU 591]

Foltz, Craig, 655 [RU 9542]

Fontaine, William Morris, 418 [RU 7395]

Foods, Section of (USNM), 37 [RU 189]; 146 [RU 240]; 395 [RU 7391]
BT Textiles, Division of (USNM)

Foote, Richard H., 579 [RU 7309]

Force, Peter, 525 [RU 7058]

Ford, Lorenzo, 124 [RU 543]

Foreign Affairs University, Beijing, China, 629 [RU 9575]

Foreign Currency Program, 31 [RU 254]; 310 [RU 180]; 311 [RU 218]
BT International Activities, Office of

Foreman, Edward R., 457 [RU 7216]

Forest Products, Hall of (NMHT), 146 [RU 240]

Forlow, William Gilson, 407 [RU 7085]

Forman, Paul, 148 [RU 250]

Fort Pierce Bureau, 31 [RU 254]; 32 [RU 329]
RT Marine Station at Link Port

Fosberg, Francis Raymond, 310 [RU 271]; 623 [RU 9572]

Foshag, William F., 120 [RU 7421]; 386 [RU 7261]; 436 [RU 7318]; 457 [RU 7281]; 549 [RU 7152]; 624 [RU 9529]

Foss, Barbara V., 282 [RU 545]

Fossil Plants, Department of (USNM), 597 [RU 7321]

Foster, George M., 128 [RU NAA 4]

Foster, Richard F., 653 [RU 9531]
Foster, Robin, 649 [RU 9553]
Four Star, 352 [RU 310]; 352 [RU 507]
14 Canadians: A Critic's Choice (exhibition), 272 [RU 481]
Fowler, Henry Weed, 78 [RU 213]; 458 [RU 7180]
Fox, Howard N., 271 [RU 469]
Francis Bacon: An Exhibition (exhibition), 272 [RU 481]
Frangiamore, Catherine Lynn, 285 [RU 282]
Frank F. Graham lawsuit, 1907-1915, 50 [RU 79]
Franklin D. Roosevelt Centennial, 22 [RU 477]
Fred Lawrence Whipple Observatory, 247 [RU 437]; 248 [RU 468]; 646 [RU 9520]; 655 [RU 9542]
    BT Smithsonian Astrophysical Observatory
    RT Mount Hopkins Observatory
Frederick A. Canfield Mineral Collection, 120 [RU 7291]
Frederick Douglass Home, 626 [RU 9558]
Frederick Hill Meserve Collection, 223 [RU 426]
Fredriksson, Kurt, 118 [RU 269]; 119 [RU 548]
Freeman, Monroe E., 356 [RU 482]
Freer, Charles Lang, 197 [RU 311]; 262 [RU 4010001]
Freer Gallery of Art, 7 [RU 31]; 8 [RU 45]; 19 [RU 137]; 21 [RU 104]; 22 [RU 477]; 329 [RU 562]; 329 [RU 637]; 366 [RU 100]; 370 [RU 92]
    BT Center for Asian Art
    RT Arthur M. Sackler Gallery of Art
Freer Gallery of Art, Building Construction Records, 264 [RU 4010003]
Freer Gallery of Art, Central Files, 262 [RU 4010001]
Freer Gallery of Art, Personnel and Special Events, 264 [RU 4010004]
Freer Gallery of Art Fund, 368 [RU 493]
Freer Medal, 262 [RU 4010001]
Freilicher, Miriam S., 612 [RU 9500]; 616 [RU 9515]; 619 [RU 9501]; 629 [RU 9502]; 634 [RU 9503]; 642 [RU 9512]; 645 [RU 9504]
French, Anthony, 653 [RU 9531]
French and Company, 443 [RU 7439]
Freudenheim, Thomas L., 25 [RU 608]
Friedmann, Herbert, 72 [RU 105]; 73 [RU 270]; 87 [RU 249]; 590 [RU 7133]; 624 [RU 9506]; 656 [RU 9539]

Friends of the Museum of the Cooper Union, 284 [RU 288]
    RT Cooper Union Museum for the Arts of Decoration
Friends of the National Zoo (NZP), 190 [RU 326]; 191 [RU 404]
Frisbee Festival (NASM), 242 [RU 339]
    BT Public Affairs, Office of (NASM)
Frisch, David, 653 [RU 9531]
Frisch, Rose, 653 [RU 9531]
Froeschner, Richard Charles, 102 [RU 418]; 554 [RU 7136]
Fudali, Robert F., 117 [RU 619]; 119 [RU 548]
Fulwyler, Mack Jett, 651 [RU 9554]
Fur animal experiment station, Saratoga Springs, New York, (USDA), 393 [RU 7143]
Fur Resources, Division of, Bureau of Biological Survey, 393 [RU 7143]
Fur Resources, Division of, Fish and Wildlife Service, 393 [RU 7143]
Fur Seal Commission, International, 574 [RU 7074]
Fur Trade Exposition and Congress, International, Leipzig, 1930, 393 [RU 7143]

G

Gabrielson, Ira N., 459 [RU 7319]
Gaetz, Ronald, 350 [RU 489]
Gage, R. B., 549 [RU 7152]
Gahan, Arthur Burton, 459 [RU 1020009]
Galapagos Science Conference, 1972, 31 [RU 254]
Gallenkamp, George, 216 [RU 443]
Galler, Sidney R., 30 [RU 108]; 31 [RU 254]; 33 [RU 150]
Garber, Paul E., 144 [RU 84]; 233 [RU 162]; 237 [RU 537]; 238 [RU 330]; 636 [RU 9590]
Garber Facility
    USE: Paul E. Garber Facility
Gardner, Julia A., 531 [RU 7327]
Gardner, Paul V., 166 [RU 406]
Garner, Floris M., 193 [RU 385]
Garrison, Wendell Phillips, 441 [RU 7073]
Garson, Inez, 272 [RU 481]
Gates, Adelia, 460 [RU 7312]
Gates, Gordon Enoch, 568 [RU 7262]
Gaudet, Charles P., 36 [RU 561]
Gauss, F. Stephen, 648 [RU 9534]
Gazenko, Oleg, 659 [RU 9551]
Gazin, Charles Lewis, 121 [RU 156]; 122 [RU 424]; 124 [RU 543]; 460 [RU 7314]

Gefland, David H., 652 [RU 9577]
Geisler, Bruno, 37 [RU 189]
Gellatly, John, 200 [RU 550]
Geller, Margaret J., 651 [RU 9546]
Gem and Mineral Hall (NMNH), 116 [RU 336]
General Accounting Office, 625 [RU 9525]
General Motors Corporation, 656 [RU 9550]
Genin, Abraham, 659 [RU 9551]
Gentner, Louis G., 461 [RU 7341]
Geographical and Geological Survey of the Rocky Mountain Region, United States
    USE: United States Geographical and Geological Survey of the Rocky Mountain Region
Geography, Inter-American Society of Anthropology and, 128 [RU NAA 4]
Geological and Geographical Surveys of the Territories, United States
    USE: United States Geological and Geographical Surveys of the Territories
Geological Commission of Brazil, 540 [RU 7078]
Geological Museum of Canada, 553 [RU 7221]
Geological Names, Committee on, United States Geological Survey, 542 [RU 7326]
Geological Society of America, 460 [RU 7314]; 542 [RU 7326]; 571 [RU 7325]
Geological Survey, Illinois, 554 [RU 7154]
Geological Survey, United States
    USE: United States Geological Survey
Geology, Department of (NMNH), 120 [RU 7421]; 122 [RU 424]; 123 [RU 328]; 403 [RU 7234]; 418 [RU 7395]; 436 [RU 7318]; 481 [RU 7349]; 502 [RU 7360]; 505 [RU 7251]; 619 [RU 9524]; 624 [RU 9529]; 644 [RU 9587]
    NT Invertebrate Paleontology and Paleobotany, Division of (NMNH)
        Vertebrate Paleontology, Division of (NMNH)
    RT Paleobotany, Department of (NMNH)
Geology, Department of (USNM), 120 [RU 7291]; 542 [RU 7326]
    NT Mineralogy and Petrology, Division of (USNM)
        Vertebrate Paleontology, Division of (USNM)
    RT Mineral Sciences, Department of (NMNH)

Geology, Department of (USNM), Biographical File, 119 [RU 7230]
George C. Marshall Library, 632 [RU 9589]
George C. Marshall Research Center, 632 [RU 9589]
George C. Marshall Research Foundation, 632 [RU 9589]
George Washington (statue), 329 [RU 562]
George Washington Memorial, 39 [RU 192]; 370 [RU 92]
George Washington Memorial Association, 8 [RU 45]; 377 [RU 7004]
George Washington, statue, 329 [RU 562]
George Washington University, 378 [RU 7006]; 608 [RU 7331]
    NT Museum Studies Program, George Washington University
Germann, Sheridan, 171 [RU 485]
Gettings, Frank B., 275 [RU 515]
Geyer, Carl Andreas, 462 [RU 7290]
Giacconi, Riccardo, 463 [RU 7416]
Gibbs, George, 407 [RU 7085]; 464 [RU 7209]; 501 [RU 7202]
Gibbs, Robert H., Jr., 71 [RU 382]; 79 [RU 415]; 80 [RU 234]; 464 [RU 7122]
Gibson, Gordon D., 68 [RU 429]; 639 [RU 9508]
Gibson, Mary S. M., 281 [RU 267]
Gibson, Terrica M., 632 [RU 9578]
Gidley, James W., 121 [RU 156]; 121 [RU 248]; 122 [RU 424]; 123 [RU 7264]; 465 [RU 7324]
Gifford, Prosser, 297 [RU 560]; 298 [RU 558]; 301 [RU 601]
Gigliotti, Joanne, 352 [RU 507]
Gilbane Building Company, 244 [RU 358]
Gilbert, Chester G., 149 [RU 297]
Gill, Theodore Nicholas, 78 [RU 213]
Gillilland, Coralee C., 176 [RU 359]
Gilmore, Charles W., 39 [RU 192]; 121 [RU 156]
Gilmore, Raymond Maurice, 81 [RU 208]
Ginsburg, Isaac, 465 [RU 7187]
Girard, Charles Frederic, 466 [RU 7190]
Gireeva, Irina, 659 [RU 9551]
Girty, George Herbert, 466 [RU 7329]
Glad, John, 299 [RU 567]
Glance, Grace E., 104 [RU 422]
Glaser, Jane R., 338 [RU 625]
Glassell, Steve A., 467 [RU 7257]
Gleason, Abbott, 299 [RU 291]; 299 [RU 567]
Glennan-Webb-Seamans Project for Research in Space History, 236 [RU 354]
Glimmer of Their Beauty, A: Black Sounds in the Twenties (exhibition), 227 [RU 361]

RT Graphic Arts, Division of (NMHT)
Graphic Arts, Division of (USNM)
Photographic History, Division of
(NMAH)
Photographic History, Division of
(NMHT)
Photography, Section of (NMHT)
Grasses, Division of (USNM), 112 [RU 229]
BT Botany, Department of (USNM)
Gravitational Redshift Space Probe Experi-
ment (SAO), 250 [RU 253]; 258 [RU 522]
BT Smithsonian Astrophysical Observa-
tory
Gray, Asa, 407 [RU 7085]; 417 [RU 7189]
Grayson, William C., 362 [RU 593]
Greager, Oswald H., 653 [RU 9531]
Great Ape House (NZP), 190 [RU 380]
Great Britain Board of Trade Committee on
Electrical Standards, 402 [RU 7214]
Great Lakes Exposition, Cleveland, 1936, 39
[RU 192]; 327 [RU 70]
Greater Texas and Pan American Exposition,
1937, 39 [RU 192]
Greeley, Frederick Atwood, 471 [RU 7307]
Greeley, Olive A., 471 [RU 7307]
Greely Relief Expedition, 1884, 37 [RU 189]
Green, Bernard R., 50 [RU 79]
Green, Stanford, 601 [RU 7112]
Greenbriar Boys, 635 [RU 9569]
Greene, Charles Tull, 472 [RU 7354]
Greene, Edward L., 473 [RU 7155]
Greene, Elizabeth E., 140 [RU 335]
Greene, John C., 485 [RU 7474]
Greene Herbarium, Edward L., 439 [RU 7272]
Greenhall, Arthur Merwin, 411 [RU 7171]
Greenwald, Irwin, 657 [RU 9536]
Greenway, James C., Jr., 453 [RU 7402]
Greenwood, Edna, 644 [RU 9586]
Gregory, John G., 248 [RU 468]
Griego, David, 654 [RU 9544]
Griffenhagen, George B., 154 [RU 244]
Griffin, Molly Ann Dwyer, 102 [RU 7422]
Griffith, Fuller O., III, 152 [RU 206]
Griffiths, David, 473 [RU 7370]
Grimmer, J. Lear, 190 [RU 380]
Griphos (computer database system), 522 [RU
7432]
Grobman, Arnold B., 473 [RU 7389]
Gronberger, Sven M., 474 [RU 7199]
Gross, M. Grant, 124 [RU 543]
Grossi, Mario, 258 [RU 517]
Grossman, Robert L., 652 [RU 9577]
Growth of the United States (exhibition), 644
[RU 9586]

Growth of the United States (NMHT), 169
[RU 261]
BT Civil History, Department of
(NMHT)
RT Domestic Life, Division of (NMHT)
Preindustrial Cultural History,
Division of (NMHT)
Gruber, Martin A., 474 [RU 7355]
Guangzhong, Dong, 262 [RU 4010001]
Guest, Grace D., 262 [RU 4010001]
Gunn, Donald, 36 [RU 561]
Gunnell, Leonard C., 333 [RU 77]
Gunnison, John W., 507 [RU 7157]
Gurney, Ashley B., 475 [RU 7300]
Gurney, Susan, 221 [RU 463]
Guthrie, Dorothy, 65 [RU 363]
Guyot, Arnold Henry, 336 [RU 60]

H

Haberstich, David E., 156 [RU 529]
Hackel, Eduard, 475 [RU 1010006]
Haeckel, Ernst, 426 [RU 7315]
Haff, Lawrence Allen, 652 [RU 9577]
Hagen, Hermann August, 490 [RU 7107]
Hagen, Joel B., 622 [RU 9559]; 645 [RU 9560]
Hagge, Carl W., 254 [RU 263]
Hahn, J. Frank, 476 [RU 7475]
Halcyon (vessel), 420 [RU 7184]
Hale, Herbert M., 386 [RU 7261]
Hale, Mason E., Jr., 107 [RU 272]; 111 [RU
428]
Half-Century book project, Smithsonian, 346
[RU 76]; 544 [RU 7081]
Haliday, Alexander Henry, 601 [RU 7112]
Hall
USE: name of hall
Hall, James, 121 [RU 248]; 517 [RU 7177]
Hall, Robert C., 39 [RU 192]
Hallion, Richard C., 240 [RU 348]
Hallock, Charles, 476 [RU 7204]
Halpert, Edith, 203 [RU 313]
Halstead, Richard, 661 [RU 9548]
Haltzel, Michael H., 301 [RU 559]
Hamarneh, Sami K., 154 [RU 244]; 155 [RU
471]
Hamilton, Susan A., 23 [RU 337]; 306 [RU
403]; 354 [RU 626]
Hamlet, Sybil E., 194 [RU 365]
Hammer, William Joseph, 39 [RU 192]
Hancock Foundation, 444 [RU 7097]
Hancock Pacific-Galapagos Expeditions, 1933-
1935, 557 [RU 7231]

Hancock South American Expedition, 1939, 557 [RU 7231]

Handbook of North American Indians, 128 [RU NAA 5]

Handbook of the Birds of India and Pakistan, 380 [RU 7008]

Handley, Charles O., Jr., 81 [RU 208]; 82 [RU 400]; 83 [RU 407]

Hanford Engineering Works (Washington), 653 [RU 9531]

Hanle, Paul A., 235 [RU 343]; 240 [RU 348]

Hans Syz Collection, 166 [RU 406]

Haptic Gallery (NPG), 226 [RU 555]

Harakal, Eileen, 350 [RU 489]

Harbridge House, 418 [RU 7304]

Harding, Robert S., 179 [RU 599]

Hardisty, William L., 36 [RU 561]

Hardy, Alan, 476 [RU 7436]

Hardy, Thora M. Plitt, 476 [RU 7144]

Harmon, Vaughan, 249 [RU 259]

Harney, Thomas R., 67 [RU 416]

Harriman Alaska Expedition, 1899, 439 [RU 7272]; 477 [RU 7243]

Harriman-Alaska Series, 8 [RU 45]

Harring, Harry K., 477 [RU 7237]

Harris, Elizabeth M., 152 [RU 206]; 153 [RU 413]

Harris, Israel H., 37 [RU 189]

Harris, Thomas R., 385 [RU 7298]

Harris, Van T., 411 [RU 7171]

Hart, Charles W., Jr., 64 [RU 384]; 88 [RU 423]; 90 [RU 414]

Hart, Harry T., 65 [RU 363]

Hart, Sidney, 230 [RU 2040001]

Hartford-Smithsonian West Indies Expedition, 1937, 557 [RU 7231]

Hartigan, Lynda Roscoe, 206 [RU 458]

Harvard College Observatory, 247 [RU 437]; 248 [RU 468]; 254 [RU 304]; 602 [RU 7431]; 646 [RU 9520]; 651 [RU 9546]
     RT Smithsonian Astrophysical Observatory

Harvard-Smithsonian Joint Center for Astrophysics, 11 [RU 613]
     BT Harvard University
     RT Center for Astrophysics

Harvard University, 247 [RU 437]; 323 [RU 168]; 380 [RU 7008]; 566 [RU 7316]; 602 [RU 7431]; 622 [RU 9559]; 636 [RU 9591]; 645 [RU 9560]; 651 [RU 9546]

Harwit, Martin O., 234 [RU 338]

Hass, Wilbert Henry, 478 [RU 7365]

Hassam, Childe, 200 [RU 550]

Hasse, William F., 65 [RU 363]

Hatch, Josiah O., 181 [RU 584]

Hatcher, John Bell, 121 [RU 248]

Hatchett, Stephen P., 512 [RU 7254]

Hathaway, Anthony N., 168 [RU 258]

Hathaway, Calvin S., 281 [RU 267]; 283 [RU 633]; 287 [RU 280]

Haverford College, 629 [RU 9575]

Hawkins, David, 653 [RU 9531]

Hawkins, Robert B., Jr., 300 [RU 571]

Hawley, Edwin H., 144 [RU 219]

Haworth, Harold L., 318 [RU 532]

Hay, Oliver Perry, 478 [RU 7188]

Hay, William Perry, 486 [RU 7469]

Hayden, Ferdinand Vandeveer, 407 [RU 7085]; 517 [RU 7177]; 533 [RU 7208]

Hayes, David, 484 [RU 7449]

Haystack Observatory (Westfield, Massachusetts), 258 [RU 517]

Hazel, Joseph E., 530 [RU 7425]

Heavy Machinery, Hall of (NMAH), 151 [RU 397]

Hebard, Morgan, 427 [RU 7162]

Hecker, Frank J., 262 [RU 4010001]

Heckscher, August, 636 [RU 9591]

Heezen, Bruce C., 479 [RU 7464]

Hegeman, Annie M., 39 [RU 192]

Heinrich, Carl, 101 [RU 7427]; 480 [RU 7125]; 618 [RU 9555]

Heller, Edmund, 480 [RU 7179]

Hemiptera, Division of (NMNH), 102 [RU 418]
     BT Entomology, Department of (NMNH)
     RT Hemiptera and Hymenoptera, Division of (NMNH)

Hemiptera and Hymenoptera, Division of (NMNH), 102 [RU 418]
     BT Entomology, Department of (NMNH)
     RT Hemiptera, Division of (NMNH)

Hemphill, Henry, 94 [RU 7418]; 95 [RU 7461]

Henderson, Amy E., 228 [RU 556]

Henderson, Charles, 481 [RU 7349]

Henderson, Edward P., 115 [RU 268]; 118 [RU 269]; 120 [RU 7421]; 386 [RU 7261]; 481 [RU 7349]; 624 [RU 9529]

Henderson, John Brooks, 481 [RU 7075]

Henderson, John Brooks, Jr., 94 [RU 7418]; 481 [RU 7075]

Henderson, Martha M., 481 [RU 7349]

Henderson, Mary Foote, 481 [RU 7075]

Henderson Island Expedition, 1987, 63 [RU 362]

Henize, Karl G., 254 [RU 263]

Henry, Harriet, 374 [RU 7001]

Henry, Joseph, 5 [RU 26]; 6 [RU 27]; 7 [RU 33]; 16 [RU 38]; 325 [RU 58]; 336 [RU 60]; 347 [RU 217]; 374 [RU 7001]; 408 [RU 7194]; 430 [RU 7080]; 441 [RU 7073]; 501 [RU 7202]; 525 [RU 7115]; 541 [RU 7070]; 543 [RU 7470]; 550 [RU 7390]; 572 [RU 7066]; 590 [RU 7055]

Henry, Mary A., 374 [RU 7001]; 572 [RU 7066]

Henry Papers, Joseph
    USE: Joseph Henry Papers

Henry statue, Joseph, 329 [RU 562]

Henry, Thomas R., 483 [RU 7347]

Henshaw, Samuel, 564 [RU 7296]

Henson, Pamela M., 612 [RU 9511]; 615 [RU 9517]; 616 [RU 9515]; 617 [RU 9514]; 618 [RU 9528]; 618 [RU 9555]; 619 [RU 9524]; 619 [RU 9570]; 620 [RU 9571]; 623 [RU 9572]; 624 [RU 9506]; 624 [RU 9529]; 624 [RU 9566]; 625 [RU 9509]; 625 [RU 9525]; 626 [RU 9573]; 627 [RU 9574]; 628 [RU 9513]; 629 [RU 9502]; 630 [RU 9507]; 630 [RU 9576]; 631 [RU 9516]; 633 [RU 9568]; 633 [RU 9579]; 634 [RU 9519]; 636 [RU 9591]; 637 [RU 9581]; 637 [RU 9582]; 638 [RU 9510]; 639 [RU 9508]; 640 [RU 9580]; 640 [RU 9584]; 641 [RU 9521]; 641 [RU 9585]; 642 [RU 9512]; 644 [RU 9586]; 644 [RU 9587]; 646 [RU 9520]; 647 [RU 9523]; 649 [RU 9553]; 659 [RU 9530]

Herbarium, United States National
    USE: United States National Herbarium

Herbarium Services Unit (NMNH), 111 [RU 428]
    BT Botany, Department of (NMNH)

"Here at the Smithsonian" (television broadcast), 360 [RU 591]

Herman, Lloyd E., 208 [RU 465]

Herpetologists, American Society of Ichthyologists and
    USE: American Society of Ichthyologists and Herpetologists

Herpetology, Department of (NMNH), 83 [RU 161]
    RT Reptiles and Batrachians, Department of (NMNH)

Herring, Jon L., 483 [RU 7343]

Hersey, David F., 356 [RU 482]

Hershkovitz, Philip, 39 [RU 192]; 500 [RU 7434]

Herzenberg, Leonard A., 651 [RU 9554]

Herzenberg, Leonore A., 651 [RU 9554]

Heyer, W. Ronald, 29 [RU 393]; 68 [RU 429]; 71 [RU 382]; 84 [RU 327]

Hibbs, Albert R., 660 [RU 9535]

Hickey, Leo J., 65 [RU 366]; 124 [RU 543]

Higgins, Robert P., 312 [RU 273]; 313 [RU 563]

High Energy Astrophysics Division (CFA), 463 [RU 7416]

High Energy Astrophysics Division (SAO), 247 [RU 437]; 257 [RU 467]

High School Scholars at the Smithsonian, 357 [RU 496]

Hildebrand, Samuel Frederick, 465 [RU 7187]

Hilgard, Julius Erasmus, 441 [RU 7073]

Hill, Elizabeth, 350 [RU 489]

Hillebrand, William F., 549 [RU 7152]

Hillwood, 19 [RU 137]; 22 [RU 281]; 329 [RU 562]
    RT Marjorie Merriweather Post estate

Hillwood Museum, 616 [RU 9515]

Hilton, George W., 160 [RU 239]

Hilton, William Atwood, 623 [RU 9572]

Hindle, Brooke, 135 [RU 276]; 136 [RU 334]

Hinners, Noel W., 234 [RU 338]

Hippisley, Alfred E., 37 [RU 189]; 39 [RU 192]

Hirohito (emperor of Japan), 262 [RU 4010001]; 497 [RU 7333]

Hiroshima (Japan), 653 [RU 9531]

Hirshhorn, Joseph H., 270 [RU 510]; 271 [RU 469]; 484 [RU 7449]; 624 [RU 9566]; 636 [RU 9591]

Hirshhorn, Olga C., 484 [RU 7449]; 624 [RU 9566]

Hirshhorn Museum and Sculpture Garden, 11 [RU 613]; 14 [RU 615]; 19 [RU 137]; 21 [RU 104]; 22 [RU 281]; 22 [RU 477]; 139 [RU 277]; 271 [RU 469]; 271 [RU 512]; 272 [RU 481]; 273 [RU 514]; 273 [RU 516]; 275 [RU 515]; 318 [RU 532]; 319 [RU 639]; 329 [RU 562]; 330 [RU 641]; 339 [RU 369]; 343 [RU 410]; 370 [RU 92]; 484 [RU 7449]; 616 [RU 9515]; 624 [RU 9566]; 636 [RU 9591]
    NT Department of Administration and Museum Support Services (HMSG)
        Education, Department of (HMSG)
        Exhibits and Design, Department of (HMSG)
    NT Painting and Sculpture, Department of (HMSG)
        Registrar, Office of the (HMSG)

Hirshhorn Museum and Sculpture Garden, Director, Office of the, 270 [RU 510]

Hirst, William P., 252 [RU 255]

Hispanic American History, Program of
(NMAH), 181 [RU 584]
Historian, Office of the (NPG), 228 [RU 556]
Historic Americans, Hall of (NMAH), 174 [RU
473]
Historic Archeology, Division of (NMHT), 170
[RU 381]
Historic Places, National Register of, 25 [RU
191]
Historic Preservation, Advisory Council on, 25
[RU 191]
Historical Society, American, 387 [RU 7057]
History, Department of (USNM), 155 [RU
396]
History, Division of (USNM), 613 [RU 9522]
History and Technology Building, 318 [RU
532]; 370 [RU 92]
    RT American History Building
History and Technology, National Museum of
    USE: National Museum of History and
        Technology
History of Common Salt, A, 521 [RU 7467]
History of Machines and Banking (exhibition),
176 [RU 359]
History of Science, Department of (NMHT),
145 [RU 375]
    NT Electricity and Modern Physics,
        Division of (NMHT)
        Mathematics, Division of (NMHT)
        Mechanisms, Division of (NMAH)
        Medical Sciences, Division of
        (NMHT)
        Physical Sciences, Division of
        (NMHT)
    RT History of Science and Technology,
        Department of the (NMAH)
History of Science and Technology, Department of the (NMAH), 145 [RU 375]
    NT Armed Forces History, Division of
        (NMAH)
        Mathematics, Division of (NMAH)
        Mechanical and Civil Engineering,
        Division of (NMAH)
        Mechanisms, Division of (NMAH)
        Medical Sciences, Division of
        (NMAH)
        Military History, Division of
        (NMAH)
        Naval History, Division of (NMAH)
        Photographic History, Division of
        (NMAH)
        Physical Sciences, Division of
        (NMAH)
        Transportation, Division of
        (NMAH)

    RT History of Science, Department of
        (NMHT)
        History of Technology, Department
        of (NMHT)
        Science and Technology, Depart-
        ment of (NMHT)
History of Science Society, 483 [RU 7363];
485 [RU 7474]; 521 [RU 7467]
History of Technology, Department of
(NMHT), 145 [RU 375]
    RT History of Science and Technology,
        Department of the (NMAH)
*History under the Sea: A Handbook for
Underwater Exploration,* 170 [RU 381]
Hitchcock, Albert Spear, 112 [RU 229]
Hobbs, Horton H., Jr., 87 [RU 249]; 486 [RU
7469]; 512 [RU 7254]; 617 [RU 9514]; 625
[RU 9509]
Hodges, Elaine R. S., 102 [RU 7422]
Hodges, Ronald William, 580 [RU 7426]
Hodgkins Fund, 7 [RU 31]; 8 [RU 34]; 8 [RU
45]; 368 [RU 493]
Hofer, William C., 201 [RU 318]
Hoffman, Regis, 658 [RU 9552]
Hoffman, Thomas E., 655 [RU 9542]
Hoffman-La Roche Corporation, 652 [RU
9577]
Hoffmann, Robert S., 29 [RU 526]; 62 [RU
374]; 64 [RU 425]
Hogan, Kevin P., 649 [RU 9553]
Hollick, Arthur, 597 [RU 7321]
Hollis, Helen R., 171 [RU 485]
Hollister, Ned, 81 [RU 208]; 189 [RU 74]; 487
[RU 7392]
Holmes, Frederic L., 485 [RU 7474]
Holmes, Julian C., 656 [RU 9539]
Holmes, Walter W., 39 [RU 192]
Holmes, William Henry, 125 [RU NAA 1]; 128
[RU NAA 5]; 197 [RU 311]; 198 [RU 312];
203 [RU 313]; 221 [RU 463]; 487 [RU
7084]
Holt collection of South American birds, 39
[RU 192]
Holton, Gerald, 485 [RU 7474]
Homage to Thomas Eakins (exhibition), 227
[RU 361]
Hong Kong Herbarium Library, 404 [RU 7271]
Hood, Leroy E., 650 [RU 9549]
Hoogstraal, Harry, 488 [RU 7454]
Hoover, Cynthia A., 165 [RU 331]; 168 [RU
258]; 171 [RU 485]
Hope, W. Duane, 68 [RU 429]; 87 [RU 249];
88 [RU 423]; 89 [RU 307]; 96 [RU 417];
639 [RU 9508]

Hope Diamond, 39 [RU 192]; 644 [RU 9587]

Hopkins, Philip S., 233 [RU 162]

Hopps, Walter, 206 [RU 458]

Horan, Henry, 317 [RU 157]

Hornaday, William Temple, 86 [RU 210]; 189 [RU 74]

Hornblower and Marshall, 370 [RU 92]

Hornig, Donald, 653 [RU 9531]

Hornig, Lillian, 653 [RU 9531]

Horsley, Jaren G., 191 [RU 404]; 193 [RU 385]

Hoth, Sue, 523 [RU 7295]

Hotton, Nicholas, III, 122 [RU 424]

Houbrick, Richard S., 93 [RU 73]; 94 [RU 7418]

Houchins, Lee, 147 [RU 383]

Hough, Walter, 128 [RU NAA 5]

Hough, William Jervis, 489 [RU 7061]

How Humans Adapt: A Biocultural Odyssey (symposium), 332 [RU 498]

Howard, Leland Ossian, 96 [RU 138]; 97 [RU 139]; 384 [RU 7305]; 490 [RU 7107]; 561 [RU 7104]; 564 [RU 7296]

Howell, Arthur Holmes, 489 [RU 7169]

Howland, Richard H., 12 [RU 618]; 164 [RU 251]; 169 [RU 261]; 177 [RU 580]

Hoyt, John Southgate Yeaton, 490 [RU 7405]

Hoyt, Sally Foresman, 490 [RU 7405]

Hrdlicka, Ales, 618 [RU 9528]; 641 [RU 9521]

Hsia, John I., 254 [RU 263]

Hubbard, Henry Guernsey, 101 [RU 7448]; 490 [RU 7107]; 561 [RU 7104]

Hubel, Gordon, 348 [RU 535]

Huber, Paul, 653 [RU 9531]

Hubert H. Humphrey Fellowship in Social and Political Thought (WWICS), 298 [RU 582]

Huchra, John, 651 [RU 9546]

Huddle, John W., 491 [RU 7398]

Hudson Bay Territory expeditions, 375 [RU 7002]

Hudson's Bay Company, 36 [RU 561]

Hueber, Francis M., 68 [RU 429]

Huffaker, E. C., 376 [RU 7003]

Hughes, Phillip S., 20 [RU 392]; 625 [RU 9525]

Hull, Frank M., 102 [RU 7422]

Hume, Ivor Noel, 166 [RU 406]

Humphrey, Hubert H., 361 [RU 587]

Humphrey, Philip S., 71 [RU 136]; 71 [RU 382]; 73 [RU 270]; 76 [RU 245]; 348 [RU 534]

Humphrey Fellowship in Social and Political Thought, Hubert H. (WWICS), 298 [RU

Hunkapiller, Michael, 650 [RU 9549]

Hurd, Harold, 648 [RU 9545]

Hurd, Paul D., Jr., 98 [RU 247]; 98 [RU 430]; 102 [RU 418]; 491 [RU 7311]

Hurlbut, Elbridge O., 33 [RU 150]; 322 [RU 470]

Huscher, Harold, 131 [RU NAA 6]

Hutchins, James S., 183 [RU 377]; 184 [RU 581]

Hutchins, Louis W., 492 [RU 7248]

Hutchinson, G. Evelyn, 636 [RU 9591]

Hutchinson, Louise Daniel, 626 [RU 9558]

Huxley, Michael R., 31 [RU 254]

Huxley, Thomas Henry, 426 [RU 7315]

Hydrogen Maser Program (SAO), 250 [RU 253]

Hyman, Harry, 33 [RU 150]

Hyman, Libby Henrietta, 626 [RU 9573]

I

Ichthyologists and Herpetologists, American Society of
    USE: American Society of Ichthyologists and Herpetologists

Iddings, Joseph Paxson, 493 [RU 7205]

Illg, Paul Louis, 89 [RU 307]

Illinois Geological Survey, 554 [RU 7154]

Illinois State Museum (Springfield), 647 [RU 9523]

Illustrated American Expedition to Southern Utah and Northern New Mexico, 37 [RU 189]

Imlay, Ralph W., 493 [RU 7380]

Immovable Objects/Lower Manhattan from Battery Park to the Brooklyn Bridge (exhibition), 288 [RU 287]; 291 [RU 547]; 293 [RU 541]

Inaugural Exhibition, 272 [RU 481]

India Space Research Organization, 258 [RU 517]

Indian Affairs, Bureau of, 622 [RU 9505]

Industries, Department of (NMHT), 10 [RU 50]

Infant Task Force, 569 [RU 7443]

Information and Education Directors, Council of, 629 [RU 9575]

Information, Office of, 342 [RU 82]; 343 [RU 371]

    RT Public Affairs, Office of

Infrared Telescope Program (SAO), 248 [RU 468]

Insect Detection and Identification Branch
(USDA), 594 [RU 7403]
  BT Insect Identification, Division of
   United States Department of
   Agriculture
Insect Identification, Division of (USDA), 98
[RU 246]; 421 [RU 7368]; 582 [RU 7339];
607 [RU 7412]
  BT Entomology and Plant Quarantine,
   Bureau of (USDA)
  RT Systematic Entomology Laboratory
   (USDA)
Insect Identification and Beneficial Insect
Introduction Institute (USDA), 576 [RU
7373]
  RT Systematic Entomology Laboratory
   (USDA)
Insect Identification and Parasite Introduction
Branch (USDA), 102 [RU 418]
Insect Identification and Parasite Introduction
Research Branch (USDA), 483 [RU 7343];
494 [RU 7458]; 580 [RU 7426]; 600 [RU
7400]
  RT Systematic Entomology Laboratory
   (USDA)
Insects, Collected Scientific Illustrations and
Photographs of, 102 [RU 7422]
Insects, Division of, 96 [RU 138]
  BT Biology, Department of (USNM)
Insects, Division of (NMNH), 97 [RU 140]; 98
[RU 430]; 400 [RU 7103]; 425 [RU 7338];
472 [RU 7354]; 570 [RU 7419]; 579 [RU
7309]; 615 [RU 9517]; 618 [RU 9555]; 619
[RU 9570]
  BT Biology, Department of (NMNH)
   Entomology, Department of
   (NMNH)
   National Museum of Natural History
  RT Entomology, Department of
   (NMNH)
Insects, Division of (USNM), 96 [RU 138]; 97
[RU 139]
  BT Biology, Department of (USNM)
   Zoology, Department of (USNM)
  RT Entomology, Department of
   (USNM)
Insect Zoo (NMNH), 65 [RU 363]; 326 [RU
503]
Institute for Astronomy (Cambridge, England),
651 [RU 9546]
Institute for Biomedical Problems (Moscow),
659 [RU 9551]
Institute for Research in Tropical America, 17
[RU 135]; 304 [RU 134]
  BT National Research Council

Institute for Social Anthropology, 128 [RU
NAA 4]
Institute of Museum Services, 26 [RU 342]
Inter-American Committee of Experts on
Nature Protection and Wild Life Preserva-
tion, 378 [RU 7006]
Inter-American Society of Anthropology and
Geography, 128 [RU NAA 4]
Interdepartmental Committee on Cooperation
with the American Republics, 518 [RU
7386]
Interdisciplinary Communications Program,
331 [RU 300]
Interdisciplinary Studies, Office of, 332 [RU
495]; 332 [RU 498]
  RT Symposia and Seminars,
   Smithsonian Office of
Interior, United States Department of the
  USE: United States Department of the
   Interior
International Activities, Office of, 27 [RU
145]; 29 [RU 526]; 31 [RU 254]; 310 [RU
91]; 312 [RU 274]
  RT Environmental Sciences, Office of
   International and Environmental
   Programs, Office of
   International Programs, Office of
International and Environmental Programs,
Office of, 31 [RU 254]; 311 [RU 218]; 312
[RU 274]
  NT Ecology Program, Office of Interna-
   tional and Environmental
   Programs
   Oceanography and Limnology
   Program
  RT Environmental Sciences, Office of
   International Activities, Office of
   International Programs, Office of
International Archeological Commission, 125
[RU NAA 1]
International Art Program, 203 [RU 313]; 217
[RU 321]
  BT National Collection of Fine Arts
   United States Information Agency
  RT Exhibitions Abroad, Office of
   (NCFA)
International Astronomical Union, 602 [RU
7431]
International Astronomical Union Taskgroup
for Lunar Nomenclature, 239 [RU 353]; 449
[RU 7415]
International Biological Program, 588 [RU
7229]
  RT United States Marine Mam-
   Program

International Botanical Congress, 1969, 439
[RU 7356]
International Boundary Commission, United
States-Mexican, 1891-1894
USE: United States-Mexican Interna-
tional Boundary Commission,
1891-1894
International Boundary Survey, United States-
Mexican, 1891-1894, 439 [RU 7272]; 515
[RU 7083]
International Catalogue of Scientific Litera-
ture, 320 [RU 65]; 333 [RU 77]; 365 [RU
93]; 366 [RU 100]
International Center Committee, Advisory
Committee for Historic Preservation, 26
[RU 342]
International Centre for Conservation in Rome,
26 [RU 342]
International Centre for the Study of the
Preservation and Restoration of Cultural
Property, 25 [RU 191]
International Commission for Military History,
510 [RU 7358]; 632 [RU 9589]
International Commission of Maritime History,
510 [RU 7358]
International Commission on Nomenclature,
1943-1983, 497 [RU 7333]
International Commission on Zoological
Nomenclature, 574 [RU 7074]; 638 [RU
9583]
International Committee on Atomic Weights,
430 [RU 7080]
International Conference on the Biology of
Whales, 588 [RU 7229]
International Conference on the History of
Cartography, Washington, D.C., August
1977, 510 [RU 7358]
International Congress of Maritime Museums,
510 [RU 7358]
International Congress of Systematic and
Evolutionary Biology, 494 [RU 7141]; 494
[RU 7145]
International Congress of Zoology, 500 [RU
7434]
International Convention Advisory Commis-
sion, 32 [RU 329]
International Convention on the Regulation of
Whaling, 495 [RU 7165]
International Council for Bird Preservation,
380 [RU 7008]; 612 [RU 9511]; 636 [RU
9591]
International Council of Museums, 24 [RU
190]; 26 [RU 342]; 137 [RU 279]; 337 [RU
624]; 349 [RU 488]; 642 [RU 9512]

International Council of Museums, Interna-
tional Committee on Museum Security, 510
[RU 7358]
International Environmental Sciences Program,
32 [RU 329]
International Exchange Service, 333 [RU 61];
334 [RU 502]; 334 [RU 509]; 365 [RU 93];
367 [RU 165]
International Exposition, Seville, Spain, 1927,
39 [RU 192]
International Exposition of Art and Technique
in Modern Life, Paris, 1937, 327 [RU 70]
International Fur Seal Commission, 574 [RU
7074]
International Fur Trade Exposition and
Congress, Leipzig, 1930, 393 [RU 7143]
International Geological Congress, 1885, 604
[RU 7238]
International Geological Congress, 1891, 604
[RU 7238]
International Geological Congress, 1913, 586
[RU 7332]
International Monetary Fund, 495 [RU 7109]
International Ornithological Congresses, 378
[RU 7006]
International Photographic Exposition,
Dresden, 1909, 39 [RU 192]
International Polar Expedition to Point Barrow,
Alaska, 1881-1883, 522 [RU 7203]
International Program for Population Analysis,
331 [RU 300]
International Program in Ecology, 310 [RU
271]
International Programs, Office of, 31 [RU
254]; 312 [RU 274]; 319 [RU 607]
    NT Center for Short-Lived Phenomena
    RT Center for Short-Lived Phenomena
        Environmental Sciences, Office of
        International Activities, Office of
        International and Environmental
            Programs, Office of
International Silk Exposition, New York, 1921,
39 [RU 192]
International Ultraviolet Explorer, 653 [RU
9543]
International Union for the Conservation of
Nature, 32 [RU 329]; 380 [RU 7008]; 636
[RU 9591]
International Union of Directors of Zoological
Gardens, 633 [RU 9568]
International Union of the History and
Philosophy of Science, 521 [RU 7467]
International Whaling Commission, 39 [RU
192]; 495 [RU 7165]; 500 [RU 7434]

International Whaling Conference, 495 [RU 7165]

International Wood Collectors Society, 606 [RU 7285]

International Year of the Quiet Sun Comet Project (SAO), 249 [RU 259]

Interpretive Programs (NASM), 243 [RU 356]
  NT Albert Einstein Spacearium (NASM)

Inventors Council, National, 562 [RU 7091]

Invertebrate Paleontology, Collected Notebooks, Manuscripts, and Photographs on, 123 [RU 7264]

Invertebrate Paleontology, Division of (NMNH), 619 [RU 9524]

Invertebrate Paleontology and Paleobotany, Division of (NMNH), 123 [RU 328]; 548 [RU 7299]; 632 [RU 9578]
  BT Geology, Department of (NMNH)

Invertebrate Zoology, Collected Manuscripts, Correspondence, Drawings, Photographs, and Notes on, 89 [RU 7260]

Invertebrate Zoology, Department of (NMNH), 87 [RU 249]; 87 [RU 292]; 88 [RU 423]; 89 [RU 307]; 90 [RU 414]; 96 [RU 417]; 501 [RU 7383]; 625 [RU 9509]; 626 [RU 9573]
  NT Crustacea, Division of (NMNH)
     Echinoderms, Division of (NMNH)
     Marine Invertebrates, Division of (NMNH)
     Mollusks, Division of (NMNH)
     Worms, Division of (NMNH)
  RT Zoology, Department of (NMNH)

Iowa Agricultural Experiment Station, 446 [RU 7137]

Irene and Herbert F. Johnson Collection, 216 [RU 443]

Isaac Stevens' survey, 437 [RU 7067]; 452 [RU 7198]
  BT Pacific Railroad Surveys

Isham, Lawrence B., 124 [RU 543]

Isis, 485 [RU 7474]; 521 [RU 7467]

Isis Editorial Advisory Board, 543 [RU 7470]

Islamic Culture and Art Archives, 262 [RU 4010001]

Isthmus of Chiriqui Expedition, 1860, 452 [RU 7198]

It All Depends (exhibition), 643 [RU 9565]

Izsak, Imre G., 496 [RU 7282]

J

Jackson, Everett A., 154 [RU 244]

Jackson, Hartley H. T., 389 [RU 7357]; 496 [RU 7172]

Jackson, Lewis A., 648 [RU 9545]

Jackson, Melvin H., 147 [RU 383]; 160 [RU 239]; 161 [RU 528]

Jacobs, Madeleine, 340 [RU 420]

James, Jack N., 660 [RU 9535]

James, Stanford, 661 [RU 9548]

James Watson Fund, 525 [RU 7115]

James Weldon Johnson (exhibition), 227 [RU 361]

Jameson, John F., 20 [RU 394]

Jamestown (Virginia) Tercentenary Exposition, 1907, 39 [RU 192]

Janssen, Barbara Suit, 174 [RU 472]

Japan, Crown Prince of, 1965, 264 [RU 4010004]

Japanese lacquer work, 144 [RU 219]

Japanese tools, collection of, 144 [RU 219]

Jarosewich, Eugene, 119 [RU 548]

Jarvis, Jennifer, 289 [RU 324]

Java Farm, 266 [RU 286]

Jazz at the Smithsonian, 181 [RU 584]

Jefferson National Expansion Memorial (St. Louis), 608 [RU 7331]; 647 [RU 9523]

Jeffreys, J. Gwyn, 37 [RU 189]; 441 [RU 7073]; 497 [RU 7092]

Jenkins, Dale W., 310 [RU 271]

Jenny, Adele, 377 [RU 7004]

Jet Propulsion Laboratory, University of California, 660 [RU 9535]

Jewell, Jerry, 655 [RU 9533]

Jewitt, A. Clive, 575 [RU 7379]

Johansen, Frits, 477 [RU 7237]

John, Stanley, 39 [RU 192]

John A. Roebling Solar Research Fund, 368 [RU 493]

John F. Kennedy Center for the Performing Arts, 19 [RU 137]; 318 [RU 532]

John F. Kennedy Library, 629 [RU 9575]

John Muir (exhibition), 227 [RU 361]

John Paul II (pope), 340 [RU 368]

Johns Hopkins University, 428 [RU 7451]
  RT Chesapeake Research Consortium, Inc.

Johnson, Charles W., 94 [RU 7418]

Johnson, Charles Y., 656 [RU 9539]

Johnson, David H., 81 [RU 208]

Johnson, J. Stewart, 285 [RU 282]

Johnson, Lady Bird, 361 [RU 587]

Johnson, Lyndon B., 270 [RU 510]; 361 [RU 587]

Johnson, Paul S., 358 [RU 586]

Johnson, Roy W., 318 [RU 532]

Johnson Sea-Link accident, 1973, 31 [RU 254]; 341 [RU 372]

Johnson-Smithsonian Deep-Sea Expedition to the Puerto Rico Trench, 1933, 9 [RU 46]
Johnson-Smithsonian Deep-Sea Expedition to the West Indies, 1933, 39 [RU 192]; 402 [RU 7089]
Johnson Wax Collection, 216 [RU 443]
Johnston, Earl S., 267 [RU 412]
Johnston, S. Paul, 233 [RU 162]; 632 [RU 9578]
Johnston, W. Robert, 209 [RU 453]
Joint Commission of Scientific Societies of Washington, D.C., 597 [RU 7099]
Joint Committee on Zoological Nomenclature for Paleontology in America, 497 [RU 7333]
Jones, Carolyn, 352 [RU 507]
Jones, Clyde J., 411 [RU 7171]
Jones, Daryl, 633 [RU 9579]
Jones, David C., 652 [RU 9577]
Jones, Frank Morton, 497 [RU 7409]
Jones, Meredith Leam, 68 [RU 429]; 89 [RU 307]; 96 [RU 417]; 626 [RU 9573]
Jones, Strachan, 36 [RU 561]
Jordan, David Starr, 78 [RU 213]
Jordan, Harry, 204 [RU 447]
Jose De Creeft, 1983 (exhibition), 205 [RU 460]
Joseph Henry Papers, 21 [RU 104]; 22 [RU 477]; 543 [RU 7470]
Joseph Henry (statue), 329 [RU 562]
Joseph, Mildred, 124 [RU 543]
Josephine Ford, 39 [RU 192]
Josiah K. Lilly, Jr., Collection, 176 [RU 359]
Journal
    USE: name of journal
Jouy, Pierre Louis, 37 [RU 189]
Juday, Chancey, 568 [RU 7262]
Judd, Neil M., 618 [RU 9528]

K

Kaeppler, Adrienne L., 128 [RU NAA 5]
Kahn Foundation for Foreign Travel of American Teachers, 8 [RU 45]
Kainen, Jacob, 152 [RU 206]; 153 [RU 413]; 208 [RU 476]; 214 [RU 455]
Kaiser, Robert J., 650 [RU 9549]
Kalashnikov, Mikhail T., 659 [RU 9532]
Kalcik, Susan, 352 [RU 507]
Kallop, Edward L., 283 [RU 633]; 287 [RU 280]
Kanazawa, Robert H., 80 [RU 234]
Kansas Settlers Society of Chicago, Illinois, 596 [RU 7123]

Kaplan, Janice, 352 [RU 507]
Kaplan, Lewis D., 660 [RU 9535]
Karisoke Research Centre, Rwanda, 191 [RU 404]
Karlstrom, Paul J., 306 [RU 403]
Karr, William W., 7 [RU 31]; 367 [RU 165]
Kassessinoff, E., 448 [RU 7468]
Kasson, John A., 600 [RU 7159]
Katz, Amron H., 657 [RU 9536]
Katz, Elena D., 652 [RU 9577]
Kauffman, Erle G., 68 [RU 429]; 124 [RU 543]; 639 [RU 9508]
Keam, Thomas V., 37 [RU 189]
Keddy, John L., 19 [RU 175]; 335 [RU 294]; 645 [RU 9504]
Keeler, David B., 212 [RU 448]; 213 [RU 451]
Keen, A. Myra, 497 [RU 7333]; 614 [RU 9526]; 627 [RU 9527]
Keim, Chris P., 653 [RU 9531]
Keith, D. Graeme, 287 [RU 280]
Keller, Brian D., 649 [RU 9553]
Kellers, Henry C., 499 [RU 7241]
Kelley, Lesley S., 652 [RU 9577]
Kellogg, A. Remington, 24 [RU 190]; 39 [RU 192]; 46 [RU 89]; 47 [RU 88]; 61 [RU 155]; 81 [RU 208]; 135 [RU 276]; 136 [RU 334]; 451 [RU 7348]; 495 [RU 7165]; 499 [RU 7170]; 500 [RU 7434]; 621 [RU 9518]; 631 [RU 9516]
Kellogg, Marguerite H., 500 [RU 7434]
Kellogg Foundation Project, 337 [RU 624]; 338 [RU 625]; 338 [RU 630]
Kelson, H. Eugene, 204 [RU 447]; 204 [RU 475]
Kendall, Amos, 590 [RU 7055]
Kendall, Edward C., 146 [RU 240]
Kendall, Sue Ann, 306 [RU 403]
Kenk, Roman, 501 [RU 7383]
Kennan Institute for Advanced Russian Studies (WWICS), 299 [RU 291]; 299 [RU 567]
Kennedy, Roger G., 136 [RU 334]; 138 [RU 583]
Kennedy Center for the Performing Arts, John F., 19 [RU 137]; 318 [RU 532]
Kennedy Library, John F., 629 [RU 9575]
Kennerly, Caleb Burwell Rowan, 408 [RU 7052]; 501 [RU 7202]
Kenney, Gilbert H., 304 [RU 401]
Kennicott, Robert, 76 [RU 7215]; 441 [RU 7073]; 502 [RU 7072]; 601 [RU 7213]
Kenny, Sister Elizabeth, 154 [RU 244]
Kensley, Brian F., 90 [RU 414]
Kenyon, Karl Walton, 412 [RU 7407]
Kerby, Catherine J., 64 [RU 384]; 312 [RU 273]

Langley-Abbot Solar Research Program (SAO), 247 [RU 437]
    BT Smithsonian Astrophysical Observatory
Langley-Wright controversy, 8 [RU 45]; 9 [RU 46]
Lansdowne, J. Fenwick, 380 [RU 7008]
Laporte, Francois de, Count Castleneau, 434 [RU 7051]
Larsen, Carl W., 339 [RU 369]; 340 [RU 420]
Larson, Clarence E., 653 [RU 9531]
Larson, Jane W., 653 [RU 9531]
Laser-10 (exhibition), 326 [RU 503]
Latham, John, 200 [RU 320]
Lawless, Benjamin W., 179 [RU 551]
Lawrence, Sidney, 274 [RU 513]
Lawson, Edward W., 273 [RU 514]
Lawton, Thomas, 262 [RU 4010001]; 264 [RU 4010004]
Lea, Isaac, 39 [RU 192]; 509 [RU 7065]
Leaf Thieves, The, 1963 (motion picture), 361 [RU 587]
Leaflets in Malacology, 410 [RU 7335]
Leapley, William T., 80 [RU 234]
Leath, Richard, 652 [RU 9577]
Leavy, Joseph B., 177 [RU 580]
Lebaron, John Francis, 37 [RU 189]
LeConte, John Lawrence, 407 [RU 7085]; 490 [RU 7107]; 561 [RU 7104]; 564 [RU 7296]
Lecture and Seminar Program (SNAP), 353 [RU 557]
Ledley, Robert S., 654 [RU 9544]
LeDoyt, Bruce, 661 [RU 9548]
Legacy of Strategic Bombing, The, 1989-1990 (lecture series), 241 [RU 355]
Legnasky, Michael, 287 [RU 531]
Lehigh University, 559 [RU 7429]
Lellinger, David B., 643 [RU 9565]
Lenman, Isobel H., 39 [RU 192]
Lennox, Thomas E., 285 [RU 282]
Leonard, Emery Clarence, 113 [RU 230]
Lepidoptera, Division of (NMNH), 103 [RU 427]
    BT Entomology, Department of (NMNH)
    RT Neuropteroids, Division of (NMNH)
"Lepidoptera of North America," 400 [RU 1020006]
Lepidopterist's Society, The, 424 [RU 7399]
Lerner, Abram, 270 [RU 510]; 271 [RU 469]
Lesley, Everett P., Jr., 287 [RU 280]
Leslie, Philip, 344 [RU 568]
Lesquereux, Charles Leo, 418 [RU 7395]; 597 [RU 7321]

Levison, Walter, 657 [RU 9536]
Levy, Florence N., 197 [RU 311]
Levy, Sandra J., 304 [RU 401]
Lewis, Cathleen S., 659 [RU 9551]
Lewis, Lester Clark, 158 [RU 293]
Lewis, Ralph H., 647 [RU 9523]
Lewis and Clark Centennial Exposition, Portland, 1905, 327 [RU 70]
Lewton, Frederick L., 146 [RU 240]; 154 [RU 244]
Lewton, Val, 213 [RU 451]
Library (CHM), 294 [RU 598]
Library, National Museum of American Art and Portrait Gallery
    USE: National Museum of American Art and Portrait Gallery Library
Library of Congress, 347 [RU 217]; 543 [RU 7470]; 545 [RU 7382]
Library
    USE: Smithsonian Institution Library
Liebhold, Peter, 656 [RU 9550]
Life and Work of Edward Greene Malbone, Miniature Painter, The, 583 [RU 7433]
Life Histories of North American Birds, 407 [RU 7120]; 406 [RU 7394]
Lilley, Arthur Edward, 258 [RU 517]
Lilly Collection, Josiah K., Jr., 176 [RU 359]
Lincoln, Frederick C., 459 [RU 7319]
Lincoln Ellsworth Expedition to Alberta and British Columbia, 1914, 480 [RU 7179]
Lincoln Memorial Commission, 39 [RU 192]
Lincoln University (Pennsylvania), 632 [RU 9578]
Lindbergh, Charles A., 39 [RU 192]
Lindsay, G. Carroll, 168 [RU 258]
Link Foundation, 10 [RU 50]
Linton, Claude, 257 [RU 303]
Little Boy (bomb), 653 [RU 9531]
Littler, Mark M., 111 [RU 428]
Liu, Li-Ing, 658 [RU 9564]
Living Animals, Department of (USNM), 86 [RU 210]; 189 [RU 74]
    RT National Zoological Park
Living Things, Hall of (NMNH), 643 [RU 9565]
Living Vertebrates, Department of (NZP), 193 [RU 385]
    RT Animal Department (NZP)
        Animal Management, Office of (NZP)
        Animal Programs, Office of (NZP)
Livingston, Audrey B., 653 [RU 9531]
Livingston, Robert S., 653 [RU 9531]
Llano, George Albert, 112 [RU 228]

Lloyd, Hoyes, 387 [RU 7150]
Loar, Peggy A., 349 [RU 488]
Local Notes, 334 [RU 298]
Lockhart, James, 36 [RU 561]
Lodge, Henry Cabot, 407 [RU 7085]
Lodge, John Ellerton, 262 [RU 4010001]; 264
   [RU 4010004]
Loeb, Morris, 39 [RU 192]
Lomax, Alan, 635 [RU 9569]
London International Fisheries Exposition,
   1883, 327 [RU 70]; 418 [RU 7193]; 468
   [RU 7050]
Long, Austin, 268 [RU 387]
Longhorn Radio Network, 301 [RU 601]
Longley, William Harding, 510 [RU 7223]
Loomis, Elias, 336 [RU 60]; 407 [RU 7085]
Loomis, Sylvia, 304 [RU 401]
Lopez, Donald S., 234 [RU 338]; 234 [RU
   346]; 238 [RU 330]
Loring, George B., 105 [RU 220]
Loring, John Alden, 510 [RU 7420]
Los Alamos National Laboratory, New Mexico,
   651 [RU 9554]
Los Alamos Scientific Laboratory (New
   Mexico), 653 [RU 9531]
Los Angeles County Museum, 623 [RU 9572]
Louis Sullivan: The Function of Ornament
   (exhibition), 293 [RU 541]
Louisiana Purchase Exposition, St. Louis,
   1904, 39 [RU 192]; 189 [RU 74]; 327 [RU
   70]
Louisville International Exposition, 1884, 58
   [RU 124]
Love, Doris, 494 [RU 7145]
Lovejoy, Thomas E. III, 72 [RU 534]; 643 [RU
   9565]
Lovell, Hin-cheung, 262 [RU 4010001]
Lovett, Sabine K., 631 [RU 9540]
Low-Beer, Fritz, 262 [RU 4010001]
Lowe, Harry, 202 [RU 444]; 203 [RU 313];
   211 [RU 314]; 212 [RU 448]
Lowe Art Gallery (Miami), 443 [RU 7439]
Lubar, Steven, 658 [RU 9552]
Lucas, Frederic Augustus, 78 [RU 203]; 121
   [RU 156]; 121 [RU 248]
Lunar Exploration Department, Bellcom, Inc.,
   449 [RU 7415]
Lundeberg, Philip K., 147 [RU 383]; 510 [RU
   7358]
Lundquist, Charles A., 250 [RU 253]; 251 [RU
   260]
Lutz, Adolpho, 432 [RU 7151]
Lutz, Bertha, 432 [RU 7151]
Lyon, Marcus Ward, Jr., 81 [RU 208]

Lyon, Rowland, 210 [RU 445]
Lytle, Richard H., 344 [RU 568]; 346 [RU 98]

M

M16 automatic rifle, 659 [RU 9532]
MacArthur, Robert H., 640 [RU 9584]
MacDonald-Wright, Stanton, 203 [RU 313]
MacFarlane, Roderick Ross, 36 [RU 561]; 37
   [RU 189]; 76 [RU 7215]; 502 [RU 7072];
   511 [RU 7207]
MacGowan, D. J., 37 [RU 189]
MacIntyre, Ian G., 123 [RU 328]
MacNab, James Arthur, 568 [RU 7262]
MacPherson, Glenn J., 119 [RU 548]
Mactavish, W., 36 [RU 561]
Made in Chicago, 1974 (exhibition), 206 [RU
   458]
Magedov, Vladimir, 659 [RU 9551]
Magnetic Telegraph Company, 590 [RU 7055]
Magruder, Colonel John H. III, 184 [RU 581]
Mahlman, F. H., 318 [RU 532]
Mahoney, James A., 65 [RU 363]; 643 [RU
   9565]
Mahy, Brian Wilfred John, 658 [RU 9564]
Makovenyi, Nadya A., 235 [RU 352]
Male, Walter, 636 [RU 9590]
Mallery, Garrick, 127 [RU NAA 2]
Malone, Adrian, 359 [RU 594]
Malone, Alice Reno, 179 [RU 599]
Maloney, James O., 512 [RU 7254]
Maltby, L. C., 376 [RU 7003]
Mammal Identification Service (NMNH), 83
   [RU 407]
     RT Mammals, Division of (NMNH)
Mammal Laboratories, Bird and
     USE: Bird and Mammal Laboratories
Mammalogy, Journal of, 389 [RU 7357]
Mammals, Collected Notes, Lists, Drawings,
   and Catalogs on, 82 [RU 7217]
Mammals, Division of (NMNH), 81 [RU 208];
   82 [RU 400]; 82 [RU 7320]; 83 [RU 407];
   621 [RU 9518]; 631 [RU 9516]
     BT Biology, Department of (NMNH)
     RT Mammal Identification Service
        (NMNH)
Mammals, Division of (USNM), 46 [RU 89];
   47 [RU 88]
     BT Biology, Department of (USNM)
        Vertebrate Zoology, Department of
        (USNM)
        Zoology, Department of (USNM)

Man and Beast: A Symposium on Comparative Social Behavior (symposium), 315 [RU 494]

Man and Beast Revisited (symposium), 332 [RU 495]; 332 [RU 498]; 357 [RU 496]; 357 [RU 497]

Man for All Seasons, A: The Life and Portraits of John Quincy Adams (exhibition), 227 [RU 361]

MAN transFORMS/Aspects of Design, 1976 (exhibition), 288 [RU 287]; 291 [RU 547]

Management Analysis Office, 335 [RU 294]; 335 [RU 486]
    RT Administrative Systems Division
        Organization and Methods Division

Mangareva Expedition, 623 [RU 9572]

Manhattan Project, 653 [RU 9531]

Manly, Charles M., 376 [RU 7003]

Mann, Albert, 434 [RU 7292]; 435 [RU 7437]

Mann, Lucile Quarry, 195 [RU 395]; 512 [RU 7293]; 628 [RU 9513]

Mann, William M., 189 [RU 74]; 190 [RU 326]; 190 [RU 380]; 195 [RU 395]; 512 [RU 7293]; 614 [RU 9526]; 628 [RU 9513]; 633 [RU 9568]

Manning, Catherine L., 177 [RU 580]

Manning, Harry F., 370 [RU 92]

Manning, Raymond B., 68 [RU 429]; 87 [RU 249]; 87 [RU 292]; 89 [RU 307]; 90 [RU 414]

Mansfield, Richard, 39 [RU 192]

Manship, Paul, 203 [RU 313]

Manufactures, Section of (USNM), 146 [RU 240]

Manville, Richard Hyde, 411 [RU 7171]; 412 [RU 7407]

Marcellini, Dale L., 191 [RU 404]

Marconi, Nello, 226 [RU 552]

Marine Biological Laboratory of the Carnegie Institution of Washington, 518 [RU 7336]

Marine Biological Laboratory (Woods Hole, Massachusetts), 559 [RU 7429]

Marine Invertebrates, Department of (NMNH), 94 [RU 202]
    NT Corals, Section of (NMNH)

Marine Invertebrates, Division of (NMNH), 88 [RU 423]; 89 [RU 307]; 91 [RU 233]; 92 [RU 235]; 93 [RU 73]; 96 [RU 417]; 548 [RU 7299]; 557 [RU 7231]
    BT Biology, Department of (NMNH)
        Invertebrate Zoology, Department of (NMNH)
        Zoology, Department of (NMNH)

    NT Corals, Section of (NMNH)
    RT Crustacea, Division of (NMNH)
        Echinoderms, Division of (NMNH)
        Mollusks, Division of (NMNH)
        Worms, Division of (NMNH)

Marine Mammal Program, United States
    USE: United States Marine Mammal Program

Marine Station at Link Port, 32 [RU 329]
    RT Fort Pierce Bureau

Marine Transportation, Section of (USNM), 160 [RU 239]
    BT Engineering, Division of (USNM)
    RT Transportation, Division of (NMHT)

Mariner 2 (satellite), 660 [RU 9535]

Marjorie Merriweather Post estate, 329 [RU 562]
    RT Hillwood

Mark, J. Carson, 653 [RU 9531]

Markoe, Francis, Jr., 525 [RU 7058]

Marland Oil Company, 440 [RU 1050101]

Marsh, Caryl Amsterdam, 214 [RU 454]

Marsh, Jane, 200 [RU 320]

Marsh, Othniel Charles, 121 [RU 248]

Marsh, Paul Malcolm, 580 [RU 7426]

Marsh-Darien expedition, 1924, 39 [RU 192]

Marshall, George C., 632 [RU 9589]

Marshall Library, George C., 632 [RU 9589]

Marshall Research Center, George C., 632 [RU 9589]

Marshall Research Foundation, George C., 632 [RU 9589]

Marshall, William B., 93 [RU 73]

Martin-Felton, Zora B., 278 [RU 390]

Martin, Joseph, 661 [RU 9548]

Marx, George, 585 [RU 7192]

Mary Agnes Chase Fund, 112 [RU 229]

Mary McLeod Bethune (exhibition), 227 [RU 361]

Maryland Historic Trust, 631 [RU 9516]

Marzio, Peter C., 153 [RU 413]; 165 [RU 331]

Mason, Brian H., 117 [RU 266]; 118 [RU 269]; 119 [RU 548]

Mason, Otis Tufton, 128 [RU NAA 5]; 325 [RU 58]; 513 [RU 7086]

Mathematics, Division of (NMAH), 159 [RU 332]
    RT Mathematics, Division of (NMHT)
        Mathematics, Section of (NMHT)
        Physical Sciences and Mathematics, Division of (NMAH)

Mathematics, Division of (NMHT), 159 [RU 332]

BT History of Science, Department of
(NMHT)
  Science and Technology, Depart-
  ment of (NMHT)
RT Medical Sciences, Division of
(NMAH)
Medical Sciences Information Exchange, 356
[RU 482]
  RT Bio-Sciences Information Exchange
  Science Information Exchange
Medical Zoology Department, Naval Medical
Research Unit No. 3, 488 [RU 7454]
Medicinal Flora of America Commission, 37
[RU 189]
Medicinal Plants Survey, 1897-1898, 439 [RU
7272]
Medicine, Division of (USNM), 39 [RU 192]
  BT Anthropology, Department of
  (USNM)
Medicine and Public Health, Division of
(USNM), 154 [RU 244]; 155 [RU 471]
  BT Engineering and Industries,
  Department of (USNM)
  RT Medical Sciences, Division of
  (NMHT)
Mediterranean Marine Sorting Center, 312
[RU 273]; 313 [RU 563]; 313 [RU 610]
  BT Oceanography and Limnology,
  Office of
Meek, Fielding B., 516 [RU 7062]
Megerian, G. K., 251 [RU 260]
Meinel, Aden, 655 [RU 9542]
Meisel, Albert, 296 [RU 275]
Mekong Basin Project, 1972, 31 [RU 254]
Melander, Axel Leonard, 516 [RU 1020010]
Melder, Keith E., 173 [RU 252]; 174 [RU 473]
Melendez, Manuel J., 181 [RU 584]
Mello, James F., 62 [RU 374]
Mellon, Andrew, 9 [RU 46]; 223 [RU 426]
Melosh, Barbara, 155 [RU 471]
Melson, William G., 68 [RU 429]; 117 [RU
266]; 119 [RU 614]
Membership and Development, Office of
(CHM), 291 [RU 436]
  BT Cooper-Hewitt Museum
Membership and Programs, Department of
(CHM), 290 [RU 284]
*Memoirs of Ira Noel Gabrielson and What
Others Have Said About Him,* 459 [RU
7319]
*Memorias de la Comision de Limites a las
ordenes del General Manuel Mier y Teran,*
408 [RU 7052]
"Memories of William Augustus Croffut," 440
[RU 7197]

Menez, Ernani G., 313 [RU 610]
Merida, Jesse, 124 [RU 543]
Merriam, Charles W., 530 [RU 7425]
Merriam, Clinton Hart, 398 [RU 7110]; 510
[RU 7420]; 564 [RU 7296]
Merriam, Clinton Levi, 516 [RU 7182]
Merriam, John Campbell, 499 [RU 7170]
Merrill, Elmer Drew, 595 [RU 7270]
Merrill, George P., 120 [RU 7421]; 517 [RU
7177]
Merzbach, Uta C., 158 [RU 293]; 159 [RU
332]
Meserve Collection, Frederick Hill, 223 [RU
426]
Meteor Research Program (SAO), 250 [RU
253]; 258 [RU 522]
  BT Smithsonian Astrophysical Observa-
  tory
Meteor Simulation Project (SAO), 250 [RU
253]
  BT Smithsonian Astrophysical Observa-
  tory
Meteorite Photography and Recovery Project
(Prairie Network) (SAO), 249 [RU 259];
250 [RU 253]; 251 [RU 302]; 602 [RU
7431]
Meteorites, Division of (NMNH), 118 [RU
269]; 119 [RU 548]; 481 [RU 7349]; 624
[RU 9529]
  BT Mineral Sciences, Department of
  (NMNH)
Meteorological Project, 336 [RU 60]
Metropolitan Mechanics Institute, 517 [RU
7064]
Metropolitan Museum of Art, 197 [RU 311];
262 [RU 4010001]
Metropolitan Museum of Art Expedition to
Egypt, 1909, 39 [RU 192]
Metropolitan Society, 434 [RU 7051]
Metropolitan State Art Contest, 197 [RU 311]
Mexican International Boundary Commission,
United States, 1891-1894
  USE: United States-Mexican Interna-
  tional Boundary Commission,
  1891-1894
Mexican-International Boundary Survey,
United States, 1891-1894
  USE: United States-Mexican Interna-
  tional Boundary Survey, 1891-
  1894
Mexican-United States Boundary Survey,
1855-1857
  USE: United States-Mexican Boundary
  Survey, 1855-1857

Meyer, Agnes E., 264 [RU 4010004]
Meyer, Robert B., 238 [RU 330]
Meyrick, Edward, 422 [RU 7129]
Mhatre, Nagesh S., 651 [RU 9554]
Miami Station, Florida, 471 [RU 7307]
Michaels, Andrew F., 317 [RU 157]; 329 [RU 562]
Mid-American Center, Arkansas, 14 [RU 605]
Middleton, Jean J., 140 [RU 335]
Mier y Teran, Manuel, 408 [RU 7052]
Mikesh, Robert C., 238 [RU 344]
Milestones of Flight (stamp issues), 238 [RU 330]
Military Affairs, 510 [RU 7358]
Military History, Division of (NMAH), 155 [RU 396]
    BT History of Science and Technology, Department of the (NMAH)
    RT Military History, Division of (NMHT)
Military History, Division of (NMHT), 155 [RU 396]
    RT Military History, Division of (NMAH)
Military History, Division of (USNM), 155 [RU 396]
    BT History, Department of (USNM)
    RT Military History, Division of (NMHT)
Millard, Charles W., 271 [RU 469]
Miller, A. J., 37 [RU 189]
Miller, Carl, 131 [RU NAA 6]
Miller, Douglass R., 580 [RU 7426]
Miller, Gerrit Smith, Jr., 81 [RU 208]; 517 [RU 7173]
Miller, J. Jefferson II, 166 [RU 406]; 613 [RU 9522]
Miller, Lillian B., 228 [RU 556]; 230 [RU 2040001]
Miller, Robert Rush, 80 [RU 234]
Miller House, 282 [RU 545]
Mills, Deborah J.
    USE: Warner, Deborah J. (Mills)
Mills, John W., 518 [RU 7336]
Mills, Robert, 370 [RU 92]
Mineral and Mechanical Technology, Divisions of (USNM), 156 [RU 216]
    RT Mechanical Technology, Division of (USNM)
        Mineral Technology, Division of (USNM)
Mineral Sciences, Collected Catalogs, Correspondence, and Specimen Lists on, 120 [RU 7291]

Mineral Sciences, Department of (NMNH), 117 [RU 266]; 117 [RU 619]; 119 [RU 548]; 119 [RU 614]; 481 [RU 7349]; 624 [RU 9529]
    NT Meteorites, Division of (NMNH)
        Petrology and Volcanology, Division of (NMNH)
    RT Geology, Department of (NMNH)
        Mineralogy and Petrology, Division of (NMNH)
Mineral Sciences, Department of, Photograph Collection (NMNH), 120 [RU 7421]
Mineral Technology, Division of (USNM), 39 [RU 192]; 149 [RU 297]; 156 [RU 216]
    BT Arts and Industries, Department of (USNM)
    RT Mechanical Technology, Division of (USNM)
Mineralogy, Division of (NMNH), 116 [RU 336]; 116 [RU 421]
Mineralogy, Division of (USNM), 120 [RU 7291]
    BT Geology, Department of (USNM)
Mineralogy and Petrology, Division of (NMNH), 115 [RU 268]; 117 [RU 266]; 117 [RU 619]; 430 [RU 7080]
    BT Geology, Department of (NMNH)
    RT Mineral Sciences, Department of (NMNH)
Miniature Painters, Sculptors and Gravers Society of Washington, 583 [RU 7433]
Mining, Section of (NMHT), 146 [RU 240]
Mint Museum of Art, 197 [RU 311]
Miro, Selected Paintings (exhibition), 272 [RU 481]
Mirrors on the Universe: The MMT Story (motion picture), 362 [RU 593]
Missonnier-Vuillemin, Marie-Therese, 317 [RU 7269]
Missouri Bureau of Mines and Geology, 605 [RU 7328]
Mitchell, James A., 370 [RU 92]
Mitman, Carl W., 47 [RU 483]; 144 [RU 84]; 148 [RU 250]; 149 [RU 297]; 160 [RU 239]; 233 [RU 162]; 518 [RU 7386]
Mobius, Karl A., 436 [RU 7255]
Modeler (USNM), 43 [RU 408]
"Models in Paleobiology," 556 [RU 7429]
Mohole Project, 508 [RU 7396]
Molecular Systematics Laboratory (NMNH), 62 [RU 374]
Molella, Arthur P., 145 [RU 375]; 149 [RU 376]

Mollusks, Collected Field Notebooks, Journals, Catalogs, Notes, and Lists on, 95 [RU 1030301]

Mollusks, Collected Notes, Lists, and Drawings on, 95 [RU 7218]

Mollusks, Collected Notes, Lists, Catalogs, Drawings, and Manuscripts on, 95 [RU 7461]

Mollusks, Division of (NMNH), 93 [RU 73]; 94 [RU 202]; 94 [RU 7418]; 441 [RU 7073]; 520 [RU 7376]; 552 [RU 7413]; 634 [RU 9519]

    BT Biology, Department of (NMNH)
       Invertebrate Zoology, Department of (NMNH)
       Zoology, Department of (NMNH)
    RT Marine Invertebrates, Division of (NMNH)

Monetary History and Medallic Art, Hall of (NMAH), 176 [RU 359]

Monnig, Oscar, 386 [RU 7261]

"Monograph on Crinoids Discovered in the State of Tennessee," 584 [RU 7301]

Monroe, Bill, 635 [RU 9569]

Monroe, Watson H., 531 [RU 7327]

Montano, Monty, 651 [RU 9554]

Montcreiffe, R. B., 37 [RU 189]

Montezuma solar observatory (Calama, Chile)
    USE: Mount Montezuma Station

Montgomery, Basil Elwood, 519 [RU 7345]

Montreal Museum of Fine Arts, 443 [RU 7439]

Moonwatch Division (SAO), 252 [RU 255]
    BT Satellite Tracking Program (SAO)

Moore, Henry, 484 [RU 7449]; 624 [RU 9566]

Moore, John Percy, 519 [RU 7265]; 568 [RU 7262]

Moore, Wayne A., 651 [RU 9554]

Mora, Giselle, 615 [RU 9561]

More Than Land or Sky: Art from Appalachia, 1981 (exhibition), 213 [RU 504]

Morgenstern Collection, 644 [RU 9586]

Morrison, Harold, 579 [RU 7309]

Morrison, Joseph P. E., 93 [RU 73]; 520 [RU 7376]

Morrison, Philip, 653 [RU 9531]

Morse, Edward Sylvester, 407 [RU 7085]

Morse, Peter, 152 [RU 206]

Morse, Samuel F. B., 148 [RU 250]; 550 [RU 7390]; 590 [RU 7055]

Morton, Conrad Vernon, 521 [RU 7303]

Moser, Joann G., 208 [RU 476]

Mosher, Stuart M., 176 [RU 359]

Mosquitoes of the South Pacific, The, 405 [RU 7381]

Moss, William W. III, 620 [RU 9571]; 629 [RU 9575]

Motheral, John G., 335 [RU 294]; 335 [RU 486]

Motherwell, Robert, 484 [RU 7449]

Mounds Survey, 127 [RU NAA 2]

Mount Brukkaros Station (Southwest Africa), 246 [RU 85]; 471 [RU 7307]

Mount Harqua Hala Station, Arizona, 471 [RU 7307]

Mount Hopkins, Arizona, 655 [RU 9542]

Mount Hopkins Observatory (SAO), 247 [RU 437]; 248 [RU 468]; 250 [RU 253]; 253 [RU 262]; 646 [RU 9520]

    BT Programs Management Office (SAO)
    RT Fred Lawrence Whipple Observatory

Mount Montezuma Station (Calama, Chile), 8 [RU 45]; 246 [RU 85]; 378 [RU 7005]; 471 [RU 7307]

Mount Saint Katherine Station, Egypt, 246 [RU 85]; 471 [RU 7307]

Mountain Lakes Biological Station, University of Virginia, 625 [RU 9509]

Moynihan, Martin Humphrey, 614 [RU 9563]; 615 [RU 9561]; 633 [RU 9579]; 640 [RU 9584]

Muesebeck, Carl Frederick William, 579 [RU 7309]; 618 [RU 9555]; 638 [RU 9583]

Muir, John, 81 [RU 208]

Muir-Wood, Helen M., 436 [RU 7318]

Muller, Fritz, 490 [RU 7107]

Mullis, Kary B., 652 [RU 9577]

Multhauf, Robert P., 135 [RU 276]; 136 [RU 334]; 138 [RU 621]; 158 [RU 293]; 158 [RU 579]; 159 [RU 332]; 485 [RU 7474]; 521 [RU 7467]; 629 [RU 9502]

Multiple-Mirror Telescope (SAO), 31 [RU 254]; 247 [RU 437]; 248 [RU 468]; 250 [RU 253]; 260 [RU 525]; 602 [RU 7431]; 646 [RU 9520]; 655 [RU 9542]

Munz, Philip Alexander, 623 [RU 9572]

Murchie, William Roger, 522 [RU 7266]

Murdoch, John, 347 [RU 217]; 522 [RU 7203]

Murphy, Edward, 661 [RU 9548]

Murphy, James M., 318 [RU 532]; 324 [RU 640]

Murray, Anne W., 167 [RU 519]; 173 [RU 252]; 174 [RU 473]

Murray, Richard N., 202 [RU 440]; 304 [RU 401]; 306 [RU 403]

Muses Flee Hitler, The (symposium), 332 [RU 495]; 357 [RU 497]

Museum Advisory Board (CHM), 282 [RU 545]

Museum Computer Network, 522 [RU 7432]

Museum Education Roundtable, 523 [RU 7295]

Museum Mile street festival, 281 [RU 492]

Museum News, 386 [RU 7450]

Museum of African Art, 307 [RU 634]
>   **RT** National Museum of African Art

Museum of Art, Archeology, and Ethnology (I-pin, China), 620 [RU 9571]

Museum of Comparative Zoology (Cambridge, Massachusetts), 566 [RU 7316]; 617 [RU 9514]; 622 [RU 9559]

Museum of Fine Arts, Boston, 262 [RU 4010001]

Museum of History and Technology
>   **USE:** National Museum of History and Technology

Museum of Modern Art, 217 [RU 321]

Museum of Natural History
>   **USE:** National Museum of Natural History

Museum of the Plains Indian (Browning, Montana), 622 [RU 9505]

"Museum Perspective, The," 510 [RU 7358]

Museum Programs, Office of, 336 [RU 629]; 337 [RU 624]; 337 [RU 631]; 338 [RU 625]; 338 [RU 630]
>   **NT** National American Museum Program

Museum Programs, Office of (NCFA), 213 [RU 466]

Museum Programs, Office of (NMAA), 213 [RU 504]; 216 [RU 456]
>   **RT** Educational Programs, Office of (NMAA)

Museum Shops, Smithsonian, 27 [RU 145]

Museum Studies Program, George Washington University, 608 [RU 7331]; 647 [RU 9523]

Museum Support Center, 11 [RU 613]; 20 [RU 394]; 26 [RU 342]; 62 [RU 374]; 64 [RU 384]; 71 [RU 382]; 123 [RU 328]; 329 [RU 562]; 616 [RU 9515]

Museum Work, 386 [RU 7450]

Museums, International Council of
>   **USE:** International Council of Museums

Museums, International Council of, International Committee on Museum Security, 510 [RU 7358]

Music at the Smithsonian, 171 [RU 485]

Music in America at the Smithsonian Institution, Conference on, 181 [RU 584]

Musical History, Division of (NMAH), 171 [RU 485]
>   **BT** Social and Cultural History, Department of (NMAH)
>   **RT** Musical Instruments, Division of (NMAH)
>   Musical Instruments, Division of (NMHT)
>   Musical Instruments, Section of (NMHT)

Musical Instruments, Division of (NMAH), 171 [RU 485]
>   **BT** Social and Cultural History, Department of (NMAH)
>   **RT** Musical History, Division of (NMAH)
>   Musical Instruments, Division of (NMHT)
>   Musical Instruments, Section of (NMHT)

Musical Instruments, Division of (NMHT), 164 [RU 251]; 168 [RU 258]; 171 [RU 485]
>   **BT** Civil History, Department of (NMHT)
>   Cultural History, Department of (NMHT)
>   **RT** Cultural History, Division of (NMHT)
>   Musical History, Division of (NMAH)
>   Musical Instruments, Division of (NMAH)
>   Musical Instruments, Section of (NMHT)

Musical Instruments, Hall of (NMAH), 171 [RU 485]

Musical Instruments, Section of (NMHT), 171 [RU 485]
>   **BT** Cultural History, Division of (NMHT)
>   **RT** Musical History, Division of (NMAH)
>   Musical Instruments, Division of (NMAH)
>   Musical Instruments, Division of (NMHT)

Musical Instruments, Section of (USNM), 171 [RU 485]
>   **BT** Ethnology, Division of (USNM)
>   **RT** Musical Instruments, Section of (NMHT)

Myers, Frank Jacob, 477 [RU 7237]

Myers, George Sprague, 78 [RU 213]; 80 [RU 234]; 524 [RU 7317]

Myers, Susan H., 166 [RU 406]; 169 [RU 261]; 644 [RU 9586]

N

NAFMAB
  USE: National Armed Forces Museum
    Advisory Board
Nagasaki (Japan), 653 [RU 9531]
Nagel, Charles, 223 [RU 426]; 224 [RU 379]
Nakian, Reuben, 214 [RU 455]
Nam Ngum Dam and Reservoir Project, 1973-
  1975 (Laos), 312 [RU 273]
Nano, George, 656 [RU 9550]
Naples Zoological Station, 8 [RU 45]
Nation of Nations, A (exhibition), 165 [RU
  331]; 598 [RU 7322]; 644 [RU 9586]
National Academy of Sciences, 8 [RU 45]; 9
  [RU 46]; 374 [RU 7001]; 377 [RU 7004];
  378 [RU 7006]; 525 [RU 7115]; 578 [RU
  7142]; 602 [RU 7431]
  NT Daniel Giraud Elliot Fund
National Advisory Committee for Aeronautics,
  8 [RU 45]; 9 [RU 46]; 10 [RU 50]; 377 [RU
  7004]
National Aeronautics and Space Administra-
  tion, 233 [RU 162]; 239 [RU 353]; 250 [RU
  253]; 251 [RU 260]; 253 [RU 262]; 254
  [RU 263]; 256 [RU 478]; 258 [RU 517];
  258 [RU 522]; 259 [RU 521]; 260 [RU
  523]; 261 [RU 538]; 267 [RU 412]; 323
  [RU 168]; 331 [RU 300]; 428 [RU 7451];
  449 [RU 7415]; 602 [RU 7431]; 632 [RU
  9578]; 653 [RU 9543]; 660 [RU 9535]
National Air and Space Administration
  Historical Committee, 521 [RU 7467]
National Air and Space Museum, 11 [RU 613];
  19 [RU 137]; 20 [RU 394]; 21 [RU 104]; 29
  [RU 526]; 30 [RU 108]; 31 [RU 254]; 32
  [RU 329]; 65 [RU 363]; 67 [RU 416]; 233
  [RU 162]; 237 [RU 351]; 237 [RU 537];
  238 [RU 330]; 238 [RU 344]; 239 [RU
  353]; 239 [RU 398]; 240 [RU 348]; 240
  [RU 480]; 241 [RU 347]; 241 [RU 355];
  241 [RU 479]; 242 [RU 339]; 242 [RU
  340]; 243 [RU 409]; 244 [RU 358]; 319
  [RU 639]; 326 [RU 503]; 339 [RU 369];
  340 [RU 368]; 449 [RU 7415]; 616 [RU
  9515]; 632 [RU 9578]; 636 [RU 9590]; 636
  [RU 9591]; 653 [RU 9531]
  NT Aeronautics, Department of
    (NASM)
    Astronautics, Department of
    (NASM)
    Center for Earth and Planetary
    Studies (NASM)
    Contractor's Files (NASM)

Cooperative Programs, Office of
    (NASM)
    Paul E. Garber Facility (NASM)
    Public Affairs, Office of (NASM)
    Silver Hill Museum (NASM)
    Space History, Department of
    (NASM)
    Space Science and Exploration,
    Department of (NASM)
    Special Events, Office of (NASM)
  RT National Air Museum
National Air and Space Museum, Assistant
  Director for Development, 236 [RU 354]
National Air and Space Museum, Assistant
  Director for Exhibits, 235 [RU 352]
National Air and Space Museum, Associate
  Director for Research, 235 [RU 343]
National Air and Space Museum, Deputy
  Director, 234 [RU 346]; 235 [RU 231]
National Air and Space Museum, Director, 233
  [RU 306]; 234 [RU 338]
National Air and Space Museum, Executive
  Officer, 237 [RU 345]
National Air and Space Museum Building, 233
  [RU 306]; 235 [RU 231]
National Air Museum, 9 [RU 46]; 10 [RU 50];
  19 [RU 137]; 237 [RU 537]; 326 [RU 503]
  RT Aeronautics, Division of (NASM)
    National Air and Space Museum
National American Museum Program, 337 [RU
  631]
  BT Museum Programs, Office of
National Anthropological Film Center, 32 [RU
  329]
National Archives and Records Service, 543
  [RU 7470]
National Armed Forces Museum Advisory
  Board, 10 [RU 50]; 12 [RU 171]; 19 [RU
  137]; 20 [RU 394]; 21 [RU 104]; 183 [RU
  377]; 184 [RU 581]; 632 [RU 9589]
  RT Dwight D. Eisenhower Institute for
    Historical Research (NMAH)
National Association of Audubon Societies,
  378 [RU 7006]
National Biomedical Research Foundation,
  Georgetown University, 654 [RU 9544]
National Collection of Fine Arts, 9 [RU 46]; 10
  [RU 50]; 12 [RU 171]; 19 [RU 137]; 21
  [RU 104]; 65 [RU 363]; 204 [RU 447]; 208
  [RU 457]; 209 [RU 453]; 210 [RU 445];
  212 [RU 448]; 212 [RU 452]; 213 [RU
  466]; 215 [RU 319]; 216 [RU 443]; 219
  [RU 596]; 220 [RU 333]; 223 [RU 426];

283 [RU 633]; 327 [RU 90]; 339 [RU 369]; 443 [RU 7439]; 583 [RU 7433]

    NT Administration, Office of (NCFA)

        Contemporary Art, Department of (NCFA)

        Contemporary Painting and Sculpture, Department of (NCFA)

        Editorial Office (NCFA)

        Education, Department of (NCFA)

        Exhibition and Design, Office of (NCFA)

        Exhibitions Abroad, Office of (NCFA)

        Fine Arts Lending Program (NCFA)

        International Art Program

        Museum Programs, Office of (NCFA)

        Painting and Sculpture, Department of (NCFA)

        Prints and Drawings, Department of (NCFA)

        Publication Editor (NCFA)

        Renwick Gallery

        Research and Professional Training, Office of (NCFA)

        Smithsonian Traveling Exhibition Service

        Twentieth Century Painting and Sculpture, Department of (NCFA)

    RT National Gallery of Art

        National Museum of American Art

        Smithsonian Gallery of Art

National Collection of Fine Arts, Assistant to the Director, 202 [RU 440]

National Collection of Fine Arts, Central Administrative File, 203 [RU 313]

National Collection of Fine Arts, Consultant Designer, 201 [RU 318]

National Collection of Fine Arts, Office of the Director, 197 [RU 311]; 198 [RU 312]; 200 [RU 320]; 200 [RU 550]; 203 [RU 313]

National Collection of Fine Arts Commission, 203 [RU 313]

National Conference of Business Paper Editors, 137 [RU 279]

National Council on the Arts, 12 [RU 171]; 203 [RU 313]

National Cultural Center, 10 [RU 50]

    RT John F. Kennedy Center for the Performing Arts

National Educational Television, 617 [RU 9541]

National Exhibition of Prints, Twenty-fifth, 1977 (exhibition), 208 [RU 457]

National Exhibition of Prints, Twenty-fourth, 1975 (exhibition), 208 [RU 457]

National Exhibition of Prints, Twenty-third, 1973 (exhibition), 208 [RU 457]

National Gallery Advisory Committee (NCFA), 197 [RU 311]

National Gallery of Art, 8 [RU 45]; 9 [RU 46]; 10 [RU 50]; 19 [RU 137]; 45 [RU 55]; 197 [RU 311]; 203 [RU 313]; 220 [RU 333]; 370 [RU 92]; 534 [RU 7306]; 583 [RU 7433]

    RT National Collection of Fine Arts

        National Museum of American Art

National Gallery of Art, Catalog of Collections I, The, 1922, 221 [RU 463]

National Gallery of Art, The, 45 [RU 55]

National Gallery of Art Commission, 197 [RU 311]

National Geodetic Satellite Program (SAO), 250 [RU 253]

National Geographic Society, 9 [RU 46]; 170 [RU 381]; 378 [RU 7006]; 630 [RU 9507]

National Geographic Society, Committee for Research and Exploration, 500 [RU 7434]

National Geographic Society-Smithsonian Archeological Expedition to Vera Cruz, Mexico, 1938-1939, 39 [RU 192]

National Geographic Society-Smithsonian Institution-Commonwealth of Australia Expedition to Arnhem Land, 1948, 80 [RU 234]; 445 [RU 7465]

National Geographic Society-Smithsonian Institution Expedition to the Dutch East Indies, 1937, 512 [RU 7293]

National Geographic Society-University of Virginia Expedition to the South Pacific Islands, 1939, 39 [RU 192]

National Geographic Society-Yale University Expedition to Peru, 1915, 39 [RU 192]; 480 [RU 7179]

National Health Council, 154 [RU 244]

National Herbarium, United States

    USE: United States National Herbarium

National Institute, 52 [RU 305]; 370 [RU 92]; 525 [RU 7058]; 540 [RU 7078]

    RT National Institution for the Promotion of Science

National Institute for Neurological Disorders and Stroke, 658 [RU 9564]

National Institutes of Health, 83 [RU 407]; 267 [RU 412]; 650 [RU 9549]; 658 [RU 9564]

National Institution for the Promotion of
Science, 387 [RU 7057]; 525 [RU 7058]
    RT National Institute
National Inventors Council, 562 [RU 7091]
National Marine Fisheries Service, 313 [RU
610]
    BT United States Department of
        Commerce
National Museum Act, 19 [RU 137]; 24 [RU
190]; 338 [RU 574]; 642 [RU 9512]
National Museum Act Advisory Council, 338
[RU 574]
National Museum Act of 1966, 26 [RU 342];
27 [RU 575]
National Museum Building, 45 [RU 55]; 51
[RU 187]
National Museum Building Commission (Arts
and Industries Building), 49 [RU 71]
National Museum construction, 1905-1909, 51
[RU 187]
National Museum of African Art, 11 [RU 613];
22 [RU 477]; 307 [RU 634]; 636 [RU 9591]
    RT Museum of African Art
National Museum of African Art, Assistant
Director, 308 [RU 635]
National Museum of African Art, Director, 307
[RU 634]
National Museum of American Art, 22 [RU
281]; 22 [RU 477]; 202 [RU 446]; 204 [RU
475]; 205 [RU 460]; 206 [RU 458]; 207
[RU 459]; 207 [RU 461]; 208 [RU 465];
208 [RU 476]; 209 [RU 453]; 210 [RU
5000101]; 211 [RU 5000102]; 212 [RU
452]; 213 [RU 451]; 213 [RU 504]; 214
[RU 454]; 216 [RU 456]; 217 [RU 321];
219 [RU 442]; 220 [RU 333]; 221 [RU 462]
    NT Administrative Services, Office of
        (NMAA)
        Assistant Director, Museum
            Resources (NMAA)
        Barney Studio House
        Curatorial Department (NMAA)
        Design and Production, Department
            of (NMAA)
        Editor, Office of the (NMAA)
        Educational Programs, Office of
            (NMAA)
        Eighteenth and Nineteenth Century
            Painting and Sculpture,
            Department of (NMAA)
        Exhibition and Design, Office of
            (NMAA)
        Graphic Arts, Department of
            (NMAA)

        Museum Programs, Office of
            (NMAA)
        Painting and Sculpture, Department
            of (NMAA)
        Prints and Drawings, Department of
            (NMAA)
        Program Support, Office of (NMAA)
        Public Affairs, Office of (NMAA)
        Registrar, Office of the (NMAA)
        Renwick Gallery
        Renwick Gallery, Office of the
            Director
        Research Support, Office of
            (NMAA)
        Twentieth Century Painting and
            Sculpture, Department of
            (NMAA)
    RT National Collection of Fine Arts
        National Gallery of Art
National Museum of American Art, Assistant
Director, 202 [RU 444]
National Museum of American Art, Assistant
Director, Museum Resources, 202 [RU 446]
    RT National Museum of American Art,
        Assistant Director, Resources
National Museum of American Art, Assistant
Director, Resources, 202 [RU 446]
    RT National Museum of American Art,
        Assistant Director, Museum
        Resources
National Museum of American Art, Deputy
Director, 201 [RU 439]
National Museum of American Art, Office of
the Director, 198 [RU 438]; 199 [RU 322]
National Museum of American Art, Staff
Meeting Coordinator, 205 [RU 464]
National Museum of American Art and Portrait
Gallery Library, 220 [RU 333]; 221 [RU
463]
National Museum of American Art Commis-
sion, 198 [RU 438]; 199 [RU 322]
National Museum of American History, 136
[RU 623]; 138 [RU 583]; 183 [RU 377];
613 [RU 9522]; 629 [RU 9502]; 632 [RU
9589]
    NT Association of Curators (NMAH)
        Dwight D. Eisenhower Institute for
            Historical Research (NMAH)
        History of Science and Technology,
            Department of the
        National Postal Museum
        National Numismatic Collection
    RT National Museum of History and
        Technology

National Museum of American History,
    Assistant Director for Administration, 140
    [RU 335]
National Museum of American History,
    Director, 136 [RU 334]; 138 [RU 583]
National Museum of Engineering and Industry,
    39 [RU 192]; 149 [RU 297]
National Museum of History and Technology,
    10 [RU 50]; 10 [RU 99]; 12 [RU 618]; 19
    [RU 137]; 21 [RU 104]; 22 [RU 281]; 24
    [RU 190]; 46 [RU 89]; 65 [RU 363]; 136
    [RU 623]; 138 [RU 583]; 185 [RU 511];
    316 [RU 160]; 326 [RU 503]; 327 [RU 90];
    504 [RU 7466]; 622 [RU 9505]; 629 [RU
    9502]; 642 [RU 9512]; 644 [RU 9586]
    NT Applied Arts, Department of
            (NMHT)
        Civil History, Department of
            (NMHT)
        Cultural History, Department of
            (NMHT)
        History of Science, Department of
            (NMHT)
        Industries, Department of (NMHT)
        Science and Technology, Department
            of (NMHT)
        Steering Committee for the History
            of Science and Technology
            (NMHT)
    RT Anthropology, Department of
            (USNM)
        Arts and Industries, Department of
            (USNM)
        Engineering and Industries, Depart-
            ment of (USNM)
        National Museum of American
            History
        United States National Museum
National Museum of History and Technology,
    Assistant Director, 139 [RU 277]
National Museum of History and Technology,
    Deputy Director, 139 [RU 277]; 139 [RU
    285]
National Museum of History and Technology,
    Director, 135 [RU 276]; 136 [RU 334]; 136
    [RU 623]; 137 [RU 278]; 137 [RU 279];
    139 [RU 277]; 139 [RU 285]; 483 [RU
    7363]; 622 [RU 9505]; 629 [RU 9502]; 642
    [RU 9512]
National Museum of History and Technology,
    Exhibition Records, 136 [RU 623]; 138 [RU
    621]
National Museum of History and Technology,
    Office of the Director, 138 [RU 621]

National Museum of History and Technology,
    Security and Fire Prevention Committee,
    510 [RU 7358]
National Museum of History and Technology,
    Special Projects, 137 [RU 279]
National Museum of History and Technology,
    Travel Reports, 48 [RU 432]
National Museum of Natural History, 10 [RU
    50]; 10 [RU 99]; 19 [RU 137]; 24 [RU 190];
    26 [RU 342]; 29 [RU 526]; 30 [RU 108]; 31
    [RU 254]; 32 [RU 329]; 46 [RU 89]; 60
    [RU 564]; 62 [RU 374]; 63 [RU 362]; 64
    [RU 425]; 65 [RU 363]; 65 [RU 366]; 67
    [RU 416]; 67 [RU 566]; 68 [RU 429]; 71
    [RU 382]; 72 [RU 391]; 101 [RU 7427];
    102 [RU 411]; 102 [RU 418]; 104 [RU
    422]; 117 [RU 619]; 123 [RU 328]; 124
    [RU 543]; 128 [RU NAA 5]; 313 [RU 610];
    326 [RU 503]; 327 [RU 90]; 403 [RU
    7234]; 418 [RU 7395]; 425 [RU 7338]; 436
    [RU 7318]; 499 [RU 7170]; 570 [RU 7419];
    608 [RU 7331]; 617 [RU 9514]; 618 [RU
    9555]; 619 [RU 9501]; 620 [RU 9571]; 623
    [RU 9572]; 625 [RU 9509]; 632 [RU 9578];
    634 [RU 9519]; 639 [RU 9508]; 641 [RU
    9521]; 643 [RU 9565]; 644 [RU 9587]; 647
    [RU 9557]
    NT American Ethnology, Bureau of
        Anthropology, Department of
            (NMNH)
        Biological Diversity Program
            (NMNH)
        Biology, Department of (NMNH)
        Birds, Division of (NMNH)
        Botany, Department of (NMNH)
        Calendar (NMNH)
        Development Office (NMNH)
        Diving Board (NMNH)
        Ecology Program (NMNH)
        Entomology, Department of
            (NMNH)
        Exhibits, Office of (NMNH)
        Exhibits Committee (NMNH)
        Geology, Department of (NMNH)
        Insects, Division of (NMNH)
        Invertebrate Zoology, Department of
            (NMNH)
        Mineral Sciences, Department of
            (NMNH)
        Molecular Systematics Laboratory
            (NMNH)
        National Museum of Natural History
            Guidebook, 1985-1986
        Paleobiology, Department of
            (NMNH)

NT Public Information Officer (NMNH)
Registrar, Office of the (NMNH)
Scholarly Studies Program (NMNH)
Senate of Scientists (NMNH)
Short-Term Visitors Program
(NMNH)
Smithsonian Oceanographic Sorting
Center (NMNH)
Smithsonian Office of Ecology
(NMNH)
Task Force on Research, 1987
(NMNH)
Vertebrate Zoology, Department of
(NMNH)
Zoology, Department of (NMNH)
RT United States National Museum
National Museum of Natural History, Assistant
Director, 619 [RU 9501]
National Museum of Natural History, Assistant
Director for Oceanography, 312 [RU 273];
312 [RU 274]; 313 [RU 563]; 313 [RU 610]
NT Smithsonian Oceanographic Sorting
Center
RT Oceanography and Limnology,
Office of
Oceanography and Limnology
Program, Office of International
and Environmental Programs
National Museum of Natural History, Assistant
to the Director for Exhibits Planning, 647
[RU 9523]
National Museum of Natural History, Associ-
ate Director for Special Projects, 64 [RU
384]
National Museum of Natural History, Director,
61 [RU 155]; 61 [RU 197]; 61 [RU 309]; 62
[RU 364]; 62 [RU 374]; 63 [RU 257]; 63
[RU 362]; 64 [RU 533]; 619 [RU 9501];
641 [RU 9521]
National Museum of Natural History, Special
Assistant to the Director, 64 [RU 425]
RT Development Office (NMNH)
National Museum of Natural History, Travel
Reports, 48 [RU 432]
National Museum of Natural History Guide-
book, 1985-1986, 64 [RU 425]
BT National Museum of Natural
History, Special Assistant to the
Director
National Museum of the American Indian, 64
[RU 384]
NT Collection Management Task Force,
National Museum of the
American Indian

National Museum, United States
USE: United States National Museum
National Numismatic Collection (NMAH), 176
[RU 359]
RT Numismatics, Division of (NMHT)
National Oceanic and Atmospheric Adminis-
tration, 267 [RU 412]
National Park Service, 314 [RU 264]; 394 [RU
7459]; 622 [RU 9505]; 626 [RU 9558]; 647
[RU 9523]
National Philatelic Collection (NMAH), 177
[RU 580]
RT Philately and Postal History,
Division of (NMHT)
Postal History, Division of (NMHT)
National Postal Museum (NMAH)
National Portrait Gallery, 10 [RU 50]; 10 [RU
99]; 12 [RU 171]; 19 [RU 137]; 21 [RU
104]; 22 [RU 477]; 224 [RU 379]; 225 [RU
2020001]; 226 [RU 552]; 226 [RU 555];
227 [RU 361]; 228 [RU 554]; 228 [RU
556]; 229 [RU 553]; 327 [RU 90]; 339 [RU
369]; 616 [RU 9515]; 626 [RU 9558]
NT Administrative Office (NPG)
Catalog of American Portraits (NPG)
Charles Willson Peale Papers (NPG)
Curatorial Departments (NPG)
Design and Production, Department
of (NPG)
Editor of Publications (NPG)
Education, Department of (NPG)
Exhibitions, Office of (NPG)
Historian, Office of the (NPG)
Painting and Sculpture, Department
of (NPG)
Photographs, Department of (NPG)
Prints and Drawings, Department of
(NPG)
Public Affairs, Office of (NPG)
Registrar, Office of the (NPG)
Time Collection (NPG)
National Portrait Gallery, Permanent Collec-
tion Records, 225 [RU 2020001]
National Postal Museum (NMAH), 177 [RU
580]
RT National Philatelic Collection
(NMAH)
Philately and Postal History,
Division of (NMHT)
Postal History, Division of (NMHT)
National Public Affairs Center for Television,
617 [RU 9541]
National Register of Historic Places, 25 [RU
191]

National Research Council, 8 [RU 45]; 9 [RU 46]; 17 [RU 135]; 304 [RU 134]; 377 [RU 7004]; 460 [RU 7314]; 499 [RU 7170]; 623 [RU 9572]
    NT Institute for Research in Tropical America
      Pacific Science Board
      Pacific Science Board, National Research Council
      Sedimentation, Committee on, National Research Council
National Resources Committee, 518 [RU 7386]
National Science Foundation, 139 [RU 277]; 267 [RU 412]; 313 [RU 610]; 323 [RU 168]; 355 [RU 627]; 394 [RU 7459]; 428 [RU 7451]; 460 [RU 7314]; 483 [RU 7343]; 578 [RU 7142]; 602 [RU 7431]
    NT United States Arctic Research Program
National Science Foundation, Panel for the History and Philosophy of Science, 543 [RU 7470]
National Science Foundation Belmont Conference, 1969-1970, 24 [RU 190]
National Security Agency, 629 [RU 9575]
National Survey of Accessibility in Museums in the United States, 1986, 213 [RU 504]; 216 [RU 456]
National Trust for Historic Preservation, Committee on Maritime Preservation, 510 [RU 7358]
National Wildlife Fund, 314 [RU 264]
National Youth Administration, 518 [RU 7386]
National Zoological Park, 7 [RU 31]; 8 [RU 34]; 9 [RU 46]; 10 [RU 50]; 11 [RU 613]; 19 [RU 137]; 29 [RU 393]; 29 [RU 526]; 30 [RU 108]; 31 [RU 254]; 189 [RU 74]; 191 [RU 404]; 192 [RU 386]; 193 [RU 385]; 193 [RU 389]; 194 [RU 365]; 195 [RU 395]; 318 [RU 532]; 320 [RU 65]; 365 [RU 93]; 367 [RU 165]; 370 [RU 92]; 419 [RU 7279]; 435 [RU 7225]; 449 [RU 7411]; 474 [RU 7355]; 480 [RU 7179]; 487 [RU 7392]; 512 [RU 7293]; 582 [RU 7337]; 596 [RU 7161]; 616 [RU 9515]; 628 [RU 9513]; 633 [RU 9568]; 645 [RU 9504]; 649 [RU 9553]
    NT Animal Department (NZP)
      Animal Management, Office of (NZP)
      Animal Programs, Office of (NZP)
      Animal Records (NZP)
      Animal Registration Records (NZP)
      Conservation and Research Center (NZP)

      Education, Office of (NZP)
      Friends of the National Zoo (NZP)
      Living Vertebrates, Department of (NZP)
      Public Affairs, Office of (NZP)
    RT Living Animals, Department of (USNM)
National Zoological Park, Assistant Director for Animal Programs, 191 [RU 404]
National Zoological Park, Assistant Director for Animal Programs, Research and Educational Activities, 191 [RU 404]
National Zoological Park, Assistant Director for Research, 191 [RU 404]
National Zoological Park, Assistant Director for Zoological Research and Educational Activities, 191 [RU 404]
National Zoological Park, Director, 190 [RU 326]; 190 [RU 380]
National Zoological Park Commission, 189 [RU 74]
Natural History, National Museum of
    USE: National Museum of Natural History
Natural History Building, 46 [RU 89]; 50 [RU 79]; 50 [RU 80]; 50 [RU 81]; 51 [RU 187]; 318 [RU 532]; 318 [RU 565]; 319 [RU 639]; 329 [RU 562]; 370 [RU 92]
Nature Magazine, 537 [RU 7252]
    BT American Nature Association
Nature of Scientific Discovery, The (symposium), 357 [RU 496]; 357 [RU 500]
Nautilus (submarine), 147 [RU 383]
Naval Architecture, Section of (USNM), 37 [RU 189]; 144 [RU 84]
    BT Arts and Industries, Department of (USNM)
Naval History, Division of (NMAH), 147 [RU 383]
    BT History of Science and Technology, Department of the (NMAH)
    RT Armed Forces History, Division of (NMAH)
Naval History, Division of (NMHT), 147 [RU 383]
    BT Armed Forces History, Department of (NMHT)
Naval History, Hall of (NMAH), 147 [RU 383]
Naval Research, Office of, 323 [RU 168]; 345 [RU 179]
Naval Research Laboratory, Washington, D.C., 656 [RU 9539]
Navy Surveying Expedition to the Phoenix and Samoan Islands, 1939, 561 [RU 7222]

NCFA
USE: National Collection of Fine Arts
Needell, Allan, 660 [RU 9535]
Nelen, Joseph A., 119 [RU 548]
Nelms, Frank A., 235 [RU 352]
Nelson, Edward William, 37 [RU 189]; 526
[RU 7364]
Neotropical Lowlands Research Program, 29
[RU 393]
RT Amazon Ecosystem Research
Program
Nepal, King of, 1960, 264 [RU 4010004]
Nepal Tiger Ecology Project, 31 [RU 254]
Nesbitt, Robert A., 459 [RU 7319]
Neuropteroids, Division of (NMNH), 104 [RU
422]
BT Entomology, Department of
(NMNH)
Neuropteroids and Diptera, Division of
(NMNH), 104 [RU 422]
BT Entomology, Department of
(NMNH)
Nevelson, Louise, 484 [RU 7449]
*New England Bird Life, Being a Manual of
New England Ornithology,* 438 [RU 7344]
New England fishing schooner logbooks, 527
[RU 7200]
New England Glaciation Collection, 528 [RU
7460]
New United Motor Manufacturing, Inc., 656
[RU 9550]
New York Botanical Garden, 439 [RU 7356];
619 [RU 9501]
New York State Conservation Consultancy,
294 [RU 544]
New York State Council on the Arts, 294 [RU
544]
New York University, 483 [RU 7363]; 617
[RU 9541]
New York World's Fair, 1939, 39 [RU 192];
327 [RU 70]
Newberry, John Strong, 597 [RU 7321]
Newcomb, Simon, 407 [RU 7085]; 600 [RU
7159]
Newland, Kenneth E., 238 [RU 330]
Newman, Marshall T., 39 [RU 192]
Newmeyer, Sarah, 264 [RU 4010004]
Newport Folk Foundation, 635 [RU 9569]
News Clipping File, 341 [RU 372]; 371 [RU
96]
BT Public Affairs, Office of
News Letter (Society of Systematic Zoology),
581 [RU 7226]
News releases, 342 [RU 370]

News Reporting, Hall of (NMHT), 153 [RU
413]
Nicastro, Richard J., 140 [RU 335]; 179 [RU
551]; 304 [RU 401]
Nichols, George, 291 [RU 436]
Nichols, Susan L., 523 [RU 7295]
Nicholson, Walter L., 362 [RU 69]; 408 [RU
7052]
Nicks, Oran W., 660 [RU 9535]
Nicollet, Jean Nicolas, 554 [RU 7275]
Nicollet Expedition, 1838, 462 [RU 7290]
*Nineteenth-Century Gallery of Distinguished
Americans, A* (exhibition), 227 [RU 361]
99th Fighter Squadron, 632 [RU 9578]
Nininger, Harvey Harlow, 39 [RU 192]; 386
[RU 7261]; 533 [RU 7284]
Nininger Meteorite Collection, Harvey Harlow,
115 [RU 268]
Nitchie, Francis R., Jr., 251 [RU 260]
Nixon, G. E. J., 575 [RU 7379]
Nixon, Richard M., 361 [RU 587]
NMHT
USE: National Museum of History and
Technology
NMNH
USE: National Museum of Natural
History
*Noble Buyer, The: John Quinn, Patron of the
Avant-Garde* (exhibition), 272 [RU 481]
Noon, Mary A., 291 [RU 547]
Norberg, Arthur L., 485 [RU 7474]
Norby, Reidar, 177 [RU 580]
Nordenskold Mesa Verde collection, 39 [RU
192]
North American Wildflowers, 8 [RU 45]; 9 [RU
46]
North Pacific Exploring Expedition, United
States
USE: United States North Pacific
Exploring Expedition
Northeast Radio Observatory Corporation, 248
[RU 256]; 258 [RU 517]
Northern Pacific Railroad Route Expedition,
123 [RU 7264]; 375 [RU 7002]
BT Pacific Railroad Surveys
Northwest Boundary Survey, 1857-1861, 464
[RU 7209]; 501 [RU 7202]; 577 [RU 7191]
Nosanow, Barbara Shissler, 216 [RU 456]
Notman, John, 370 [RU 92]
Nozaki, Thomas, Jr., 651 [RU 9554]
Nucleus of National Collections (NPG), 229
[RU 553]

Numismatics, Division of (NMHT), 176 [RU 359]
    BT Applied Arts, Department of (NMHT)
        Civil History, Department of (NMHT)
    RT National Numismatic Collection (NMAH)
Numismatics, Division of (USNM), 39 [RU 192]; 176 [RU 359]
    BT History, Department of (USNM)
    RT Numismatics, Division of (NMHT)
Numismatics, Hall of (NMAH), 176 [RU 359]
Nutting, Charles Cleveland, 481 [RU 7075]

O

O'Brien, Roy, 318 [RU 532]
Ocana, Gilberto, 630 [RU 9576]; 649 [RU 9553]
Oceanographic Sorting Center, Smithsonian
    USE: Smithsonian Oceanographic Sorting Center
Oceanography and Limnology, Office of, 31 [RU 254]; 312 [RU 273]; 312 [RU 274]; 313 [RU 563]; 313 [RU 610]
    NT Smithsonian Oceanographic Sorting Center
    RT National Museum of Natural History, Assistant Director for Oceanography
        Oceanography and Limnology Program, Office of International and Environmental Programs
Oceanography and Limnology Program, Office of Environmental Sciences, 312 [RU 273]
Oceanography and Limnology Program, Office of International and Environmental Programs, 312 [RU 273]; 313 [RU 563]
    RT National Museum of Natural History, Assistant Director for Oceanography
        Oceanography and Limnology, Office of
Odell, J. Scott, 171 [RU 485]
Odetics Incorporated (Anaheim, California), 658 [RU 9552]
Oehser, Paul H., 348 [RU 535]; 630 [RU 9507]
Office
    USE: name of office
"Office Memoranda," 335 [RU 486]
Official White House China: 1789 to the Present, 504 [RU 7466]
Ogden, Herbert Gouvernour, 37 [RU 189]

Ohio Valley and Central States Exposition, Cincinnati, 1888, 58 [RU 124]; 78 [RU 203]
Okada, Kaoru Kitajima, 649 [RU 9553]
O'Keeffe, Georgia, 484 [RU 7449]
Old Sturbridge Village (Massachusetts), 598 [RU 7322]; 644 [RU 9586]
Oldroyd, Ida Shepard, 627 [RU 9527]
Oldroyd, Thomas, 627 [RU 9527]
Oldroyd collection of Lincoln relics, 39 [RU 192]
O'Leary, Daniel, 282 [RU 545]
Olin, Charles H., 321 [RU 576]
Olin, Jacqueline S., 321 [RU 576]
Oliver, Lawrence L., 317 [RU 157]
Oliver, Smith Hempstone, 144 [RU 84]; 160 [RU 239]; 161 [RU 528]
Olivier, Charles P., 386 [RU 7261]
Olmsted, Arthur J., 156 [RU 529]
Olson, Storrs L., 72 [RU 391]
Omaha, Trans-Mississippi, and International Exposition, 1898, 58 [RU 124]; 327 [RU 70]
Oman, Paul Wilson, 506 [RU 7352]; 528 [RU 7346]; 579 [RU 7309]
Optical and Infrared Astronomy Division (SAO), 247 [RU 437]
Orbiting Astronomical Observatory, 251 [RU 260]
    RT Celescope, Project
Orcutt, Charles Russell, 37 [RU 189]; 39 [RU 192]; 473 [RU 7155]; 529 [RU 7088]
O'Reilly, Henry, 590 [RU 7055]
O'Reilly, Laurence P., 65 [RU 363]
Organ, Robert M., 321 [RU 576]
Organic Chemistry, Section of (USNM), 146 [RU 240]
Organization and Methods Division, 335 [RU 294]
    RT Administrative Systems Division
        Management Analysis Office
Organization of Government Scientific Work, Committee on, 377 [RU 7004]
Organs in America, 171 [RU 485]
Origin of Chemistry, The, 521 [RU 7467]
Ornithological Club, Potomac Valley, 537 [RU 7111]
Ornithological Club of Washington, D.C., Baird, 398 [RU 7110]; 496 [RU 7172]
Ornithological reprints (NMNH), 75 [RU 1060108]
Ornithologists' Union, American
    USE: American Ornithologists' Union

Ornithology, Department of (USNM), 72 [RU 105]
    RT Birds, Division of (NMNH)
Ortner, Donald J., 68 [RU 429]; 128 [RU NAA 5]
Osborn, Henry Fairfield, 121 [RU 248]
Osborn, Henry Leslie, 529 [RU 7387]
Osborne collection of Guatemalan textiles, 39 [RU 192]
Osburn, Raymond Carroll, 530 [RU 7246]; 550 [RU 7408]
Osiris, 485 [RU 7474]
Osmun, William R., 287 [RU 280]
Osten-Sacken, Charles Robert, 601 [RU 7112]
Osteological preparator (USNM), 43 [RU 408]
Ostroff, Eugene N., 152 [RU 206]; 153 [RU 413]; 156 [RU 529]
O'Sullivan, Judith, 216 [RU 456]; 352 [RU 507]
O'Toole, Dennis A., 226 [RU 555]
Outlook for Space (symposium), 357 [RU 500]
Outreach Services Branch (AM), 278 [RU 390]
    BT Education Department (AM)
Owen, David Dale, 489 [RU 7061]
Owen, Richard, 426 [RU 7315]
Owen, Richard E., 651 [RU 9554]
Owen collection of fossils, 37 [RU 189]

P

Pachter, Marc, 228 [RU 556]; 629 [RU 9575]; 635 [RU 9569]
Pacific Islands Scientific Expedition, Proposed, 1939-1940, 89 [RU 307]
Pacific Ocean Biological Survey Program, 76 [RU 245]
    RT Birds, Division of (NMNH)
Pacific Railroad Survey of the 47th and 49th parallels, 577 [RU 7191]
    BT Pacific Railroad Surveys
Pacific Railroad Survey of the 38th parallel, 507 [RU 7157]
    BT Pacific Railroad Surveys
Pacific Railroad Surveys, 375 [RU 7002]; 437 [RU 7067]; 507 [RU 7157]; 577 [RU 7191]
    NT Isaac Stevens' survey
        Northern Pacific Railroad Route Expedition
        Pacific Railroad Survey of the 47th and 49th parallels
        Pacific Railroad Survey of the 38th parallel
Pacific Science Board, National Research Council, 623 [RU 9572]

Pacific Science Board of the National Research Council, 1953, 89 [RU 307]
Pacific Science Congress, 623 [RU 9572]
Packard, Alpheus Spring, 564 [RU 7296]
Packard, George R., 297 [RU 560]
Pageant of Progress Exposition, Chicago, 1922, 39 [RU 192]
Pain and Its Relief (exhibition), 155 [RU 471]
Paine, Richard G., 85 [RU 508]
Painter, Joseph Hannum, 109 [RU 225]
Painting and Sculpture, Department of (HMSG), 271 [RU 469]; 272 [RU 481]
    BT Hirshhorn Museum and Sculpture Garden
Painting and Sculpture, Department of (NCFA), 205 [RU 317]
Painting and Sculpture, Department of (NMAA), 205 [RU 460]; 207 [RU 461]
    RT Curatorial Department (NMAA)
        Eighteenth and Nineteenth Century Painting and Sculpture, Department of (NMAA)
        Twentieth Century Painting and Sculpture, Department of (NMAA)
Painting and Sculpture, Department of (NPG), 225 [RU 2020001]
Painting and Sculpture, Department of Contemporary (NCFA), 206 [RU 315]
Painting and Sculpture, Department of Twentieth Century (NCFA), 206 [RU 315]
Palache, Charles, 549 [RU 7152]
Palearctic Migratory Bird Survey, 77 [RU 435]
    RT Birds, Division of (NMNH)
Paleobiology, Department of (NMNH), 122 [RU 424]; 123 [RU 328]; 124 [RU 543]; 493 [RU 7380]; 502 [RU 7360]; 619 [RU 9524]; 621 [RU 9518]; 647 [RU 9557]
    NT Vertebrate Paleontology, Division of (NMNH)
Paleobotany, Department of (NMNH), 123 [RU 328]
    RT Geology, Department of (NMNH)
Paleontological Society, 571 [RU 7325]
Paleontological Society of America, 502 [RU 7360]
Paleontology, Division of Vertebrate (NMNH), 121 [RU 156]; 122 [RU 424]; 460 [RU 7134]
Paleontology, Division of Vertebrate (USNM), 121 [RU 248]
Paleontology, Journal of, 502 [RU 7360]
Paleontology, Section of (USGS), 605 [RU 7328]

Paleontology, Section of Vertebrate (NMNH), 121 [RU 156]

Paleontology and Stratigraphy, Section of (USGS), 478 [RU 7365]; 531 [RU 7327]
    RT Coastal Plain Investigations, Section of (USGS)

Paleontology and Stratigraphy Branch (USGS), 123 [RU 328]; 530 [RU 7425]

Paley, Albert, 370 [RU 92]

Palmer, Edward, 37 [RU 189]; 532 [RU 7442]

Palmer, William, 39 [RU 192]

Palmer Peninsula (Antarctica) Survey, 1962-1963, 557 [RU 7231]

Pan-American Exposition, Buffalo, New York, 1901, 58 [RU 124]; 189 [RU 74]; 327 [RU 70]

Pan American Union, 197 [RU 311]

Panama, Glass Plate Negatives of, *circa* 1927, 532 [RU 7455]

Panama, sloth and anteater research, 1971-1977, 449 [RU 7411]

Panama-California Exposition, San Diego, 1912-1916, 8 [RU 45]

Panama-California Exposition, San Diego, 1916, 39 [RU 192]; 366 [RU 100]; 327 [RU 70]

Panama Canal Alternatives Study, 1973-1983, 29 [RU 526]

Panama Canal Zone, 616 [RU 9567]

Panama Canal Zone, Biological Survey of the, 1911-1912, 8 [RU 45]; 39 [RU 192]

Panama-Pacific International Exposition, San Francisco, 1915, 8 [RU 45]; 39 [RU 192]; 189 [RU 74]; 327 [RU 70]

Pangels, Henning, 658 [RU 9552]

Panzer, Nora M., 216 [RU 456]

Paper Conservation Laboratory (CHM), 294 [RU 544]

Paradis, Charlie, 661 [RU 9548]

Parents Association (SEEC), 569 [RU 7443]

Parish-Smithsonian Expedition, 1930, 534 [RU 7306]

Park Service, National
    USE: National Park Service

Parkinson, Robin, 287 [RU 531]

Parks, David R., 651 [RU 9554]

Parsons, James A., 653 [RU 9531]

Partello, Dwight J., 39 [RU 192]

Pasahow, Lynn H., 652 [RU 9577]

Pate, Vernon Sennock Lyonesse-Liancour, 533 [RU 1020004]

Patent Office Building, 12 [RU 171]; 201 [RU 318]; 203 [RU 313]; 319 [RU 639]; 329 [RU 562]; 329 [RU 637]; 370 [RU 92]

    RT Fine Arts and Portrait Galleries
    Fine Arts and Portrait Galleries Building

Patent Office Building, opening, 1968, 212 [RU 448]

Patent Office collections, United States, 39 [RU 192]

Patrick, Ruth, 608 [RU 7385]

Paul E. Garber Facility (NASM), 653 [RU 9531]; 636 [RU 9590]

Paul, Stella, 306 [RU 403]

Pawson, David L., 68 [RU 429]; 87 [RU 249]; 87 [RU 292]; 88 [RU 423]; 89 [RU 307]; 90 [RU 325]

Payroll Records, Federal, 368 [RU 501]

Payroll Records, Private, 368 [RU 493]

Peabody Museum of Natural History, Yale University, 380 [RU 7008]; 636 [RU 9591]

Peace Corps Environmental Program, Smithsonian Institution
    USE: Smithsonian Institution-Peace Corps Environmental Program

Peacock Room, 264 [RU 4010003]

Peale, Albert Charles, 533 [RU 7208]

Peale, Anna Claypoole, 230 [RU 2040001]

Peale, Charles Willson, 230 [RU 2040001]; 535 [RU 7054]

Peale, James, 230 [RU 2040001]

Peale, Raphael, 230 [RU 2040001]

Peale, Rembrandt, 230 [RU 2040001]; 535 [RU 7054]

Peale, Rubens, 535 [RU 7054]

Peale, Sarah Miriam, 230 [RU 2040001]

Peale, Titian Ramsay, 230 [RU 2040001]; 535 [RU 7054]; 587 [RU 7186]

Peale Family Papers (NPG), 230 [RU 2040001]

Pearce, Franklin L., 124 [RU 543]

Pearce, John N., 168 [RU 258]

Pearis, Ella B. Howard, 631 [RU 9540]

Pearlman, Michael R., 256 [RU 478]

Pearson, Louise M., 644 [RU 9587]; 645 [RU 9504]

Pearson, Sandra L., 275 [RU 515]

Peary, Robert Edwin, 37 [RU 189]

Pederson, Harry, 557 [RU 7231]

Pele Expedition, 1967, 94 [RU 7418]

Pele Expedition to Indonesia, 1970, 552 [RU 7413]

Pelikan Committee Review of International Programs (WWICS), 298 [RU 558]

Pell Collection, Alfred Duane, 8 [RU 45]; 166 [RU 406]

Penfield, Samuel Lewis, 549 [RU 7152]

Pennak, Robert W., 494 [RU 7145]

Pennsylvania Railroad Company, 599 [RU 7268]

Pennsylvania Society of Miniature Painters, 197 [RU 311]

Perez, Rolando A., 649 [RU 9553]

Performing Arts, Division of, 27 [RU 145]; 181 [RU 584]; 635 [RU 9569]
    RT Public Programs, Department of (NMAH)

Perkin-Elmer Corporation, 652 [RU 9577]

Perkins, Frederick S., 37 [RU 189]

Perkins, G. Holmes, 370 [RU 92]

Perkins, Leonard F., Sr., 653 [RU 9531]

Perkins, R. C. L., 575 [RU 7379]

Permanent Collection Illustrated Checklist (NPG), 225 [RU 2020001]; 229 [RU 553]

Perrot, Paul N., 24 [RU 190]; 25 [RU 608]; 26 [RU 342]; 27 [RU 575]; 338 [RU 574]; 643 [RU 9565]

Perry, John, 633 [RU 9568]

Perry, Kenneth M., 160 [RU 239]

Perry, Stuart H., 533 [RU 7284]; 624 [RU 9529]

Perrygo, Watson M., 534 [RU 7306]; 631 [RU 9516]

Peter and Stubbins, 370 [RU 92]

Peters, James A., 83 [RU 161]; 84 [RU 327]; 534 [RU 7175]

Peterson, John, 617 [RU 9541]

Peterson, Mendel L., 147 [RU 383]; 170 [RU 381]; 184 [RU 581]

Petrology and Volcanology, Division of (NMNH), 119 [RU 614]
    BT Mineral Sciences, Department of (NMNH)

Pettibone, Marian H., 89 [RU 307]; 96 [RU 417]

Pfister, Harold F., 281 [RU 492]

Phanerogams, Division of (NMNH), 113 [RU 230]
    BT Botany, Department of (NMNH)

Phenomenon of Change, The, 281 [RU 492]

Philadelphia (ship), 147 [RU 383]

Philadelphia Museum, 535 [RU 7054]

Philadelphia Museum Company, 535 [RU 7054]

Philately, Division of (USNM), 177 [RU 580]
    BT History, Department of (USNM)
    RT Philately and Postal History, Division of (NMHT)

Philately, Hall of (NMAH), 177 [RU 580]

Philately and Postal History, Division of (NMHT), 177 [RU 580]
    BT Civil History, Department of (NMHT)

    RT National Philatelic Collection (NMAH)
        National Postal Museum (NMAH)
        Postal History, Division of (NMHT)

Philips, Frederic M., 339 [RU 369]

Philosophical Society of Washington, 374 [RU 7001]; 536 [RU 7079]; 600 [RU 7159]

Photograph Collection, Smithsonian Archives, 369 [RU 95]

Photographic Exposition, International, Dresden, 1909, 39 [RU 192]

Photographic History, Division of (NMAH), 156 [RU 529]
    BT History of Science and Technology, Department of the (NMAH)
        Social and Cultural History, Department of (NMAH)
    RT Graphic Arts and Photography, Division of (NMHT)
        Photographic History, Division of (NMHT)
        Photography, Section of (NMHT)

Photographic History, Division of (NMHT), 156 [RU 529]
    BT Applied Arts, Department of (NMHT)
        History of Technology, Department of (NMHT)
    RT Graphic Arts and Photography, Division of (NMHT)
        Photographic History, Division of (NMAH)
        Photography, Section of (NMHT)

Photographs, Department of (NPG), 225 [RU 2020001]

Photography, Hall of (NMAH), 156 [RU 529]

Photography, Section of (NMHT), 156 [RU 529]
    BT Graphic Arts, Division of (NMHT)
    RT Graphic Arts and Photography, Division of (NMHT)
        Photographic History, Division of (NMAH)
        Photographic History, Division of (NMHT)

Photography, Section of (USNM), 156 [RU 529]
    BT Graphic Arts, Division of (USNM)
    RT Photography, Section of (NMHT)

Physical and Chemical Geology, Division of (NMNH), 115 [RU 268]
    BT Geology, Department of (NMNH)
    RT Mineralogy and Petrology, Division of (NMNH)

Physical Anthropology, Division of (NMNH), 641 [RU 9521]

Physical Sciences, Division of (NMHT), 158 [RU 293]; 158 [RU 579]; 159 [RU 332]
    BT Science and Technology, Department of (NMHT)
    NT Mathematics and Antique Instruments, Section of (NMHT)

Physical Sciences and Mathematics, Division of (NMAH), 159 [RU 332]; 174 [RU 473]
    BT History of Science and Technology, Department of the (NMAH)
    RT Mathematics, Division of (NMAH)
    Mathematics, Division of (NMHT)
    Mathematics, Section of (NMHT)
    Mathematics and Antique Instruments, Section of (NMHT)
    Physical Sciences, Division of (NMHT)

Physical Sciences and Measurement, Section of (USNM), 158 [RU 293]; 159 [RU 332]; 158 [RU 579]
    BT Engineering, Division of (USNM)
    RT Physical Sciences, Division of (NMHT)

Physics, Hall of (NMAH), 145 [RU 375]

Physics, Mathematics, and Astronomy, Hall of (NMHT), 158 [RU 293]

Picasso, Pablo, 484 [RU 7449]; 624 [RU 9566]

Pickering, Charles, 417 [RU 7189]; 587 [RU 7186]

Picozza, Enrico, 652 [RU 9577]

Pierce, Jack W., 68 [RU 429]

Pigliucci, Riccardo, 652 [RU 9577]

Pilgrim, Dianne H., 281 [RU 492]

Pilling, James, 127 [RU NAA 2]

Pilsbry, Henry A., 481 [RU 7075]; 497 [RU 7333]

Pinchot, Mrs. James W., 39 [RU 192]

Pine, Ronald H., 83 [RU 407]

Pittier, Henri, 39 [RU 192]

Pitts, Edward, 661 [RU 9548]

Pizzini, Andre del Campo, 102 [RU 7422]

PKM machine gun, 659 [RU 9532]

Planetary Sciences Division (SAO), 247 [RU 437]

Plant Industry, Bureau of (USDA), 110 [RU 227]; 415 [RU 7430]
    NT Agrostology Section (USDA)

Plant Quarantine, Bureau of Entomology and (USDA)
    USE: Entomology and Plant Quarantine, Bureau of (USDA)

Plant Taxonomy, International Association for, 494 [RU 7141]

Plant World, 108 [RU 222]

Plants, Collected Notes, Lists, and Catalogs on, 114 [RU 1010014]

Plants, Division of (USNM), 105 [RU 220]; 106 [RU 221]; 107 [RU 236]; 107 [RU 272]; 108 [RU 222]; 108 [RU 223]; 109 [RU 224]; 109 [RU 225]; 109 [RU 226]; 111 [RU 428]; 113 [RU 230]; 114 [RU 237]
    BT Biology, Department of (NMNH)
    Biology, Department of (USNM)
    RT Botany, Department of (USNM)
    United States Department of Agriculture
    United States National Herbarium

Platt, Charles A., 262 [RU 4010001]; 370 [RU 92]

Platt, Louise, 298 [RU 570]

Platt, Robert, 95 [RU 7461]

Pogue, Forrest C., 183 [RU 377]; 632 [RU 9589]

Poinsett, Joel Roberts, 525 [RU 7058]

Polar Expedition to Point Barrow, Alaska, International, 1881-1883, 522 [RU 7203]

Polaris Expedition, 1871-1873, 339 [RU 68]

Political History, Division of (NMAH), 174 [RU 473]; 613 [RU 9522]
    BT Social and Cultural History, Department of (NMAH)
    RT Political History, Division of (NMHT)

Political History, Division of (NMHT), 173 [RU 252]; 174 [RU 473]
    BT Civil History, Department of (NMHT)
    NT American Costume, Section of (NMHT)
    Growth of the United States (NMHT)
    RT Political History, Division of (NMAH)

Pollard, Charles Louis, 108 [RU 222]

Pollock, George Freeman, 619 [RU 9570]

Polymerase Chain Reaction, History of the, 652 [RU 9577]

Pomona College, 623 [RU 9572]

Poole, Robert K., 314 [RU 264]

Poore, Richard Z., 530 [RU 7425]

Pope, Annemarie H., 220 [RU 316]

Pope, John A., 262 [RU 4010001]; 264 [RU 4010004]

Poplar Islands, 267 [RU 419]

Poplar Islands, Erosion Control Study, 266 [RU 286]
    BT Chesapeake Bay Center for Environmental Studies

Population Dynamics Quarterly, 331 [RU 300]
Port Antonio, Jamaica, marine laboratory,
   Johns Hopkins University, 606 [RU 7235]
Port-au-Prince Bicentennial Exposition, Haiti,
   1949, 39 [RU 192]
Port Orford meteorite, 1933, 39 [RU 192]
Porter, Holbrook Fitz John, 149 [RU 297]
Portland Museum of Art (Maine), 443 [RU
   7439]
Portland Zoological Park, 633 [RU 9568]
Portrait Gallery
      USE: National Portrait Gallery
Portraits, Catalog of American
      USE: Catalog of American Portraits
Portraits from the American Stage, 1771-1971
   (exhibition), 227 [RU 361]
Portraits from "The Americans: The Demo-
   cratic Experience" (exhibition), 227 [RU
   361]; 229 [RU 553]
Post, Jeffrey E., 116 [RU 421]
Post, Robert C., 161 [RU 528]
Post estate, Marjorie Merriweather, 329 [RU
   562]
Post Office Building, 264 [RU 4010003]
Postal History, Division of (NMHT), 177 [RU
   580]
      BT Applied Arts, Department of
         (NMHT)
      RT National Philatelic Collection
         (NMAH)
         National Postal Museum (NMAH)
         Philately and Postal History,
            Division of (NMHT)
Postcards from the National Collection of Fine
   Arts, 213 [RU 466]
Potomac-Side Naturalists' Club, 536 [RU
   7210]
Potomac Valley Ornithological Club, 537 [RU
   7111]
Potter, Mary Grace, 363 [RU 600]
Poultry Congress and Exposition, World's
   (Seventh), Cleveland, 1939, 327 [RU 70]
Powell, John Wesley, 125 [RU NAA 1]; 127
   [RU NAA 2]; 407 [RU 7085]
Powell Survey
      USE: United States Geographical and
         Geological Survey of the Rocky
         Mountain Region
Power and the Early Steam Engine (exhibi-
   tion), 151 [RU 397]
Prairie Network (SAO)
      USE: Meteorite Photography and
         Recovery Project (SAO)
Preble, Edward Alexander, 537 [RU 7252]

Preindustrial Cultural History, Division of
   (NMHT), 169 [RU 261]
      RT Domestic Life, Division of (NMHT)
         Growth of the United States
            (NMHT)
Preparator, Arts and Industries, Department of
   (USNM), 43 [RU 408]
Preserving the History of the Aerospace
   Industry, April 1990 (symposium), 241 [RU
   355]
Presidents' Medals, 1789-1977 (exhibition),
   227 [RU 361]
Presidents on Wheels, 174 [RU 473]
Press, Smithsonian Institution, 27 [RU 145];
   348 [RU 535]
Pribilof Islands, Alaska, 585 [RU 7181]
Priestley, Joseph, 39 [RU 192]
Primate Space Flight Training Facility
   (U.S.S.R.), 659 [RU 9551]
Princeton University, 651 [RU 9546]
Pringle, Cyrus Guernsey, 37 [RU 189]
Printer (USNM), 43 [RU 408]
Printing and Publication, Advisory Committee
   on, 8 [RU 34]
Printing Ink Exhibition, The (exhibition), 152
   [RU 206]
Prints and Drawings, Department of (NCFA),
   208 [RU 457]
Prints and Drawings, Department of (NMAA),
   208 [RU 476]
      RT Graphic Arts, Department of
         (NMAA)
Prints and Drawings, Department of (NPG),
   225 [RU 2020001]
Proceedings of the American Society of
   Zoologists, 390 [RU 7351]
Proceedings of the Biological Society of
   Washington, 410 [RU 7185]
Proctor, Joseph O., Jr., 529 [RU 7387]
Proctor, Roy, 257 [RU 303]
Program Coordinator, Office of the (CHM),
   289 [RU 324]
Program Support, Office of (NMAA), 217 [RU
   321]
      RT Exhibitions Abroad, Office of
         (NCFA)
Programs Management Office (SAO), 253 [RU
   262]
      NT Mount Hopkins Observatory (SAO)
Progress Exposition, New Haven, 1926, 39
   [RU 192]
Project
      USE: name of project

Property and Supplies, Department of, 59 [RU 78]

Property Clerk, 59 [RU 78]

Psychology and the Social Sciences, Research Group in, 345 [RU 179]

Public Affairs, Office of, 27 [RU 145]; 323 [RU 373]; 324 [RU 82]; 340 [RU 368]; 340 [RU 420]; 341 [RU 372]; 341 [RU 405]; 342 [RU 370]; 343 [RU 371]; 343 [RU 410]; 343 [RU 549]; 358 [RU 586]; 361 [RU 587]; 372 [RU 106]
    BT Coordinator of Public Information
    NT News Clipping File
       Radio Smithsonian
    RT Information, Office of
       Smithsonian Museum Service
       Telecommunications, Office of

Public Affairs, Office of (HMSG), 274 [RU 513]
    BT Administration and Support Services, Department of (HMSG)
    RT Publications and Information Service Department (HMSG)

Public Affairs, Office of (NASM), 242 [RU 339]
    NT Frisbee Festival (NASM)

Public Affairs, Office of (NMAA), 214 [RU 454]

Public Affairs, Office of (NMAH), 180 [RU 360]
    NT Public Information (NMAH)
       Special Events (NMAH)
    RT Public Affairs, Office of (NMHT)

Public Affairs, Office of (NMHT), 180 [RU 360]; 182 [RU 595]
    NT Special Events, Office of (NMAH)
    RT Public Affairs, Office of (NMAH)

Public Affairs, Office of (NPG), 228 [RU 554]

Public Affairs, Office of (NZP), 194 [RU 365]

Public Affairs, Office of (Smithsonian Resident Associate Program), 355 [RU 632]

Public Affairs, Office of, Director, 339 [RU 369]

Public Affairs, Office of, Telecommunications Coordinator, 617 [RU 9541]

Public and Academic Programs, Office of (NMAH), 181 [RU 584]
    RT Public Programs, Department of (NMAH)

Public Information (NMAH), 180 [RU 360]
    BT Public Affairs, Office of (NMAH)

Public Information, Office of, 358 [RU 586]

Public Information and Education, Division of (NMHT), 179 [RU 599]
    RT Education and Visitor Information, Division of (NMAH)

Public Information Office (CHM), 291 [RU 547]

Public Information Officer (NMNH), 67 [RU 416]

Public Programs, Department of (NMAH), 181 [RU 584]
    RT Performing Arts, Division of
       Public and Academic Programs, Office of (NMAH)

Public Programs, Office of (NMAA), 214 [RU 455]

Public Relations, Office of (SITES), 350 [RU 489]
    BT Smithsonian Institution Traveling Exhibition Service

Public Relations Officer, Smithsonian Institution, 630 [RU 9507]

Public Service, Assistant Secretary for, 27 [RU 145]

Publication Editor (NCFA), 215 [RU 319]
    RT Editorial Office (NCFA)

Publications, Committee on, 1894-1896, 585 [RU 7181]

Publications and Information Service Department (HMSG), 274 [RU 513]
    RT Public Affairs, Office of (HMSG)

Publius, 300 [RU 571]

Purnell, Louis R., 632 [RU 9578]

Pursuit of Science in Revolutionary America, The, 483 [RU 7363]

Q

Quadrangle Complex, 343 [RU 410]
    RT Quadrangle Museum Project
       South Quadrangle Project

Quadrangle Museum Project, 27 [RU 575]
    RT Quadrangle Complex
       South Quadrangle Project

Quality of Man's Environment (symposium), 315 [RU 494]

Quartermaster Corps (United States Army), 512 [RU 7293]

Quartermaster General, Office of, 632 [RU 9578]

R

Radford, Tom, 523 [RU 7295]
Radiation and Organisms, Division of, 9 [RU 46]; 267 [RU 412]; 268 [RU 387]
    BT Smithsonian Astrophysical Observatory
    NT Carbon-Dating Laboratory
    RT Chesapeake Bay Center for Environmental Studies
        Radiation Biology Laboratory
        Smithsonian Environmental Research Center
Radiation Biology Laboratory, 29 [RU 526]; 30 [RU 108]; 31 [RU 254]; 32 [RU 329]; 267 [RU 412]; 267 [RU 419]; 268 [RU 387]
    NT Carbon-Dating Laboratory
    RT Chesapeake Bay Center for Environmental Studies
        Radiation and Organisms, Division of
        Smithsonian Environmental Research Center
Radio and Geoastronomy Division (SAO), 247 [RU 437]; 256 [RU 478]; 258 [RU 517]
    NT Satellite Tracking Program (SAO)
"Radio Dialogue" (WWICS) (radio broadcast), 301 [RU 601]; 302 [RU 602]; 302 [RU 603]; 302 [RU 604]
    RT "Dialogue" (WWICS) (radio broadcast)
Radio Meteor Project (SAO), 249 [RU 259]; 250 [RU 253]; 254 [RU 304]; 602 [RU 7431]
    BT Harvard College Observatory
"Radio Smithsonian" (radio broadcast), 358 [RU 586]; 359 [RU 296]; 360 [RU 589]; 360 [RU 591]; 361 [RU 588]; 361 [RU 590]
    BT Telecommunications, Office of
Rafinesque, Constantine Samuel, 538 [RU 7250]
Railroad History, 603 [RU 7384]
Rails of the World, 380 [RU 7008]
Rainey, Paul J., 480 [RU 7179]
Rainey African Expedition, 1911-1912, 39 [RU 192]; 480 [RU 7179]
Ralph, William LaGrange, 74 [RU 1060102]
Rambo, James I., 287 [RU 280]
Ramsey, Norman F., Jr., 653 [RU 9531]
Ranck, Gary L., 83 [RU 407]
RAND
    USE: Research and Development (RAND) Corporation

Rand, A. Stanley, 633 [RU 9579]; 640 [RU 9580]; 649 [RU 9553]
Rand, Harry Z., 205 [RU 460]; 206 [RU 458]; 207 [RU 461]
Rand, Patricia, 640 [RU 9580]
Random Records of a Lifetime, 487 [RU 7084]
Raney, Edward C., 389 [RU 7149]
Ransom, Brayton Howard, 568 [RU 7262]
Rasetti, Franco Dino, 538 [RU 7240]
Rasmussen, Knud, 562 [RU 7091]
Rasmussen Expedition, Knud,1920, 562 [RU 7091]
Rathbun, Mary Jane, 91 [RU 233]; 467 [RU 7257]; 539 [RU 7256]; 557 [RU 7231]; 568 [RU 7262]
Rathbun, Richard, 38 [RU 201]; 39 [RU 192]; 42 [RU 112]; 45 [RU 55]; 50 [RU 79]; 91 [RU 233]; 197 [RU 311]; 453 [RU 7446]; 540 [RU 7078]; 568 [RU 7262]
Rathbun, Seward Hume, 540 [RU 7078]
Ratzenberger, Katherine, 221 [RU 463]
Rau, Charles, 541 [RU 7070]
Rau, Phil, 494 [RU 7458]
Raven, Henry Cushier, 541 [RU 7178]
Ravenel, William deC., 39 [RU 192]; 48 [RU 167]; 197 [RU 311]; 198 [RU 312]; 327 [RU 70]; 568 [RU 7262]
Ray, Clayton E., 122 [RU 424]; 451 [RU 7348]; 621 [RU 9518]
Ray, G. Carleton, 588 [RU 7229]
Ray, Louis L., 542 [RU 7393]
Ray, Man, 484 [RU 7449]; 624 [RU 9566]
Read, Benjamin H., 296 [RU 275]
Read, Robert W., 65 [RU 366]
Reading Is Fundamental Inc., 27 [RU 145]
Reagon, Bernice Johnson, 181 [RU 584]
Receipt for Packages, 58 [RU 129]
    RT Registrar
Recent Acquisitions (NPG), 229 [RU 553]
Recktenwald, Diether J., 651 [RU 9554]
Record of Storage (USNM), 57 [RU 126]
    RT Registrar (USNM)
Reed, Daniel J., 228 [RU 556]
Reed, Fred C., 146 [RU 240]
Reed, Michael, 655 [RU 9542]
Reed, R. L., 376 [RU 7003]
Reed, Theodore H., 189 [RU 74]; 190 [RU 326]; 190 [RU 380]; 633 [RU 9568]; 649 [RU 9553]
Reeside, John B., Jr., 530 [RU 7425]; 542 [RU 7326]
Regents, Board of
    USE: Board of Regents
Regional Events Program (SNAP), 353 [RU 557]

Registrar (USNM), 24 [RU 190]; 52 [RU 305]; 52 [RU 6999T]; 54 [RU 75]; 54 [RU 127]; 54 [RU 128]; 54 [RU 199]; 55 [RU 120]; 55 [RU 186]; 55 [RU 434]; 56 [RU 109]; 56 [RU 110]; 56 [RU 111]; 56 [RU 118]; 57 [RU 121]; 57 [RU 122]; 57 [RU 126]; 58 [RU 124]; 58 [RU 125]; 59 [RU 123]; 644 [RU 9587]

Registrar, Annual Reports (USNM), 54 [RU 128]

Registrar, Office of the, 26 [RU 342]; 344 [RU 568]

Registrar, Office of the (CHM), 292 [RU 540]; 293 [RU 541]; 293 [RU 542]

Registrar, Office of the (HMSG), 275 [RU 515]

Registrar, Office of the (NMAA), 209 [RU 453]; 210 [RU 5000101]; 211 [RU 5000102]

Registrar, Office of the (NMNH), 67 [RU 566]

Registrar, Office of the (NPG), 225 [RU 2020001]

Registrarial Council of the Smithsonian Institution, 67 [RU 566]; 292 [RU 540]
  RT Council of Registrars
     Smithsonian Institution Registrar's Council

Registrars, Council of
  USE: Council of Registrars

Regusa, Robert P., 652 [RU 9577]

Rehabilitative Medicine, Hall of (NMHT), 154 [RU 244]

Rehder, Harald A., 93 [RU 73]; 94 [RU 7418]; 634 [RU 9519]

Reid, Earl D., 80 [RU 234]

Reid-Henry, D. M., 453 [RU 7402]

Reines, Frederick, 653 [RU 9531]

Reingold, Nathan, 185 [RU 511]; 485 [RU 7474]; 543 [RU 7470]; 634 [RU 9503]

Reinhardt, John E., 22 [RU 477]; 307 [RU 634]

Reinhardt, Leslie, 230 [RU 2040001]

Reiss, Phillip K., 329 [RU 562]

Relations Between the Smithsonian and the Congress, 625 [RU 9525]

Relief Association, Smithsonian Institution, 349 [RU 86]

Religious Society of Friends, 497 [RU 7333]

Remensnyder Collection of American Stoneware, 644 [RU 9586]

Renwick Gallery, 10 [RU 99]; 22 [RU 281]; 22 [RU 477]; 201 [RU 318]; 203 [RU 313]; 212 [RU 448]; 213 [RU 451]; 220 [RU 333]; 318 [RU 532]; 329 [RU 562]; 636 [RU 9591]

  BT National Collection of Fine Arts
     National Museum of American Art

Renwick Gallery, Office of the Director, 208 [RU 465]
  BT National Museum of American Art

Reptiles and Amphibians, Collected Notes, Lists, and Catalogs on, 85 [RU 1060501]

Reptiles and Amphibians, Division of (NMNH), 83 [RU 161]; 84 [RU 327]; 432 [RU 7151]; 534 [RU 7175]
  BT Vertebrate Zoology, Department of (NMNH)
     Zoology, Department of (NMNH)

Reptiles and Amphibians, Division of (USNM), 85 [RU 7445]
  NT Turtles, Collected Notes, Photographs and Graphic Illustrations on (USNM)

Reptiles and Batrachians, Department of (NMNH), 83 [RU 161]
  RT Herpetology, Department of (NMNH)

Reptiles and Batrachians, Division of (NMNH), 83 [RU 161]
  BT Biology, Department of (NMNH)

Reptiles and Batrachians, Division of (USNM), 85 [RU 508]

Reptiles, Department of (NMNH), 83 [RU 161]

Reptiles, Department of (USNM), 610 [RU 7166]

Research and Development (RAND) Corporation, 657 [RU 9536]

Research and Professional Training, Office of (NCFA), 219 [RU 596]

Research Awards Program, Smithsonian
  USE: Smithsonian Research Awards Program

Research Corporation, 8 [RU 45]; 10 [RU 50]; 17 [RU 46TB]; 17 [RU 51]

Research Group in Psychology and the Social Sciences, 345 [RU 179]

Research in Tropical America, Institute for, 17 [RU 135]; 304 [RU 134]

Research Support, Office of (NMAA), 219 [RU 442]
  RT Slides and Photography, Office of (NCFA)

Resser, Charles Elmer, 377 [RU 7004]; 544 [RU 7232]; 619 [RU 9524]

Return to Albion: Americans in England, 1760-1940 (exhibition), 229 [RU 553]

Reunion: Memories of an American Experience (motion picture), 362 [RU 593]

Rhees, William Jones, 320 [RU 64]; 374 [RU 7000]; 489 [RU 7061]; 544 [RU 7081]

Rhinehart, B. L., 376 [RU 7003]

Rhoad, Vincent, 661 [RU 9548]

Rhoades, Georgia M., 215 [RU 319]

Rhoades, Katherine N., 262 [RU 4010001]

Rhode River Environmental Education Project, 266 [RU 286]

    BT Chesapeake Bay Center for Environmental Studies

Rhode River Review, 267 [RU 419]; 268 [RU 399]

Rhode River Watershed Program, 266 [RU 286]

    BT Chesapeake Bay Center for Environmental Studies

Rice, Mary E., 96 [RU 417]

Rice Institute (Texas), 645 [RU 9560]

Richard, John H., 575 [RU 7441]

Richards, Horace G., 93 [RU 73]

Richards, William N., Jr., 25 [RU 608]; 26 [RU 342]; 27 [RU 575]; 338 [RU 574]

Richardson, Edgar P., 304 [RU 401]; 305 [RU 402]

Richardson, Elliott L., 300 [RU 571]

Richardson, Harriett, 89 [RU 7260]

Richmond, Charles Wallace, 37 [RU 189]; 72 [RU 105]; 74 [RU 1060103]; 545 [RU 7382]

Richmond, Edward Avery, 546 [RU 7374]

Richter, Anders, 348 [RU 535]

Rickey, George, 203 [RU 313]

Ricklefs, Robert Eric, 640 [RU 9584]

Ridgway, John L., 547 [RU 7211]

Ridgway, Robert, 72 [RU 105]; 74 [RU 1060102]; 75 [RU 1060104]; 415 [RU 7071]; 547 [RU 7167]; 590 [RU 7133]

Riesenberg, Saul H., 128 [RU NAA 5]; 639 [RU 9508]

Rifkin, Ned, 271 [RU 469]

Riggs, George, 204 [RU 447]

Riggs Collection of Arms and Armor, 37 [RU 189]

Riley, Charles Valentine, 96 [RU 138]; 97 [RU 139]; 101 [RU 7448]; 547 [RU 7076]

Riley, Joseph Harvey, 72 [RU 105]; 548 [RU 7118]

Ringgold Expedition

    USE: United States North Pacific Exploring Expedition

Rinzler, Ralph, 28 [RU 367]; 635 [RU 9569]; 636 [RU 9591]

Rio, Luis del, 140 [RU 335]

Ripley, Mary Livingston, 264 [RU 4010004]

Ripley, S. Dillon, 10 [RU 99]; 11 [RU 613]; 72 [RU 105]; 203 [RU 313]; 264 [RU 4010004]; 380 [RU 7008]; 551 [RU 7447]; 616 [RU 9515]; 624 [RU 9566]; 625 [RU 9525]; 626 [RU 9558]; 635 [RU 9569]; 636 [RU 9591]

Ritterbush, Philip C., 266 [RU 286]; 315 [RU 102]; 315 [RU 494]

River Basin Surveys, 9 [RU 46]; 128 [RU NAA 5]; 131 [RU NAA 6]

River House, 318 [RU 532]

Rivers, Larry, 484 [RU 7449]

Road after 1984: High Technology and Human Freedom (symposium), 332 [RU 495]; 332 [RU 498]; 357 [RU 496]; 357 [RU 497]

Robbins, Warren H., 307 [RU 634]

Robert Adam and Kedleston Hall (exhibition), 293 [RU 542]

Robert Rauschenberg, 1973-1974 (exhibition), 206 [RU 458]

Roberts, Frank H. H., 39 [RU 192]

Roberts, Henry B., 548 [RU 7299]

Roberts, Richard Brooke, 549 [RU 7160]

Robertson, Charles J., 201 [RU 439]; 202 [RU 446]; 204 [RU 475]

Robertson, Robert, 627 [RU 9527]

Robinson, C. J., 95 [RU 7218]

Robinson, Douglas, 275 [RU 515]

Robinson, Louise W., 204 [RU 447]

Robinson, Michael H., 190 [RU 380]

Robinson, Theodore, 648 [RU 9545]

Roche Molecular Systems, 652 [RU 9577]

Rock, Joseph Francis, 548 [RU 7118]; 549 [RU 7287]; 595 [RU 7270]

Rockefeller Archive Center Council, 543 [RU 7470]

Rockefeller Brothers Fund, 314 [RU 264]

Rockefeller Foundation, 562 [RU 7091]

Rocketry Division, Naval Research Laboratory, 656 [RU 9539]

Rockhill, William Woodville, 37 [RU 189]

Roddenberry, Gene, 239 [RU 398]

Roderick, Walter R., 636 [RU 9590]

Rodriguez-Martinez, Pablo, 637 [RU 9581]

Roebling, Washington A., 39 [RU 192]; 120 [RU 7421]; 549 [RU 7152]

Roebling Solar Research Fund, John A., 368 [RU 493]

Rogers, Anne M., 626 [RU 9558]; 628 [RU 9538]

Rogers, David, 494 [RU 7145]

Rogers, Henry J., 550 [RU 7390]

Rogers, Isaiah, 370 [RU 92]

Rogick, Mary Dora, 550 [RU 7408]

Rohlfing, H. Christian, 281 [RU 267]; 281 [RU 492]; 282 [RU 545]; 287 [RU 280]

Rohwer, Sievert Allen, 579 [RU 7309]

Rolff, Jan, 254 [RU 263]

Rondon, Candido Mariano da Silva, 551 [RU 7472]

Roosevelt, Franklin Delano, 149 [RU 376]; 557 [RU 7231]

Roosevelt, Theodore, 480 [RU 7179]; 551 [RU 7472]

Roosevelt African Expedition, 1909
    USE: Smithsonian-Roosevelt African Expedition, 1909

Roosevelt Memorial Association, Inc., 551 [RU 7472]

Roosevelt-Rondon South American Expedition, 551 [RU 7472]

Root, Joseph, 661 [RU 9547]

Roper, Clyde F. E., 68 [RU 429]; 88 [RU 423]; 93 [RU 73]

Roschwalb, Susanne, 228 [RU 554]

Rose, Eileen, 349 [RU 488]

Rose, Joseph Nelson, 39 [RU 192]; 105 [RU 220]; 106 [RU 221]; 109 [RU 225]

Rosenberg, Dorothy, 13 [RU 620]; 551 [RU 7447]

Rosenfeld, Alvin, 340 [RU 420]

Rosenzweig, Phyllis, 272 [RU 481]

Rosewater, Joseph, 87 [RU 249]; 93 [RU 73]; 94 [RU 7418]; 552 [RU 7413]

Ross, Bernard Rogan, 36 [RU 561]; 39 [RU 192]; 76 [RU 7215]; 553 [RU 7221]

Roth, Herbert E., 252 [RU 255]

Roth, Rodris C., 164 [RU 251]; 165 [RU 331]; 167 [RU 519]; 168 [RU 258]; 169 [RU 261]

Roth, Waldfried T., 193 [RU 385]

Rotman, Marcos Boris, 651 [RU 9554]

Roundtable Reports, 523 [RU 7295]

Roundy, Paul V., 553 [RU 7330]

Rowe, Benson, 257 [RU 467]

Roy, Robert H., 428 [RU 7451]

Roy Neuberger Collection, 216 [RU 443]

Royal Entomological Society of London, 580 [RU 7323]

Royal Industrial Museum of Scotland, 553 [RU 7221]

Royal Pavilion at Brighton, The (exhibition), 293 [RU 542]

RPK74 machine gun, 659 [RU 9532]

Rubinoff, Ira, 614 [RU 9563]; 637 [RU 9582]; 649 [RU 9553]

Ruetzler, Klaus, 90 [RU 325]

Ruhe, Benjamin, 200 [RU 320]; 214 [RU 454]

Rusk, Jeremiah M., 105 [RU 220]

Russell, James Townsend, 39 [RU 192]

Russell, Louise M., 102 [RU 418]

Russian-American Telegraph Expedition, 441 [RU 7073]; 601 [RU 7213]

Rydberg, Per Axel, 439 [RU 7272]

S

Saarinen, Eliel, 9 [RU 46]; 198 [RU 312]

Sabrosky, Curtis W., 638 [RU 9583]

Sachet, Marie-Helene, 623 [RU 9572]

Sackler, Arthur M., Collection of Oriental Art, 11 [RU 613]

Sackler Gallery of Art
    USE: Arthur M. Sackler Gallery of Art

Sadik, Marvin, 223 [RU 426]; 226 [RU 555]; 227 [RU 361]; 228 [RU 554]

Safford, William Edwin, 37 [RU 189]; 554 [RU 7275]

Sage, Nancy, 275 [RU 515]

Saiki, Randall K., 652 [RU 9577]

Sailer, Reece Ivan, 554 [RU 7136]; 579 [RU 7309]

Salan, Jean M., 307 [RU 634]; 308 [RU 635]

Samaniego, Mirna, 649 [RU 9553]

Samuel Yellin Metalworkers, 370 [RU 92]

San Diego Natural History Museum, 444 [RU 7097]

Sanderson, Geraldine B., 180 [RU 360]; 182 [RU 595]

Sandhouse, Grace, 555 [RU 7456]

San Francisco Earthquake, 1906, 410 [RU 7335]

Santamaria, Dilia, 649 [RU 9553]

Santiago, Margaret A., 67 [RU 566]; 352 [RU 507]

Sao Paulo Biennale exhibitions, 1967, 1969, 1973, 214 [RU 454]

Saratoga Springs, New York, fur animal experiment station, (USDA), 393 [RU 7143]

Satellite Tracking and Data Acquisition Department (SAO), 254 [RU 263]
    BT Satellite Tracking Program (SAO)

Satellite Tracking Program (SAO), 247 [RU 437]; 248 [RU 256]; 248 [RU 468]; 249 [RU 259]; 250 [RU 253]; 252 [RU 255]; 254 [RU 263]; 256 [RU 301]; 256 [RU 478]; 258 [RU 517]; 258 [RU 522]; 602 [RU 7431]; 613 [RU 9556]; 646 [RU 9520]
    BT Radio and Geoastronomy Division (SAO)
        Smithsonian Astrophysical Observatory

Skarstrom, Eugenie Beth, 301 [RU 601]
Skog, Laurence E., 111 [RU 428]
Skyland Resort (Virginia), 619 [RU 9570]
Slides and Photography, Office of (NCFA),
219 [RU 442]
    RT Visual Resources, Office of
(NMAA)
Sliter, William V., 530 [RU 7425]
Slocum, John J., 13 [RU 341]
Slosson, Edwin E., 562 [RU 7091]
Sloth and anteater research, Panama, 1971-
1977, 449 [RU 7411]
Slud, Paul, 72 [RU 391]; 73 [RU 270]
Slutzkey, Joel, 658 [RU 9552]
Small, Gordon B., Jr., 567 [RU 7414]
Small Mammal House (NZP), 190 [RU 380]
Smiley, Charles W., 567 [RU 7206]
Smillie, Thomas W., 156 [RU 529]
Smith, Alan P., 649 [RU 9553]
Smith, Albert C., 46 [RU 89]; 61 [RU 155];
452 [RU 7096]
Smith, Alice Kimball, 653 [RU 9531]
Smith, Arthur, 102 [RU 7422]
Smith, Bruce D., 65 [RU 366]
Smith, Cyril, 653 [RU 9531]
Smith, Fletcher A., 278 [RU 390]
Smith, Francis O. J., 590 [RU 7055]
Smith, Frank, 568 [RU 7262]
Smith, Hugh McCormick, 39 [RU 192]
Smith, Jean Chandler, 639 [RU 9588]
Smith, John Bernhard, 96 [RU 138]; 97 [RU
139]; 101 [RU 7427]; 564 [RU 7296]
Smith, John Donnell, 106 [RU 221]; 114 [RU
237]
Smith, Jung Lea, 102 [RU 7422]
Smith, Lloyd M., 650 [RU 9549]
Smith, Lyman Bradford, 568 [RU 7276]
Smith, Neal G., 621 [RU 9562]; 633 [RU
9579]; 640 [RU 9584]
Smith, Ralph, 626 [RU 9573]
Smith, Ralph Clifton, 152 [RU 206]
Smith, Sidney Irving, 585 [RU 7192]
Smithmeyer, J. L., 370 [RU 92]
Smithson, James, 374 [RU 7000]
Smithson Bicentennial, 18 [RU 142]; 137 [RU
279]; 158 [RU 293]; 341 [RU 372]; 343
[RU 410]
Smithson Bicentennial (symposium), 315 [RU
494]
Smithson crypt gate, 370 [RU 92]
Smithson Memorial, 370 [RU 92]
Smithsonian, Conference on the Future of,
1927, 9 [RU 46]
"Smithsonian, The" (television broadcast), 361
[RU 587]

"Smithsonian Announcements," 335 [RU 486]
Smithsonian Archeological Expedition to
Mexico, 452 [RU 7096]
Smithsonian Archives, 21 [RU 104]; 22 [RU
281]; 29 [RU 526]; 346 [RU 98]; 370 [RU
94]
    RT Smithsonian Institution Archives
    Smithsonian Institution Archives,
    Office of
Smithsonian Art Commission, 19 [RU 137];
198 [RU 312]; 203 [RU 313]; 209 [RU 453]
Smithsonian Art Index (NCFA), 219 [RU 442]
Smithsonian Associates, 12 [RU 171]; 12 [RU
618]; 27 [RU 145]; 354 [RU 626]; 355 [RU
627]; 636 [RU 9591]
    RT Smithsonian Resident Associate
Program
Smithsonian Astrophysical Observatory, 8 [RU
34]; 8 [RU 45]; 9 [RU 46]; 10 [RU 50]; 12
[RU 171]; 19 [RU 137]; 29 [RU 393]; 29
[RU 526]; 30 [RU 108]; 31 [RU 254]; 32
[RU 329]; 246 [RU 85]; 246 [RU 474]; 247
[RU 188]; 247 [RU 437]; 248 [RU 468];
257 [RU 467]; 258 [RU 517]; 258 [RU
522]; 259 [RU 521]; 259 [RU 530]; 260
[RU 523]; 260 [RU 524]; 260 [RU 525];
261 [RU 538]; 267 [RU 412]; 323 [RU
168]; 365 [RU 93]; 370 [RU 92]; 378 [RU
7005]; 455 [RU 7463]; 471 [RU 7307]; 602
[RU 7431]; 612 [RU 9500]; 613 [RU 9556];
616 [RU 9515]; 646 [RU 9520]; 651 [RU
9546]; 655 [RU 9542]
    NT Atomic and Molecular Physics
Division (SAO)
    Boyden Observatory
    Celescope, Project (SAO)
    Central Bureau for Astronomical
Telegrams
    Contracts and Procurement Office
(SAO)
    Flight Operations, Department of
(SAO)
    Fred Lawrence Whipple Observatory
(SAO)
    Gravitational Redshift Space Probe
Experiment (SAO)
    High Energy Astrophysics Division
(SAO)
    Infrared Telescope Program
    Langley-Abbot Solar Research
Program (SAO)
    Meteor Research Program (SAO)
    Mount Hopkins Observatory
    Multiple-Mirror Telescope (SAO)

NT Optical and Infrared Astronomy
Division (SAO)
Planetary Sciences Division (SAO)
Radio and Geoastronomy Division
(SAO)
Satellite Tracking Program (SAO)
Solar and Stellar Physics Division
(SAO)
Southwest Meteor Spectral Patrol
(SAO)
Theoretical Astrophysics Division
(SAO)
Very Long Baseline Interferometer
(SAO)
RT Center for Astrophysics
Harvard College Observatory
Smithsonian Astrophysical Observatory,
Assistant Director, 248 [RU 468]
RT Smithsonian Astrophysical Observa-
tory, Assistant Director (Admin-
istration)
Smithsonian Astrophysical Observa-
tory, Deputy Director
Smithsonian Astrophysical Observatory,
Assistant Director (Administration), 248
[RU 256]; 248 [RU 468]
RT Smithsonian Astrophysical Observa-
tory, Assistant Director
Smithsonian Astrophysical Observa-
tory, Assistant Director (Man-
agement)
Smithsonian Astrophysical Observa-
tory, Deputy Director
Smithsonian Astrophysical Observatory,
Assistant Director (Management), 249 [RU
259]
RT Smithsonian Astrophysical Observa-
tory, Assistant Director (Admin-
istration)
Smithsonian Astrophysical Observatory,
Assistant Director (Science), 250 [RU 253]
Smithsonian Astrophysical Observatory,
Deputy Director, 248 [RU 468]
RT Smithsonian Astrophysical Observa-
tory, Assistant Director
Smithsonian Astrophysical Observa-
tory, Assistant Director (Admin-
istration)
Smithsonian Astrophysical Observatory,
Director, 247 [RU 437]
Smithsonian-Bredin-Archbold Biological
Survey of Dominica, 452 [RU 7096]; 625
[RU 9509]

Smithsonian-Bredin Belgian Congo Expedition, 1955, 557 [RU 7231]
Smithsonian-Bredin Caribbean Expeditions,
1956-1959, 557 [RU 7231]
Smithsonian-Bredin Expedition to Yucatan,
1960, 557 [RU 7231]
Smithsonian-Bredin Society Islands Expedi-
tion, 1957, 557 [RU 7231]
Smithsonian Building Committee, 489 [RU
7061]
RT Smithsonian Institution Building
Smithsonian Buildings, 22 [RU 477]; 27 [RU
145]; 49 [RU 71]; 51 [RU 187]; 203 [RU
313]; 248 [RU 468]; 266 [RU 286]; 279
[RU 378]; 308 [RU 635]; 318 [RU 532];
329 [RU 562]; 329 [RU 637]; 370 [RU 92]
NT American History Building
Anacostia Museum
Arthur M. Sackler Gallery of Art
Arts and Industries Building
Barney Studio House
Barro Colorado Island
Belmont Conference Center
Carnegie Mansion
Cooper-Hewitt Museum
Fine Arts and Portrait Galleries
Fine Arts and Portrait Galleries
Building
Fred Lawrence Whipple Observatory
Hirshhorn Museum and Sculpture
Garden
History and Technology Building
Java Farm
Multiple-Mirror Telescope
Museum Support Center
National Gallery of Art
National Museum Building
National Museum of African Art
National Portrait Gallery
National Zoological Park
Natural History Building
Renwick Gallery
River House
Smithsonian Astrophysical
Observatory
Smithsonian Institution Building
South Quadrangle Project
Smithsonian Chemist, Office of the, 346 [RU
241]
Smithsonian Child Care Center, 569 [RU
7443]
Smithsonian-Chrysler Expedition to East
Africa, 1926, 189 [RU 74]; 512 [RU 7293]

Smithsonian Early Enrichment Center, 352
[RU 507]; 569 [RU 7443]
  NT Board of Directors (SEEC)
     Parents Association (SEEC)
Smithsonian Environmental Alert Pilot
Program, 319 [RU 607]
Smithsonian Environmental Research Center,
29 [RU 393]; 29 [RU 526]; 32 [RU 329];
267 [RU 412]; 268 [RU 387]; 268 [RU
399]; 636 [RU 9591]
  NT Carbon-Dating Laboratory
  RT Chesapeake Bay Center for Environ-
     mental Studies
     Radiation and Organisms, Division
     of
     Radiation Biology Laboratory
Smithsonian Environmental Research Center,
Office of the Director, 267 [RU 412]
Smithsonian-Firestone Expedition to Liberia,
1940, 189 [RU 74]; 512 [RU 7293]
Smithsonian Folklife Studies, 635 [RU 9569]
Smithsonian Foreign Currency Program, 260
[RU 524]
"Smithsonian Galaxy" (radio broadcast), 358
[RU 586]; 359 [RU 296]; 360 [RU 589];
361 [RU 588]; 361 [RU 590]
Smithsonian Gallery of Art, 198 [RU 312]; 370
[RU 92]
  RT National Collection of Fine Arts
Smithsonian Gallery of Art Commission, 197
[RU 311]
Smithsonian-Geographic Society Archeological
Expedition to Vera Cruz, Mexico, 1938-
1939
  USE: National Geographic Society-
     Smithsonian Archeological
     Expedition to Vera Cruz,
     Mexico, 1938-1939
Smithsonian-Geographic Society Expedition to
the Dutch East Indies, 1937
  USE: National Geographic Society-
     Smithsonian Institution
     Expedition to the Dutch East
     Indies, 1937
Smithsonian Half-Century book project, 346
[RU 76]; 544 [RU 7081]
Smithsonian-Hartford West Indies Expedition,
1937, 557 [RU 7231]
Smithsonian-Harvard expedition to Altai
Mountains, Siberia, 1912, 39 [RU 192]
Smithsonian History of Aviation Project
(NASM), 235 [RU 343]
Smithsonian Illustrated Library of Antiques,
281 [RU 492]

Smithsonian Infant Care Center, 352 [RU 507]
Smithsonian Information Center
  USE: Visitor Information and Associ-
     ates' Reception Center
Smithsonian Institution, centennial, 10 [RU
50]
*Smithsonian Institution, 1846-1896, The
History of Its First Half-Century, The,* 346
[RU 76]
Smithsonian Institution, history, 551 [RU
7447]
Smithsonian Institution, visitors registers, 364
[RU 62]
Smithsonian Institution Archives, 370 [RU 94];
629 [RU 9575]
  RT Smithsonian Archives
     Smithsonian Institution Archives,
     Office of
Smithsonian Institution Archives, Office of,
370 [RU 94]
  RT Smithsonian Archives
     Smithsonian Institution Archives
Smithsonian Institution Archives and Special
Collections Council, 629 [RU 9575]
Smithsonian Institution Building, 19 [RU 137];
264 [RU 4010003]; 318 [RU 532]; 318 [RU
565]; 329 [RU 562]; 347 [RU 217]; 370
[RU 92]; 518 [RU 7386]
  NT Children's Room of the Smithsonian
     Institution Building
Smithsonian Institution-Commonwealth of
Australia-National Geographic Society
Expedition to Arnhem Land, 1948, 80 [RU
234]; 445 [RU 7465]
*Smithsonian Institution: Documents Relative
to its Origin and History, 1835-1899,* 544
[RU 7081]
Smithsonian Institution Employees Federal
Credit Union Newsletter, 347 [RU 299]
Smithsonian Institution Libraries, 29 [RU
526]; 639 [RU 9588]
Smithsonian Institution Library, 320 [RU 65];
333 [RU 61]; 347 [RU 217]; 545 [RU 7382]
Smithsonian Institution-Peace Corps Environ-
mental Program, 310 [RU 271]; 314 [RU
264]
  BT Ecology Program, Office of Environ-
     mental Sciences
     Ecology Program, Office of Interna-
     tional and Environmental
     Programs
Smithsonian Institution Press, 27 [RU 145];
348 [RU 535]
  RT Editorial and Publications Division
     Editorial Division

Smithsonian Institution Registrar's Council, 292 [RU 540]
    RT Council of Registrars
        Registrarial Council of the
          Smithsonian Institution
Smithsonian Institution Relief Association, 349 [RU 86]
Smithsonian Institution Traveling Exhibition Service, 10 [RU 50]; 24 [RU 190]; 26 [RU 342]; 27 [RU 575]; 211 [RU 314]; 220 [RU 333]; 327 [RU 90]; 349 [RU 290]; 350 [RU 489]; 350 [RU 518]; 351 [RU 487]; 351 [RU 536]
    NT Public Relations, Office of (SITES)
    RT Smithsonian Traveling Exhibition Service
Smithsonian Institution Traveling Exhibition Service, Exhibition Posters, 351 [RU 490]
Smithsonian Institution Traveling Exhibition Service, Office of the Director, 349 [RU 488]
Smithsonian Institution with S. Dillon Ripley, Secretary, The (motion picture), 358 [RU 586]
Smithsonian Institution with S. Dillon Ripley, Secretary, The (television broadcast), 362 [RU 593]
Smithsonian Institution Women's Council, 352 [RU 310]; 352 [RU 507]; 569 [RU 7443]
Smithsonian-Johnson Deep-Sea Expedition to the Puerto Rico Trench, 1933, 9 [RU 46]
Smithsonian-Johnson Deep-Sea Expedition to the West Indies, 1933
    USE: Johnson-Smithsonian Deep-Sea Expedition the West Indies, 1933
Smithsonian Journal of History, The, 185 [RU 193]
    BT National Museum of History and Technology
Smithsonian magazine, 27 [RU 145]; 345 [RU 308]; 353 [RU 557]; 354 [RU 626]; 636 [RU 9591]
Smithsonian Museum Service, 342 [RU 370]; 358 [RU 586]; 643 [RU 9565]
    RT Public Affairs, Office of
Smithsonian Museum Shops, 27 [RU 145]
Smithsonian Museum Support Facility, 14 [RU 605]
    RT Museum Support Center
Smithsonian National Associates Program, 10 [RU 99]; 353 [RU 557]; 360 [RU 592]
    NT Contributing Membership Program (SNAP)

Lecture and Seminar Program (SNAP)
Regional Events Program (SNAP)
Selected Studies Program (SNAP)
Smithsonian Oceanographic Sorting Center, 10 [RU 50]; 312 [RU 273]; 313 [RU 563]; 313 [RU 610]
    BT National Museum of Natural History, Assistant Director for Oceanography
        Oceanography and Limnology, Office of
        Oceanography and Limnology Program
Smithsonian Oceanographic Sorting Center (NMNH), 10 [RU 50]
    BT National Museum of Natural History
Smithsonian Office of Anthropology (NMNH), 128 [RU NAA 5]
    RT Anthropology, Department of (NMNH)
Smithsonian Office of Ecology, 310 [RU 271]
    BT National Museum of Natural History
    NT Chesapeake Bay Center for Field Biology
Smithsonian Office of Educational Research, 354 [RU 388]
Smithsonian Office of Symposia and Seminars
    USE: Symposia and Seminars, Smithsonian Office of
"Smithsonian Project Discovery" (proposed television production), 359 [RU 594]
Smithsonian Research Awards Program, 31 [RU 254]; 33 [RU 150]; 260 [RU 524]
Smithsonian Research Foundation, 260 [RU 524]
Smithsonian Research Subcommittee, 46 [RU 89]
Smithsonian Resident Associate Program, 10 [RU 99]; 355 [RU 632]
    NT Public Affairs, Office of (Smithsonian Resident Associate Program)
Smithsonian Resident Associate Program, Director, 354 [RU 626]; 355 [RU 627]
    RT Smithsonian Associates
Smithsonian-Roosevelt African Expedition, 1909, 8 [RU 45]; 39 [RU 192]; 189 [RU 74]; 480 [RU 7179]; 515 [RU 7083]; 551 [RU 7472]
Smithsonian Science Information Exchange, 10 [RU 50]; 12 [RU 171]; 19 [RU 137]; 30 [RU 108]; 31 [RU 254]; 32 [RU 329]; 356 [RU 482]

Space Science and Exploration, Department of (NASM), 240 [RU 348]; 241 [RU 347]
   RT Astronautics, Department of (NASM)
Space Telescope History Project (NASM), 235 [RU 343]
Space Telescope Science Institute, 463 [RU 7416]
Spaeth, Eloise, 304 [RU 401]
Spangler, Paul J., 102 [RU 411]; 570 [RU 7419]
Specht, Robert D., 657 [RU 9536]
Special Assistant to the Assistant Secretary for Museum Programs, 26 [RU 342]
Special Assistant to the Secretary, 12 [RU 618]; 13 [RU 620]
Special Assistant to the Secretary for Bicentennial Planning, 13 [RU 341]
Special Assistant to the Secretary for Fine Arts, 12 [RU 441]
Special Assistant to the Secretary for Scientific Matters, 315 [RU 102]
Special Consultant to the Secretary, 14 [RU 615]
Special Events (NMAH), 180 [RU 360]
   BT Public Affairs, Office of (NMAH)
Special Events, Office of, 323 [RU 373]
   BT Coordinator of Public Information
Special Events, Office of (NASM), 242 [RU 340]; 243 [RU 409]
Special Events, Office of (NMAH), 182 [RU 595]
   RT Public Affairs, Office of (NMHT)
Special Events, Office of (WWICS), 298 [RU 570]
"Special Memoranda," 335 [RU 486]
Special Museum Programs, Office of, 24 [RU 190]
Species Survival Program (NZP), 633 [RU 9568]; 649 [RU 9553]
Specimen Catalogs, Division of Birds (NMNH), 75 [RU 1060107]
Specimen Distribution Record Books (USNM), 55 [RU 120]
   RT Registrar (USNM)
Specimen Distribution Records (USNM), 55 [RU 186]
   RT Registrar (USNM)
Spectra, 522 [RU 7432]
Speier, Hans, 657 [RU 9536]
Spencer, Herbert, 426 [RU 7315]
Sperry gyrocompass, 147 [RU 383]
Spina, W. J., 82 [RU 7217]

Spirit of Fact, The: The Daguerreotypes of Southworth and Hawes, 1843-1862 (exhibition), 227 [RU 361]
Spirit of St. Louis (exhibition), 39 [RU 192]
Spitz, Armand N., 252 [RU 255]
Spofford, Sally Hoyt, 490 [RU 7405]
Spottswood, Henry N., 59 [RU 78]
Sprague, Katherine M. (Tkac), 569 [RU 7443]
Springer, Victor G., 79 [RU 415]; 80 [RU 234]
Sprouls, Ellen V., 352 [RU 507]
Sputnik (satellite), 613 [RU 9556]
Squires, Donald F., 87 [RU 249]; 87 [RU 292]; 626 [RU 9573]
Squires, Hubert G., 39 [RU 192]
St. John, Harold, 623 [RU 9572]
St. John, Orestes Hawley, 554 [RU 7154]
St. John Fisher College, 615 [RU 9517]
Staff, Volunteer, and Intern Services (VIARC), 363 [RU 600]
Stage, Gerald I., 102 [RU 418]
Stahlman, William, 485 [RU 7474]
Stam, Deirdre, 522 [RU 7432]
Standley, Paul Carpenter, 109 [RU 224]; 109 [RU 226]
Stanford University, 497 [RU 7333]; 524 [RU 7317]; 627 [RU 9527]; 646 [RU 9520]; 651 [RU 9554]
Stanley, John Mix, 572 [RU 7066]
Stanton, Timothy William, 530 [RU 7425]; 571 [RU 7325]
Star Catalogue (SAO), 250 [RU 253]
"Star Trek" (television series), 239 [RU 398]
Starr, S. Frederick, 299 [RU 291]
State and Local Government Program (WWICS), 300 [RU 571]
State, United States Department of, 128 [RU NAA 4]
State University of Iowa Expedition to Barbados and Antigua, 577 [RU 7138]
Station Operations Division (SAO), 254 [RU 263]
   BT Satellite Tracking Program (SAO)
"Statistical Review of the Vessel Fisheries of the United States in 1880," 447 [RU 7196]
Steam Engine in the Graphic Arts, The (exhibition), 153 [RU 413]
Steam Transportation, Section of (USNM), 599 [RU 7268]
   BT Arts and Industries, Department of (USNM)
Stearns, Robert Edwards Carter, 93 [RU 73]; 94 [RU 7418]; 95 [RU 7461]; 573 [RU 7077]; 614 [RU 9526]
Stearns, Winfrid Alden, 37 [RU 189]; 438 [RU 7344]

Steele, Edward Strieby, 573 [RU 7277]

Steering Committee for the History of Science and Technology (NMHT), 185 [RU 511]

Stein, Robert, 37 [RU 189]

Stejneger, Leonhard, 69 [RU 143]; 69 [RU 242]; 83 [RU 161]; 85 [RU 508]; 85 [RU 7445]; 398 [RU 7110]; 574 [RU 7074]; 575 [RU 7441]; 628 [RU 9513]

Stelfox, Arthur Wilson, 575 [RU 7379]

Steller, Georg Wilhelm, 574 [RU 7074]

Stephens, Carlene E., 151 [RU 397]; 661 [RU 9548]

Stephens, James Francis, 601 [RU 7112]

Stephenson, Lloyd William, 531 [RU 7327]

Stern, Harold P., 262 [RU 4010001]; 264 [RU 4010004]

Stern, William L., 107 [RU 272]; 111 [RU 428]; 606 [RU 7285]

Stevens, Charles E., 489 [RU 7061]

Stevens' survey, Isaac
> USE: Isaac Stevens' survey

Stevenson, Matilda Coxe, 127 [RU NAA 2]

Stewart, Julian H., 128 [RU NAA 4]

Stewart, Thomas Dale, 30 [RU 108]; 61 [RU 155]; 61 [RU 197]; 128 [RU NAA 5]; 618 [RU 9528]; 641 [RU 9521]

Steyermark, Julian Alfred, 110 [RU 227]

Steyskal, George C., 576 [RU 7373]

Still Life by Henry Lee McFee, 1986 (exhibition), 211 [RU 449]

Stimpson, William, 91 [RU 233]; 441 [RU 7073]; 528 [RU 7253]; 576 [RU 7093]

Stimson, Dorothy, 485 [RU 7474]

Stirling, Matthew William, 39 [RU 192]; 127 [RU NAA 3]; 618 [RU 9528]; 641 [RU 9521]

Stockwell, Elizabeth, 627 [RU 9574]

Stone, Alan, 577 [RU 7340]

Stoner, Dayton, 577 [RU 7138]

Stoner, Eugene M., 659 [RU 9532]

Stovel, Richard T., 651 [RU 9554]

Strassmann, Elizabeth, 209 [RU 453]

Stratigraphic Paleontology, Division of (NMNH), 619 [RU 9524]

Stratigraphic Paleontology, Division of (USNM), 377 [RU 7004]
> BT Geology, Department of (USNM)

Stratmon, David L., 307 [RU 634]

Strekalovsky, Nicholas, 448 [RU 7468]

Strekalovsky, Roman, 448 [RU 7468]; 577 [RU 1020011]

Strong, William Duncan, 325 [RU 87]

Stuckenrath, Robert, 268 [RU 387]

Stuckert, Juan V. Theodoro, 475 [RU 1010006]

Suckley, George, 577 [RU 7191]

Sullivan, J. Kevin, 266 [RU 286]; 267 [RU 419]

"Summary of the Gellatly Collection, A," 1932, 200 [RU 550]

Summer Ecology Program, 268 [RU 399]

Summer Institute in Systematics, 61 [RU 197]; 581 [RU 7226]

Superintendent of Buildings, 317 [RU 157]

Superintendent of Construction for the United States National Museum Building, 50 [RU 81]

Suratt, Samuel T., 346 [RU 98]

Survey
> RT Expedition
> USE: Archbold-Bredin-Smithsonian Biological Survey of Dominica
> Bikini Scientific Resurvey, 1947
> Bikini Scientific Survey, 1946
> Biological Survey of the Panama Canal Zone, 1911-1912
> *Comision de Limites,* Mexico, 1827-1828
> Crossroads Operation
> Fish and Wildlife Survey of Guatemala, 1946-1947
> Illinois Geological Survey
> Isaac Stevens' survey
> Medicinal Plants Survey, 1897-1898
> Northwest Boundary Survey, 1857-1861
> Pacific Ocean Biological Survey Program
> Pacific Railroad Survey of the 47th and 49th parallels
> Pacific Railroad Survey of the 38th parallel
> Pacific Railroad Surveys
> Palearctic Migratory Bird Survey
> Panama Canal Zone, Biological Survey of the, 1911-1912
> United States Geological and Geographical Survey of the Territories, 1871-1877
> United States Geographical and Geological Survey of the Rocky Mountain Region
> United States-Mexican Boundary Survey, 1855-1857
> United States-Mexican International Boundary Survey, 1891-1894

Surveys
> USE: River Basin Surveys

Sustainable Growth Program, 296 [RU 275]
  BT Woodrow Wilson International
      Center for Scholars
Suter, Lisa, 354 [RU 626]; 283 [RU 633]
  RT Taylor, Lisa Suter
Swallen, Jason Richard, 107 [RU 272]; 110
  [RU 227]; 111 [RU 428]
Swan-Brush electrical apparatus collection, 39
  [RU 192]
Swarthmore College, 635 [RU 9569]
Swartout, Edgerton, 461 [RU 7471]
Swedish Academy of Sciences, 405 [RU 7105]
Sweeney, Charles W., 653 [RU 9531]
Sweet, Richard G., 651 [RU 9554]
Sweetser, Susan, 291 [RU 436]
Switzer, George S., 116 [RU 336]; 117 [RU
  266]
Symposia and Seminars, Smithsonian Office
  of, 10 [RU 99]; 27 [RU 145]; 332 [RU 495];
  332 [RU 498]; 357 [RU 496]; 357 [RU
  497]; 357 [RU 500]; 358 [RU 499]
  RT Interdisciplinary Studies, Office of
      Seminars, Division of, Office of
      Academic Programs
Systematic and Evolutionary Biology, Interna-
  tional Congress of, 494 [RU 7141]; 494
  [RU 7145]
Systematic Biology Resource Management
  Project, 578 [RU 7142]
Systematic Biology Symposium, 578 [RU
  7142]
Systematic Entomology Laboratory (USDA),
  421 [RU 7368]; 469 [RU 7359]; 475 [RU
  7300]; 483 [RU 7343]; 576 [RU 7373]; 579
  [RU 7309]; 580 [RU 7323]; 580 [RU 7426];
  582 [RU 7339]; 594 [RU 7403]; 600 [RU
  7400]; 604 [RU 7404]; 607 [RU 7412]; 638
  [RU 9583]
  RT Insect Identification, Division of
      (USDA)
      Insect Identification and Beneficial
      Insect Introduction Institute
      (USDA)
      Insect Identification and Parasite
      Introduction Research Branch
      (USDA)
Systematic Zoology, Journal of, 581 [RU
  7226]
Systematic Zoology, Society of
  USE: Society of Systematic Zoology
Systematics Collections, Conference of
  Directors of, 578 [RU 7142]
Systematics, Summer Institute in, 61 [RU
  197]; 581 [RU 7226]

T

Table Mountain Station, California, 246 [RU
  85]; 378 [RU 7005]; 471 [RU 7307]
Talbot, Frank H., 62 [RU 374]
Talbot, Lee Merriam, 310 [RU 271]
Tamblyn and Brown conferences, 9 [RU 46]
Tanguy, Peter S., 658 [RU 9552]
Tapley, James, 632 [RU 9589]
Tasev, Atanas, 582 [RU 7337]
Task Force on Research, 1987 (NMNH), 63
  [RU 362]
Tatarewicz, Joseph, 657 [RU 9536]
Taxidermist (USNM), 43 [RU 408]; 86 [RU
  210]; 87 [RU 433]; 631 [RU 9516]
Taxonomic Data File, Division of Birds
  (NMNH), 75 [RU 1060104]
Taylor, Frank A., 14 [RU 605]; 24 [RU 190];
  46 [RU 89]; 61 [RU 155]; 135 [RU 276];
  136 [RU 334]; 138 [RU 621]; 144 [RU 84];
  160 [RU 239]; 233 [RU 162]; 338 [RU
  574]; 629 [RU 9502]; 635 [RU 9569]; 642
  [RU 9512]; 644 [RU 9586]
Taylor, Frederick W., 346 [RU 241]
Taylor, Joshua C., 199 [RU 322]; 203 [RU
  313]; 204 [RU 447]; 208 [RU 465]; 214
  [RU 455]; 219 [RU 596]
Taylor, Lawrence E., 323 [RU 373]
Taylor, Lisa Suter, 281 [RU 267]; 281 [RU
  492]; 283 [RU 633]; 354 [RU 626]
  RT Suter, Lisa
Taylor, Lonn W., 181 [RU 584]
Taylor, Michael E., 530 [RU 7425]
Taylor, Theodore W., 12 [RU 171]
Taylor, Walter W., Jr., 39 [RU 192]
Taylor, William Ralph, 79 [RU 415]; 80 [RU
  234]
Te Vega Expedition to Malaysia, Thailand, and
  Indonesia, 1963, 552 [RU 7413]
Tecumseh (ship), 183 [RU 377]; 184 [RU 581]
Telecommunications, Office of, 358 [RU 586];
  359 [RU 296]; 359 [RU 594]; 360 [RU
  589]; 360 [RU 591]; 360 [RU 592]; 361
  [RU 587]; 361 [RU 588]; 361 [RU 590];
  362 [RU 593]
  NT "Radio Smithsonian" (radio
      broadcast)
  RT Public Affairs, Office of
Telecommunications, Office of, Director, 617
  [RU 9541]
Telegrams, 55 [RU 434]
  BT Registrar (USNM)
Telephone, The (exhibition), 179 [RU 551]

Tennessee Centennial Exposition, Nashville, 1897, 58 [RU 124]; 327 [RU 70]

Terrestrial Mollusks of the Family Urocoptidae in the Island of Cuba, 402 [RU 7089]

Texas Centennial Exposition, Dallas, 1936, 39 [RU 192]; 327 [RU 70]

Texas Project, 1979-1985 (AAA), 304 [RU 401]

Textile Hall (NMAH), 174 [RU 472]

Textiles, Department of (CHM), 288 [RU 539]

Textiles, Division of (NMAH), 174 [RU 472]
    BT Social and Cultural History, Department of (NMAH)
    RT Textiles, Division of (NMHT)

Textiles, Division of (NMHT), 174 [RU 472]
    BT Applied Arts, Department of (NMHT)
        History of Technology, Department of (NMHT)
    RT Textiles, Division of (NMAH)

Textiles, Division of (USNM), 39 [RU 192]; 144 [RU 84]
    BT Arts and Industries, Department of (USNM)
    NT Chemical Technology, Section of (USNM)
        Foods, Section of (USNM)
        Organic Chemistry, Section of (USNM)

Textiles, Section of (USNM), 174 [RU 472]
    BT Crafts and Industries, Division of (USNM)
    RT Textiles, Division of (NMHT)

Tharp, Marie, 479 [RU 7464]

Theatre Mart, 400 [RU 7473]

Theoretical Astrophysics Division (SAO), 247 [RU 437]

Thi Le, Tam, 661 [RU 9548]

This New Man: A Discourse in Portraits (exhibition), 227 [RU 361]

Thomas, Alma, 216 [RU 456]

Thomas, Cyrus, 37 [RU 189]

Thomas, George S., 154 [RU 244]

Thomas, Michael Rogers Oldfield, 517 [RU 7173]

Thomas, Toni E., 234 [RU 346]

Thomas Alva Edison (exhibition), 227 [RU 361]

"Thomas Christian and the Diatomists of Richmond," 434 [RU 7292]

Thomas M. Evans Special Exhibition Gallery (NMNH), 26 [RU 342]; 62 [RU 374]

Thompson-Starrett lawsuit, 1907-1915, 50 [RU 79]

Thorington, Richard W., Jr., 68 [RU 429]; 71 [RU 382]; 81 [RU 208]; 82 [RU 400]

Thorpe, Janet, 285 [RU 282]

Threads of History, 174 [RU 473]

332nd Fighter Group, 632 [RU 9578]

Thwaites, George Henry Kendrick, 601 [RU 7112]

Tiffany & Company, 507 [RU 1040101]

Tillinghast, Carlton W., 248 [RU 256]; 249 [RU 259]; 335 [RU 468]

Tillotson, Robert G., 140 [RU 335]; 177 [RU 580]

Time, 223 [RU 426]

Time Collection (NPG), 225 [RU 2020001]

Time Incorporated, 223 [RU 426]

Tinian Island airbase, 653 [RU 9531]

Tkac, Katherine M. (Sprague), 569 [RU 7443]

Tobey, James A., 154 [RU 244]

Todd, Edward L., 582 [RU 7339]

Todd, Ruth, 440 [RU 1050101]

Tolman, Ruel P., 152 [RU 206]; 153 [RU 413]; 197 [RU 311]; 198 [RU 312]; 583 [RU 7433]

Tomas Barrera expedition to Cuba, 1914, 402 [RU 7089]

Topographical Data Project, 362 [RU 69]

Torch, The, 340 [RU 420]; 343 [RU 371]

Torre y de la Huerta, Carlos de la, 94 [RU 7418]; 402 [RU 7089]

Torrey, Herbert, 417 [RU 7189]

Torrey, John, 417 [RU 7189]

Totten and Rogers, 370 [RU 92]

Tougas, Charles, 253 [RU 262]

"Toward Our Third Century" Bicentennial Awards Program, 22 [RU 281]; 583 [RU 7227]

Tower Concert (concert series), 171 [RU 485]

Townsend, Charles Henry Tyler, 384 [RU 7305]; 564 [RU 7296]

Toyota Motor Corporation, 656 [RU 9550]

Tracy, Evarts, 461 [RU 7471]

Tracy, Samuel Mills, 584 [RU 7278]

Tracy and Swartwout, 370 [RU 92]

Transportation and Engineering, Section of (USNM), 599 [RU 7268]
    BT Arts and Industries, Department of (USNM)

Transportation Clerk, Receipt for Packages, 58 [RU 129]

Transportation, Division of (NMAH), 161 [RU 528]; 603 [RU 7384]
    BT History of Science and Technology, Department of the (NMAH)
    RT Transportation, Division of (NMHT)

Transportation, Division of (NMHT), 160 [RU 239]; 161 [RU 528]
  BT History of Technology, Department of (NMHT)
    Industries, Department of (NMHT)
    Science and Technology, Department of (NMHT)
  RT Transportation, Division of (NMAH)
Transportation Receipts (USNM), 59 [RU 123]
  RT Registrar (USNM)
Transportation Records (USNM), 57 [RU 122]
  RT Registrar (USNM)
Travel Reports
  USE: name of organizational unit
Traveling Exhibition Service, Smithsonian Institution
  USE: Smithsonian Institution Traveling Exhibition Service
Traver, Jay R., 385 [RU 7298]
Treasures from the Smithsonian Institution at the Royal Scottish Museum, 1984 (exhibition), 28 [RU 367]
Treasury Relief Art Project, 1963-1964 (AAA), 304 [RU 401]
Trembly, Royal H., 317 [RU 157]
Trinity Test Site (New Mexico), 653 [RU 9531]
Troost, Gerard, 584 [RU 7301]
Troost collection of Crinoids, 37 [RU 189]
Tropical Forest Dynamics Project (STRI), 649 [RU 9553]
Tropp, Henry S., 159 [RU 332]
True, Frederick William, 38 [RU 201]; 42 [RU 112]; 45 [RU 55]; 69 [RU 143]; 69 [RU 242]; 78 [RU 203]; 81 [RU 208]; 122 [RU 424]; 347 [RU 217]; 585 [RU 7181]
True, Webster Prentiss, 348 [RU 535]
Truettner, William H., 205 [RU 460]; 207 [RU 459]
Trujillo, Jurencio, 649 [RU 9553]
Tsai, Lung-We, 658 [RU 9552]
Tucara Commission to Argentina, 446 [RU 7137]
Tung, Kuang-zung, 262 [RU 4010001]
Turley, Frank, 370 [RU 92]
Turner, George T., 177 [RU 580]
Turner, Lucien M., 585 [RU 7192]
Turtles, Collected Notes, Photographs and Graphic Illustrations on, 85 [RU 7445]
  BT Reptiles and Amphibians, Division of (USNM)
Tuskegee Airmen, 632 [RU 9578]
Twentieth Century Painting and Sculpture, Department of (NCFA), 206 [RU 315]

Twentieth Century Painting and Sculpture, Department of (NMAA), 206 [RU 458]
Twigg, Homer, 654 [RU 9544]
Tyler, James C., 62 [RU 374]; 234 [RU 338]
Tyrone Station, New Mexico, 246 [RU 85]

U

Ubelaker, Douglas H., 65 [RU 366]; 128 [RU NAA 5]
Udall, Sharyn, 304 [RU 401]
Uhuru (satellite), 463 [RU 7416]
Ulke, Henry, 586 [RU 7424]
Ulke, Titus, 586 [RU 7424]
Ulrich, Edward Oscar, 377 [RU 7004]; 403 [RU 7234]; 436 [RU 7318]; 586 [RU 7332]; 619 [RU 9524]
Uncapher, Keith, 657 [RU 9536]
Under Secretary, 616 [RU 9515]; 625 [RU 9525]
Under Secretary, Office of the, 19 [RU 137]; 20 [RU 392]; 20 [RU 394]
  RT Assistant Secretary for Administration
Underwater Exploration, Hall of (NMHT), 170 [RU 381]
Underwater Exploration Project, 170 [RU 381]
Underwood, Todd, 649 [RU 9553]
United Auto Workers, 656 [RU 9550]
United Nations Economic and Social Council, 26 [RU 342]
United Nations Educational, Scientific, and Cultural Organization, 562 [RU 7091]
United States Air Force, 233 [RU 162]; 252 [RU 255]; 254 [RU 263]; 258 [RU 522]; 260 [RU 523]; 323 [RU 168]; 636 [RU 9590]; 657 [RU 9536]
United States Arctic Research Program, 313 [RU 610]
  BT National Science Foundation
United States Army, 155 [RU 396]; 233 [RU 162]; 258 [RU 522]; 418 [RU 7304]; 515 [RU 7083]; 624 [RU 9529]; 512 [RU 7293]
  NT Quartermaster Corps (United States Army)
United States Book Exchange, 632 [RU 9578]
United States Capitol, 264 [RU 4010003]
United States Census of 1880, 447 [RU 7196]; 567 [RU 7206]
United States Civil Service Commission, 91 [RU 209]; 363 [RU 182]

United States Coast and Geodetic Survey, 396
[RU 7068]; 397 [RU 7053]; 441 [RU 7073]
RT National Oceanic and Atmospheric
Administration
United States Coast Survey
USE: United States Coast and Geodetic
Survey
United States Commission of Fish and
Fisheries
USE: United States Fish Commission
United States Commission on Military History,
510 [RU 7358]
United States Department of Agriculture, 97
[RU 140]; 98 [RU 430]; 101 [RU 7427];
102 [RU 418]; 102 [RU 7422]; 103 [RU
427]; 104 [RU 422]; 106 [RU 221]; 110
[RU 227]; 391 [RU 7367]; 400 [RU 7103];
414 [RU 7366]; 421 [RU 7368]; 423 [RU
7362]; 424 [RU 7399]; 432 [RU 1020008];
469 [RU 7359]; 472 [RU 7354]; 483 [RU
7343]; 494 [RU 7458]; 528 [RU 7346]; 576
[RU 7373]; 577 [RU 7340]; 579 [RU 7309];
580 [RU 7323]; 580 [RU 7426]; 582 [RU
7339]; 594 [RU 7403]; 600 [RU 7400]; 604
[RU 7404]; 618 [RU 9555]; 623 [RU 9572];
628 [RU 9513]; 638 [RU 9583]
NT Agricultural Research Services
(USDA)
Animal Husbandry Research
Division (USDA)
Entomology, Bureau of (USDA)
Entomology and Plant Quarantine,
Bureau of (USDA)
Insect Detection and Identification
Branch (USDA)
Insect Identification, Division of
(USDA)
Insect Identification and Beneficial
Insect Introduction Institute
(USDA)
Insect Identification and Parasite
Introduction Branch (USDA)
Insect Identification and Parasite
Introduction Research Branch
(USDA)
Plant Industry, Bureau of (USDA)
Systematic Entomology Laboratory
(USDA)
RT Plants, Division of (USNM)
United States Department of Commerce, 313
[RU 610]
NT National Marine Fisheries Service
United States Department of Energy, 267 [RU
412]; 394 [RU 7459]; 625 [RU 9525]

United States Department of the Interior, 420
[RU 7084]; 420 [RU 7168]
NT Biological Survey, Bureau of
Fisheries, Bureau of
United States Department of State, 128 [RU
NAA 4]
United States Experimental Grass and Forage
Station, Garden City, Kansas, 105 [RU 220]
United States Exploring Expedition, 417 [RU
7189]; 458 [RU 7180]; 525 [RU 7058]; 587
[RU 7186]
United States Fish and Wildlife Service
USE: Fish and Wildlife Service
United States Fish Commission, 38 [RU 54];
42 [RU 112]; 78 [RU 213]; 89 [RU 7260];
91 [RU 233]; 327 [RU 70]; 375 [RU 7002];
404 [RU 7224]; 420 [RU 7184]; 421 [RU
7438]; 427 [RU 7258]; 468 [RU 7050]; 540
[RU 7078]
RT Biological Survey, Bureau of
Bird and Mammal Laboratories
Fish and Wildlife Service
Fisheries, Bureau of
Fishes, Division of
United States Geographical and Geological
Survey of the Rocky Mountain Region, 127
[RU NAA 2]
United States Geological and Geographical
Surveys of the Territories, 1871-1877, 450
[RU 7369]; 517 [RU 7177]
United States Geological Survey, 123 [RU
328]; 125 [RU NAA 1]; 377 [RU 7004];
418 [RU 7395]; 422 [RU 7377]; 430 [RU
7080]; 441 [RU 7073]; 446 [RU 7397]; 466
[RU 7329]; 478 [RU 7365]; 493 [RU 7380];
503 [RU 7245]; 507 [RU 1040101]; 508
[RU 7396]; 530 [RU 7425]; 531 [RU 7327];
542 [RU 7326]; 553 [RU 7330]; 560 [RU
7233]; 571 [RU 7325]; 586 [RU 7332]; 597
[RU 7321]; 605 [RU 7328]; 619 [RU 9524];
623 [RU 9572]; 624 [RU 9529]; 647 [RU
9557]
NT Coastal Plain Investigations, Section
of (USGS)
Geological Names, Committee on
Paleontology, Section of
Paleontology and Stratigraphy,
Section of (USGS)
Paleontology and Stratigraphy
Branch (USGS)
United States in the World, The (symposium),
332 [RU 495]; 332 [RU 498]; 357 [RU 500]
United States Information Agency, 217 [RU
321]
NT International Art Program

United States Light-house Board, 374 [RU 7001]; 397 [RU 7053]

United States Marine Mammal Program, 588 [RU 7229]

  RT International Biological Program

United States-Mexican Boundary Survey, 1855-1857, 375 [RU 7002]; 501 [RU 7202]; 515 [RU 7083]

United States-Mexican International Boundary Commission, 1891-1894, 37 [RU 189]; 39 [RU 192]

United States-Mexican International Boundary Survey, 1891-1894, 439 [RU 7272]; 515 [RU 7083]

United States Mint, 176 [RU 359]

United States National Herbarium, 39 [RU 192]; 105 [RU 220]; 106 [RU 221]; 108 [RU 222]; 108 [RU 223]; 112 [RU 229]; 365 [RU 93]; 595 [RU 7270]

  RT Botany, Department of (NMNH)
      Botany, Department of (USNM)
      Plants, Division of (USNM)

United States National Museum, 10 [RU 50]; 43 [RU 408]; 44 [RU 133]; 54 [RU 75]; 54 [RU 127]; 54 [RU 128]; 54 [RU 199]; 55 [RU 434]; 57 [RU 126]; 85 [RU 508]; 144 [RU 219]; 320 [RU 65]; 365 [RU 93]; 367 [RU 165]; 377 [RU 7004]; 378 [RU 7006]; 395 [RU 7391]; 504 [RU 7466]; 534 [RU 7306]; 540 [RU 7078]; 545 [RU 7382]; 571 [RU 7325]; 583 [RU 7433]; 613 [RU 9522]; 615 [RU 9517]; 617 [RU 9514]; 619 [RU 9501]; 619 [RU 9570]; 622 [RU 9505]; 629 [RU 9502]; 631 [RU 9516]; 634 [RU 9519]; 641 [RU 9521]; 642 [RU 9512]; 644 [RU 9586]; 644 [RU 9587]

  NT Arts and Industries, Department of (USNM)
      Correspondence and Documents, Division of (USNM)
      Correspondence and Documents, Office of (USNM)
      Correspondence and Records, Office of
      Foods, Section of (USNM)
      Registrar (USNM)
      Reptiles and Batrachians, Division of (USNM)

  RT Chief Clerk
      Disbursement Clerk
      Exposition records
      National Museum Building
      National Museum of History and Technology

National Museum of Natural History Superintendent of Construction

United States National Museum, Accession Records, 52 [RU 305]; 52 [RU 6999T]; 56 [RU 109]; 56 [RU 110]; 56 [RU 111]; 56 [RU 118]

United States National Museum, Administrative Assistant, 45 [RU 215]; 48 [RU 167]; 49 [RU 198]; 50 [RU 80]

United States National Museum, Assistant Director, 642 [RU 9512]

United States National Museum, Associate Director, 47 [RU 483]

United States National Museum, Curators' Annual Reports, 44 [RU 158]

United States National Museum, Director, 19 [RU 175]; 24 [RU 190]; 46 [RU 89]; 47 [RU 88]; 48 [RU 432]; 61 [RU 155]; 136 [RU 334]; 642 [RU 9512]

  RT Assistant Secretary
      Assistant Secretary in charge of the United States National Museum
      Director General of Museums

United States National Museum, Editor, 630 [RU 9507]

United States National Museum, Executive Curator, 42 [RU 112]; 44 [RU 117]; 585 [RU 7181]

United States National Museum, Exhibits Modernization Committee, 24 [RU 190]; 642 [RU 9512]

United States National Museum, Exhibits Modernization Program, 123 [RU 328]; 326 [RU 503]; 622 [RU 9505]; 624 [RU 9506]; 631 [RU 9516]; 641 [RU 9521]; 642 [RU 9512]

United States National Museum, Modeler, 43 [RU 408]

United States National Museum, Osteological Preparator, 43 [RU 408]

United States National Museum, Permanent Administrative Files, 39 [RU 192]

  RT Accession Records

United States National Museum, Preparators' Annual Reports, 43 [RU 408]

United States National Museum, Printer, 43 [RU 408]

United States National Museum, Register of Package Announcements, 58 [RU 125]

United States National Museum, Taxidermist, 43 [RU 408]; 86 [RU 210]; 87 [RU 433]; 631 [RU 9516]

United States National Museum, Transportation Receipts, 59 [RU 123]

United States National Museum, Transportation Records, 57 [RU 122]

United States National Museum, Travel Reports, 48 [RU 432]

United States National Museum, visitors registers, 364 [RU 62]

United States National Museum Bulletin 50, 590 [RU 7133]

United States Naval Observatory, 648 [RU 9534]

United States Naval Observatory Eclipse Expedition to Nivafoou Island, 1930, 499 [RU 7241]

United States Naval Observatory Eclipse Expedition to the Philippine Islands, 1929, 499 [RU 7241]

United States Navy, 147 [RU 383]; 233 [RU 162]; 260 [RU 523]; 629 [RU 9575]

United States Navy Expedition to Guam, 1899, 37 [RU 189]

United States Navy Galapagos Expedition, 1941-1942, 557 [RU 7231]

United States North Pacific Exploring Expedition, 91 [RU 233]; 375 [RU 7002]; 528 [RU 7253]; 576 [RU 7093]

United States Ordnance Department, 650 [RU 9537]

United States Patent Office collections, 39 [RU 192]

United States Postal Service, 619 [RU 9570]

United States Public Health Service, 594 [RU 7403]; 607 [RU 7412]

United States Rubber Company, 507 [RU 7435]

United States Studies Program (WWICS), 300 [RU 569]
    RT American Society and Politics Program (WWICS)

United States Treasury Department, 176 [RU 359]

"Unity of the Universal Existence," 595 [RU 7094]

Universal Film Manufacturing Company-Smithsonian African Expedition, 1920, 39 [RU 192]

University of Arizona, 655 [RU 9542]

University of California, Berkeley, 491 [RU 7311]; 651 [RU 9546]

University of California, Los Angeles, 405 [RU 7381]

University of Chicago, 559 [RU 7429]; 620 [RU 9571]

University of Florida, 625 [RU 9509]

University of Hawaii, 623 [RU 9572]

University of Maryland at College Park, 428 [RU 7451]; 658 [RU 9552]
    RT Chesapeake Research Consortium, Inc.

University of Massachusetts, 385 [RU 7298]

University of Michigan, 628 [RU 9513]

University of Missouri, 605 [RU 7328]

University of Nebraska, 565 [RU 7082]

University of North Dakota, 645 [RU 9560]

University of Panama, 630 [RU 9576]

University of Pennsylvania, 623 [RU 9572]; 650 [RU 9537]

University of Pennsylvania expedition to Babylonia, 1887-1888, 39 [RU 192]

University of Southern California, 444 [RU 7097]

"University of the Air" (proposed television production), 359 [RU 594]

University of Virginia, 625 [RU 9509]
    NT Mountain Lakes Biological Station, University of Virginia

University of Virginia-National Geographic Society Expedition to the South Pacific Islands, 1939
    USE: National Geographic Society-University of Virginia Expedition to the South Pacific Islands, 1939

University of Washington, 638 [RU 9510]

University Workshop on the History of Aviation, 1988, 241 [RU 355]

Unpublished Papers submitted to the Smithsonian Institution, 363 [RU 63]

Upper Atmosphere Studies Division (SAO), 254 [RU 263]
    NT Satellite Tracking Program (SAO)

USS *Constellation* (vessel), 147 [RU 383]

USS *Constitution* (vessel), 147 [RU 383]

Utterback, Teresa, 658 [RU 9564]

V

Vail, Alfred, 148 [RU 250]; 550 [RU 7390]; 590 [RU 7055]

Vail, Amanda, 590 [RU 7055]

Vail, George, 590 [RU 7055]

Vail, James Cummings, 590 [RU 7055]

Vail, Stephen, 590 [RU 7055]

Vail Telegraph Collection, 590 [RU 7055]

Valmas, John, 661 [RU 9548]

Van Cleave, Harley J., 426 [RU 7315]

Van Dilla, Marvin A., 651 [RU 9554]

Van Tyne, Jocelyn, 387 [RU 7440]

Vance, David, 522 [RU 7432]

Vanderburgh, Richard C., 252 [RU 255]
Vanstrum, Paul R., 653 [RU 9531]
Varden, John, 591 [RU 7063]
Vasey, George, 105 [RU 220]; 591 [RU 7087]
Vaughan, T. Wayland, 531 [RU 7327]; 592 [RU 1050102]
Vaughn, Peter P., 121 [RU 156]
Veizades, Nicholas, 651 [RU 9554]
Venable, George L., 102 [RU 7422]
Venice Biennale, 1968, 1970, 1972, 214 [RU 454]
Venice Biennale exhibitions, 217 [RU 321]
Venter, J. Craig, 650 [RU 9549]; 658 [RU 9564]
Vermont Structural Slate Company (Fair Haven, Vermont), 661 [RU 9547]
Verrill, Addison Emery, 70 [RU 431]; 415 [RU 7071]; 429 [RU 7183]; 441 [RU 7073]
Vertebrate and Invertebrate Paleontology, Collected Notebooks, Manuscripts, and Photographs on, 123 [RU 7264]
Vertebrate Paleontology, Collected Notebooks on, 123 [RU 1050401]
Vertebrate Paleontology, Department of (NMNH), 121 [RU 156]
Vertebrate Paleontology, Division of (NMNH), 121 [RU 156]; 122 [RU 424]; 460 [RU 7314]
    BT Geology, Department of (NMNH)
      Paleobiology, Department of (NMNH)
Vertebrate Paleontology, Division of (USNM), 121 [RU 248]
    BT Geology, Department of (USNM)
Vertebrate Paleontology, Section of (NMNH), 121 [RU 156]
    BT Stratigraphic Paleontology, Division of (NMNH)
Vertebrate Zoology, Department of (NMNH), 71 [RU 136]; 71 [RU 382]; 83 [RU 161]; 612 [RU 9511]
    NT Birds, Division of (NMNH)
      Fishes, Division of (NMNH)
      Mammals, Division of (NMNH)
      Reptiles and Amphibians, Division of (NMNH)
    RT Zoology, Department of (NMNH)
Vertebrate Zoology, Department of (USNM), 71 [RU 136]
Very Long Baseline Interferometer (SAO), 250 [RU 253]
Vesey, Louis X. de, 609 [RU 7212]
Veterans Administration, 625 [RU 9525]; 644 [RU 9587]

Victor (vessel), 1879, 529 [RU 7387]
Victory at Yorktown (exhibition), 155 [RU 396]
Villard, Oswald Garrison, 441 [RU 7073]
Vin Fiz (airplane), 636 [RU 9590]
Viola, Herman J., 68 [RU 429]
Virginia Geological Survey, 422 [RU 7377]
Virginia Institute of Marine Science, 428 [RU 7451]
    RT Chesapeake Research Consortium, Inc.
Visitor Information and Associates' Reception Center, 363 [RU 600]
    NT Seven Day Information Service (VIARC)
      Staff, Volunteer, and Intern Services (VIARC)
Visitors Registers of the Smithsonian Institution and United States National Museum, 364 [RU 62]
Visscher, John Paul, 593 [RU 7239]
Visual Resources, Office of (NMAA), 219 [RU 442]
    RT Slides and Photography, Office of (NCFA)
Vitola, Francisco, 615 [RU 9561]; 637 [RU 9581]
Vivarium Society, 594 [RU 7163]
Vivian, James R. III, 226 [RU 555]
Vizcaya Art Museum (Miami), 443 [RU 7439]
Vogel, Robert M., 151 [RU 397]
Vogt, George B., 594 [RU 7403]
Volkert, James W., 213 [RU 451]; 216 [RU 456]
Volunteer Flight Officer Network, 252 [RU 255]
    BT Moonwatch Division (SAO)
von Baer, Karl Ernst, 426 [RU 7315]
Von Steuben (exhibition), 155 [RU 396]

W

Wadley, F. M., 505 [RU 7251]
Wahlen, Ralph K., 653 [RU 9531]
Wait, Wesley, 595 [RU 7094]
Wakefield, E. A., 39 [RU 192]
Walcott, B. Stuart, 377 [RU 7004]
Walcott, Charles D., 8 [RU 45]; 9 [RU 46]; 38 [RU 201]; 39 [RU 192]; 45 [RU 56]; 121 [RU 248]; 127 [RU NAA 2]; 197 [RU 311]; 198 [RU 312]; 262 [RU 4010001]; 377 [RU 7004]; 403 [RU 7234]; 461 [RU 7471]
Walcott, Mary Vaux, 8 [RU 45]

Walcott Research Fund, Charles D. and Mary
　　Vaux, 8 [RU 45]; 368 [RU 493]
Walker, Egbert Hamilton, 404 [RU 7271]; 595
　　[RU 7270]
Walker, Ernest Pillsbury, 190 [RU 380]; 596
　　[RU 7161]
Walker, William B., 221 [RU 463]
Wallen, Irvin Eugene, 266 [RU 286]; 310 [RU
　　271]; 312 [RU 273]; 312 [RU 274]; 313
　　[RU 563]
Waller, Thomas R., 68 [RU 429]
Walpole, Frederick A., 439 [RU 7272]
Walsh, Benjamin Dann, 596 [RU 7123]
Walter Rathbone Bacon Traveling Scholarship
　　expedition to the West Indies, 1928-1930,
　　402 [RU 7089]
Waltham Clock Company, 661 [RU 9548]
　　RT Waltham Watch Company
Waltham Watch Company, 661 [RU 9548]
　　RT Waltham Clock Company
Walton, Anne, 182 [RU 595]
War Committee, Smithsonian
　　USE: Smithsonian War Committee
War Production Board, 496 [RU 7172]
War Risk Insurance, Bureau of, 39 [RU 192];
　　50 [RU 80]
Ward, David C., 230 [RU 2040001]
Ward, Henry Baldwin, 596 [RU 7247]
Ward, Lester Frank, 597 [RU 7321]
Ward, Robert, 39 [RU 192]
Ware, Willis, 657 [RU 9536]
Warner, Deborah J. (Mills), 158 [RU 293]
Warner, William W., 27 [RU 145]
Warren, Owen G., 370 [RU 92]
Washburn, Wilcomb E., 173 [RU 252]; 174
　　[RU 473]; 316 [RU 160]; 316 [RU 609]
Washington, Henry Stephens, 120 [RU 7421]
Washington Academy of Sciences, 377 [RU
　　7004]; 460 [RU 7314]; 597 [RU 7099]
*Washington Academy of Sciences, Journal of
　　the,* 597 [RU 7099]
Washington Area School Study Council, 137
　　[RU 279]
Washington Biologists' Field Club, 378 [RU
　　7006]; 598 [RU 1020005]; 612 [RU 9511]
Washington City Museum, 591 [RU 7063]
Washington *Evening Star,* 483 [RU 7347]
*Washington: From Banneker to Douglass,
　　1791-1870* (exhibition), 227 [RU 361]
Washington in the New Era, 1870-1970
　　(exhibition), 227 [RU 361]
Washington Memorial Association, George, 8
　　[RU 45]; 377 [RU 7004]
Washington Memorial, George, 39 [RU 192];
　　370 [RU 92]

Washington Monument, 264 [RU 4010003]
Wasshausen, Dieter C., 111 [RU 428]
Watkins, C. Malcolm, 164 [RU 251]; 165 [RU
　　331]; 168 [RU 258]; 169 [RU 261]; 598
　　[RU 7322]; 644 [RU 9586]
Watkins, Charles H., 644 [RU 9586]
Watkins, J. Elfreth, 59 [RU 78]; 148 [RU 250];
　　317 [RU 157]; 347 [RU 217]; 599 [RU
　　7268]
Watkins, Lura Woodside, 644 [RU 9586]
Watkins, William N., 146 [RU 240]; 174 [RU
　　472]
Watson, Doc, 635 [RU 9569]
Watson, George E., 71 [RU 136]; 71 [RU 382];
　　72 [RU 391]; 73 [RU 270]; 77 [RU 435]
Watson, George H., 644 [RU 9586]
Watson, Robert, 652 [RU 9577]
Watson Fund, James, 525 [RU 7115]
Watters, Thomas R., 240 [RU 480]
Watts, Frederick, 105 [RU 220]
WCBS-TV, 617 [RU 9541]
We the People (exhibition), 174 [RU 473]
We Were But a Handful (exhibition), 228 [RU
　　554]
Wead, Charles K., 600 [RU 7159]
Weart, Spencer, 485 [RU 7474]
Weaver, James M., 171 [RU 485]; 181 [RU
　　584]
Webb, Philip Baxter, 95 [RU 7218]
Weber, Walter A., 72 [RU 105]
Wedderburn, Alexander J., 156 [RU 529]
Wedel, Waldo R., 128 [RU NAA 5]
*Wedgewood Portraits and the American
　　Revolution* (exhibition), 227 [RU 361]
Weinberg, Alvin M., 653 [RU 9531]
Weisman, Donald M., 600 [RU 7400]
Weiss, Helena M., 644 [RU 9587]
Weitzman, Stanley H., 79 [RU 415]; 80 [RU
　　234]
Welch, Paul Smith, 568 [RU 7262]
Welch, Richard, 661 [RU 9548]
Weld, Lewis Hart, 600 [RU 7127]
Wells, Albert, 644 [RU 9586]
Wells, Samuel F., Jr., 301 [RU 559]
Wells Historical Museum (Sturbridge,
　　Massachusetts), 598 [RU 7322]; 644 [RU
　　9586]
Welsh, Peter C., 169 [RU 261]; 185 [RU 193]
Welsh, William W., 465 [RU 7187]
Welt Als Uhr, Die (The World as a Clock)
　　(motion picture film), 151 [RU 397]
Wenley, Archibald G., 262 [RU 4010001]; 264
　　[RU 4010004]
Werner, Albert, 252 [RU 255]

Werner, Dagmar, 633 [RU 9579]
West China Border Research Society, 620 [RU 9571]
West European Program (WWICS), 301 [RU 559]
Western Society of Malacologists, 497 [RU 7333]
Western Union Telegraph Expedition, 441 [RU 7073]; 601 [RU 7213]
Westin, Sandra, 228 [RU 554]
Westinghouse Research Laboratory, 323 [RU 168]
Westwood, John Obadiah, 601 [RU 7112]
Wetmore, Alexander, 9 [RU 46]; 10 [RU 50]; 39 [RU 192]; 46 [RU 89]; 135 [RU 276]; 136 [RU 334]; 189 [RU 74]; 197 [RU 311]; 378 [RU 7006]; 386 [RU 7261]; 467 [RU 7257]; 534 [RU 7306]; 617 [RU 9514]; 619 [RU 9524]; 631 [RU 9516]; 644 [RU 9587]; 645 [RU 9504]; 647 [RU 9523]
Wettergreen, David, 658 [RU 9552]
Weymann, Ray J., 655 [RU 9542]
Whaling Commission, International
    USE: International Whaling Commission
Whaling Conference, International, 495 [RU 7165]
Whaling, International Convention on the Regulation of, 495 [RU 7165]
Wheatley, Thomas, 658 [RU 9552]
Wheeler, George C., 645 [RU 9560]
Wheeler, William Morton, 645 [RU 9560]
Wheels and Wheeling: The Smithsonian Cycle Collection, 161 [RU 528]
Wherry, Edgar Theodore, 549 [RU 7152]
Whipple, Fred Lawrence, 247 [RU 437]; 249 [RU 259]; 251 [RU 260]; 602 [RU 7431]; 646 [RU 9520]; 655 [RU 9542]
Whipple Observatory, Fred Lawrence
    USE: Fred Lawrence Whipple Observatory
White, Charles Abiathar, 571 [RU 7325]
White, David, 418 [RU 7395]
White, Eileen, 291 [RU 436]
White, John H., Jr., 160 [RU 239]; 161 [RU 528]; 603 [RU 7384]
White, John S., Jr., 116 [RU 336]; 116 [RU 421]
White, Thomas J., 652 [RU 9577]
White House art program, 203 [RU 313]
White House Fellows' Seminar on American Art, 200 [RU 320]
Whitebread, Charles, 154 [RU 244]
Whitehead, Donald R., 604 [RU 7404]

Whitehead, Kenneth, 310 [RU 180]
Whitelaw, John, 237 [RU 345]
Whitlock, Herbert Percy, 549 [RU 7152]
Whitmarsh, Thomas, 601 [RU 7112]
Whitmore, Frank C., Jr., 647 [RU 9557]
Whittaker, William, 658 [RU 9552]
Why Not A Woman (exhibition), 228 [RU 554]
Widunas, Joseph, 652 [RU 9577]
Wigner, Eugene P., 653 [RU 9531]
Wilcox, Timothy E., 37 [RU 189]
"Wild Blackberries and Dewberries in the District of Columbia and Vicinity," 573 [RU 7277]
Wild Fur Animal Investigations, Section of (Fish and Wildlife Service), 412 [RU 7407]
    BT Fish and Wildlife Service
    RT Bird and Mammal Laboratories
Wilderness Society, 612 [RU 9511]
Wildlife Research, Branch of (Fish and Wildlife Service), 610 [RU 7174]
Wildlife Service, Fish and
    USE: Fish and Wildlife Service
Wilkes, Charles, 417 [RU 7189]
Wilkes Expedition
    USE: United States Exploring Expedition
Williams, Alwyn, 436 [RU 7318]
Williams, Henry Shaler, 604 [RU 7238]
Williams, James Steele, 605 [RU 7328]
Williams, Joseph T., 655 [RU 9542]
Williams, Ken, 655 [RU 9533]
Williams, Roberta, 655 [RU 9533]
Williams, Talcott, 37 [RU 189]
Williamson, Francis S. L., 266 [RU 286]; 267 [RU 419]
Williamson, Linwood, 649 [RU 9553]
Willis H. Dupont Collection, 176 [RU 359]
Willits, Edwin, 105 [RU 220]
Wills of the United States Presidents, 174 [RU 473]
Wilson, Archie F., 606 [RU 7285]
Wilson, Charles Branch, 606 [RU 7235]
Wilson, Jane S., 653 [RU 9531]
Wilson, Mildred S., 89 [RU 307]
Wilson, Robert, 653 [RU 9531]
Wilson International Center for Scholars, Woodrow
    USE: Woodrow Wilson International Center for Scholars
Wilson Quarterly, The (WWICS), 303 [RU 572]; 303 [RU 573]; 303 [RU 578]
Winds of the Northern Hemisphere, 433 [RU 7060]
Windsor, Donald M., 649 [RU 9553]

Winlock, William Crawford, 149 [RU 297]

Winnecook Ranch Company, 410 [RU 7335]

Winnie Mae (airplane), 636 [RU 9590]

Wirth, Willis W., 607 [RU 7412]

Wisconsin Academy of Sciences, Arts and Letters, 496 [RU 7172]

Withuhn, William L., 161 [RU 528]

Wohlstetter, Albert, 657 [RU 9536]

Wolle, Philip W., 608 [RU 7385]

Wolle, Francis, Rev., 608 [RU 7385]

Women in Museums Network, 352 [RU 507]

Women in Science (exhibition), 155 [RU 471]

Woodbury, Richard B., 128 [RU NAA 5]

Woodbury, Robert S., 160 [RU 239]

Woodend Mansion, 395 [RU 7294]

Woodenworks, 1972-1975 (exhibition), 208 [RU 465]

Woodring, Wendell P., 531 [RU 7327]

Woodrow Wilson International Center for Scholars, 10 [RU 99]; 19 [RU 137]; 21 [RU 104]; 297 [RU 585]; 298 [RU 558]; 298 [RU 570]; 298 [RU 582]; 299 [RU 567]; 300 [RU 569]; 300 [RU 571]; 301 [RU 559]; 301 [RU 601]; 302 [RU 602]; 302 [RU 603]; 302 [RU 604]; 303 [RU 572]; 303 [RU 573]; 303 [RU 578]; 636 [RU 9591]

    NT "Dialogue" (WWICS) (radio broadcast)

    "Focus" (WWICS) (radio broadcast)

    Hubert H. Humphrey Fellowship in Social and Political Thought (WWICS)

    Kennan Institute for Advanced Russian Studies (WWICS)

    Pelikan Committee Review of International Programs (WWICS)

    "Radio Dialogue" (WWICS) (radio broadcast)

    Special Events, Office of (WWICS)

    State and Local Government Program (WWICS)

    United States Studies Program (WWICS)

    West European Program (WWICS)

    Wilson Quarterly, The (WWICS)

Woodrow Wilson International Center for Scholars, Deputy Director, 297 [RU 560]

Woodrow Wilson International Center for Scholars, Office of the Director (WWICS), 296 [RU 275]

Woods, Loren P., 80 [RU 234]

Wooldridge, Edmund T., Jr., 238 [RU 330]

Woolf, Harry, 485 [RU 7474]

Woolfe, Henry D., 37 [RU 189]

Woolfenden, William E., 304 [RU 401]; 305 [RU 402]

Woollcott, Alexander, 628 [RU 9513]

Work-Learn Program in Environmental Studies, 268 [RU 399]

World Food Prize (symposium), 332 [RU 495]; 332 [RU 498]

World Health Organization, 658 [RU 9564]

"World Is Yours, The" (radio broadcast), 144 [RU 84]; 324 [RU 83]; 360 [RU 592]

    RT Radio Smithsonian

"World Is Yours, The," 9 [RU 46]

    RT Radio Smithsonian

World War I, 393 [RU 7378]

World War II, 262 [RU 4010001]; 617 [RU 9514]; 618 [RU 9528]; 632 [RU 9578]; 646 [RU 9520]; 648 [RU 9545]; 650 [RU 9537]; 653 [RU 9531]

World's Columbian Exposition, Chicago, 1893, 39 [RU 192]; 58 [RU 124]; 327 [RU 70]; 439 [RU 7272]; 507 [RU 1040101]; 528 [RU 7460]

World's Industrial and Cotton Centennial Exposition, New Orleans, 1884-1885, 327 [RU 70]

World's Poultry and Congress Exposition (Seventh), Cleveland, 1939, 327 [RU 70]

Worley, Charles, 648 [RU 9534]

Worms, Division of (NMNH), 96 [RU 417]; 626 [RU 9573]

    BT Invertebrate Zoology, Department of (NMNH)

    RT Marine Invertebrates, Division of (NMNH)

Worthington, William III, 661 [RU 9547]

Woudenberg, Timothy M., 652 [RU 9577]

Wright, A. Gilbert, 65 [RU 363]; 608 [RU 7331]; 647 [RU 9523]

Wright, Wakefield A., 653 [RU 9531]

Wright-Langley controversy, 8 [RU 45]; 9 [RU 46]

Wunder, Richard P., 205 [RU 317]; 281 [RU 267]; 283 [RU 633]

Wytsman, P., 427 [RU 7162]

XYZ

X-ray telescope, 463 [RU 7416]

Xantus, John, 378 [RU 7006]; 609 [RU 7212]

Xayavong, Savay, 661 [RU 9548]

Yale University, 380 [RU 7008]; 619 [RU 9524]; 636 [RU 9591]

Yale University-National Geographic Society Expedition to Peru, 39 [RU 192]; 480 [RU 7179]

Yallico, Ernesto, 649 [RU 9553]

Yangtze River, 262 [RU 4010001]

Yarrow, Henry Crecy, 83 [RU 161]; 127 [RU NAA 2]; 610 [RU 7166]

Yashiro, Yuko, 262 [RU 4010001]

Yates, Hugh E., 318 [RU 532]

Yelavich, Susan, 289 [RU 324]

Yellin Metalworkers, Samuel, 370 [RU 92]

Yellis, Kenneth, 226 [RU 555]; 523 [RU 7295]

Yellow Fever Service, Rockefeller Foundation, 622 [RU 9559]

Yochelson, Ellis L., 659 [RU 9530]

Young, David A., Jr., 506 [RU 7352]; 528 [RU 7346]

Young, David K., 312 [RU 273]

Young, Kenneth, 228 [RU 556]

Young, Stanley Paul, 411 [RU 7171]; 412 [RU 7407]; 610 [RU 7174]

Youth Advisory Council, 278 [RU 390]
    BT Education Department (AM)

Yvonne (vessel), 420 [RU 7184]

Zapruder, Marjorie S., 209 [RU 453]

Zeman, Robert, 654 [RU 9544]

Zetek, James, 94 [RU 7418]; 95 [RU 7461]; 304 [RU 134]; 564 [RU 7296]; 611 [RU 7462]; 615 [RU 9561]; 621 [RU 9562]; 627 [RU 9574]; 645 [RU 9504]

Zichterman, Harry W., 204 [RU 447]

Zilczer, Judith K., 271 [RU 469]; 624 [RU 9566]

Zindt, Linda, 639 [RU 9588]

Zisfein, Melvin B., 234 [RU 346]; 235 [RU 352]

Zoo to Art, 1985 (exhibition), 211 [RU 449]

Zoologia, Departamento de (Sao Paulo, Brazil), 633 [RU 9579]

Zoological Nomenclature, International Commission on, 574 [RU 7074]; 638 [RU 9583]

Zoological Park, National
    USE: National Zoological Park

Zoological Station, Naples, 8 [RU 45]

Zoology, Department of (NMNH), 69 [RU 143]; 70 [RU 243]; 71 [RU 136]; 83 [RU 161]; 87 [RU 249]; 87 [RU 292]; 557 [RU 7231]; 612 [RU 9511]; 624 [RU 9506]; 625 [RU 9509]; 626 [RU 9573]
    NT Birds, Division of (NMNH)

Zoology, Department of (USNM), 69 [RU 143]
    BT National Museum of Natural History

    NT Birds, Division of (USNM)
    Echinoderms, Division of (USNM)
    Fishes, Division of (USNM)
    Insects, Division of (USNM)
    Mammals, Division of (USNM)
    Reptiles and Amphibians, Division of (USNM)
    RT Biology, Department of (USNM)
    Vertebrate Zoology, Department of (USNM)

Zug, George R., 68 [RU 429]; 71 [RU 382]; 84 [RU 327]

Zusi, Richard L., 72 [RU 391]; 73 [RU 270]